THE

INDIAN ARROWHEADS

IDENTIFICATION AND PRICE GUIDE

Other **CONFIDENT COLLECTOR** Titles of Interest

The Overstreet Comic Book Companion Identification And Price Guide
by Robert M. Overstreet

The Overstreet Comic Book Price Guide
by Robert M. Overstreet

The Overstreet Comic Book Grading Guide
by Robert M. Overstreet and Gary M. Carter

THE OVERSTREET

INDIAN ARROWHEADS

IDENTIFICATION AND PRICE GUIDE

Third Edition

Robert M. Overstreet
and Howard Peake

About the front cover: For decades the state of Oregon has been known for its gem quality arrowheads found along the Columbia, John Day and other rivers. The cover of this edition is a small sampling of these high quality Oregon points. All are included in this edition. The center point is a red and green agate Klickatat Dagger point, one of the finest known.

Important Notice: All of the information, including valuations, in this book has been compiled from the most reliable sources, and every effort has been made to eliminate errors and questionable data. Nevertheless, the possibility of error always exists in a work of such immense scope. The publisher and the author will not be held responsible for losses which may occur in the purchase, sale, or other transaction of property because of information contained herein. Readers who feel they have discovered errors are invited to *write* and inform us so the errors may be corrected in subsequent editions.

THE CONFIDENT COLLECTOR: THE OVERSTREET INDIAN ARROWHEADS IDENTIFICATION AND PRICE GUIDE (3rd edition) is an original publication of Avon Books. This work has never before appeared in book form.

AVON BOOKS
A division of
The Hearst Corporation
1350 Avenue of the Americas
New York, New York 10019

Published by arrangement with Overstreet Publications Inc.
Library of Congress Catalog Card Number: 92-97109
ISBN: 0-380-77186-1

Cover photographed by Denford Jones Photographics

First Avon Books Trade Printing: June 1993

Printed in the U.S.A.

10 9 8 7 6 5 4 3 2 1

TABLE OF CONTENTS

ACKNOWLEDGMENTS

A very special thanks is due Erwin and Howard Peake and Stephen Addison for their time devoted to traveling and photographing needed types, and especially to Erwin and Howard for locating collections for shooting and their endless hours spent in point classification and pricing. This book contains many photos from the collections of Blake Warren, Roland Callicutt, Ralph Allen and Floyd Ritter.

We wish to sincerely thank these people especially for making their collections available to us. Hundreds of new photographs were provided for this edition from the collections of Tommy Beutell, Leo Paul Davis and others who spent their valuable time with us.

Our gratitude goes to Kevin Pipes and John Parker for their advice and help with this project. Many of their points are illustrated throughout this edition. We would also like to thank a new friend in Florida, Susan Crowe who sent many photos of personal finds for this edition and to Scott Tickner who also provided photographs of needed types.

Special thanks is due the Cherokee Museums in North Carolina and in Tahlequah for their support. One of the finest displays of point types in a museum is in the Indian Mound and Museum in Florence, Alabama. Charles Moore was very generous in allowing us to photograph the museum's collection for our first edition.

We are also indebted to the Late A.W. Beinlich Jr. and Dr. Hollifield whose collections also appear in this edition.

Acknowledgement is also due those who wish their names not to be listed and especially to the following people who either provided photographs, points for photographing or additional data:

David Amos
Jim Catoe
Owen Collins
Brad Cooley
Dr. Jay Goldberg
Les Grubbe
Newell Harrison
Patrick Keefe
Ray Kilgore
Steve Langly
Jimmy Mabe
Sandy McConnell
Sam Murphy
Frank Nifong
John Retherford
Jamie Richardson
Philip Richardson
Hank Senn
George W. Shanks, Jr.
David Shaw
Charles Shewey
Scott C. Tickner
Dale Strader
Mark Wagoner
Becky Wilkes
Jeff Wilkes
Jimmy Wilkes
Louise Young

INTRODUCTION

> All points illustrated in this book are believed to be genuine prehistoric artifacts. We have gone to great lengths to insure that only authentic points are included. Any errors discovered will be deleted in future editions. This is not a "for sale" list of points. The illustrated examples are for identification and value purposes only.

Hunting arrowheads has been a popular pastime for many Americans over the past one hundred years. Even the Indians themselves cherished and collected rock crystals, gem stones and points. In the past, large collections were put together with very little effort, since few people hunted and the supply of good artifacts was plentiful. Plowed fields along creeks and rivers, as well as river banks, are the most popular sources for hunting relics, as the early Indians built their villages and hunted game in such locations. The Indians' food supply, such as fish, mussels, game, etc. lived in, or migrated to, or along a water supply such as rivers, creeks, springs, ponds, swamps and lakes. Early man preyed on this abundant food supply, migrating along these water routes, moving from place to place in search of better hunting grounds, as the game became depleted.

Fields are plowed in the Fall or Spring of each year. The most likely sites for hunting, of course, would be the large flat areas close to the original river or creek banks areas that may be large enough to support a small village and are on high ground, protected from a flooding river especially places where a creek converges with a larger river. Go field hunting after a hard rain which will wash-out relics and make them easy to see. Look for washed-out areas or gulleys. Here is where you can get lucky, especially if you are the first person in the field. Be sure to ask permission before entering private property. Most farmers are friendly and will give permission to enter their land if asked in a nice way.

Plowed fields next to springs and cave openings have also produced relics. Such a place is Castillian Springs, just above Nashville, Tennessee. Here, next to the spring, there are salt licks for animals. The Indians occupied and lived in this area for thousands of years from Paleo to Woodland periods and later. The herd animals would always migrate here for salt and watering, providing the Indians with plentiful meat and nourishment right in their own back yard. Erosion around the spring has, in the past, produced many excellent artifacts from fluted points to Doves, to Lost Lakes, to stemmed types. Another similar site is Nickajack Cave and its surrounding fields just below Chattanooga, Tennessee. Overhangs and rock shelters along rivers and creeks where early man lived, as well as river islands, have produced fine artifacts as well.

In the 1930s the blow-outs or dust storms in the plains states produced many fine projectile points. The top layer of soil blew away, exposing relics left centuries ago by the Indians.

Sand bar hunting along the Tennessee River became possible after the Tennessee Valley Authority built their dams and began controlling the river level in the 1930s. During the development of the TVA system, hunting was excellent. Lake levels were dropped during the winter months exposing the sand bars which were originally high areas in the now inundated fields along the river channel areas where the early Indians built their villages and camp sites. As winter storms raged through the Tennessee Valley, the lake levels would rise and fall and the racing river would cut into the sand bars, exposing relics for anyone to merely come along and pick up.

Today most of the sand bars and plowed fields in many states have been "hunted out." But the energetic hunter can still find new sites that produce if he gathers his facts, follows all leads, studies maps of likely areas and hunts whenever he can. Sooner or later he will get lucky.

However, most collectors are neither energetic nor imaginative, and build their collections by systematically purchasing specimens one at a time. ***Genuine*** points can be found for sale at relic shows, and sometimes local collections come up for sale in your area. Warning: More than any other collectible field, fake relics, all recently made and aged, are being offered to the public everywhere as genuine prehistoric artifacts. Knowing the history or pedigree of a point is very important in the process of determining whether or not it is a genuine pre-Columbian piece. Before purchasing a relic from anyone, be sure the dealer will guarantee it to be a genuine, old pre-Columbian piece, and will also give you your money back should you later discover otherwise. Many reputable dealers will give you a money back guarantee. Whenever possible, you should have an expert acquaintance examine any and every piece for its authenticity before you buy.

WHY COLLECT PROJECTILE POINTS?

Whether you collect ancient Chinese cloisonne, Egyptian tomb pieces, or projectile points, there is a particular satisfaction in possessing a piece of history from the distant past-to hold in your hands an object that was made by someone thousands of years ago.

Projectile points may very well be the earliest evidence of man's ability to create, style and manufacture objects of symmetry and beauty. If you ever have the priviledge of seeing an exceptional piece, made of the finest material, and flaked to perfection, take a close look. You will soon realize that these early tools of man were made for two reasons: function and beauty. They represent a unique art form crafted by the world's earliest artist. Unique, because, like snowflakes, each specimen is an original and no two are exactly alike.

Many different materials were utilized from crude slate, conglomerate or quartzite to high quality flint, agate, petrified wood or volcanic obsidian. Even the Indians went to great lengths to obtain high quality material from the popular flint and chert quarries known to them, such as Dover in Northwest Tennessee, Flint Ridge in Ohio, and the many obsidian sources of the West. It is believed that extensive trade networks for flint and other objects were established in the earliest times and extended over vast areas from coast to coast.

The variations in shape and flaking style are clues to dating and identifying point types. The novice should study points from the different periods illustrated in this book and will soon become familiar with the various styles produced. Generally speaking, the older Paleo and Archaic types are better made, exhibiting the finest flaking, thinness, edgework and symmetry ever produced by man. The earliest points are all auriculate or eared. Some are grooved in the center or fluted. Later, these forms basically became side-notched, corner-notched or basal-notched or stemmed. With the introduction of the bow, most points became smaller and lighter with stemmed bases. However, during the Woodland period, Paleo auriculate and Archaic notched forms reappeared for a short period of time.

Some collectors specialize in a particular type, while others try to assemble a collection of many shapes and types. Most collectors are only interested in points from their immediate locale, and only if found by them. However, this author has learned after many years of hunting, that the only way to put together a quality collection is through intelligent buying. It's a rare occurrence today to find an outstanding piece for your collection by hunting in the field.

HOW TO GRADE POINTS

Before a point's true value can be assessed, its condition or state of preservation as well as quality must be determined. The better the quality and condition, the larger the size, the more valuable the point. Perfect points that are thin, made of high quality material with perfect symmetry, flaking and are classic for the type are worths several times the price of common, but complete low grade field points.

The following factors influence the grade and value of a point:

Condition: Perfection is the rule. Nicks, chips, breakage reduce value.

Size: Everything else being equal, a larger point will grade higher than a smaller point and larger points are worth more.

Form: The closer a point comes to being a classic for the type, the higher the grade and value.

Symmetry: Points with good balance and design are higher grade and worth more.

Flaking: Points with precision percussion and secondary flaking, a minimum of hinge fractures and problem areas are higher grade and worth more. Points with unusual flaking patterns, such as collateral or oblique transverse enhances grade and value.

Thinness: The thinner the better.

Material & Color: Quality as well as type of material enhances grade and value. Points made from colorful or high quality material such as agate, petrified wood, agatized coral, quartz crystal, flint, jasper, Horse Creek chert, Buffalo River chert, conglomerate, Flint Ridge chert, Carter Cave chert, Dover chert, etc. increases grade and value. Some materials become glassier and more colorful when heat treated by the Indians and would enhance the grade. Certain local materials are more collectible in various states, such as ryolite in North and South Carolina, Dover in Tennessee, Carter Cave chert or Kentucky hornstone in Kentucky, Flint Ridge chert in Ohio, Knife River chert in South Dakota or petrified wood in Arizona and New Mexico. Usually, points that have pretty colors alone will sell for higher prices.

However, most points are made of medium grade gray to brownish cherts and the grade and value is more influenced by the other factors listed above.

After all the above steps have been considered, then the reader can begin to assign a grade to his point. Points are graded on a scale of 1 to 10, where a 10 is the best and a 1 is the lowest grade for a complete point.

GRADING DEFINITIONS

Grade 10: Perfect in every way which includes thinness, flaking, symmetry and form. The best example you would ever expect to see of any given type. This grade is rarely seen and is extremely rare. This grade applies to medium to large size points that normally occurs in a given type. A point does not necessarily have to be the largest known to qualify for this grade.

Grade 8 or 9: Near perfect but lacking just a little in size or material or thinness. It may have a small defect to keep it out of a 10 category. Still very rare and most high grade points would fall in this category.

Grade 6 or 7: Better than the average grade but not quite nice enough to get a high ranking. Flaking, size and symmetry are just a little above average. Points in this grade are still very hard to find in most states. A very collectible grade.

Grade 4 or 5: The average quality that is found. The size is medium, the flaking, thickness and symmetry is average. 2 or 3 very minute nicks may be seen, but none that would be considered serious.

Grade 1-3: Field grade points that have below average overall quality. Better points with more serious faults or dings would fall in this grade. The most common grade found and correspondingly, the least valuable.

Broken points: Usually little to no value. However, good high grade broken backs of high demand type points have fetched good prices. Such as paleo points and many of the rare beveled and notched types.

PRICING POINTS

After a point has been graded and assigned a grade number, it sould be compared with similar points in the alphabetical listing. The prices listed will give the reader a guide as to the probable value of his point. But be careful, compare grade with grade. If your point has a little ear or tip broken, the value is affected drastically. Of course, state of perfection, thinness, rarity of type, quality of material and flaking and size all enter into determining a value. Usually with everything being equal, the larger the size the higher the price.

PRICING IN THIS BOOK: Prices listed in this book are for your information only. None of the points shown are for sale. Under each type, we have attempted to show a photographic spread of size, quality and variation of form (where available), from low to high grade, with corresponding prices. A price range is given for each illustration.

The low price is the *wholesale price* (the price dealers may pay for that point).

The high price is the *retail price* (the price a collecto rmay pay for that point).

Each illustration also gives a brief description pointing out special features when applicable. The prices listed have been averaged from the highest and lowest prices we have seen, just prior to publication. We feel that this will give you a fair, realistic price value for each piece illustrated. If your point matches the illustrated example in both size, color and quality, the listed value would then apply.

Many factors affect value and should be considered when determining a price for your point. Besides those listed under Grading Points, the following should also be considered:

More factors that influence the value of a point:

Provenance: When a point has been properly documented as to where and when it was found and by who, the value increases. Points from famous sites such as the Clovis site in New Mexico, the Quad site in Alabama, the Nuckolls site in Tennessee, the Hardaway site in North Carolina, etc. increases value. Well documented points from famous collections increases value. Points that have been published increases demand and makes them easier to sell (the wise investor should have all points checked before purchase, whether published or not, because many fakes have been published as genuine). Local points usually bring higher prices than imports from other states.

Rarity: Obviously, some point types are scarcer and much harder to find than others. For instance, Clovis which is found in most of North America is more common than Folsom which is rarely found in just a few western states. But both these types are much rarer than Pickwick or Adena which occur in large quantities.

Popularity of Type: Market demand for certain point types can greatly influence the supply and value. The value of these points can vary with changing market demands and available supplys.

Points with slight damage, such as a nick off the tip or wing, suffer a cut in value of about 60 percent. Medium damage, such as a wing missing, will cut the value by about 90 percent. Field grade pieces and halves are usually sold at five dollars per gallon. The very best points have no top retail price and are always in very high demand. Local points are usually always worth more in the area where they are found.

Fire damaged points: Points made of flint, chert, chalcedony and other materials are susceptible to damage when in close contact with fire and heat. This can occur when points shot at the animal are left in the butchered meat that is cooked over a fire. Fire damaged flint reflects a rather unique appearance, usually a circular pitted, or pock-marked look not unlike miniature moon craters.

There have been theories that the intense heat of fire actually brings about a molecular change, or rearrangement of the molecules. This undue stress or tension causes a change in the material which induces the pock-marks to form. This has been questioned and critized by some geologists who flatly state that no such action takes place.

The acceptable and more logical explanation is that the change is purely physical. That is, that the heat from the fire is applied and transferred in such a random and uneven manner that the coefficients of contraction and expansion causes the damage or pitting.

The resultant conflict of expansion and non-expansion coefficients flake off the flint material due to tensions within itself. The resultant flake is quite different from a pressure or percussion flake in that it is circular and, of course, non-controllable. The following illustrations show points with the typical pitting associated with fire damage.

(Examples of fire damaged points)

Impact fractures: When spears and arrow points are thrown or shot, they sometimes collide with hard objects such as bone in animals or rock or wood when the target is missed. If the angle at the point of impact is just right, the resulting blow will fracture the point, forming a flute or channel that runs from the tip toward the base. In other examples the fracturing will run up the side or the tip of the point will simply snap off. Occasionally these broken points with impact fluting are remade in to new points with the flute channel still visible (see illo). These should not be confused with real fluted Paleo points that were found by later Indians and rechipped into a more recent point, also with the fluting still present. Points with well defined impact fractures are interesting additions to any collection and should not be overlooked when going through the junk boxes.

Impact Fractures (continued)

A unique example of a point with an impact fracture that was rechipped into a complete point.

Fracture extends along the right side from the tip through the base. Excellent example.

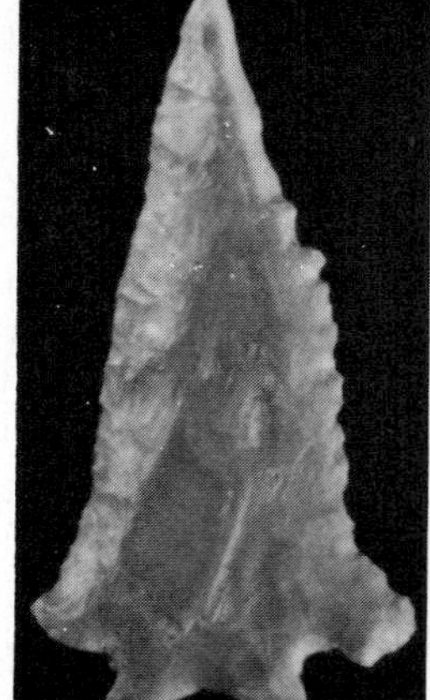

Fluted from the base.
Impact fracture from the tip.

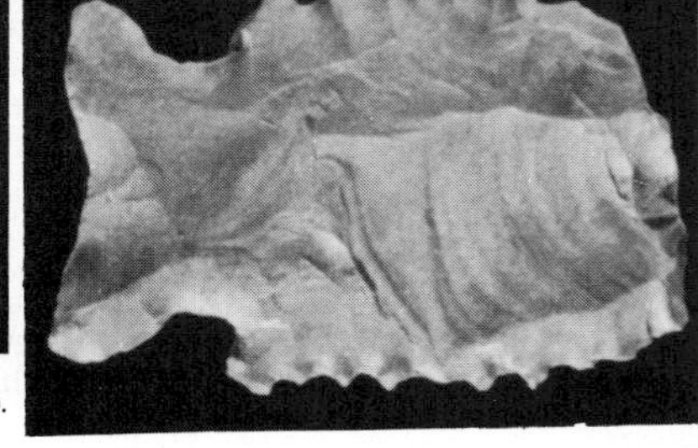

Hafting: Sinew, gut and rawhide were used to lash the stone points or knives onto a shaft or handle. Fibres from hair and plants (grasses, tree bark, yucca, vines, etc.) were also employed for lashing. Pitch and asphalt were used as adhesives (when available) to glue the lashings to the stone and shaft. On rare occasions arrows and knives have been found with hafting completely intact.

Right: A complete knife with bone handle and flint blade recovered 4 feet below the floor of a dry cave in the Fort Rock desert in south central Oregon. Note the tally marks at the rear of the handle. The gut hafting and the gum or asphaltum adhesive cementing the blade to the handle.

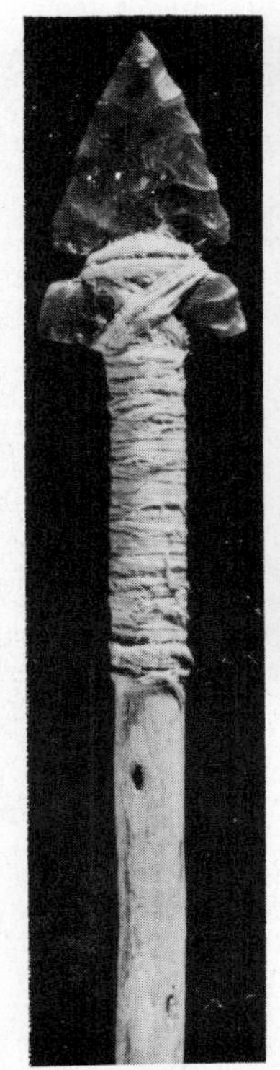

A rare example of a hafted arrowpoint on a wooden shaft. This arrow was found in a cave in Las Cruces, NM. The binding is fashioned of fibres from a local plant.

A Kirk Corner-Notched point found on the Hiwassee River in SE Tenn. Note the petrified hafting around the base of the point. A brown stain and remnants of the hafting extends all around the stem .

DATING AND NAMING POINT TYPES

For decades professional archaeologists and collectors have been interested in the age and classification of projectile points. Of course the best information has come from archaeologically controlled scientific excavations where exact locations, cultural association and carbon dating of associated matter with point types was made.

This is done through stratigraphic excavation where artifacts are carefully removed and catalogued from each cultural layer. Carbon deposits from animal and vegetable remains are also taken from these layers and dated through the carbon 14 and other techniques. This gives an age for each layer and its associated artifacts.

Many of these sites were occupied for thousands of years by various peoples who left projectile points around their campfires and buried with their dead. The face of the land next to rivers, where many of these sites are, is always changing due to flooding. Indian villages and campsites were either being eroded away or buried under silt deposited by the flooding river. Soon the sites that were destroyed would become occupied again, waiting for the next inundation. Over a period of thousands of years, these sites accumulated many stratified layers of silt, some of which contain evidence of human occupation. The most recent culture would be near the top with the oldest at the deepest levels.

Some of these excavated areas produced important point types which were named after the site from which they were found. These "type sites" are located all across the country. Some of the more famous ones are Eva in northwest Tennessee, Quad and Pine Tree in northwest Alabama, Clovis near Clovis, New Mexico, Folsom near Folsom, New Mexico, Columbia Gem Points from the Northwest and Sandia from Sandia Cave near Albuquerque, New Mexico. There are many more sites, too numerous to list here.

These excavations have provided valuable information about point types and their cultural relationships, and the papers published about them by the archaeologists became the first attempt at typing or classifying projectile points. These papers and books are still important reference sources today and belong in every reference library.

WHY ANOTHER TYPE BOOK?

The authors of this book have felt the need for a more comprehensive type book; a book that would not only show more detail in each illustration, but a spread of variations for each type as well. Many of the existing type books give only one example of each type, usually a pen and ink drawing. Since most point types have many variations, it is difficult and frustrating to classify a collection from only one example of each type. There is also a problem classifying from artwork because we are at the mercy of the artist to show accurately the subtleties of each type illustrated.

We believe that it takes photographs to show the flaking technique, patination, and other factors that are important in cultural period classification. Also the texture of the material, beveling, serrations, etc. are shown in much more detail with photographs. In this volume, where we felt there was a need, several specimens of a type are shown. We have also included additional supportive information to insure that this book is the most helpful and comprehensive of its kind to collectors.

All mistakes are our own. We have gone to great lengths to insure that only genuine pre-Columbian artifacts are used for the illustrations. Where there was any question of a point's authenticity, we did not include it. There were also problems in classifying some of the variants and placing the photographs under their proper types. Again errors in this area, as they occur, will be remedied in future editions.

This reference work is not inclusive of all known types, although hundreds are named and listed. These will be added in future editions as good examples become available for us to photograph. We solicit your comments, critique, and type suggestions for future editions of this work.

Cores: Cores are made from spalls which are large chunks of flint broken off nodules for the manufacture of projectile points and knives. Long, thin, slender flakes are struck off the spall, eventually creating a circular core. Points are then fashioned from the flakes. As more and more flakes are removed, the spall takes on a conical shape. The flakes are struck from the round base towards the point. Eventually, the cone becomes too small to produce flakes of proper size and is then discarded. The illustrations (reduced to about half size) are examples of spent cores.

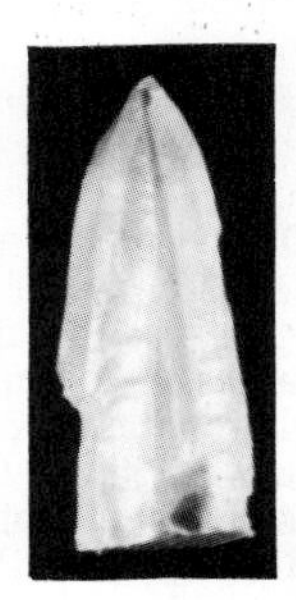

(Examples of spent cores made from spalls)

FINDING VERSUS BUYING POINTS

Why would a collector want to buy points instead of just finding his own? The answer to this question is very simple. Many people who collect just don't have the time to spend hunting in the field. In most cases, you can buy points cheaper than you can find them, when you consider travel, lodging, food and the money you could be earning if you were at home. But the best reason for buying is to acquire quality pieces that are not available or found in your immediate area of hunting. Not all collectors are fortunate enough to live in an area that produces high quality material.

One of the authors lived and hunted in central Alabama and Mississippi for ten years, keeping every piece that was found. Later, when he took a realistic look at his collection, it was only worth about $1,000.00 and looked very common. He began selling everything but the most perfect pieces. He used the money to finance hunting trips to other areas that were strong with quality points, and also began to buy nice pieces as they became available. His previous collection was basically all the same color. He soon found that points from other areas were more colorful, and within three years he had built a large collection that anyone would be proud to own. He kept up this style of collecting for several years and has owned many super quality pieces worth a substantial amount of money. If he had not ventured out into other hunting areas, his collection today would still be worth little and of low quality. Try possessing a quality item, whether it be stone, bone, pottery or flint. After all, isn't this what collecting is all about?

HOW TO SPOT THE BEST RIVER SITES

The best place to begin is at the mouth of any tributary that feeds the river. There are usually high slopes on both sides where the Indians lived. A favorite site for early man was a point coming off a large hill, that flattened out near the river. If you are in an area with a lot of low bottom land, you should look for the higher spots along the shoreline. Another good area to check (in the case of dammed rivers) is the backwaters or sloughs and tributaries off the main channel. These places are usually lined with peninsulas or islands that receive constant weathering on their beaches. The lake level is always fluctuating depending upon rains and water flow through the dams. The rising and falling of the water is always lashing at the exposed river banks and beaches.

Many people use boats on the lakes to reach the sites, whether they are hunting river banks or fields along the river. On large rivers, the best hunting is usually the second or third ridge away from the river. The Indians would set up camp here due to the river changing its course and, most of all, flood waters. An exception would be a large ridge along the river bank that is already high enough from the flood waters. On the smaller streams, the best area is the first hump or ridge back from the stream. Timing is very important. Being the first person on a producing site just after bank erosion has occurred is the name of the game. This information should aid the beginner collector. Good luck and happy hunting!

RIVER LAYER HUNTING

Depth of layers in feet: A-(1'-2'), B-(2'-3'), C-(3'-5'), D-(8'-10'), E-(14'-16'), F-(18'-20'), G-(20'-22'), H-(26')

Note that the area or gaps between the layers (A-H) represent the silt that separates the occupied layers. These silt layers would have some correlation in time elapsed between the occupied layers. **Layer** A-Mississippian; bird points and pottery. **Layer** B-Copena, celts, pottery. **Layer** C-Woodland; stemmed points, stone tools, pottery, atlatl. **Layer** D-Late Archaic; Benton layer, stone tools, atlatl. **Layer** E-Early Archaic and Transitional Paleo points and uniface tools. **Layer** F-Transitional Paleo points and unfluted Paleo points. **Layer** G-Paleo points and uniface tools. **Layer** H-Original hard clay and stone river bank.

Here are some interesting facts about certain layers. The deeper or lower the layer, the older the point. **Layer** C-The *Little Bear Creek* and *Mulberry Creek* points are near the top of this layer; whereas the *Pickwick* and *Big Slough* are near the bottom, proving they are the most ancient. **Layer** E-From the top of this layer down to the middle comes fractured base *Decatur, LeCroy,* and most of all, *Pine Tree.* The *Lost Lake* and *Plevna (Dovetail)* are next, followed by an occasional *Eva* and several *Kirk Corner Notched* points. At the very bottom of the layer were many fine *Greenbrier* points. **Layer** F-At the top of this layer are a few *Greenbrier* points with classic *Daltons* just three inches below them. Toward the bottom of the layer are *Beaver Lake* and unfluted *Clovis* points. **Layer** G-All points and even damaged pieces have been fluted. The Cumberland points are near the middle of the layer and the Clovis points are toward the bottom. This proves that Clovis points are older, yet Cumberland points are more valuable due to their limited distribution and rarity.

HOW TO BUY AUTHENTIC RELICS

The best way to recognize an old point is by knowing how both river and field patination affects the type of flint from which the point is made. Each point type also has its own style of chipping that you should study and understand. A Paleo point never has random flaking, while Archaic and Woodland points do. You should understand that changes in patination along the edges or near the point of an arrow are signs of rechipping. Hinge fractures are good indicators to the authenticity of a point. An old point will patinate underneath the hinge fracture.

If you go to a show, flea market, or someone's house to buy relics, you must decide if the person selling the relics is trustworthy. If this person has a piece that you definitely want, and he looks untrustworthy, you should ask for a guarantee in writing. If the person seems to be of good character, you should ask for a satisfaction guarantee. This means that if you do get a piece that becomes questionable, you would be able to trade it for another item of equal value that you feel is a good authentic piece. This arrangement would help you feel more secure about what you are buying.

There is a lot of competition in the Indian relic market. Some people will condemn a competitor's piece to persuade you to buy from them. They will also try to buy a good item from you at a cheap price. Others may say a relic is bad just to convince you that they are experts. To be truely knowledgeable in Indian relics, this book will help, but you need to learn as much as you can. Study the flint types of your collecting area and how they look with natural patination. Learn to match flaking styles with types. Simply look at as many good authentic points as you can. Remember, the people who think they know more than everyone else are usually the ones who get burned.

MARKET REPORT

We have had a very interesting couple of years. The Indian artifact field has received more publicity than any time in the past. On one hand, we have the influence of the Washington Paleo cache (valued at $450,000). Then on the other hand, you have court cases over digging, fines for just surface hunting, and people charged with trespassing for surface hunting in plowed fields. This publicity and controversy has brought many new collectors, dealers, and investors into the artifact field. The demand for high grade classic point types, has caused prices to continue to soar. Pedigree and authentification in writing still has a great influence over the value of a point. There has been an increase in value of all grades of points, with the greatest influence on grade 9 and 10. Even the field grade points (guide grades 1-2) are bringing more than in the past.

There is an old saying, “Paleo is King.” You hear this at shows around the country, and they are referring to the fluted points. They show the most rapid increase in value over all other types. Paleo and Transitional Paleo points, usually sell fast and are purchased above the Overstreet guide prices when there is no question about the authenticity of the point. Even fluted points, grades 4-5, have doubled in the last few years. Many collectors and dealers continue to skower the richest areas that produce Paleo points. The following are a few recent sales:

Clovis-$13,000; Cumberland-$15,000 (turned down); Redstone-$8,000; Folsom-$4,000 (turned down); Clovis-$7,500; Clovis-$5,000; Debert-$2,000; Greenbrier-$2,500; Quad-$4,000; Sloan-$3,500 and a Fishtail-$1,500.

Not far behind the fluted point is the value of the classic bevels of the early Archaic period. The super Dovetails, Thebes, Hardins, Lost Lakes, large Fracture Bases, and Saint Charles are sold in the thousands instead of the hundreds. Even more dynamic, are the long ceremonial cache points made during the late Archaic period. These cache points are very rare and valuable. They are in high demand with an extremely limited quantity. Some recent observations follow:

Dovetail-$1500; Kirk-$1500; Lost Lake-$2500; Pine Tree-$1000; Hardin-$7000; Fractured Base-$1200, and Thebes-$1200.

Late Archaic cache points sold: 14” Benton-$8500; 13” Turkeytail (early form)-$6500; 12” Benton-$7500; 10” Elk River-$2200; 9” double notched Turkeytail-$5500 and a 16” killed Turkeytail-$1000.

There are more Woodland points found than points of any other cultural period. This is the only time period where you can still buy a good spearpoint at an affordable price when compared to earlier point types. Even with the greater demand for points today, there are an abundant supply of Woodland points (grades 1-6). Therefore, these points are escallating just as in the other cultural periods. A few of the known point sales follow: Snyders-$1800; Motley-$2500; Mulberry Creek-$600; Mud Creek-$600; Pickwick-$1800; Copena-$2000; Little Bear-$750 and a North-$600.

Nearly every collector in the country wants a selection of small Mississippian points. These points in grades 9-10 have doubled in value in the last couple years. Mississippian points are also found in caches, which are sought by collectors in every state. Whether its a cache of Caddo points, agate points of the Northwest, warpoints from the Southwest or birdpoints of the Southeast, demand is high and so are the prices. Some recent sales include: Columbia River-$450; Maud-$300; Nodena-$250; Jacks Reef Pentagonal-$200; Hayes-$280; Agee-$450; Rogue River-$350; Knight Island-$800 (offer rejected); Talco-$350; Cahokia-$350; Hayes Double Notch-$500 and a Perdiz-$400.

We are often asked "How do you acquire high grade or cache quality points?" After consulting several dealers, we have compiled the following advice toward answering this question. First, go into areas that are known to produce the type of point that you want to obtain. There, you either spend a lot of time hunting yourself, or contact the local collectors who may sell some of their points. As a general rule, when you get a local collector's help, they can direct you to the other local relic hunters. Going to an Indian relic show, is another way to get a rare point. However, at the shows, prices are usually at or above the Overstreet Guide Value.

Many times, buying a super point at a show or from a known dealer, is the only chance for a collector to obtain a rare grade 9-10 point. This is especially true for collectors in areas that are archeologically important, when choosing a relic show to attend. They also attract the largest point dealers as well as the best local pieces that are for sale.

IDENTIFICATION OF ARCHEOLOGICAL SITES

There are several methods that hunters use to locate new sites. Some like to talk to the old time collectors who tell them about sites they once searched. Others try topographic maps, airplanes, color of soil and even buying sites so they have exclusive rights. The best advice for beginners would be to find the first hump or ridge just away from the river. When this area is part of a plowed field, you will usually find signs of early man. A collector who really has a good background can ride any road and point out many sites just by conditions being right. The same is true for boating on the rivers. There are also bluff shelters that were used by the Indians nearly in every occassion. The one place that seems to always have the strongest concentrated evidence of early man, is the first high area back from the mouth of a tributary stream, that feeds a larger stream. Some hunters find nice pieces by hunting in the creek beds during low water. In some areas, where there are cliffs close to the river, Indians would build villages and mounds on the flat top part of the cliff. Indians also lived near natural scenery such as waterfalls, springs, caves, rock bridges and canyons. A young person resently wrote "How can I find a good arrowhead?" Our instructions were as follows:

Go to any river bottom (flat lands along many rivers), and hunt on the high spots during the Spring plow season. If the land is disced, you will find a lot of damaged pieces. But if the land has been turned by the deep running, breaking plows, you stand a chance of finding something perfect and possibly large. We hope this information helps and wish you good luck in your hunting efforts.

The above lake site has produced thousands of artifacts over the years. When the lake drops for Winter pool, long peninsulas or sand bars will extend and wash from the heavy rains. Collectors simply walk the beaches in search of relics.

The above site is a perfect high area with a stream in the woods just past it. Anytime the first high area away from a stream is plowed, it is a good place to hunt. This site may produce some of the late Archaic cache points. Look for similar sites along streams and rivers in your area.

You may also want to try hunting the shell middens along the river which are known to produce excellent arrowheads. They are very easy to spot. Note shell deposits (white areas) along beach illustrated above.

A closeup of the beach at the site in the top photo showing the mix of shell, rocks and flint flakes. The best advice on river hunting is to concentrate on areas of fresh heavy shore erosion.

A site being protected against erosion for a future excavation project.

Above: Closeup of the site in the top photograph. This site has a Copena burial layer about the middle of the bank and a thick layer of late Archaic flaking near the base of the bank.

Many collectors enjoy boating and stopping along the banks where there are sites. As far as the information to date, we can look the river except for state and federal lands, such as: Wildlife reserves, parks, national forests, etc. As for the plowed fields, we have heard of little problems for just surface hunting with permission from the landowners. However, there were a few trespassing tickets from wildlife resource agents given to hunters without written permission from the owner. We have some people who hunt creek beds, gravel and sand bars, who have been asked to leave. No one seems to know where we stand on digging. Is all digging illegal? What about digging on your own land in a village site? The laws seem to have different interpretation in different parts of the country.

Let's have an open mind and take a look at what is going on in different situations. First we'll take plowed fields. The surface material is of almost no archeological significance because it has been disturbed and all that will happen to the artifacts is that they will be broken and destroyed by the plows. Surely, no one can find fault with saving these pieces by surface hunting. Next, we'll look at hunting in creek beds. Again, the pieces are not in their original layer. They too are destroyed by swift water and other rocks. We can't fault in saving these pieces for people to see, enjoy and praise.

Digging is the most controversial part of the collecting of artifacts. Some people think that private collectors should surface hunt only and not dig at all. Most believe they should be able to do as they please on land they own or lease. Generally, many think (where the law permits) that digging village sites and trash pits are acceptable, but not burial or ceremonial sites. We feel that there is no harm in digging villages or trash pits on private property with permission or on your own land. There should be more cooperation between professionals and the private collectors. Professionals could possibly post sites that contain human remains and let the amateurs hunt on the village sites. We share the same interest, why not work together, instead of being like the President and Congress.

Most everyone we talk to would go along with not disturbing sites with human remains. This is the type of site that the government was intending to protect. Now, it has been blown out of proportion and used to fine people for hunting pieces that would have been destroyed or lost forever. If revenue is the problem, why not sell a relic hunting license that would be good for all surface hunting and flood area river hunting. This would be more practical than citizens not knowing what the laws are and hating government and professionals. Let's protect the burial or ceremonial mounds, and leave the good citizens alone who like this wholesome family hobby.

There are some hard feelings about river hunting being prohibited in certain areas such as parks, forest and wildlife reserves. Now, this may sound like a good idea. But lets look at the collectors point of view also.

Above: Photograph showing a typical river bank along a major river system. Toward the bottom of the picture is a dark layer or village of the late Archaic period which contains aritfacts. Note the heavy erosion taking place where large chunks of soil have fallen into the water below.

Here is a close-up of the dark layer in the previous photograph. There are several areas of exposed bone. There are thousands of scenes like this along the major U.S. rivers. The exposed point is an early form of Benton with an early system of flaking. Lets take a look at what will happen to this Benton point.

This is the beach below the river bank that has been shown. Large chunks of bank fall and are dissolved to form these sandy beaches. The Benton point (from the previous illustration), bone, tools and everything else end up on this beach for a short time. The future of this artifact can take three possible results. First, it can be found by someone who can cherish and display it for others to enjoy. Second, it can be pulled off the bank by waves (as in the photograph) only to be lost forever in mud. Third, it can be dredged up by gravel barges where it will be destroyed by the shaking, screening and falling. Note the photograph below:.

Above: River banks are constantly being dredged in the production of sand and gravel for consumers. Of course the archaeological sites are located in these river banks and are being destroyed by this process.

Stopping collectors from hunting these beaches seems rediculous. This doesn't even make sense on wildlife reserves either (where currently many tickets are being written to offenders). Consider points not on the river banks, such as under bluff shelters or in the sandy parks of the western states. They will lay there for years if not disturbed. This is simply not the case when it comes to river banks. We can't see any harm in a family out hunting arrows in the flood plain (below the high water mark) which is always changing with water fluctuation. This goes for wildlife flood zones also because in this case, it is not preserving, it is losing. We submit "fine the diggers, leave good people who are surface hunting alone."

Left: This photograph shows a fine Mississippian burial mound. Indian rights groups want all sites like this one protected from looters. There are hundreds of sites like this one along the major waterways of our nation. This mound is being destroyed by two factors neither is digging. First, high water is eating away at its base and large pleasure ships or barges are sending large waves against the banks. This causes the large piles of fresh soil to slide into the river along with artifacts and human remains. As we pointed out, this is only one of many sites with the same destruction taking place daily. Only a small percentage of these sites are attacked by diggers. So, the vast majority of destruction seems to be done by water transportation and energy systems.

We believe it is better for a young person to be walking a beach, searching for an arrow, than roaming the streets looking for trouble. We have not seen any human remains at artifact shows, Just tools and weapons they made to survive. Most collectors are from good families that hunt as a hobby and should not fear the government taking their time away. We think originally the legislation was meant to protect certain ceremonial sites, but then the interpretation was later expanded to include many other areas, and today has completely overdone things to the point that private citizens are being fined for walking the beaches hunting points.

If the government is for stopping citizens from walking the river banks, and for protecting the river sites from being destroyed, then lets do it 100% or not at all. The cause of over 90% of the destruction of the river sites is man-made erosion. Erosion is caused by large pleasure craft and barges. So to satisfy a few, we must eliminate all river traffic. Erosion is also caused by the water level being raised to the height of the sites. So to satisfy the law, we would have to shut down the energy producing dams, to get the water down to below the sites. If we are going to overdo the protection of river sites, lets lay the blame where it belongs, not just on the collector.

The answer to river hunting should be admissible. The answer to plowed fields should be to permit except where land is posted and violators would be guilty of trespassing. The answer to digging-not allowed on any government land or anywhere there are human remains.

HOW TO USE THIS BOOK

IMPORTANT

All illustrations in the book are actual size unless otherwise noted.

CLASSIFICATION: Projectile points come in many shapes, colors and sizes. Their quality varies from thick, crude forms to very thin, beautifully flaked, symmetrical specimens. Over the past fifty years, hundreds of points have been classified and given names. The names of people, rivers, creeks, lakes, mountains, towns, etc. have been used in naming point types. Many of the types come from sites that were excavated from undisturbed stratigraphic layers and carbon dating was made. These data are important in placing each type in time and showing the relationship of one type to another. You will soon see that most of the early types evolved into the later forms.

The scope of this book is to include as many point types as possible with the idea of expanding to more types in future updated editions as the information becomes available to us. The point types are arranged in alphabetical order. The archeological period and approximate dates of popular use are given for each point type. A general distribution area is given, along with a brief description of each type. There are several factors that determine a given type: **1**-Shape or form. 2-Size. **3**-Style or flaking. **4**-Thickness or thinness. **5**-Kind of material.

IDENTIFYING FORMS: All points fall into four basic forms: 1. Lanceolate. 2. Auriculate. 3. Notched base. 4. Stemmed.

Examples of these forms are illustrated on the following pages and should serve as a quick guide in determining the shape or type of a given point. Just compare your point with the illustrated examples to determine if it is lanceolate, auriculate, side notched, corner notched, basal notched or stemmed. Once you have determined the basic shape, then go to the list of types associated with the form which your point matched. One by one, compare your point with each type listed, leafing through the book until a perfect match is found. Please pay attention to type or style of flaking, beveling (if any), as well as shape and size. Most of the early points (Paleo and Archaic) exhibit parallel or collateral flaking from the edge to the center of the point. Woodland and later points were not made this way. Sometimes, this is your only clue in determining a type when you have found several forms from different periods that seem to match your point.

Although hundreds of points have been named, there are still dozens of forms that have not been identified. During the Woodland Period, the use of the bow brought about myriad variations in the stemmed point. Here is where the novice will have his greatest problem in determining types. Many of these forms will not be found in any type book, so don't get discouraged when you cannot find a match.

IDENTIFICATION AND CLASSIFICATION OF POINT SHAPES AND FEATURES

LANCEOLATE FORMS
(BASE SHAPES)

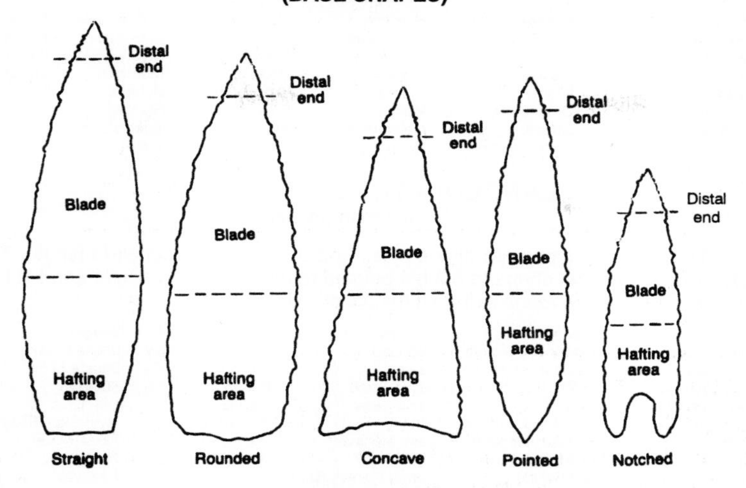

LANCEOLATE FORMS
(BLADE SHAPES)

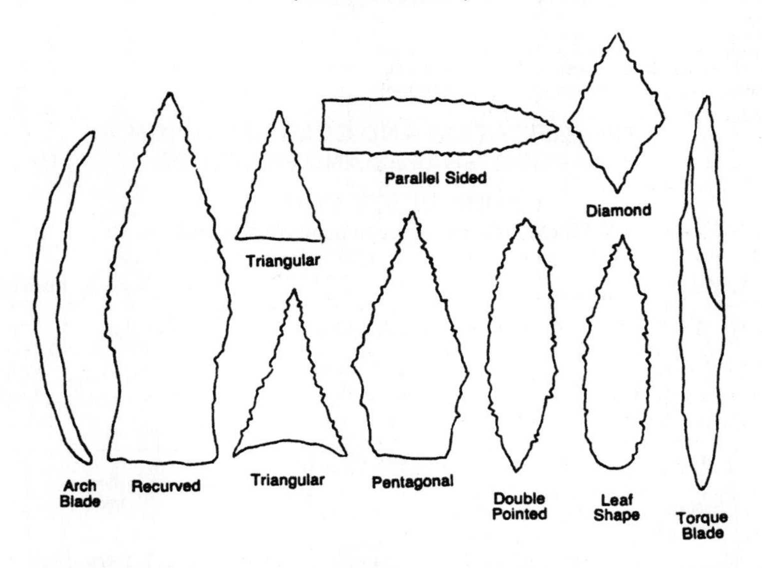

NOTE: The above forms apply to all sizes. Your actual point may be much larger or smaller than the shapes illustrated. The lanceolate form originated in Paleo times and persisted through all the archaeological periods.

LANCEOLATE FORMS LISTED
(Small size)

The following types are all small size (under two inches) with no stem, and vary in form from leaf shape to triangular to parallel sided to pentagonal. Each type can be found in the alphabetical listings.

Addison Micro-Drill
Brewerton, Eared-Triangular
Camp Creek
Catan
Clarksville
Cottonwood Triangle
Drill
Ebenezer
Flint River Spike
Fort Ancient
Fresno
Graver
Greeneville
Guerrero
Guntersville
Hamilton
Jacks Reef Pentagonal
Levanna
Lozenge
Madison
Matamoros
Maud
McGloin
Montgomery
Mouse Creek
Nodena
Nolichucky
O'Leno
Papago
Pinellas
Rogue River U- Back
Sand
Mountain
Scraper
Shetley
Spedis
Starr
Talco
Tampa
Valina
Young

LANCEOLATE FORMS LISTED
(Medium to large size)

The following types are all stemless and are over two inches in length. They vary in form from leaf shape to double pointed to triangular to concave and flat base shapes. They can be found in the alphabetical listings.

Abasolo
Adena Blade
Agate Basin
Angostura-East
Angostura-West
Benjamin
Benton Blade
Bone Pin
Browns Valley
Caddoan Blade
Candy Creek
Cascade Leaf
Cobbs Triangular
Copena Classic
Copena Round Base
Copena Triangular
Cotaco
Covington
Cowhouse Slough
Decatur Blade
Drill
Eden
Fort Ancient Blade
Fort Ancient Knife
Fox Creek
Lanceolate
Frazier
Friday
Gahagan
Greeneville
Guilford Round Base
Guilford Straight Base
Harahey
Hardaway Blade
Hell Gap
Hi-Lo
Jacks Reef
Pentagonal
Kinney
Lake Mohave
Lancet
Lerma Pointed Base
Lerma Rounded Base
Llano
Milnesand
Morrow Mountain Rounded Base
Morse Knife
Nebo Hill
Nolichucky
North
Paint Rock Valley
Paleo Knife
Pandora
Pelona
Plainview
Ramey Knife
Red Ochre
Refugio
Rio Grande
Ross
Sabine
Safety Harbor
Sandia
Scottsbluff I
Scottsbluff II
Scraper
Searcy
Sedalia
Snake Creek
Square Knife
Stanfield
Tear Drop
Tennessee River
Texas Blade
Tortugas
Turkeytail
Victoria
Wadlow

IDENTIFICATION AND CLASSIFICATION OF POINT SHAPES AND FEATURES

AURICULATE FORMS
(These drawings apply to points of all sizes)

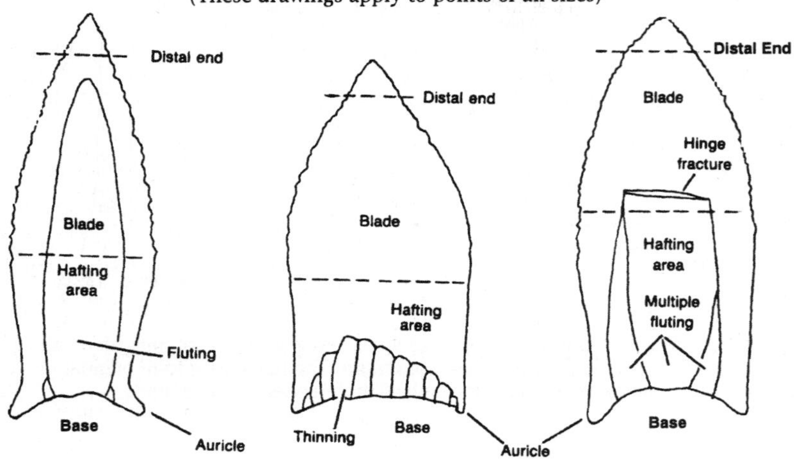

AURICULATE FORMS (continued)

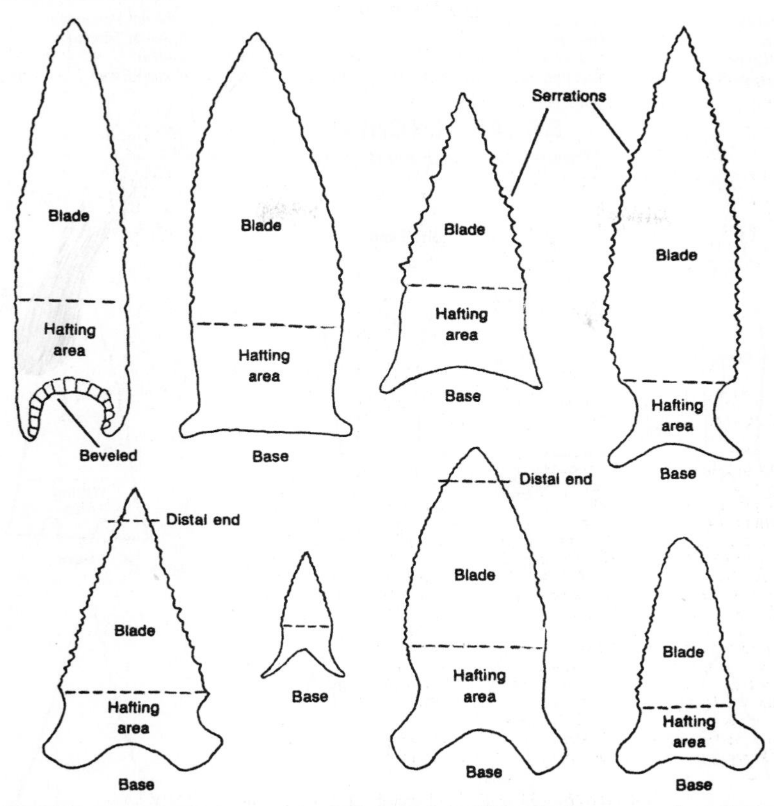

Note: This is the basic form of the Paleo Period, although there are a few shapes here of a later time. Flaking tends to be parallel and the entire hafting area edges are usually smoothed (ground) on most early examples.

AURICULATE FORMS LISTED

The following types have auriculate or eared bases. Included here are weakly side notched and corner notched forms with eared or auriculate bases, even though they are also listed again under their proper form. All can be found in the alphabetical listings.

Alamance
Angostura
Barber
Bassett
Beaver Lake
Big Sandy
Big Sandy Contracted Base
Big Sandy E-Notched
Brewerton, Eared-Triangular
Candy Creek
Carrizo
Chipola
Clovis
Clovis-Unfluted
Conerly
Copena-Auriculate
Cumberland
Dalton-Breckenridge
Dalton-Classic
Dalton-Colbert
Dalton-Greenbrier
Dalton-Hemphill
Dalton-Nuckolls
Dalton-Santa Fe
Dalton-Tallahassee
Debert
Drill
Durant's Bend
Edwards
Fairland
Folsom
Frio
Gilchrist
Golondrina
Gower
Graham Cave
Greenbrier
Guilford-Yuma
Hardaway
Hardaway-Dalton
Hardaway-Palmer
Haw River
Hemphill
Hi-Lo
Holland
Humboldt
Jeff
Kirk Serrated
Leighton
Lott
Marianna
McKean
Meserve
Midland
Mouse Creek
Mule Ear
Nolichucky
Nova
Orient
Oxbow
Paint Rock
Valley
Pedernalis
Pelican
Pine Tree
Pine Tree Corner Notched
Pinto Basin

AURICULATE FORMS LISTED (co(continued)

Plainview
Quad
Redstone
Rodgers Side-Hollowed
Rogers Creek
Rowan
Russell Cave
San Patrice
Sandia
Simpson
Steubenville
Suwannee
Waratan
Wheeler Excurvate
Wheeler Expanded Base
Wheeler Recurvate
Wheeler Triangular
Yadkin
Yadkin-Eared

BASAL NOTCHED FORMS

(These drawings apply to points of all sizes)

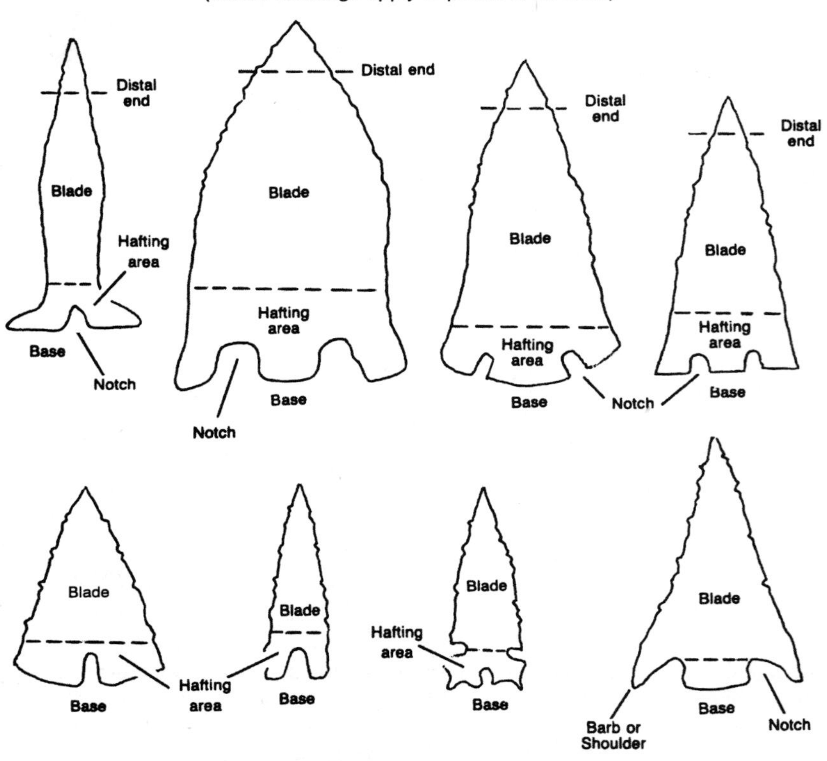

Note: Basal notched forms appeared in the early Archaic period and reappeared in the Woodland Period. This form of hafting was not very popular with only a handful of types known.

BASAL NOTCHED FORMS LISTED

The following types all have one or more basal notch or are forms with long barbs that may appear to be basal notched. All can be found in the alphabetical listings.

Andice
Base Tang Knife
Cahokia
Calf Creek
Carizzo
Citrus
Clay County
Culbreath
Culbreath-Snapped Base
Cuney
Drill
Ensor Split-Base
Eva
Frio
Garza
Hamilton Stemmed
Harrell
Haskell
Haw River
Hernando
Hillsborough
Kirk Snapped Base
Limeton Bifurcate
Lost Lake
McKean
Mehlville
Parowan
Pedernalis
Pine Tree
Rockwall
San Saba
Shumla
Smith
Smithsonia
Snyders
Toyah
Wade
Wheeler

CORNER NOTCHED FORMS

(These drawings apply to points of all sizes)

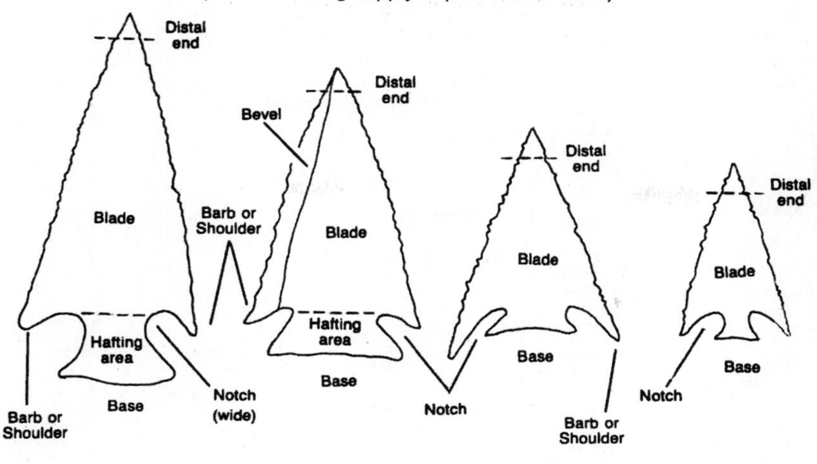

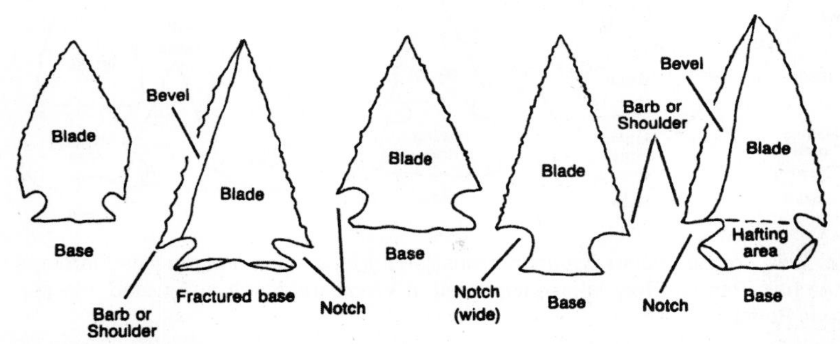

Note: Corner notched forms appeared in the early Archaic period and went out of style in the later Archaic. They appeared again in the Woodland and lasted to Historic times.

CORNER NOTCHED FORMS LISTED

The following types are notched in the basal corners and vary in size from very small to very large. All can be found in the alphabetical listings.

Afton
Agee
Autauga
Benton
Big Creek
Big Slough
Bolen Bevel
Brewerton Corner Notched
Buck Creek
Castroville
Catahoula
Clay County
Conejo
Corner Tang Knife
Crawford Creek
Cupp
Cypress Creek
Dardanelle
Decatur
Desert Corner Notched
Dovetail
Drill
Edgefield Scraper
Edgewood
Edwards
Elko
Ellis
Ensor
Ensor Split-Base
Fairland
Fountain Creek
Fox Valley
Frio
Garth Slough
Gibson
Godley
Greenbrier
Hamilton Stemmed
Hardin
Hopewell
Jacks Reef Corner Notched
Keota
Kirk Corner Notched
Knight Island
Lafayette
Lost Lake
Mad River
Marcos
Marshall
Martindale
Martis
Merom
Montell
Motley
Ocala
Palmer
Perforator
Perkinsville
Pine Tree Corner Notched
Potts
Rockwall
St. Charles
Scallorn
Sequoyah
Sinner
Snyders
Stilwell
Taylor
Thebes
Wade

SIDE NOTCHED FORMS

(These drawings apply to points of all sizes)

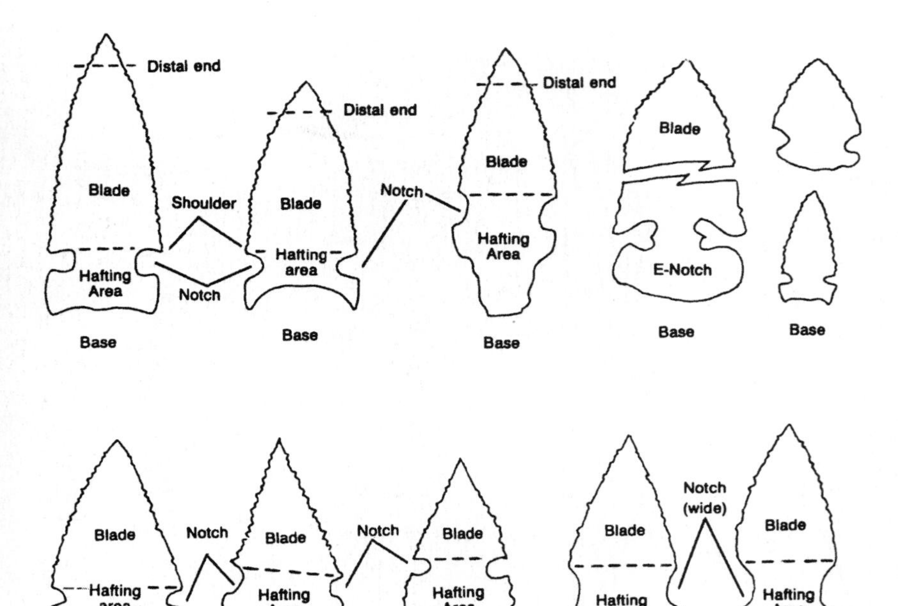

Note: Side notched points began in Transitional Paleo times and persisted through the Archaic Period. They later reappeared in Woodland times and lasted into the Historic Period.

SIDE NOTCHED FORMS LISTED

The following types have notches on each side of the blade and range from very small to very large. All can be found in the alphabetical listings.

Agee
Benton
Besant
Big Sandy
Big Sandy-Broad Base
Big Sandy-Contracted Base
Big Sandy E-Notched
Black Rock
Bolen Bevel
Bolen Plain
Brewerton Side Notched
Cache River
Cahokia
Coosa
Cottonwood Triangle
Damron
Dardanelle
Desert Side Notched
Drill
Durst
Duval
Ecusta
Edgefield Scraper
Evans
Exotic Forms
Fishspear
Flint Creek
Fountain Creek
Fox Ear
Fresno
Frio
Godar
Godley
Graham Cave
Greenbrier
Halifax
Hanna
Harpeth River
Harrell
Haskell
Hemphill
Holston
Huffaker
Keota
Klunk Side-Notched
Knight Island
Leighton
Leon
MacPherson
Matanzas
Merom
Mount Albion
Northern Side Notched
Ohio Double Notched
Orient
Osceola
Osceola-Greenbrier
Otter Creek
Oxbow
Paisano
Perforator
Pine Tree
Raddatz
Reed
Rowan
Russell Cave
San Patrice
Savage Cave
Schild Spike
Schugtown
Snake Creek
Sublet Ferry
Swan Lake
Taylor
Temporal
Thebes
Toyah
Turkeytail (Fulton)
Turkeytail (Harrison)
Union Side Notched
Washita

STEMMED FORMS
(Hafting Area Types)
(These drawings apply to points of all sizes)

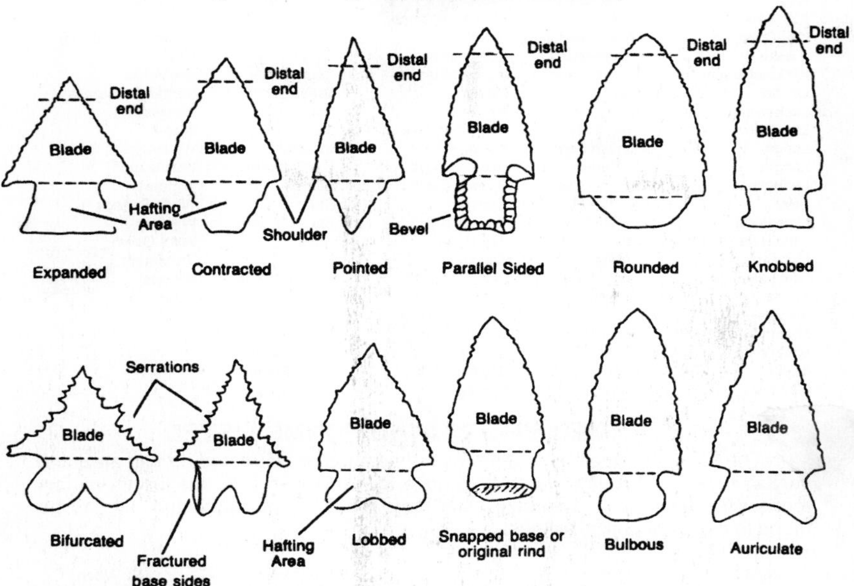

Note: Stemmed types began as early as the Paleo Period, but didn't really become popular until the Woodland Period. Consequently, this form has the most types and is the most difficult to classify.

STEMMED FORMS LISTED

The following types have shoulders and stems and vary in size from very small to very large. Excluded from this list are all stemmed forms that have a bifurcated base which are listed elsewhere. All can be found in the alphabetical listings.

Abbey
Adena
Adena-Dickson
Adena-Narrow Stem
Adena-Notched Base
Adena-Robbins
Adena-Waubesa
Adena-Wells
Afton
Alachua
Alaska Points
Alba
Appalachian
Ashtabula
Augustin
Bakers Creek
Bare Island
Bascom
Bassett
Beacon Island
Benton
Benton-Narrow Blade
Big Creek
Big Slough
Blevins
Boggy Branch-Type I
Boggy Branch-Type II
Bonham
Bradford
Bradley Spike
Brazos
Broad River
Broward
Buck Creek
Buggs Island
Bulbar Stemmed
Bulverde
Calapooia
Carrolton
Castroville
Catahoula
Cave Spring
Chesapeake Diamond
Clifton
Coahuila
Cody Knife
Colbert
Coldwater
Colonial
Columbia
Conejo
Coosa
Cotaco Creek
Cotaco-Wright
Cottonbridge
Crawford Creek
Crescent Knife
Crump Lake Stemmed
Culbreath
Cupp
Cypress Creek
Cypress Creek
Dallas
Darl
Datil
Deadman
Delhi
Double Tip
Drill
Duval
Ebenezer
Eden
Edgefield Scraper
Eiffel Tower
Elam
Elk River
Elko
Elora
Epps
Etley
Evans (Side notched)
Exotic Forms
Fairland
Flint Creek
Flint River
Flint River Spike
Friley
Garth Slough
Gary
Gilchrist
Guilford-Stemmed
Gunther
Gypsum Cave
Halifax
Hamilton
Hamilton Stemmed
Hardee Beveled
Hardin
Harpeth River
Hayes
Heavy Duty
Hidden Valley
Hillsborough
Holland
Holmes
Homan
Howard
Jerome
John Day River
Johnson
Jude
Kalapuyan

STEMMED FORMS LISTED (continued)

Kays
Kent
Kirk Serrated
Kirk-Snapped Base
Klickatat Dagger
La Jita
Lackawaxen
Lamoka
Lange
Langtry
Ledbetter
Levy
Limestone
Little Bear Creek
Livermore
Lost Lake
Maples
Marcos
Marion
Martindale
Martis
McIntire
Merom
Morhiss
Morrill
Morrow Mountain
Morrow Mountain Straight Base
Motley
Mouse Creek
Mount Albion
Mountain Fork
Mud Creek
Mulberry Creek
New Market
Newnan
Nolan
Oauchita
Orient
Palmillas
Pandale
Pedernalis
Pelican
Perdiz
Perforator
Perkinsville
Pickwick
Pine Tree Corner Notched
Ponchartrain I
Ponchartrain II
Putnam
Randolph
Rheems Creek
Rogue River
Rose Springs
Russell Cave
Sabinal
San Jose
San Pedro
Sandia
Santa Cruz
Sarasota
Savannah River
Schild Spike
Scottsbluff I
Scottsbluff II
Searcy
Seminole
Sequoyah
Sinner
Six Mile Creek
Smithsonia
South Prong Creek
Stanly
Steiner
Steuben
Steubenville
Stilwell
Stocton
Stone Square Stem
Sumter
Susquehanna Broad
Table Rock
Taylor
Thonotosassa
Trade Points
Travis
Trinity
Turkeytail (Harrison)
Turkeytail (Hebron)
Umatilla
Val Verde
Ventana-Amargosa
Wacissa
Wade
Waller Knife
Washington
Wateree
White Springs
Williams
Will's Cove
Yarbrough
Yavapai Stemmed
Zorra

STEMMED-BIFURCATED FORMS LISTED

The following types have a prominent notched or bifurcated hafting area and vary in size from small to large. We have also included with this listing various forms with deeply concave bases that may appear to be bifurcated. All can be found in the alphabetical listings.

Arredondo
Baker
Big Sandy-Contracted Base
Black Rock
Buzzard Roost Creek
Cave Spring
Chiricahua
Conejo
Cuney
Dalton-Greenbrier
Darl
Decatur
Drill
Duncan
Edgewood
Edwards
Fairland
Fox Valley
Frio
Garza
Gower
Hanna
Harpeth River
Harrell
Holland
Hoxie
Jetta
Jude
Kanawha
Kirk Serrated-Bifurcated
Lake Eerie
Lampasos
LeCroy
Limeton Bifurcate
Lott
MacCorkle
Montell
Morris
Orient
Osceola
Oxbow
Patrick
Pedernalis
Pine Tree
Pine Tree Corner Notched
Pinto Basin
Rice Lobbed
Rogers Creek
Russell Cave
St. Albans
Sallisaw
San Jose
Savannah River
Southampton
Stanly
Stanly Narrow Blade
SW Hanna
Toyah
Uvalde
Washita
Wheeler

BLADE BEVELING TYPES

(These drawings apply to points of all sizes)

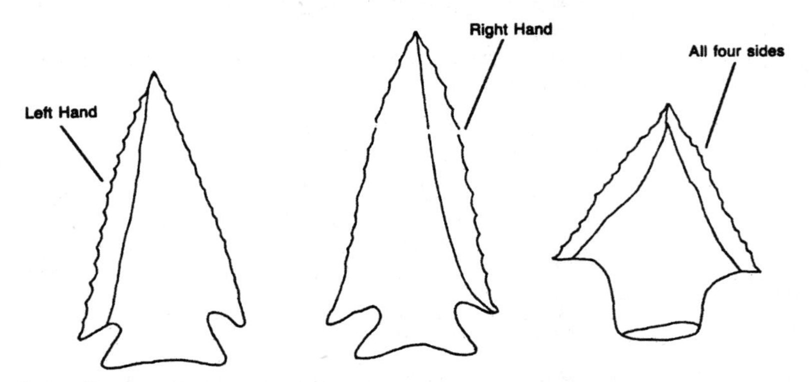

Note: Alternate blade beveling began in the early Archaic Period and continued into the Woodland Period. Beveled points are very popular among collectors.

BLADE EDGE TYPES

(These drawings apply to points of all sizes)

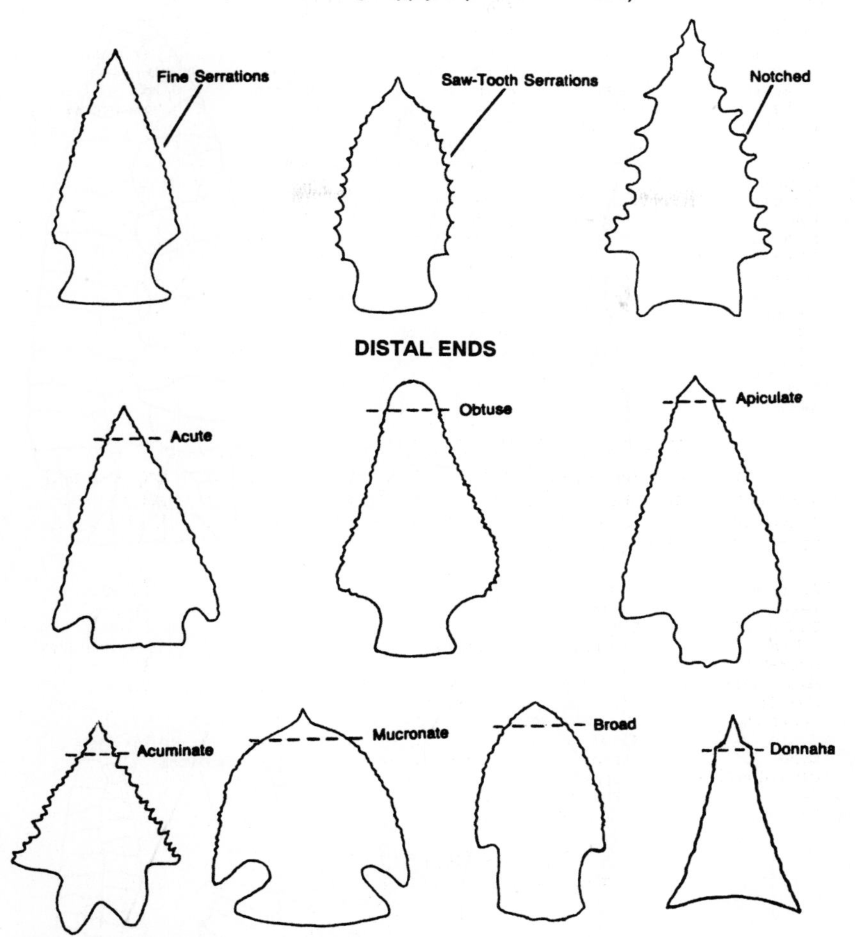

Note: The distal end of a point is located at the very tip and describes the shape of the penetrating part of the knife or projectile point.

POINT CROSS SECTIONS

(These drawings apply to points of all sizes)

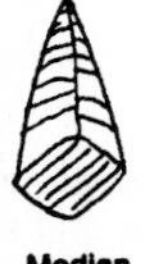

Elliptical · Round · Uniface or Plano-convex · Median ridged · Rhomboid · Flattened · Fluted

Note: The cross section of a point represents its form if broken at mid-section.

FLAKING TYPES

(These drawings apply to points of all sizes)

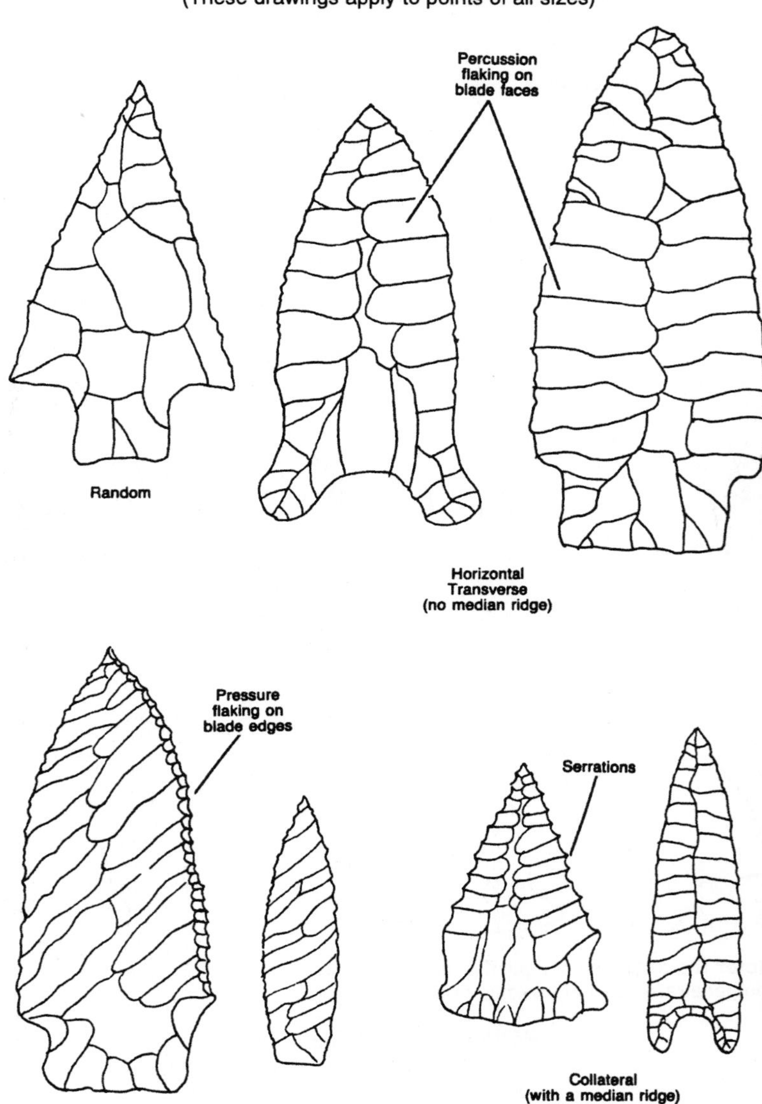

Note: Points are rough shaped with an elk antler billet or hammer stone. Then fine pressure flaking is applied to the blade and stem edges with a sharp pointed antler. Billet and deer antler are alternated until the point is finally finished. During the flaking process, edges are lightly ground to prevent hinge fracturing on the blade edges.

STEMMED FORMS
BASAL EDGE TYPES
(These drawings apply to points of all sizes)

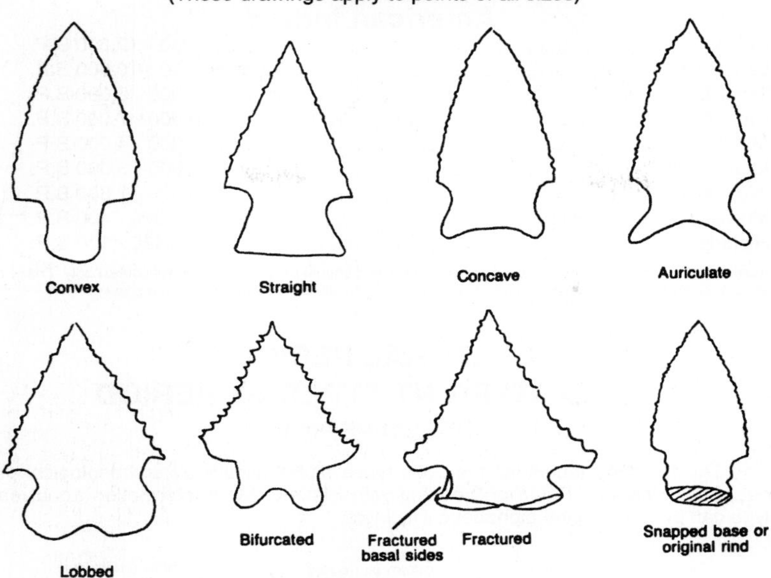

STEMMED FORMS
SHOULDER TYPES
(These drawings apply to points of all sizes)

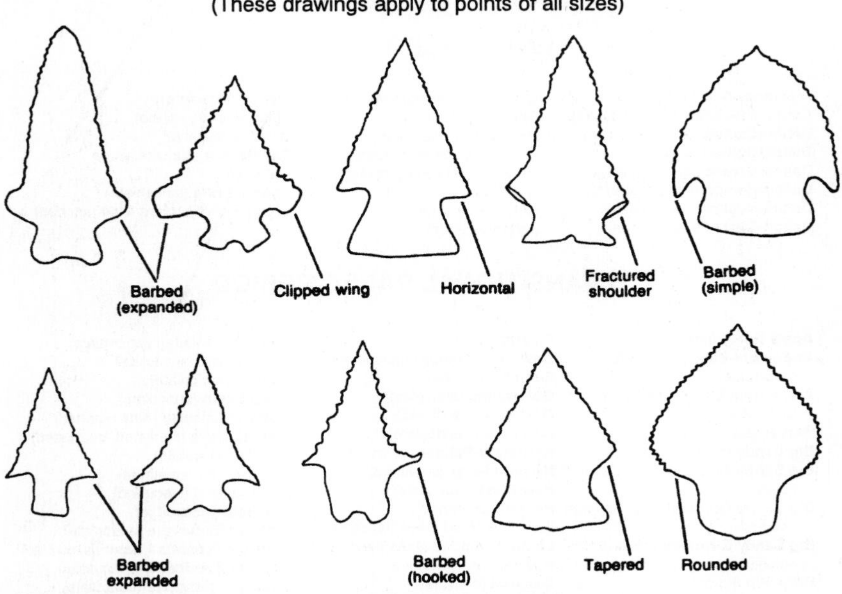

Note: The shoulder devides the blade from the hafting area.

CULTURAL PERIODS of the American Indian

Paleo ....c. 40,000 - 12,000 B.P.
Late Paleo ....c. 15,000 - 10,000 B.P.
Transitional Paleo.................... c. 12,000 - 9,000 B.P.
Early Archaic .... c. 10,000 - 7,000 B.P.
Middle Archaic....................c. 7,000 - 4,000 B.P.
Late Archaic. .... c. 4,000 - 3,000 B.P.
Woodland ....c. 3,000 - 1,300 B.P.
Mississippian ....c. 1,300 - 400 B.P.
Historic ....c. 450 - 170 B.P.

Note: The dates given above are only approximations and should be used in a general context only. These data are constantly being revised as new information becomes available. B.P. means "before present."

CULTURAL PERIODS INDEX TO POINT TYPES BY PERIOD

PALEO PERIOD

The following tables list the point types alphabetically by archaeological periods, beginning with Paleo and ending with Historic. More information about each type can be found in the alphabetical listings.

Beaver Lake (auriculate)
Clovis (auriculate)
Clovis-Unfluted(auriculate)
Cumberland (auriculate)
Folsom (auriculate)
Graver (lanceolate)
Lancet (lanceolate)
Midland (auriculate)
Redstone (auriculate)
Scraper (lanceolate)
Simpson (auriculate)
Suwanee (auriculate)

LATE PALEO PERIOD

Alamance (auriculate)
Dalton-Breckenridge (auriculate)
Dalton-Classic (auriculate)
Dalton-Colbert (auriculate)
Dalton-Greenbrier (auriculate)
Dalton-Hemphill (auriculate)
Dalton-Nuckolls (auriculate)
Dalton-Santa Fe (auriculate)
Dalton-Tallahassee (auriculate)
Debert (auriculate)
Hardaway (auriculate)
Hardaway Blade (lanceolate
Hardaway-Dalton (ariculate)
Hell Gap (lanceolate)
Hi-Lo (auriculate)
Jeff (auriculate)
Llano (lanceolate)
Plainview (auriculate)
Quad (auriculate)
San Patrice (auriculate/side notched)
Square Knife (lanceolate)
Union Side Notched (side notched)

TRANSITIONAL PALEO PERIOD

Agate Basin (lanceolate)
Angostura-East (auriculate, lanceolate)
Angostura-West (auriculate, lanceolate)
Barber (auriculate)
Big Sandy (side notched)
Big Sandy-Broad Base (side notched)
Big Sandy-Contracted Base (side notched)
Big Sandy E-Notched (side notched
Bone Pin (lanceolate)
Browns Valley (lanceolate)
Cave Spring (stemmed)
Carrizo (auriculate)
Cowhouse Slough (lanceolate)
Eden (lanceolate)
Golondrina (auriculate)
Graham Cave (fluted)
Greenbrier (auriculate)
Hardaway-Palmer (auriculate)
Harpeth River (stemmed)
Haw River (auriculate)
Holland (stemmed)
Lerma-Pointed Base (lanceolate)
Lerma-Rounded Base (lanceolate)
McKean (auriculate)
Meserve (auriculate)
Milnesand (lanceolate)
Osceola-Greenbrier (side notched)
Paint Rock Valley (lanceolate)
Paleo Knife (lanceolate)
Pelican (auriculate)
Pinto Basin (auriculate)
Rowan (auriculate, side notched)
Russell Cave (stemmed, bifurcated)
Sandia (auriculate)
Scottsbluff I (stemmed)
Scottsbluff II (stemmed)
Stanfield (lanceolate)
Wheeler Excurvate (auriculate)
Wheeler Expanded Base (auriculate)
Wheeler Recurvate (auriculate)
Wheeler Triangular (auriculate)

EARLY ARCHAIC PERIOD

Abasolo (lanceolate)
Alaska Points (stemmed)
Andice (basal notched)
Autauga (corner notched)
Baker (bifurcated)
Boggy Branch-Type I (stemmed)
Boggy Branch-Type II (stemmed)
Bolen Bevel (side notched)
Bolen Plain (side notched)
Brazos (stemmed)
Cache River (side notched)
Calf Creek (basal notched)
Chesapeake Diamond (stemmed)
Chipola (auriculate)
Cobbs Triangular (lanceolate)
Cody Knife (stemmed)
Crawford Creek (stemmed)
Crump Lake (stemmed)
Damron (side notched)
Datil (stemmed)
Decatur (corner notched)
Decatur Blade (lanceolate)
Dovetail (corner notched)
Ecusta (side notched)
Edgefield Scraper (side, corner notched, stemmed)
Elk River (stemmed)
Eva (basal notched)
Fishspear (side notched)
Fountain Creek (side or corner notched
Fox Ear (side notched)
Fox Valley (bifurcated)
Garth Slough (stemmed)
Gilchrist (auriculate)
Gower (bifurcated)
Graham Cave (side notched)
Gypsum Cave (stemmed)
Hamilton (stemmed)
Hardee Beveled (stemmed)
Hardin (stemmed)
Heavy Duty (stemmed)
Hemphill (side notched)
Hoxie (bifurcated)
Jetta (bifurcated)
Johnson (stemmed)
Jude (stemmed)
Kanawha (bifurcated)
Kirk Corner Notched
Kirk Serrated (stemmed)
Kirk Serrated-Bifurcated
Kirk Snapped Base (stemmed)
Lake Erie (bifurcated)
Lake Mohave (lanceolate)
Lampasos (bifurcated, auriculate)
LeCroy (bifurcated)
Leighton (side notched)
Limeton Bifurcate (bifurcated)
Lost Lake (corner notched)
MacCorkle (bifurcated)
Mad River (corner notched)
Martindale (corner notched & stemmed)
Mule Ear (auriculate)
Nebo Hill (lanceolate)
Northern Side Notched
Osceola (side notched)
Palmer (corner notched)
Perforator (corner, side notched)
Pine Tree (side notched, auriculate)
Pine Tree Corner Notched
Rice Lobbed (bifurcated)
Rio Grande (lanceolate)
St. Albans (bifurcated)
Savage Cave (side notched)
Searcy (stemmed)
Sedalia (lanceolate)
Southampton (bifurcated)
Spedis (lanceolate)
Stanly (bifurcated)
Stanly Narrow Blade (bifurcated)
Steubenville (stemmed)
Stilwell (corner notched)
Stocton (stemmed)
Taylor (corner notched)
Tennessee River (lanceolate)
Thebes (corner notched)
Victoria (lanceolate)
Wacissa (stemmed)
Waller Knife (stemmed)
White Springs (stemmed)

MIDDLE ARCHAIC PERIOD

Abbey (stemmed)
Afton (corner notched)
Appalachian (stemmed)
Arredondo (bifurcated)
Augustin (stemmed)
Bascom (stemmed)
Benton (stemmed)
Benton Blade (lanceolate)
Benton-Narrow Blade (stemmed)
Big Slough (stemmed)
Brewerton Corner-Notched
Brewerton, Eared-Triangular
Brewerton Side-Notched
Buck Creek (stemmed)
Bulverde (stemmed)
Buzzard Roost Creek (bifurcated)
Carrizo (bifurcated)
Carrolton (stemmed)
Cascade Leaf (lanceolate)
Chiricahua (bifurcated)
Clay County (corner notched)
Conerly (auriculate)
Copena-Auriculate
Cottonbridge (stemmed)
Crescent Knife (stemmed)
Cypress Creek (stemmed)
Cypress Creek (stemmed)
Dawson (stemmed)
Frazier (lanceolate)
Frio (side & corner notched)
Guilford-Round Base (lanceolate)
Guilford-Stemmed (stemmed)
Guilford-Straight Base (lanceolate)
Guilford-Yuma (auriculate)
Halifax (side notched)
Hidden Valley (stemmed)
Hillsborough (stemmed)
Holston (side notched)
Kays (stemmed)
Kinney (lanceolate)
La Jita (stemmed)
Lange (stemmed)
Langtry (stemmed)
Ledbetter (stemmed)
Maples (stemmed)
Marion (stemmed)
Marshall (corner notched)
McIntire (stemmed)
Mehlville (basal notched)
Montell (bifurcated)
Morrow Mountain (stemmed)
Morrow Mtn Rounded Base (lanceolate)
Morrow Mtn Straight Base (stemmed)
Mount Albion (side notched)
Mountain Fork (stemmed)
Newnan (stemmed)
Nolan (stemmed)
Otter Creek (side notched)
Palmillas (stemmed)
Pandale (stemmed)
Pedernalis (bifurcated)
Pelona (lanceolate)
Pickwick (stemmed)
Putnam (stemmed)
Ramey Knife (lanceolate)
Refugio (lanceolate)
San Jose (stemmed)
Savannah River (stemmed & bifurcated)
Six Mile Creek (stemmed)
Smith (basal notched)
Stone Square Stem (stemmed)
Sumter (stemmed)
SW Hanna (bifurcated)
Thonotosassa (stemmed)
Tortugas (lanceolate)
Travis (stemmed)
Uvalde (bifurcated)
Val Verde (stemmed)
Ventana-Amargosa (stemmed)
Williams (stemmed)
Yavapai Stemmed (stemmed)
Zorra (stemmed)

LATE ARCHAIC

Adena (stemmed)
Adena Blade (lanceolate)
Adena-Narrow Stem (stemmed)
Adena-Notched Base (stemmed)
Adena-Robbins (stemmed)
Adena-Wells (stemmed)

LATE ARCHAIC PERIOD (continued)

Corner Tang Knife (corner notch)
Cottonwood Triangle (lanceolate & side notched)
Covington (lanceolate)
Culbreath (basal notched)
Culbreath-Snapped Base (basal notched)
Dallas (stemmed)
Duncan (bifurcated)
Elam (stemmed)
Ellis (corner notched)
Elora (stemmed)
Ensor (corner notched)
Ensor Split-Base (corner notched)
Epps (stemmed)
Etley (stemmed)
Evans (side notched)
Flint River (stemmed)
Gary (stemmed)
Godar (side notched)
Godley (side notched)
Hanna (bifurcated & side notched)
Hernando (basal notched)
Holmes (stemmed)
Kent (stemmed)
Lafayette (corner notched)
Lamoka (stemmed)
Levy (stemmed)
Limestone (stemmed)
Little Bear Creek (stemmed)
Marcos (corner notched)
Matamoros(lanceolate)
Matanzas (side notched)
Merom (side notched)
Morhiss (stemmed)
Motley (corner notched)
Mud Creek (stemmed)
Mulberry Creek (stemmed)
Orient (side notched)
Oxbow (side notched)
Pandora (lanceolate)
Patrick (bifurcated)
Pinto Basin (bifurcated)
Pontchartrain (Type I) (stemmed)
Pontchartrain (Type II) (stemmed)
Raddatz (side notched)
Sabine (lanceolate)
St. Charles (corner notched)
San Pedro (stemmed)
Seminole (stemmed)
Smithsonia (stemmed)
Snake Creek (side notched)
South Prong Creek (stemmed)
Swan Lake (side notched)
Table Rock (stemmed)
Texas Blade (lanceolate)
Trinity (stemmed)
Turkeytail (Fulton) (side notched)
Turkeytail (Harrison) (side notched and stemmed)
Turkeytail (Hebron) (stemmed)
Wade (stemmed)

WOODLAND PERIOD

Addison Micro-Drill (lanceolate)
Adena-Dickson (stemmed)
Adena-Waubesa (stemmed)
Alba (stemmed)
Bakers Creek (stemmed)
Benjamin (lanceolate)
Besant (side notched)
Black Rock (bifurcated)
Bradford (stemmed)
Bradley Spike (stemmed)
Broad River (stemmed)
Broward (stemmed)
Camp Creek (lanceolate)
Candy Creek (auriculate)
Coldwater (stemmed)
Columbia (stemmed)
Coosa (stemmed & side notched)
Cotaco Creek (stemmed)
Cotaco-Wright (stemmed)
Cupp (corner notched)
Darl (stemmed)
Darl Blade (lanceolate)
Delhi (stemmed)
Desert Corner Notched
Desert Side Notched
Durant's Bend (auriculate)
Durst (side notched)
Duval (side notched & stemmed)
Ebenezer (stemmed)
Edgewood (corner notched)
Edwards (corner notched)
Elko (corner notched)
Exotic Forms (notched)
Fairland (stemmed)
Flint Creek (stemmed)
Flint River Spike (stemmed)
Fox Creek Lanceolate
Friday (lanceolate)
Friley (stemmed)
Gahagan (lanceolate)
Gibson (corner notched)
Greeneville (lanceolate)
Gunther (stemmed)
Hamilton (lanceolate)
Hamilton-Stemmed
Hopewell (corner notched)
Humboldt (auriculate)
Jacks Reef Corner Notched
Jacks Reef Pentagonal (lanceolate)
Kalapuyan (stemmed)
Klunk Side-Notched
Knight Island (side notched)
Lackawaxen (stemmed)
Leon (side notched)
Levanna (lanceolate)
MacPherson (side notched)
Martis (corner notched & stemmed)
Montgomery (lanceolate)
Morrill (stemmed)
Morse Knife (lanceolate)
Mouse Creek (pentagonal)
New Market (stemmed)
Nolichucky (lanceolate)
North (lanceolate)
Nova (auriculate)
Oauchita (stemmed)
Ocala (corner notched)
Ohio Double Notched (side notched)
O'Leno (lanceolate)
Paisano (side notched)
Parowan (basal notched)
Pontcharatrain II (stemmed)
Potts (corner notched)
Randolph (stemmed)
Red Ochre (lanceolate)
Reed (side notched)
Rheems Creek (stemmed)
Rockwall (corner notched)
Rogers Creek (auriculate)
Rose Springs (stemmed)
Ross (lanceolate)
San Saba (basal notched)
Sand Mountain (lanceolate)
Santa Cruz (stemmed)
Sarasota (stemmed)
Scallorn (corner notched)
Schild Spike (stemmed)
Shumla (basal notched)
Sinner (stemmed, corner notched)
Snyders (corner nothced)
Steuben (stemmed)
Sublet Ferry (side notched)
Susquehanna Broad (stemmed)
Taylor (stemmed)
Tear Drop (lanceolate)
Valina (lanceolate)
Wadlow (lanceolate)
Waratan (auriculate)
Washington (stemmed)
Wateree (stemmed)
Will's Cove (stemmed)
Yadkin (auriculate)
Yadkin-Eared (auriculate)
Yarbrough (stemmed)

MISSISSIPPIAN PERIOD

Agee (side notched)
Bassett (stemmed)
Blevins (stemmed)
Bonham (stemmed)
Bulbar Stemmed (stemmed)
Caddoan Blade (lanceolate)
Cahokia (side notched)
Calapooia (stemmed)
Catahoula (stemmed)
Clarksville (lanceolate)
Clifton (stemmed)
Colbert (stemmed)
Colonial (stemmed)
Dardanelle (side notched)
Deadman (stemmed)
Double Tip (stemmed)
Eiffel Tower (stemmed)
Fort Ancient (lanceolate)
Fort Ancient Blade (lanceolate)
Fresno (lanceolate & side notched)

MISSISSIPPIAN PERIOD (continued)

Garza (basal notch)
Guntersville (lanceolate)
Harahey (lanceolate)
Harrell (side & base notched)
Haskell (side notched)
Hayes (stemmed)
Homan (stemmed)
Howard (stemmed)
Huffaker (side notched)
Jerome (stemmed)
John Day River (stemmed)
Keota (side notched)
Klickatat Dagger (Stemmed)
Livermore (stemmed)
Lott (auriculate)
Lozenge (lanceolate)
Madison (lanceolate)
Maud (lanceolate)
McGloin (lanceolate)
Morris (bifurcated)
Nodena (lanceolate)
Papago (lanceolate)
Perdiz (stemmed)
Perkinsville (corner notched & stemmed)
Pinellas (lanceolate)
Rogue River (stemmed)
Rogue River U-Back (lanceolate)
Sabinal (stemmed)
Safety Harbor (lanceolate)
Sallisaw (bifurcated)
Schugtown (side notched)
Sequoyah (stemmed)
Shetley (lanceolate)
Starr (lanceolate)
Steiner (stemmed)
Talco (lanceolate)
Tampa (lanceolate)
Temporal (side notched)
Toyah (side & base notched)
Umatilla (stemmed)
Washita (side notched)
Young (lanceolate)

HISTORIC PERIOD

Cuney (bifurcated)
Guerrero (lanceolate)
Trade Points

CHRONOLOGICAL DATA
IMPORTANT EVENTS IN THE HISTORY OF EARLY MAN

It is a clearly established fact that the Indian (or man), in the Western Hemisphere, did not originate from those sources that have long been proposed and advocated by non-scientific theories. Such ideas as the lost continent of Mu, the lost tribe of Israel, the sunken continent of Atlantis, the Vikings, the Phoenicians, the Polynesians, lost Egyptian seamen, etc. can only be considered as legends of Western man's origins and have no true basis in fact.

Evidence now clearly indicates that neither the Indian himself, nor his pre-historic ancestors, such as Cro-Magnon, Neanderthal, Peking, Java, Swanscomb, and the many others, evolved in the Western Hemisphere. But rather (it is generally accepted), that whoever he was, or wherever he came from, he appeared as a full-fledged Homosapiens (man), and entered the unpopulated new world of our Western Hemisphere. He is still with us today.

Likewise, it is generally accepted, with few reservations, that this ancestor of the American Indian (and later the American Eskimo), was none other than the Mongolian peoples. There now seems to be little or no reluctance to accept this theory as to the origin of the American Indian's ancestry.

From a genetic point of view, the evidence is overwhelming; scant beard, prominent cheekbones, straight black coarse hair, broad face, large torso, short legs, dark brown-red skin, a tendency to slanted eyes and the epicanthus fold.

These nomadic people followed the herds of mammoth elephants, and other animals, as the herds moved to new grazing lands. These people followed the herds for one reason: they were his prey and they ate these animals. Without them he starved.

These ancestors of the American Indian migrated from inner Mongolia to the Western Hemisphere by way of the Alaskan land-bridge that came into being during the glacier epochs. This land-bridge was over a thousand miles wide and was the direct result of a large percentage of the ocean's water being tied up in glacier ice and snow. This ice and snow (several miles thick in places), was so vast that the resultant weight-burden was great enough that the continents themselves were actually depressed into the Earth's mantle.

The Indians of North America peopled two continents and filled its earth, sea, rivers and sky with a pantheon of Spirits and Gods long before the Bronze Age had even dawned in Europe and Asia.

The men of profound knowledge in Europe overlooked an enormous truth while trying to explain the origins of the Indian within the context of the Bible, which was the basic document of European thought. In truth, the New World contained as varied, and as complex, human societies and communities as did the Old World, but this thought was unacceptable to the Old World.

When Hernando Cortes invaded the Aztecs of Mexico, he encountered an empire that boasted astronomy, writing, a calendar more accurate than that of Europe, monumental architecture, a floating capital city with causeways, canals, and a vast and complex monarchy that ruled thousands of square miles, with millions of people in a number of different tribes.

Francisco Pizarro encountered much of these same cultural advances when he invaded the Incas of Peru. Here the business of a monarchy was more complex due to the empire's incredible size, varied cultures, and the inhospitable Andes Mountain range.

These, and other Indians of North, Central and South America are a source of wonder, awe and puzzlement to the savants of Europe. Who were these people? Where did they come from? What was their history?

For nearly two centuries, answers to these questions remained unanswered, or rather farfetched. But, beginning with Thomas Jefferson, an inquiry into questions of American Indian cultural history was put on a systematic and scientific basis. Such a detailed approach could be expected of Jefferson since he is considered worldwide as The Renaissance Man.

The course of search, study, and inquiry has been arduous, steep, and involved. Due to the immensity of the subject, and the nature of the scholarly discipline required, entirely new methods and records of archaeological techniques had to be developed. New data, hypotheses, and ideas are constantly examined, compared and re-examined. We now know much, but many old (and new) questions remain for future generations to answer.

Please note that this chronology is obviously subject to critique, revision and correction. Indulgence is a must. Compiling this listing and the research was, as the saying goes, "like putting shoes on a running horse."

As archaeological money and interests increase, as methods and techniques are developed and improved, along with the inclusion of such fields as paleoanthropology, geochemistry, the pedologists, the palynologist, and others, we are covered each day with a mass of theories, proof, facts and evidence. We are now rapidly learning about man, his origin and his history.

For this reason the chronology that follows includes the total picture of man so as to lead up to one of man's descendants who was the progenitor, or ancestor of our special interests the American Indian.

CHRONOLOGY

3,750,000 B.P.-Dr. Mary D. Leaky of The National Geographic Society, discovers five footprints of an ancient man who's mud prints turned into fossilized, stone imbeded prints of this age. The prints found at Laetolil Tanzania were of an individual who was four feet tall.

3,350,000 B.P.-The earliest known fossil remains of ancient man discovered by Mary Leaky in December, 1974, in the area called Laetolil, 25 miles from Olduvai Gorge in Tanzania. The date was proven out by radio isotope techniques on fossilized teeth and jawbones of eleven different individuals.

3,000,000 B.P.-Dr. Donald C. Johanson and a team at Hadar, Ethiopia in 1974 discover Lucy, a partial female skeleton. Other finds of 60 individuals there, and at Laetoli, Tanzania, led to the naming of a new species of Hominidae, Australopithecus afarensis.

2,500,000 B.P.-Stone tools, similar to the Oldowan tools, found in Ethiopia appear.

2,000,000 B.P.-In 1924 a skull of this age was found in a South African cave by Professor Raymond Dart, of The Anatomy Department at Witwatersrand at Johannesburg, South Africa. It is the skull of a six year old child, gathered with other fossils from the limestone quarry which had exposed the cave. Later Prof. Dart announced his discovery as the famous Taung Child, which he named Australopithecus africanus. Overnight, the 32 year old Dart was a celebrity.

1,500,000 B.P.-The skull of a Homo Erectus boy is found (in 70 pieces), and fitted together. Found by Richard Leakey, and Kamoya Kimeu near West Turkana locale.

1,500,000 B.P.-Fossilized footprints of ancient man were discovered along the shore of Lake Turkana in northern Kenya. These footprints were discovered in August and July of 1978, by Dr. Anna K. Behrensmeyer of Yale University and the University of California. Announced by the National Science Foundation, the ancient footprints were made by an individual who was 5 feet 6 inches tall and weighed 120 lbs.

1,500,000 B.P.-Man's first standardized tool, the handaxe, appeared. The earlier ones were crudely chipped and called abbevillian, and the later forms were more elegant and called acheulian and chellean.

1,500,000 B.P.-First documented evidence of man using or playing with fire. C.K. Brain (Transvaal Museum in Pretoria) and Andrew Sillen (Univ. of Cape Town) found bone fragments which indicate that the fire was used for warmth, cooking or keeping wild beasts away at the site in Kenya.

1,200,000 B.P.-The Ice Age begins. First glacier movement South.

800,000 B.P.-The oldest unquestionable site of hominid occupation in Europe is Soleilhac, the Massif Central of France. Based on the many tools found there.

500,000 B.P.-Northeast of Madrid, Spain, at Ambrona and Torralba, on the Spanish plain, butchering sites of Mammoth elephants were found. Excavations by anthropologists Clark Howell and Leslie Freeman revealed thousands of stone tools, traces of fires and well preserved elephant bones and tusks.

400,000 B.P.-At the Terra Amata site on the French Riviera, a footprint of Homo Erectus is unearthed in 1966.

300,000 B.P.-Swanscombe skull fragments, Britain's oldest known human remains, are so dated.

160,000 B.P.-Utility flake tools were in wide use. These Middle Paleolithic tools were known as mousterian and levalloisian.

125,000 B.P.-Neanderthal Man appears on the scene in Europe, based on finds in the Neander Valley near Dusseldorf in Germany, starting in 1956.

120,000 B.P.-Excavations at the mouth of the Klasies River in South Africa indicate that ancient people lived there at this time. The occupational levels are as distinct as the layers of a cake and reveal much about our ancestors of that period.

60,000 B.P.-Carbon 14 dates on wood remains unearthed at Amersfoart, Netherlands.

60,000 B.P.-Kebara Cave, overlooking an Israeli banana plantation, has yielded a Neanderthal burial dating back to this time.

50,000 B.P.-Fragments of anatomically modern humans, found in caves at Klasies River mouth on South Africa's Indian Ocean coast, are dated back to this period in the past.

50,000 B.P.-Excavations by an Israeli-French team in 1983, at the Kebara Cave on Israel's Mount Carmel, reveals for the record that at this early time, deliberate burials were already in vogue.

50,000 B.P.-In 1951, Ralph and Rose Solecki, excavating in Shanidar Cave in Ira for the Smithsonian, discovers several remains of Neanderthal Man dating to this age. Remains of a variety of small plant pollen gave clues that certain mortuary rites (flowers) already had begun. Now referred to as the "Flower People."

47,000 B.P.-Start of the Paleolithic Age.

47,000 B.P.-Modern man, Homosapiens, appears in Europe.

47,000 B.P.-Pedra Furada in northeast Brazil has a hugh rock shelter with cave paintings of deer, birds, armadillos, stick figure people, hunting, sex and childbirth. Niede Guidon of the Institute of Advanced Social Science in Paris believes this site was occupied at the same time Neanderthals were living in Europe.

42,000 B.P.-Modern man, Homosapiens, appears in the Middle East.

41,000 B.P.-A fossilized skull with many stone implements was found at the Florisbad site near Bloemfortein, South Africa, and has been given this tentative date.

40,000 B.P.-Late Paleolithic flaked tools known as Solutrean Perigondian and Aurignacian appeared (Similar to the later Lerma type of the new world).

40,000 B.P.-At Orogrande cave in southern New Mexico, archaeologist Richard Mac Neish uncovered chipped stones and the toe bone of a horse with a spear point embedded in it; also, a fireplace with human fingerprints in the clay.

37,000 B.P.-Carbon tests on charcoal from firepits near Lewisville, Texas suggest that man was in that part of North American by this time.

34,160 B.P.-Charcoal from a fire pit in a rock shelter in Brazil gives a radiocarbon test date of 34,160 B.C., discovered in 1986.

33,000 B.P.-A peat bog site was discovered by Tom Dillehay of the University of Kentucky at Monte Verde, west of the Andes in south-central Chile. Many items were found in excellent condition under the bog including plant remains, wooden artifacts, digging sticks, mortars, spear tips and building foundations. 65 plant species with 15 plants having medicinal properties still used by local indians today were found.

32,000 B.P.-A wealth of ornaments, tools, and animal remains points to a complex of early Ice Age people located on the windswept steppes of Kostienki, along the Don River in the U.S.S.R. These Siberian shelters were mostly made of mammoth tusks, bones, large mandibles and hides.

32,000 B.P.-An ivory carved body of a man, dating to this time, was found in a cave at Hohlenstein, West Germany. Years after the discovery, a small lion muzzle was found at the same site and the same level. They fit together. This is the oldest anthropomorphic figure known.

32,000 B.P.-It is now generally agreed that prehistoric people had invented the bow and arrow by this time. This enabled man to much improve his standard of living by his increased ability to kill animals from a distance. The Egyptians were the first to adopt the bow and arrow as a standard weapon of war, quickly followed by the neighboring countries.

32,000 B.P.-In Brazil, excavations by N. Guidon have revealed remains dating back to 32,000 B.P. and 27,000 B.P. in a rock shelter located in arid polygon in the state of Piaui. The deep levels of Toco-do-Boqueirac-da-Pedra-Furado produced finds in support of these dates. Other caves in the same area lend further support to these dated eras.

30,000 B.P.-Neanderthal man appears to be fading from the scene in Europe.

27,000 B.P.-Jacques Cinq-Mars of the Archaeological Survey of Canada has found evidence of episodic human activity at Bluefish Caves in the Yukon. He also found the leg bone of a mammoth from which flakes were chipped. Also broken mammoth bones were found at Old Crow Basin.

26,000 B.P.-This seems to be the approximate period of time in which Ice-Age man began to create works of art with his hands. Of course, those which have lasted long enough for us to find are made of ivory. A small bust of an Ice-Age male was found in 1890 in Dolri Vestonice. Starting in 1920, archaeologists have found many additional items of Ice-Age man's art at this site.

The very realistic likeness of an Ice-Age man has recently been re-examined by Alexander Marshook after special requests for his evaluation. Exhaustive tests reveal the age of this eight-centimeter Czechoslovakian art at this date.

26,000 B.P.-One of the earliest known statues of man was discovered at Brno, Czechoslovakia. This rare human symbol is unique in that it has a mobile left arm, was carved of ivory, and touched with ocher.

23,800 B.P.-Material felt to be of human origin is charcoal from an ancient lake bed deposit near Tule Springs, Nevada. Carbon 14 test indicates age of more than 23,800 years old.

22,000 B.P.-At Valsequillo, Mexico, geologically dated artifacts suggest man's presence in Middle America at this date.

20,000 B.P.-Cro-Magnon man invents the bone needle, followed by the spear-thrower, the bone fish hook, the bow and arrow (millennia later in Europe), musical instruments of bone and decorative ornaments.

20,000 B.P.-Despite hazards brought about by glaciers that gripped North America, Paleo man continued to flood across the land bridge from Asia. Ice-Age hunters, armed with fragile spears, pursued the Wooly Mammoth elephant which stood 13 feet in height. Their descendants peopled the Western Hemisphere from Alaska and the Bering Sea, south to Terre del Fuego at the southern tip of South America.

20,000 B.P.-In southwestern Pennsylvania a jagged overhang juts out from a sand stone cliff. In this shelter archaeologists have evidence of human occupation many millenniums ago. A piece from a mat or basket woven 19,600 years ago and hearths, stone tools, deer bones lined with knife marks were found there. Dubbed "Meadowcroft," the resident hunters-gatherers traded with others in areas we know as Ohio and West Virginia.

20,000 B.P.-In July 1953, Keith Glasscock, amateur archaeologist, finds fluted points and bones of an ancient man at the Scharbauer Ranch near Midland, Texas. The Smithsonian Institute announced a year later that these bones and points date back to this time.

20,000 B.P.-Pikimachay (Cave of the Fleas) is located in the temperate basin of the Ayacucho, Peru, at an altitude of 9,400 ft. In this harsh environment the cave deposits indicate human occupation until 12,000 B.P. and indicates the Indians' adaptability for the 8,000 year period.

18,000 B.P.-A paleolithic camp beneath an overhanging rock bluff near Les Eyzies was long used as an Atlantic Salmon fishing camp.

17,000 B.P.-At Laguna Beach, California a human skull was found that dates to 15,000 years B.C. the oldest human remains yet found in North America.

15,500 B.P.-Stone-Age man leaves his pre-historic cave paintings on the walls in Lascaux Cave in Southwestern France and other caves in Europe. Amazingly accurate, it is man's first blush at the art of depicting living creatures. His earlier forms of art were decorative for himself and for his weapons.

15,000 B.P.-Excavated at Malta, Siberia, an ivory plaque incised with dots may have been an early attempt at a calendar or of record keeping.

15,000 B.P.-The global Ice-Age ends, although some glaciers persisted to 11,000 B.P. Last retreat of the glaciers, raising the global ocean level by 300 feet, and flooding the coastal areas of all continents.

15,000 B.P.-Mesolithic Period significant by Magdalenian burins and lancets.

14,000 B.P.-Discovered in 1912, the Tuc d'Audoubert cave in the French Pyrenees has been found to contain statues of hand shaped bison molded of wet clay and dated to this time.

14,000 B.P.-A spectacular discovery was made in Chile by T. Dillehay and a Chilean team of archaeologists. The remains of an encampment of mastodon hunters previously unknown in South America dated to 14,000 B.P. and found in a peat bog. There were 14 dwellings made of wood and skin housing about 56 people for many seasons. The occupants did not use worked or flaked points. The hunting weapons were stone balls (the oldest bolas in America).

14,000 B.P.-Small bands of eary man in South America hunted horse, mastodon and the giant sloth (all later extinct) in this period. These hunters did not use bifacial stone points, nor did they use flaked or delicately fashioned tools in general. A. Krieger referred to this in 1964 as the "Pre-Projectile Phase" on the South American scene, characterized by the absence of bifacial points. It appears that these early South American hunters were very few in number and had not yet mastered the technique of the pressure flaking art.

13,500 B.P.-Artistic caveman wall art on a sandstone tablet was found in Enlene Cave in the French Pyrenees. Found by Robert Begouen and Jean Clottes.

13,000 B.P.-Taima-taima in northwest Venezuela contains the remains of a mastodon elephant slain at this approximate date. Spear points and tools were also found by archaeologist Ruth Gruhn of the University of Alberta at Edmonton.

13,000 B.P.-Part of a fossilized jawbone was found south of the equatorial sites in Kenya and Ugonda. Believed to be the earliest known and first example of what scientists call Miocene Hominoids. Called "Otavipithecus Namibiensis," the fossil, like those from East Africa, is one of the closest to the evolutionary split, says researcher Glen Conroy, professor of anatomy and anthropology at the Washington Medical School in St. Louis.

12,000 B.P.-In 1924 a fluted point campsite was found by C.C. Coffin in eastern Colorado. Over a decade later, bison bones were found during excavation. The points found here were of the same type found one year later on the Folsom site.

12,000 B.P.-In 1925 the Folsom site was found by George McJunkin near Folsom, New Mexico. The remains of Ice-Age buffalo (bison) were found with fluted projectile points, the first proof that early man hunted bison.

12,000 B.P.-Midland, Texas. A skull of Midland Man was found and dated back to 12,000 years ago.

12,000 B.P.-Lake dwellers in Switzerland begin a culture that grew out of the need for protection from marauders at that time.

12,000 B.P.-In 1987, Moises Aquirre dug up an enormous Clovis spearpoint. He and his foreman, Mark Mickles, of the R. and R. Orchard, at Wenatchee, Washington, by day's end had found 19 stone tools and 6 large Clovis spearpoints. This was confirmed in 1988 by subsequent excavations in a formal archaeological dig by Dick Daughtery of Washington State University. The largest number of Clovis points ever found (20) in one place, authenticated, with one matched pair 9 inches long, are the largest ever found. They are excellent in workmanship and made of translucent chalcedony.

12,000 B.P.-In 1927, Anna Le Guillon Mitchell-Hedges, adopted daughter of F.A. Mitchell-Hedges, found a skull of human size and appearance. Carved from a single piece of clear crystal, it is an object unlike any other on earth. Shrouded in mysticism, it was found in the ruins of the Lubaantun Tomb, in a large Myan citadel located in Honduras.

11,200 B.P.-In 1936, the Clovis site was found near Clovis, New Mexico. The area is called Llano Estacado. The location excavated was called Blackwater Draw No. 1 where Clovis fluted points were found with mammoth bones, and identified as a "kill" site. Radiocarbon dates are: Clovis level - 11,200

B.C.; Folsom, Midland level - 10,300 B.P.; Agate Basin level - 9,800 B.P.

11,200 B.P.-In Colorado, the Dent Site produced Clovis points in association with debris that dates back to this time.

11,000 B.P.-Last major advance of the glacier period's ice sheet nears present day Milwaukee, Wisconsin.

11,000 B.P.-Unmistakable recent evidence of human occupation found in Fells' Cave, near the Strait of Magellon in Chile. Already, the wanderers who crossed the land bridge from Asia into Alaska had traversed two continents and arrived at the southernmost tip of South America.

11,000 B.P.-In Flint Run, Virginia, numerous quarries and campsites were dated from 9,000 B.C.

10,600 B.P.-At Debert, Nova Scotia, 4,000 flint tools and hunting points (Dalton variants) were found and dated to 10,600 years old.

10,240 B.P.-A man of Mongolian decent was found entombed in a lake at Warm Mineral Springs, Florida, in association with a Sabre Tooth Tiger and a Giant Ground Sloth. A spear thrower or atlatl was also found. Carbon 14 dating of this age was obtained. It is not known if the American Indians invented the Atlatl themselves or acquired it by way of Asia. A revolutionary improvement for the Indian. This allowed for increasing the impact energy by 200 times as well as extending the range.

10,000 B.P.-Start of the Mesolithic Age.

10,000 B.P.-In Scharbauer, Texas, a woman's skull was found that dated to 8,000 B.C.

10,000 B.P.-At the Hell Gap Site in Eastern Wyoming are found Agate Basin, Alberta and Hell Gap points.

10,000 B.P.-In 1951, the Quad site on Beaver Creek near Decatur, Alabama, two miles from the Tennessee River, was discovered, producing a new type, the Quad point.

10,000 B.P.-In 1936, Sandia Cave in the Sandia Mountains near Albuquerque, New Mexico was hunted by Kenneth Davis. He found relics there and took them to Dr. Hibben of the University of New Mexico, who excavated the cave. About 19 Sandia points were found, and a radiocarbon date of 19,000 B.P. was reported in the earliest levels, but is today believed to be much later.

10,000 B.P.-Wyoming Thunderbird site. Clovis type projectile points, fragments, and flint napping evidence dated.

10,000 B.P.-Modoc Rock Shelter in Southern Illinois, yields evidence of early man at the lower levels of the cave-like site.

10,000 B.P.-Footprints of ancient man was found in the mud of a cave in France.

10,000 B.P.-In 1951, the Bull Brook site, near Ipswich, Massachussets (Essex County), was found to produce fluted points. Radiocarbon dated at 10,000 B.P., these Paleo points were brought to light by William Eldridge as well as Tony, Frank, Joseph and Nicola Vaccaro. Their help and cooperation with John and Beth Brimes (Peabody Museum staff members) clearly establishes es the Paleo culture in New England. This is a classic example of how persistent and determined amateur archaeologists such as Eldridge and the Vaccaro brothers can add much to our knowledge of early man.

10,000 B.P.-An archaeological survey of the Shattuck farm near Andover, Mass. revealed that this site has a complex record of cultures of the Archaic and Woodland periods. Now known as the Andover Technological Center, this site has produced 77 known extensive private collections and added much to the cultural knowledge of the Archaic and Woodland periods in Massachusetts.

10,000 B.P.-First known site in America of a maritime adaption is that of Anangula on the Aleutian Islands. Microlithic tools and microdrills in evidence suggest their wide use in the working of bone and ivory.

9,000 B.P.-In Fort Rock Cave, Oregon, sandals made of shredded sagebrush bark are found which date back 90 centuries ago.

8,400 B.P.-Numerous excavations in Utah's Hogup Cave revealed hunting and gathering evidence of Indians using this site as a shelter for both seasonal hunts as well as a permanent dwelling place.

8,000 B.P.-In 1956, the Pine Tree site on Beaver Creek near Decatur, Alabama, west of the Quad site, was excavated, naming the Pine Tree point.

7,210 B.P.-In Windover, Florida, 170 individuals were found in a peat bog and carbon 14 dated to this time. Unique in all history is that ancient human brain tissue was found still in an excellent state of preservation. This allowed biologists from the University of Florida at Gainesville to study actual DNA from human brain cells of the first Americans. Finely woven fabrics made from palm fronds were also preserved for study.

7,000 B.P.-Evidence points to this date as the start of corn (maize) being a food product cultivated by the Indians in Mexico. Maize was the end product of cross-breeding corn grass with tripsacum and teosinte.

7,000 B.P.-Neolithic ware of the stone implements appears. Agriculture and metal working begins.

7,000 B.P.-In the early 1930s, the Eden site near Eden, Wyoming, was found. The site was excavated and Eden points were found with fossil bison. Radiocarbon dated at 7,000 B.P.

7,000 B.P.-In 1932, the Scottsbluff site was found in Scottsbluff County, Nebraska. The site was excavated and Scottsbluff points were found with fossil bison. A radiocarbon date of 7,000 B.P. was obtained for the site.

6,500 B.P.-Start of the Copper Age.

6,000 B.P.-Shoreline villages of long term occupation at Cape Kiusensfenn, Alaska.

5,600 B.P.-Building of the great Egyptian pyramids begins.

5,500 B.P.-Start of the Bronze Age.

5,500 B.P.-Invention of the wheel in the Caucasus, or in Mesopotania.

5,000 B.P.-Earliest evidence of corn in North America was discovered in Bat Cave, New Mexico, and dates back 5,000 years.

5,000 B.P.-Wyoming's Mummy Cave yields evidence of 5,000 years of human habitation and 38 layers of artifacts including agate projectile points in one of the topmost layers.

5,000 B.P.-Weapons, tools and ornaments are hammered from nuggets of copper by Indians of the Great Lakes area.

5,000 B.P.-A recent series of archaeological finds in South America shows that the Incas were merely the final act in the many civilizations of the Andes. New excavations reveal stone pyramids and monuments back to this date along with seeds, potatoes and fragments of nets and fabrics.

5,000 B.P.-12 large wooden boats were found at Abydos, Egypt in 1991. 50 to 60 feet long, these boats are the earliest royal ships ever found, the greatest number of ancient ships ever found at one site and the oldest boats ever found anywhere. The site is 280 miles south of Cairo and 8 miles from the Nile River. Each boat was inside a mud-brick coffin and buried in a pit with pottery. The boats were to serve as magical vehicles to transport the dead pharaohs through the sky. Found by David O'Conner, curator of the Egyptian section of the University Museum of Pennsylvania and the Egyptian Antiquities Organization.

5,000 B.P.-Johan Reinhard with Chicago's Field Museum of Natural History in LaPaz Bolivia has been studying high-altitude ceremonial sites in the Andean peaks. It seems that the Inca Indians believed these high peaks were their ancestors which had to be venerated by sacrifice. Reinhard located, studied and excavated hundreds of "offerings" and human sacrifices to these Inca gods. The sites are located on almost inaccessible peaks and crags, at heights of 17,000 to 22,000 feet. The Incas built ceremonial centers here in the rocks and gravel, so isolated that they were undisturbed for 500 to 1,000 years. At these antiseptic, very high altitudes, the sites and mummified contents were actually in a "deep-freeze" locale. The cold is so extreme that even the flesh on the mummies is well preserved. Young women, boys and girls were sacrificed here. Blood types, diseases and last food consumed before death was discernable.

4,600 B.P.-In 1991 a frozen and mummified prehistoric man was found at an elevation of 10,500 feet in a melting Similaur glacier in the Alps on the Italian side. Dated from the Neolithic age, a pure copper axe (not bronze), a bow, quiver, arrows, flint knife, flint fire starter with kindling in a leather pouch were found with the remains. This is the oldest naturally preserved corpse ever found of a European man.

4,500 B.P.-Clay tablets found in nothwestern Syria reveal that an ancient city named Ebla once rivaled Egypt and Mesopotamia as major powers of the ancient world. Dr. Paolo Matthiae of the University of Rome, while on an archaeological mission in Syria, discovered more than 15,000 cuneiform tablets in a mound called Tell Mardikh. The early Bronze Age city of Ebla is clearly stated many times. The cities of Sodom and Gomoriah as well as Iram, a city mentioned in the Koran, are referred to for the first time.

4,500 B.P.-A giant fish weir was built near Boston, Mass.

4,400 B.P.-Records and relics found in Peru take the record of western man, the Indian, back to still further distant epochs about the year 2,400 B.C.

4,000 B.P.-Finds on the surface and later archaeological digs in recent decades date the inhabitation of Russell Cave in Alabama.

4,000 B.P.-Mashkan-Shapin, a Mesopotamian city is discovered in January of 1989. Found by Archaeologist Elizabeth C. Stone of the State University of New York at Stony Brook.

3,800 B.P.-Tell Leilan, a Mesopotamian city is discovered in 1985 and dated to this time.

3,600 B.P.-Bronze Age in China begins.

3,600 B.P.-Start of the Iron Age.

3,500 B.P.-Near the confluence of the Arkansas and Mississippi Rivers in Louisiana, the Poverty Point Culture evolved. This enigmatic cultural site is one square mile in size, but contains six miles of ridges built by hauling in 1,500,000,000 pounds of dirt by hand.

3,000 B.P.-The Maya culture begins which lasted for 2,000 years.

3,000 B.P.-In late 1989, Richard Hansen, who discovered the ancient Mayan city of Nakbe, unearthed another significant city of Nakbe in that it is built over an even earlier Mayan village dating back to 1,000 B.C. that had been preserved underneath it like a modern-day Pompeii.

3,000 B.P.-Rise of the Adena culture in Ohio. A turkey-tail point (Adena culture) made of Indiana hornstone found in Indiana was dated to 3,000 years ago.

2,600 B.P.-Advent of Stonehenge on the Salisbury Plain in England.

2,600 B.P.-The Mayan Indian calendar of the Central American Indian began in 613 B.C. (based on actual Mayan calendar date).

2,600 B.P.-Tikal, a Mayan super city begins, consisting of 3,000 constructions in a 6 square mile area, with more than 10,000 earlier structures lying beneath these. Here stands the tallest ancient structure, made by Indians, in the Western Hemisphere, erected in 741 A.D. This culture lasted through to 900 A.D.

2,600 B.P.-In a remote Quatamalan jungle in 1989, Richard Hanson, a U.C.L.A. archaeologist, excavated what may be the oldest known Mayan center of civilization. Known as Nakbe, it consists of 75 major structures and hundreds of mounds and has been dated to this time.

2,600 B.P.-In 1932, the greatest single treasure was discovered at Monte Alban (Olmec culture). Found were over 500 pieces of Mixtec jewelry, including gold, silver, jade, turquoise, rock crystal and intrically carved bone.

2,600 B.P.-At Copan "City of Kings" in Honduras, William L. Fash, JNr. of Northern Illinois Univ., and Ricardo Agurcias Fasquelle of the Honduran Institute of Anthropology discovered a Mayan temple. This buried temple had 200-250 years of construction beneath it and three major structures atop it. The 18 by 12 meter temple had been completely plastered over and sealed up before the later temples were built over it. In the temple were found nine eccentric flints of intricate quality with scraps of cloth wrapping clinging to their surface. Each piece was individually wrapped and then all together in a bundle.

2,500 B.P.-The bow is introduced in North America, after having been used in Europe for several thousand years.

2,290 B.P.-The National Geographic Society discovers a Mayan monument in the Yucatan in 1939, which bears the date of Nov. 4th, 291 B.C. (Spinden correlation), the earliest known work dated by man himself found in the New World thus far.

2,250 B.P.-Rise of Olmec civilization and culture in Central America.

2,000 B.P.-In 1837, a woman's body was found in Haraldskjaer Fen, Denmark in a peat bog, perfectly preserved with hair, clothes, and skin all intact. On May 8th, 1950, Tollund Man was found in a peat bog near Aarhu, Denmark. He was so perfectly preserved that the undigested remains of his last meal were still in his digestive tract. With more discoveries, these bog people were dated to 1500 to 2000 years old.

2,000 B.P.-In 1954 the Camp Creek site in Greene County, Tennessee, at the convergence of Camp Creek and the Nolichucky River, was excavated. Camp Creek and Nolichucky points found here became new types. Radiocarbon dates of 2,000 B.P. were acquired.

2,000 B.P.-The Snaketown site of Hohokam culture near Gila, Arizona yields some 3,000 beautifully chipped arrowheads in one ceremonial area. Called Saw-Toothed Icicles, they are of unique beauty. The World's first acid etching was done by the Hohokam.

1,700 B.P.-Known as the "Moche,"a culture of Indians in the Lambrayeque valley of Peru lived by farming the land from about A.D. 100 to A.D. 800. Ever since 1532, when the Spanish appeared, their tombs have been looted of gold and artifacts even to this day. In February 1987, some looters were caught with part of their bounty. Investigations by the authorities and the Bruning Museum of Peru resulted in the discovery of an adjacent tomb never before opened. Now considered one of the richest and most significant tombs ever found in the Americas, this excavation reveals much about the culture of the "Moche."

1,500 B.P.-At Lake Titicaca, in Bolivia, the Andean Empire of the Tiahuanaco flourished. Their knowledge of hydrology and farming to produce irrigated fields outproduced modern farming methods by a yield of seven times as great. This was done without modern farm technology and equipment by using the Tiahuanaco technique of raised fields and water channels.

1,500 B.P.-A recent dig in South America has uncovered a Peruvian King Tut in an elaborate tomb containing his 1,500 year old remains. Buried with him were hundreds of priceless gold and silver artifacts.

24 A.D.-In 1890, Frank H. Cushing of the Smithsonian Institution discovers and partially excavates the site of Key Marco, Florida. He finds several hundred wooden artifacts and works of art over 1,000 years old, yet still preserved.

100 A.D.-Rise of the culture preceding the Aztecs, known as Teotihuacan

(Yucatan). This civilization built the two famous structures known as The Pyramid of the Sun and The Pyramid of the Moon, the first great city in the New World.

100 A.D.-Caracol, an ancient Mayan city flourishes. Remains of buildings at this city in the Yucatan were taller than any building in the Americas until the construction in 1896 of the Flatiron Building in New York City.

200 A.D.-Rise of the Hopewell culture in midwestern United States.

200 A.D.-Largest effigy mound in America was built, the Serpent Mound in Ohio.

575 A.D.-Zimbabwe, the mystery city of Southern Rhodesia is dated by Carbon 14 test to this date.

600-1200 A.D.-Mississippian ceremonial centers evolved rapidly in the Southeast. Spiro in Oklahoma, Etowah in Georgia, Cahokia near St. Louis, all of whose names are legendary.

879 A.D.-A stela bearing this Mayan date (converted) was found at Chichen Itza. This Mayan city was a center of advanced civilization. Here was the sacred sacrificial Cenote (lake) where children were sacrificed amid great treasure and artifacts.

900 A.D.-The Turks develope an advanced bow and arrow. Their laminated bows were made of a combination of special woods, animal horns and tendons.

924 A.D.-In 1924, L. L. Loud, of the University of California, found several duck decoys in Lovelock Cave in Northwestern Nevada. Dated at 1,000 years of age, these decoys were made of bouyant rushes, and some were covered with duck feathers; more proof of the masterful adaptions made by the American Indians.

1000 A.D.-The sophisticated pre-Inca Indians created the incredible giant art of Peru's Nazea plain. Giant spiders, reptiles, birds, insects, fish and monkeys are included with lines and geometrical figures so vast that they were not discernible until the advent of aircraft.

1064 A.D.-Construction of the Tenayuca Pyramid (The Pyramid of the Serpents), near present day Mexico City.

1100 A.D.-The crossbow becomes the most popular weapon in Europe. It fired a smaller and shorter arrow, but it was a deadly and accurate projectile called a bolt.

1100 A.D.-The rise of the Toltec civilization and culture in Mexico.

1100 A.D.-Wetherill and Mason, in December 1888, discover the cliff dwellings at Mesa Verde, Colorado built nearly 800 years earlier by the Anasazi. This one site had 23 kivas and 200 rooms.

1100 A.D.-Cahokia, in Illinois, becomes the largest town in North America.

1100 A.D.-Pueblo Bonito, in New Mexico, becomes the largest Pueblo village in North America.

1200 A.D.-Easter Island statues were erected.

1200 A.D.-Rise of the civilization and culture of the Aztecs.

1200-1400 A.D.-The large Mississippian town of Moundville in western Alabama flourishes.

1325 A.D.-Founding by the Aztecs of Tenochititlan (now Mexico City), built on a marshy island in Lake Texcoco. Alliance with Texcoco and Tlacopan, along with subjugation of Tlatelelco, forged the highest civilization in the Western Hemisphere prior to the advent of Columbus. By the time of its conquest by Hernando Cortes, this city had a population of 300,000. A city of canals and causeways, its beauty awed the Spanish Conquistadors. As they were aware that no city in Europe could compare to it, the Spaniards promptly proceeded to destroy it.

1438 A.D.-Dawn of the Inca Empire in Peru. Forged by the emperor Pachacuti, ninth in the dynasty of Incas, lords of Cuzco.

1492-Christopher Columbus lands at San Salvadore and claims all land in the

Western world for Spain.

1500 A.D.-A bison kill site was discovered in 1969 by a surveying crew laying out an interstate just east of Sundance Wyoming. Now known as the "Vore Buffalo Jump" this site has revealed that between 1500 and 1800 A.D. an estimated 20,000 animals died and were butchered here by the Indians. The bison were periodically driven by the Indians over a 55 foot drop in small groups, as needed for food and etc. The drop killed, injured or stunned the bison for slaughter. This site was used by the Arapaho, Cheyenne, Kiowa, Apache, Crowe, Shoshone and the Sioux Indians.

1519 A.D.-On Good Friday, Hernando Cortes with 508 soldiers, 16 horses, and 14 cannon landed at San Juan de Ulua (modern day Veracruize). From here Cortes started the looting and destruction of an innocent people consisting of many cultures and civilizations, not to end until 1525 A.D. with the conquest of the Maya (Guatemala).

1540 A.D.-The earlier Mississippian ceremonial centers were quickly followed by satellite cultures such as Hiwassee Island, Citico, and Tellico, in Tennessee. Weeden Island, Coles Creek, Natchez, Coosa, and Ocmulgee complexes were next. Many of these were encountered by DeSoto on his explorations, including the older Etowah center at Cartersville, Georgia.

1540 A.D.-Hernando DeSoto, the Spaniard explorer, seeking gold, starts his explorations at the Southeastern areas of what is now Florida, Georgia, Alabama, Tennessee, Mississippi, as well as touching the western areas of North and South Carolina. As a result of this expedition, the Indian population in the Southeast was nearly wiped out within 10 years.

1706-1714 A.D.-The Cherokee Indian replaced the Creeks and the Yuchi (Children of the Sun), in the area of what is now Tennessee.

1797 A.D.-John Frere found a flint axe in association with a Pleistocene elephant tooth near Hoxie, England.

1801 A.D.-Thomas Jefferson published a volume describing his investigations and excavations of a mound near his home, Monticello, in Virginia. The first organized site work. Jefferson concluded that these mounds were the work of the ancestors of the Indians of his time, a view not generally accepted until 100 years later.

1838 A.D.-The removal of the Cherokees and other Indians from lands east of the Mississippi River was effected by the U.S. Army under the command of General Winfield Scott.

1891 A.D.-Eugene Dubois, a Dutchman, finds the skull of Java Man. The find was the result of extensive search and excavation on the banks of the Solo River in Java. Now called Homo Erectus, this was for many years the oldest of early man's evidence.

1894 A.D.-Duck River cache found in Tennessee, dated to 1,500 A.D. This is the finest assemblage of flaked artifacts ever found.

1911 A.D.-Hiram Bingham finds the timeless city of the Incas, Machu Picchu. The mountain-locked city perched on a jungle crag of the Andes in Peru.

1911 A.D.-On the 9th of August, Ishi, a Yahi Indian is captured. He was the last wild Indian in North America.

1929 A.D.-In China, in 1927, a young paleontologist named W. D. Pei found a skull cap embedded in deposits in a limestone cave at Zhoukoudian, near Beijing. Called Peking Man, it is a counterpart to Java Man.

1941 A.D.-A fluted point site was found near Enterline, Pennsylvania. The points were made from Onondago chert originating from a quarry about 200 miles away. These points had multiple fluting which is now called the Enterline method of fluting, and is considered to be an early form of fluting technique. The Williamson site in Dinwiddie County, Virginia and the Joffre Coe site in North Carolina also used the Enterline method of fluting.

1955 A.D.-The LeCroy site, seven miles north of Harrison Bay State Park in Hamilton County, Tennessee, was named after Archie LeCroy who had worked the site for ten years. This site produced points from Paleo to Mississippian. A large quantity of bifurcated stemmed points were found here and given his name.

1955 A.D.-Wheeler point named by James W. Cambron after the Wheeler Basin of North Alabama.

1959 A.D.-Mary D. Leakey makes a startling find–the skull of Zinjan thropus, or Australopithecus boisei, at the site of Tanzania's Olduval Gorge.

1972 A.D.-Richard Leakey finds a skull similar to Zinjan. The site of the find was at lake Turkana in Africa.

THE SLAUGHTER OF THE BUFFALO

by Stephen O. Addison

Historians insist that in the 15th Century there were at least 100 million buffalo in the area that comprises the United States. They roamed the land from California to the east coast, and from the Gulf of Mexico to the forests of Canada. Yet, by 1830 there were no buffalo east of the Mississippi River.

It is estimated that about the time of the Revolutionary War there were at least 60 million of these giant beasts west of the Mississippi. Gertz Cortez was the first European to see a buffalo (in Mexico) and Alvar Nunez Cabeza de Vaca was the first European to see the buffalo in its wild state and to make notes of his observations (in Texas).

Giants these animals were, and until the year 1880 the buffalo in America were the most numerous hooved animals on earth.

Some earlier locomotives were forced to wait as much as eight hours due to buffalo crossing the railroad tracks–so great was the number of some herds.

Col. R.I. Dodge watched a herd of these animals in 1871. The herd, he said, was 25 miles wide and 50 miles deep (an estimated 4 million buffalo in one herd).

But now a tragic doom awaited the buffalo. The crowning, ignominous act was ours and was done to control and eliminate the Indian. We slaughtered this quiet and docile animal by the millions. It was an unprecedented sacramental violation.

At the behest of General Phil Sheridan, military commander of the Southeast, the slaughter, which had already begun, was not only allowed to continue, but was aided and encouraged to still greater numbers by the general. "Let the hunters kill until the buffalo is exterminated," he said. "These hunters have done more to solve the Indian problem than the Army has been able to do in 30 years."

Yes, there were many protests. The questionable logic of the red-whiskered general who overdramatized the necessity of destroying the buffalo (to the last animal) was without question a tragic error of history.

Indian-hater Sheridan pulled enough weight with President Grant, his old Civil War comrade-in-arms, to push through his extermination program.

Within a short period, the 60 million buffalo were reduced to a total of only 600.

This is 1/100,000th of 1 percent which survived in the year 1889 as compared to a century before. This was the death knell of the Indian in the West.

After 400,000 years of needing only physical ruggedness to survive, it was inevitable that the buffalo would succumb to an increase of man into his territory. One or two men could stampede a massive herd of our buffalo.

However The Cape Buffalo of Africa would not tolerate such impertinence of man. If anyone tried to stampede them they would be placing their lives in jeopardy. As many as two or three would attack the perpetrater who would be lucky to escape death.

The name of "Buffalo" itself is a misnomer which was applied by white man himself erroneously. In truth this North American oxlike ruminant's correct name is Bison, (sometimes called "wisent").

But, with man on the scene it was different, and one man, O.A. "Brick" Bond, of

Dodge City, Kansas, killed 5,575 buffalo in a 60-day period "to help the government control the Indian," he said.

How could the buffalo be so important to the Indian's existence? Let's take a look.

The buffalo was the Indian's source of fresh meat. "Jerky" was meat dried in the sun and was a staple food item. "Pemmican" was dried meat pounded into a powder and mixed with berries.

Sizzling hot buffalo steaks were the best of food, along with the buffalo bread eaten raw with the steaks. This was the dry fat under the hide along the backbone and it tasted like bread.

Buffalo tongues were cooked on spits of green sticks over the fire. Buffalo marrow was cooked in the bone and served as dessert. The bones were placed in the fire and the marrow cooked by the heat transmitted from the bones. The bones were then split open by a blow from a stone or club, and the marrow eaten. It was said to be a gourmet's morsel.

Buffalo meat was more easily digested than that of domestic cattle. One could eat his fill of buffalo meat and eat without fear of indigestion. Few foods are more nourishing than buffalo meat.

In short, the buffalo's flesh was food and his blood was drink for the Indian. The Indian fashioned moccasins and leggings from the tanned hides. He scrapped and stitched the hides together to cover tepees, and slept under warm buffalo robes. Beds, clothes and belts were made from the hide, as were bull-boats and parfleche bags.

The Indian used rawhide for saddles, ropes, bands, bags, straps and handles. Green hides were used as cooking pots. The tough neck hide was made into shields and would turn the blow of a club, stop an arrow and even small caliber bullets. Ribs were used for runners on the dog sleds, club handles and for bow components. Small bones were made into various tools, knives, needles, awls, combs, ear trinkets and breast ornaments. Large bones made digging tools, hoes, shovels and weapons.

Buffalo hair made ropes, small game traps, snares, nets and fishing lines. By boiling the buffalo hooves, an excellent glue was made and for which there were many uses, including the fletching, (feathers), of arrows and binding reinforcements on bows. The horns were made into cups, bowls, spoons, ladles, weapons and warbonnets. Sinew made bowstring, thread and lashing for making arrows, bows and war clubs.

The dried bladders were used as canteens for holding water. Even the tail was dried and used as a club and for knife scabbards.

On the treeless prairie, buffalo chips fueled the Indian campfire and warmed his tepee. Blood and brains were used in the tanning of hides. The liver and tongue were a delicacy. Even the gallstones were treasures as a talisman and used for war paint. In effect, to the Indian, a buffalo was a walking department store and provided all he needed to sustain himself and his people. Equally important, it was always there and awaiting his use.

It is indeed a sad commentary on our so-called civilization that this bountiful natural meat supply was destroyed by the white man in a mad massacre. The great beasts were slaughtered literally by the millions, their hides ripped off, and the meat left to rot on the prairie. No wonder the Indian fiercely opposed the white man's wanton destruction of the buffalo herds.

Once the buffalo were gone, the Indian could not survive, and he ceased to be a threat or danger to the frontier immigrants.

Today the buffalo is no longer an endangered species. By 1903 their numbers had increased from a low of 600 to 969. Since then, with renewed effort and a dedicated commitment their numbers are now over 80,000 buffalo in the U.S. alone.

TERMINOLOGY

The following terms are used in the point collecting market and are listed here for your information.

Agate-A semi-precious chalcedony formed as quartz fossils of a previous geological age. The colors are cloudy, clear to banded.
Agatized Coral-Found in Florida and used to produce beautifully flaked points. All coral has small polyps visible under magnification.
Archaic-The archaeological period that falls between Paleo and Woodland.
Asymmetrical-A term used to describe points that are not of the same form on both sides.
Auriculate-Refers to rounded or pointed ears that project from the base or stem of certain points.
Barb-A protruding shoulder that forms a point. Also see *wing.*
Basal Edge-The bottom edge of a point.
Basal Grinding-When the edge around the hafting area of a point has been smoothed so that the lashings would not be cut.
Basal Notch-When the basal edge of a point is notched for hafting.
Basal Polish-A polishing of the faces of the hafting area that occurs on certain Paleo points.
Base-The bottom part of a point used for hafting.
Baton-A hand-held ceremonial object made of flinty material used in the eagle dances of the Mississippian peoples.
Beavertail-Refers to a point made by the Adena peoples that has a stem in the form of a beaver's tail.
Bevel-The sloped edge of a blade or stem.
Bifurcated-Refers to the stem of points that have a central notch splitting the stem in two ears.
Bird Point-A term used to describe very small arrow points, believed by some to have been used for shooting birds. Actually, small triangular points have been found embedded in the bodies of deceased Indians during archeaological digs, suggesting they were used in war. Most of the Mississippi culture arrow points fall into this catagory.
Blade-The area of a point between the tip and the stem or base.
Blank-See *preform.*
Blunt-Refers to a point with has a short, broad, rounded tip. Also called *stunner* or *scraper.* These points were actually used as knives and scrapers.
B.P.-Before present.
Buffalo River Chert-A colorful middle Tennessee chert with specks and bands of browns to reds to purples used in point production.
Bulbous-A term used to describe a circular or rounded shape and is usually applied to point stems.
Burin-A lancet with one end fractured off at an angle, producing a sharp point.
Burlington Chert-A fossil bearing quartz found in Illinois and Missouri.
Cache-A group of points deposited in the same place, usually of the same type and origin.
Callche-Calcium deposited on points found in Texes and adjoining states.
Carter Cave Chert-Found in Northeastern Kentucky, a high quality, beautifully colored material of tans to orange to reds.
Ceremonial-Any object made for a specific use in a rite or ceremony denoting authority or power; i.e., *Duck River cache.*
Chalcedony-A quartz-like material with a waxy luster.
Chert-A flintlike quartz that often occurs in limestone. (*Webster*).
Classic Example-A term used to refer to a point that represents the truest form of a particular type.
Clipped Wing-A barbed shoulder that has been fractured off or clipped.
Collateral-Refers to a flaking style where parallel flakes are removed from each side of a blade and meet in the center, forming a median ridge.
Concholdal Fracture-The breakage of rock in concentric circles or in a shell-like pattern.
Conglomerate-A metamorphic rock that is geologically recombined and is composed of clay, sand, mud and pebbles.
Contracting-Refers to the width of a stem or point that is diminishing.
Concave-Slanting inward.
Convex-Slanting outward.
Core-A cone-shaped form of flint or chert produced from spalls. Long slivers are struck off the circular base used in point production.
Corner Notch-When the basal corners of a point are notched for hafting.
Corner Tang-When a single tang is located on one of the basal corners in a diagonal posture.
Coshocton Chert-From south central Ohio, a grey to blue to black chert used in point production.
Cross Section-A mid-section representation of the shape and thickness of a point.
Crystal Quartz-Clear, pure, hard silica from the quartz crystal, used in rare instances for points.
Distal End-The area of the tip of a point.
Dovetail-The other type name for *Plevna,* which refers to the shape of the base of this corner notched point.

Dover Chert-A high quality brownish to black material that comes from an ancient quarry located near Dover, Tennessee. This material is used in point production and has been popular with all cultures from Paleo to the current day.
Duck River Cache-The world's largest and best-known group of ceremonial flint objects ever found; from the Duck River in West Tennessee.
Duckbill Scraper-A long, ovoid-shaped, uniface tool in the form of a duck's bill, steeply beveled on the broad end.
Eagle Claw-A ceremonial object made of flinty material in the form of an eagle's claw, made by the Mississippian peoples and used in their ceremonial eagle dances.
Ears-Pointed or rounded projections from the base of certain points
Edwards Plateau Chert-A Texas material found in limestone and ranging in color from browns, tans to greys.
Effigy Flints-Extremely rare flinty forms chipped into the shape of various animals such as human heads, turtles, snakes, eagles, etc.
E-Notch-The same as *Key notch.*
Enterline-Refers to an early method of fluting used by the Paleo Indians first recognized on a site near Enterline, Pennsylvania. Two parallel flutes are struck on each face before the final central flute.
Expanding-Refers to the width of a stem or point that is getting larger.
Fake-A modern reproduction that is sold as an authentic ancient artifact.
Fishhook-Authentic fishhooks made of flinty material are extremely rare, if they exist at all. Beware of recently made examples for sale.
Fishtail-A term used to describe auriculate or points with expanding ears.
Flaking-Refers to the chipping or shaping of the stone.
Flint-A greyish to black or brown quartz with a high silica content that produces a conchoidal fracture. It is usually found in association with chalk, limestone and other rock deposits which contain lime. It commonly occurs in small and large ovoid nodules, as well as in veins. Impure flint is known as chert, which varies widely as to texture, color, grain and knapping characteristics. Pure flint is so hard and even-grained that its use by early man was a vital necessity in producing arrowheads, spearheads, knives, ceremonial objects, and other utility tools such as lancets, drills and other implements. Late Stone-Age man learned that when struck with high iron content rocks, the flint gave off sparks. Thus, it became Iron-Age man's chief method of producing fire.
Flint Ridge Chert-A high quality, multi-colored material that is used in flint knapping from Paleo times to the present day. The quarry is located near Columbus, Ohio.
Flute-A grooved channel on one or both faces of a point struck from the base. A technique used in Paleo times.
Fort Payne Chert-An Alabama material found in tans, greys, browns and whites mixed.
Fractured Base-See *Snapped Base.*
Gem Quality-When a point is made of semi-precious material such as agate, petrified wood, jade, etc.
Graver-A Paleo flint uniface tool with sharp projections for puncturing or incising purposes.
Grinding-See *Basal grinding.*
Heat Treated-A process used by early Indians to improve the quality of the stone for easier flaking. The stone would be buried in sand under a fire and exposed to temperatures exceeding 500 degrees for several days. This would change the molecular structure as well as the color of the original material.
Hemitite-(ironstone)-A reddish to purplish-brown iron oxide sometimes used in point manufacture.
Hinge Fracture-The termination point of a struck flake where it breaks off.
Historic-The archaeological period following Mississippian when the Indians came in contact with Europeans.
Horizontal Transverse—Refers to a flaking style where horizontal parallel flakes are removed that extend from one side of the blade, across the face to the other side.
Hornstone-A bluish to grey chert from Indiana and Kentucky.
Horse Creek Chert-A rare red, yellow and blue material from West Tennessee that is highly prized among collectors.
Impact Fracture-A grooved channel that begins at the tip of a point and runs towards the base, occurring during impact when the point is thrown or shot.
Jasper Chert-A reddish to yellow to brown variety of quartz used in point production.
Key Notch-A blade notching technique that produces a spur or ridge at the base of the notch in the form of an E. See *Thebes* points.
Lanceolate-A term used to describe a stemless point.
Lancet-A thin, long, narrow flake of flinty material used for slicing.
Limestone-A sedimentary material formed primarily of calcium.
Lobbed-Refers to the base portion of a point that is eared. The ears are rounded and are formed by the meeting of two circles creating a lobbed effect.
Mace-A hand-held ceremonial object made of flinty material used in the eagle dances by the Mississippian peoples.
Median Ridge-Refers to a high ridge that forms in the center of a blade due to angled parallel flaking.
Mississippian-The archaeological period that occurred after Woodland and before Historic, about 1000 to 1500 A.D.
Mottled-Any point material that contains spots of different colors or shades.
Nodule-A concretion of chert, flint and other substances that occurs in chalks and lime-

stones. Nodules are broken into spalls which are chipped into cores.
Oblique Transverse-Refers to a flaking style where oblique parallel flakes are removed that extend from one side of the blade, across the face to the other side.
Obsidian-A dark glassy volcanic rock.
Opaque-When a substance will permit light to penetrate but with no detail or torm.
Paleo-The earliest archaeological period.
Patina-A chemically created coating caused by oxidation due to long exposure to oxides.
Percussion Flaking-The first stage in the process of shaping a point or blade when flakes are removed by striking the edge with a blunt tool.
Perforator-Usually an arrowhead that has been rechipped with a sharp needle-like point for puncturing or incising purposes.
Petrified Palm Wood-A highly collected form of agate from the south central region used in point production.
Petrified Wood-A colorful agatized chalcedony used in point production.
Polished-See *Basal polish.*
Pre-Columbian-Occurring before Columbus (1492 A.D.).
Preform-A roughly shaped elliptical blank prepared for later finishing into a point or blade.
Pressure Flaking-The final stage of shaping a point or blade when flakes are removed with the point of a tool through forced pressure rather than blows.
Projectile-A body impelled or projected through the air.
Pudding Stone-See *Conglomerate.*
Quartzite-See *Sugar quartz & Tallahatta quartzite.*
Reproduction-A recent facsimile of an ancient artifact.
Sandstone-A metamorphic stone composed of layers of sand.
Scraper-A tool that is made either from scratch or from broken points used to scrape hides. See *Duckbill Turtleback Thumb & Side Scraper.*
Serrated Edge-A saw-toothed cutting edge pressure flaked on the blade edge.
Shoulder-The area of a point that divides the blade from the stem.
Side Notch-Refers to a notch in the side of a point for either hafting purposes or decoration.
Side Scraper-A lanceolate shaped uniface blade with a prepared edge on one or more sides for scraping.
Slate-A metamorphic sedimentary material that forms in thin layers and contains various amounts of organic material.
Snapped Base-A term used to describe points that have a part of the base intentionally fractured or snapped off. See *Decatur and Kirk*
Spall-A chunk of flint or chert broken off a nodule from which long slivers can be fractured off for point production. Spalls are converted into cores.
Stem-The area of a point behind the shoulders that is used for hafting.
Striking Platform-A raised area prepared on the base of Paleo points from which a flute can be struck. See example under *Clovis.*
Stunner-A short blunt arrow point believed by some to have been used only to stun the animal for capture. These were probably used as knives and scrapers.
Sugar Quartz-Also known as quartzite, a granular low grade form of quartz used in the production of some point types.
Sun Disc-A circular ceremonial effigy form of the Sun made from flinty material.
Tallahatta Quartzite-A greyish fossiliferous stone used in point production. This material oxidizes easily resulting in a pitted appearance and a reduction in mass.
Tang-A projection that extends from the base of a point (see *Ears*).
Thumb Scraper-A short stubby ovoid shaped unitace tool that is steeply beveled on one end for scraping.
Thunderbird-A legendary bird-beast that the Indian believed had power over all. Flint effigies have occurred ot this animal but most are recently made.
Torque Blade-Refers to a blade that twists or turns in one direction from base to point. This occurs during the manufacturing process when a piece of flint is fractured off a round spall at an angle.
Transitional Period-The time period involved between two cultural periods.
Translucent-When a substance will permit a great amount of light to penetrate but with no detail or form.
Turkeytail-A narrow point with a diamond shaped stem in the Adena family.
Turtleback Scraper-An elliptical shaped uniface scraper in the form of a turtle's back.
Typology-The study of point types.
Umbrella Tangs-Shoulder projections that droop downward.
Unfluted-A term used to describe points that usually occur fluted but are not.
Uniface-A point or tool finished only on one face (see *Double uniface*).
Upper Mercer Chert-From south central Ohio a black chert used in point production.
War Point-Small triangular points that were used by the Indians against each other in war. These points have been found in excavations embedded in the bodies of Indians.
Willow Leaf-A long slender ovate point in the form of a willow leaf.
Wing-Same as barb.
Woodland-The archaeological period that is after the Archaic Period but before the Mississippian.

ABASOLO - Early to Mid Archaic, 7000 - 5000 B.P.

(Also see Catan, Desmuke, Montgomery & Morrow Mountain)

G2, $2-$5
Travis Co., TX.

G2, $2-$5
Travis Co., TX.

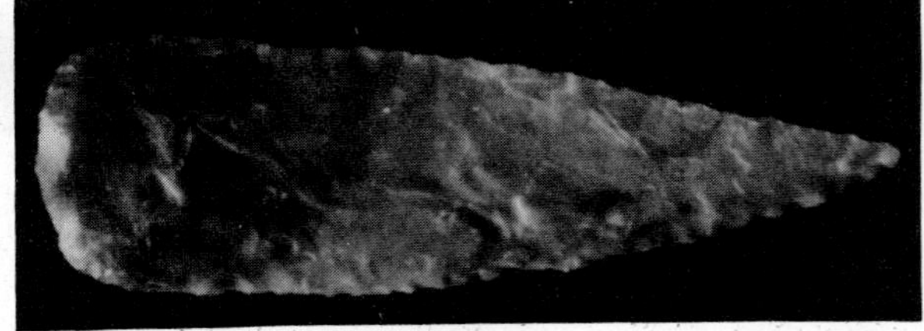

G5, $15-$25
Bell Co., TX.

G4, $8-$5
Austin, TX.

G5, $15-$25. Pyramid Lake, NV.

LOCATION: Midwestern states and Mexico. **DESCRIPTION:** A medium to large size, broad, lanceolate point with a rounded base. The blade can be beveled on one side of each face and the base can be thinned. **I.D. KEY:** Early form of flaking on blade with good secondary edgework and rounded base.

ABBEY - Early to Mid Archaic, 6000 - 4000 B.P.

(Also see Alachua, Cottonbridge, Levy, Pickwick, Savannah River, South Prong Creek & Wacissa)

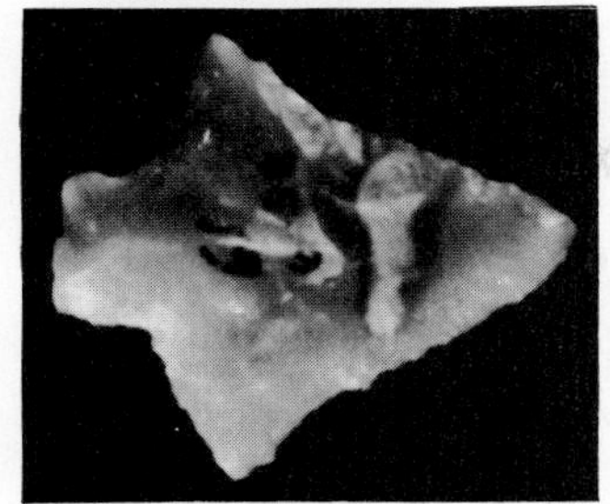

G3, $5-$10
Henry Co., AL.

G4, $8-$12
Escambia Co., AL.

G5, $20-$35
Terrell Co., GA. Note unusual notched base.

G7, $50-$75
Burke Co., GA.

G7, $50-$80
Warner Robbins, GA. Classic example. Note fine blade serrations.

LOCATION: GA, AL, FL. **DESCRIPTION:** A medium sized, broad, stemmed point that is fairly thick and is steeply beveled on all four sides of each face. Blade edges are concave to straight. Shoulders are broad and tapered. A relationship to Elora, Maples and Pickwick has been suggested. **I.D. KEY:** Expanded barbs & fine edgework.

G7, $150-$200
Cuthburt, GA. Note unusual fractured wings.

G5, $25-$35
Alexander City, AL.

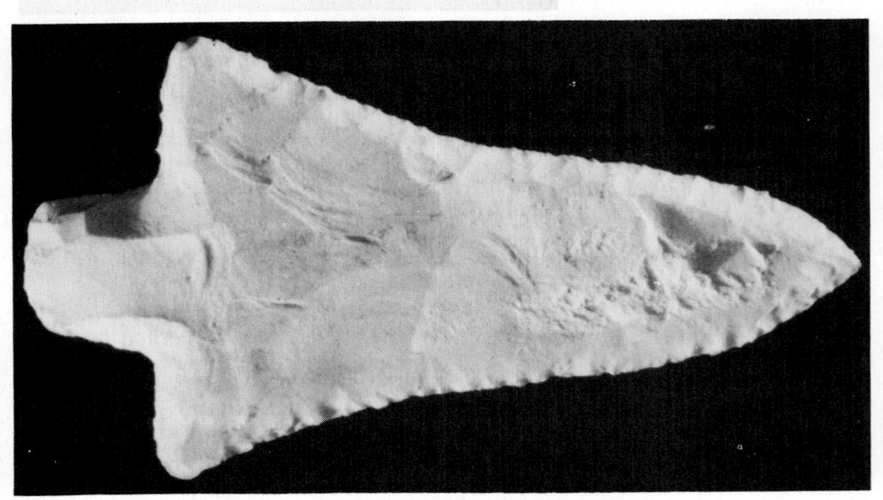

G10, $350-$600
Blakely, GA.

ADDISON MICRO-DRILL - Late Woodland to Mississippian, 2000 - 1000 B.P.

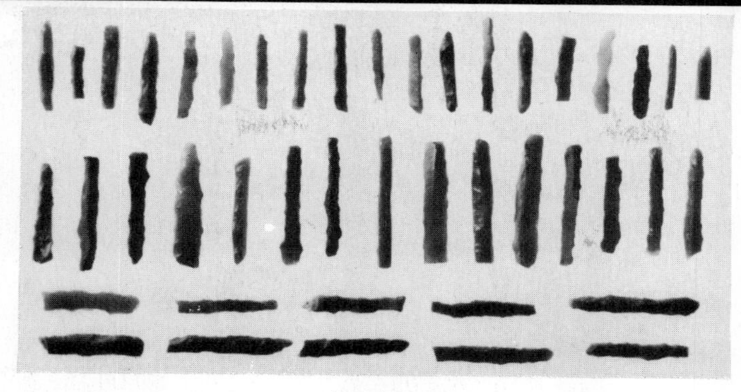

$3.00-$5.00
Shown actual size. All found in Bradley & Hamilton Co., TN.

LOCATION: Examples have been found in Alabama, North Carolina, North Georgia and Tennessee. **DESCRIPTION:** Very small to medium size, narrow, slivers, flattened to rectangular in cross section. Theory is that this is the final form of a drilling process. The original form were flint slivers with sharp edges that were used as drills. As the sliver was turned in the drilling process, the opposite edges in the direction of movement began to flake off. As the drilling operation proceeded, the edges became steeper as more and more of each side was flaked. Eventually a thin, steeply flaked, rectangular drill form was left and discarded. Unique in that these micro artifacts are not made and then used, but are created by use, and discarded as the edges became eroded away by extremely fine flaking, thus reducing their effectiveness as a cutting edge.

ADENA - Late Archaic to late Woodland, 3000 - 1200 B.P.

G3, $5-$8
MO.

G3, $5-$8
Humphreys Co., TN. Dover chert.

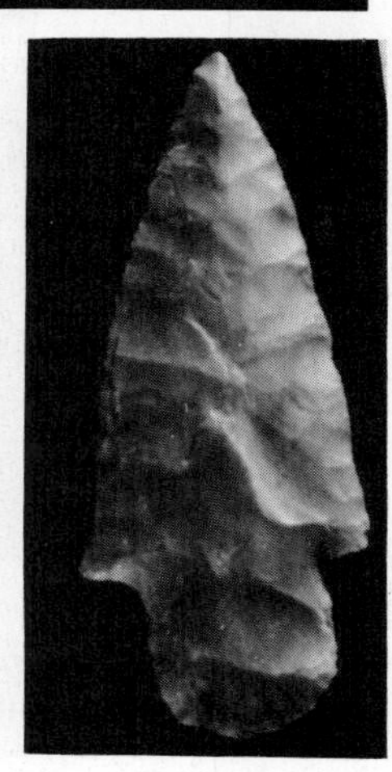

G3, $5-$8
Humphreys Co., TN.

ADENA (continued)

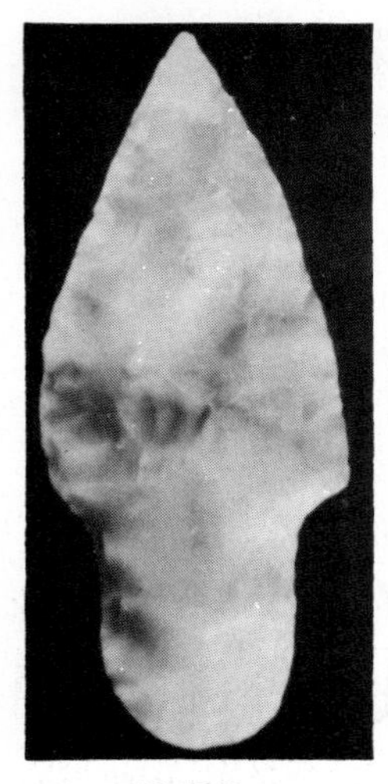

G3, $5-$8
Cleveland, OH. Flint Ridge flint

G5, $25-$40
Parsons, TN. Classic "beavertail" base.

G6, $30-$50
Parsons, TN.

G5, $25-$40
Hardin Co., TN. Pink chert.

G4, $10-$20
White Co., TN.

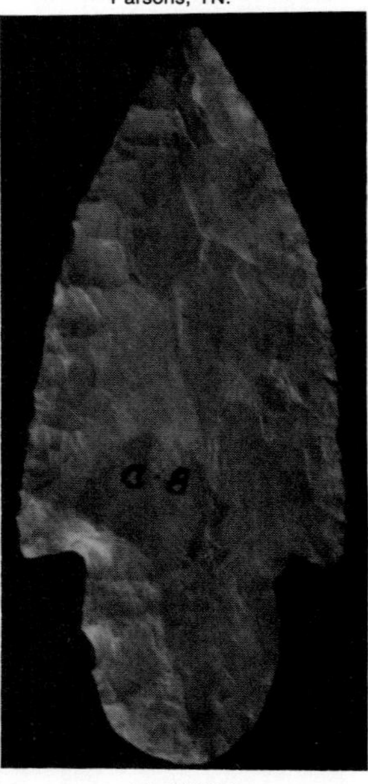

G4, $15-$25
Humphreys Co., TN.

LOCATION: Eastern to Southeastern states. **DESCRIPTION:** A medium to large, thin, narrow, triangular blade that is sometimes serrated, and with a medium to long, narrow to broad rounded "beaver tail" stem. Most examples are from average to excellent quality. Bases can be ground. Has been found with *Nolichucky, Camp Creek, Candy Creek, Ebenezer* and *Greenville* points (Rankin site, Cocke Co., TN). **I.D. KEY:** Rounded base, woodland flaking.

G7, $40-$75
White Co., TN.

G6, $40-$75
Humphreys Co., TN.

G8, $150-$250
Butler Co., KY. Excellent form and quality.

G10, $450-$800
Clifton, TN. Super color.

G8, $180-$300
Parsons, TN. "Bell" shaped stem.

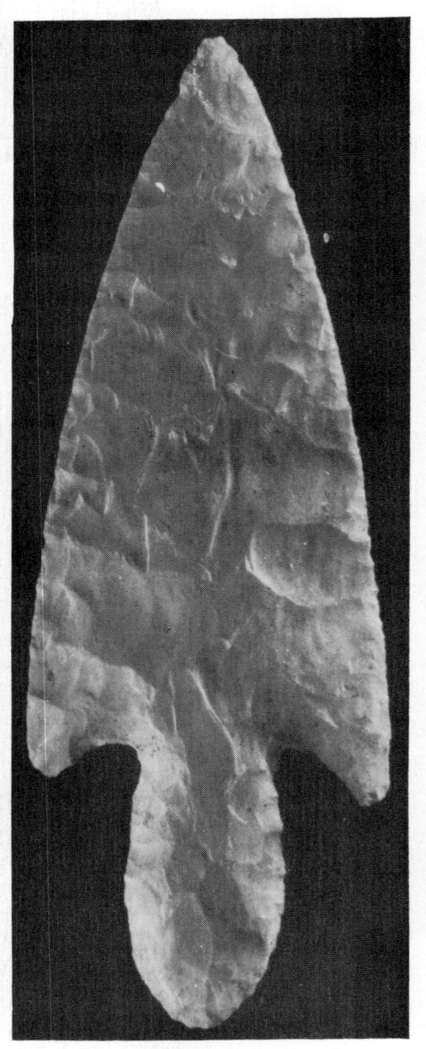

G9, $250-$400
Louisville, KY. Minor tip damage.
Cache quality point.

ADENA (continued)

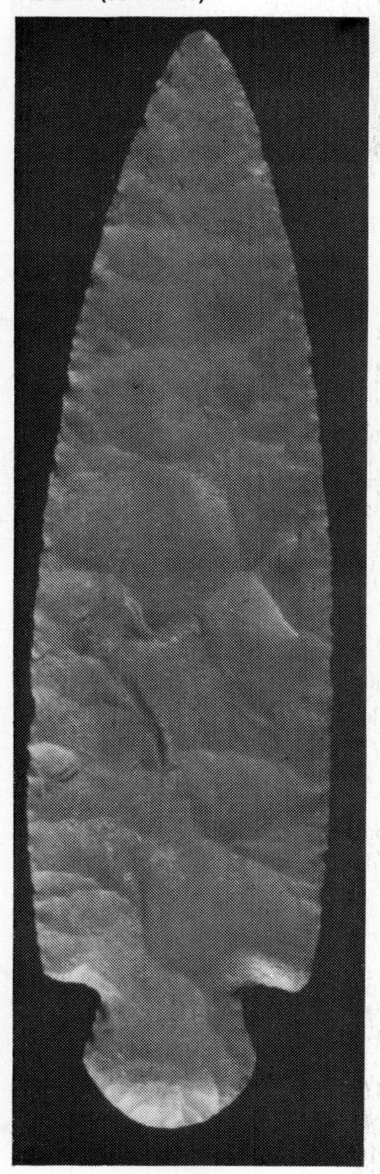

G10, $700-$1000
Lexington, KY. Boiled chert.

G10, $700-$1200
Perry Co., TN. Very thin and excellent. Note "bell" shaped stem.

ADENA BLADE - Late Archaic to Woodland, 3000 - 1200 B.P.

(Also see Copena, Pandora, Tear Drop and Tennessee River)

G7, $80-$120
Humphreys Co., TN. Cache point.

G8, $150-$250
Humphreys Co. TN. Cache point.

LOCATION: Midwestern to Eastern states. **DESCRIPTION:** A large size, thin, broad, ovate blade with a rounded base and is usually found in caches. **I.D. KEY:** Woodland flaking, large direct strikes.

ADENA-DICKSON - Woodland, 2500 - 1600 B.P.

(See Gary, Levy, Marion, Morrow Mountain and Newnan)

G4, $10-$20
Meigs Co., TN.

G3, $5-$10
Cooper Co., MO.

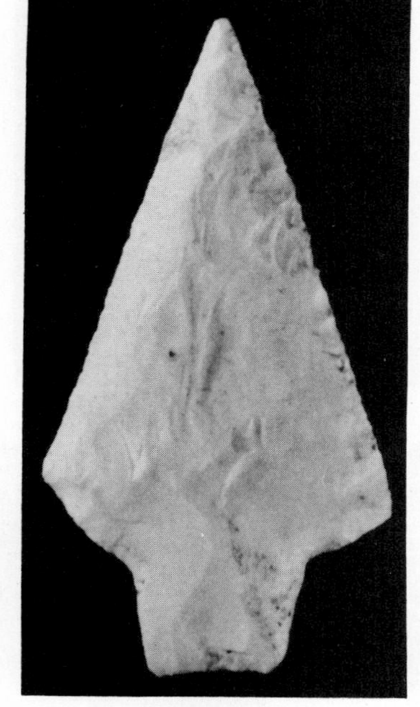

G5, $45-$75
MO.

G6, $75-$125
MO.

LOCATION: Midwestern states. **DESCRIPTION:** A medium to large size point with tapered shoulders and a contracting stem. High quality flaking and thinness is evident on most examples. **I.D. KEY:** Basal form.

G6, $90-$150
ILL.

G7, $180-$300
IND.

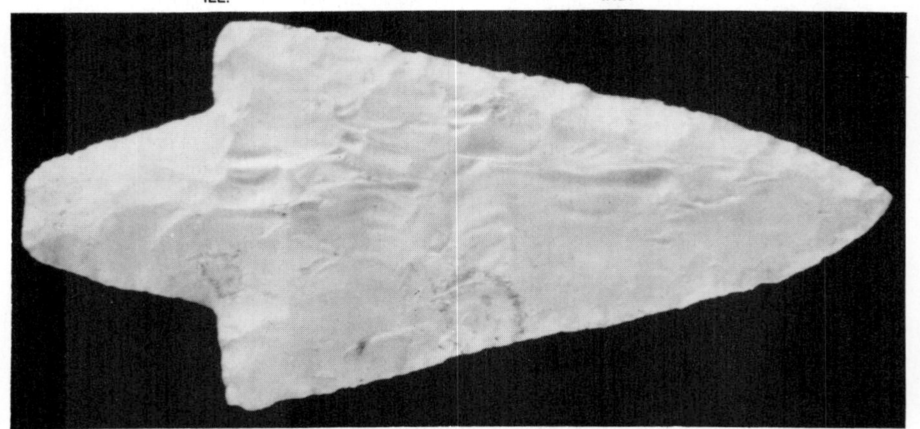

G8, $250-$450
ILL.

G10, $400-$750
CO.

G10, $450-$800
MO/ILL.

ADENA-NARROW STEM - Late Archaic to Woodland, 3000 - 1200 B.P.

(Also see Little Bear Creek)

G5, $15-$25
W. TN. Buffalo River chert.

G3, $5-$6
Meigs Co., TN.

G3, $3-$6
Humphreys Co., TN.

G5, $15-$25
Humphreys Co., TN.

G5, $25-$40
W. TN.

G3, $5-$6
S.E. TN.

G5, $25-$35
Humphreys Co., TN.

LOCATION: Eastern to Southeastern states. **DESCRIPTION:** A medium to large, thin, narrow triangular blade that is sometimes serrated, and a medium to long, narrow, rounded stem. Most examples are well made. **I.D. KEY:** Narrow rounded base with more secondary work than ordinary *Adena*.

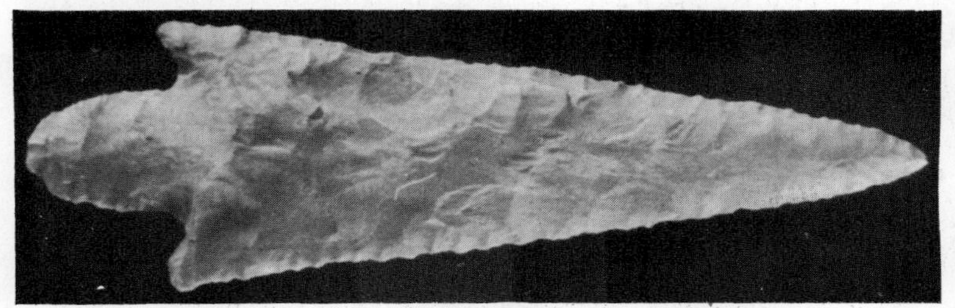

G9, $150-$250
W. TN. Note fine serrations. Very thin.

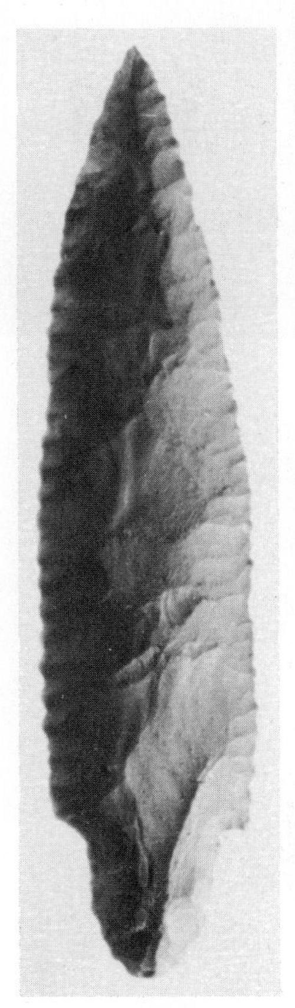

G7, $50-$80
W. TN. Note fine serrations.

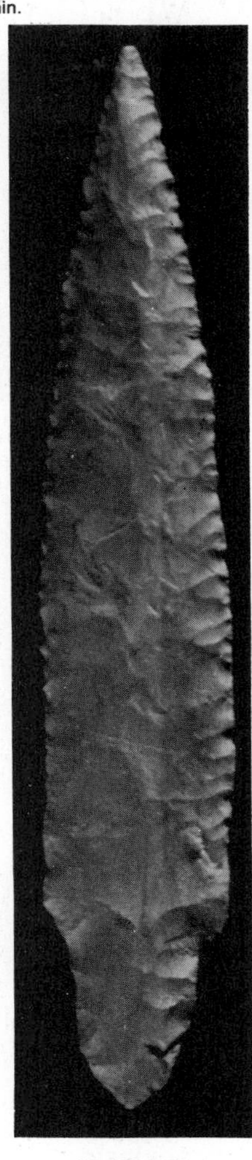

G8, $70-$100
KY.

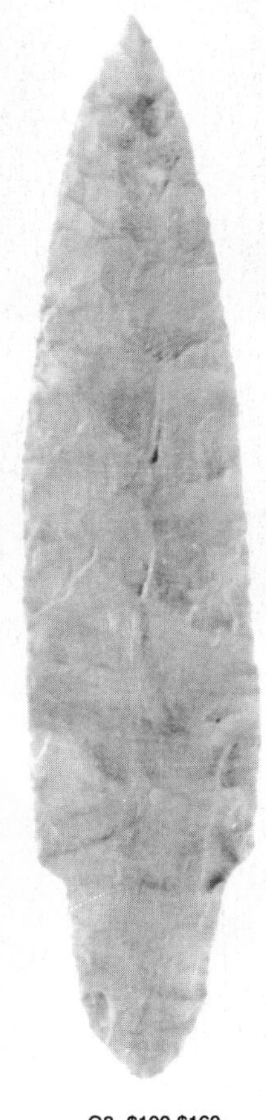

G8, $100-$160
Humphreys Co., TN. Excellent quality and thinness.

ADENA-NOTCHED BASE - Late Archaic to Woodland, 3000 - 1200 B.P.

G4, $10-$15
MO.

G5, $15-$25
MO.

G4, $10-$15
Humphreys Co., TN.

G6, $25-$35, Parsons, TN.

G5, $15-$25, Parsons, TN.

LOCATION: Southeastern states. **DESCRIPTION:** Identical to Adena, but with a notched or snapped-off concave base. **I.D. KEY:** Basal form different.

ADENA-ROBBINS - Late Archaic to Woodland, 3000 - 1800 B.P.

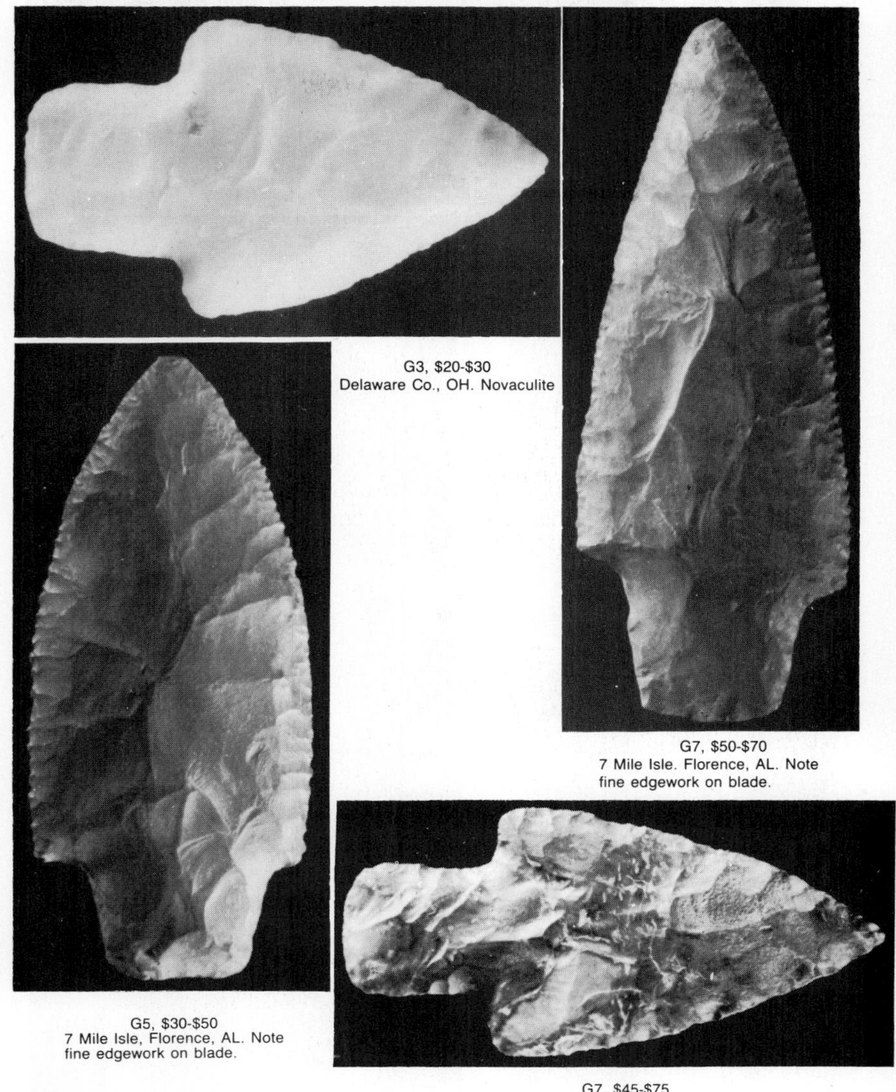

G3, $20-$30
Delaware Co., OH. Novaculite

G7, $50-$70
7 Mile Isle. Florence, AL. Note fine edgework on blade.

G5, $30-$50
7 Mile Isle, Florence, AL. Note fine edgework on blade.

G7, $45-$75
Cleveland, OH. Classic form.

LOCATION: Eastern to Southeastern states. **DESCRIPTION:** A large, broad, triangular point that is thin and well made with a long, wide, rounded stem that is parallel sided. The blade has convex sides and square shoulders. Many examples show excellent secondary flaking on blade edges. **I.D. KEY:** Squared base, heavy secondary flaking.

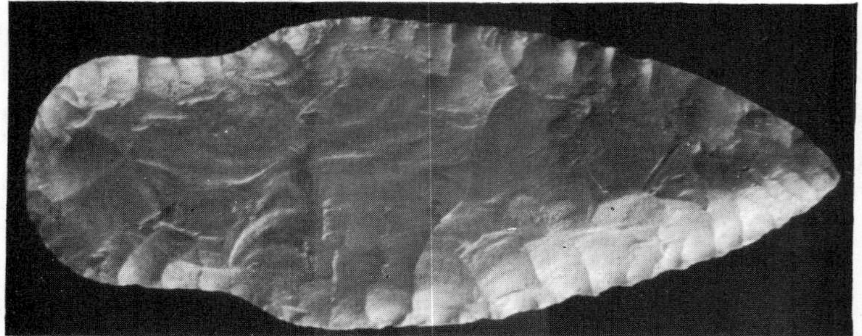

G6, $40-$60
Allen Co., KY.

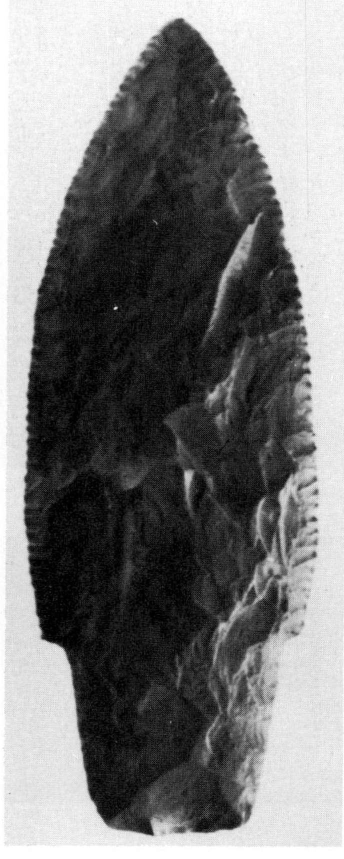

G10, $600-$1000
Trigg Co., KY. Outstanding example. Thin with fine serrations. Very rare in this size and quality.

G8, $150-$250
Cooper River, SC. No edge work.

ADENA-WAUBESA - Woodland, 2500 - 1500 B.P.

G4, $25-$35
Humphreys Co., TN.

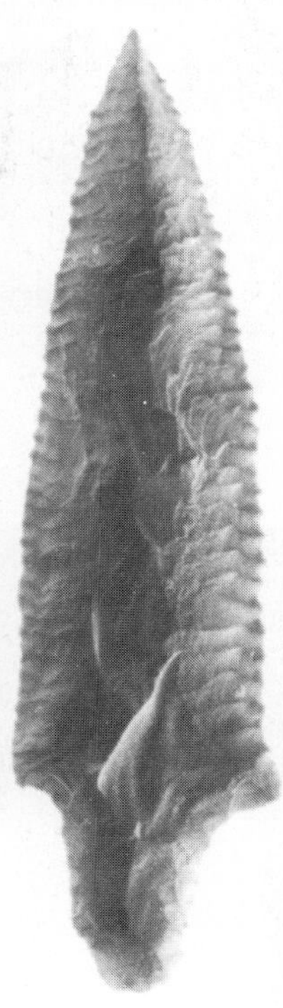

G8, $200-$300
Parsons, TN. Older form. High quality with sawtooth serrations. Dark Dover chert with a needle tip. Found 12' deep in the Tenn. River bank.

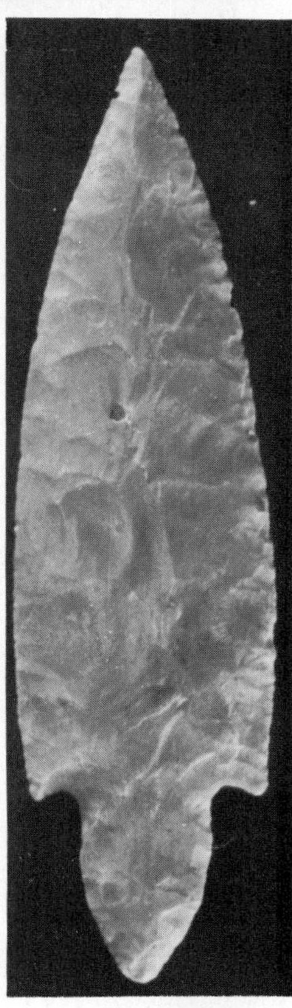

G9, $250-$400
Nashville, TN. Cache quality point.

G9, $250-$400, Humphreys Co. TN. Very thin and excellent.

LOCATION: Eastern to Southeastern states. **DESCRIPTION:** A medium to large, narrow, thin, well made point with a contracting stem that is rounded or pointed. Some examples exhibit unusually high quality flaking and saw-tooth serrations. Blades are convex to recurved. Shoulders are squared to barbed. **I.D. KEY:** Basal form pointed or near pointed, good secondary flaking and thin.

G6, $50-$75
Hamilton Co., OH.

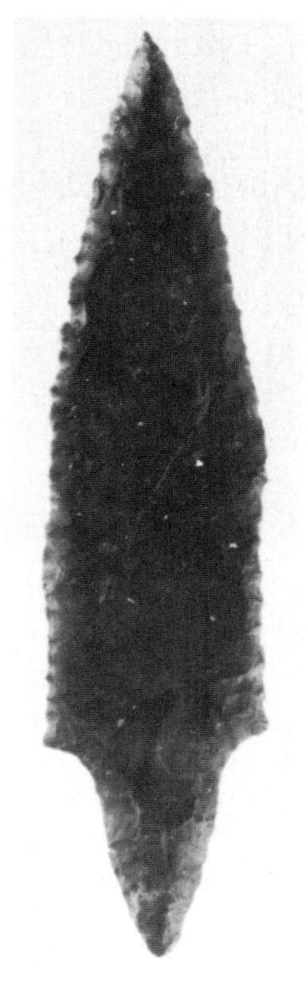

G8, $120-$180
Humphreys Co., TN. Dark dover chert. Very thin, excellent quality.

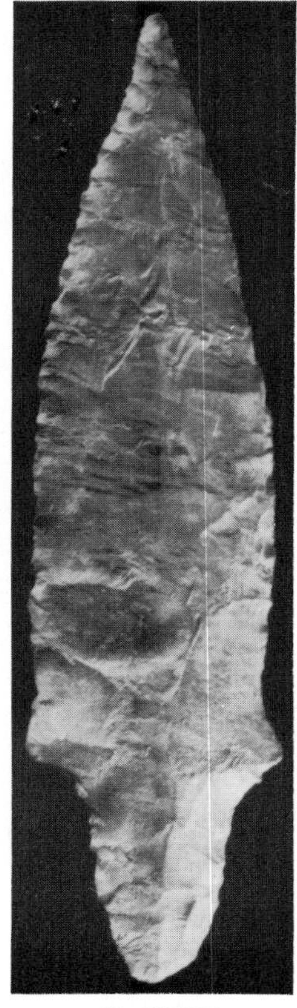

G7, $90-$150
Humphreys Co., TN. Dover chert.

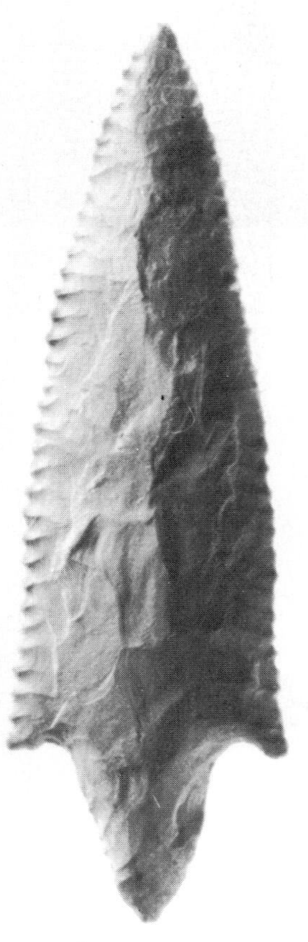

G10, $400-$650
Humphreys Co., TN. Outstanding speciment with saw-tooth serrations, very thin and excellent form.

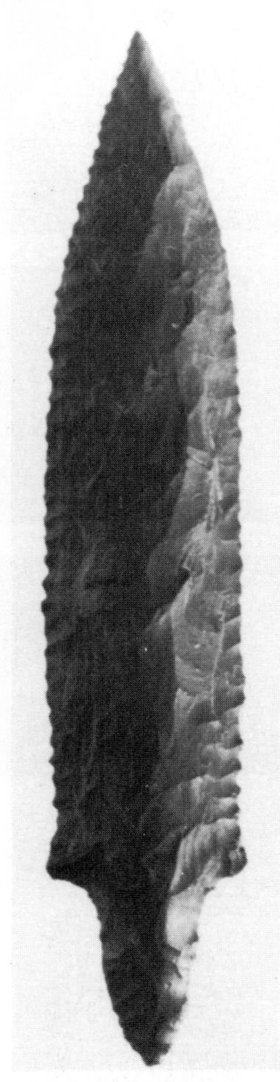

G10, $900-$1500
Parsons, TN. Outstanding example. Very thin with saw-tooth serrations. Points of this quality are very rare.

G10, $750-$1000
Parsons, TN. Very high quality, thin, with excellent form. Note unusual tapered shoulders.

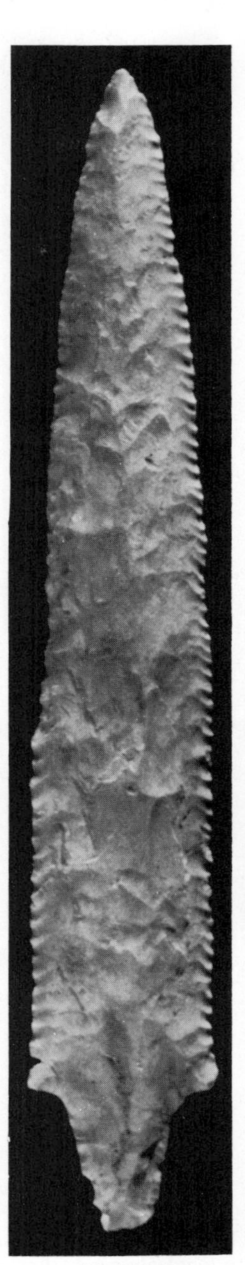

G10, $500-$800
Humphreys Co., TN. Note fine edgework.

ADENA-WELLS - Early to Mid Archaic, 8000 - 5000 B.P.

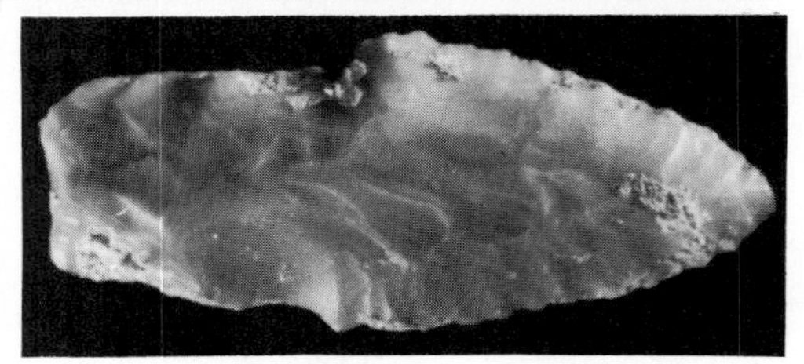

G4, $15-$20, Austin, TX.

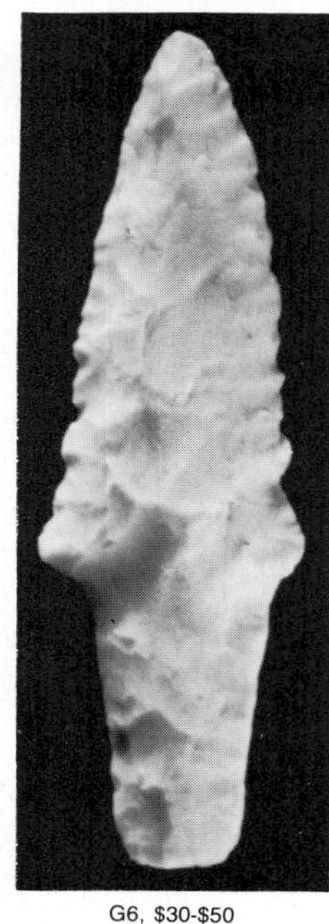

G6, $30-$50
Austin, TX.

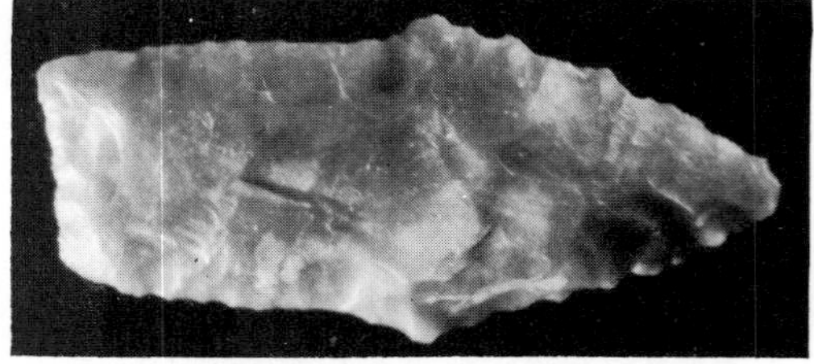

G4, $12-$20, Austin, TX. Early form.

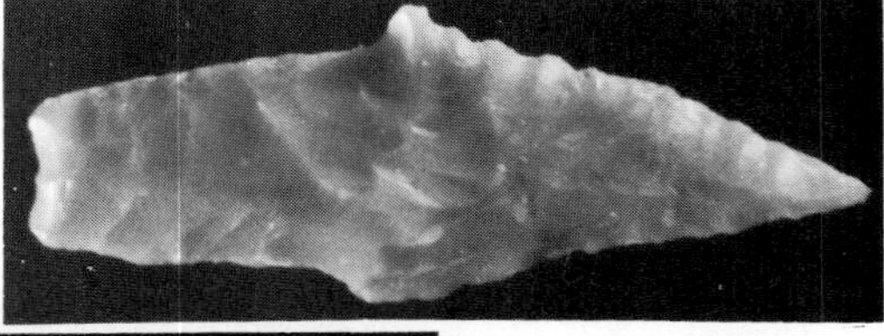

G3, $3-$7
Comanche Co., TX.

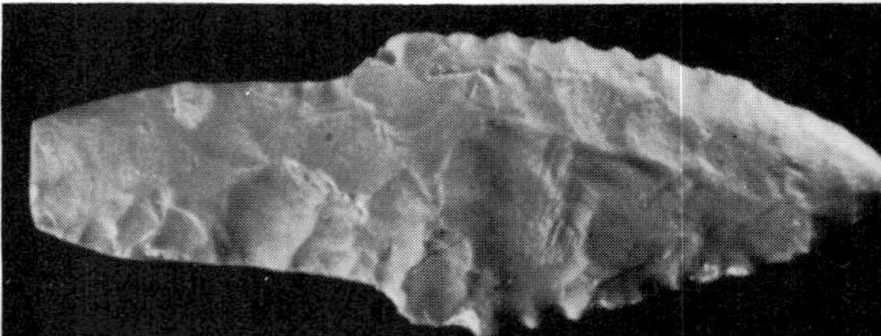

G6, $30-$50
Austin, TX.

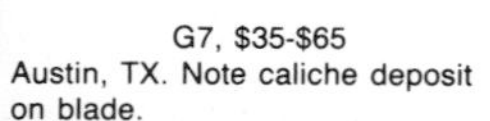

G7, $35-$65
Austin, TX. Note caliche deposit on blade.

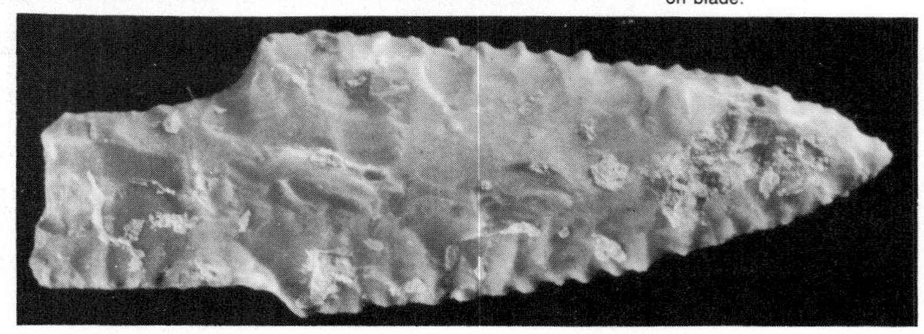

LOCATION: Eastern Texas. **DESCRIPTION:** A medium to large size, thin, point with a long, narrow contracting to parallel stem that has a rounded to straight base. Shoulders can be tapered, horizontal or barbed. **I.D. KEY:** Basal form, extended and squared up. Early flaking style.

AFTON - Mid-Archaic to early Woodland, 5000 - 2000 B.P.

(Also see Jacks Reef Corner Notched)

G4, $15-$25
OH.

G6, $40-$60
OH.

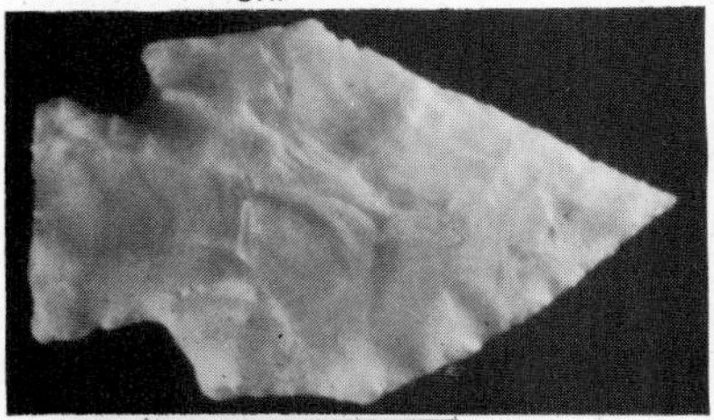

G4, $15-$25
MO.

G3, $10-$20
MO.

G5, $20-$35
Pulaski Co., KY.

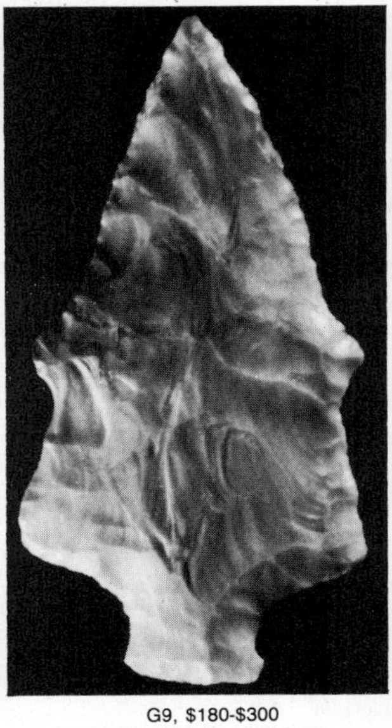

G9, $180-$300
Hardin Co., TN. Colorful heat treated chert.

G7, $45-$70
Dayton, TN.

LOCATION: Midwestern states and is rarely found in some Eastern and Southeastern states. **DESCRIPTION:** A medium to large size pentagonal shaped point with a flaring or corner notched stem. Some examples are base notched and some are stemmed. **I.D. KEY:** blade form.

AFTON (continued)

G10, $350-$600
Seneca Co., OH. Note unusual "knobbed" blade corners.

G6, $35-$60
MO.

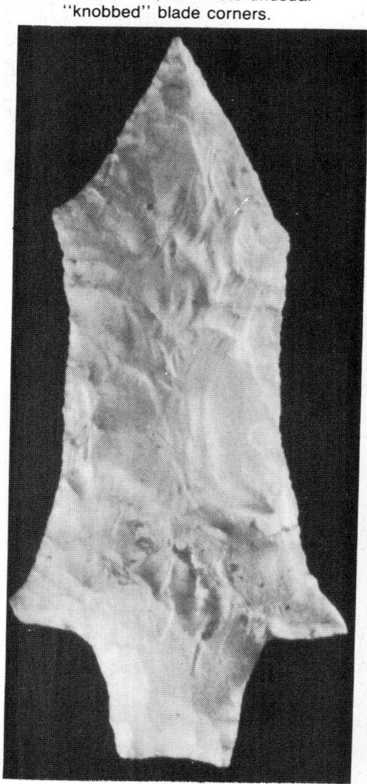

G8, $180-$300
MO.

G9, $250-$400
Webster Co., MO.

AGATE BASIN - Transitional Paleo to early Archaic, 9500 - 8000 B.P.

(Also see Allen, Angostura, Eden, Guilford, Lerma, Nebo Hill & Sedalia)

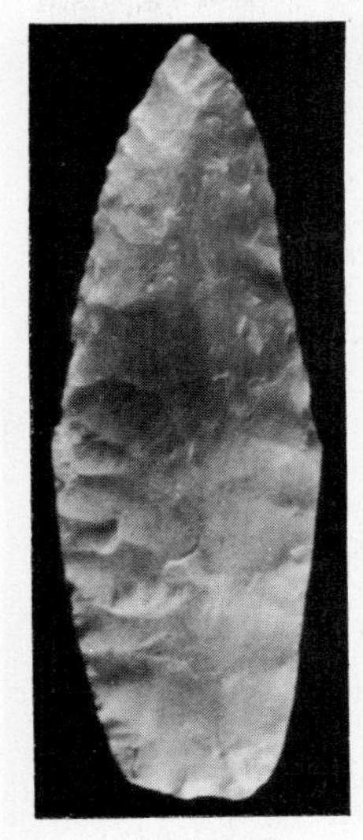

G5, $60-$100
Benton Co., KY. Note collateral flaking.

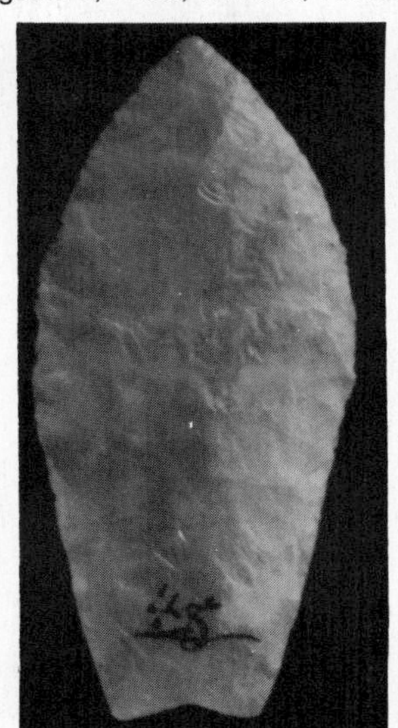

G6, $180-$300
ILL.

G5, $65-$100
Union Parrish, LA.

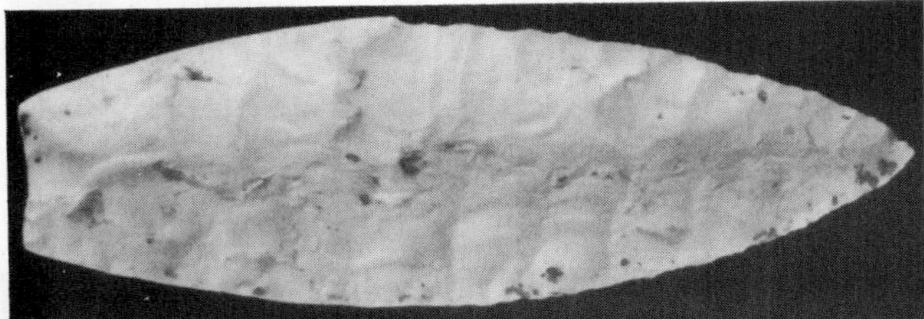

G7, $250-$450
Pike Co., ILL. Note resharpening on left edge above hafting area.

G6, $180-$300
Schuyler Co., ILL.

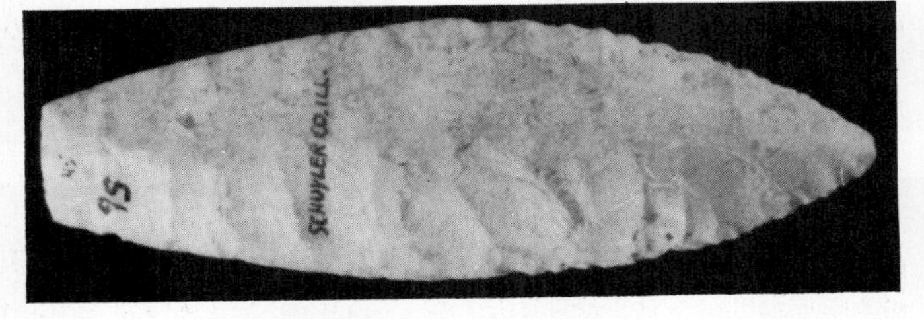

LOCATION: Midwestern states. **DESCRIPTION:** A medium to large size lanceolate blade of unusually high quality. Bases are either convex, concave or straight, and are usually ground. Some examples are median ridged and have random to parallel flaking. **I.D.KEY:** Basal form and flaking style.

G9, $350-$650
Alton, ILL.

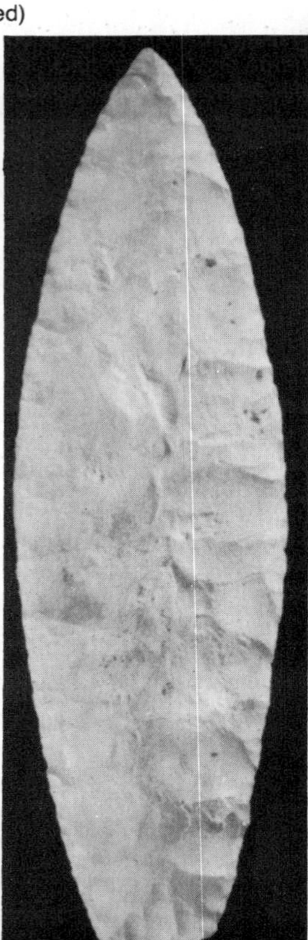

G9,$450-$750
ILL.

G10, $350-$650
St. Charles Co., MO.

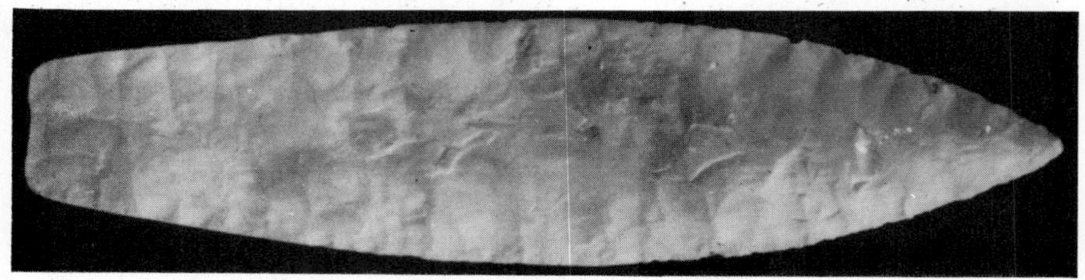

G10, $600-$1000, Pearl, ILL.

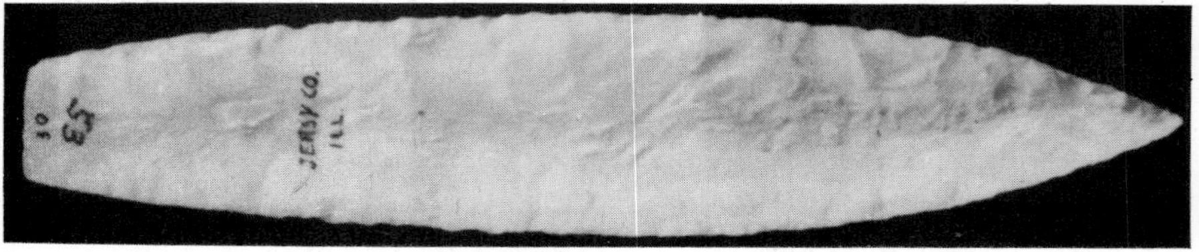

G9, $350-$600, Jersey Co., ILL.

AGATE BASIN (continued)

G10, $600-$1000
Calaway Co., MO.

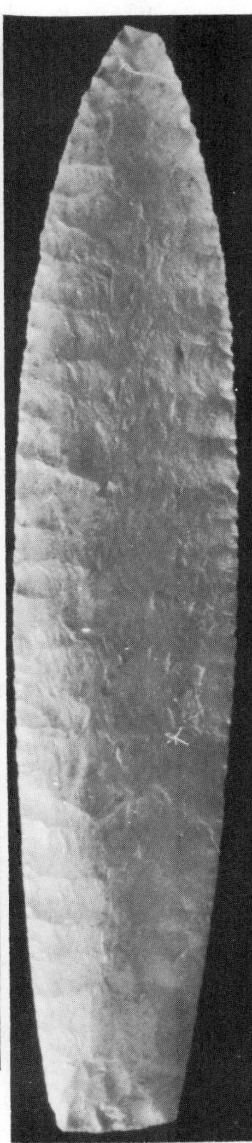

G8, $250-$400
Pike Co., ILL. Tip nick.

G8, $250-$400
MO. Several blade nicks.

AGEE - Mississippian, 1200 - 700 B.P.

(Also see Alba, Hayes, Homan & Keota)

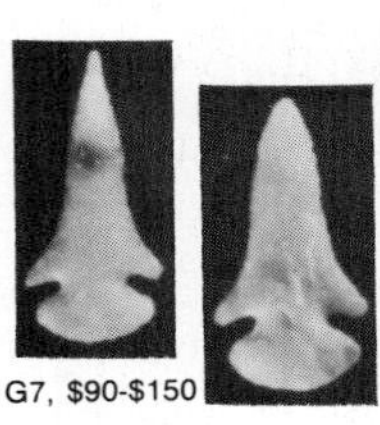
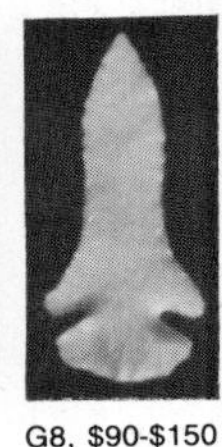
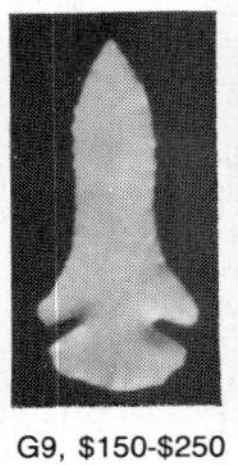
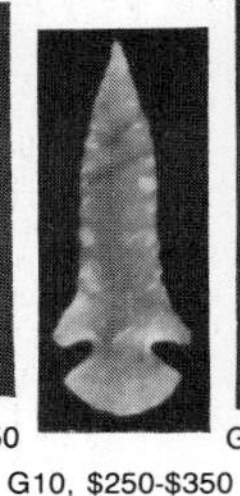
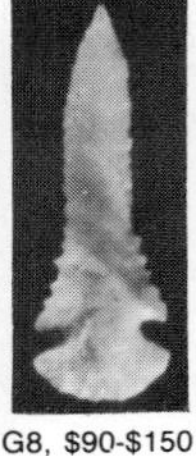

G7, $90-$150 G7, $80-$125 G8$80-$125 G8, $90-$150 (Little River Co., AR) G9, $150-$250 G10, $250-$350 G8, $90-$150 G6, $50-$75 Miller Co., AR.

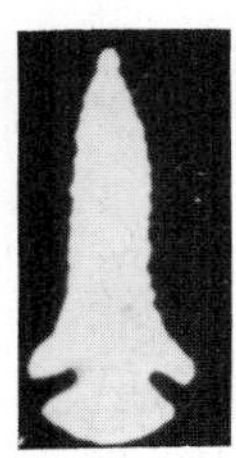
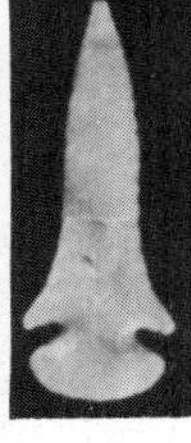
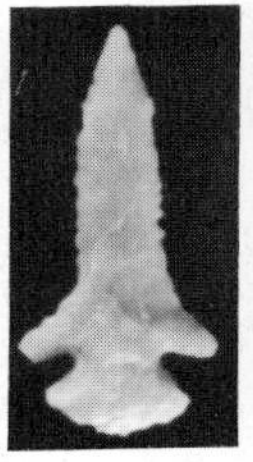
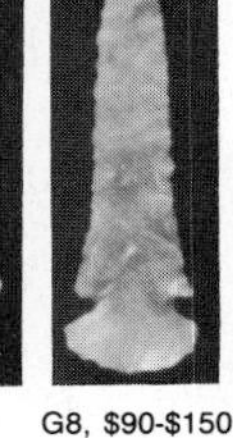
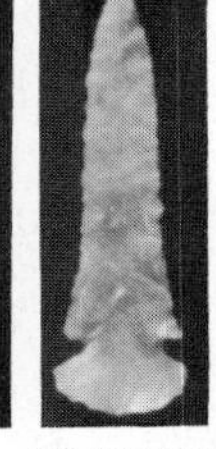

G7, $90-$125 G8, $80-$125 G7, $75-$120 G8, $90-$150 (Little River Co., AR.)

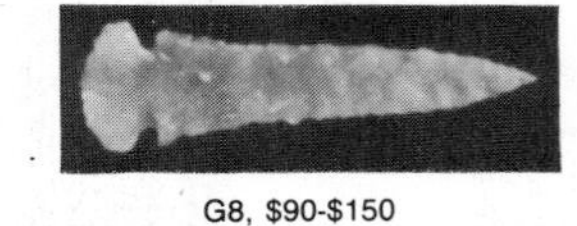

G8, $90-$150

G10, $180-$300

LOCATION: Midwestern states. **DESRIPTION:** A small to medium size, narrow, expanded barbed, corner notched point. Tips are needle sharp. Some examples are double notched at the base. A rare type. **I.D. KEY:** Basal form and barb expansion.

ALACHUA - Late Archaic to Woodland, 4000 - 2500 B.P.

(Also see Cypress Creek, Hardee Beveled, Levy, Marion, Morror Mountain, Newnan, Putnam and Sumter)

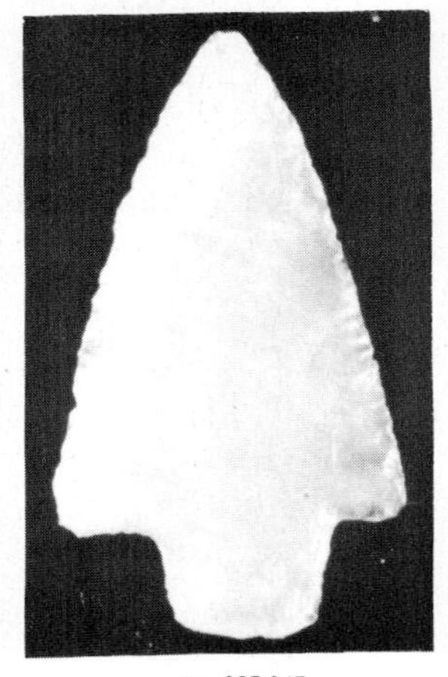

G4, $35-$45
Hillsborough Co., FL.

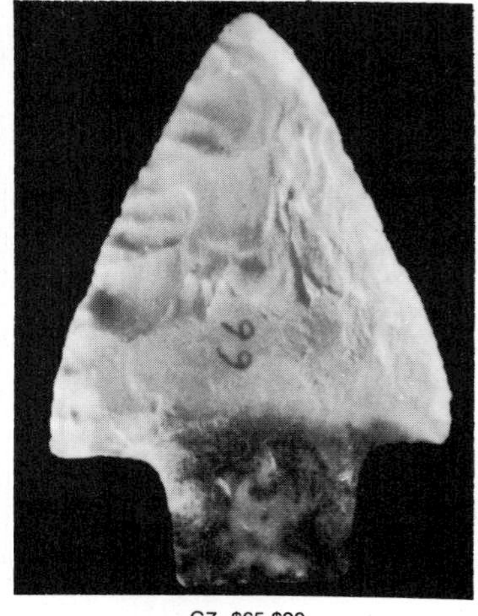

G7, $65-$90
Alachua Co., FL, Newnan's Lake.
Classic.

ALACHUA (continued)

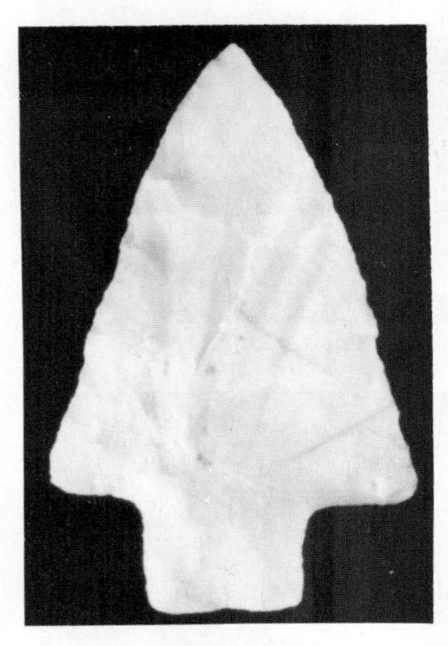

G7, $60-$90
Miller Co., GA. Banded chert.

G9, $120-$200
Early Co., GA. Tang nick.

LOCATION: Florida, Georgia and Alabama. **DESCRIPTION:** A medium to large size, very broad point with a rectangular stem. Shoulders can be horizontal to barbed and blade edges can be convex to straight. **I.D. KEY:** Squared base, one barb shoulder.

ALAMANCE - Late Paleo, 10000 - 8000 B.P.

(Also see Dalton, Hardaway & Haw River)

G4, $50-$75
Cent. NC.

G8, $150-$250
Cranville Co., NC.

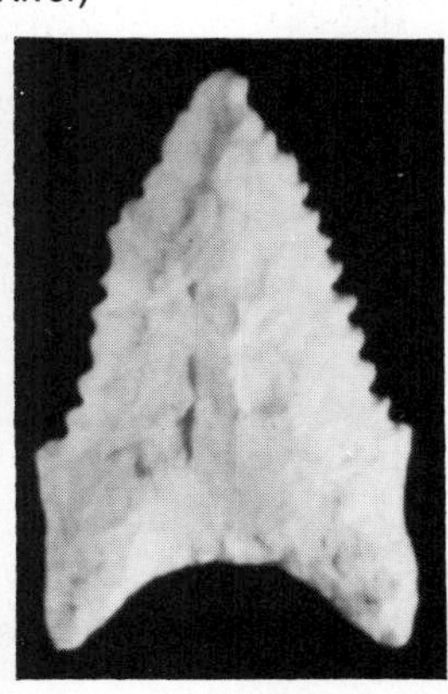

G6, $60-$75
Warner Robbins, GA.

ALAMANCE (continued)

G9, $250-$400
Durham Co., NC. Rhyolite.

G8, $125-$200
Johnson Co., NC. Rhyolite.

G7, $90-$150
Central NC.

G9, $200-$350
Moore Co., NC. Fluted.

G8, $125-$200
Montgomery Co., NC.

LOCATION: Coastal states from Virginia to Florida. **DESCRIPTION:** A broad, short, auriculate point with a deeply concave base. The broad basal area is usually ground and can be expanding to parallel sided. A variant form of the *Dalton-Greenbrier* evolving later into the *Hardaway* type. **I.D. KEY:** Width of base and strong shoulder form.

ALAMANCE (continued)

G9, $200-$350
Surry Co., NC.

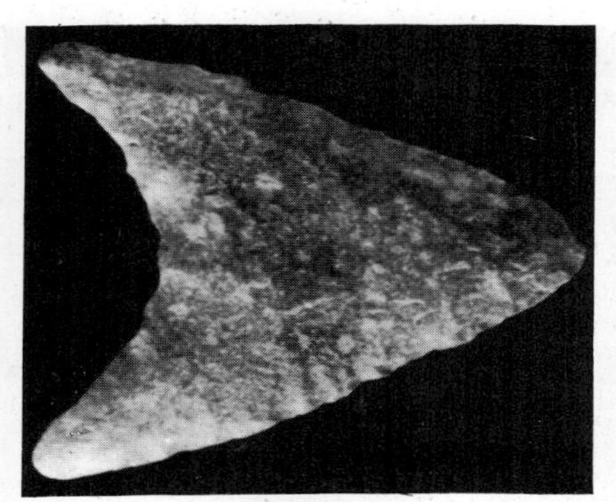

G8, $150-$250
Guilford Co., NC. Rhyolite.

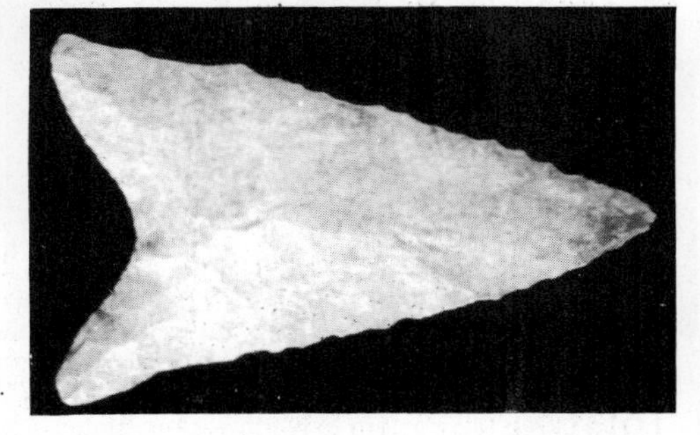

G9, $280-$450
Chesterfield Co., SC.

ALASKA POINTS

(See Crescent Knife)

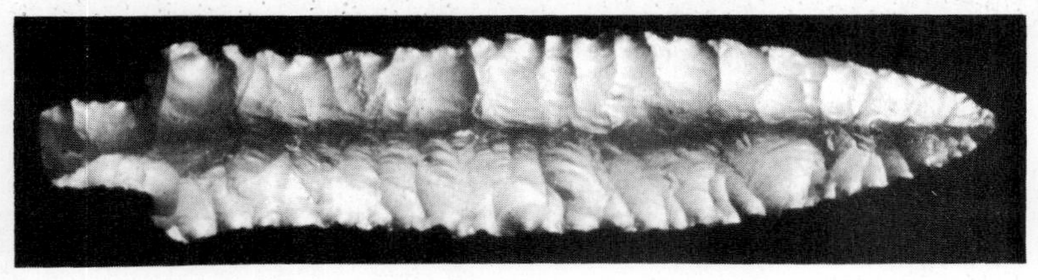

$60-$100
Alaska.

$15-$25
Alaska.

DESCRIPTION: Type names are unknown. The examples shown appear to be Archaic in age.

ALBA - Woodland to Mississippian, 2000 - 400 B.P.

(Also see Agee, Bonham, Cuney, Hayes, Homan, Keota, Perdiz, Scallorn & Sequoyah)

G3, $2-$5
Lincoln Parrish, LA.

G3, $3-$6

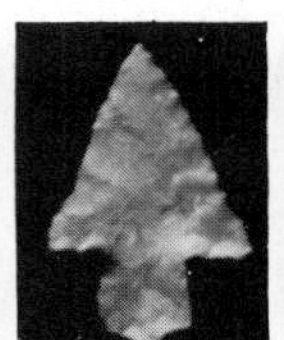
G3, $2-$5

G2, $1-$3

G6, $20-$35

(All Comanche Co. TX.)

G6, $20-$35
Comanche Co., TX.

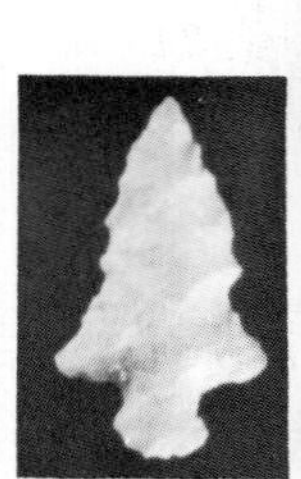
G4, $10-$20
Lincoln Parrish, LA.

G7, $35-$65
Columbia Rv. WA.

G7, $30-$55
Comanche Co., TX.

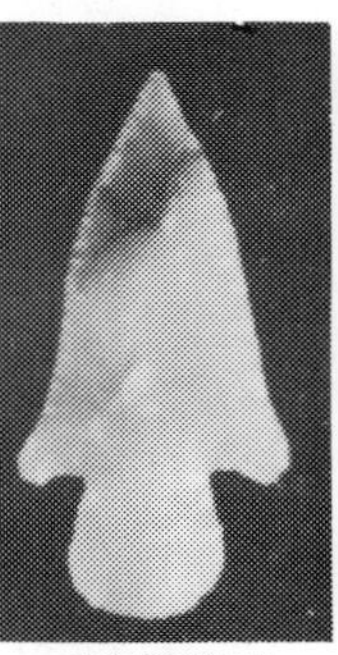
G9, $60-$100
Columbia Rv. WA.

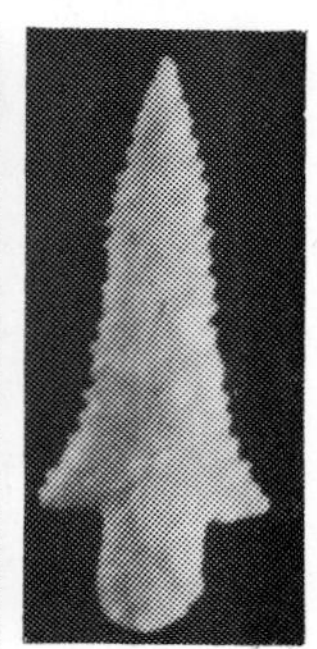
G8, $50-$80
IL.

LOCATION: Midwestern to Northwestern states. **DESCRIPTION;** A small to medium size, narrow, well made point with prominent tangs, a recurved blade and a bulbous stem. Some examples are serrated. **I.D. KEY:** Rounded base and expanded barbs.

ALLEN - Transitional Paleo to early Archaic, 9000 B.P. - 7500 B.P.

(Also see Angostura, Browns Valley, Clovis, Cochise and Plainview)

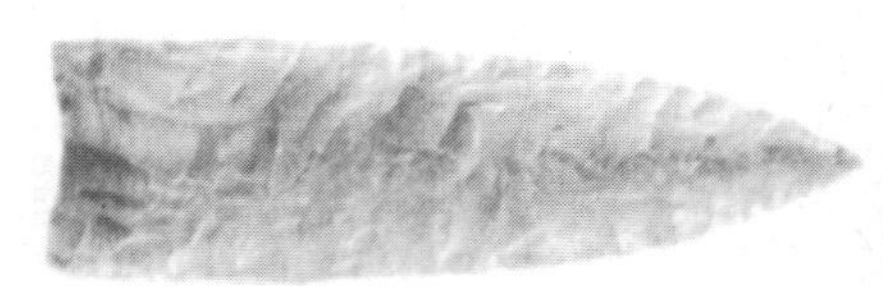
G7, $150-$200
McIntosh Co., OK. Note very fine secondary flaking and basal thinning. Excellent quality.

G1, $10-$20
CO/TX. Broken back.

G2, $20-$30
CO/TX. Broken tip.

LOCATION: Midwestern states to Canada. **DESCRIPTION:** A medium to large size lanceolate point that has oblique transverse flaking and a concave base. Basal area is ground. **I.D. KEY:** Flaking style and blade form.

ALLEN (continued)

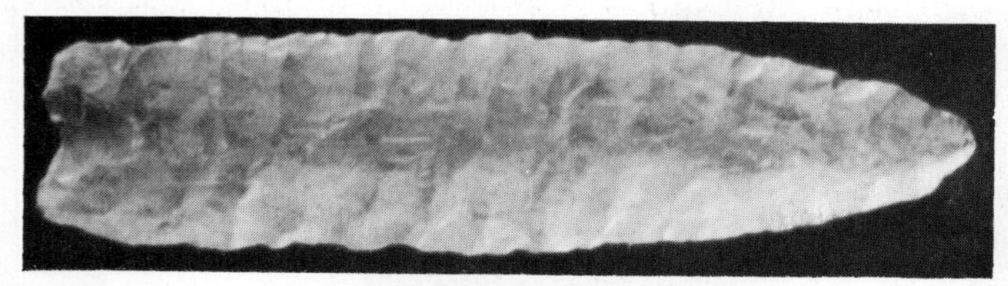

G4, $80-$120
Iowa. Note oblique flaking. Minor edge and tip nicks.

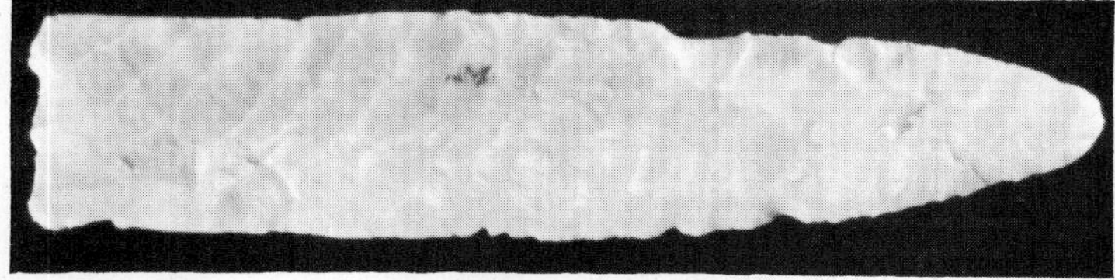

G5, $100-$150
McIntosh Co., OK. Note collateral flaking. Minor edge and tip nicks.

ANDICE - Early Archaic, 8000 - 5000 B.P.

(Also see Calf Creek)

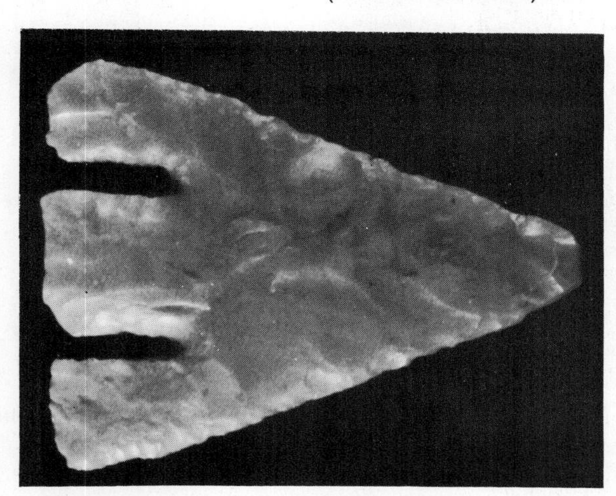

G5, $150-$250
TX. Tip damage.

LOCATION: Midwestern states. **DESCRIPTION:** A broad, thin, triangular point with very deep, parallel basal notches. Larger than *Calf Creek* points.

ANGELICO CORNER-NOTCHED (See Decatur)

ANGOSTURA-EAST - Transitional Paleo to mid-Archaic, 10000 - 8000 B.P.

(Also see Browns Valley, Clovis-unfluted, Eden, Guilford, Llano, Midland, Milnesand, Paint Rock Valley, Plainview and Wheeler)

G7, $60-$100
Giles Co., TN. Narrow form.

G10, $180-$300
Humphreys Co., TN. Very thin and excellent. Dover chert.

G8, $70-$120
Huntsville, AL.

G8, $80-$120, Humphreys Co., TN.

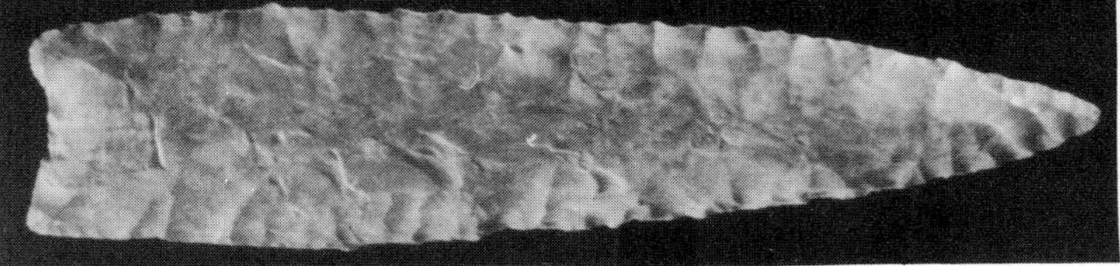

G10, $250-$400, Humphreys Co., TN.

LOCATION: Eastern to Southeastern states. **DESCRIPTION:** A medium to large size lanceolate blade with a contracting, concave base. Both broad and narrow forms occur. Flaking can be parallel oblique to random. Bases are not usually ground but are thinned. **I.D. KEY:** Basal form, early flaking on blade.

ANGOSTURA-WEST -Transitional Paleo to mid-Archaic, 10000 - 8000 B.P.

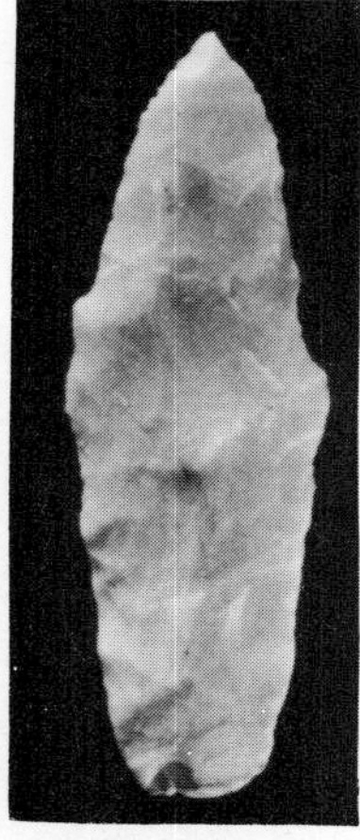

G3, $25-$40
Comanche Co., TX.
Resharpened form.

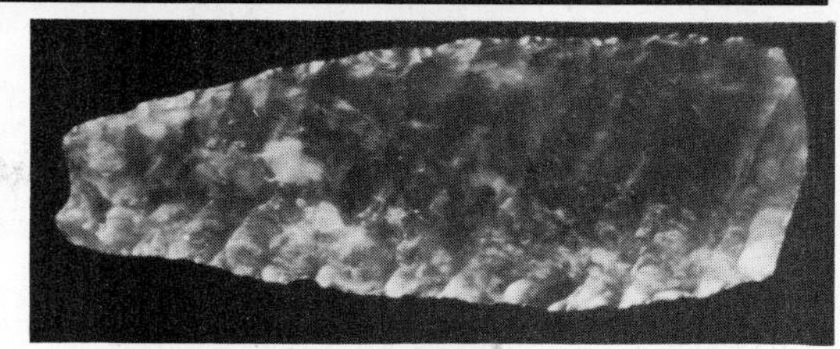

G1, $5-$10, CO/TX. Note oblique flaking. Broken back.

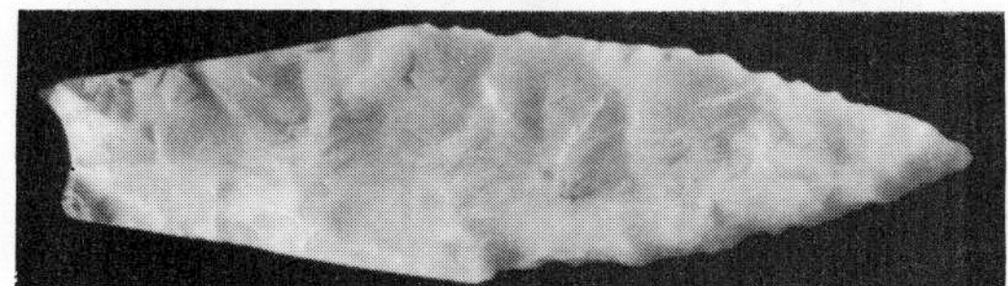

G8, $180-$280
Comanche Co., TX. Resharpened form. Note right-hand bevel on blade edge. Classic example.

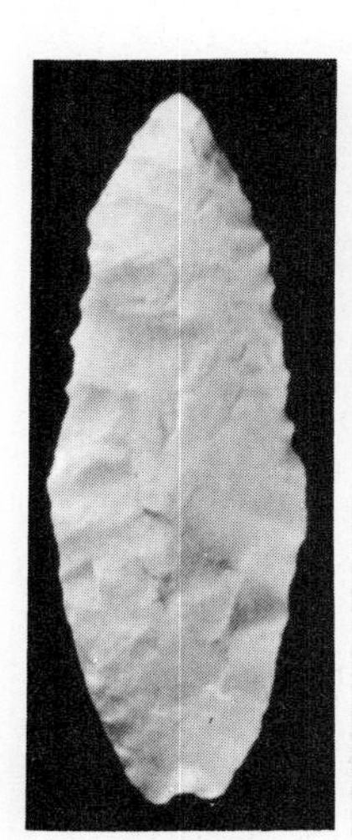

G6, $80-$120
Comanche Co., TX.
Resharpened form.

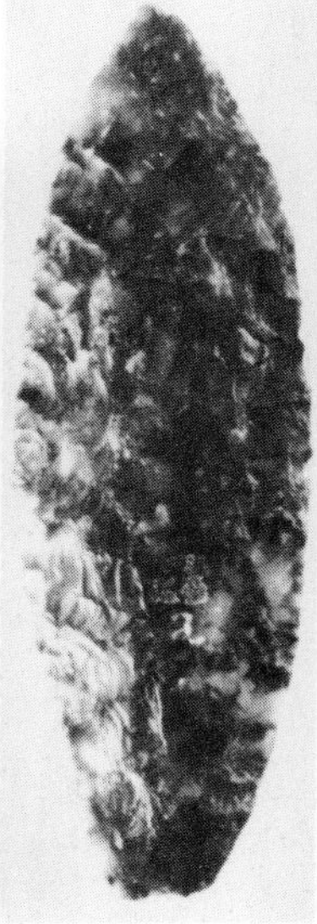

G7, $150-$250
Austin, TX. Agate.

G9, $250-$400
So. Platt River, NEB.

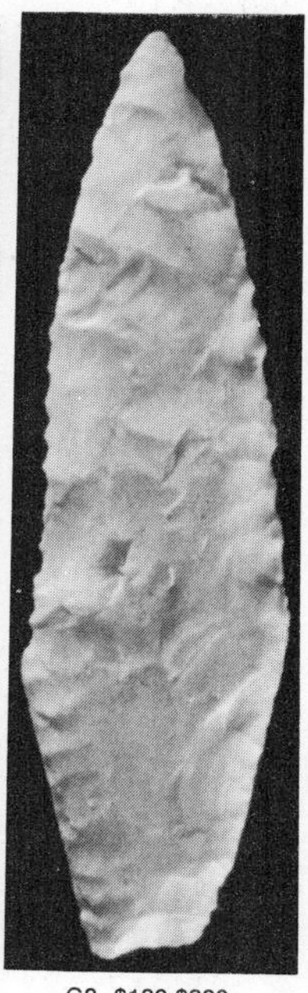

G8, $180-$300
Comlanche Co., TX. Note beveling on right side of each face.

LOCATION: Midwest to Western states. **DESCRIPTION:** A medium to large size lanceolate blade with a contracting, concave, straight or convex base. Both broad and narrow forms occur. Flaking can be parallel oblique to random. Blades are commonly steeply beveled on one side of each face; some are serrated and most have basal grinding. Formerly called *Long* points. **I.D. KEY:** Basal form, flaking on blade which can be beveled.

ANGOSTURA-WEST (continued)

G6, $85-$140
Austin, TX.

G9, $300-$450
Cooper Co., MO. Note Oblique flaking.

G9, $250-$400
Comanche Co., TX. Note excellent oblique parallel flaking across blade face.

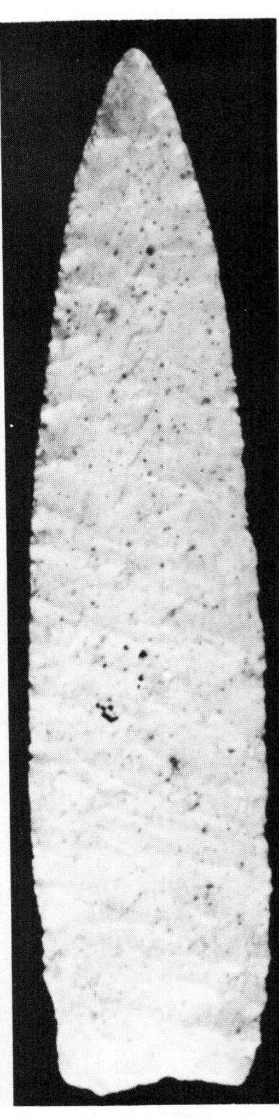

G10, $400-$700
Ralls Co., MO. Note superior oblique parallel flaking across blade face. Excellent example

APPALACHIAN - Mid-Archaic, 6000 - 3000 B.P.

(Also see Hamilton and Savannah River)

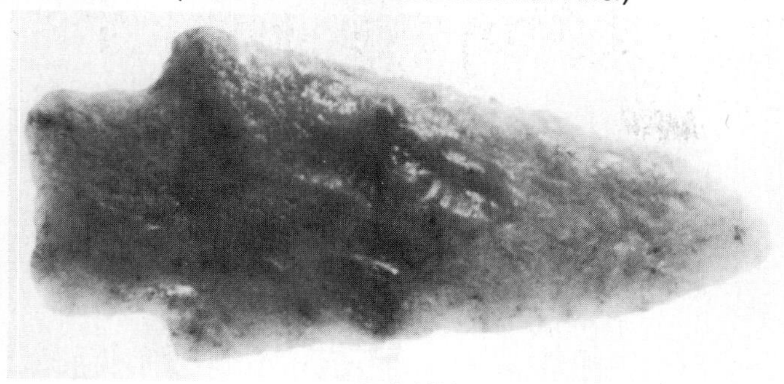

G7, $40-$50
Florence, AL. Quartzite.

G8, $120-$200
Warner Robbins, GA. Quartzite.

G3, $10-$15
Polk Co., GA. Quartzite.

LOCATION: Southeastern states. **DESCRIPTION:** A medium to large size, rather crudely made stemmed point with a concave base. Most examples are made of quartzite. Shoulders are tapered and the base is usually ground. **I.D. KEY:** Basal form.

G5, $55-$90
Blythe Ferry, Rhea Co., TN.
Quartzite. Note glued break above midsection.

G9, $250-$400
Cent. NC.

ARREDONDO - Mid to Late Archaic, 5000 - 3000 B.P.

(Also see Buzzard Roost Creek, Kirk Serrated and Savannah River)

G2, $3-$7
Walker Co., GA.

G4, $25-$40
Levy Co., FL.

G6, $35-$60
Levy Co., FL.

G9, $85-$150
Marion Co., FL.

LOCATION: AL, GA, FL. **DESCRIPTION:** A thick, small to medium size point with a short, broad blade and a wide, bifurcated base which can be thinned. Could be related to *Savannah River* points. **I.D. KEY:** Basal form and thickness.

ASHTABULA - Late Archaic, 4000 - 1500 B.P.

(Also see Susquehanna Broad)

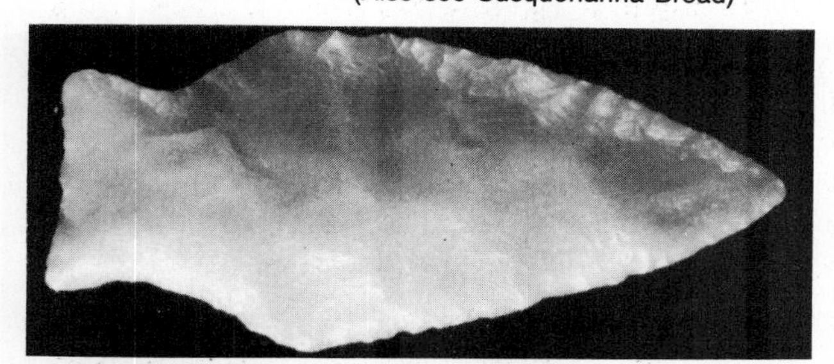

G4, $45-$70
AR. Novaculite.

LOCATION: Northeastern states, especially Northeastern Ohio and Western Penn. **DESCRIPTION:** A medium to large size, broad, thick, expanded stem point with tapered shoulders. **I.D. KEY:** Basal form, one barb round and the other stronger.

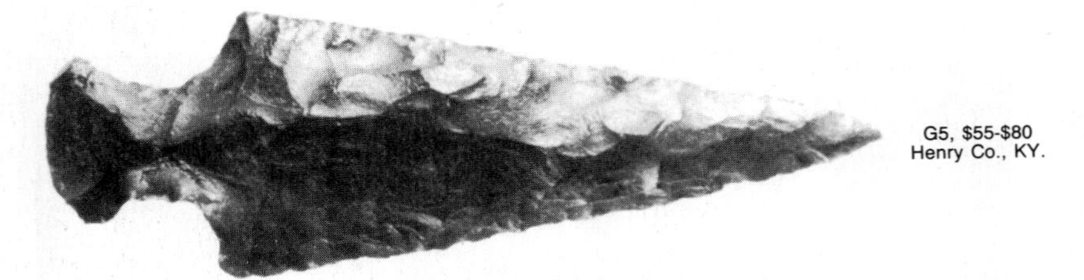

G5, $55-$80
Henry Co., KY.

G7, $150-$250
Ohio

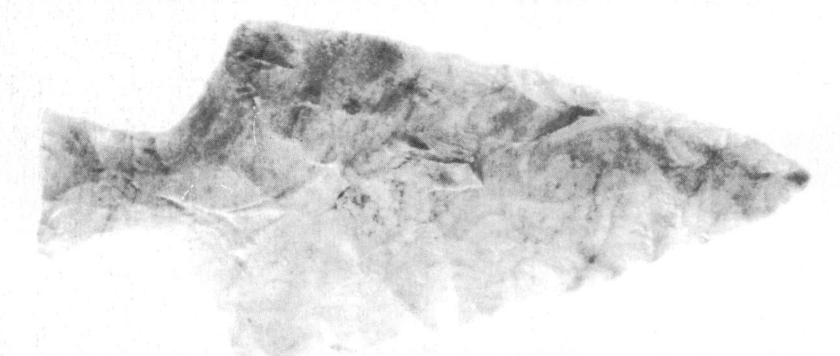

G8, $250-$350
OH.

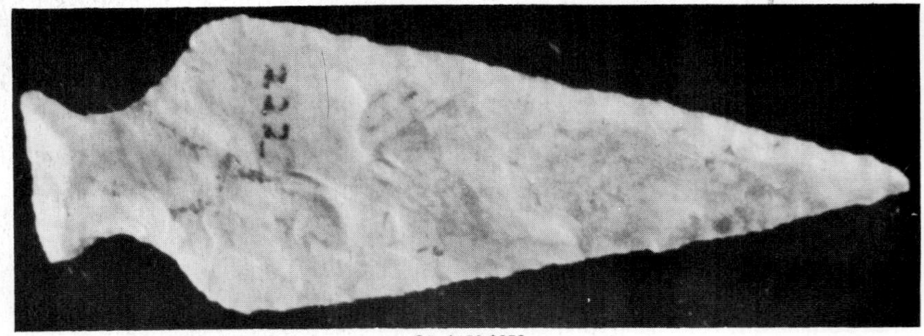

G7, $150-$250
OH.

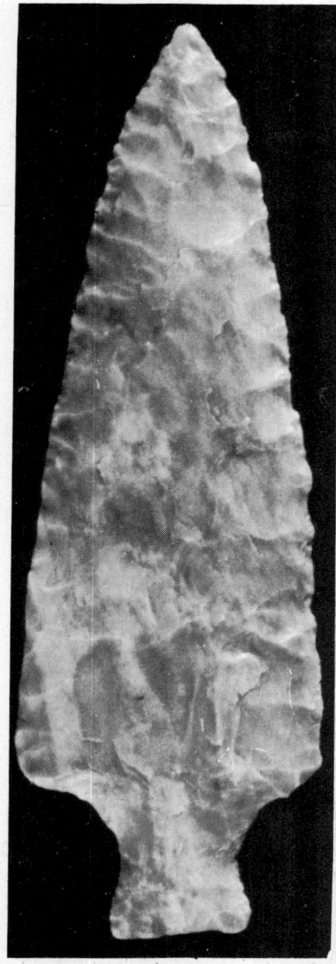

G9, $350-$600
OH.

G9, $450-$600
OH.

AUGUSTIN - Middle Archaic, 7000 - 5000 B.P.

(Also see Gypsum Cave, Jerome, Morrow Mountain and Santa Cruz)

G4, $8-$12
Yavapai Co., AZ.

G3, $6-$10
Yavapai Co., AZ.

G2, $2-$5
Yavapai Co., AZ.

LOCATION: Southwestern states. **DESCRIPTION:** A small to medium size, triangular point with weak shoulders and a contracting base.

AUTAUGA - Early Archaic, 9000 - 7000 B.P.

(Also see Brewerton, Ecusta and Palmer)

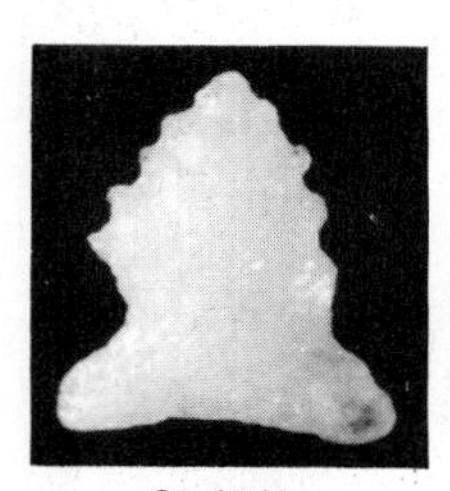

G5, $3-$6
Chattanooga, TN.
Milky quartz.

G4, $5-$10
Lafayette Co., MS

G7, $15-$25
Autauga Co., AL.

G5, $8-$15
Sussex Co., VA.

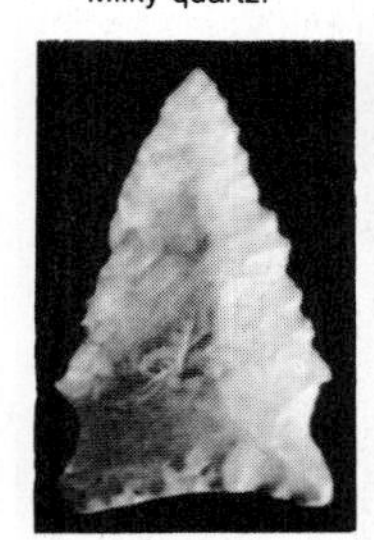

G5, $8-$15
Lafayette Co., MS.

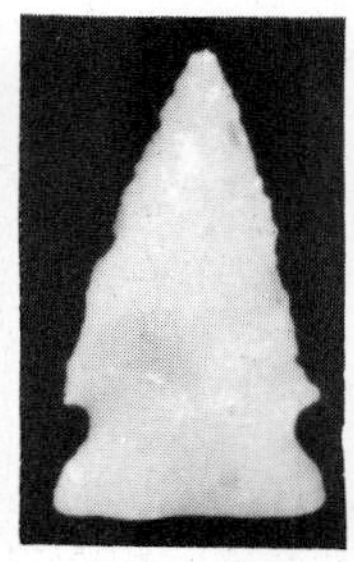

G7, $15-$25
Autauga Co., AL.

G6, $10-$20
Humphreys Co., TN.
Tang nick.

G9, $25-$40
Tishimingo Co., MS.

LOCATION; Southeastern states. **DESCRIPTION:** A small weakly corner notched point with a straight base, that is usually ground, and straight blade edges that are serrated. Blades can be beveled on one side of each face. **I.D. KEY:** Archaic flaking on blade.

AUTAUGA (continued)

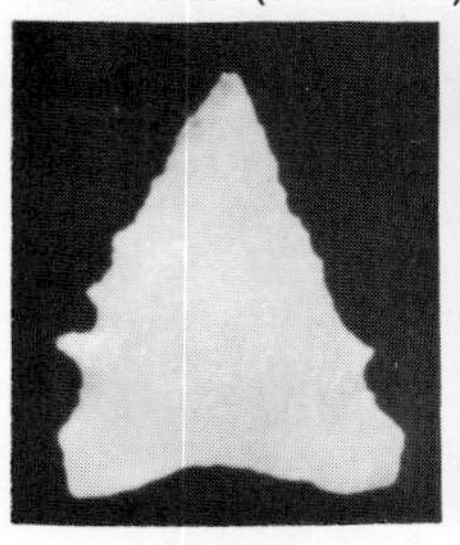

G5, $5-$10
Autauga Co., AL., Milky quartz.

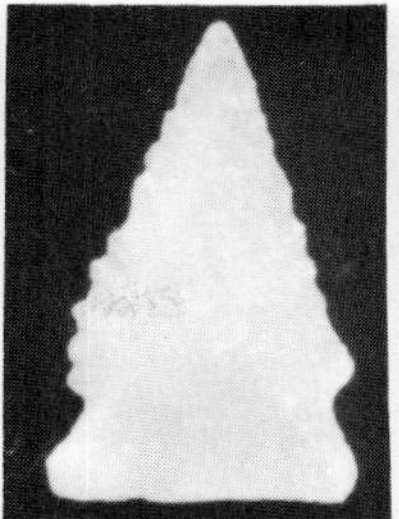

G6, $10-$20
Autauga Co., AL.

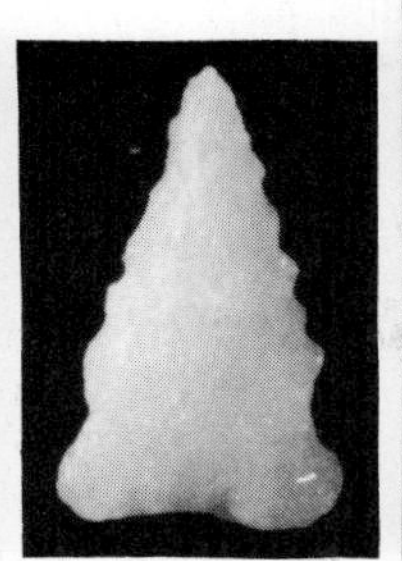

G5, $8-$15
Dalton, GA.

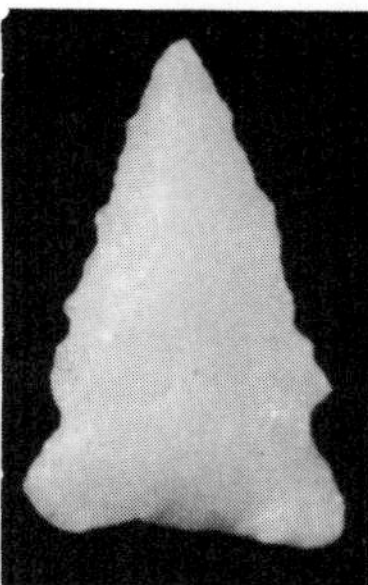

G5, $15-$25
Dalton, GA.

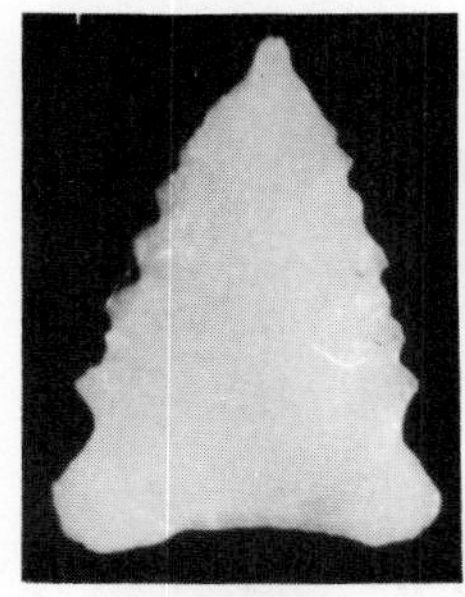

G8, $18-$30
Dalton, GA.

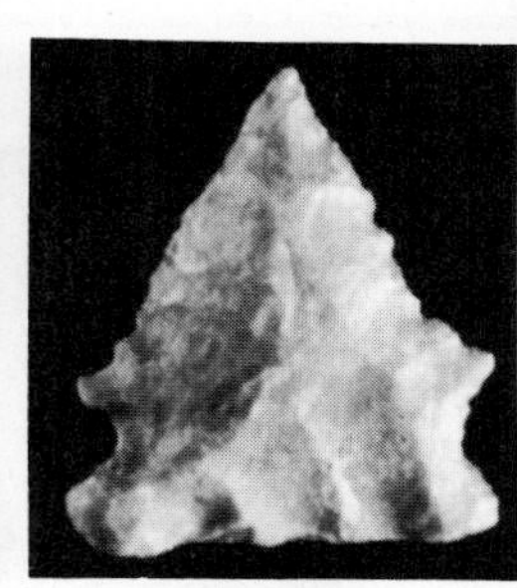

G8, $15-$25
Hamilton Co., TN.

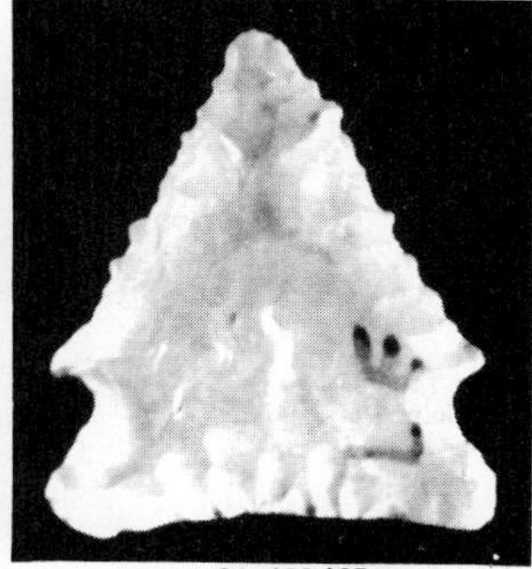

G9, $20-$35
Walker Co., AL.

BAKER - Early Archaic, 8000 - 6000 B.P.

(Also see Pedernalis and Uvalde)

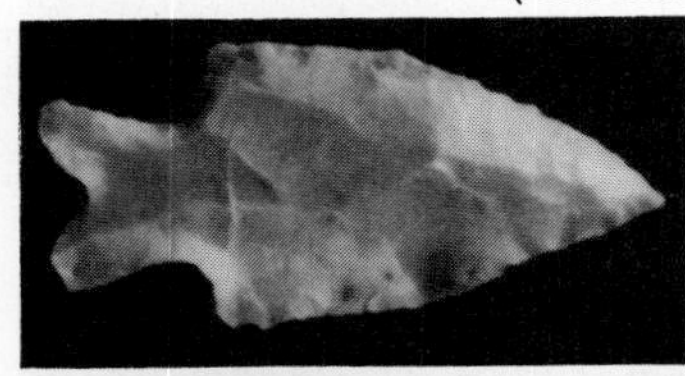

G5, $20-$30
Cent. TX.

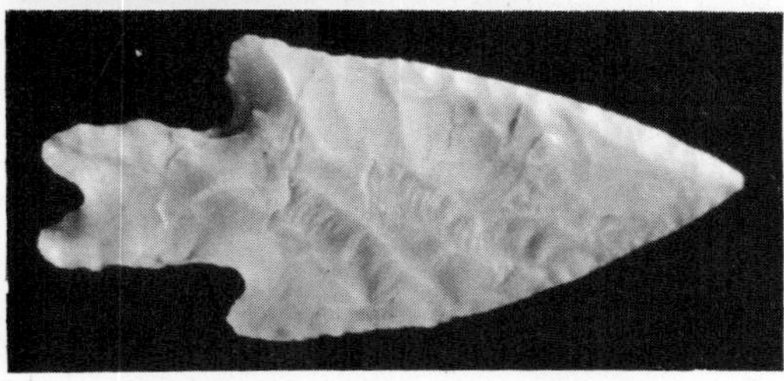

G8, $60-$100
Comanche Co., TX. Note long strikes across face of blade.

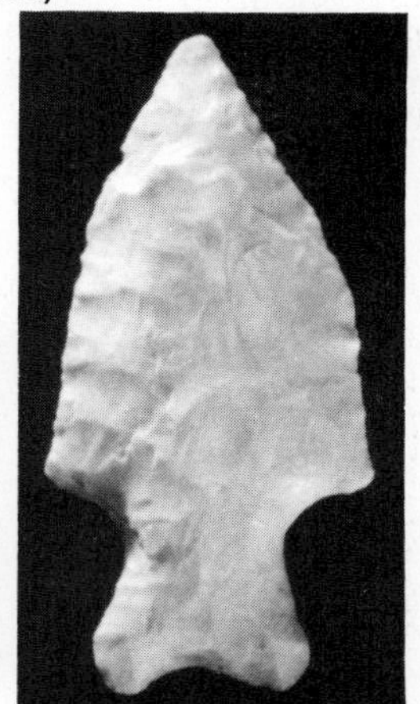

G5, $20-$30
Comanche Co., TX.

LOCATION: Midwestern states. **DESCRIPTION:** A medium size, narrow point with a long expanding to parallel stem that is bifurcated. Shoulders are horizontal to slightly barbed. Similar to the *Uvalde* type. **I.D. KEY:** Base extended and bifurcated, early flaking.

BAKER (continued)

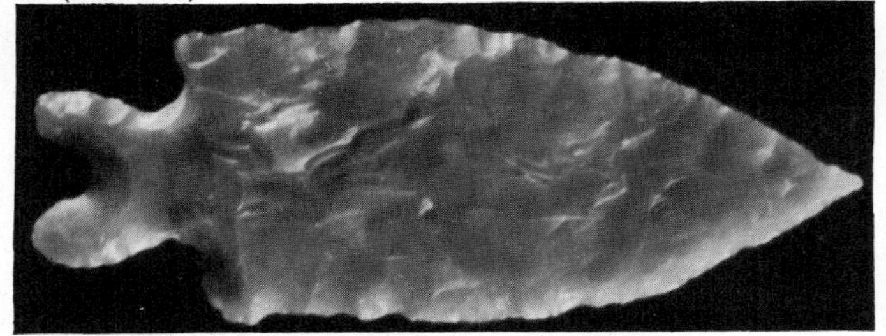

G9, $150-$280
Austin, TX. Georgetown flint.

BAKERS CREEK - Woodland, 4000 - 1300 B.P.

(Also see Bradford, Copena, Edgewood, Ellis, Harpeth River, Mud Creek, Steuben and Swan Lake)

G4, $4-$8
S.E. TN.

G2, $2-$5
S.E. TN.

G2, $2-$4
Meigs Co., TN.

G3, $3-$6
MS.

G2, $2-$5
N. AL.

G3, $8-$15
Humphreys Co., TN.

G4, $10-$20
Florence, AL. Resharpened from a much larger point.

LOCATION: Southeastern states. **DESCRIPTION:** A small to large size expanded stem point with tapered or barbed shoulders. Bases are concave, convex to straight. Related to Copena (found with them in caches) and are called *Stemmed Copenas* by some collectors. Called *Lowe* and *Steuben* in Illinois. **I.D. KEY:** Expanded base, usually thin.

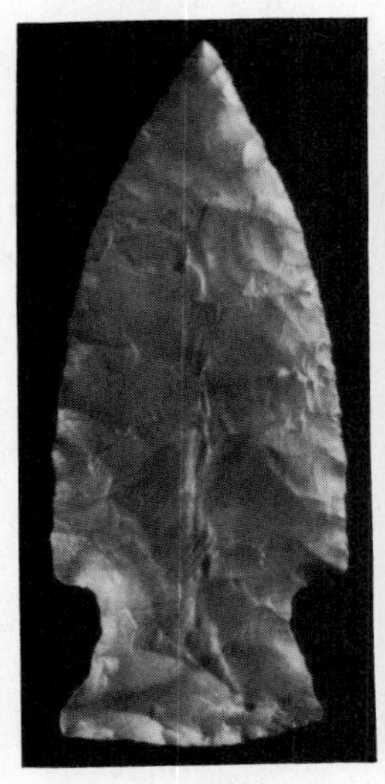

G6, $30-$40
Parsons, TN.

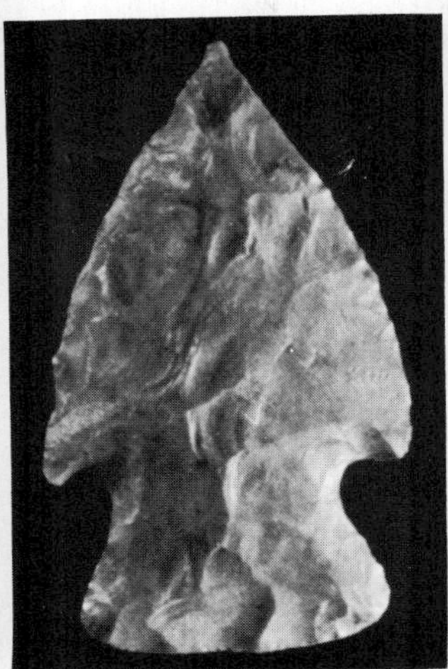

G5, $20-$35
Florence, AL.

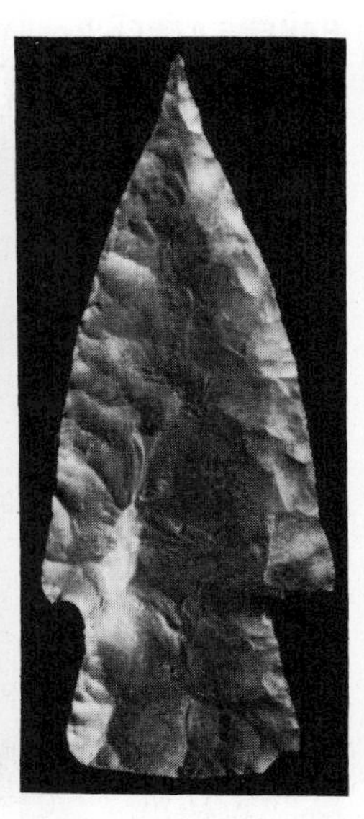

G8, $60-$100
Clifton, TN.

G7, $45-$70
Humphreys Co., TN. Dover chert. Very thin and high quality. Cache point.

G4, $15-$25
Humphreys Co., TN.

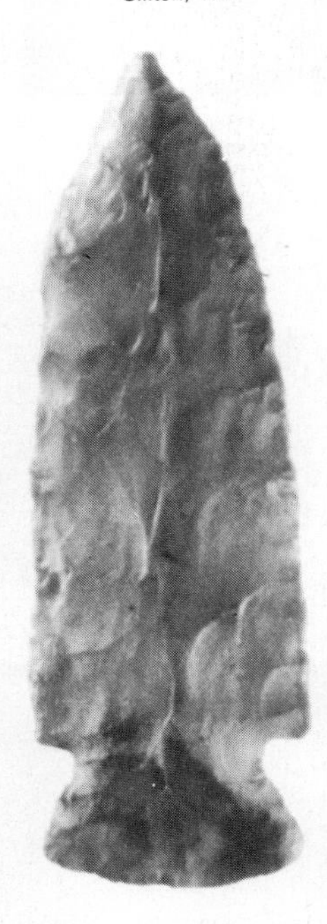

G7, $40-$70
Florence, AL. Excellent form and quality.

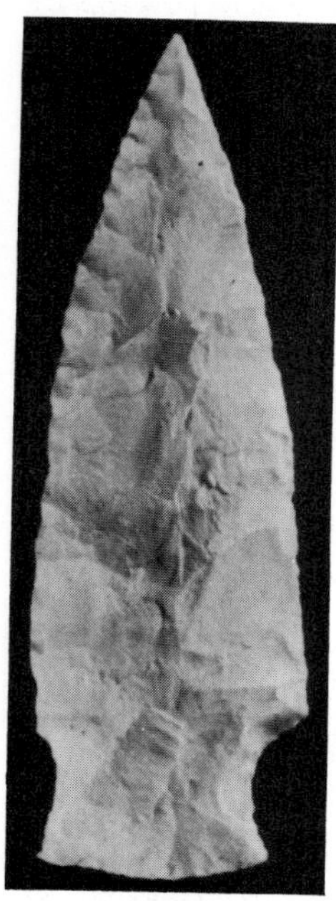

G6, $35-$45
Humphreys Co., TN.

G8, $60-$100
Humphreys Co., TN. Dover chert. Very thin and high quality. Cache point.

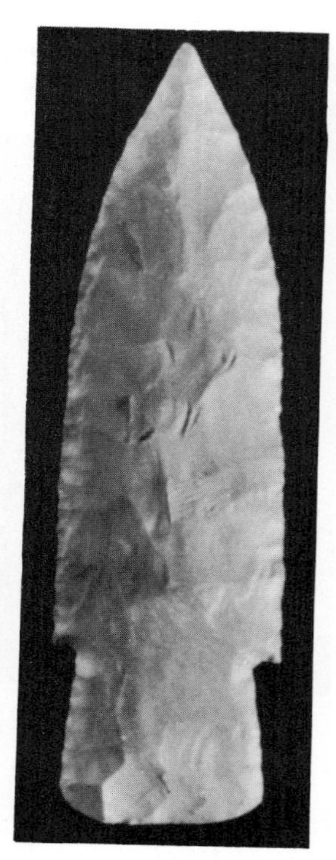

G9, $200-$300
Lauderdale Co., AL. Outstanding, thin, high quality example.

G8, $75-$100, Humphreys Co., TN. Dover chert.

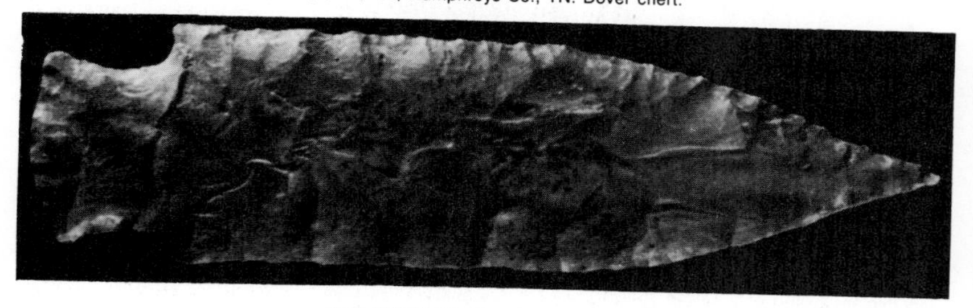

G10, $250-$400, Humphreys Co., TN.

BANDY (See Martindale)

BARBER - Transitional Paleo, 10000 - 7000 B.P.

(Also see Beaver Lake, Copena Auriculate and Kinney)

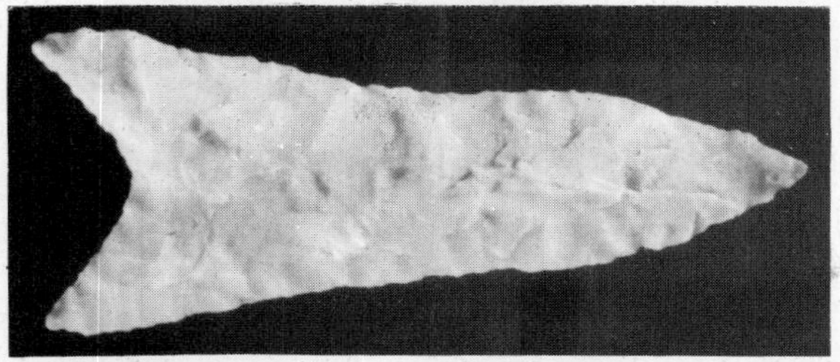

G9, $150-$250
Comanche Co., TX.

G10, $180-$300, Austin, TX. Thin and excellent quality.

Location: Midwestern states. **DESCRIPTION:** A medium to large size lanceolate point with a recurved blade, a deeply concave base and pointed ears. **I.D. KEY:** Very early flaking.

BARE ISLAND - Late Archaic, 4500 - 1500 B.P.

(Also see Kent, Little Bear Creek and Travis)

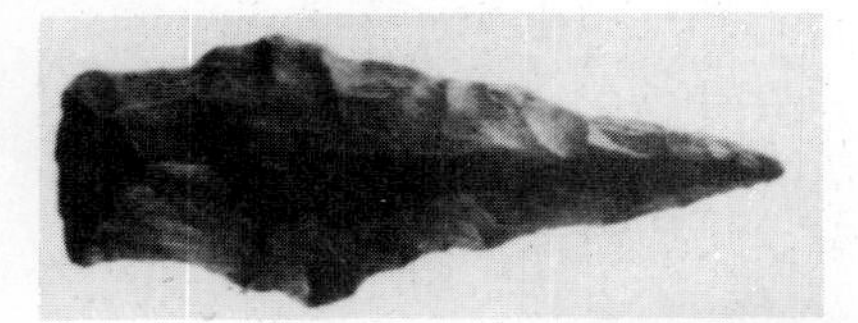

G6, $15-$25
S.E. TN.

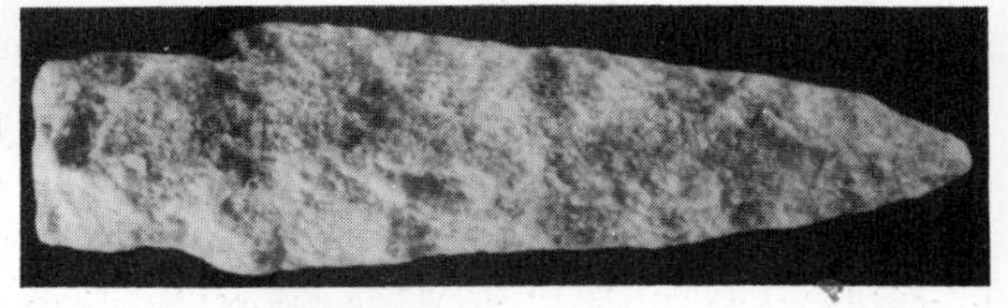

G7, $20-$25
Lane Co. PA.

LOCATION: Southeastern states. **DESCRIPTION:** A medium to large size, thick, stemmed point with tapered shoulders. One shoulder is higher than the other and the blade has one convex edge and one concave to straight edge.

BASCOM - Mid to late Archaic, 4500 - 3500

(Also see Appalachian, Maples, Morrow Mountain and Savannah River)

G6, $30-$50
Henry Co., AL.

G10, $350-$600
Savannah, GA., Briar Creek.
Outstanding example.

BASCOM (continued)

LOCATION: AL, GA. **DESCRIPTION:** A large size, broad point with shoulders tapering to the base which is usually straight. Possibly a variant form of the *Maples* point. **I.D. KEY:** Basal form.

BASE TANG KNIFE - Late Archaic to Woodland, 4000 - 2000 B.P.

(Also see Corner Tang and San Saba)

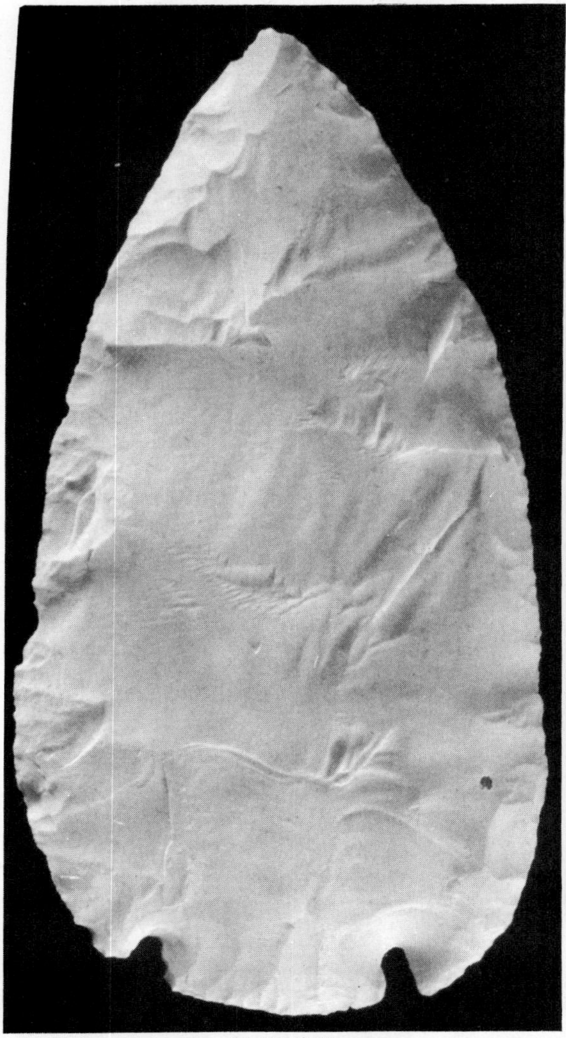

G7, $120-$200
Comanche Co., TX.

G8, $200-$250
Austin, TX.

LOCATION: Midwestern states. **DESCRIPTION:** A large size, broad blade with basal notches and a convex base.

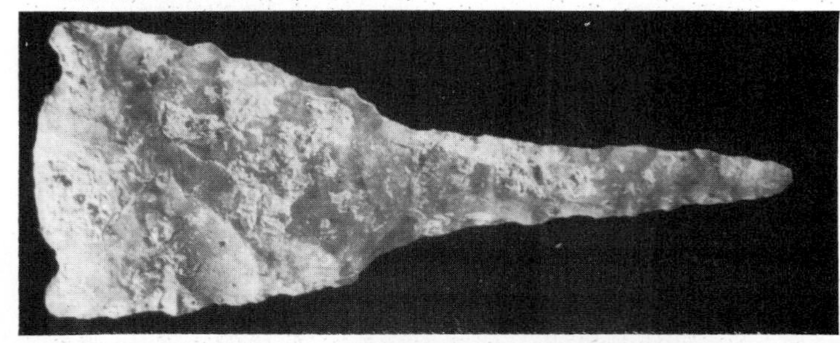

G6, $100-$180
Austin, TX. Note Caliche on blade.

G9, $200-$350
Austin, TX. Very thin cross section.

G10, $350-$500
Comanche Co., TX. A corner tang cross form.

BASSETT - Mississippian, 800 - 400 B.P.

(Also see Clifton, Ebenezer and Perdiz)

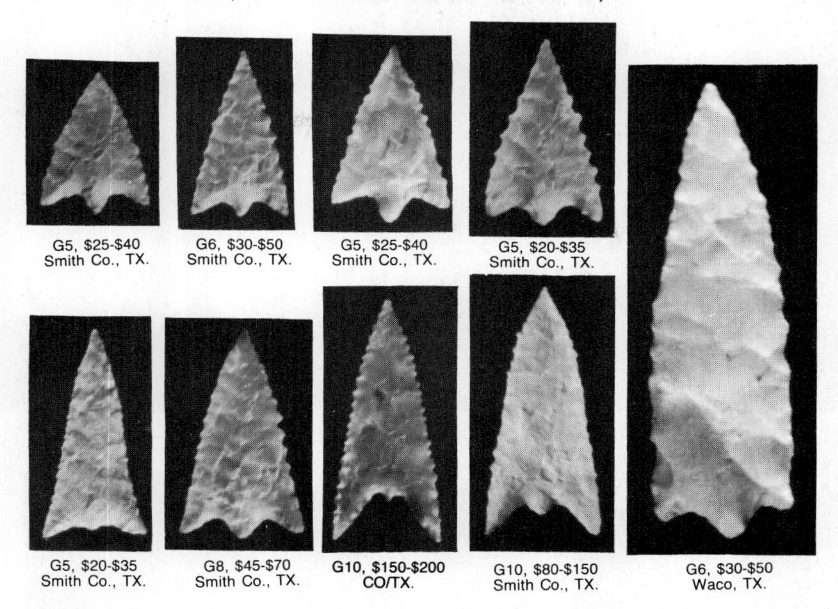

G5, $25-$40 Smith Co., TX. — G6, $30-$50 Smith Co., TX. — G5, $25-$40 Smith Co., TX. — G5, $20-$35 Smith Co., TX.

G5, $20-$35 Smith Co., TX. — G8, $45-$70 Smith Co., TX. — **G10, $150-$200 CO/TX.** — G10, $80-$150 Smith Co., TX. — G6, $30-$50 Waco, TX.

LOCATION: Midwestern states. **DESCRIPTION:** A small size, thin, triangular point with pointed tangs and a small pointed base. High quality flaking is evident on most examples. **I.D. KEY:** small pointed base.

BEACON ISLAND - Late Archaic, 4000 - 3000 B.P.

(Also see Big Slough, Elk River, Flint Creek and Palmillas)

G2, $1-$3 S.E. TN. — G2, $2-$4 E. TN. — G3, $5-$8 Meigs Co., TN. — G2, $2-$4 Lauderdale Co., AL.

LOCATION: Southeastern to Midwestern states. **DESCRIPTION:** A small to large size triangular point with a bulbous stem. Shoulders are usually well defined and can be barbed. Called *Palmillas* in Texas. **I.D. KEY:** Rounded base.

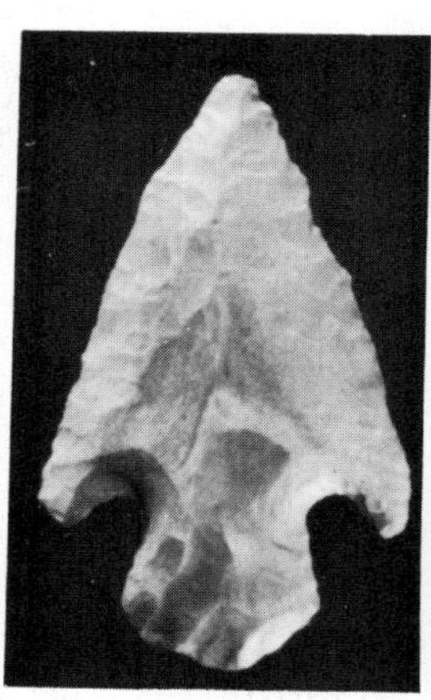

G4, $8-$12
Lauderdale Co., AL:.

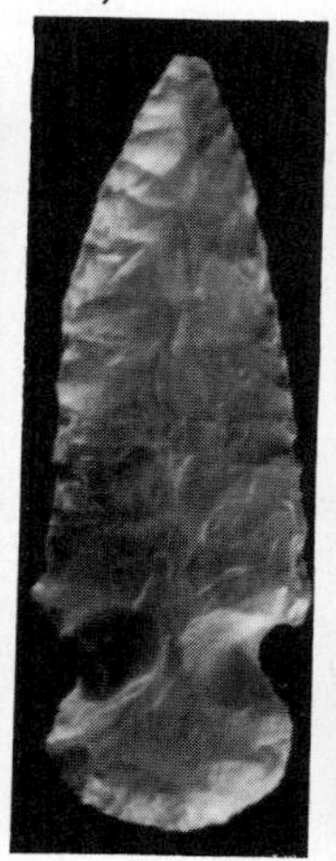

G2, $2-$4
Lauderdale Co., AL.

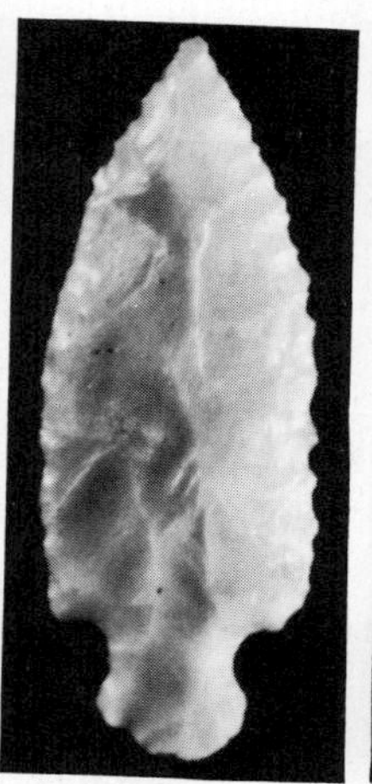

G3, $4-$8
White Co., TN.

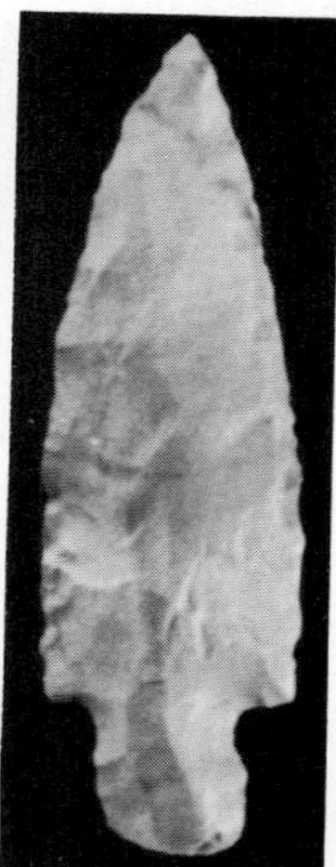

G2, $2-$4
Florence, AL.

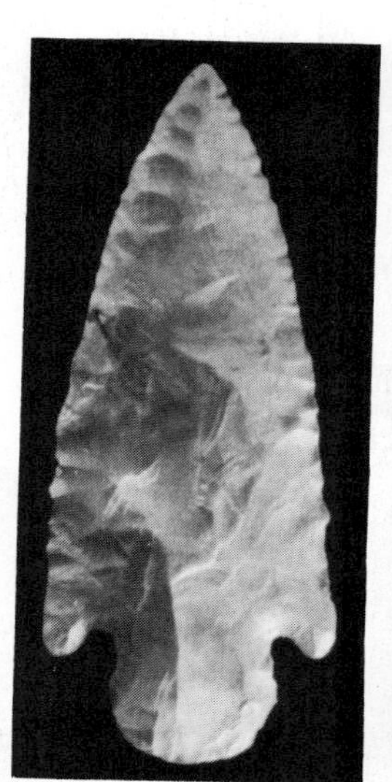

G5, $15-$25
Morgan Co., AL.

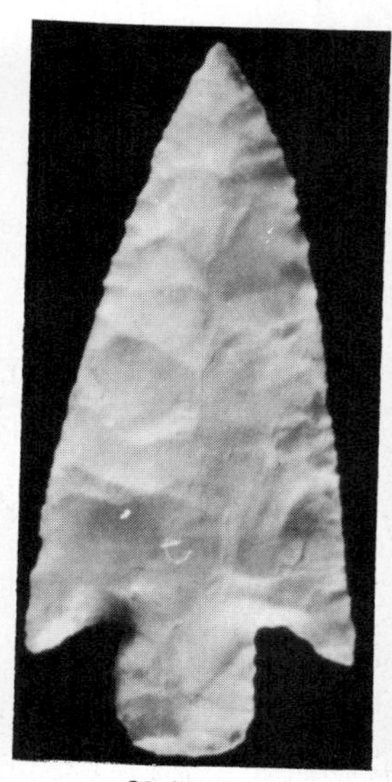

G6, $25-$40
Humphreys Co., TN.

G6, $25-$35
Decatur, AL.

G5, $10-$20
Lauderdale Co., AL.

G6, $25-$40
Humphreys Co., TN.

G8, $40-$70
Florence, AL.

G9, $70-$100
7 Mile Isle, Florence, AL. Classic example.

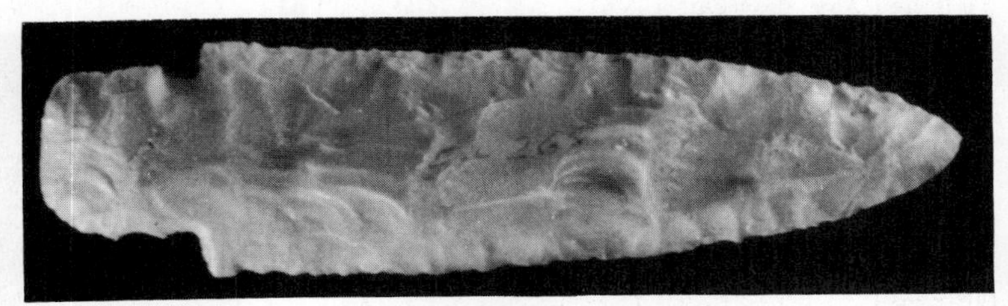

G6, $25-$40
Morgan Co., AL.

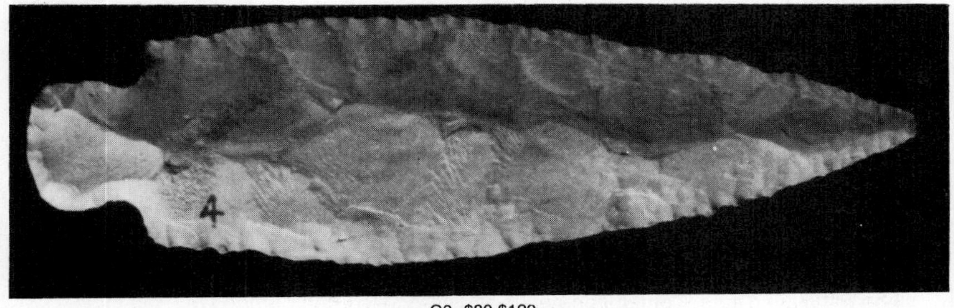

G9, $80-$120
7 Mile Isle, Florence, AL.

BEAVER LAKE - Paleo, 12000 - 8000 B.P.

(Also see Barber, Candy Creek, Cumberland, Golondrina, Midland, Quad, Simpson and Suwannee)

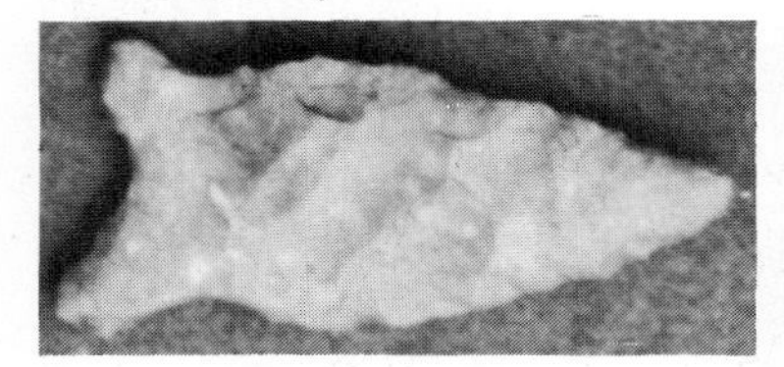

G3, $25-$35
Marion Co., FL.

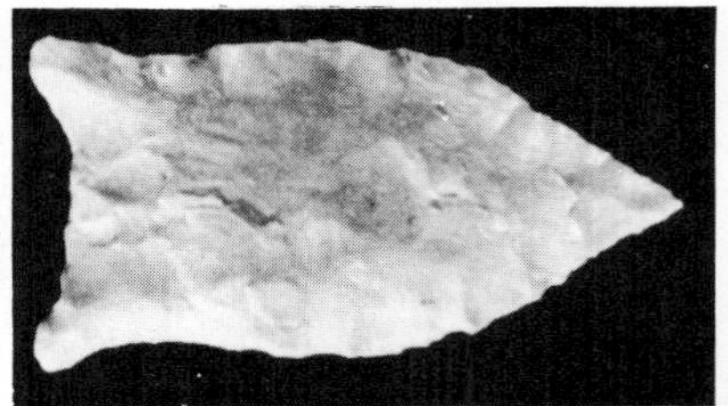

G5, $60-$85
Elk River, Giles Co., TN.

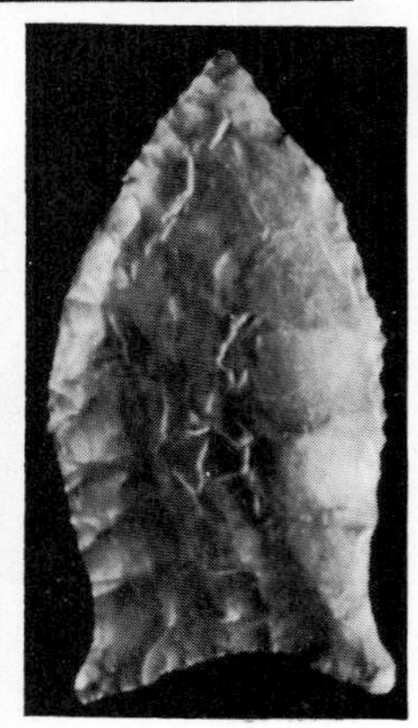

G6, $60-$100
Humphreys Co., TN.

G3, $25-$35
Lawrence Co., AL.
Tip & tang nicks.

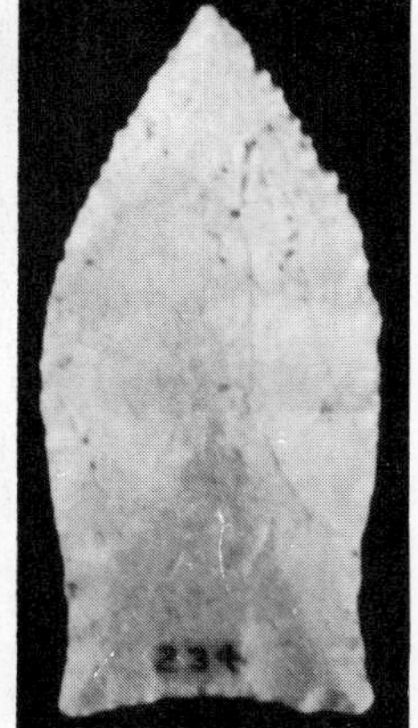

G7, $90-$150
AR.

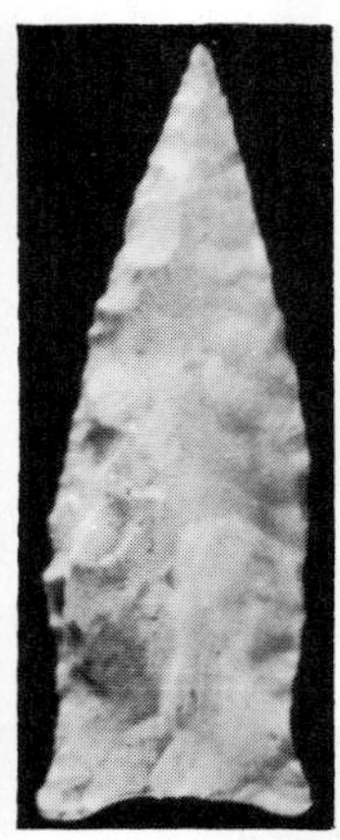

G5, $60-$100
Columbia Co., FL.

G7, $90-$150
Scott Co., MO.

G9, $250-$350
W. TN. Dover chert.

LOCATION: Southeastern states. **DESCRIPTION:** A medium to large size lanceolate blade with flaring ears. Contemporaneous and associated with *Cumberland*, but thinner than unfluted *Cumberlands*. Bases are ground and blade edges are recurved. **I.D. KEY:** Paleo flaking, shoulder area.

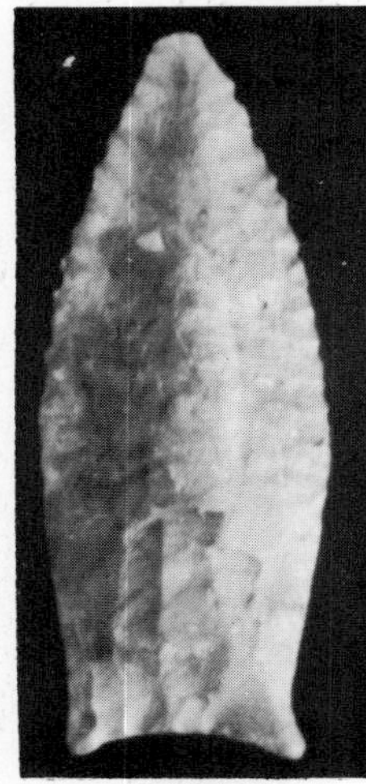

G6, $60-$100
Humphreys Co., TN. Note thinning strikes on base. Tip nick.

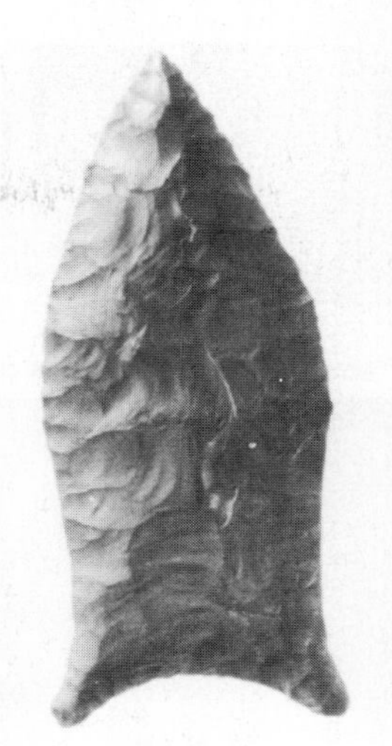

G9, $250-$400
Parsons, TN. Classic. High quality with field patina. Dover chert.

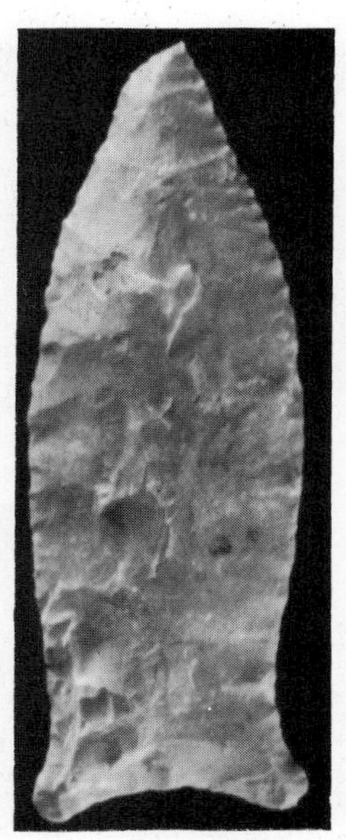

G7, $90-$150
Lauderdale Co., AL. Tip nick.

G8, $180-$300
Bullitt Co., KY.

G9, $250-$350
Humphreys Co., TN. Dover chert. Very thin and excellent.

G9, $250-$400
Henry Co., TN.

G9, $450-$600, Florence, AL. Fort Payne chert. Slight arc to blade.

G9, $250-$400, Obion Co., TN.

G8, $180-$300
Smith Co., TN. Classic form with minor tip damage. Note collateral flaking to a median ridge.

G7, $150-$200
Lauderdale Co., AL. Restored ear.

G8, $180-$300
Limestone Co., AL. Thick cross section.

BENJAMIN - Woodland, 3000 - 1600 B.P.

(Also see Abasolo, Catan, Copena-Round Base, Montgomery and Refugio)

G5, $3-$5
Morgan Co., AL.

G4, $2-$4
Morgan Co., AL.

G2, $2-$3
Madison Co., AL.

G2, $1-$3
Limestone Co., AL.

G4, $2-$4
Morgan Co., AL.

LOCATION: Southeastern states. **DESCRIPTION:** A medium to large size, thin, narrow, lanceolate point with a rounded base. This point has been found in association with *Copena*.

BENTON - Middle Archaic, 6000 - 4000 B.P.

(Also see Buzzard Roost Creek, Elk River and Turkeytail)

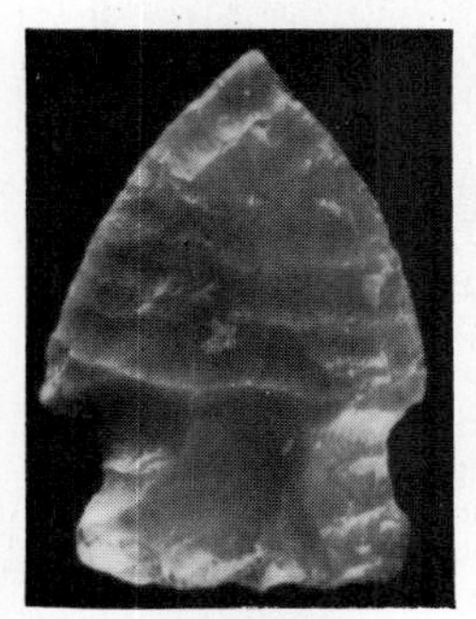

G2, $2-$3
Bethany, WV.

G5, $15-$25
Burke Co., GA.

BENTON (continued)

G3, $3-$5
Meigs Co., TN.

G3, $2-$5
Florence, AL.

G5, $15-$25
Florence, AL.

G5, $15-$25
Florence, AL. Note oblique flaking.

G7, $65-$95
MO. Rare gound & polished form

G4, $10-$15, Burke Co., GA.

LOCATION: Southeastern to Midwestern states. **DESCRIPTION:** A medium to very large size, broad, stemmed point with straight to convex sides. Bases can be corner or side notched, double notched, knobbed, bifurcated or expanded. Some examples show parallel oblique flaking. All four sides are beveled and basal corners usually have tangs. Examples have been found in Arkansas with a steeply beveled edge on one side of each face (Transition form?). Found in caches with Turkeytail points in Mississippi on Benton sites. Bentons and Turkeytails as long as 16¾'' were found together on this site and dated to about 4000 B.P. **I.D. KEY:** Wide squared base.

G3, $8-$12
Meigs Co., TN.

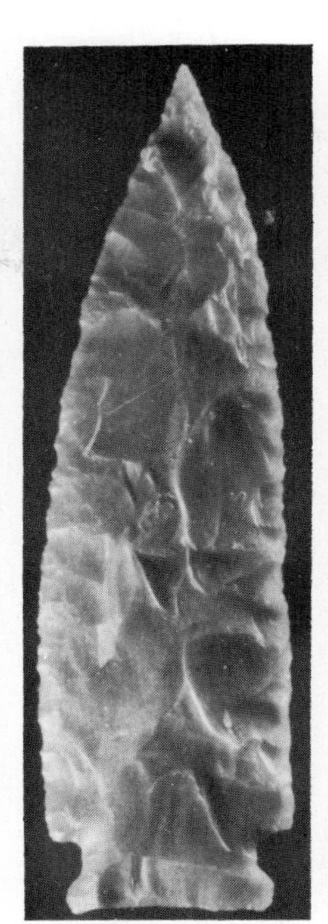

G6, $45-$65
White Co., TN.

G5, $20-$30
Decatur, AL.

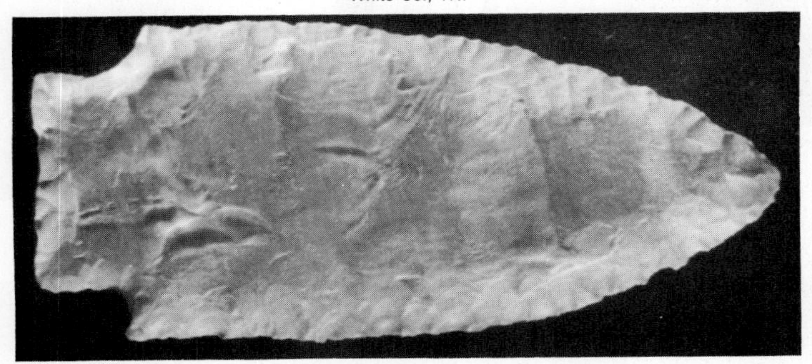

G6, $30-$50. Florence, AL. Fort Payne chert.

G8, $100-$200, Florence, AL. Note oblique parallel flaking on blade.

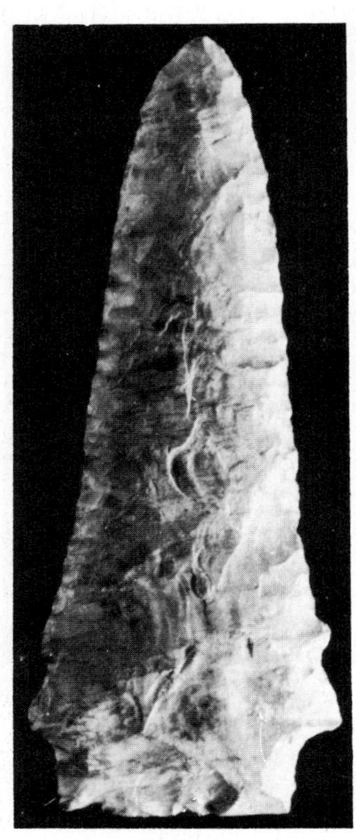

G6, $35-$60
Cheatham Co., TN. Note unusual side notching. This double notched form is rare.

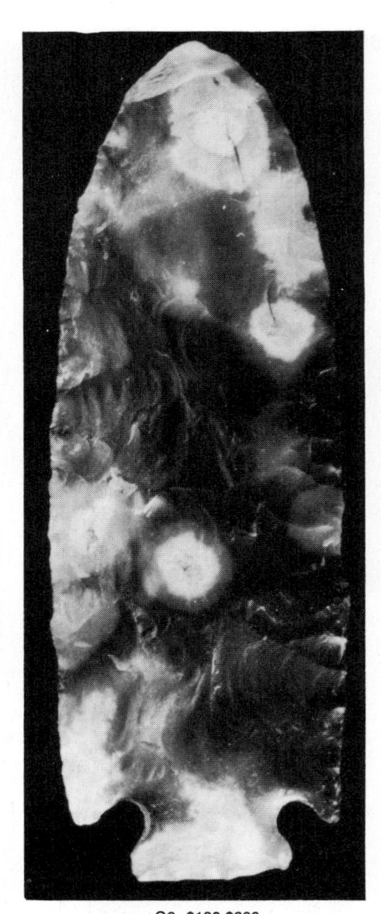

G8, $180-$300
Sumner Co., TN. Colorful chert with yellow spots.

G7, $65-$90, KY.

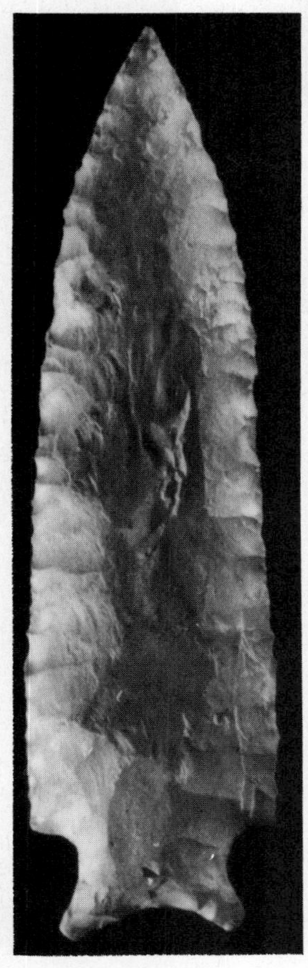

G9, $250-$350
Humphreys Co., TN.

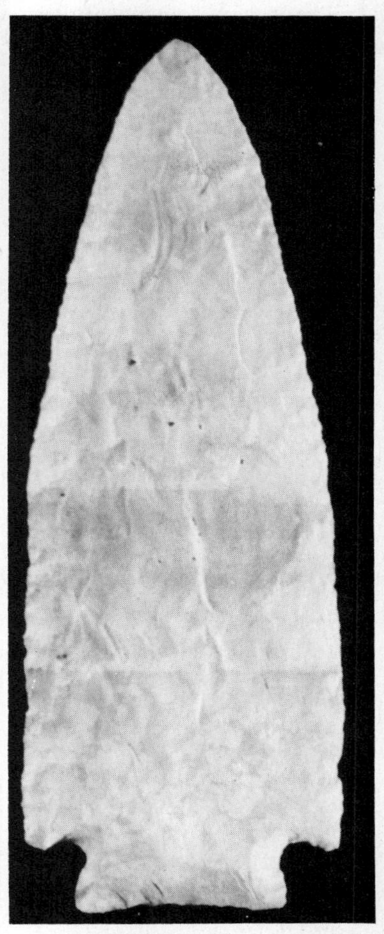

G10, $450-$600
Hiwassee Isle, Meigs Co., TN.

G9, $400-$600
Humphreys Co., TN. Colorful Buffalo River chert. Note parallel, oblique flaking.

G9, $400-$600
Humphreys Co., TN. Dover chert.

G8, $180-$300
Lauderdale Co., AL. Dover chert.

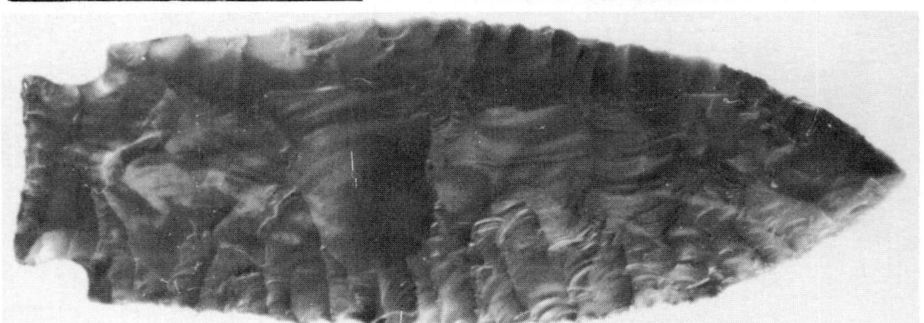

G10, $450-$650, Hardin Co., TN. Colorful heat treated Buffalo River chert.

G10, $600-$1000
Humphreys Co., TN. Note excellent oblique flaking.

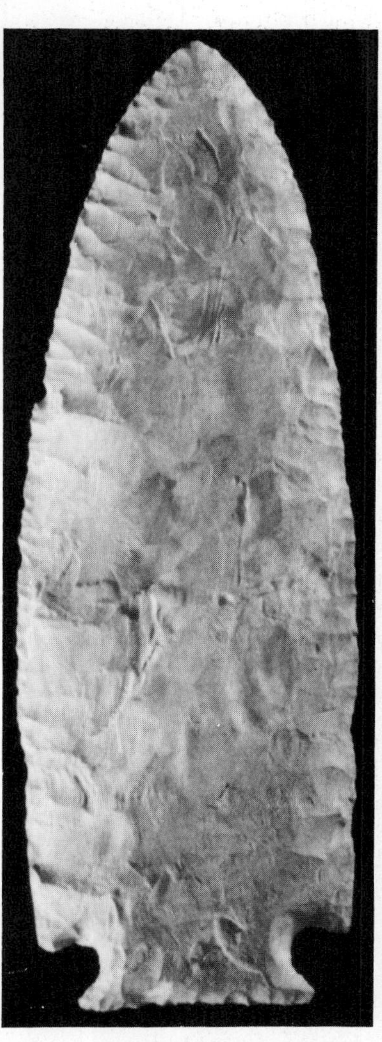

G10, $600-$1000
Hardin Co., TN. Outstanding example for quality and thinness. Found with a Buzzard Roost of equal size and quality.

G9, $350-$500
Sumner Co., TN. Note oblique, parallel flaking. Tip is rounded, not damaged.

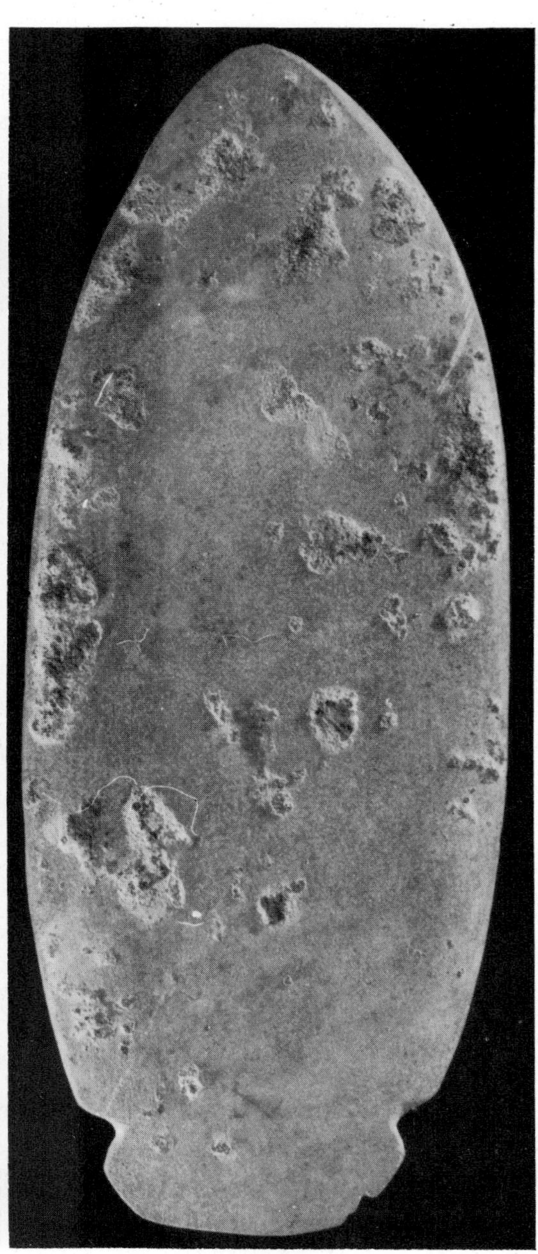

G10, $2500 - ?
Lee Co., MS. Only known ground greenstone Benton known. Rarest relic you can find.

BENTON (continued)

G10, $800-$1600
Clifton, TN. Note oblique flaking.

G10, $2500-$3500
Lee Co., MS. Rare double notch

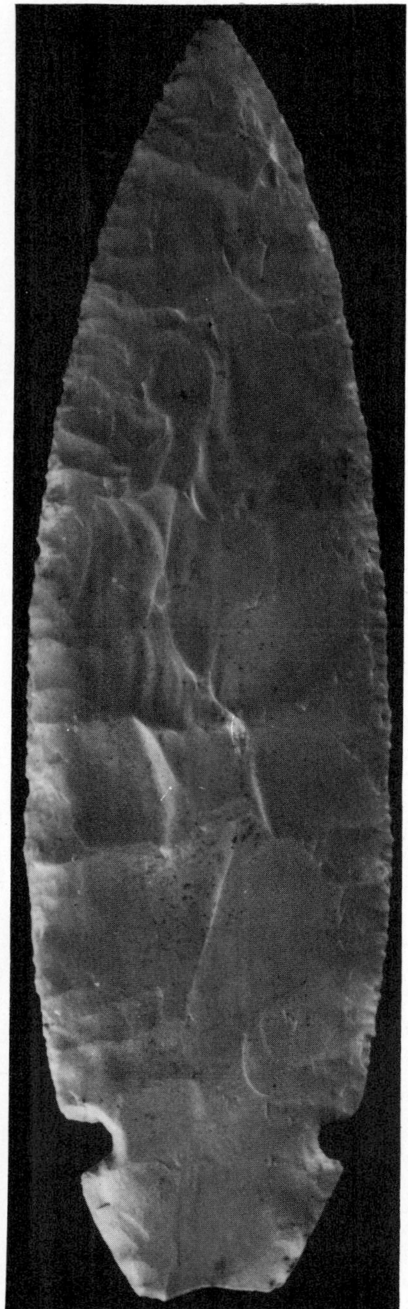

G10, $1500-$2500
Lee Co., MS. Rare Benton/Turkey cross type.

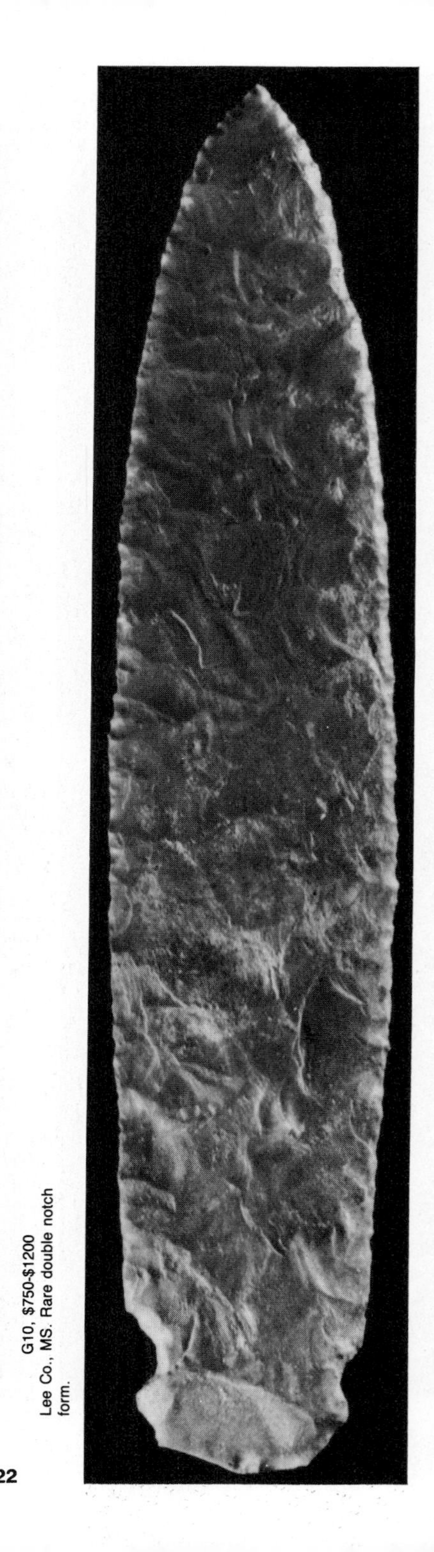

G10, $750-$1200
Lee Co., MS. Rare double notch form.

BENTON BLADE - Middle Archaic, 6000 - 4000 B.P.

(Also see Benton and Copena)

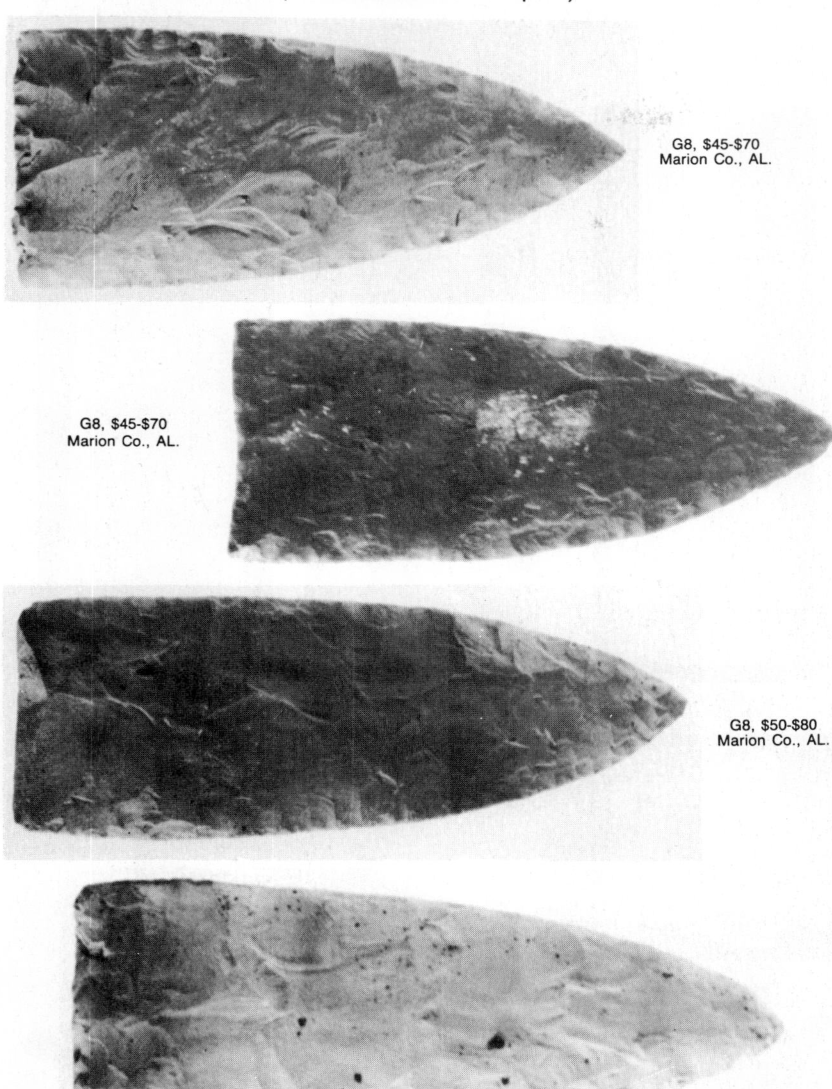

G8, $45-$70
Marion Co., AL.

G8, $45-$70
Marion Co., AL.

G8, $50-$80
Marion Co., AL.

G8, $50-$80
Marion Co., AL.

LOCATION: Southeastern to Midwestrn states. **DESCRIPTION:** A medium to very large size, broad, finished blade used either as a knife or as a preform for later knapping into a *Benton* point. Usually found in caches. **I.D. KEY:** Archaic flaking similar to the *Benton* type.

BENTON-NARROW BLADE - Mid-Archaic, 6000 - 4000 B.P.

(Also see Elk River)

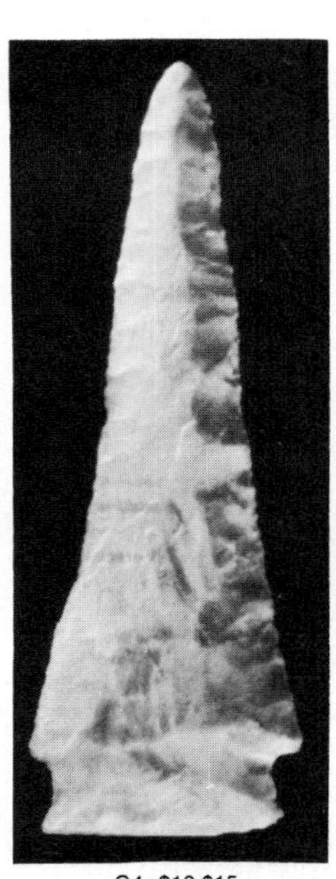

G4, $10-$15
Morgan Co., AL.

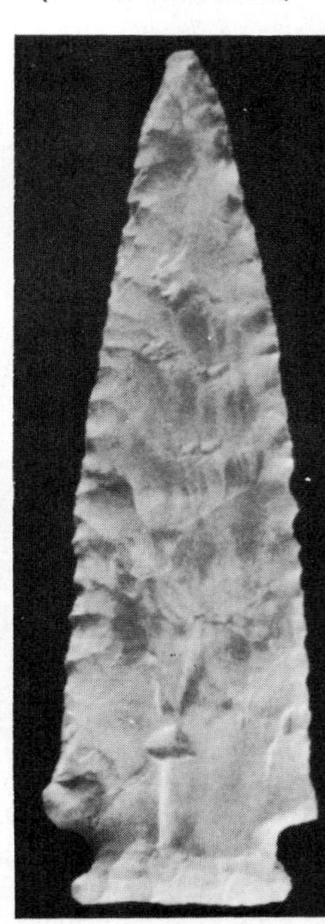

G5, $12-$20
Morgan Co., AL.

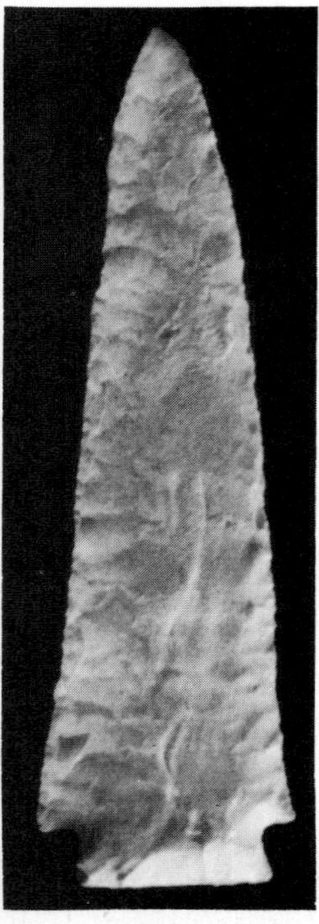

G6, $30-$35
Morgan Co., AL.

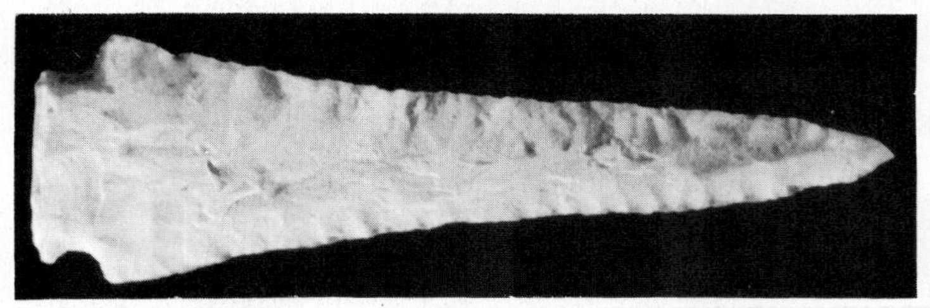

G7, $30-$45
Morgan Co., AL.

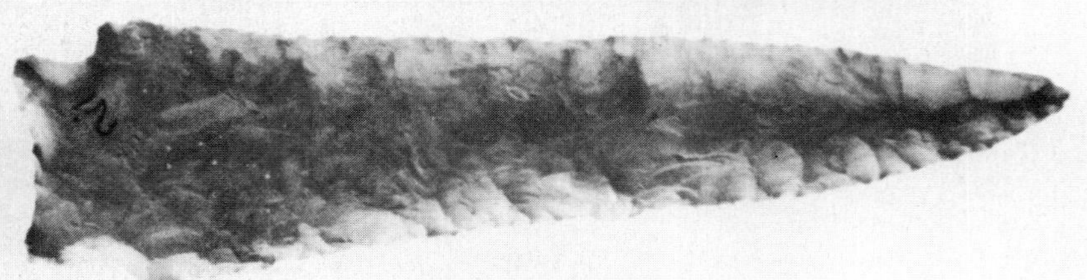

G8, $70-$120
Florence, AL.

LOCATION: Southeastern to Midwestern states. **DESCRIPTION:** A medium to large size, narrow, stemmed variant of the *Benton* form.

BESANT - Late Woodland, 1500 B.P.

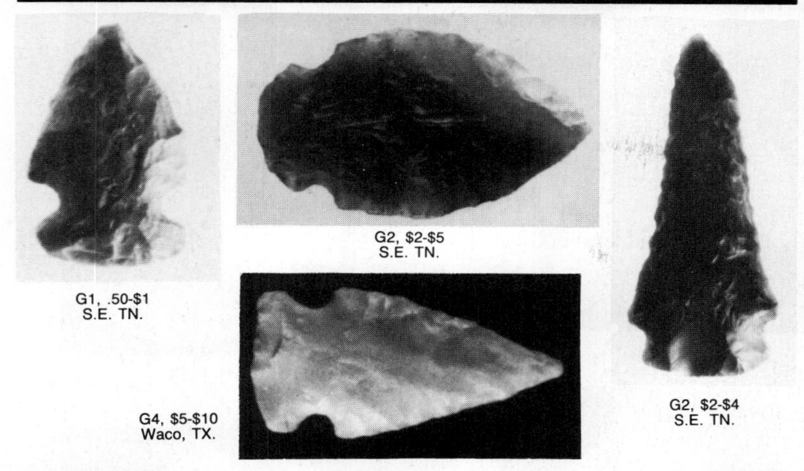

G1, .50-$1
S.E. TN.

G2, $2-$5
S.E. TN.

G4, $5-$10
Waco, TX.

G2, $2-$4
S.E. TN.

LOCATION: Midwestern states. **DESCRIPTION:** A small to medium size, short, broad, side notched point with a rounded base.

BIG CREEK - Late Archaic to early Woodland, 3500 - 2500 B.P.

(Also see Big Slough, Marcos and Williams)

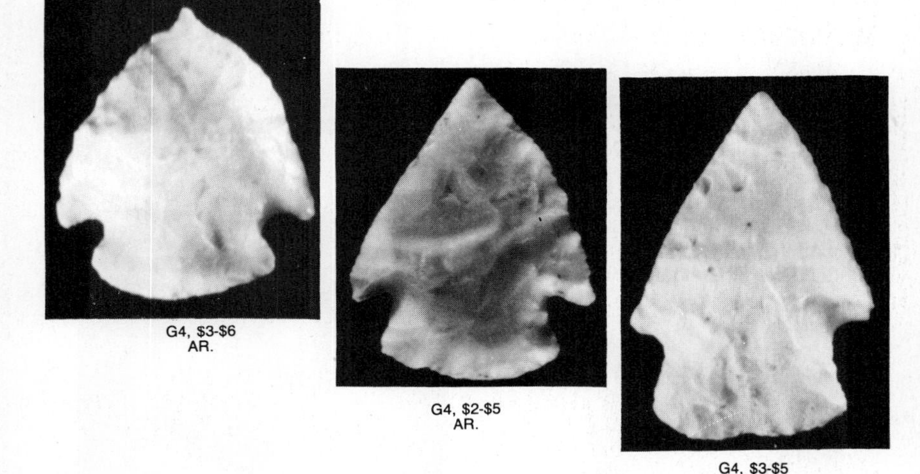

G4, $3-$6
AR.

G4, $2-$5
AR.

G4, $3-$5
N.E. AR.

LOCATION: Midwestern states. **DESCRIPTION:** A small to medium size, short, broad, corner notched point with a bulbous base. Believed to be related to *Marcos* points. The tips are needle sharp on some examples, similar to *Mud Creek* points. Tangs can be weak to very long. Small *Big Slough* points would be indistinguishable to this type. **I.D. KEY:** Rounded base and barbs drop.

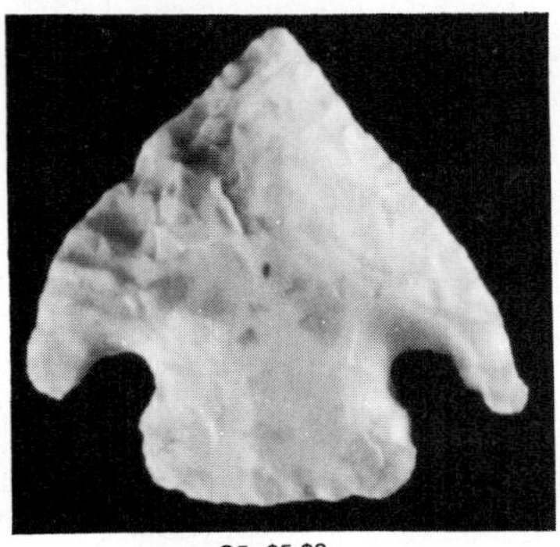

G5, $5-$8
AR.

G4, $3-$6
AR.

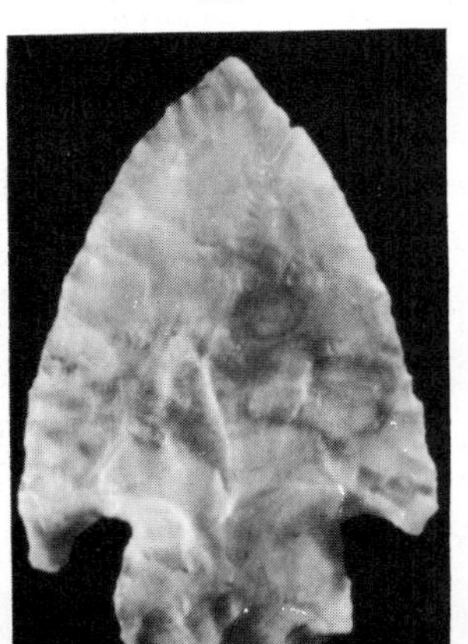

G4, $5-$6
AR.

G3, $2-$4
AR.

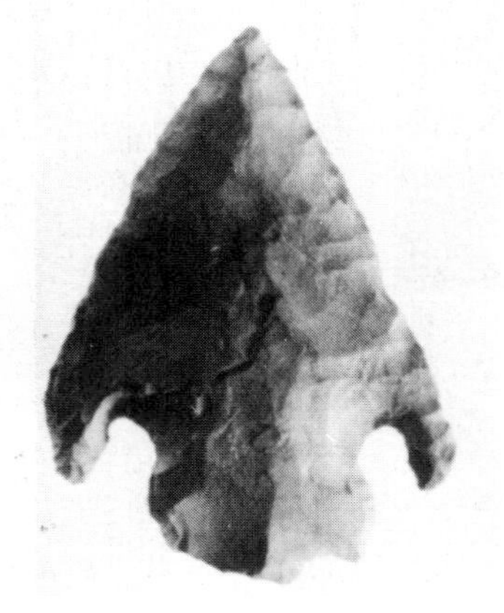

G6, $10-$12
AR.

G5, $5-$8
AR.

BIG SANDY - Transitional Paleo to late Archaic, 10000 - 3000 B.P.

(Also see Black Sand, Bolen Bevel, Cache River, Frio, Godar, Osceola, Pine Tree, Raddatz, Rowan & Savage Cave)

G2, $2-$3
Meigs Co., TN.

G2, $1-$3
Macon Co., AL.
Milky quartz.

G3, $2-$5
Autauga Co., AL.
Milky quartz.

G2, $2-$3
Meigs Co., TN.

G5, $7-$12
NE AL.

G5, $8-$10
Meigs Co., TN.

G4, $4-$7
Autauga Co., AL.
Milky quartz.

G5, $5-$10
Marion Co., AL.

G5, $7-$12
Henegar, AL.

G6, $20-$35
NE AL.

G6, $15-$25
NE AL.

G6, $20-$35
NE AL.

LOCATION: Southeastern states. **DESCRIPTION:** A small to medium size, side-notched point with early forms showing heavy basal grinding, serrations, and horizontal flaking. This type may be associated with the *Frazier* point, being an unnotched form. Some examples have been carbon dated to 10,000 B.P., but most are associated with Mid-Archaic times. **I.D. KEY:** Basal form & blade flaking.

G5, $8-$15
New Era, TN. Note
Leighton type base.

G7, $50-$75
Humphreys Co., TN.

G7, $40-$70
Coffee Lake, Florence, AL.

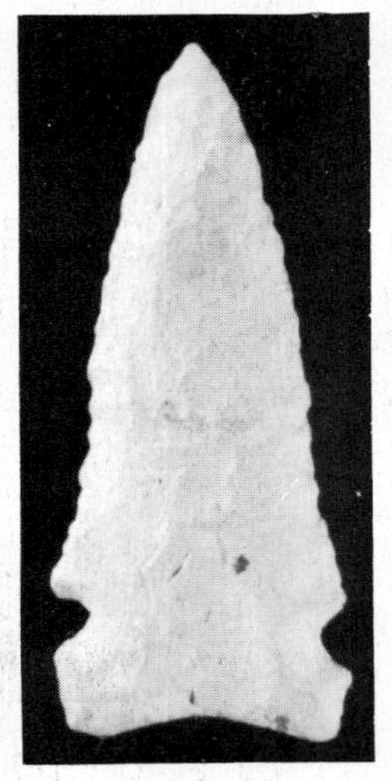

G6, $20-$35
Guilford Co., NC

G8, $80-$125
Florence, AL. Note collateral
flaking.

G8, $75-$100
Humphreys Co., TN.

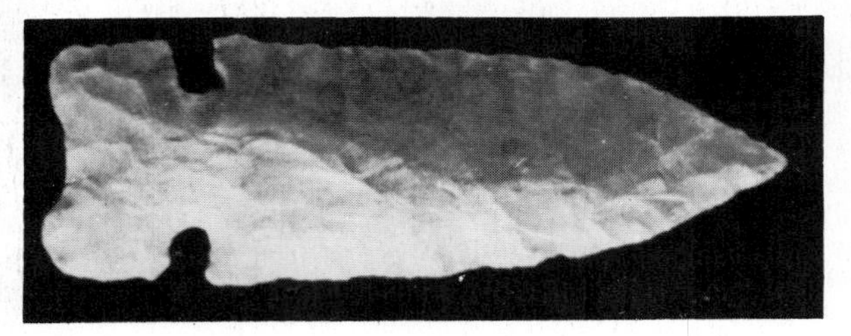

G9, $90-$150
Humphreys Co., TN.

BIG SANDY-BROAD BASE - Transitional Paleo to early Archaic, 10000 - 7000 B.P.

(Also see Rowan)

G4, $10-$12
Meigs Co., TN.

G4, $8-$12
Mid-TN.

G4, $10-$15
TN/KY. Black chert.

G8, $55-$80
Humphreys Co., TN.

G4, $15-$20
Davidson Co., TN.

G8, $60-$90
Humphreys Co., TN.

G9, $120-$220
Humphreys Co., TN.

LOCATION: Southeastern states. **DESCRIPTION:** A small to medium size, side-notched point with a broad base that is usually ground. The base is wider than the blade.

BIG SANDY-CONTRACTED BASE - Transitional Paleo to early Archaic, 10000 - 8000 B.P.

(Also see Graham Cave, Frio, Oxbow, Rowan and Uvalde)

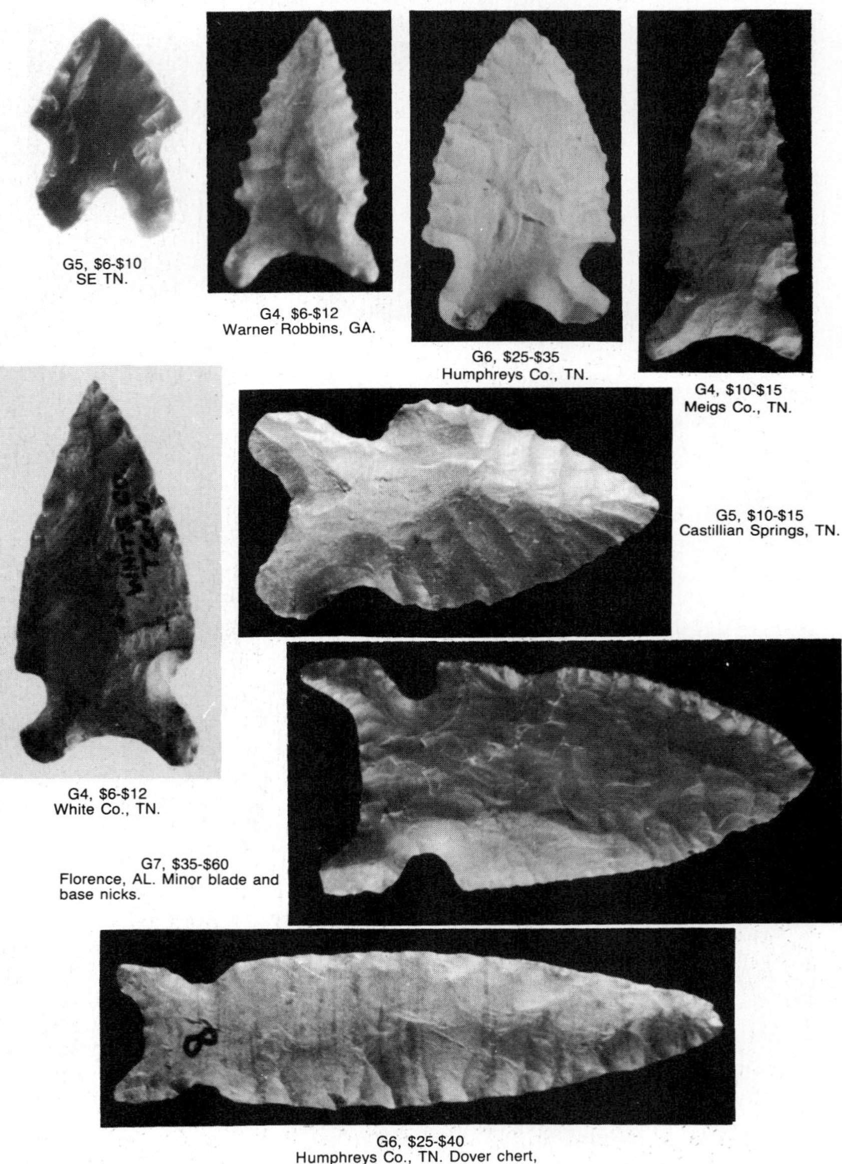

G5, $6-$10
SE TN.

G4, $6-$12
Warner Robbins, GA.

G6, $25-$35
Humphreys Co., TN.

G4, $10-$15
Meigs Co., TN.

G5, $10-$15
Castillian Springs, TN.

G4, $6-$12
White Co., TN.

G7, $35-$60
Florence, AL. Minor blade and base nicks.

G6, $25-$40
Humphreys Co., TN. Dover chert, tip nick.

LOCATION: Southeastern states. **DESCRIPTION:** A small to medium size, side-notched point with a deeply concave base, that is ground, and dropping ears. Some examples exhibit nice parallel flaking.

BIG SANDY E-NOTCHED - Transitional Paleo to early Archaic, 10000 - 7000 B.P.

(Also see Bolen Bevel and Thebes)

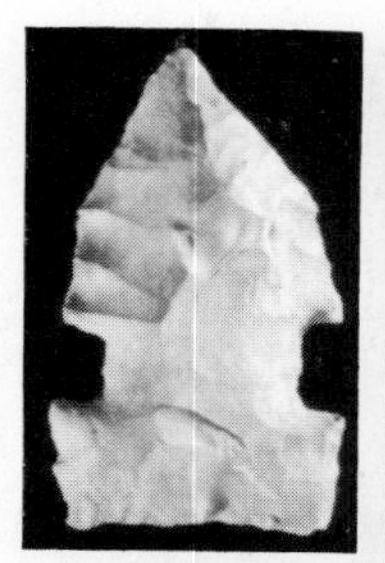
G2, $3-$5
Humphreys Co., TN.

G3, $6-$10
Humphreys Co., TN.

G2, $5-$8
Coffee Lake, Florence, AL.

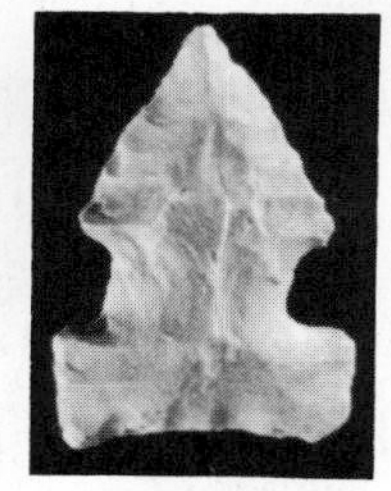
G2, $3-$5
Humphreys Co., TN.

G7, $30-$50
Humphreys Co., TN.

G8, $45-$70
Humphreys Co., TN. Tip nick.

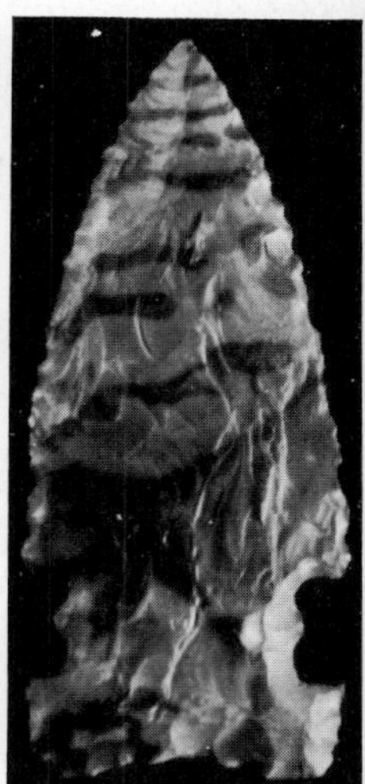
G10, $300-$500
Humphreys Co., TN. Colorful Buffalo River chert.

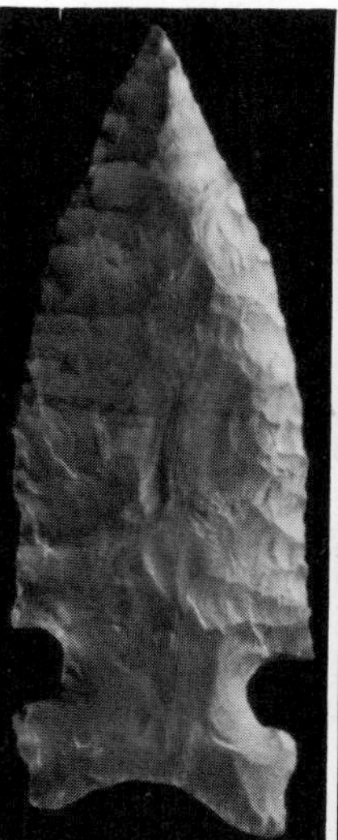
G10, $120-$200
Coffee Lake, AL.

G10, $150-$250
Humphreys Co., TN.

LOCATION: Southeastern states. **DESCRIPTION:** A small to medium size expanded side-notched point. The notching is unique and quite rare for the type. This type of notch is angled into the blade to produce a high point or nipple in the center, forming the letter E. Also called Key-notched. Rarely, the base is also E-Notched. The same notching occurs in the *Bolen* and *Thebes* types. **I.D. KEY:** Two flake notching system.

BIG SLOUGH - Mid-Archaic, 7000 - 4000 B.P.

(Also see Beacon Island, Big Creek, Boggy Branch, Elk River and Williams)

G5, $10-$20
Florence, AL.

G4, $8-$15
Jonesboro, AR.

G8, $45-$80
W. TN.

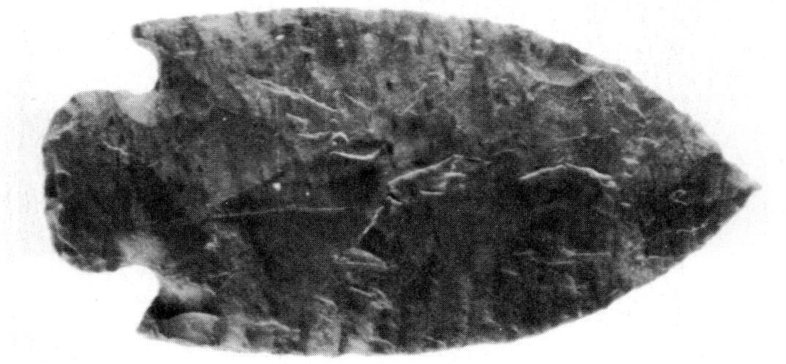

G9, $80-$120
Humphreys Co., TN.
Dover chert. Very thin & excellent.

LOCATION: Southeastern states. **DESCRIPTION:** A medium to large size, broad, stemmed point with a bulbous base. The blade is convex to recurved. The shoulders may show a weak to medium tang. **I.D. KEY:** Basal form and barbs.

BIG SLOUGH (continued)

G4, $8-$15
Parsons, TN.

G9, $80-$120
Humphreys Co., TN. Very thin and excellent.

G9, $80-$120
Humphreys Co., TN.

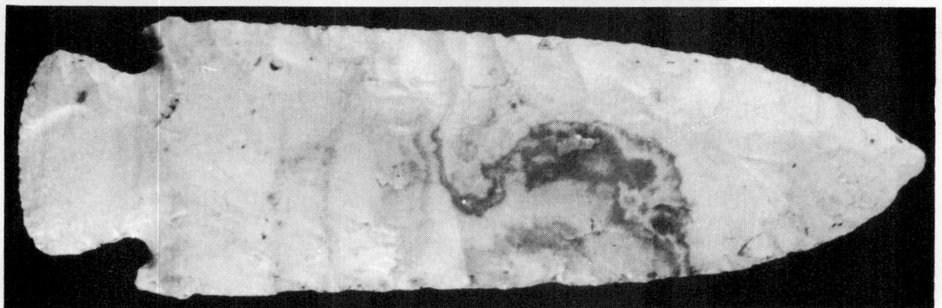

G9, $80-$150
St. Clair Co., IL.

BLACK ROCK - Woodland, 3000 - 1000 B.P.

(Also see Desert)

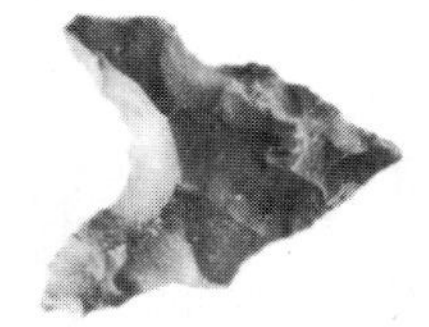

G4, $7-$12
Yavapai Co., AZ

LOCATION: Western to Midwestern states. **DESCRIPTION:** A small size lanceolet to triangular point with a concave base.

BLEVINS - Mississippian, 1200 - 600 B.P.

(Also see Hayes and Howard)

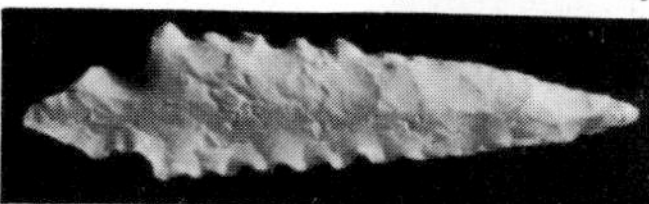

G8, $45-$80
W. AR.

LOCATION: Midwestern states. **DESCRIPTION:** A small size, narrow spike point with two or more notches on each blade side. The base is diamond shape. A cross between *Hayes* and *Howard*.

BLUNT - Paleo to Woodland, 12000 to 1000 B.P.

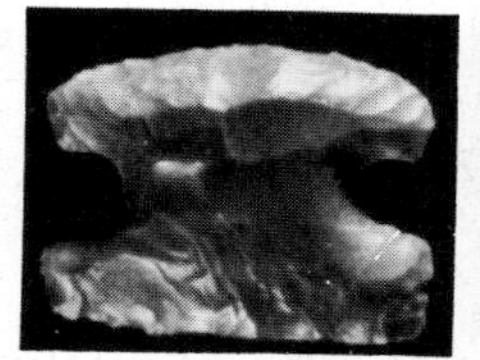

$1-$2
IN/IL., Big Sandy

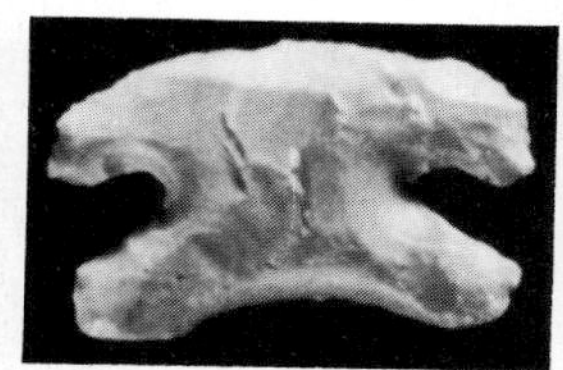

$1-$2
IN/IL., Big Sandy

$1-$2
Mid TN.

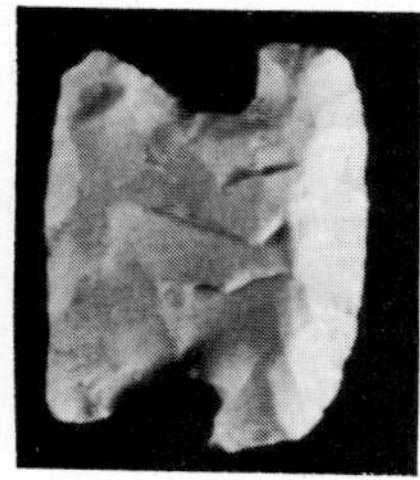

$1-$2
IN/IL.

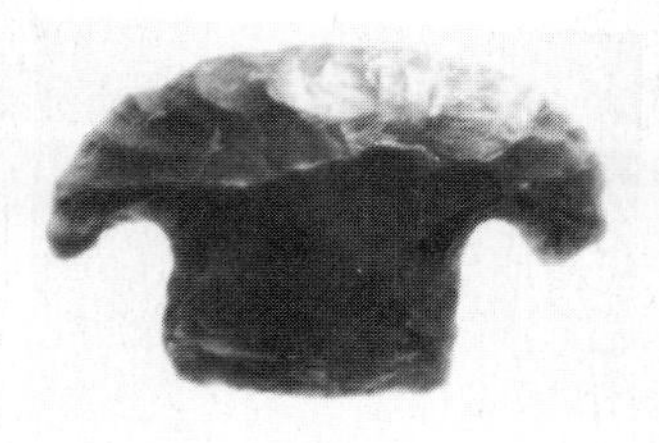

$1-$2
IN/IL. Elk River

$1-$2
IN/IL. Kirk Corner Notched.

LOCATION: North American continent everywhere. **DESCRIPTION:** Blunts are usually made from broken points that are rechipped into this form, but can be made from scratch. All point types can occur as blunts. Some collectors call this form *Stunners* believing they were made to stun animals, not to kill. However, most archaeologists think they were used as knives and for scraping hides.

BLUNT (continued)

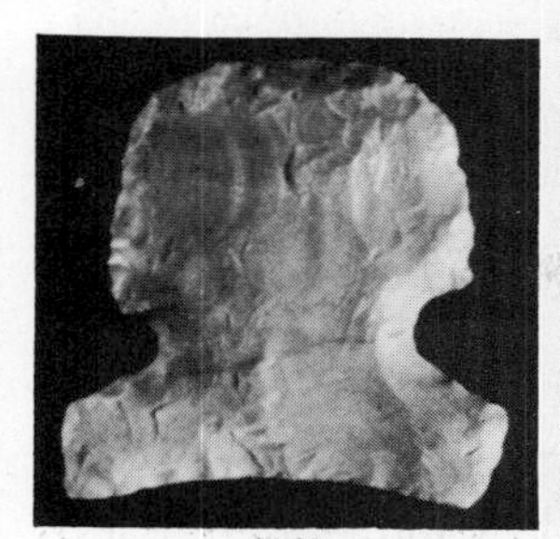

$1-$2
Mid-TN. Big Sandy.

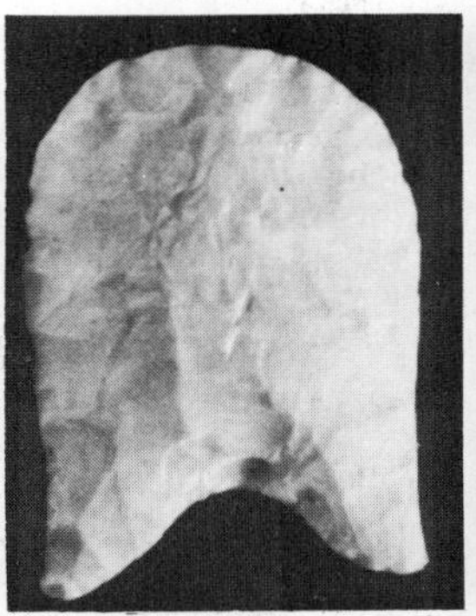

$8-$10
IN/IL. Dalton.

$4-$6
Mid-TN. Turkey Tail.

$6-$8
IN/IL. Thebes

$2-$3, IN/IL.

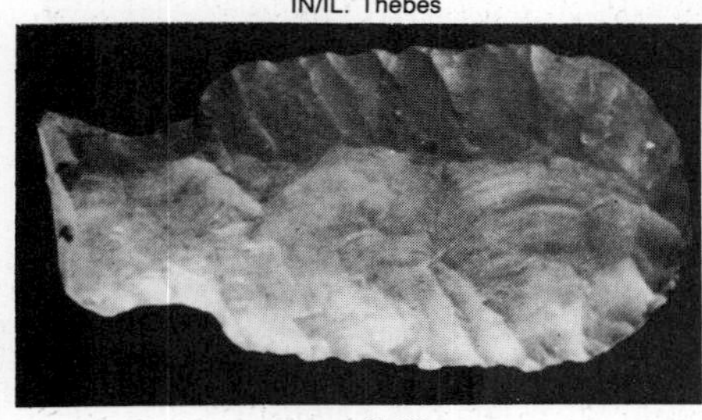

$1.00
Mid-TN. Elk River

$1-$2
IN/IL.

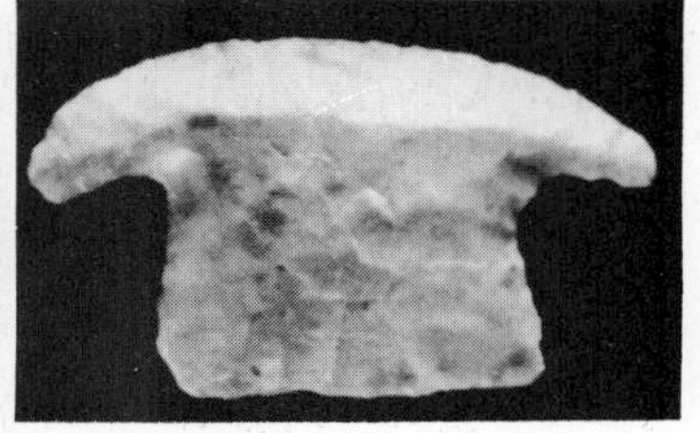

$1-$2
IN/IL.

BOGGY BRANCH-TYPE I- Early to Mid-Archaic, 9000 - 6000 B.P.

(Also see Big Slough, Fountain Creek and Kirk Serrated)

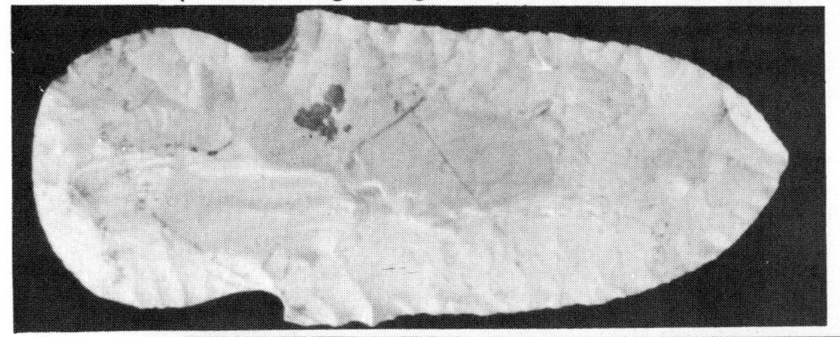

G7, $70-$100
Henry Co., AL.

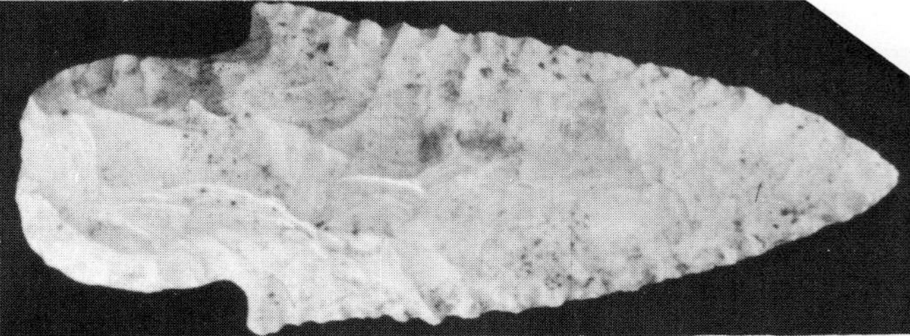

G8, $150-$250
Henry Co., AL.

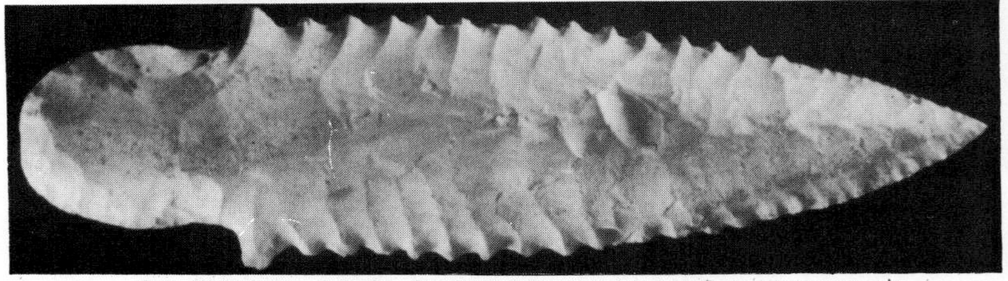

G10, $2500-$3500, Early Co., GA. Outstanding, rare example. One of the best known.

LOCATION: Small area in SE AL & SW GA. **DESCRIPTION:** A medium to large size serrated point with weak shoulders and a large bulbous base which is usually ground. Blade flaking is similar to *Kirk Serrated*. Very rare in the small type area. **I.D. KEY:** Basal form and edgework.

BOGGY BRANCH-TYPE II - Early to Mid-Archaic, 9000 - 6000 B.P.

(Also see Big Slough, Fountain Creek and Kirk Serrated)

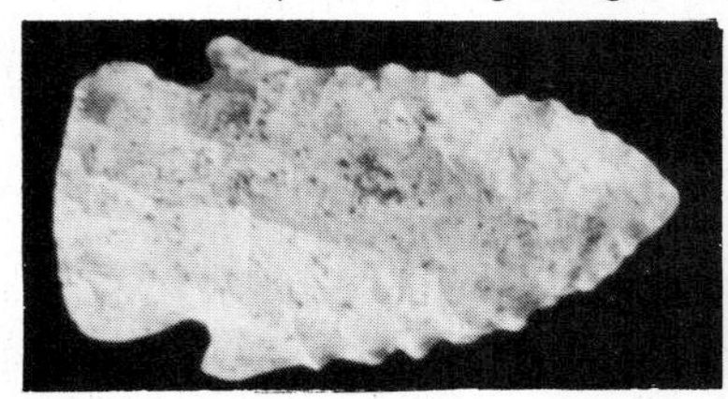

G5, $25-$40
Henry Co., AL.

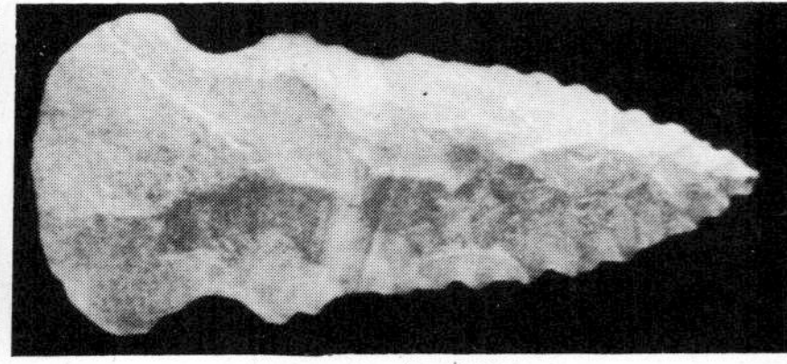

G5, $25-$40
Randolph Co., NC

LOCATION: Southern Southeastern states. **DESCRIPTION:** A small to medium size serrated point with weak shoulders and a bulbous base which is usually ground. The base is shorter and smaller than in type I. **I.D. KEY:** Basal form and early flaking.

BOGGY BRANCH-TYPE II (continued)

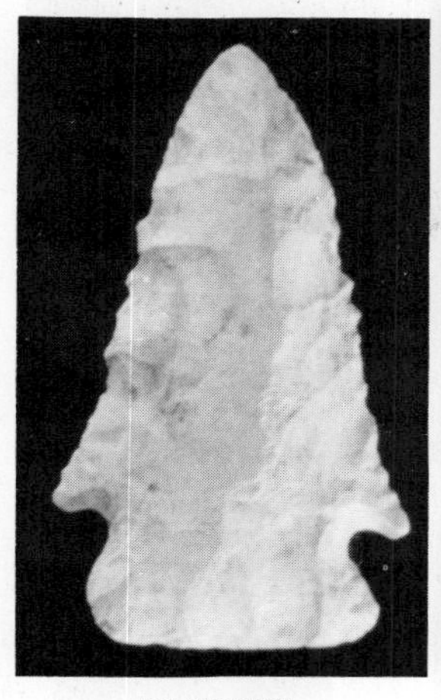

G8, $70-$100
Henry Co., AL.

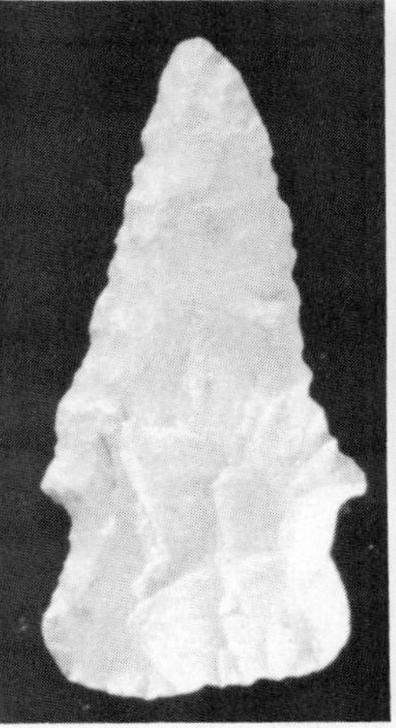

G3, $8-$12
Henry Co., AL.

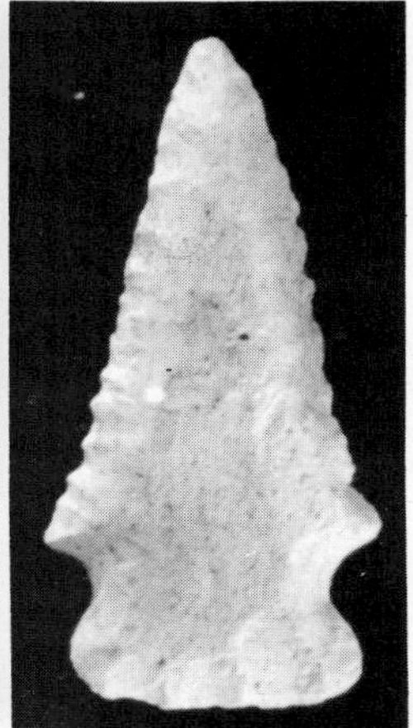

G4, $10-$20
Henry Co., AL.

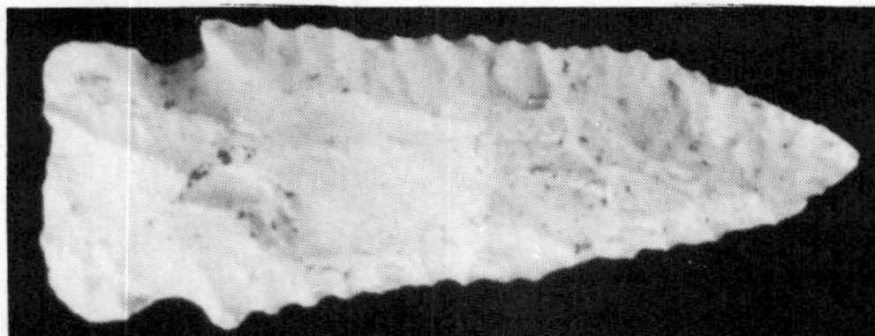

G4, $12-$20
Henry Co., AL.

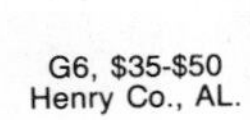

G6, $35-$50
Henry Co., AL.

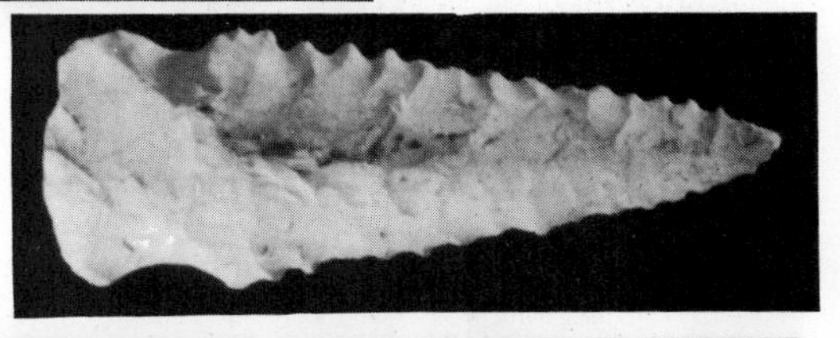

BOLEN BEVEL - Early Archaic, 10000 - 7000 B.P.

(Also see Big Sandy, Clay, Godar, Lafayette, Osceola and Raddatz)

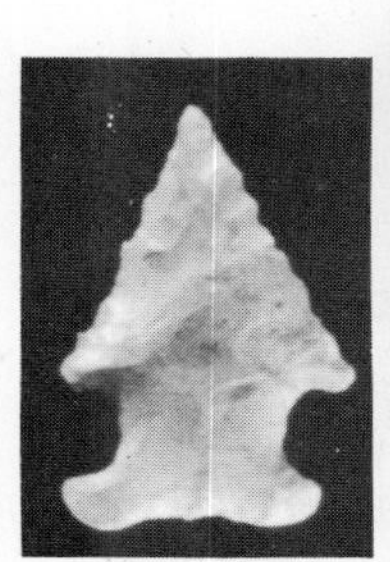

G3, $4-$8
Henry Co., AL.

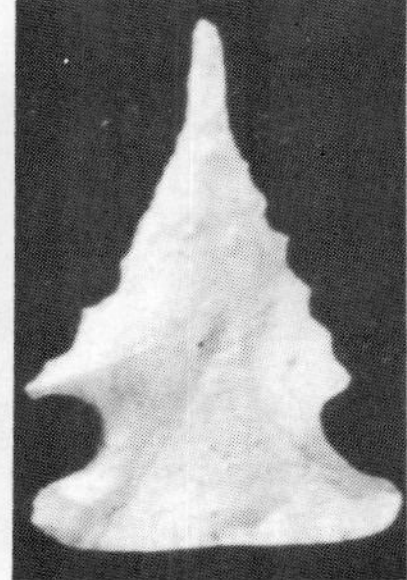

G3, $6-$10
Henry Co., AL.

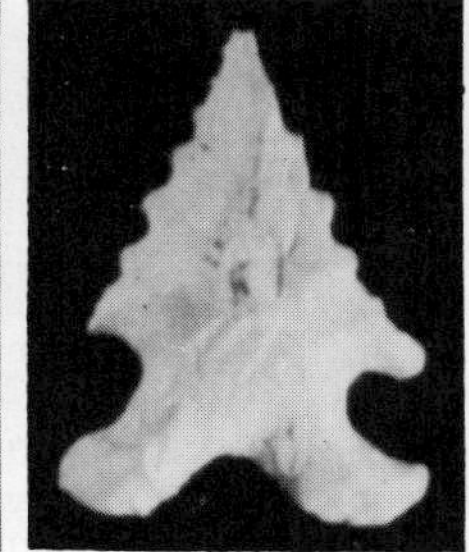

G5, $25-$40
Warner Robbins, GA.

G3, $4-$8
Henry Co., AL.

BOLEN BEVEL (continued)

G6, $90-$150
St. Marks Rv., FL.

G7, $120-$200
NW Cent. FL.

G5, $60-$90
Suwannee RV., FL.

G4, $50-$80
Henry Co., AL.

G8, $250-$350
Worth Co., GA.

G5, $60-$100
Lexington Co., SC.

G4, $45-$70
Jasper Co., SC.

G8, $250-$350
Lake Marion, SC.

G5, $80-$120
Lexington Co., SC.

LOCATION: Eastern states including Florida. **DESCRIPTION:** A small to medium size, side-notched point with early forms showing basal grinding, beveling on one side of each face, and serrations. Bases can be straight, concave or convex. The side notch is usually broader than in *Big Sandy* points. E-notching or expanded notching also occurs on early forms. **I.D. KEY:** Basal form and notching.

BOLEN BEVEL (continued)

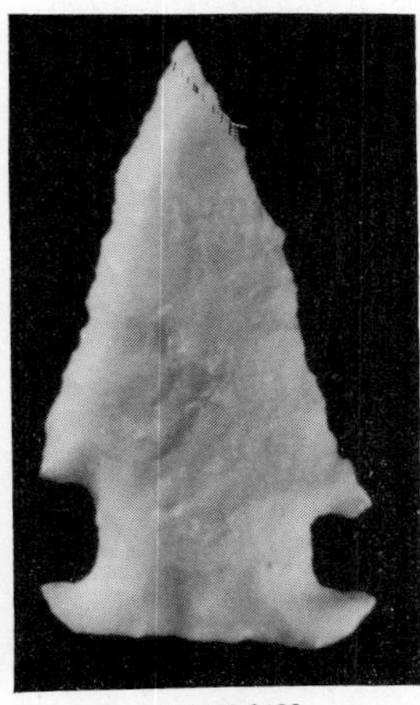

G6, $100-$180
Dougherty Co., GA.

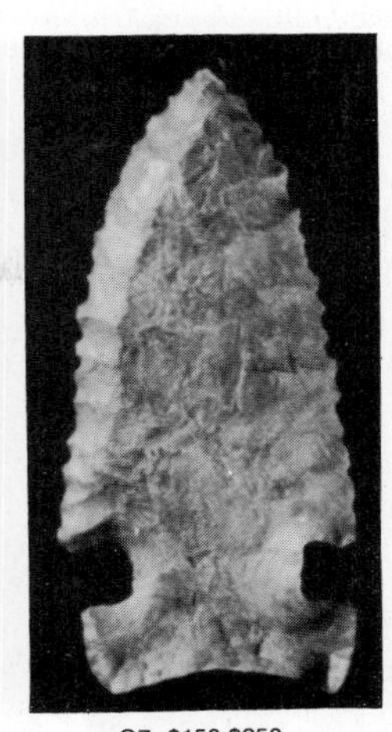

G7, $150-$250
Suwannee RV., FL.

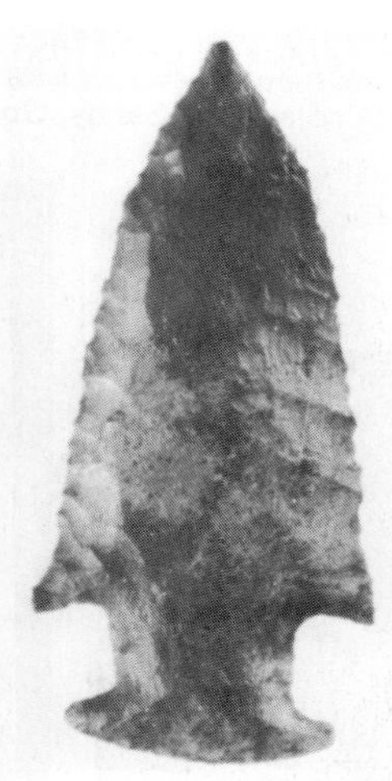

G8, $250-$350
Sante Fe RV., FL.

G6, $125-$200
Silver Lake, FL. Yellow coral, tang nick.

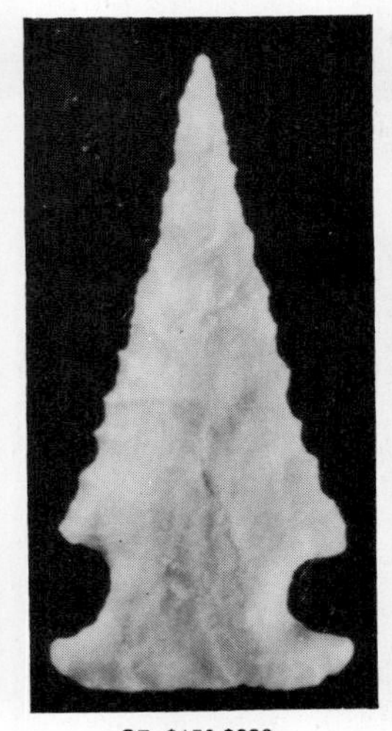

G7, $150-$280
Taylor Co., FL.

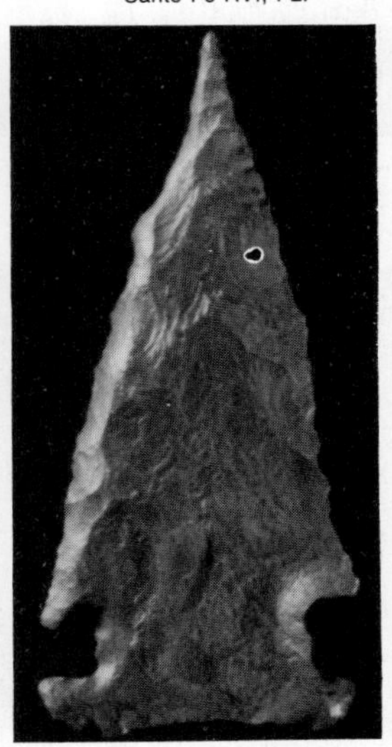

G8, $250-$350
Suwannee RV., FL.

G10, $600-$1000
Columbia Co., FL.

BOLEN PLAIN - Early Archaic, 9000 - 7000 B.P.

(Also see Big Sandy, Godar, Osceola, Osceola Greenbrier, Raddatz & Taylor)

G6, $125-$220
Aucilla RV., FL.

G7, $150-$220
Sante Fe RV., FL.

G7, $120-$200
Baker Co., GA.

G5, $80-$140
Suwannee RV., FL.

G7, $150-$250
Suwannee RV., FL.

G7, $150-$280
Aucilla RV., FL.

LOCATION: Eastern states. **DESCRIPTION:** A small to medium size, side-notched point with early forms showing basal grinding and serrations. Bases are straight, concave or convex. The side-notches are usually broader than in the *Big Sandy* type, and can be expanded to E-notched on some examples. **I.D. KEY:** Basal form and flaking on blade.

BONE PIN - Transitional Paleo, 12,000 - 9000 B.P.

$25-$75 each

LOCATION: Florida. **DESCRIPTION:** Medium to large size, slender, double pointed spear pins made from Mammoth tusks. Found in Florida associated with Mammoth kills. The ivory is usually blackened with age.

BONHAM - Woodland to Mississippian, 1200 - 600 B.P.

(Also see Alba, Bulbar Stemmed, Cuney, Hayes, Perdiz, Rockwall and Scallorn)

G3, $6-$10
Columbia Rv., WA

G4, $10-$15
Comanche Co., TX.

G4, $10-$15
OR.

G4, $10-$15
Comanche Co., TX.

G4, $10-$15
Waco, TX.

G6, $30-$40
WA/OR.

G7, $40-$50
Waco, TX.

G8, $60-$75
WA/OR.

G8, $60-$75
Comanche Co., TX.

G4, $8-$12
Comanche Co., TX.

G7, $40-$50
Wasco Co., OR

G6, $20-$35
Comanche Co., TX.
Tip nick.

G8, $60-$75
Comanche Co., TX.

G7, $25-$40
Clearwater Co., ID.

G8, $50-$60
Comanche Co., TX.

G9, $45-$90
Clearwater Co., ID.

G9, $60-$100
Cent. TX.

G9, $75-$100
Comanche Co., TX.

G9, $45-$90
Comanche Co., TX.

G6, $30-$40
McCurtain Co., OK.

G6, $20-$35
MO.

LOCATION: Northwest to Southeastern states. **DESCRIPTION:** A small to medium size, thin, well made triangular point with a short to long squared or rounded stem. Many examples are finely serrated and are made of agate. Blade edges are straight, concave, convex or recurved. Shoulders are squared to barbed. **I.D. KEY:** Long straight base, expanded barbs.

BRADFORD - Woodland to Mississippian, 2000 - 800 B.P.

(Also see Bakers Creek and Broward)

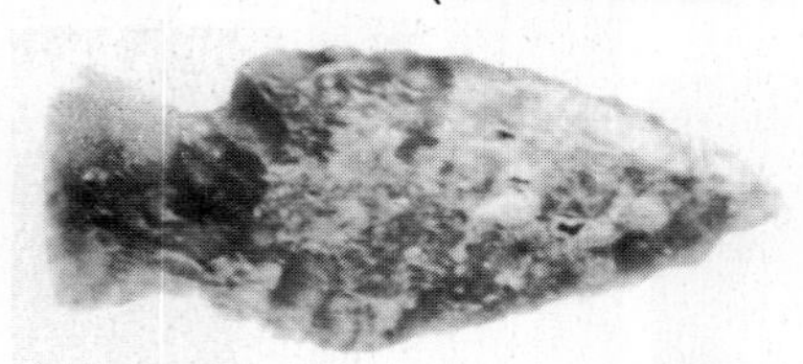

G3, $2-$5
Hillsborough Co., FL.

LOCATION: Southern Southeastern states. **DESCRIPTION:** A medium size, narrow, expanded stem point with tapered to rounded shoulders.

BRADLEY SPIKE - Woodland, 4000 - 1800 B.P.

(Also see Duval, Flint River Spike, Mountain Fork, New Market, Randolph and Schild Spike)

G1, .50-$1 Dunlap, TN.

G1, .50-$1 Dunlap, TN.

G2, $1-$2 Dunlap, TN.

G3, $1-$3 Dunlap, TN.

G6, $6-$10 Morgan Co., AL.

G5, $4-$6 Limestone Co., AL.

G7, $8-$10 Marion Co., TN.

G8, $8-$15 Limestone Co., AL.

G8, $8-$15 Decatur, AL.

G5, $4-$6 Limestone Co., AL.

LOCATION: Southeastern states. **DESCRIPTION:** A small to medium size, narrow, thick, spike point. The shoulders are tapered and the stem contracts. The base on some examples shows the natural rind of the native material used.

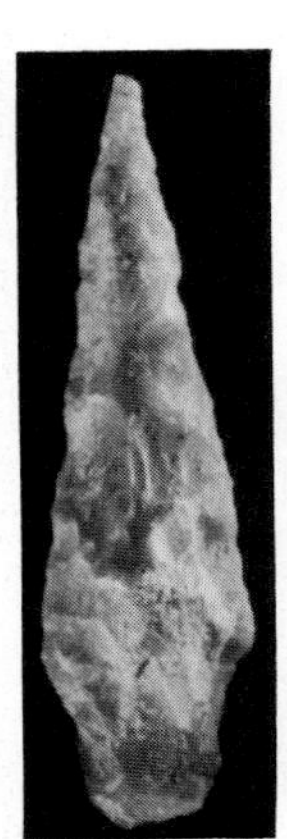
G6, $6-$8
Marion Co., AL.

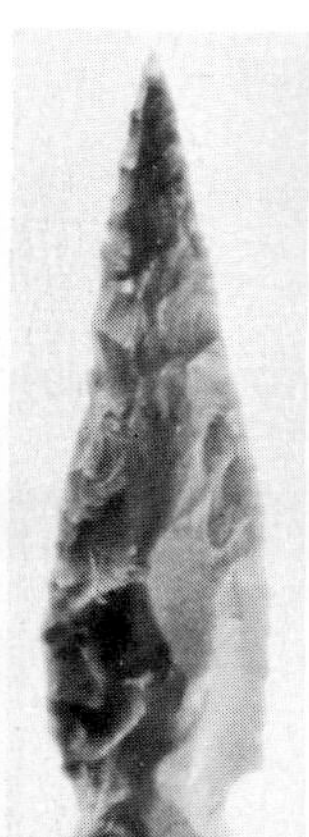
G6, $6-$10
Limestone Co., AL.

G7, $8-$12
Limestone Co., AL.

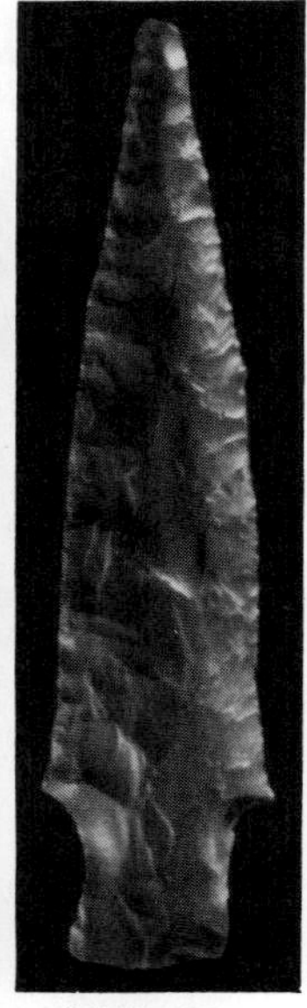
G10, $30-$40
Florence, AL.

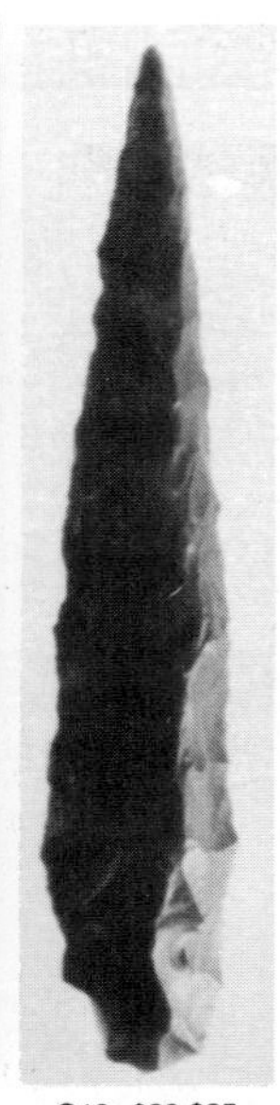
G10, $20-$35
Madison Co., AL.
Black chert.

BRAZOS - Early Archaic, 8000 - 5000 B.P.

(Also see Darl, Hoxie and Lampasos)

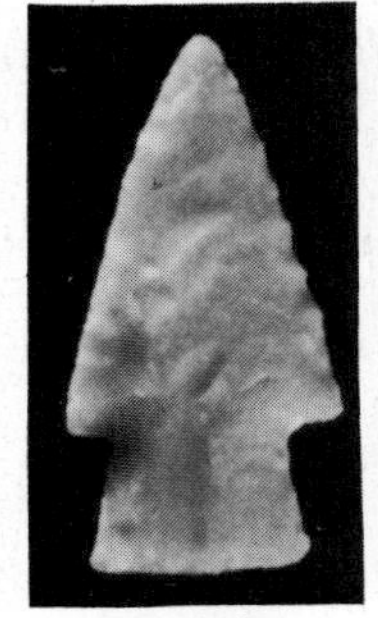
G3, $5-$8
Comanche Co., TX.

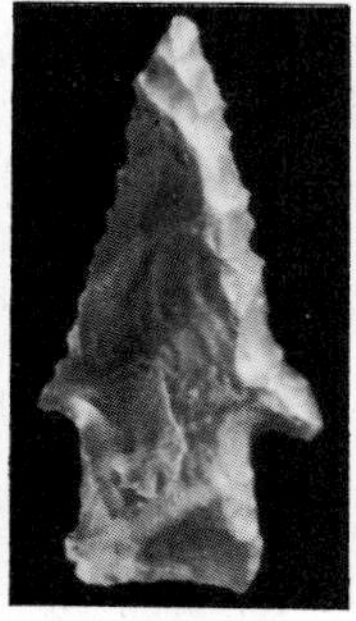
G3, $6-$10
Comanche Co., TX.

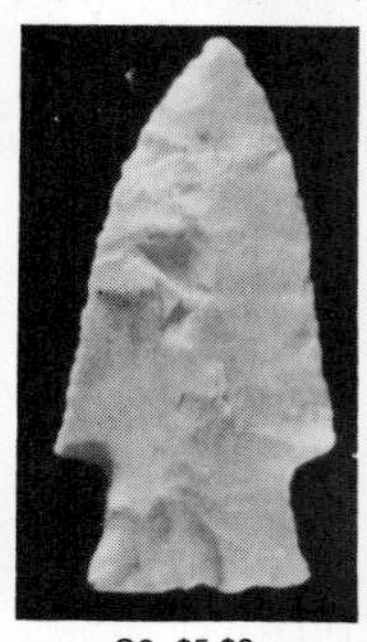
G3, $5-$8
Comanche Co., TX.

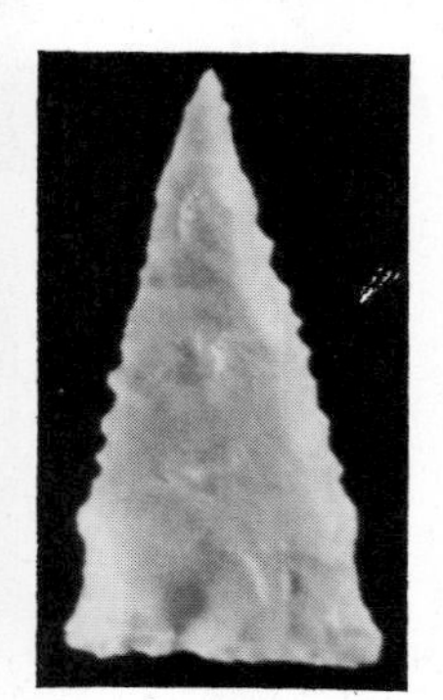
G4, $8-$15
Austin, TX.

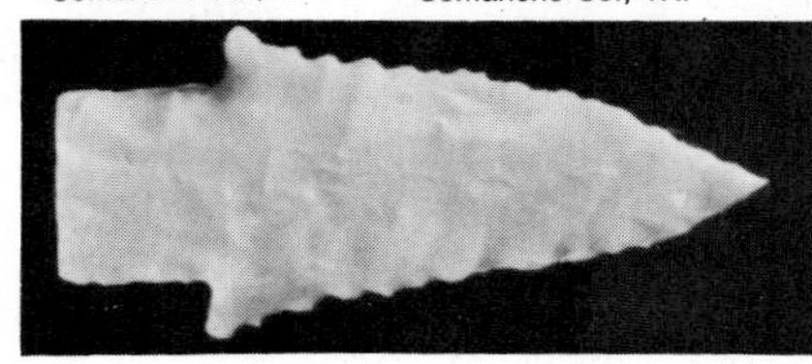
G8, $40-$65
Comanche Co., TX.

LOCATION: Midwestern states. **DESCRIPTION:** A medium to large size, narrow point with horizontally barbed shoulders and an expanding to square stem. The blades on most examples are steeply beveled on one side of each face. Flaking is early parallel and is of much higher quality than *Darl*.

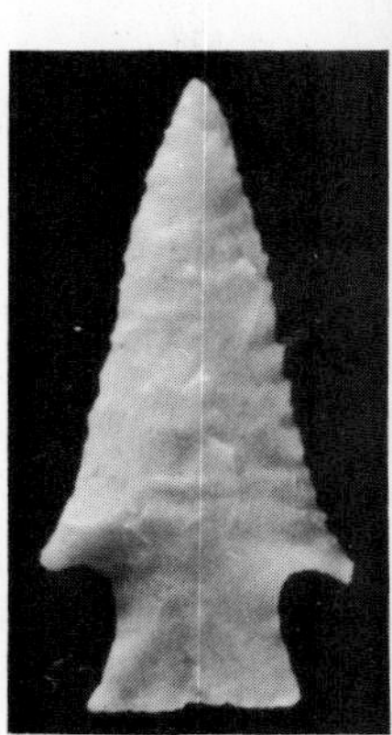

G6, $25-$40
Comanche Co., TX.

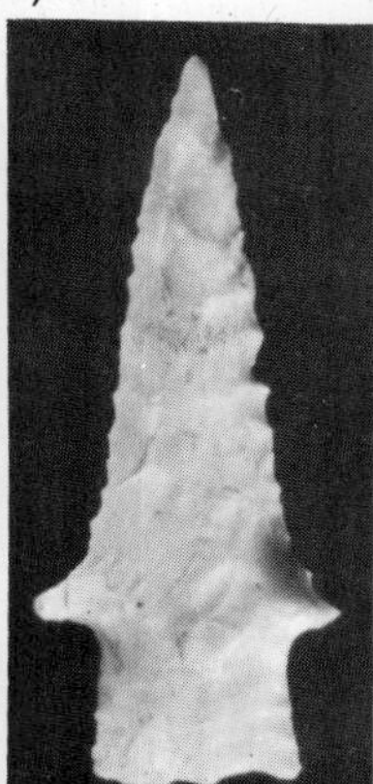

G5, $15-$25
Comanche Co., TX.

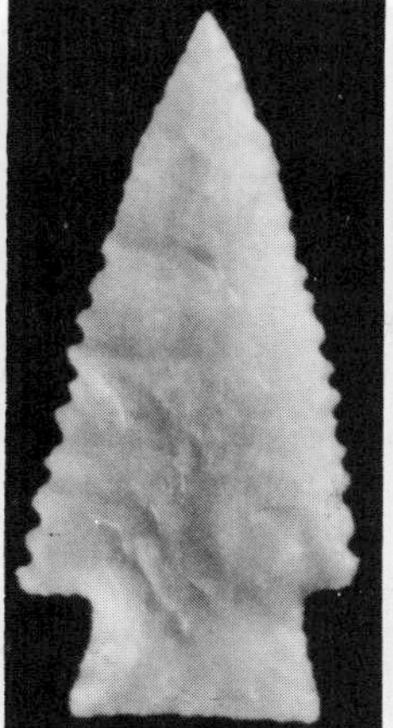

G8, $60-$75
Austin, TX.

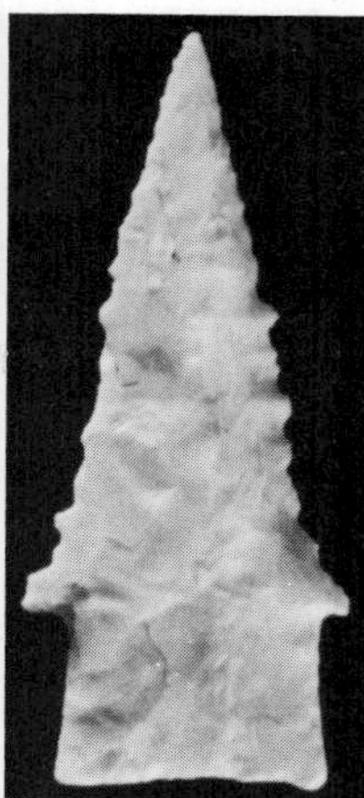

G9, $70-$100
Comanche Co., TX.

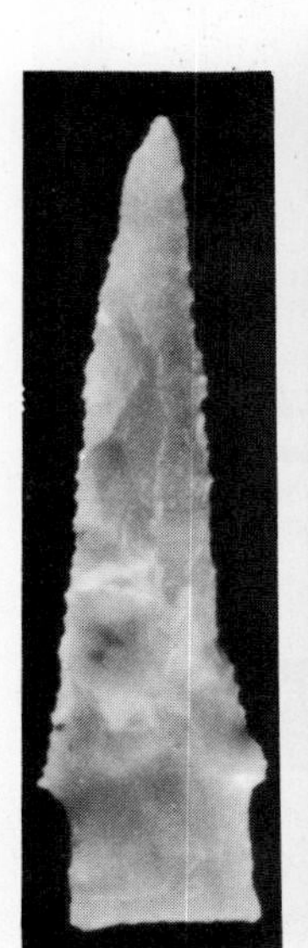

G5, $20-$30
Comanche Co., TX. Right-hand bevel on blade.

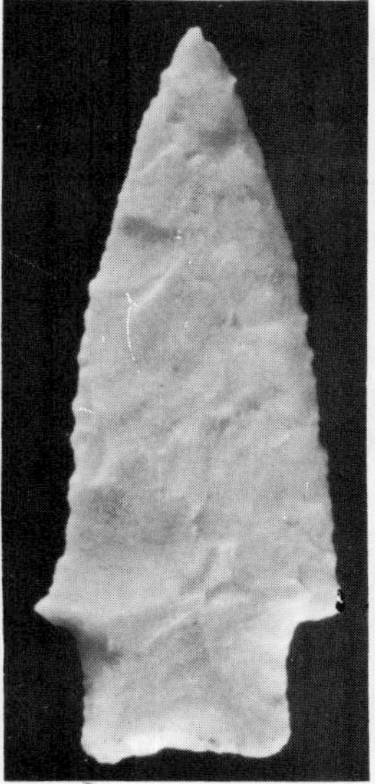

G9, $55-$90
Comanche Co., TX.

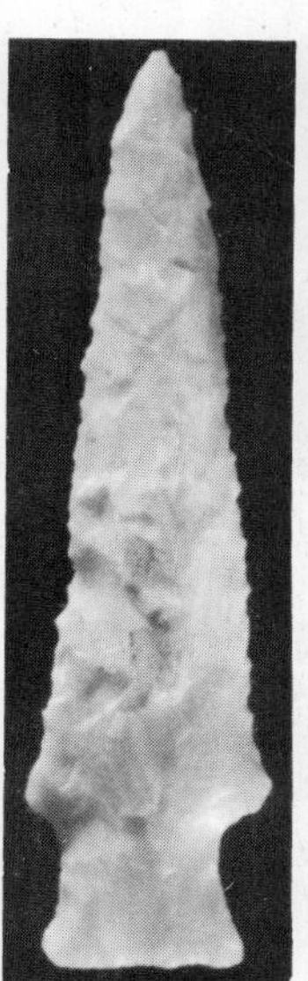

G7, $35-$60
Comanche Co., TX.

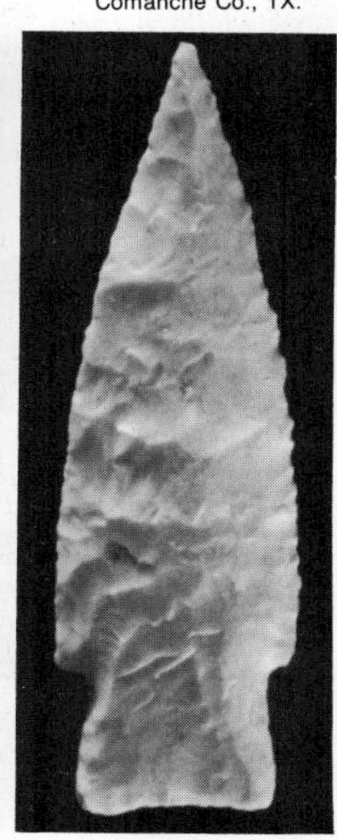

G9, $80-$120
Comanche Co., TX. Right-hand bevel on blade.

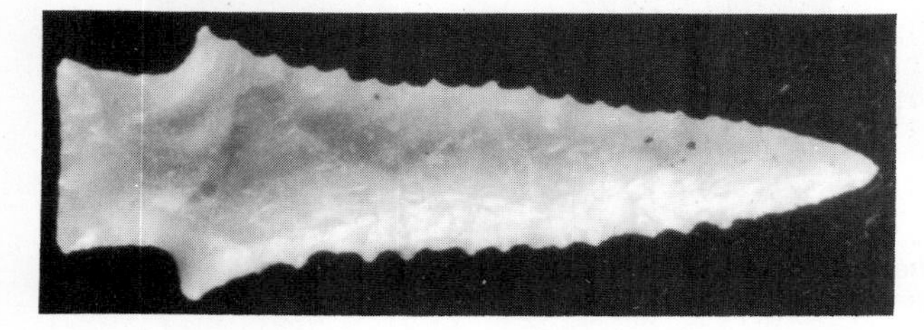

G10, $180-$300
Austin, TX.

BRAZOS (continued)

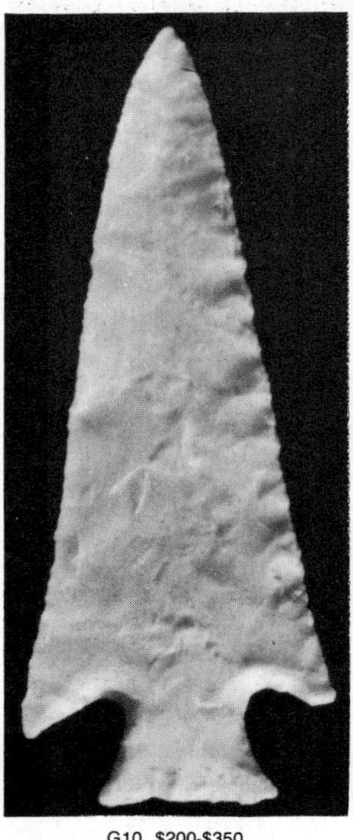

G10, $200-$350
Austin, TX.

G8, $45-$80
Comanche Co., Tx. Note left-hand bevel on blade. Base nick.

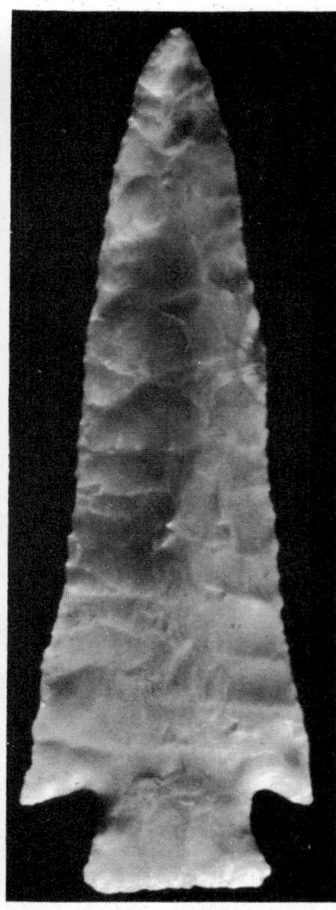

G10, $250-$400
Austin, TX. Note collateral flaking.

BRECKENRIDGE (See Dalton-Breckenridge)

BREWERTON CORNER-NOTCHED - Mid to late Archaic, 6000 - 4000 B.P.

(Also see Autauga)

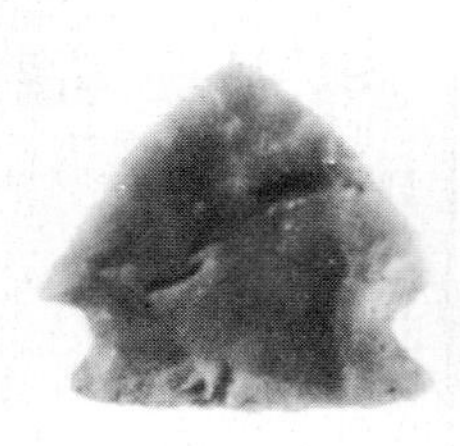

G2, $1-$3
SE TN.

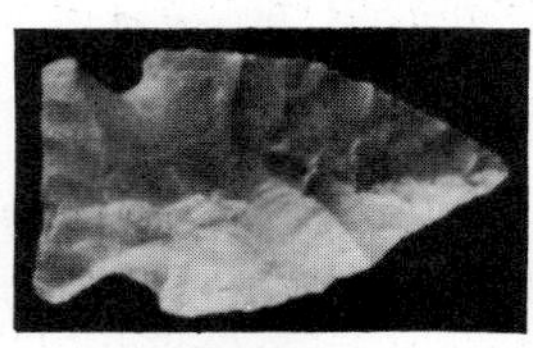

G5, $5-$10
Bethany WV.

G8, $12-$20
N. AL.

LOCATION: Southeastern states. **DESCRIPTION:** A small size, triangular point with faint corner notches and a concave base. Called *Freeheley* in Michigan. **I.D. KEY:** Width, thickness.

BREWERTON CORNER-NOTCHED (continued)

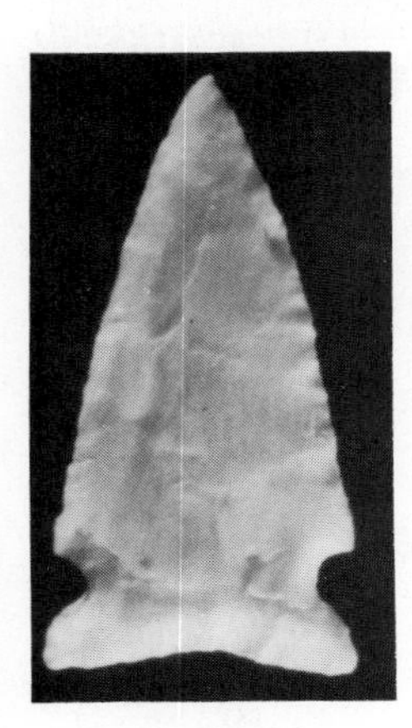

G8, $25-$30
MO.

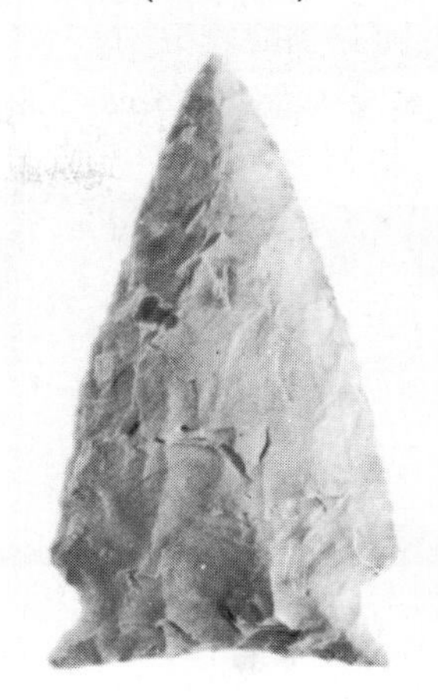

G10, $35-$45
Humphreys Co., TN.

G6, $10-$15
MO.

BREWERTON, EARED-TRIANGULAR - Mid to late Archaic, 6000 - 4000 B.P.

(Also see Autauga & Yadkin)

G8, $5-$7
Cent. PA.

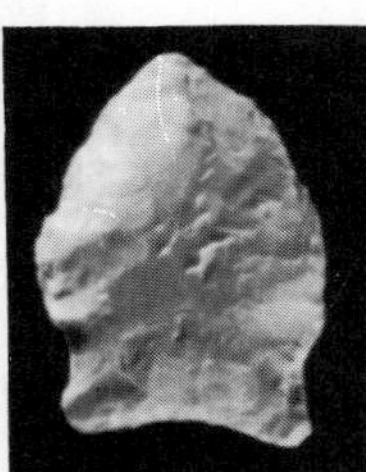

G2, .50-$1
NE AL.

G7, $3-$5
Autauga Co., AL.

G4, $1-$2
Dunlap, TN.

G5, $1-$3
Walker Co., AL.

G3, .50-$1.25
Harrison Co., IN

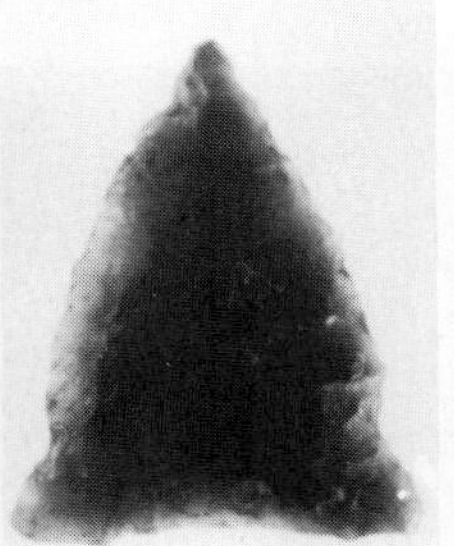

G10, $12-$20
SE TN.

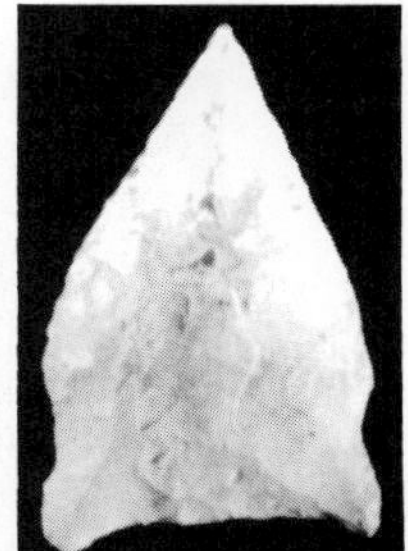

G9, $6-$12
AR.

LOCATION: Southeastern states. **DESCRIPTION:** A small size, triangular, eared, point with a concave base.

BREWERTON SIDE-NOTCHED - Mid to late Archaic, 6000 - 4000 B.P.

(Also see Autauga, Big Sandy & Ecusta)

G3, $1-$2
Chickamauga, GA.

G3, $1-$3
Harrison Co., IN.

G4, $1-$3
Seymor, IN.

G4, $2-$4
Harrison Co., IN.

G3, .75-$1.25
Harrison Co., IN.

G8, $5-$10
OH.

G4, $2-$4
Waco, TX.

G4, $1-$3
Dinwiddie Co., VA.

LOCATION: Southeastern states. **DESCRIPTION:** A small size, triangular point with shallow side notches and a concave base.

BROAD RIVER - Woodland, 3000 - 1500 B.P.

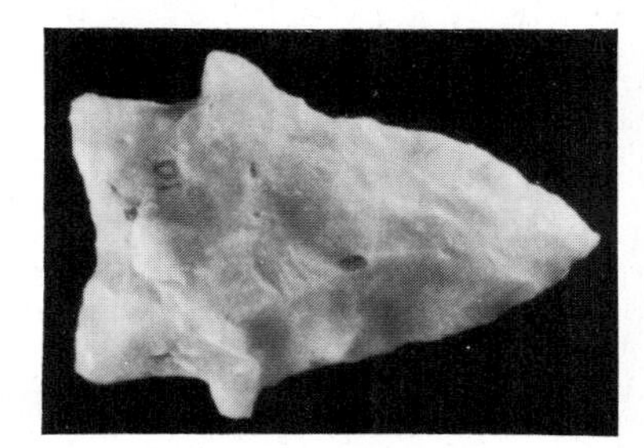

G7, $8-$12
Beaufort Co., SC.

LOCATION: Southern Southeastern states. **DESCRIPTION:** A small size, thick point with small shoulder barbs, a parallel sided stem and a straight to concave base.

BROWARD - Woodland to Mississippian, 2000 - 800 B.P.

(Also see Bradford)

G3, $10-$20
Seminole Co., GA.

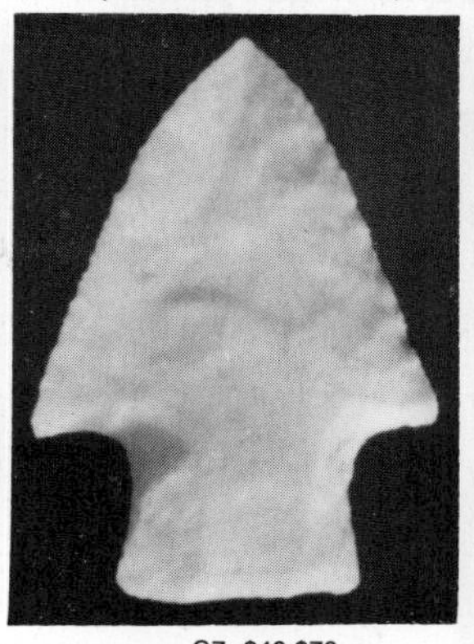

G7, $40-$70
Pasco Co., FL.

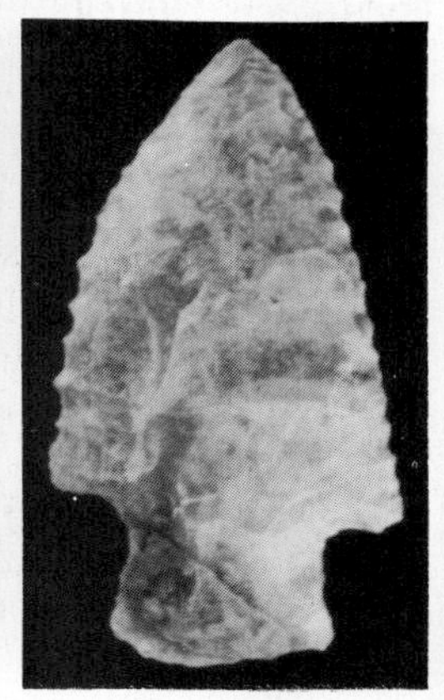

G5, $25-$40
Hillsborough Co., FL.

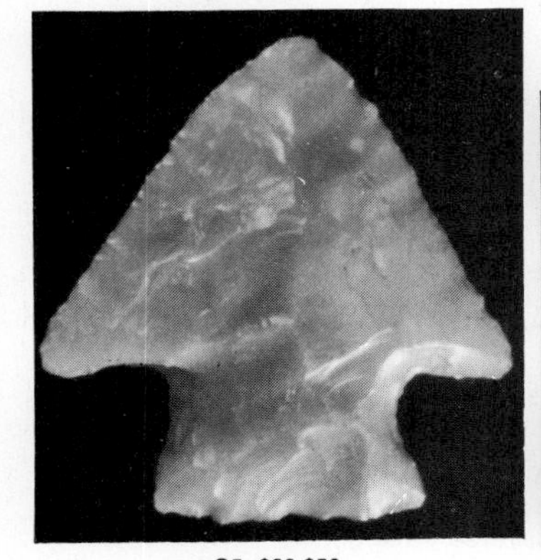

G5, $30-$50
Madison Co., FL.

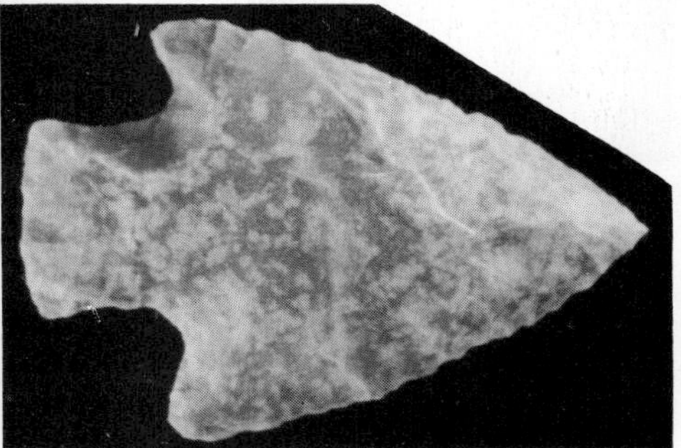

G8, $45-$80
Silver Lake, FL.

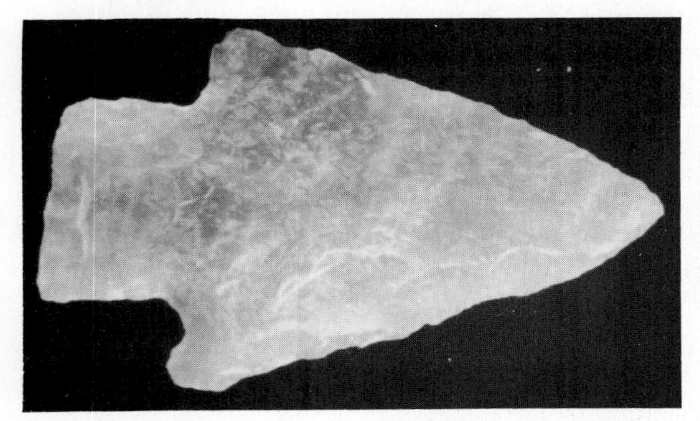

G4, $20-$30
Pasco Co., FL.

LOCATION: Southern Southeastern states. **DESCRIPTION:** A medium to large size triangular point with tapered to square shoulders and a short expanding base. The base can be straight, concave or convex. Basal corners can be sharp to rounded. **I.D. KEY:** High and low barbs.

BROWNS VALLEY - Transitional Paleo, 10000 - 8000 B.P.

(Also see Agate Basin, Allen, Angostura, Clovis, Midland, Plainview & Sedalia)

G6, $100-$180
Cent. IL. Note oblique parallel flaking which is characteristic of the type.

G7, $150-$250
Morgan Co., AL. Note oblique flaking & steeply beveled base.

G8, $350-$500
NE AR. Translucent Knife River flint. Note excellent oblique flaking.

LOCATION: Midwestern states. **DESCRIPTION:** A medium to large, thin, lanceolate blade with usually oblique to horizontal transverse flaking and a concave to straight base which can be ground. **I.D. KEY:** Paleo transverse flaking.

BUCK CREEK - Mid to late Archaic, 6000 - 3500 B.P.

(Also see Hamilton, Motley, Smithsonia, Table Rock and Wade)

G4, $25-$40
Humphreys Co., TN., Dover chert

G5, $35-$60
Humphreys Co., TN., Dover chert.

LOCATION: Kentucky and surrounding states. **DESCRIPTION:** A large, thin, broad, stemmed point with strong barbs and high quality flaking. Some have needle tips, blade edges are convex to recurved. Blade width can be narrow to broad. **I.D. KEY:** Barb expansion and notching.

BUCK CREEK (continued)

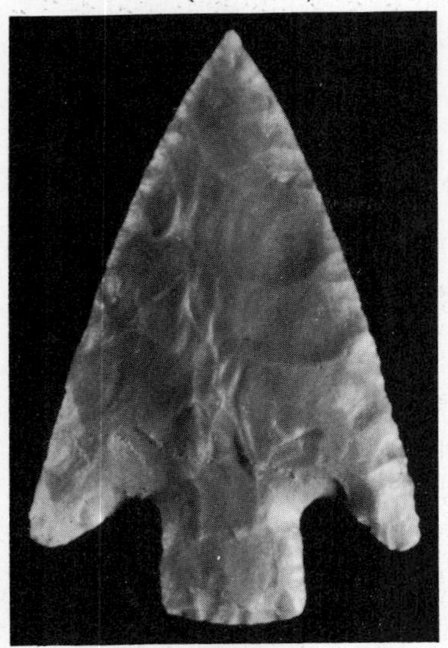

G8, $80-$150
Livingston Co., KY.

G7, $35-$65
Mid-TN.

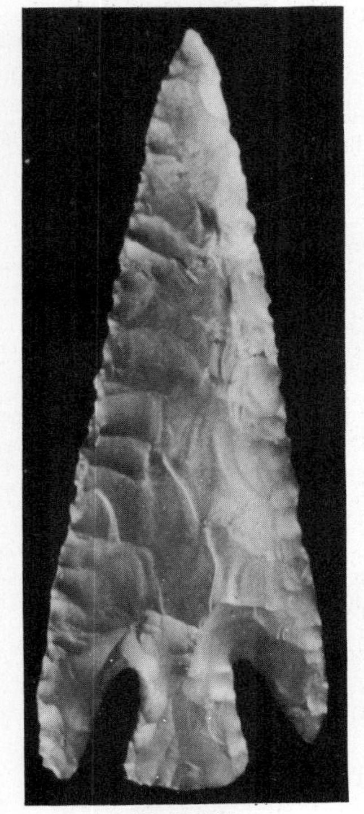

G8, $70-$110
Hendersonville, TN.

G7, $75-$90
Livingston Co., KY.

G10, $250-$400
Humphreys Co., TN.

G8, $150-$250
Humphreys Co., TN. Dover chert.

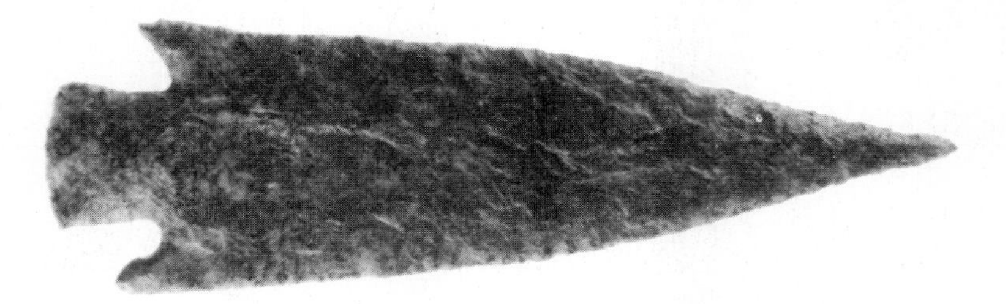

G10, $1200-$1800, Dickson Cave, KY. One of a chache of four.

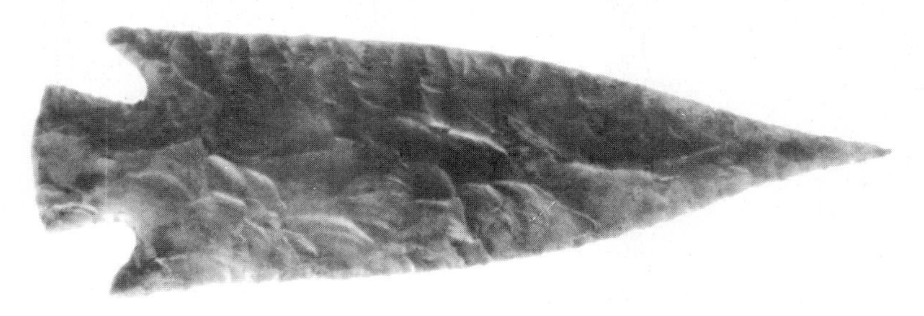

G10, $2000-$3500, Dickson Cave, KY. One of a cache of four.

BUGGS ISLAND - Late Archaic, 5500 - 3500 B.P.

(Also see Dallas, Ebenezer and Langtry)

G3, $1-$3
Bristol, TN.

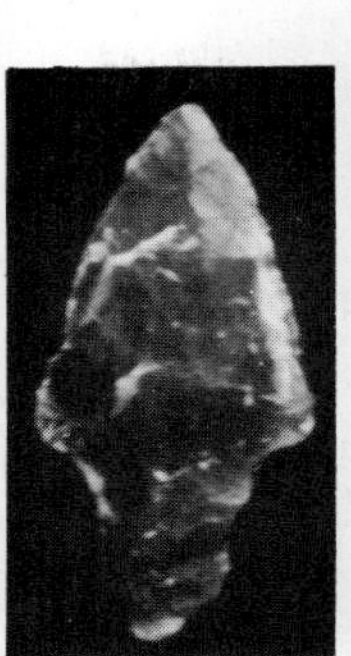

G2, $1-$2
Bristol, TN.

G3, $1-$3
Dunlap, TN.

G4, $2-$3
Florence, AL.

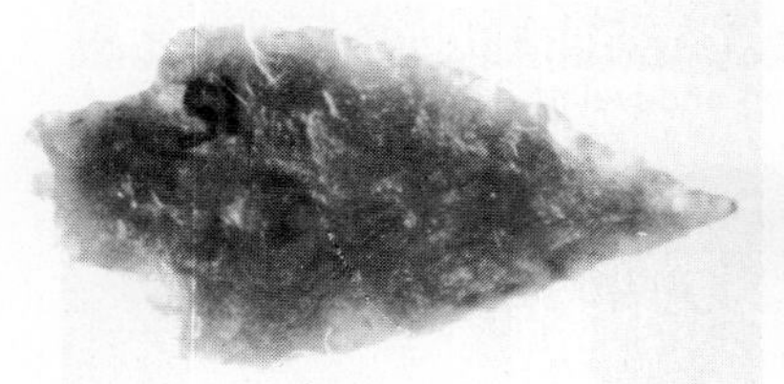

G5, $3-$5
Meigs Co., TN.

G6, $4-$6
S.E. TN.

LOCATION: Eastern states. **DESCRIPTION:** A small to medium size point with a contracting stem and tapered shoulders. The base is usually straight.

BULBAR STEMMED - Mississippian, 1000 - 500 B.P.

(Also see Bonham)

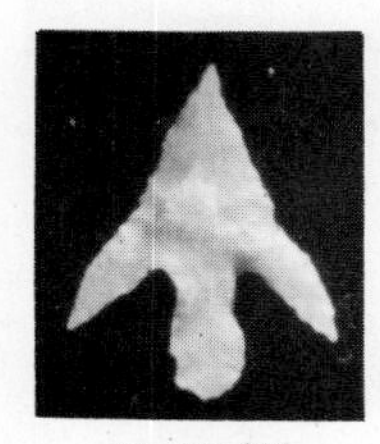

G6, $25-$45
Comanche Co., TX.

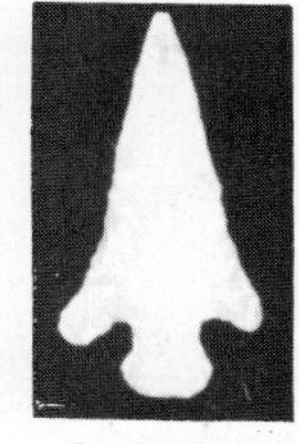

G4, $12-$20
Clearwater Co., ID.

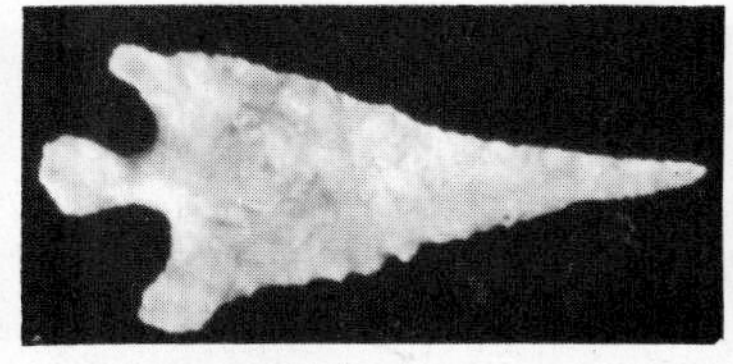

G7, $30-$50
Comanche Co., TX.

LOCATION: Midwestern states. **DESCRIPTION:** A small size, very thin, barbed point with a bulbous base. Blade edges are sometimes finely serrated. **I.D. KEY:** Extended bulbous base.

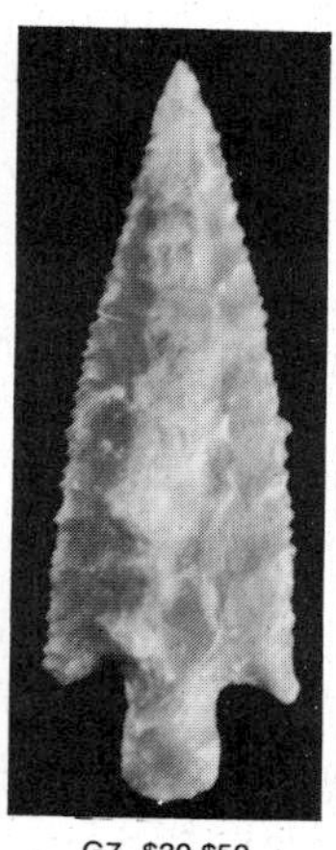
G7, $30-$50
Cent. TX.

G9, $60-$100
Cent. TX. Very thin with arch blade. Excellent quality.

G10, $120-$200
Cent. TX. Excellent.

BULVERDE - Mid-Archaic to Woodland, 5000 - 1000 B.P.

(Also see Carrolton and Delhi)

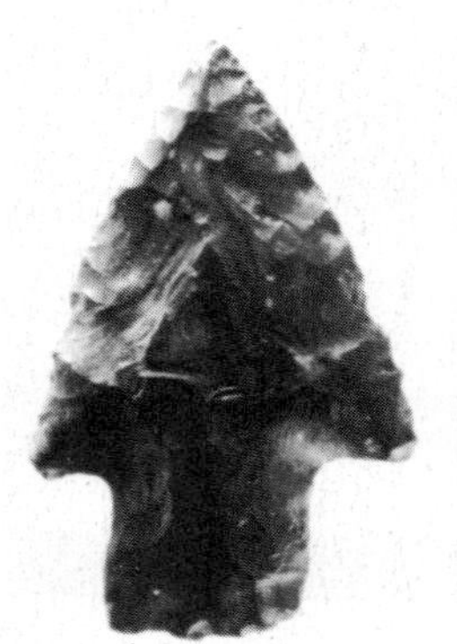
G3, $3-$5
Comanche Co., TX.

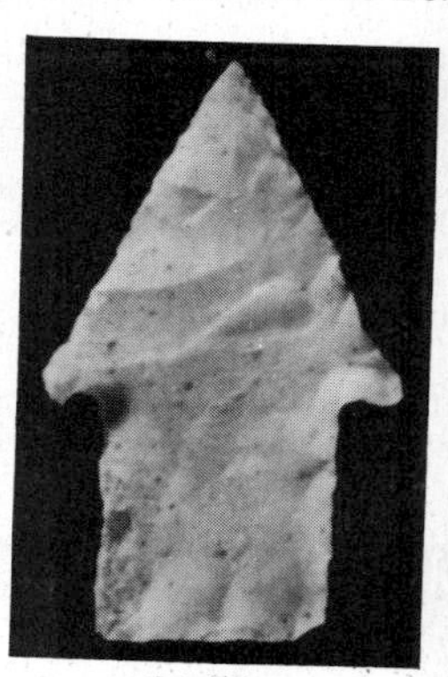
G4, $7-$8
Cent. TX.

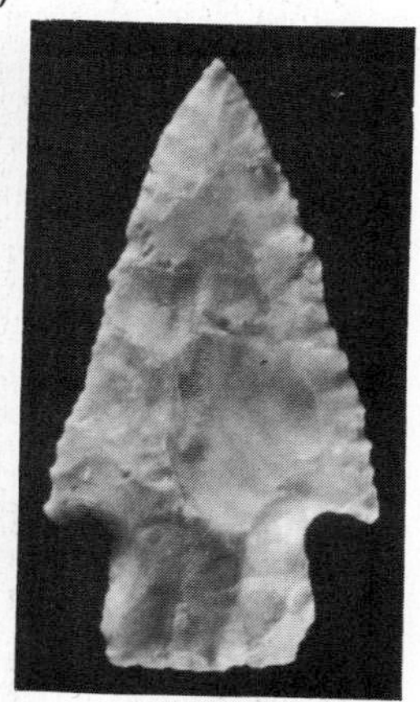
G5, $6-$10
Comanche Co., TX.

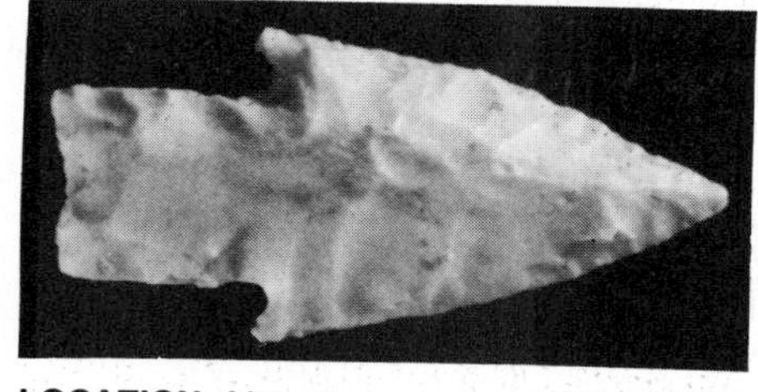
G6, $10-$20
Comanche Co., TX.

LOCATION: Midwestern states. **DESCRIPTION:** A medium size, long rectangular stemmed point with usually barbed shoulders. Believed to be related to *Carrolton*. **I.D. KEY:** Squared base and barbs.

BULVERDE (continued)

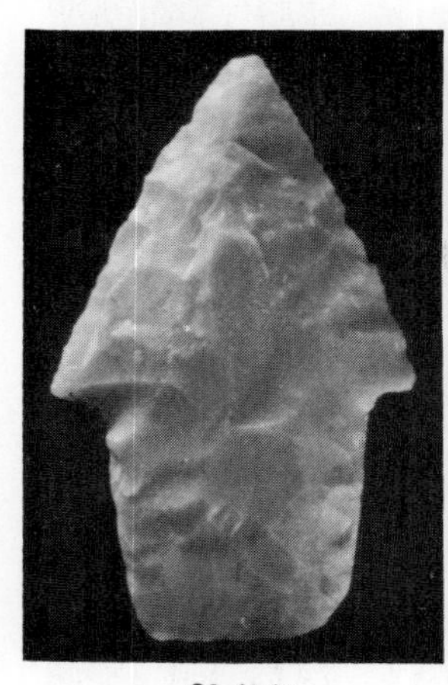

G3, $3-$5
Comanche Co., TX.

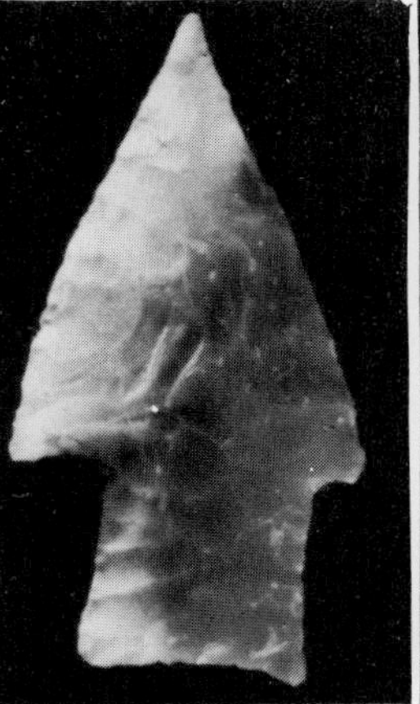

G4, $5-$8
Austin, TX.

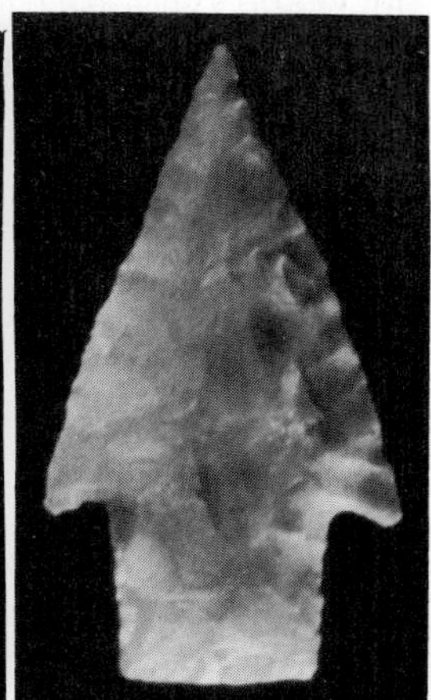

G8, $35-$50
Bell Co., TX.

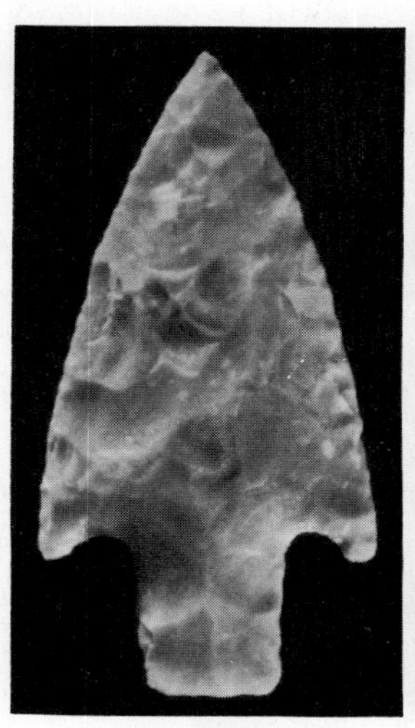

G8, $25-$40
Comanche Co., TX.

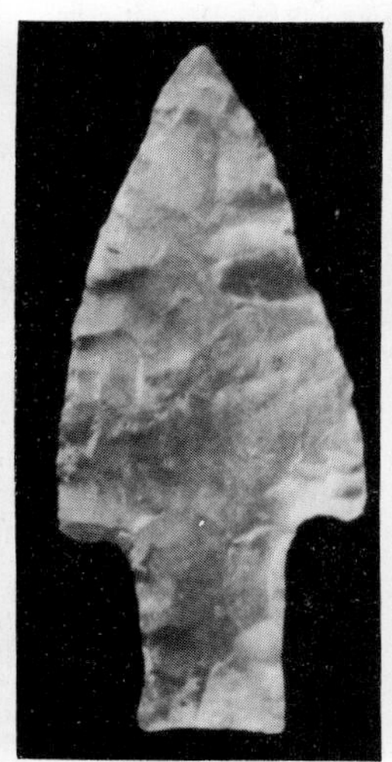

G4, $5-$8
Bell Co., TX.

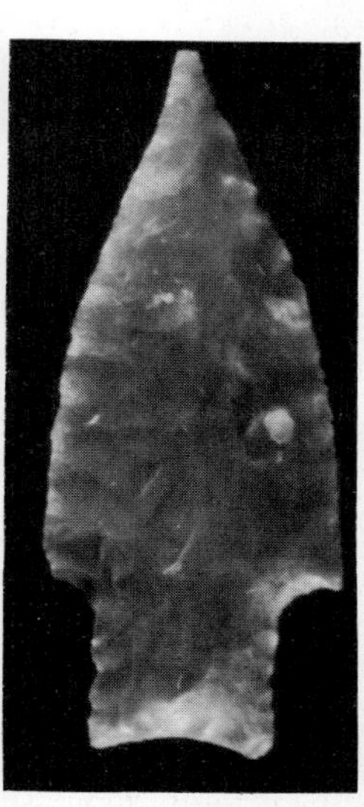

G4, $5-$8
Bell Co., TX.

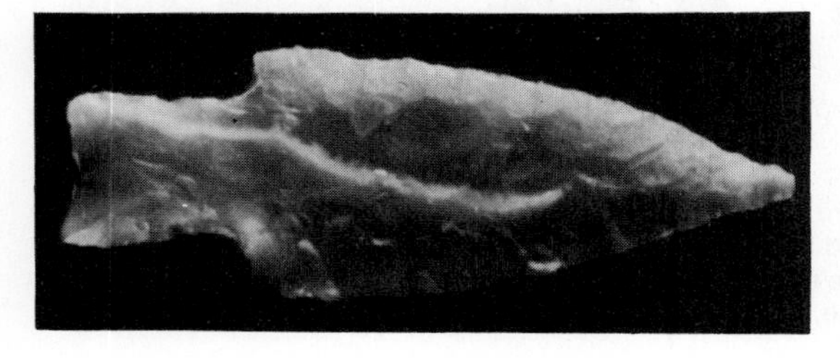

G5, $8-$12
Travis Co., TX.,

BULVERDE (continued)

G7, $15-$25
Comanche Co., TX.

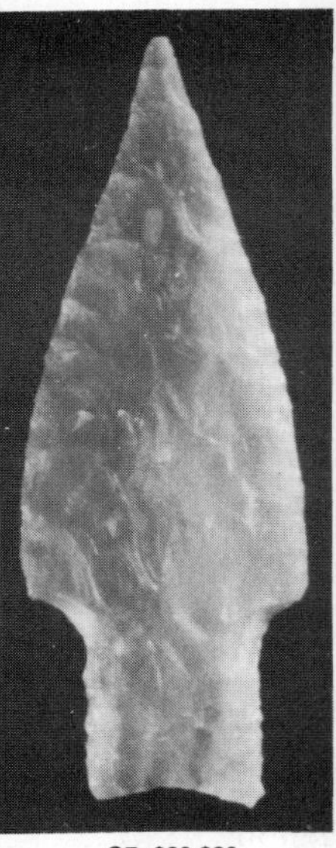
G7, $20-$30
Comanche Co., TX.

G6, $10-$20
Comanche Co., TX.

BUZZARD ROOST CREEK - Early to mid-Archaic 6000 - 4000 B.P.

(Also see Arredondo, Benton, Kirk Serrated and Southampton)

G2, $3-$4
Marion Co., TN.

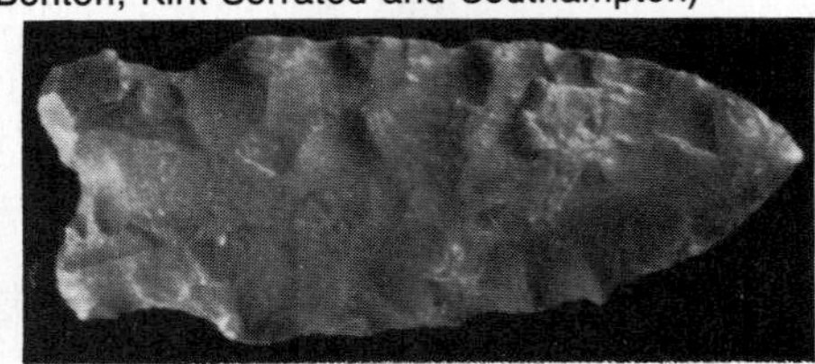
G3, $4-$5
Meigs Co., TN.

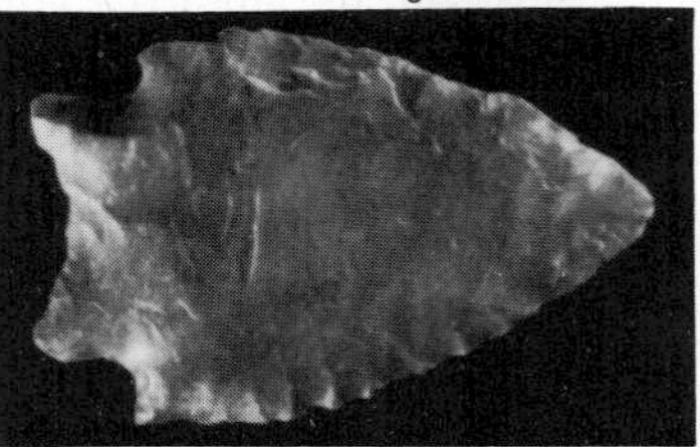
G4, $6-$10
Meigs Co., TN.

LOCATION: Southeastern states. **DESCRIPTION:** A medium to large size, stemmed point with a bifurcated base. Believed to be related to the *Benton* point. Found in Arkansas with the blade steeply beveled on one side of each face (transition form?). **I.D. KEY:** Bifurcated base, width of base found with *Benton* points. A notched base *Benton*.

BUZZARD ROOST CREEK (continued)

G3, $2-$5
N. AL.

G2, $2-$4
Dallas Co., AL. Hematite.

G4, $8-$10
Humphreys Co., TN.

G5, $10-$15
Decatur, AL.

G4, $6-$10
Hamilton Co., IL.

G7, $45-$80
Florence, AL. Coffee Lake.

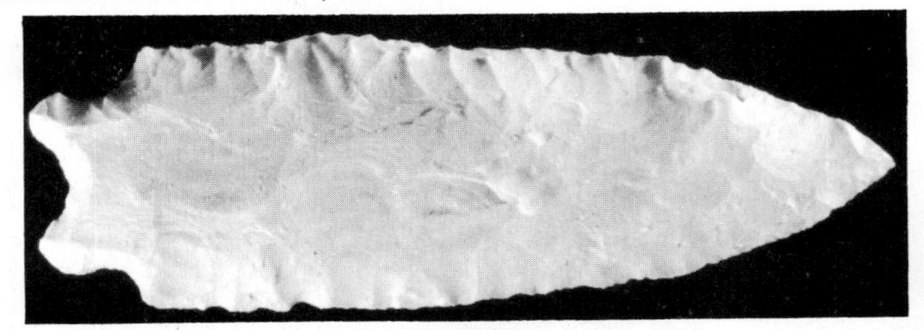

G7, $40-$70
Giles Co., TN.

G7, $45-$80
Florence, AL. Fort Payne chert.

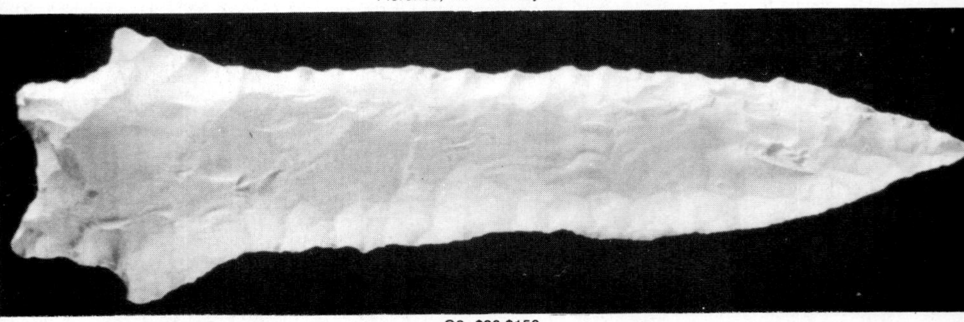

G8, $90-$150
Hardin Co., TN.

G8, $120-$150
Parsons, TN.

G10, $450-$700
Clifton, TN. Outstanding high quality example. Found with a Benton of equal quality and size.

G10, $400-$750
Marshall Co., AL. Colorful chert.

CACHE RIVER - Early to mid-Archaic, 8000 - 5000 B.P.

(Also see Big Sandy, Bolen Plain, Graham Cave, Knight Island and Rowan)

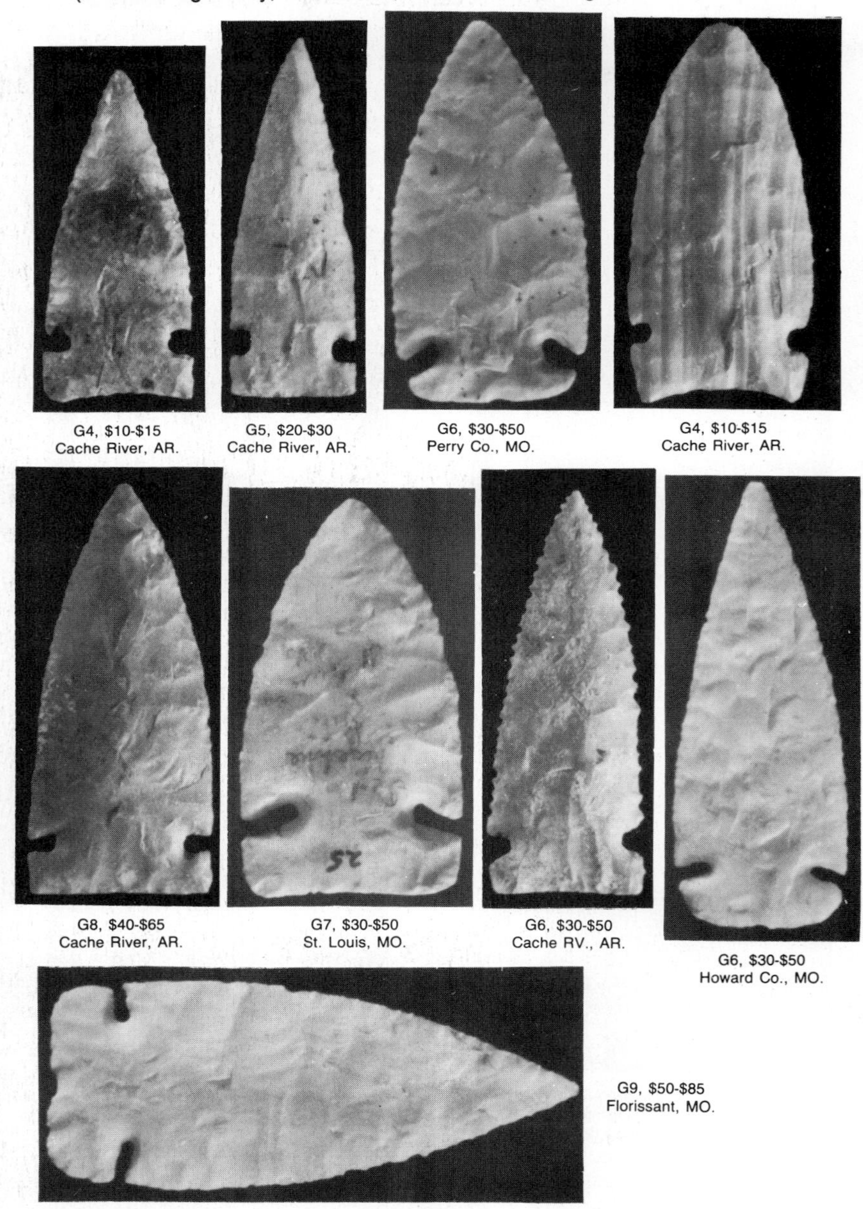

G4, $10-$15
Cache River, AR.

G5, $20-$30
Cache River, AR.

G6, $30-$50
Perry Co., MO.

G4, $10-$15
Cache River, AR.

G8, $40-$65
Cache River, AR.

G7, $30-$50
St. Louis, MO.

G6, $30-$50
Cache RV., AR.

G6, $30-$50
Howard Co., MO.

G9, $50-$85
Florissant, MO.

LOCATION: Midwestern states. **DESCRIPTION:** A small to medium size, fairly thin, side-notched, triangular point with a concave base. Could be related to *Big Sandy* points. **I.D. KEY:** Base form, narrow notched & flaking of blade.

CADDOAN BLADE - Mississippian, 800 - 600 B.P.

(Also see Adena Blade)

G9, $600-$1000
Little River Co., AR. Excellent example.

LOCATION: Midwestern states on Caddo culture sites. **DESCRIPTION:** A large size, thin, double pointed, elliptical, ceremonial blade with serrated edges. Examples with basal side notches have been found in Texas. Beware of fakes. **I.D. KEY:** Edgework, flaking style on blade.

G9, $800-$1500
Little River Co., AR. Outstanding example.

CAHOKIA - Mississippian, 1000 - 500 B.P.

(Also see Desert, Harrell, Reed and Washita)

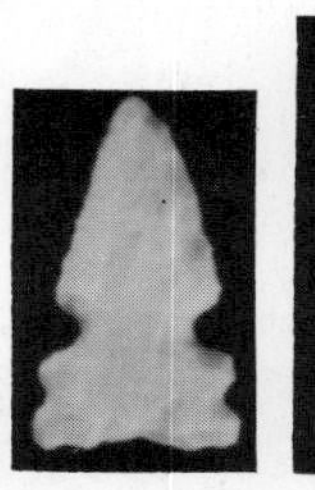
G4, $25-$40
IL.

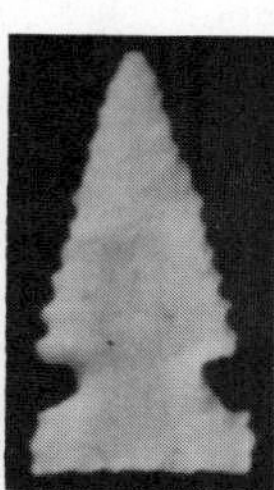
G5, $30-$50
IL.

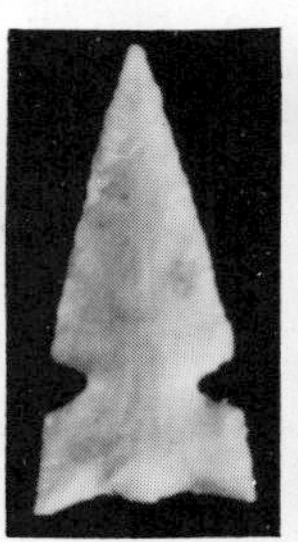
G6, $60-$100
Cahokia, IL.

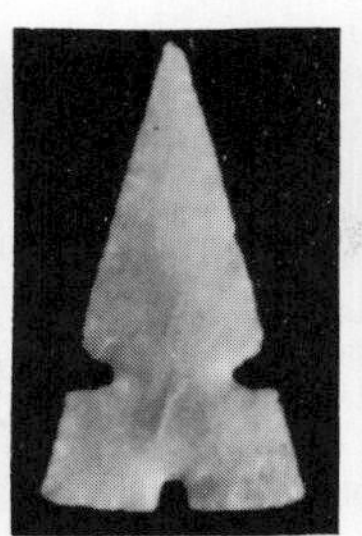
G6, $60-$100
Cahokia, IL.

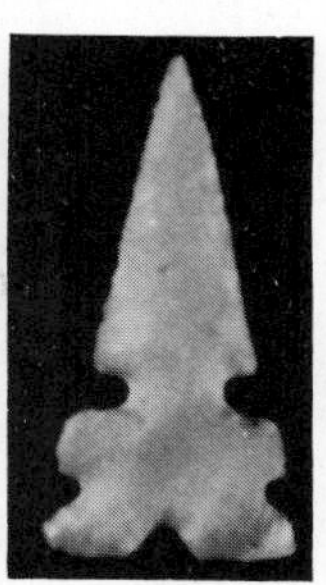
G8, $150-$250
Cent. IL.

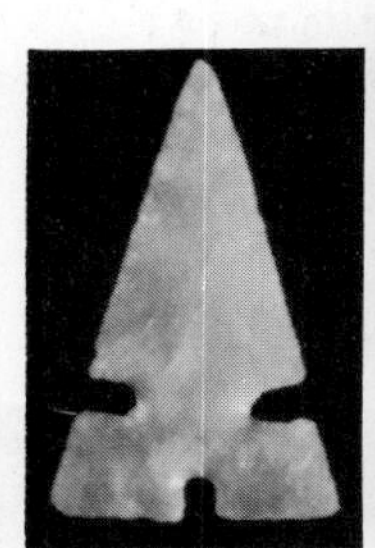
G7, $90-$150
Cahokia, IL.

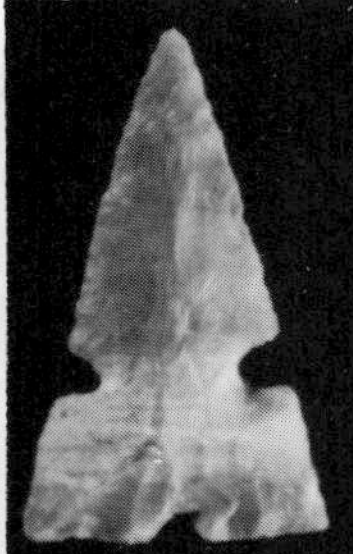
G6, $60-$100
Cahokia, IL.

G6, $60-$100
Cent. IL.

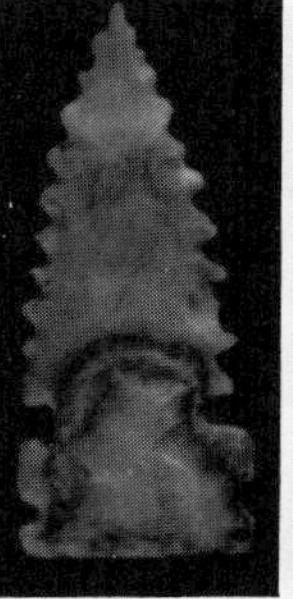
G8, $150-$250
Cent. IL.

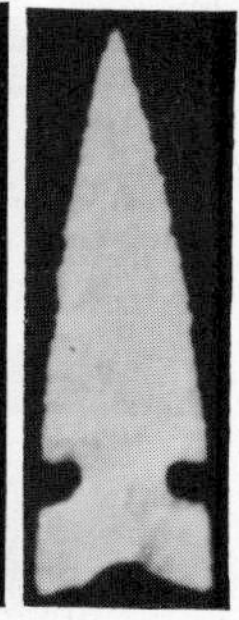
G7, $100-$200
Spiro Mound, OK.

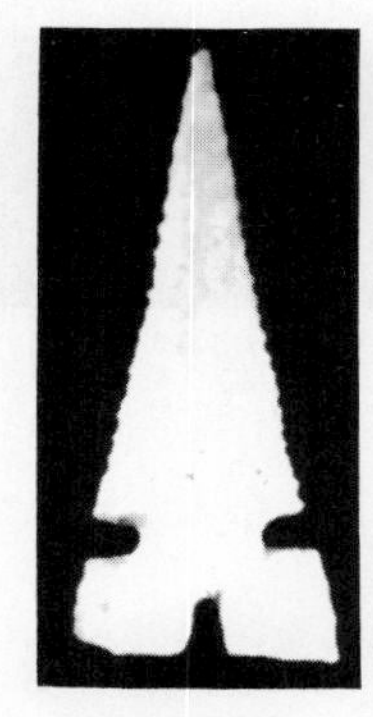
G5, $45-$70
Cent. IL.

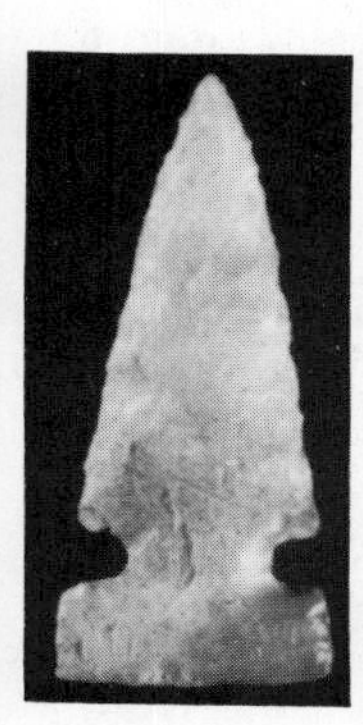
G6, $60-$100
Cent. IL.

G5, $30-$60
Cent. IL.

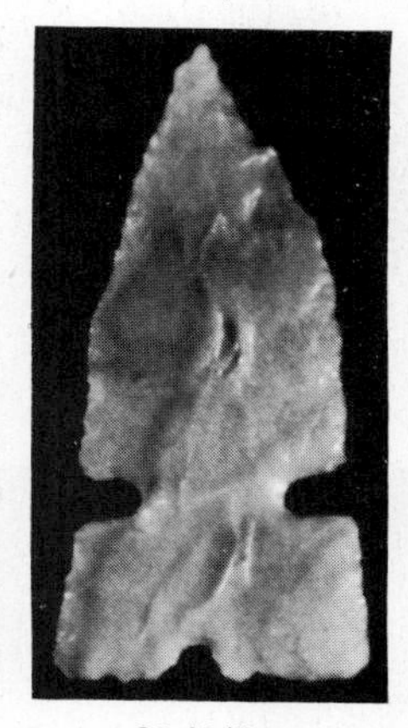
G3, $2-$5
Cent. IL. Blade nicks.

LOCATION: Midwestern states. The famous Cahokia mounds are located in Illinois. **DESCRIPTION:** A small to medium size, thin, triangular point that can have one or more notches on each blade edge. The base is either plain or has a center notch. Associated with the Caddo culture.

CALAPOOIA - Mississippian, 1000 - 600 B.P.

(Also see Rogue River & Rogue River U-Back)

G2, $5-$8

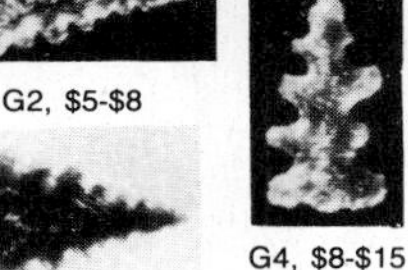

G2, $5-$8

G4, $8-$15
Fern Leaf

G5, $10-$20
Fern Leaf

(Lane Co., OR.)

G4, $10-$15
Fern Leaf

G4, $8-$15

G4, $8-$15

(Lane Co., OR.)

G4, $8-$15

G9, $35-$60

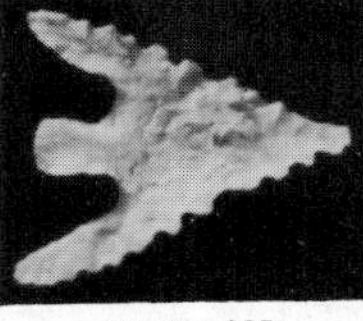

G7, $20-$35

(Lane Co., OR.)

G7, $20-$35
Wasco Co., OR.

LOCATION: Northwestern states. **DESCRIPTION:** A small size, thin dart point with serrated to strongly barbed blade edges. Stems are short and slightly expanding and shoulders are strong. The barbed edge variant is call a *Fern Leaf* point.

CALF CREEK - Early to mid-Archaic, 8000 - 5000 B.P.

(Also see Andice)

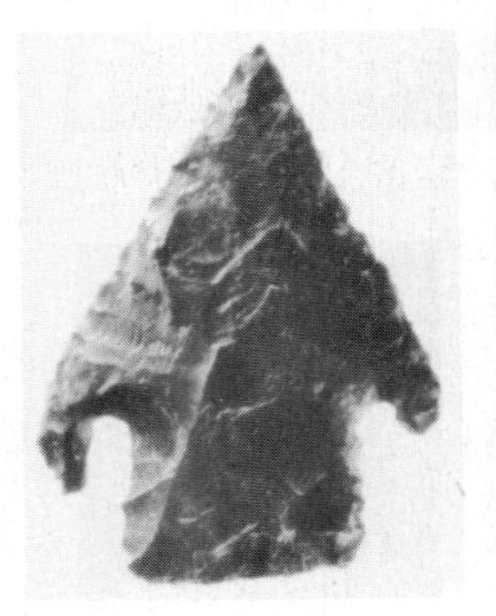

G2, $25-$35
AR.

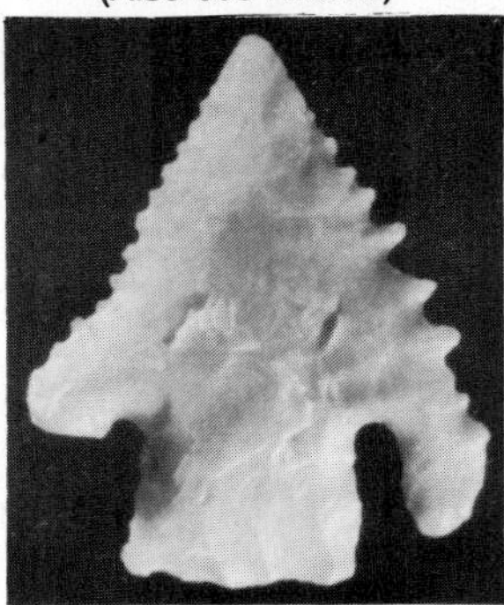

G2, $25-$35
TX/AR. Broken tang.

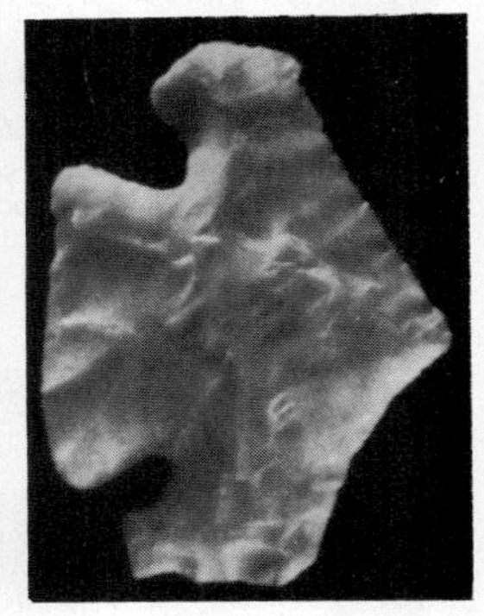

G1, $15-$25
MO.

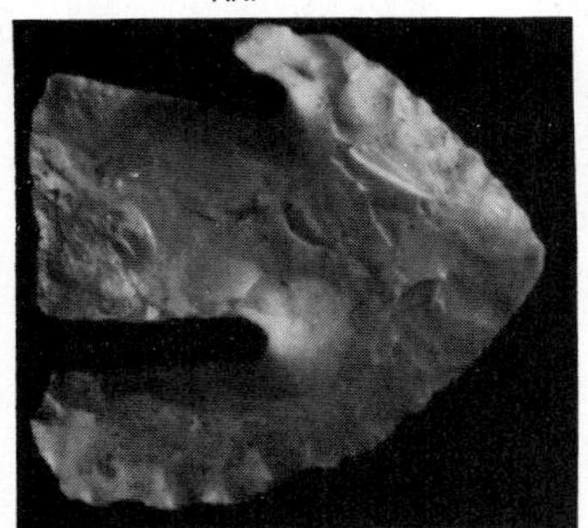

G2, $20-$35
MO. Broken tang.

G2, $25-$35
TX/AR. Broken tang.

CALF CREEK (continued)

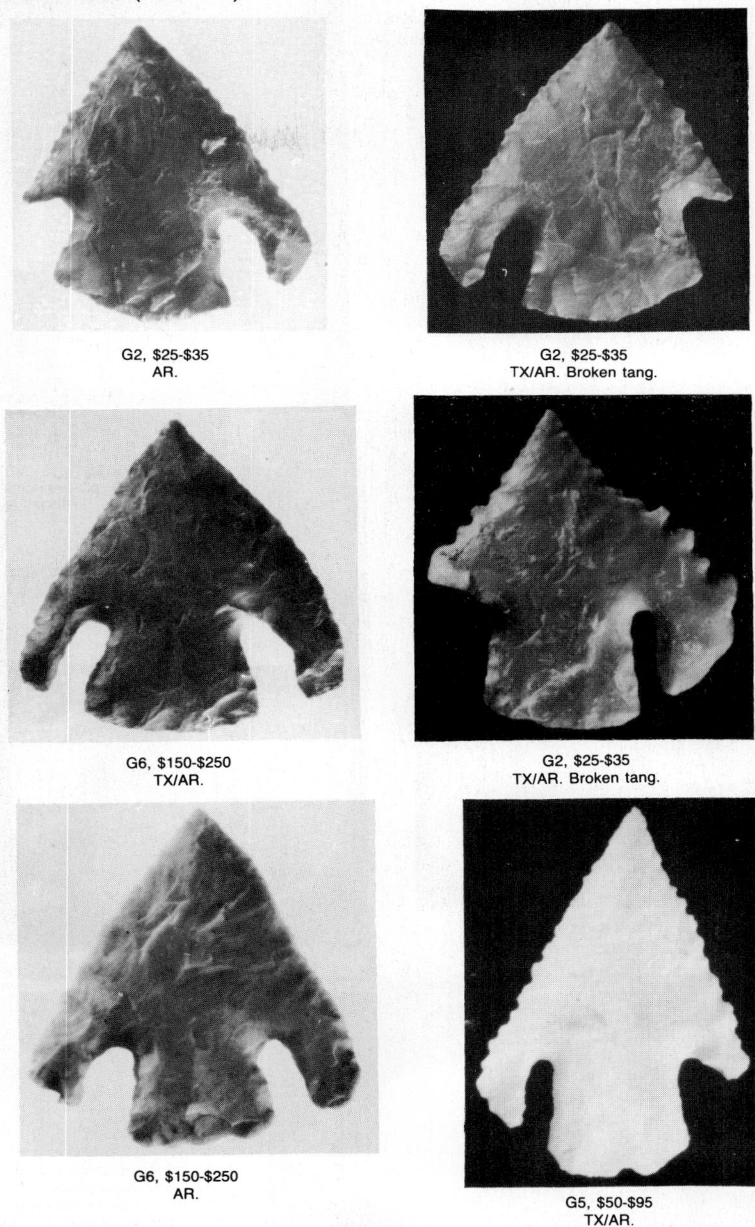

G2, $25-$35
AR.

G2, $25-$35
TX/AR. Broken tang.

G6, $150-$250
TX/AR.

G2, $25-$35
TX/AR. Broken tang.

G6, $150-$250
AR.

G5, $50-$95
TX/AR.

LOCATION: Midwestern states. **DESCRIPTION:** A medium to large size, thin, triangular point with very deep parallel basal notches. Large examples would fall under the *Andice* type while small examples are called *Bell* points. Very rare in type area. **I.D. KEY:** Notches almost straight up.

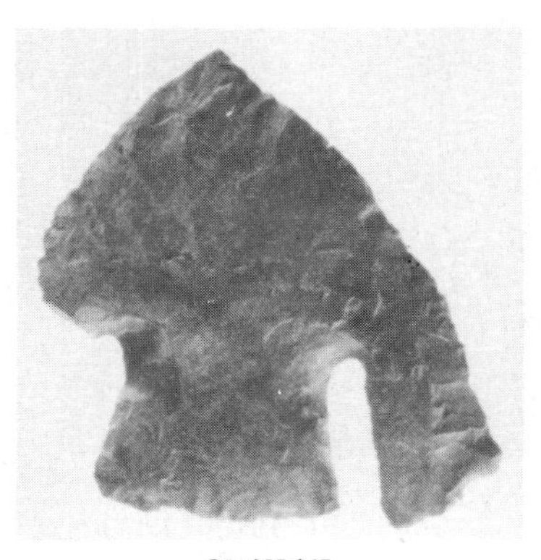

G3, $35-$45
AR. Broken tang.

G5, $50-$90
AR. Type site.

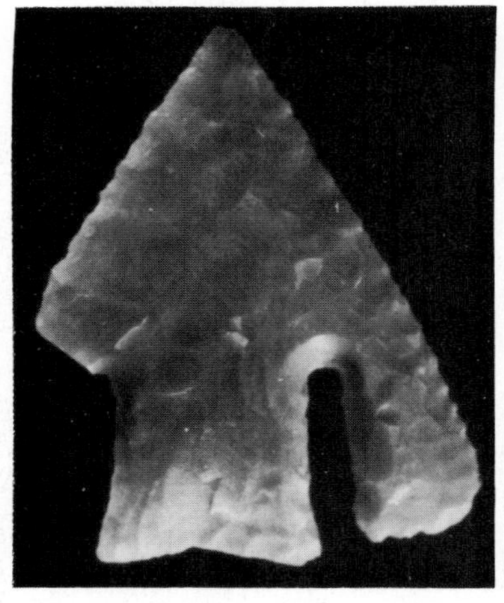

G4, $40-$65
TX. Broken tang.

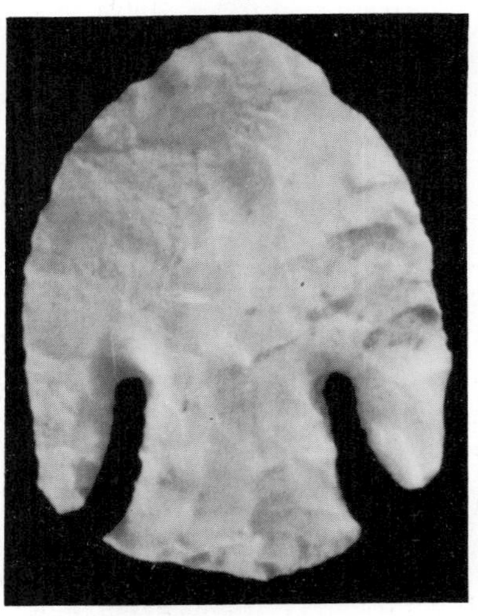

G6, $100-$180
TX/AR.

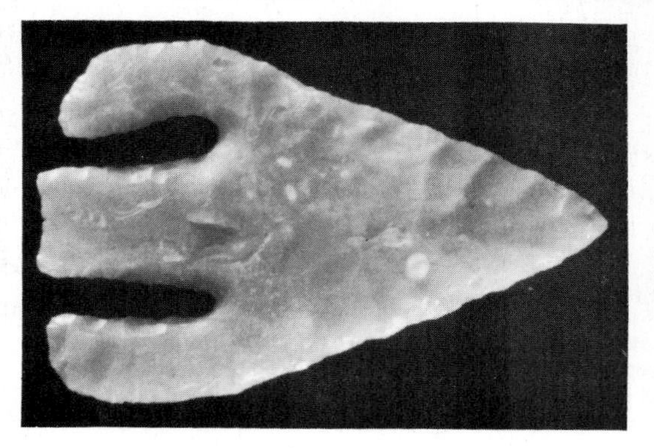

G10, $2000-$3500
Comanche Co., TX. Excellent quality and thinness. Hard to find complete and unsharpened with wings flaring in toward the base. Best example we've seen.

G8, $400-$550
AR. Type site.

G5, $50-$90
Yell Co., AR. Broken wing.

CAMP CREEK - Woodland, 3000 - 1500 B.P.

(Also see Greeneville, Hamilton, Madison, Nolichucky and Yadkin)

G2, .50-$1
Parsons, TN.

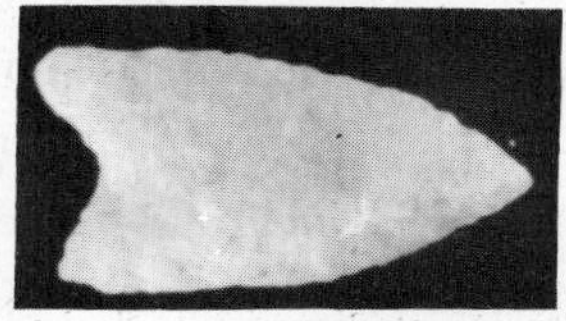

G3, $1-$2
Autauga Co., AL.

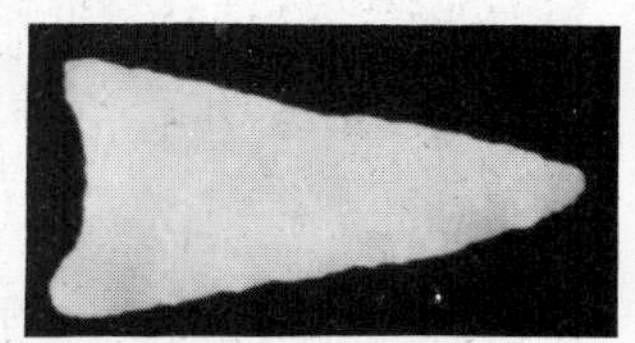

G3, $1-$2
Montgomery Co., AL.

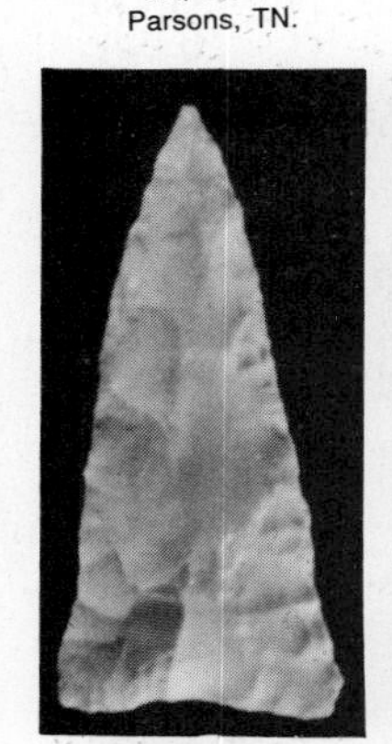

G3, $1-$2
Morgan Co., AL.

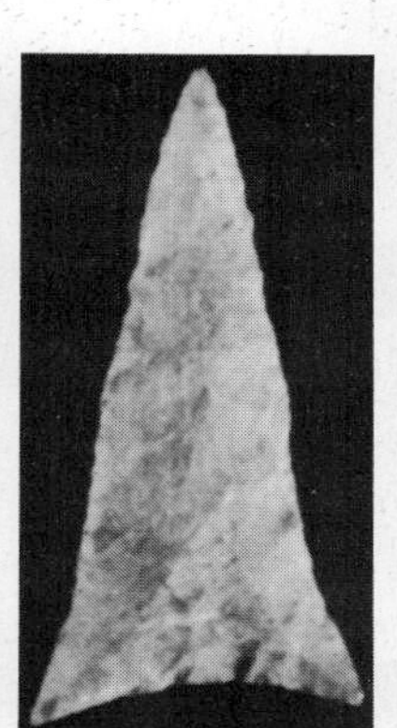

G8, $45-$70
Sevier Co., TN.

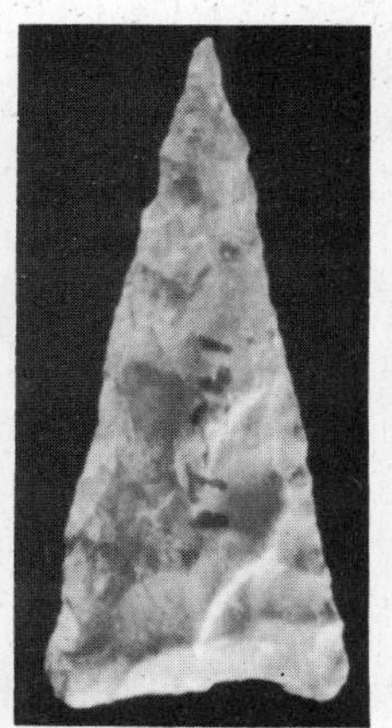

G3, $1-$3
Morgan Co., AL.

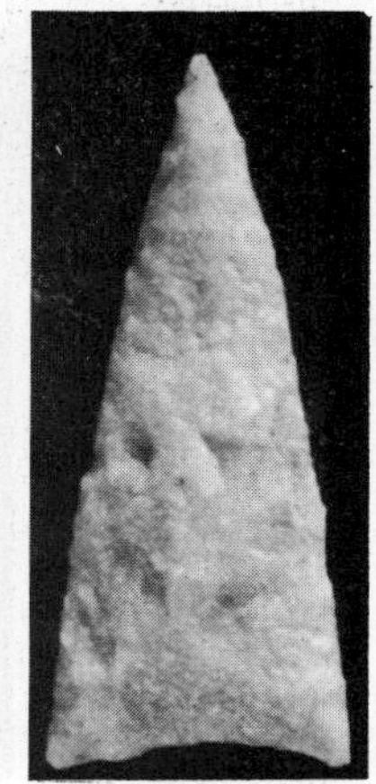

G7, $40-$70
Johnson City, TN. Quartzite.

LOCATION: Southeastern states. **DESCRIPTION:** A small to medium size triangular point with straight to convex sides and a concave base. Believed to have evolved into *Hamilton* points; related to *Greeneville* and *Nolichucky* points. Has been found with *Adena* stemmed in caches (Rankin site, Cocke Co., TN).

CAMP CREEK (continued)

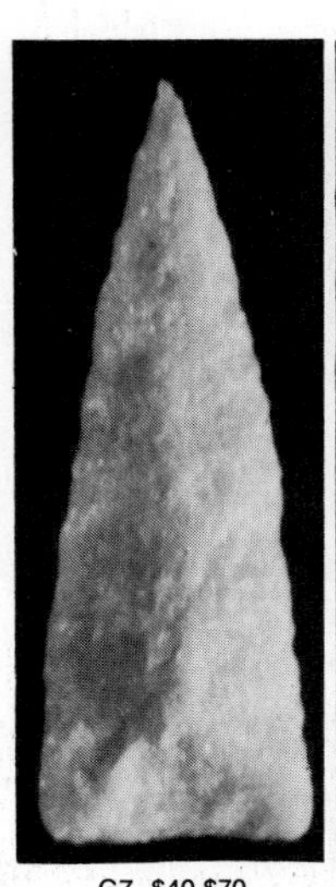

G7, $40-$70
Sevier Co., TN. Quartzite.

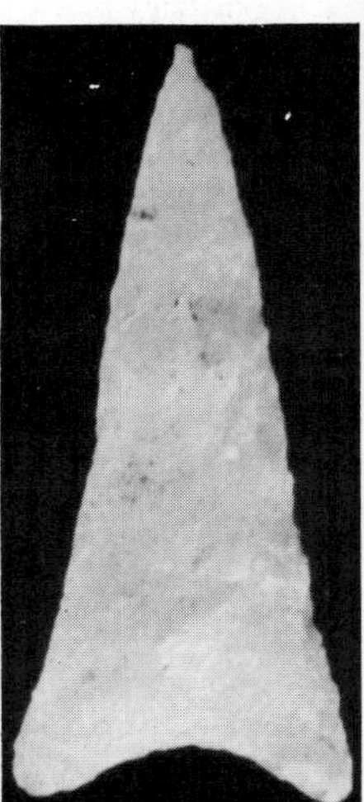

G8, $70-$120
Dayton, TN. Quartzite.

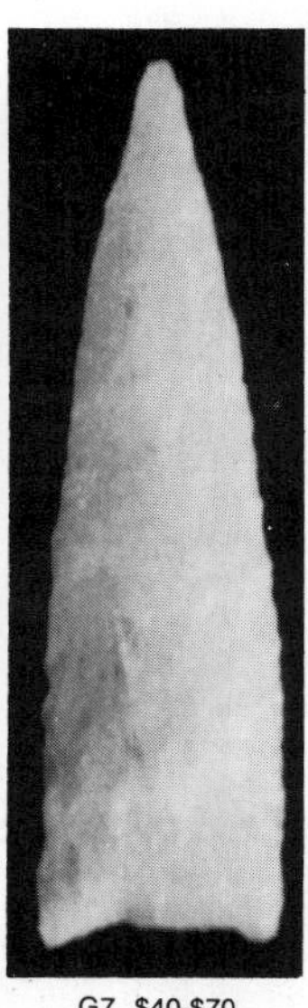

G7, $40-$70
Sevier Co., TN. Quartzite.

G6, $20-$40
Bristol, TN. Black flint.

G6, $15-$35
Bristol, TN. Black flint.

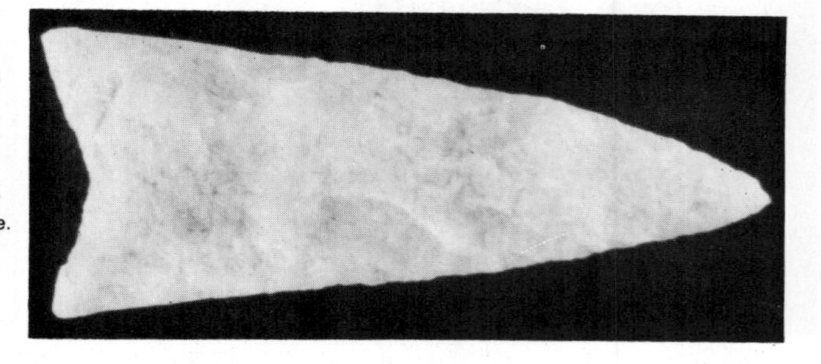

G9, $90-$135
Dayton, TN. Quartzite.

CANDY CREEK - Early Woodland, 3000 - 1500 B.P.

(Also see Beaver Lake, Camp Creek, Copena, Dalton, Nolichucky, Paisano, Quad and Yadkin)

G2, $2-$4
Putnam Co., TN.

G4, $4-$6
Hamilton Co., TN.

G7, $15-$20
Marion Co., TN.

G7, $10-$20
Houston Co., TN.

G8, $25-$35
Marion Co., TN.

G9, $35-$45
Meigs Co., TN.

G7, $10-$20
Dayton, TN.

G9, $30-$45
Dayton, TN.

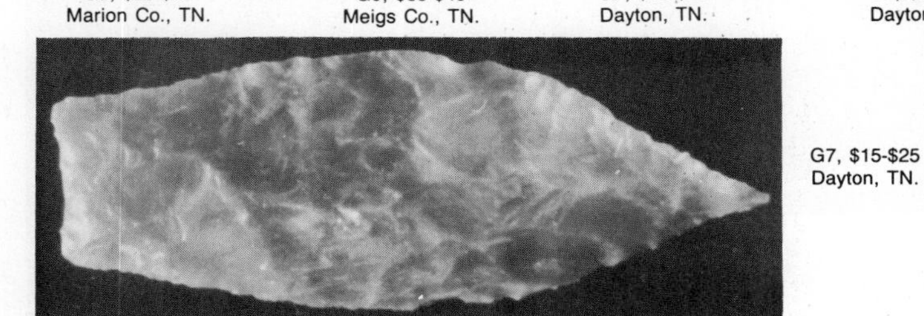

G7, $15-$25
Dayton, TN.

LOCATION: Southeastern states. **DESCRIPTION:** A medium size, lanceolate, eared point with a concave base and recurved blade edges. Bases may be thinned or fluted and lightly ground. Flaking is of the random Woodland type and should not be confused with the earlier auriculate forms that have the parallel flaking. These points are similar to *Cumberland, Beaver Lake, Dalton* and *Quad*, but are shorter and of poorer quality. It is believed that Paleo people survived in East Tennessee to 3,000 B.P., and influenced the style of the *Candy Creek* point. Believed to be related to *Copena, Camp Creek, Ebenezer, Greenville* and *Nolichucky* points. **I.D. KEY:** Ears, thickness and Woodland flaking.

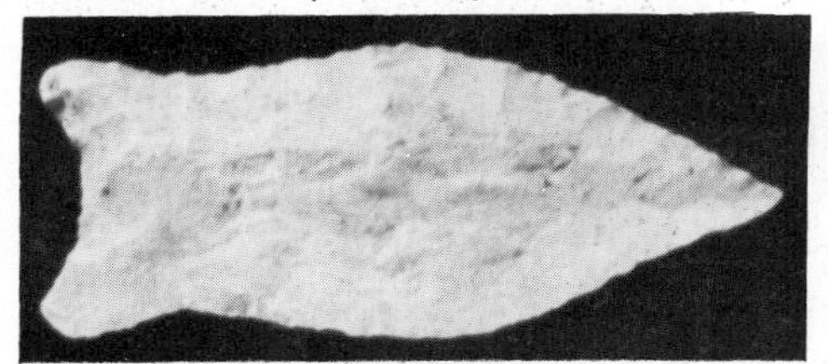

G8, $15-$25
Dayton, TN.

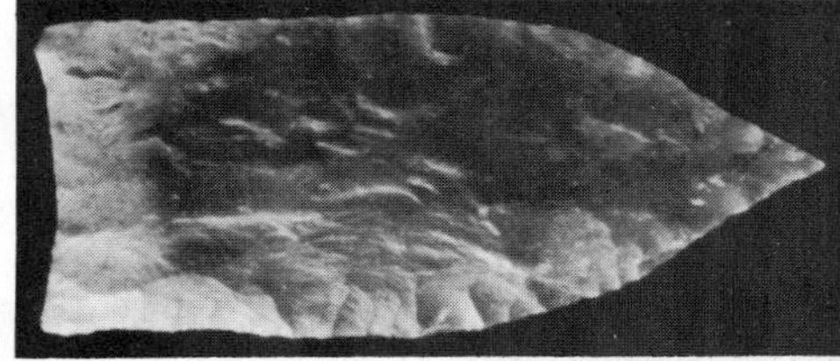

G9, $30-$45
Hamilton Co., TN.

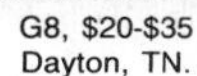

G8, $20-$35
Dayton, TN.

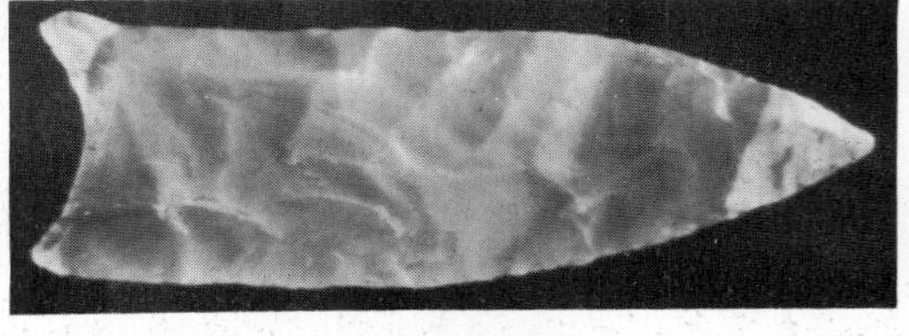

G9, $30-$45
Dayton, TN.

CARRIZO - Mid-Archaic, 7000 - 4000 B.P.

(Also see Limeton Bifurcate, Llano and Tortugas)

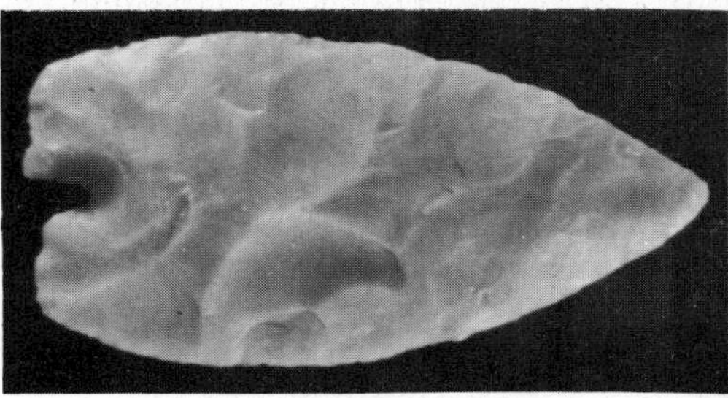

G8, $50-$80
Austin, TX.

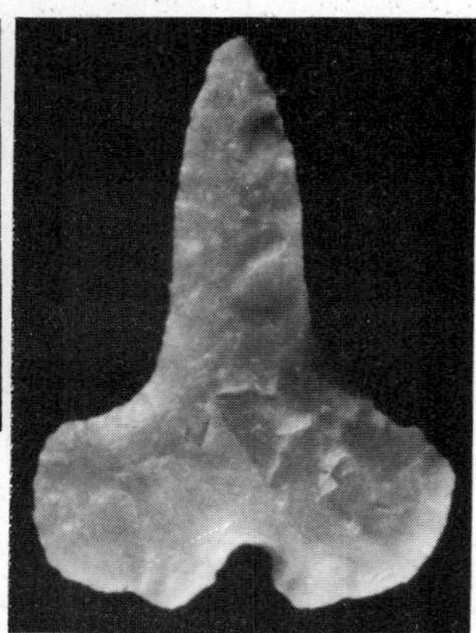

G7, $35-$45
Austin, TX. Drill form.

LOCATION: Midwestern states. **DESCRIPTION:** A small to medium size, triangular point with a deep single notch or a concave indention in the center of the base. Flaking is parallel to random. Blade edges are rarely serrated. Similar examples are found in the Southeast but are much cruder and more recent in age. **I.D. KEY:** Basal notch.

CARROLTON - Mid to Late Archaic, 5000 - 3000 B.P.

(Also see Adena Wells, Bulverde and Dallas)

G2, $2-$4
Cent. TX.

G2, $3-$4
Comanche Co., TX.

G2, $3-$4
Cent. TX.

G2, $2-$4
Comanche Co., TX.

G6, $15-$25
Comanche Co., TX.

G6, $10-$20
Austin, TX.

G4, $5-$10
Bell Co., TX.

G1, .50-$1
Waco, TX.

G7, $20-$35
Comanche Co., TX.

LOCATION: Midwestern states. **DESCRIPTION:** A medium to large size, long, parallel stemmed point with a square base. Workmanship is crude to medium grade. Believed to be related to *Bulverde* points.

CASCADE LEAF - Mid-Archaic, 8000 - 5000 B.P.

(Also see Allen & Angostura)

G9, $40-$60
Deschutes Co., OR.
Dietz Cache point.

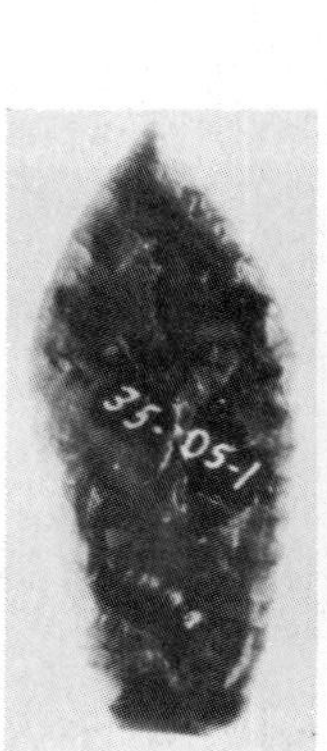

G3, $25-$35
Deschutes Co., OR.
Dietz cache point.

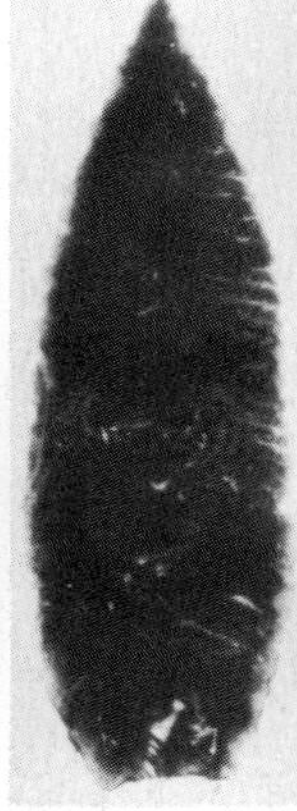

G8, $35-$50
Deschutes Co., OR.
Dietz Cache point.

G9, $40-$60
Deschutes Co., OR.
Dietz Cache point.

G10, $75-$125, Lake Co., OR.

LOCATION: Northwestern states. **DESCRIPTION:** A medium to large size, narrow, thin blade that usually exhibits oblique parallel flaking. Base can be convex or concave. The famous Dewey Dietz cache of 2130 blades was found in Oregon decades ago. **I.D. KEY:** Oblique, parallel flaking.

CASTROVILLE - Late-Archaic to Woodland, 4000 - 1500 B.P.

(Also see Lange, Marcos and Marshall)

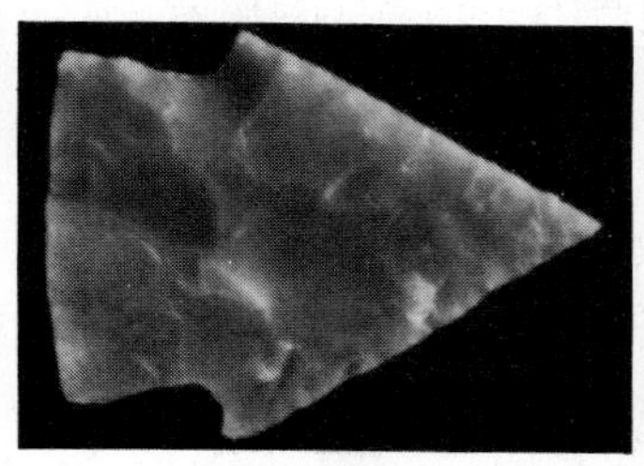

G2, $5-$10
Bell Co., TX.

G4, $10-$20
Austin, TX.

LOCATION: Midwestern states. **DESCRIPTION:** A medium to large size, broad, corner notched point with an expanding base and prominent tangs that can reach the basal edge. The base can be straight to convex and is usually broader than in *Lange*.

G5, $12-$20
Comanche Co., TX.

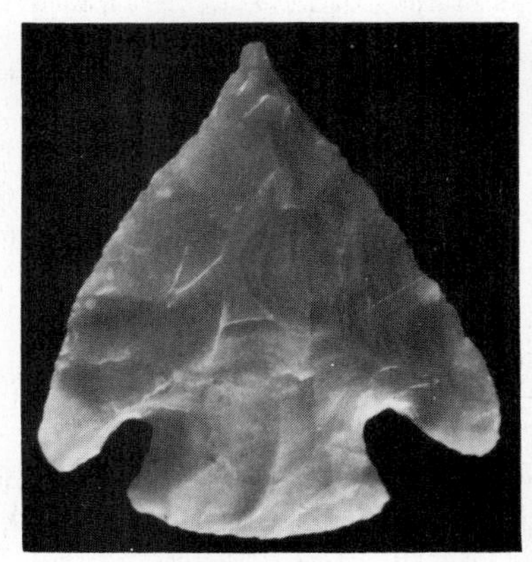

G5, $12-$20
Comanche Co., TX.

G8, $50-$80
Austin, TX.

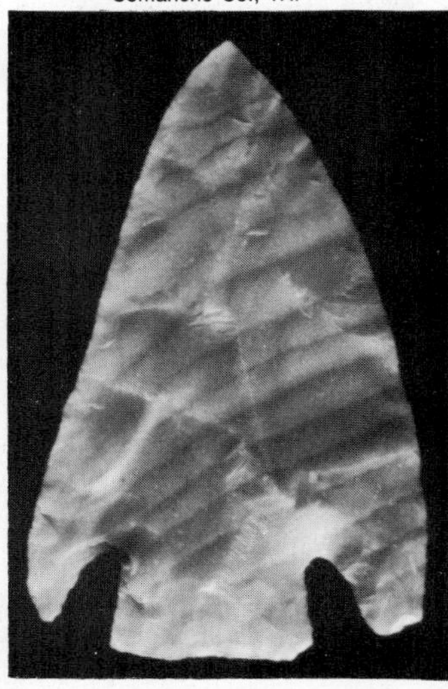

G6, $20-$35
Austin, TX. Georgetown Flint.

G5, $8-$15
Comanche Co., TX. Blade nick.

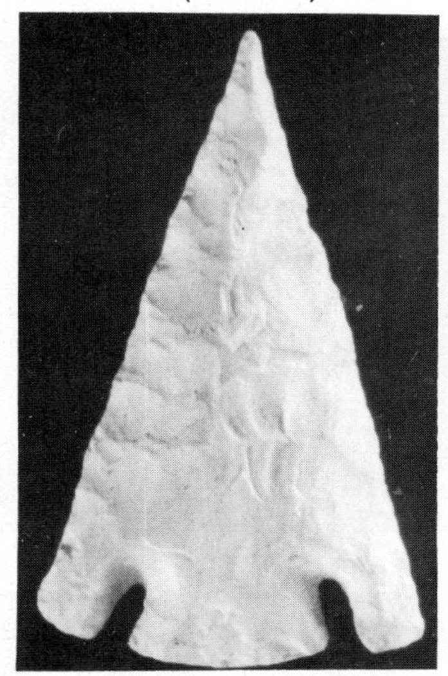

G9, $100-$180
Austin, TX.

G9, $100-$150
Austin, TX.

G10, $150-$250
Austin, TX.

G10, $250-$350
Austin, TX.

CATAHOULA - Mississippian, 800 - 400 B.P.

(Also see Garth Slough, John Day River and Scallorn)

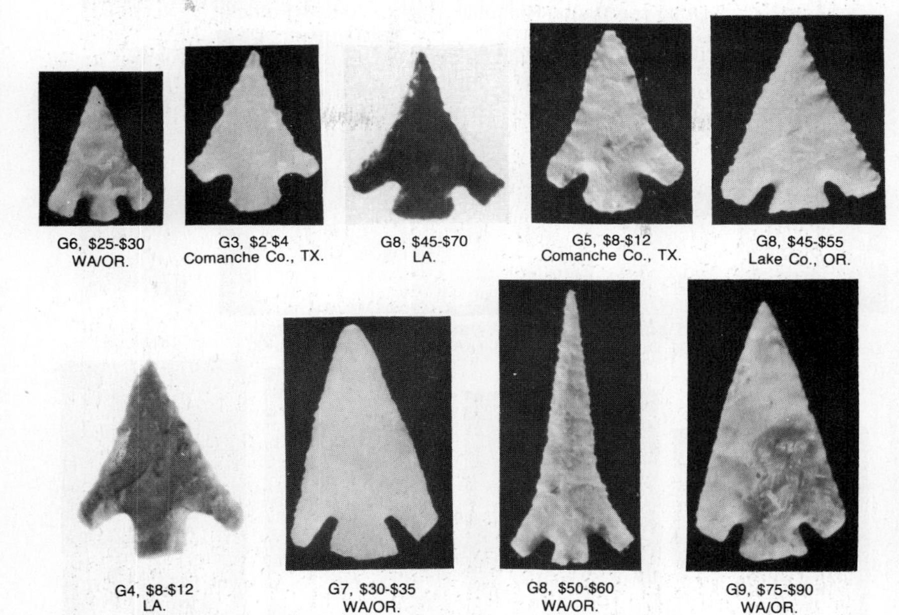

G6, $25-$30
WA/OR.

G3, $2-$4
Comanche Co., TX.

G8, $45-$70
LA.

G5, $8-$12
Comanche Co., TX.

G8, $45-$55
Lake Co., OR.

G4, $8-$12
LA.

G7, $30-$35
WA/OR.

G8, $50-$60
WA/OR.

G9, $75-$90
WA/OR.

LOCATION: Midwestern states. **DESCRIPTION:** A small size, thin, point with broad, flaring, squared tangs. The stem is parallel sided to expanding. The base is straight to concave.

CATAN - Late Archaic to Mississippian, 4000 - 300 B.P.

(Also see Abasolo, Benjamin, Matamoros, Montgomery and Young)

G4, $5-$10
Cent. TX.

G3, $3-$5
Cent. TX.

G5, $8-$12
Cent. TX.

G7, $15-$20
W. TX.

LOCATION: Midwestern states. **DESCRIPTION:** A small lanceolate point with a rounded base. Large examples would fall under the *Abasolo* type.

CAVE SPRING - Transitional Paleo to early Archaic, 9000 - 8000 B.P.

(Also see Dalton-Hemphill, Hanna, Jude & Patrick)

G3, $4-$8 Limestone Co., AL.

G3, $4-$8 SE TN.

G8, $25-$40 Colbert Co., AL.

G7, $15-$25 Christian Co., KY.

G7, $15-$25 Colbert Co., AL.

G2, $1-$2 Morgan Co., AL.

G10, $30-$50 Humphreys Co., TN.

G7, $20-$35 Morgan Co., AL.

G8, $35-$45 Hardin Co., TN.

LOCATION: Southeastern states. **DESCRIPTION:** A small to medium size, stemmed point with a shallow bifurcated base. Blade edges are usually straight; shoulders are either tapered or barbed, and the stem usually expands with a tendency to turn inward at the base which is usually ground. **I.D. KEY:** Early Archaic flaking.

CHESAPEAKE DIAMOND - Early Archaic, 7000 - 5000 B.P.

(Also see Morrow Mountain)

G6, $5-$10 Dallas Co., AL.

LOCATION: Far Eastern states. **DESCRIPTION:** A small to medium size diamond shaped point that is pointed at both ends. Unique in that the base and tip are indiscernable and evidence indicates that both ends of the point were used as tips.

CHIPOLA - Early Archaic, 10,000 - 8000 B.P.

(Also see Dalton, Hardaway & San Patrice)

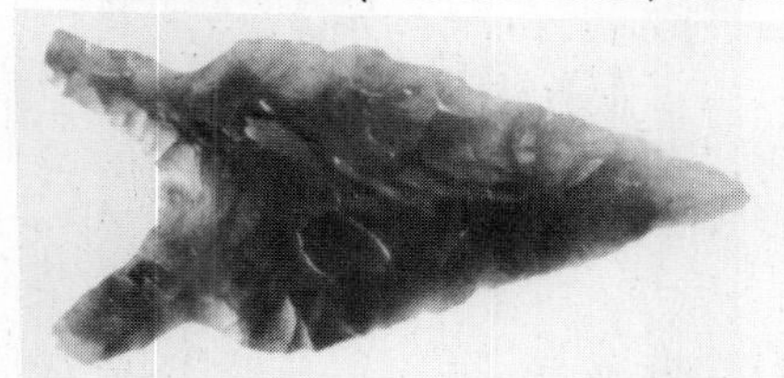

G8, $75-$125
Chipola River, FL.

LOCATION: Southern Southeastern states. **DESCRIPTION:** A small to medium size triangular point with long, expanding auricles and a tapered shoulder. Bases are deeply concave and are thinned. Rare in type area.

CHIRICAHUA - Mid to late Archaic, 5000 - 4000 B.P.

(Also see Palmer and SW Hanna)

G1, .25-.50
Yavapai Co., AZ.

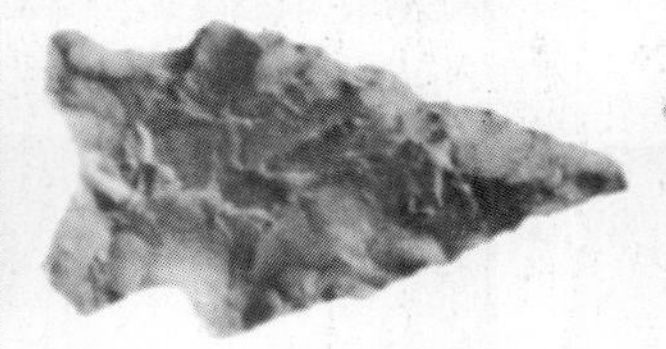

G4, $4-$6
Yavapai Co., AZ.

G5, $5-$8
Yavapai Co., AZ.

LOCATION: Southwestern states. **DESCRIPTION:** A small to medium size side-notched to eared point with a concave base. Shoulders are tapered.

CITRUS - Late Archaic to Woodland, 3500 - 2000 B.P.

(Also see Culbreath, Eva, Hernando, Parowan, Rockwall and San Saba)

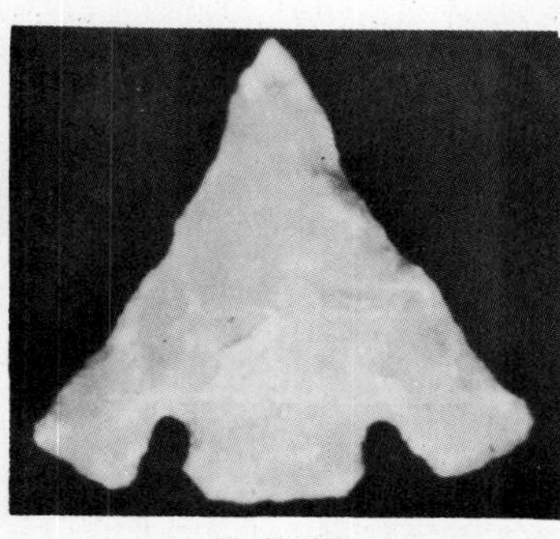

G2, $25-$35
Marion Co., FL.

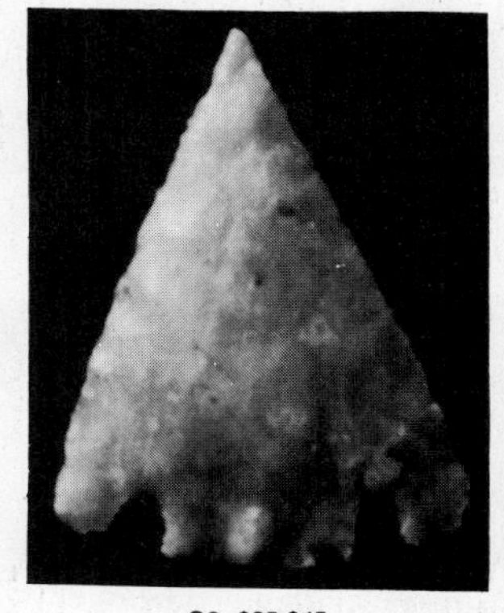

G3, $35-$45
Hillsborough Co., FL.

LOCATION: Southern Southeastern states including Florida. **DESCRIPTION:** A medium to large size basal-notched point. The stem is wider than *Hernando*. **I.D. KEY:** Notches and later flaking on blade.

G7, $180-$300
NW Cent. FL.

G4, $35-$45
NW Cent. FL.

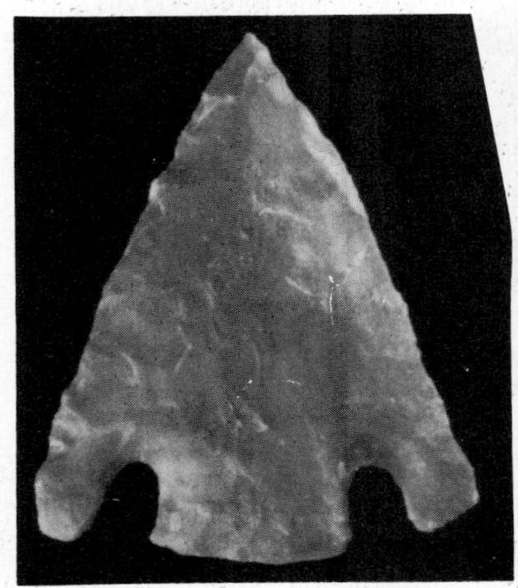

G6, $80-$150
Pasco Co., FL.

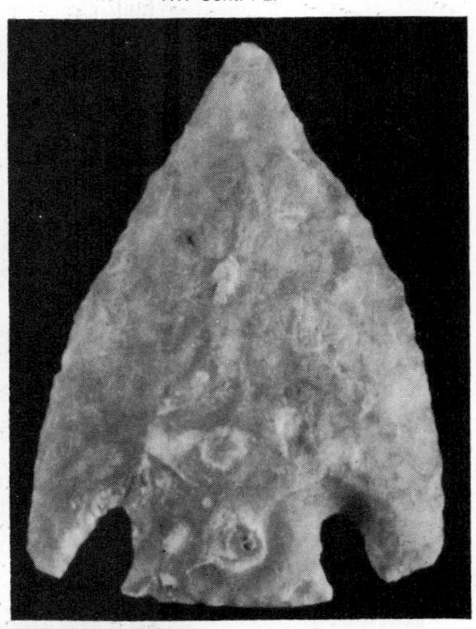

G5, $50-$90
NW Cent. FL.

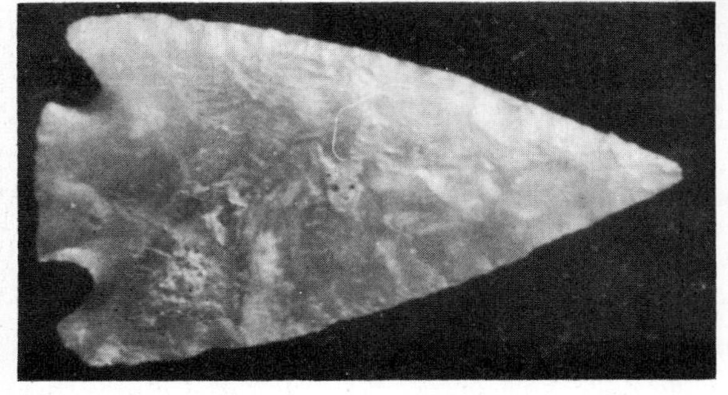

G7, $180-$300
NW Cent. FL. Agatized coral.

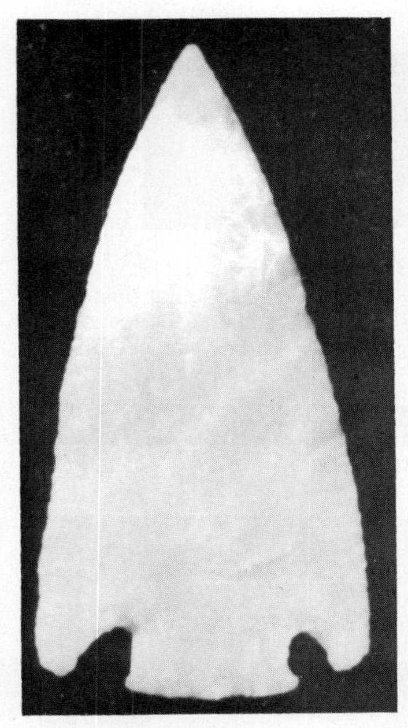

G8, $450-$650
NW Cent. FL. Coral.

G9, $500-$800
NW Cent. FL. Agatized coral.

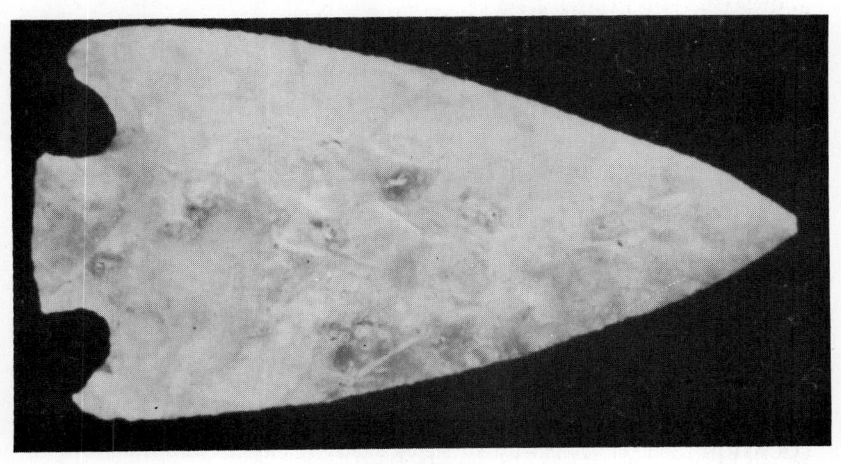

G7, $350-$550
NW Cent. FL. Small tip nick.

CLARKSVILLE - Mississippian, 1000 - 500 A.D.

(Also see Caraway, Levanna, Madison and McGloin)

G4, $4-$6
Wilkes Co., NC.

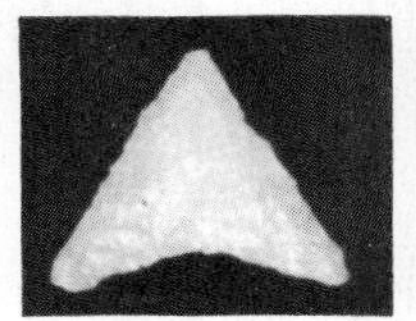
G2, $1-$3
Union Co., SC

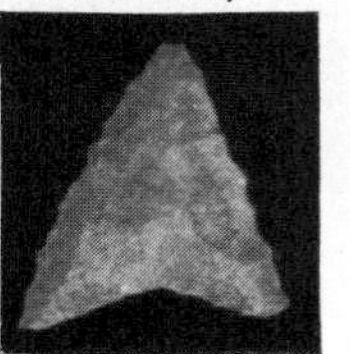
G2, $1-$3
Newberry Co. SC. Slate.

LOCATION: Far Eastern states. **DESCRIPTION:** A small size triangular point with all three sides approx. the same width. The base is straight to slightly concave. Examples made from Quartzite and quartz tend to be thick in cross section.

CLAY COUNTY - Middle to Late Archaic, 5000 - 3500 B.P.

(Also see Kirk Corner-Notched and Lafayette)

G2, $45-$60
Sou. GA. Ginny area.

G5, $90-$150
Albany, GA.

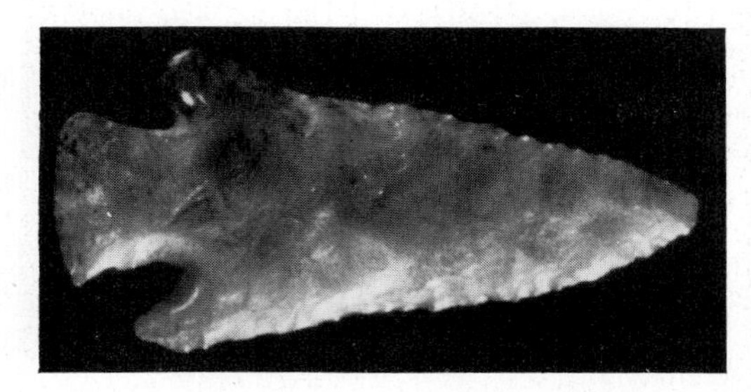
G2, $45-$60
Sou. GA. Suwannee RV.

LOCATION: Southern Southeastern states including Florida. **DESCRIPTION:** A medium to large size corner-notched point with outward-flaring, squared shoulders (clipped wing). Blades are recurvate. **I.D. KEY:** Deep notches and squared barbs.

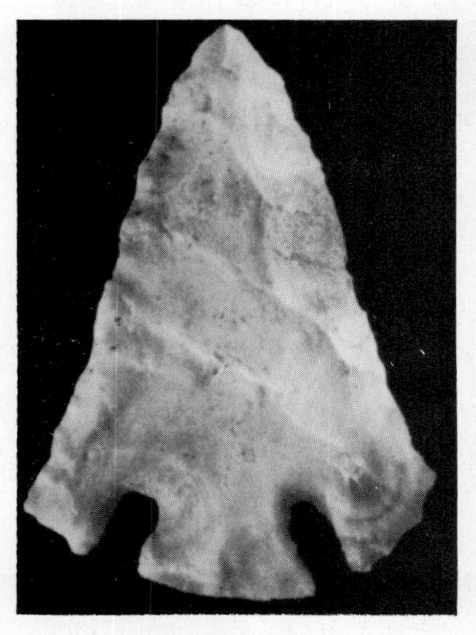

G7, $150-$250
Lee Co., GA.

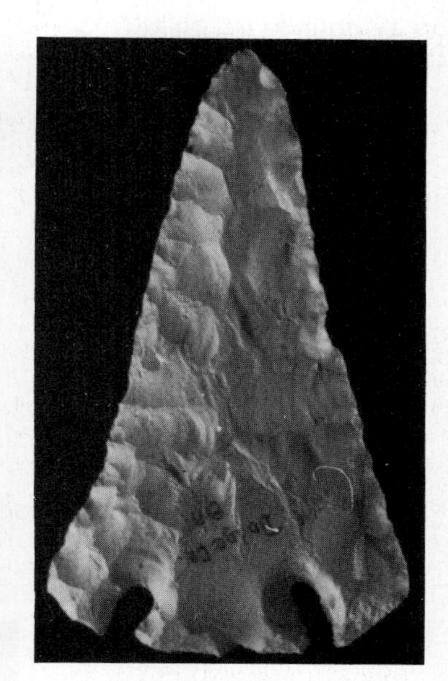

G7, $150-$250
Dodge Co., GA.

G3, $50-$80
Marion Co., FL.

G8, $225-$350
Dodge Co., GA.

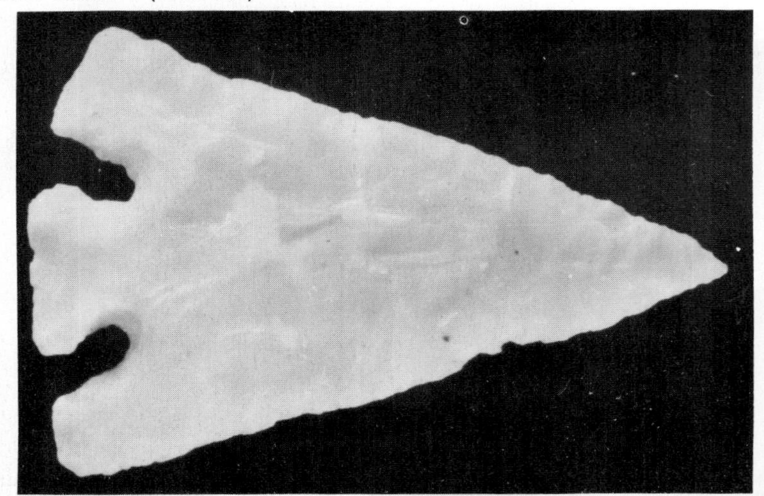

G9, $350-$550
Cherokee Co., AL.

G8, $225-$375
NW Cent. FL.

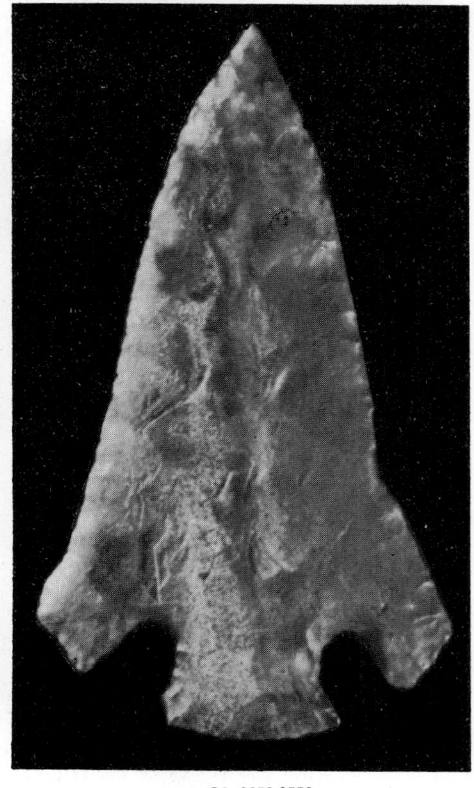

G9, $350-$550
NW Cent. FL.

CLIFTON - Mississippian, 1200 - 500 B.P.

(Also see Bassett and Ebenezer)

G6, .70-$1
Waco, TX.

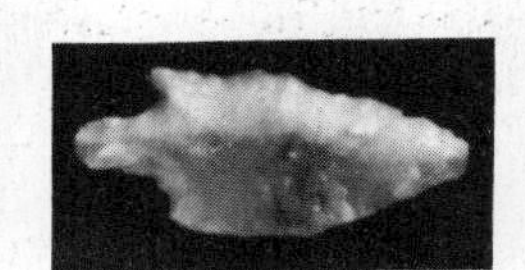

G1, .20-.50
Waco, TX.

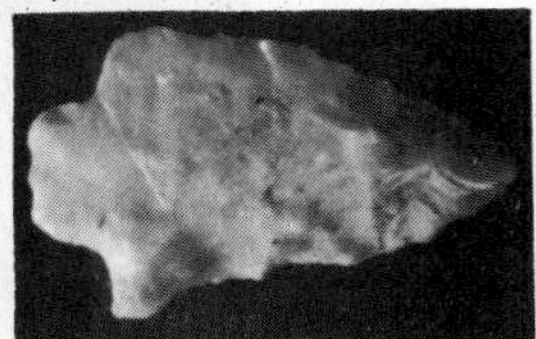

G3, .50-.90
Comanche Co., TX.

LOCATION: Midwestern states. **DESCRIPTION:** A small size, crude point that is usually made from a flake and is uniface. The base is sharply contracting to pointed.

CLOVIS - Early Paleo, 15000 - 9000 B.P.

(Also see Allen, Angostura, Browns Valley, Cochise, Conerly, Copena Auriculate, Cumberland, Dalton, Debert, Llano, Plainview, Redstone, Simpson & Suwanee)

G1, $40-$50
IL.

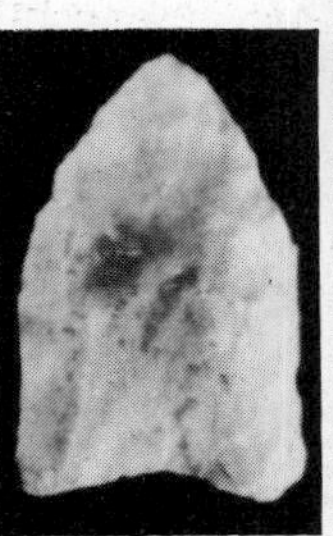

G1, $40-$50
Southampton Co., VA.

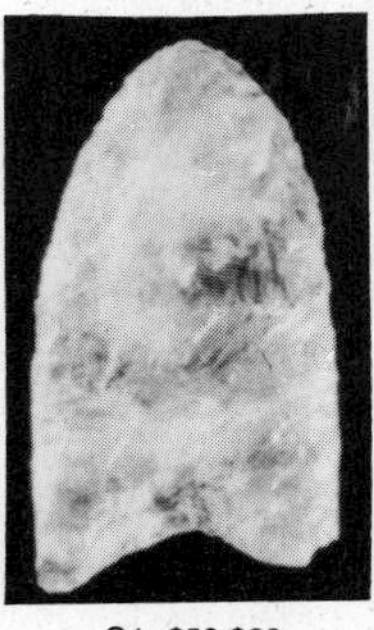

G1, $50-$60
Greenville Co., VA.

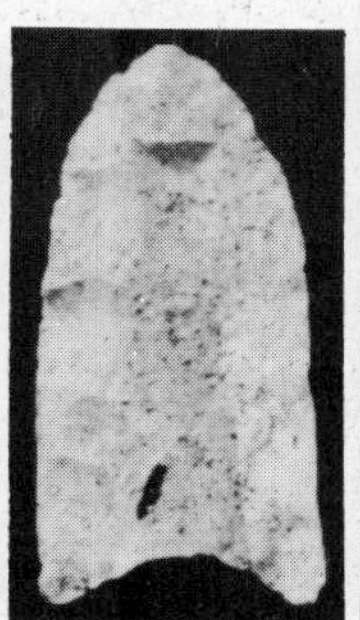

G2, $85-$100
MO.

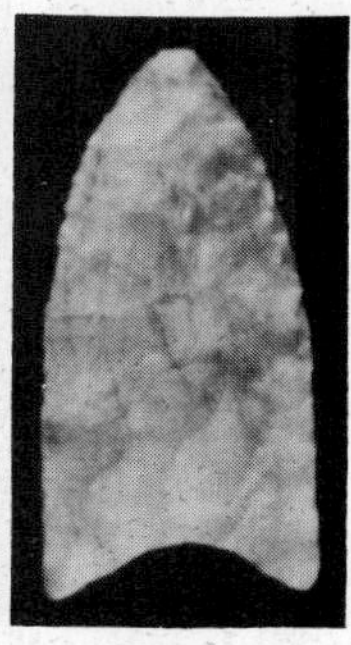

G3, $100-$125
Charleston, SC., Cooper RV.

G3, $125-$200
Suwannee RV, FL.

G6, $300-$480
Ontario, Canada

LOCATION: All of North America. **DESCRIPTION:** A medium to large size, auriculate, fluted, lanceolate point with convex sides and a concave base that is ground. Most examples are fluted on both sides about ⅓ the way up from the base. The flaking can be random to parallel. *Clovis* is the earliest point type in this hemisphere. It is believed that this form was developed here after early man crossed the Bering Straits to reach this continent about 50,000 years ago. Current theories place the origin of *Clovis* in the Southeastern U.S. since more examples are found in Florida, Alabama and Tennessee than anywhere else. **I.D. KEY:** Paleo flaking, shoulders, batan fluting instead of indirect style.

G2, $60-$100
Mecklenburg Co.,
VA. Crystal.

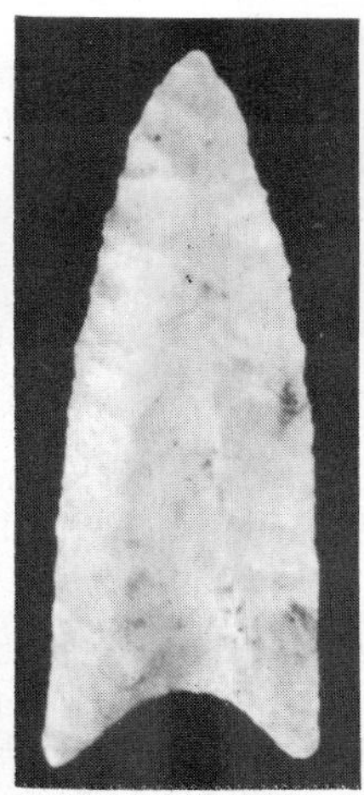

G4, $180-$300
MO.

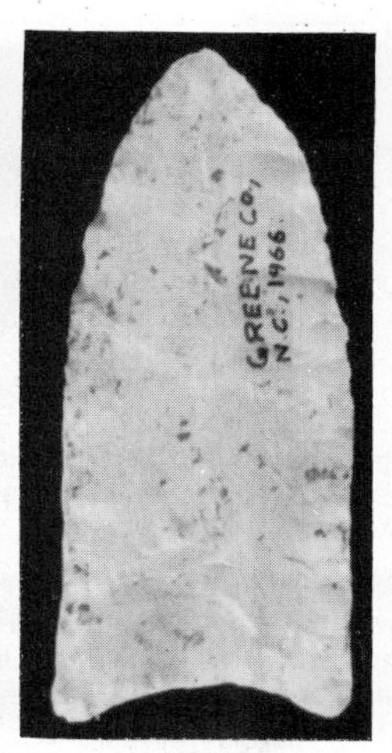

G5, $250-$450
Greene Co., NC.

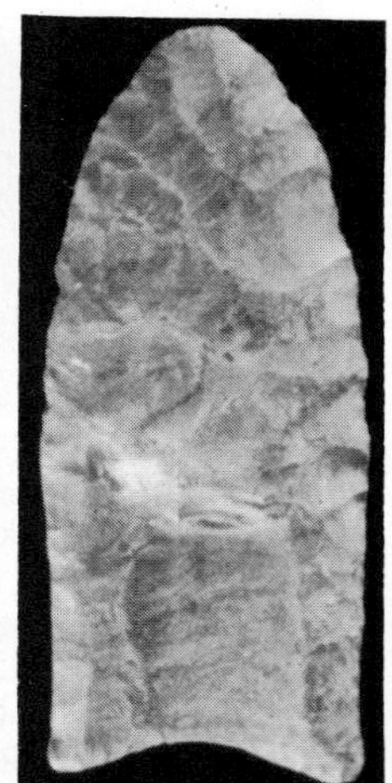

G5, $250-$450
Greensville Co., VA.

G5, $250-$400
Rowan Co., NC.

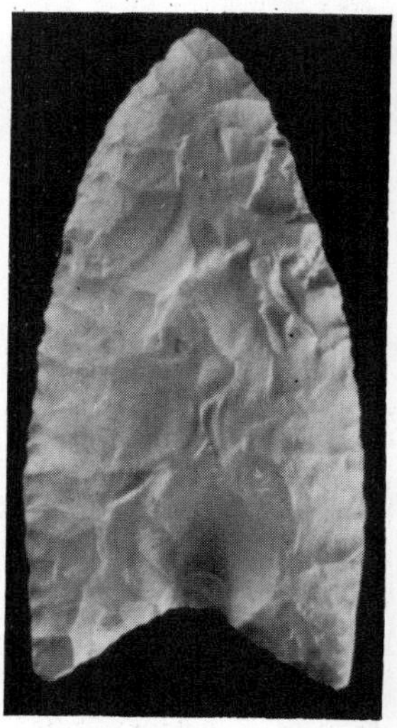

G5, $250-$450
Vernon Parrish, LA.

G5, $250-$400
Smith Co., VA.

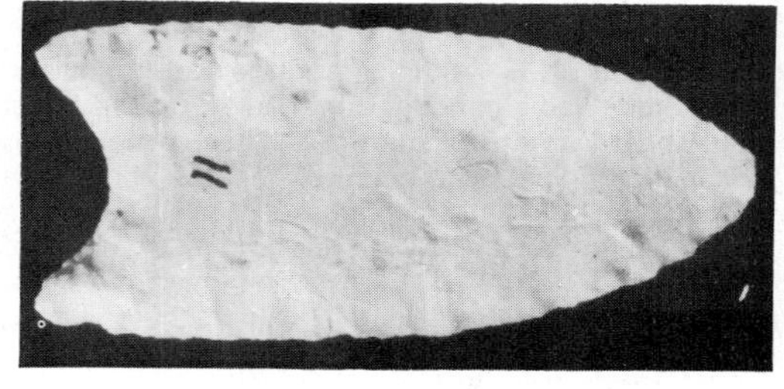

G5, $250-$400
MO.

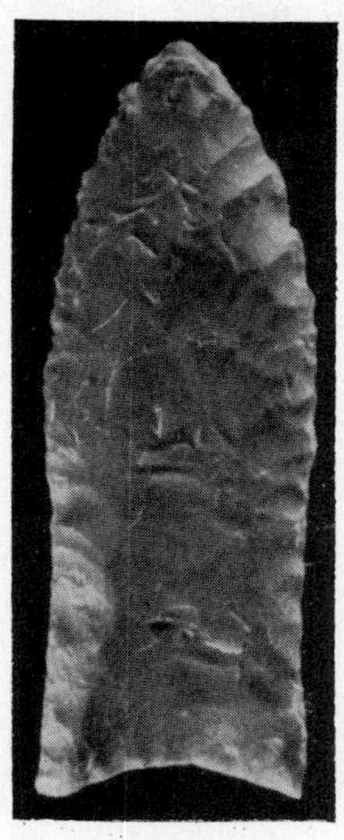

G7, $450-$700
Brunswick Co., VA.

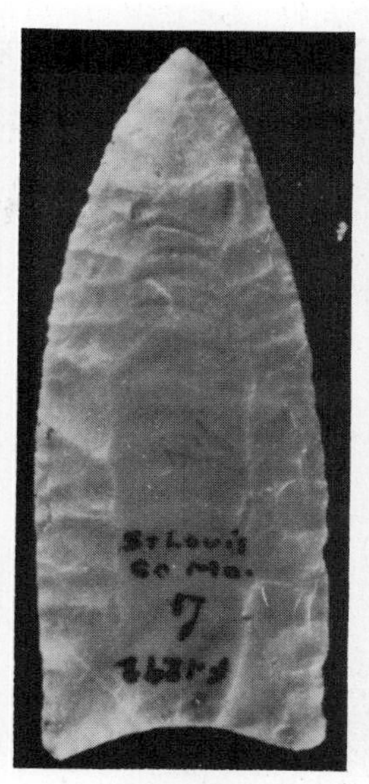

G7, $450-$700
St. Louis Co., MO.

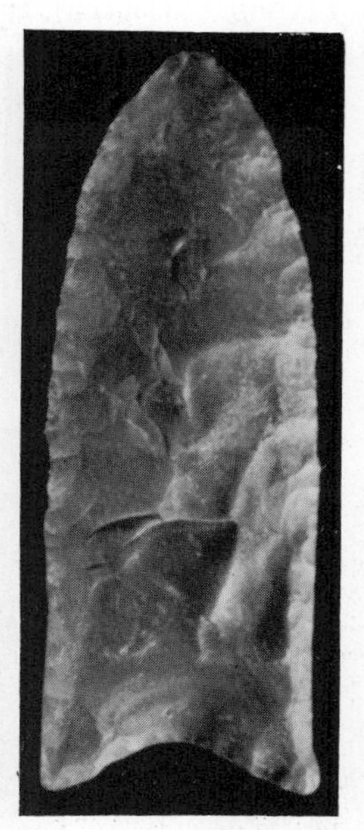

G7, $450-$700
Greensville Co., VA.

G5, $280-$450
Kershaw Co., SC.

G7, $450-$750
Clinton Co., IL.

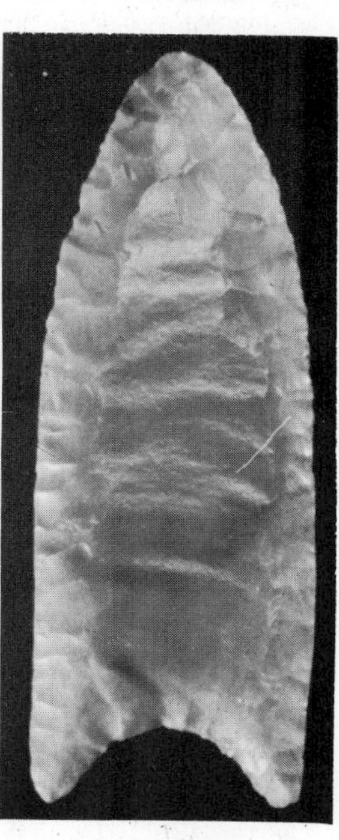

G8, $850-$1400
Humphreys Co., TN.

CLOVIS (continued)

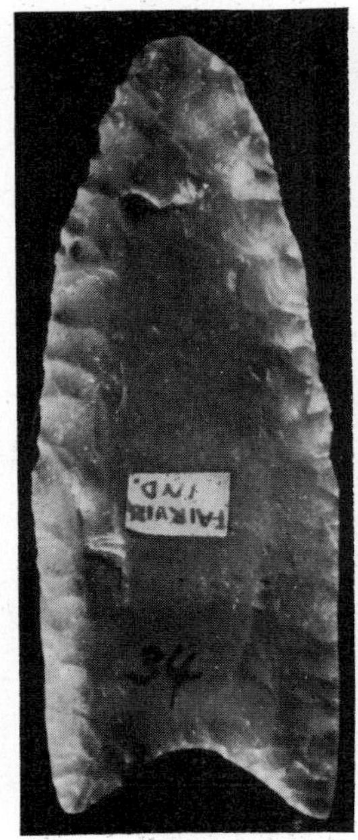
G7, $500-$950
Fairview, IN.

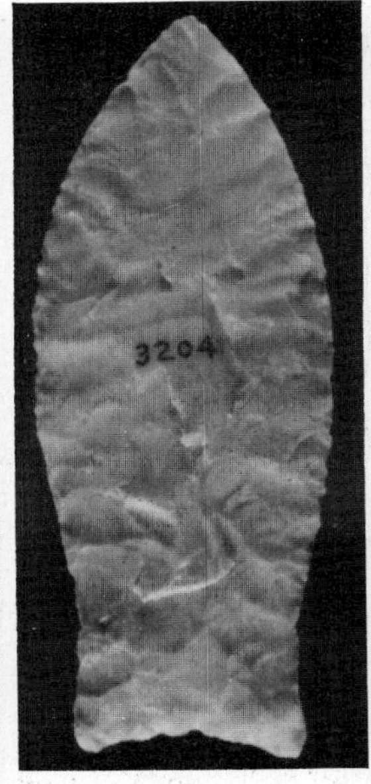

G7, $500-$850
Cent. IL. Nice color.

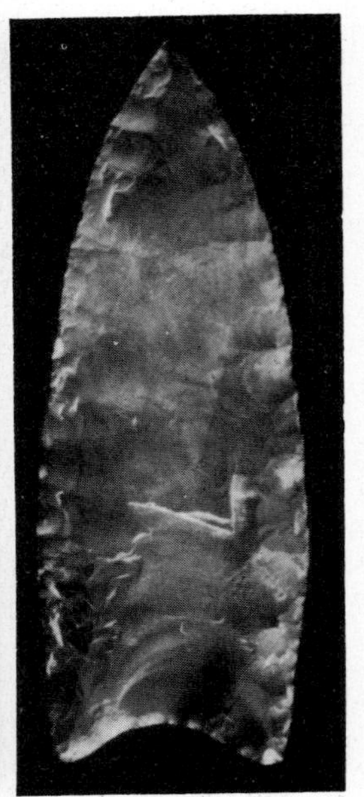
G6, $400-$700
Ohio.

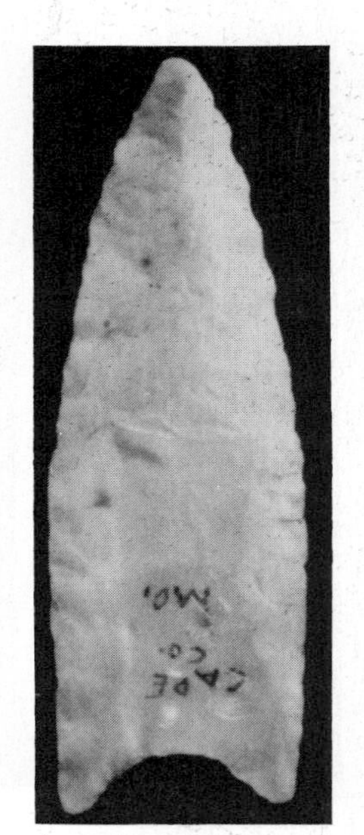
G6, $450-$700
Cape Co., MO.

G7, $500-$750
Calhoun Co., GA.

G6, $400-$650
Chipola RV., FL.

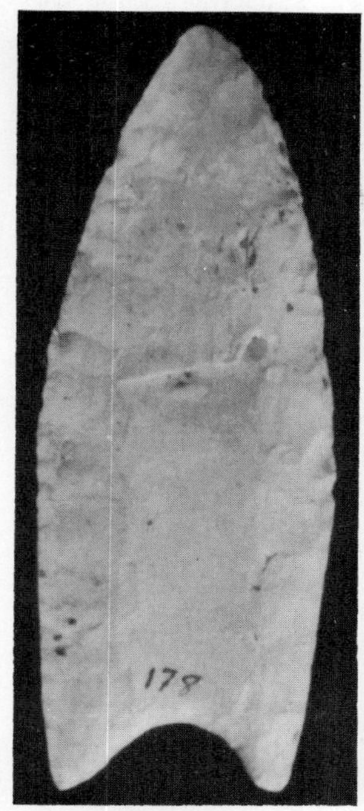

G8, $800-$1500
IL.

G6, $450-$750
Pittsylvania Co., VA.

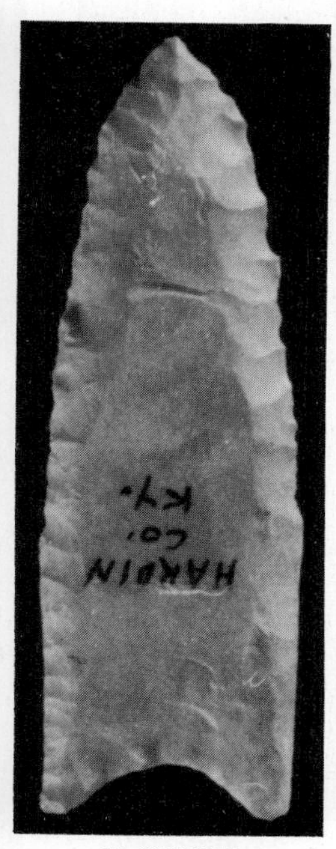

G6, $450-$750
Hardin Co., KY.

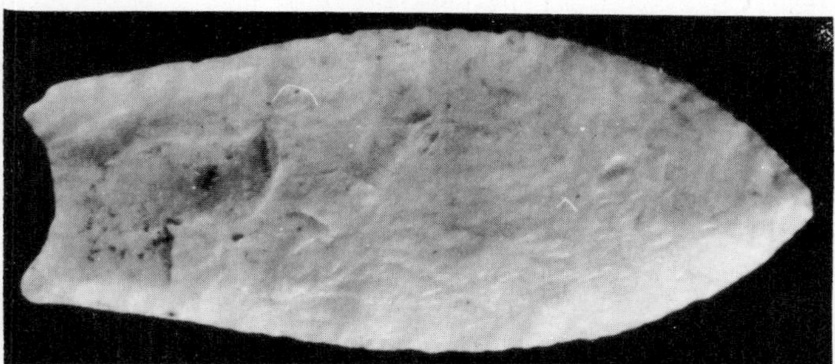

G6, $450-$750, Pulaski Co., KY. Ear nick.

G7, $600-$900, IL, Ross County form.

CLOVIS (continued)

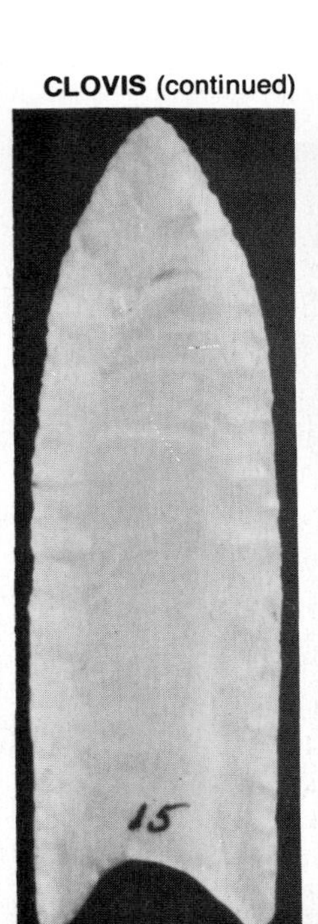

G9, $1500-$2800
Fulton Co., IL. Excellent form and fluting.

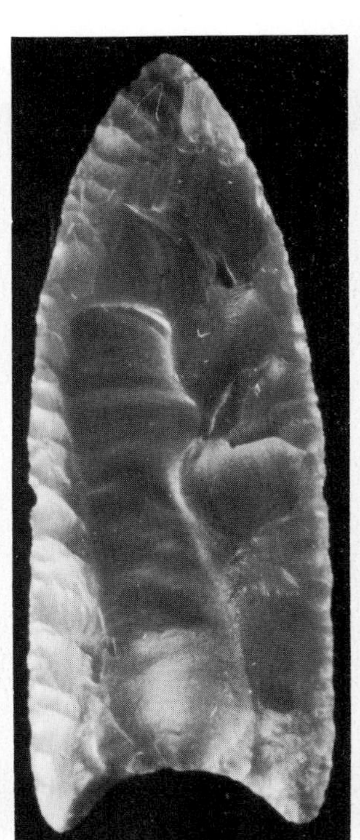

G8, $1000-$1500
Sand Mtn., AL.

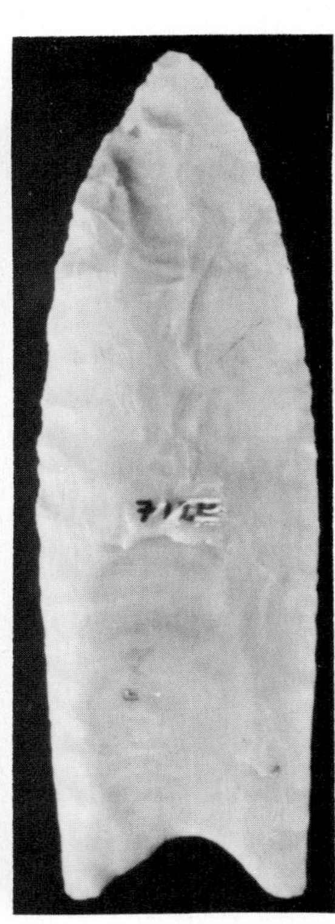

G8, $900-$1500
KY/OH.

G8, $1000-$1500, Metcalf Co., KY.

G9, $1500-$2800, Decatur Co., GA.

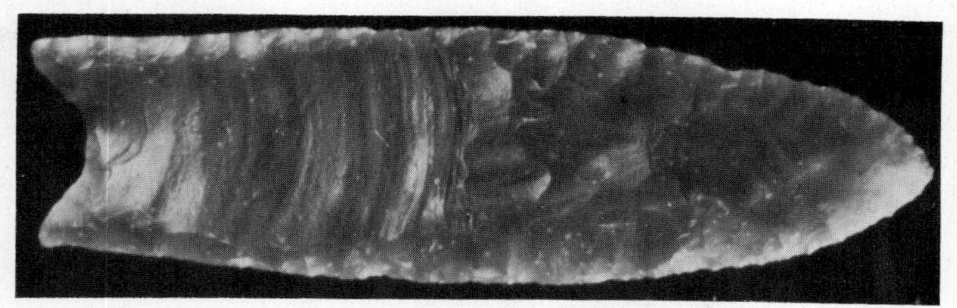

G8, $1000-$1350, Mid. TN., high grade flint.

G7, $550-$900, MO. Early form for the type. Ear nick.

G8, $900-$1200, MO.

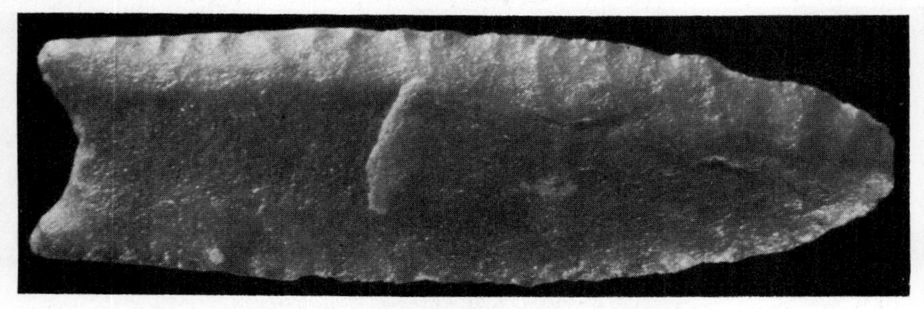

G7, $600-$1000, Sumner Co., TN. Quartzite material. Tip nick.

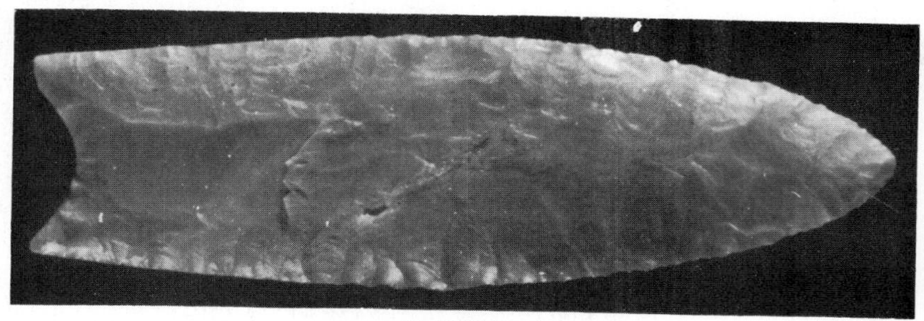

G9, $1500-$2500
Williamson Co., TN. Kentucky
hornstone. Field patination.

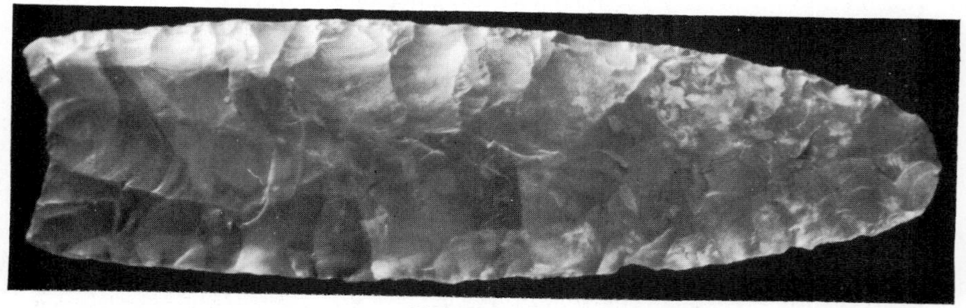

G8, $1200-$2000
Clovis, NM, Curry Co., Blanco Cr. Made of colorful alibaates chert. Thick cross section.

G9, $1500-$2200
Cherokee Co., NC.

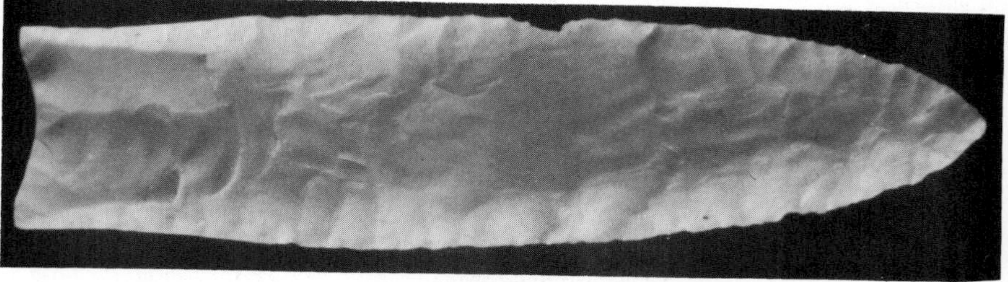

G7, $500-$900
Fulton Co., IL. Blade nick.

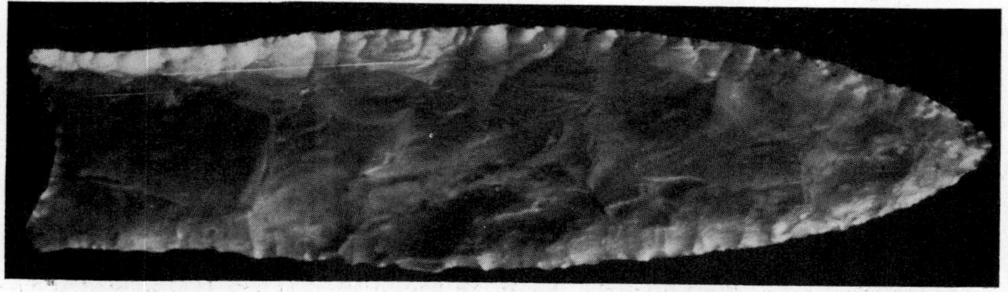

G9, $1500-$2500
W. TN.

G10, $3500-$5500
Humphreys Co., TN. Buffalo River chert. Base is heavily ground. Ross County form.

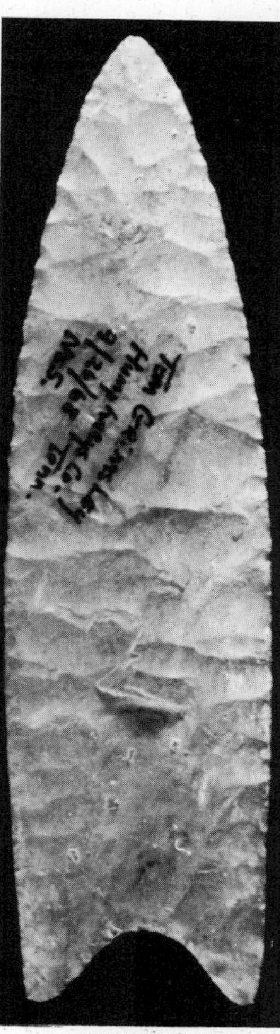

G10, $5000-$6500
Humphreys Co., TN. Patinated Buffalo River chert. Classic.

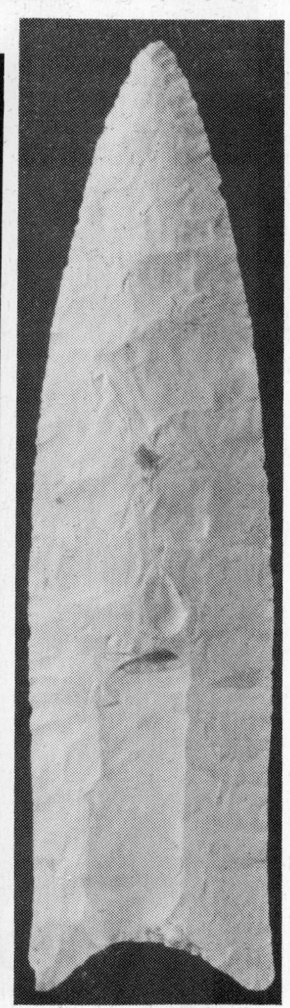

G9, $1500-$2500
KY. Ear damage.

G10, $10,000-$12,000
Limestone Co., AL. Fluted only on one side due to thinness. Very rare in this size. Note parallel, oblique flaking on face of blade. Base is lightly ground. Perfect points are rare.

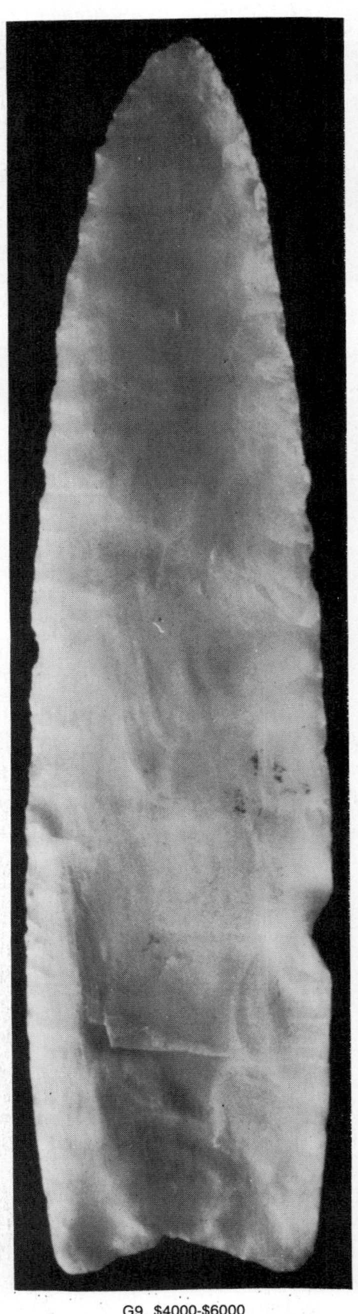

G9, $4000-$6000
CO/WY. Minor blade nicks.

CLOVIS-UNFLUTED - Paleo, 12000 - 9000 B.P.

(Also see Angostura, Beaver Lake, Candy Creek, Golondrina, Plainview, Simpson & Suwanee)

G5, $100-$185
Florecne, AL.

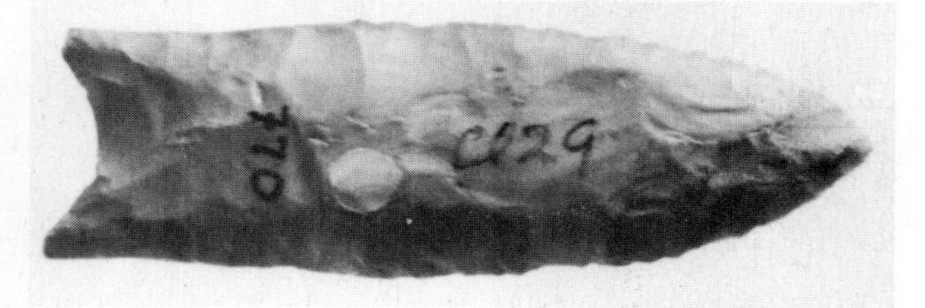

G6, $175-$250
W. TN. Ear nick.
Thinned base.

LOCATION: All of North America. **DESCRIPTION:** A medium to large size, auriculate point identical to fluted *Clovis*, but not fluted. A very rare type.

COAHUILA - Late Archaic to Woodland, 4000 - 2000 B.P.

(Also see Adena-Waubesa)

G3, $8-$15
Comanche Co., TX.

G7, $35-$50
Comanche Co., TX.

LOCATION: Southern Midwestern states. **DESCRIPTION:** A medium to large size, narrow point with tapered shoulders and a long, pointed, contracting stem.

COBBS TRIANGULAR - Early Archaic, 8000 - 5000 B.P.

(Also see Abasolo, Decatur, Dovetail, Lerma and Lost Lake)

G7, $70-$90
Colbert Co., AL.

G7, $70-$100
Florence, AL. Note needle tip.
Classic form.

G7, $75-$85
Florence, AL. Decatur site.
Classic form.

LOCATION: Southeastern states. **DESCRIPTION:** A medium to large size, thin, lanceolate blade with a broad, rounded to squared base. One side of each face is usually steeply beveled. These are un-notched preforms for early Archaic beveled types such as *Decatur, Dovetail, Lost Lake*, etc.

G8, $100-$180
Florence, AL.

G7, $80-$90
Savannah RV., GA, Briar Creek.

G8, $90-$150
Benton Co., TN.

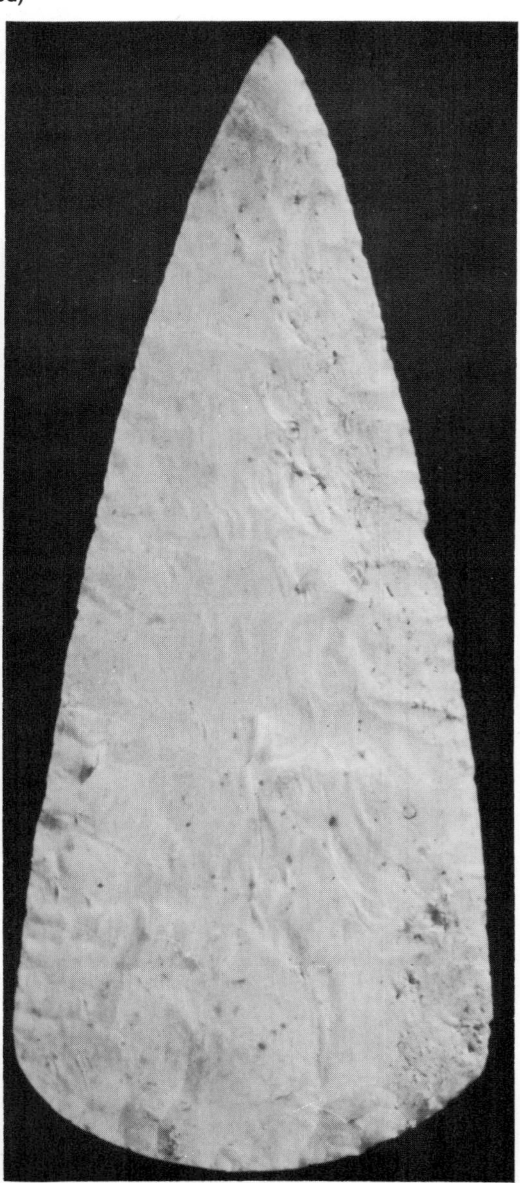

G10, $350-$600
Grafton, IL., Northern form.

G10, $350-$550
Montgomery Co., MO. Southern form.

G9, $180-$300
Humphreys Co., TN. High quality Dover chert. Thin and excellent.

G9, $180-$300
Humphreys Co., TN. Dover chert.

COCHISE - Late Paleo, 11,500 - 10,000 B.P.

(Also see Allen, Angostura and Clovis)

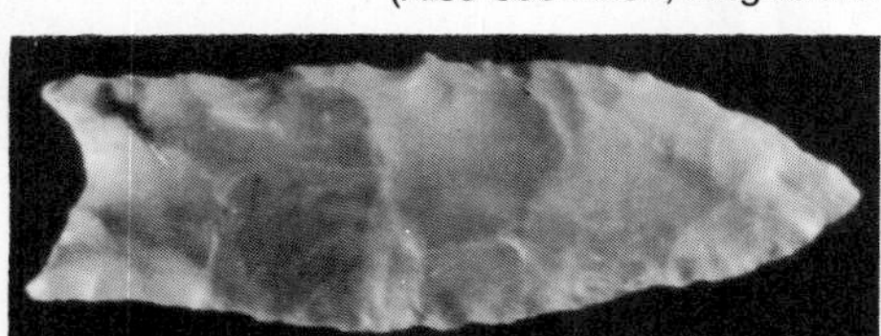

G4, $60-$80
McIntosh Co., OK. Green Potato Hills flint.

LOCATION: Southwestern states. **DESCRIPTION:** A medium to large size lanceolate point that is usually fluted. Base is concave and is ground.

CODY KNIFE - Early Archaic, 8000 - 5000 B.P.

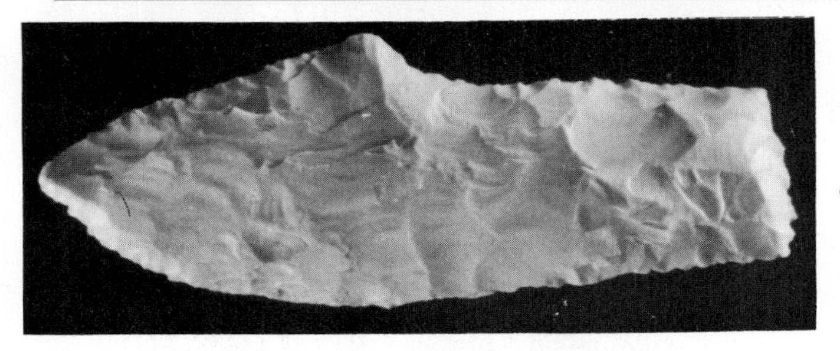

G5, $45-$70
Comanche Co., TX.

LOCATION: Midwestern states. **DESCRIPTION:** A large size asymmetrical blade with one shoulder and a long parallel sided to slightly contracting stem. Stem edges are ground on early examples.

COLBERT (See Dalton-Colbert)

COLBERT - Mississippian, 1000 - 400 B.P.

(Also see Scallorn)

G6, $25-$40
Lincoln Parrish, LA.

LOCATION: Midwestern states. **DESCRIPTION:** A small size point with broad horizontal shoulders and a short, bulbous stem with a straight base.

COLDWATER - Woodland, 3000 - 1000 B.P.

(Also see Gilchrist)

G3, $2-$5
Marion Co., AL.

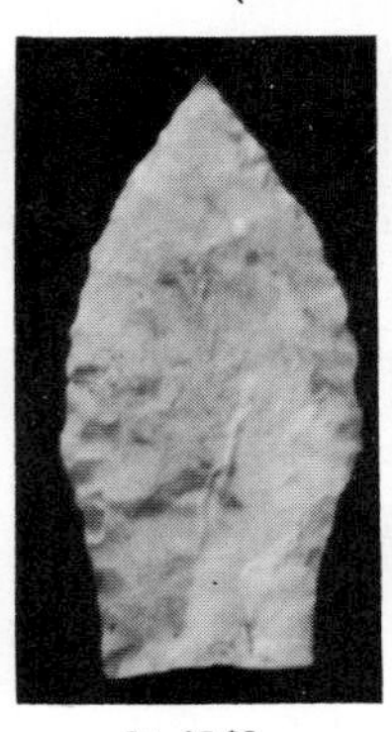

G4, $5-$8
Marion Co., AL.

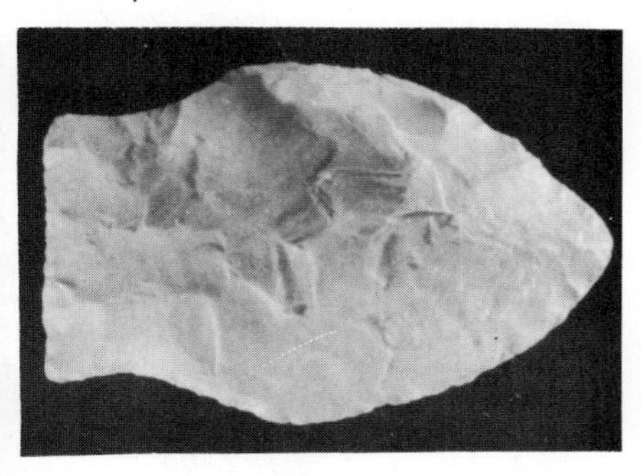

G6, $10-$20
Franklin Co., MS.

LOCATION: Southern Gulf states. **DESCRIPTION:** A medium size lanceolate point with weak tapered shoulders, a short stem and a straight base. **I.D. KEY:** One high shoulder.

COLONIAL - Mississippian, 1200 - 800 B.P.

(Also see Rose Springs and Ventana-Amargosa)

G2, $2-$5
Yavapai Co., AZ.

G3, $4-$6
Yavapai Co., AZ.

G4, $8-$12
Yavapai Co., AZ.

LOCATION: Southwestern states. **DESCRIPTION:** A small size tapered shoulder point with a medium to long stem.

COLUMBIA - Woodland, 2000 - 1000 B.P.

(Also see Hamilton)

G7, $30-$40
Marion Co., FL. Nice color.

G3, $5-$8
Marion Co., FL. Tip nick.

G3, $5-$8
Hamilton Co., FL.

LOCATION: Southern Southeastern states. **DESCRIPTION:** A medium to large size stemmed point. Shoulders are tapered to horizontal and are weak. Stem is short and slightly expanding. Base is straight.

CONEJO - Late Archaic, 4000 - 3000 B.P.

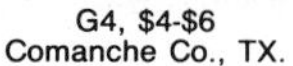

G4, $4-$6
Comanche Co., TX.

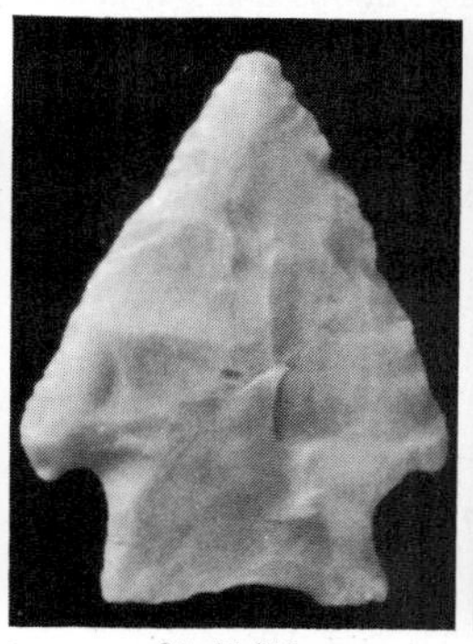

G5, $6-$10
Comanche Co., TX.

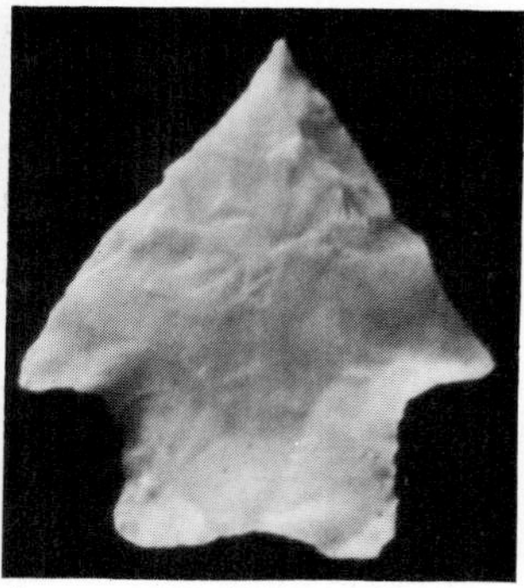

G7, $10-$15
Austin, TX.

LOCATION: Midwestern states. **DESCRIPTION:** A medium size, corner notched point with an expanding, concave base and tangs that turn towards the base.

CONERLY - Mid-Archaic, 7500 - 4500 B.P.

(Also see Beaver Lake, Browns Valley, Guilford, Midland, Simpson & Suwanee)

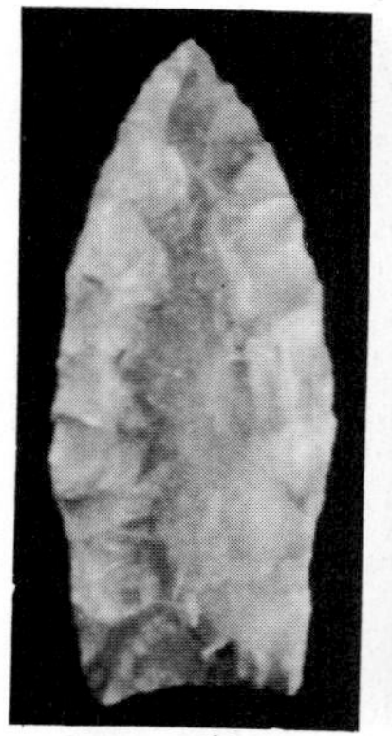

G6, $30-$45
Putnam Co., TN.

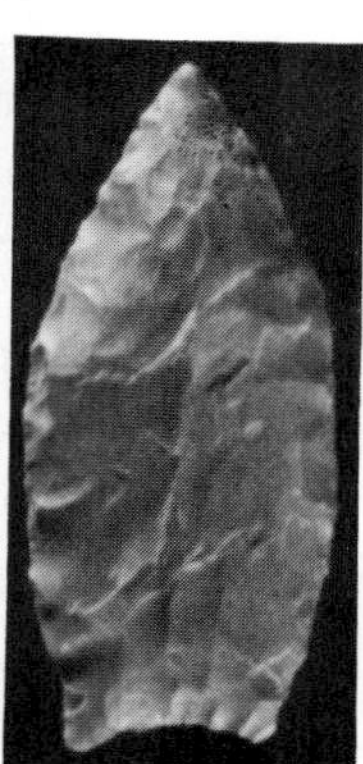

G5, $20-$35
Marion Co., TN.

G8, $45-$70
Meigs Co., TN. Hiwassee Isle.

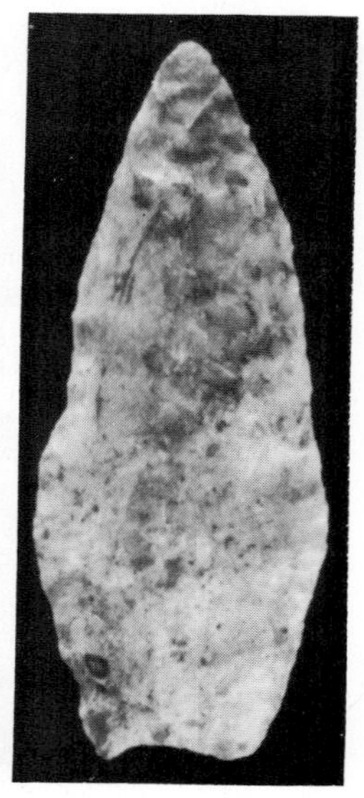

G4, $15-$20
Beaufort Co., SC.

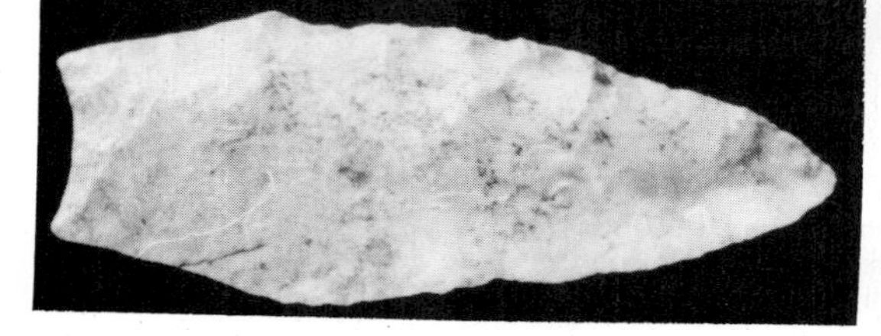

G8, $50-$80
Briar Creek, GA.

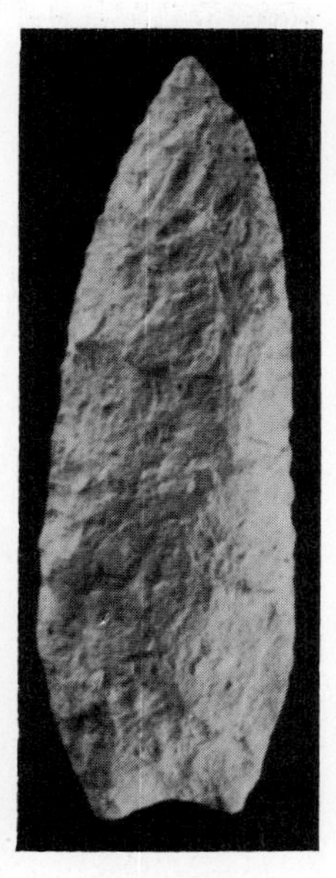

G8, $45-$70
Screven Co., GA.

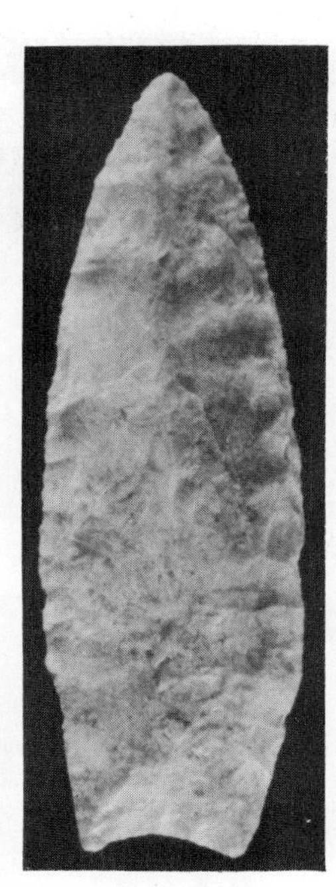

G10, $150-$250
Jasper Co., SC.

G9, $65-$100
Burke Co., GA.

G10, $100-$150
Burke Co., GA.

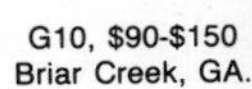

G10, $90-$150
Briar Creek, GA.

LOCATION: Southern Southeastern states, especially Tennessee, Georgia and Florida. **DESCRIPTION:** A medium to large auriculate point with a contracting, concave base which can be ground. On some examples, the hafting area can be seen with the presence of very weak shoulders. The base is usually thinned. Believed to be related to the *Guilford* type. **I.D. KEY:** Base concave, thickness, flaking.

COOSA - Woodland, 2000 - 1500 B.P.

(Also see Crawford Creek)

G7, $3-$5
Dunlap, TN.

G4, $1-$2
Jackson Co., AL.

G4, $2-$3
Marion Co., TN.

G5, $5-$8
Meigs Co., TN.

G7, $10-$12
Marion Co., TN.

G6, $8-$10
Meigs Co., TN.

G3, $1-$3
Meigs Co., TN.

G9, $15-$20
Meigs Co., TN.

LOCATION: Southeastern states. **DESCRIPTION:** A medium size, usually serrated medium grade point with a short stem. Some examples are shallowly side-notched. Shoulders are roughly horizontal.

COPENA-AURICULATE - Mid-Archaic to Woodland, 5000 - 2500 B.P.

(Also see Candy Creek, Beaver Lake, Clovis, Quad and Yadkin)

G6, $15-$20
Marion Co., TN.

G5, $10-$15
Marion Co., TN.

LOCATION: Southeastern states. **DESCRIPTION:** A medium to large size, lanceolate point with straight to recurved blade edges and a concave, auriculate base. Could be confused with *Beaver Lake, Candy Creek, Clovis, Cumberland* or other auriculate forms. Look for the random Woodland flaking on this type. **I.D. KEY:** concave base.

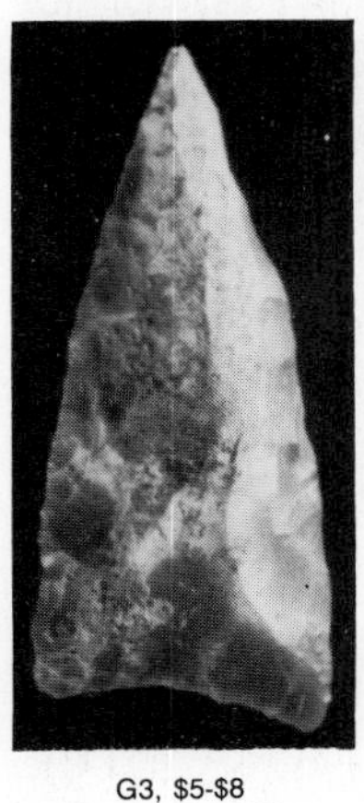

G3, $5-$8
Marion Co., TN.

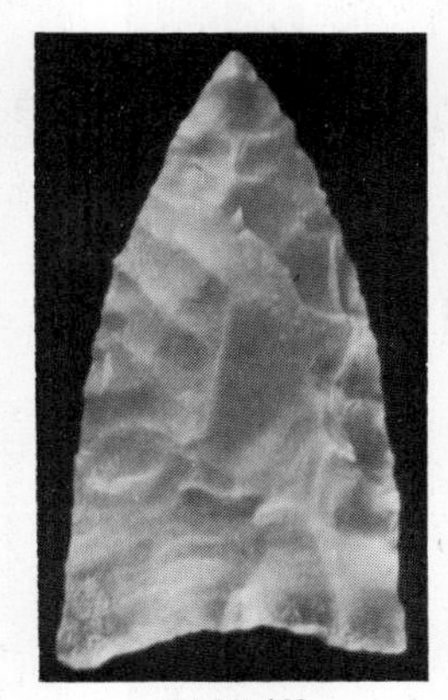

G6, $15-$20
Dayton, TN.

G6, $15-$20
Marion Co., TN.

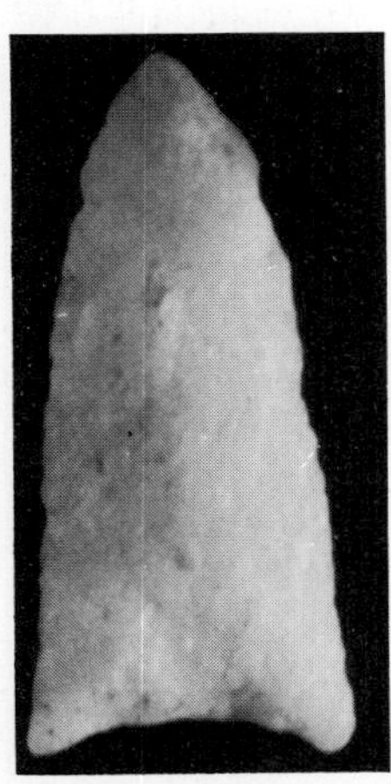

G7, $25-$35
NE AL. Quartzite.

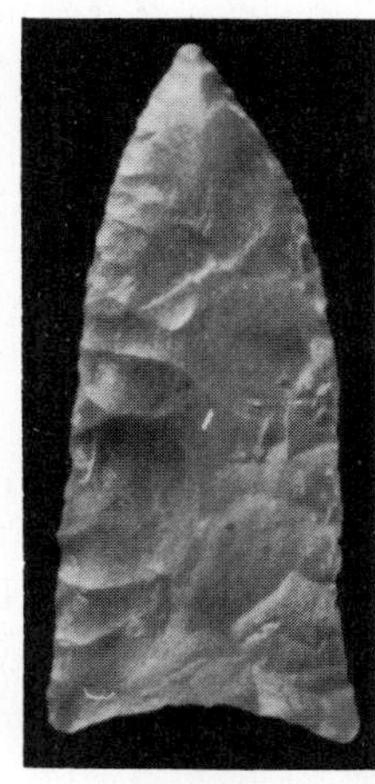

G7, $25-$35
Decatur, AL.

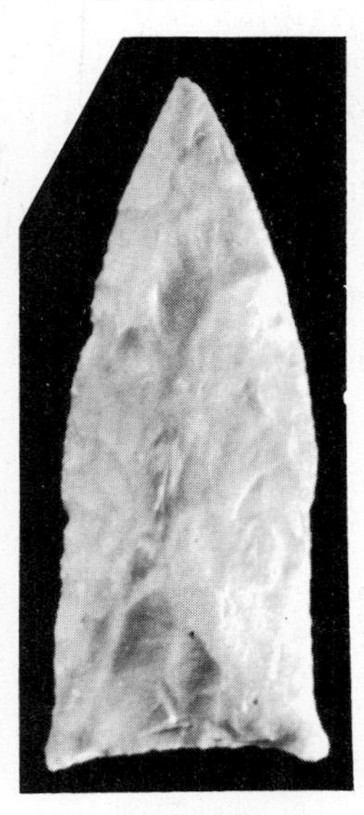

G6, $15-$20
Rhea Co., TN.

G8, $40-$65
Hardin Co., TN.

COPENA-AURICULATE (continued)

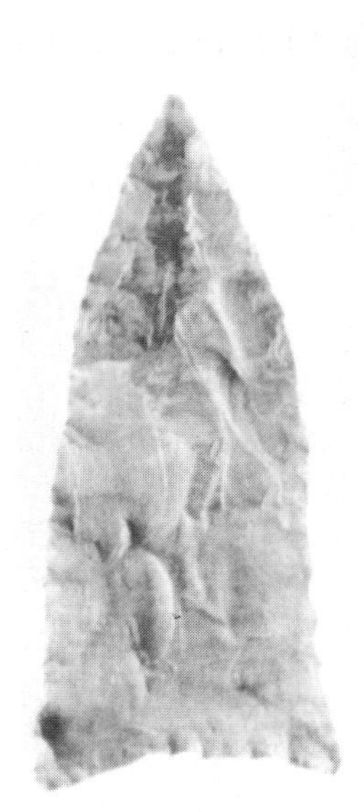

G7, $20-$35
Humphreys Co., TN. Dover chert.

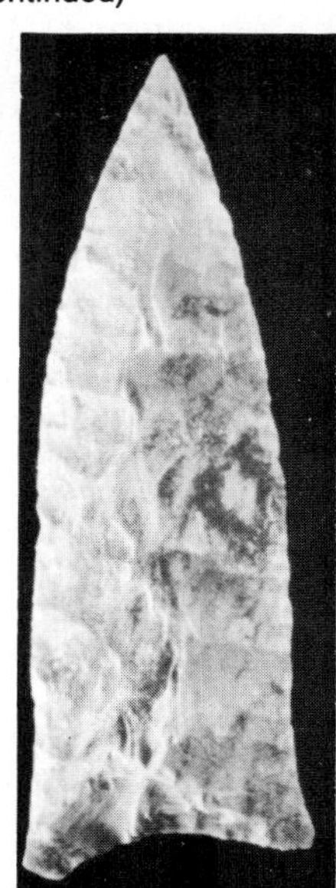

G9, $60-$90
Meigs Co., TN. Hiwassee River.
Cache point.

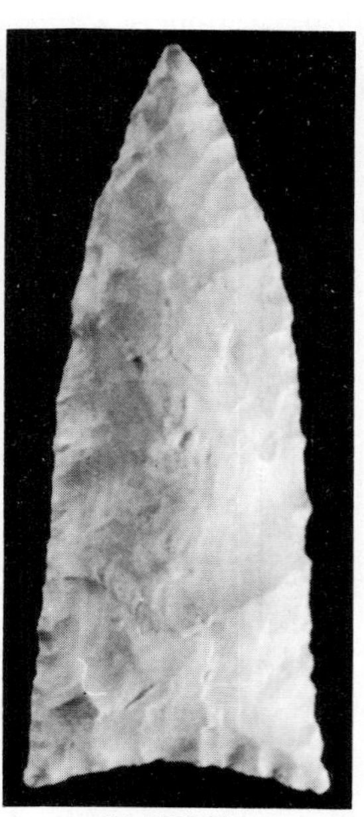

G9, $80-$120
Humphreys Co., TN.

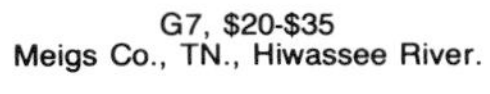

G7, $20-$35
Meigs Co., TN., Hiwassee River.

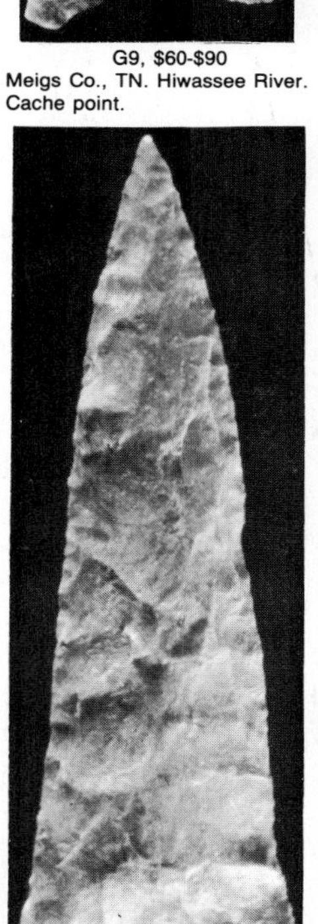

G9, $60-$90
Meigs Co., TN. Hiwassee River.
Cache point.

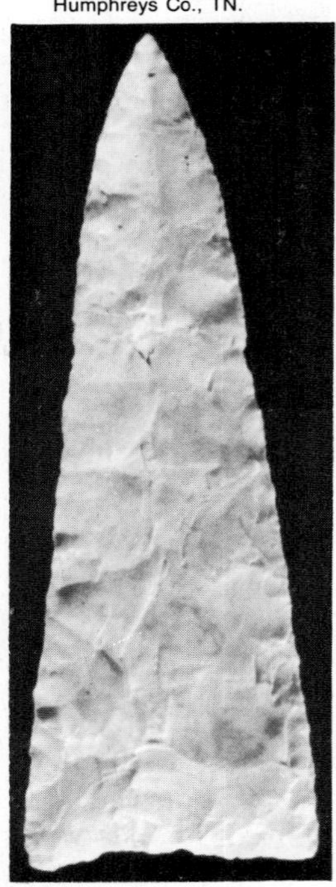

G8, $40-$70
Meigs Co., TN., Hiwassee River.
Cache point.

COPENA-CLASSIC (Shield form) - Late Archaic to Woodland, 4000 - 1200 B.P.

(Also see Friday, Nolichucky)

G2, $1-$2
Hamilton Co., TN.

G3, $4-$6
Parsons, TN.

G5, $10-$20
Dayton, TN.

G4, $5-$8
Humphreys Co., TN.

G7, $50-$80
Florence, AL.

G9, $150-$200
Decatur Co., TN. Note Bakers Creek look at base.

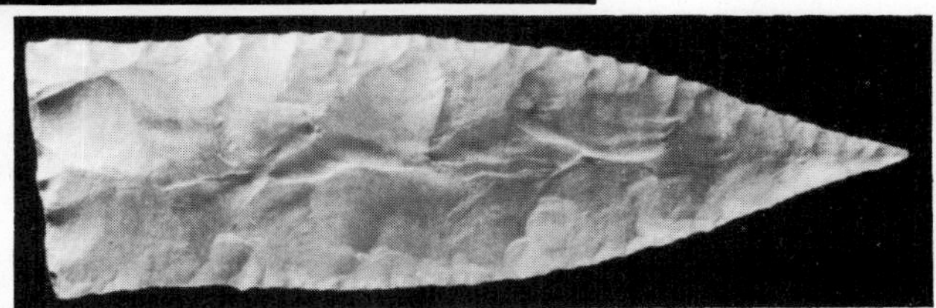

G8, $90-$160, Humphreys Co., TN.

LOCATION: Southeastern states. **DESCRIPTION:** A medium to large size, lanceolate point with recurved blade edges and a straight to slightly convex base. This point usually occurs in Woodland burial mounds, but is also found in late Archaic sites in Tennessee. The Alabama, Tennessee forms are usually very thin with high quality primary and secondary flaking.

G7, $80-$120
Florence, AL.

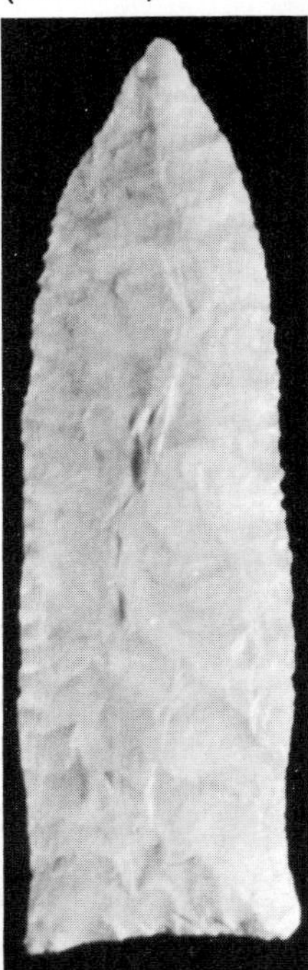

G9, $150-$250
Humphreys Co., TN. Note unusual oblique, parallel flaking. Excellent quality.

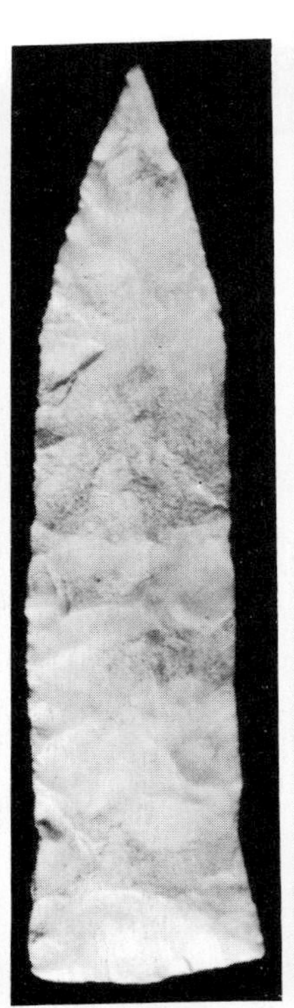

G7, $50-$80
Savannah, TN.

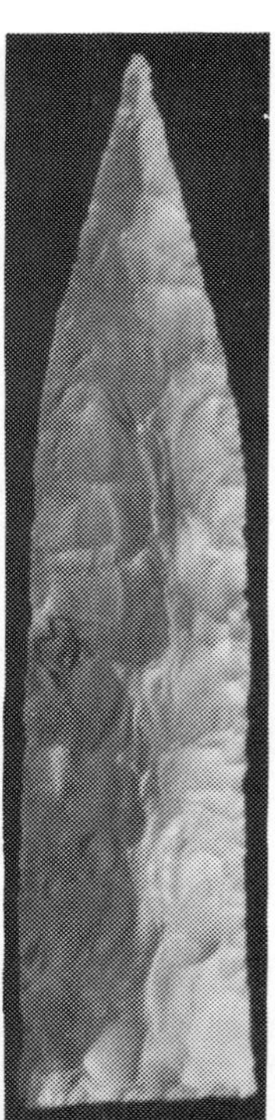

G8, $120-$220
Humphreys Co., TN.

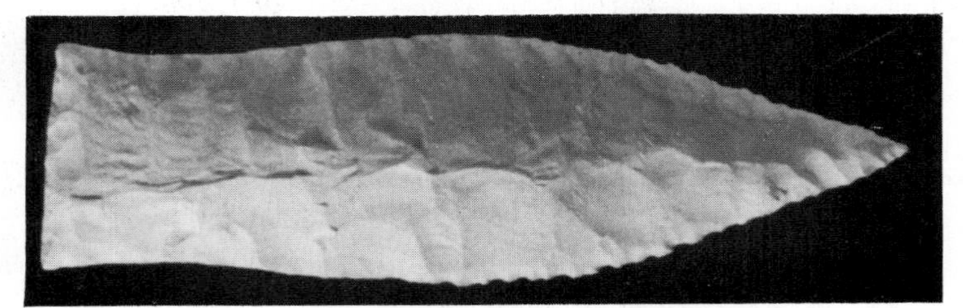

G9, $180-$280, Humphreys Co., TN.

G10, $900-$1250
Parsons, TN. High grade Dover chert and very thin with torque blade. Basal grinding. Classic form.

G10, $500-$850
Humphreys Co., TN. Thin with basal grinding. Excellent quality.

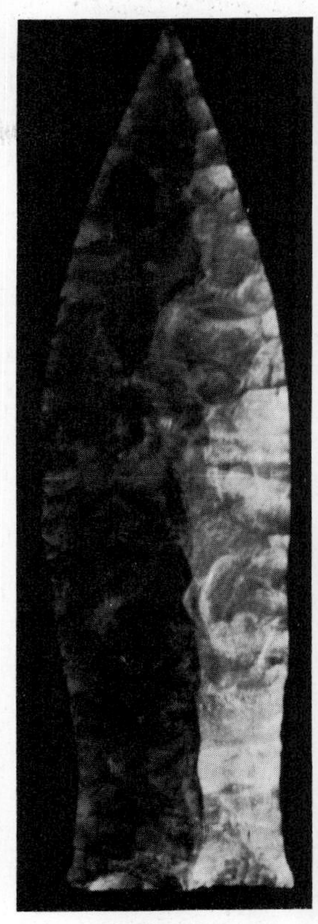

G9, $350-$500

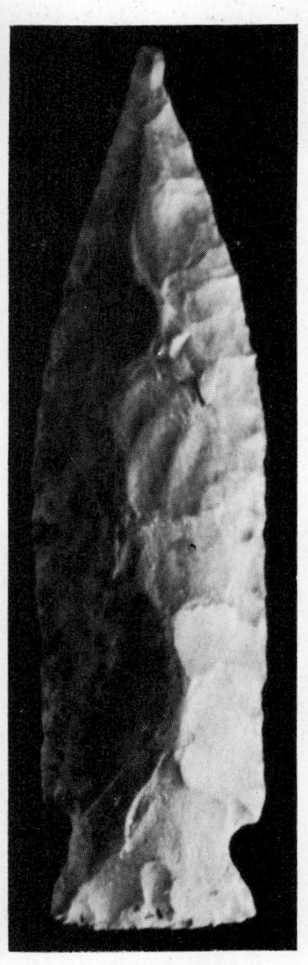

G9, $250-$350

Humphreys Co., TN. A two point cache found together, a Copena (left) and a Bakers Creek (right). Both are made of patinated Dover chert and are probably made by the same person. More proof of the close relationship of these two types.

G8, $130-$250
Humphreys Co., TN.

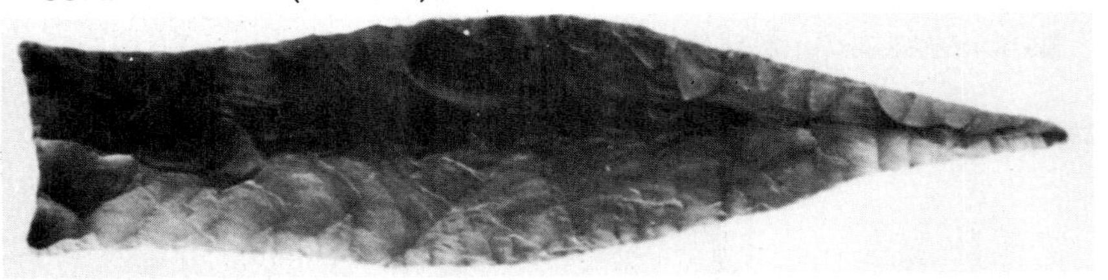

G10, $350-$500
Humphreys Co., TN. Nice needle tip.

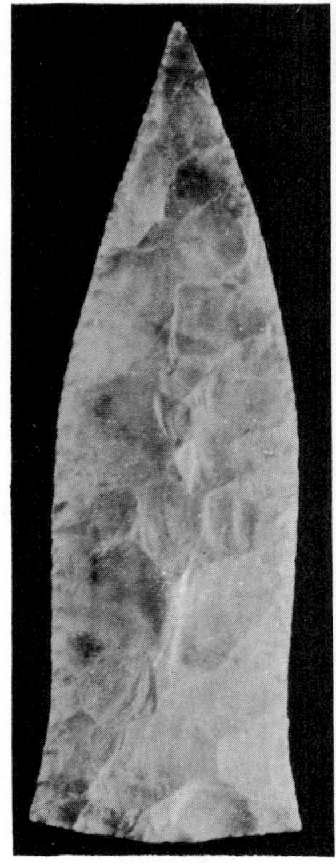

G9, $250-$350
Humphreys Co., TN.

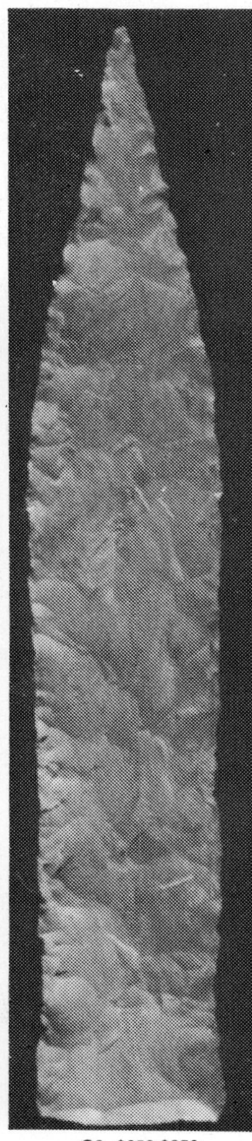

G9, $250-$350
Reelfoot Lake, KY.

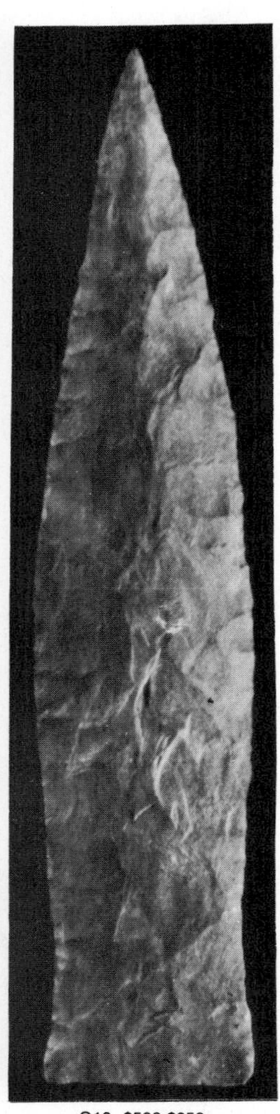

G10, $500-$850
Humphreys Co., TN. Very thin and excellent quality. Basal area is ground. Torque blade.

COPENA-ROUND BASE - Late-Archaic to Woodland, 4000 - 1200 B.P.

(Also see Tennessee River)

G3, $4-$6
W. TN.

G4, $8-$12
Parsons, TN.

G5, $10-$20
Lauderdale Co., AL.

G6, $15-$25
Davidson Co., TN.

G5, $12-$20
Decatur, AL.

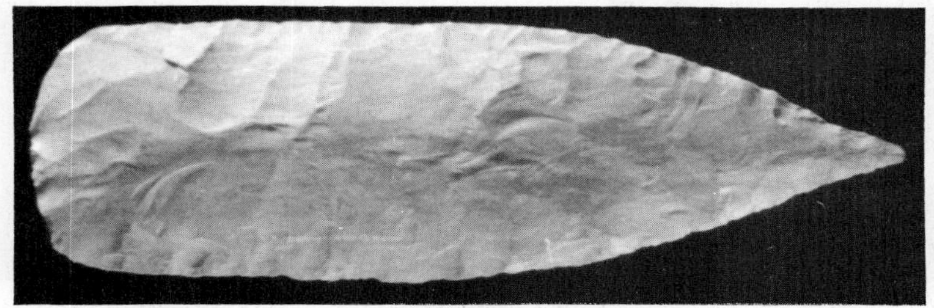

G8, $45-$80
Savannah, TN., Snake Creek.
Pink chert. Excellent quality.

LOCATION: Southeastern states. **DESCRIPTION:** A medium to large size lanceolate blade with a rounded base. Blade edges become parallel towards the base on some examples.

COPENA-TRIANGULAR - Late Archaic to Woodland, 4000 - 1800 B.P.

(See Benton Blade)

G4, $6-$10
Hardin Co., TN.

G5, $10-$20
N. AL.

G4, $6-$10
W. TN.

G5, $8-$15
Florence, AL.

G5, $8-$15
Fort Payne, AL.

G5, $8-$15
New Era, TN.

G6, $20-$35
Humphreys Co., TN.

LOCATION: Southeastern states. **DESCRIPTION:** A medium to large size lanceolate blade with a straight base. Blade edges become parallel towards the base. Some examples show a distinct hafting area near the base where the blade edges form a very weak shoulder and become slightly concave.

G7, $35-$45
Meigs Co., TN.

G8, $45-$60
Hardin Co., TN.

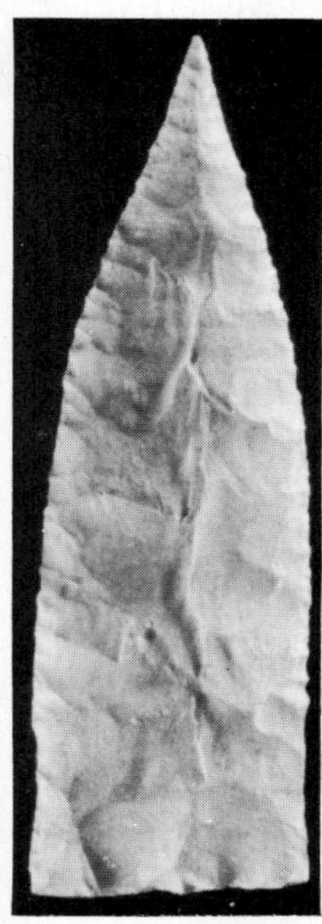

G9, $80-$120
Decatur Co., TN. Needle tip.
Ground basal area.

G9, $125-$225, Hardin Co., TN. Note definite break between blade and hafting area. Needle tip.

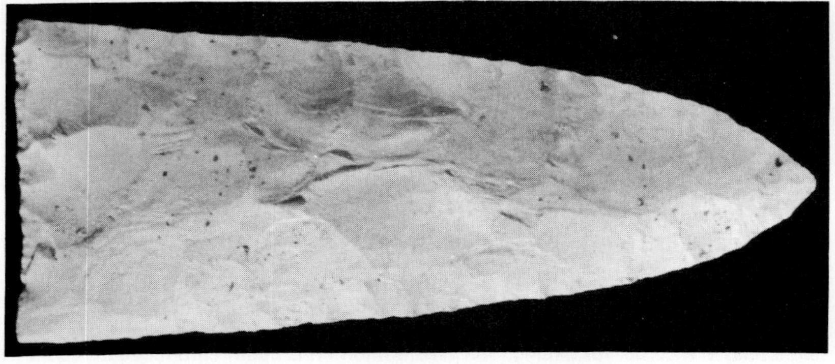

G9, $90-$150. Humphreys Co., TN. Outstanding wide-base form.

CORNER TANG KNIFE - Late Archaic to Woodland, 4000 - 2000 B.P.

(Also see Base Tang Knife)

G1, $6-$10
W. TN.

G7, $150-$250
Austin, TX.

G1, $6-$10
W. TN.

G1, $6-$10
W. TN.

G9, $450-$750
Comanche Co., TX. Note caliche deposit on blade surface.

G8, $250-$400
Stenette, TX.

LOCATION: Western to Southeastern states. **DESCRIPTION:** The Eastern form is a medium size blade with only one of the basal corners notched for hafting. On some examples, the opposite basal corner expands. The Western form is notched producing a tang at a corner for hafting. The Western form has been reproduced in recent years.

G9, $350-$500
Austin, TX.

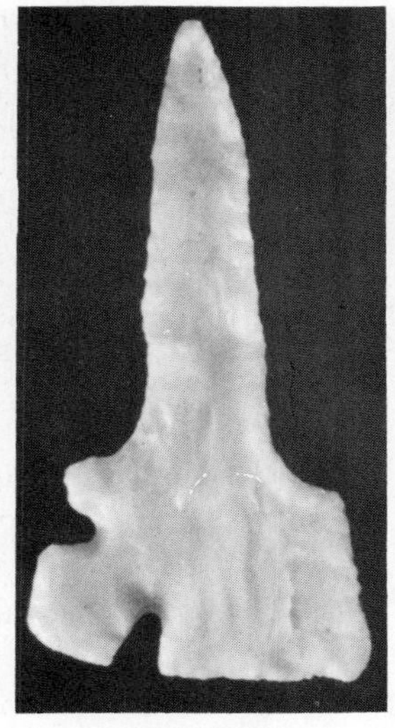

G8, $250-$400
Comanche Co., TX.

G7, $150-$250
Comanche Co., TX.

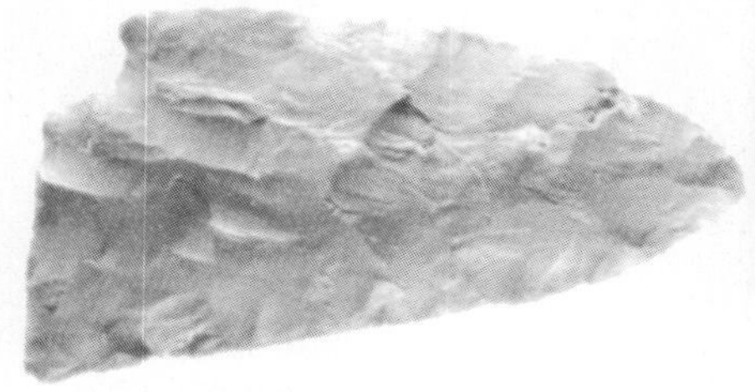

G2, $10-$20
W. TN.

COTACO CREEK - Woodland, 2500 - 2000 B.P.

(Also see Flint Creek and Little Bear Creek)

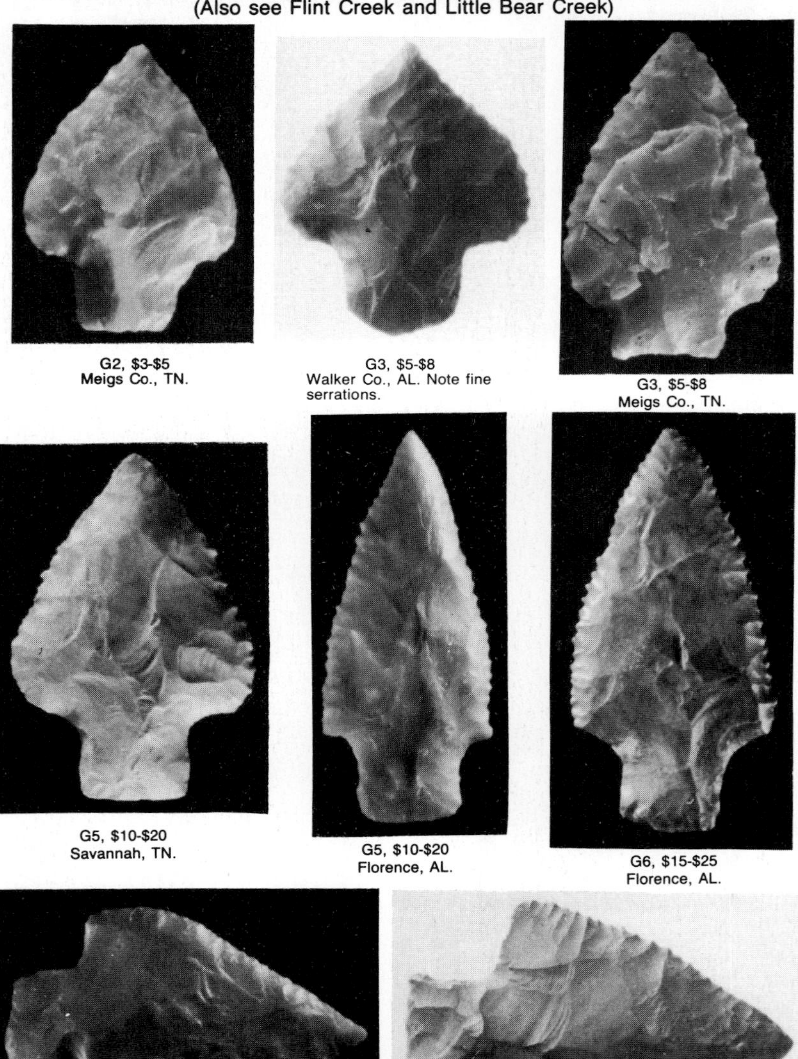

G2, $3-$5
Meigs Co., TN.

G3, $5-$8
Walker Co., AL. Note fine serrations.

G3, $5-$8
Meigs Co., TN.

G5, $10-$20
Savannah, TN.

G5, $10-$20
Florence, AL.

G6, $15-$25
Florence, AL.

G5, $10-$20
Decatur, AL.

G6, $20-$35, Parsons, TN.

LOCATION: Southeastern states. **DESCRIPTION:** A small to medium size, well made, broad, triangular stemmed point with wide rounded to square shoulders. Blade edges are usually finely serrated and some examples have blunt tips. **I.D. KEY:** Edgework and rounded shoulders.

G6, $15-$25
Savannah, TN.

G6, $20-$35
Decatur, AL.

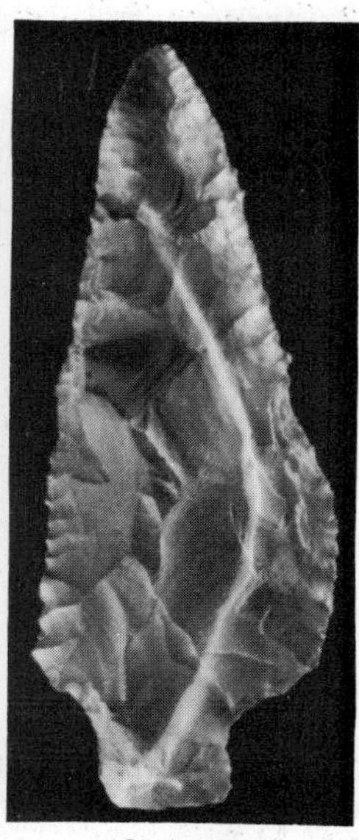

G7, $50-$80
Clifton, TN. Horse Creek chert.

G9, $250-$350
Florence, AL. Classic high quality example..

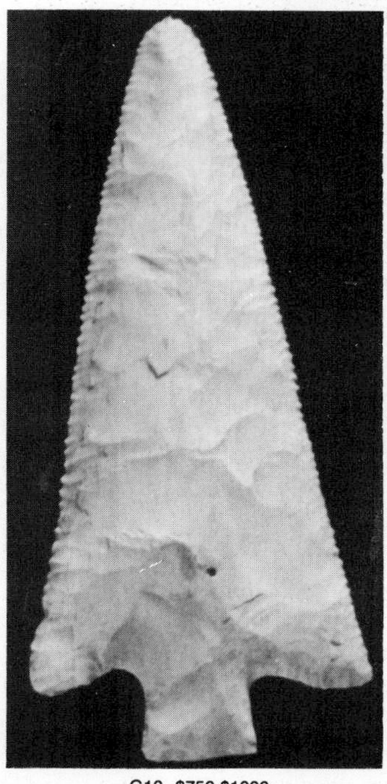

G10, $750-$1000
Ramar, TN. Very unusual fine serrated edges which occur on all four sides and extend around the tip. Excellent quality.

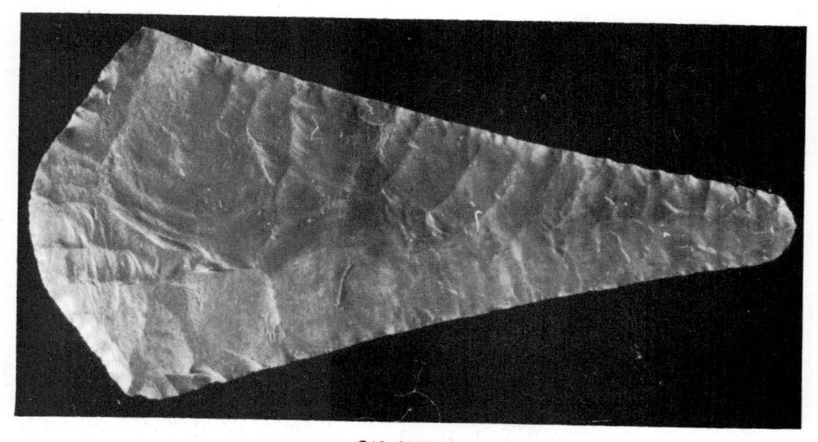

G10, $280-$400
W. TN. This is a very rare preform found in a cache with the other two points on this page. All of these points are very thin and of excellent quality. The prices listed are for individual points. If sold as a cache, they would bring much more.

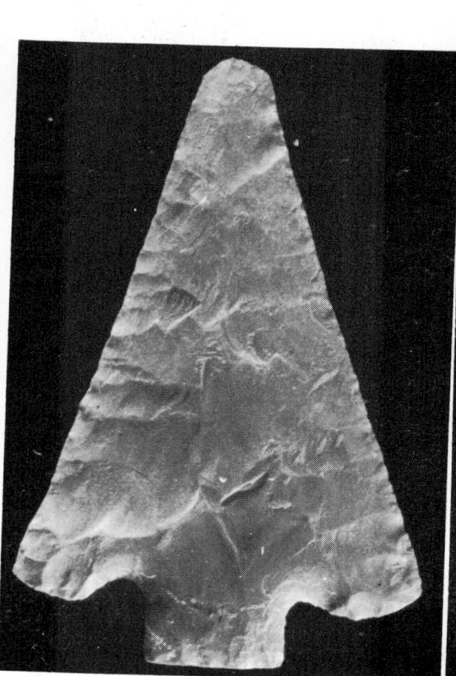

G10, $450-$650
W. TN. Cache.

G10, $350-$600
W. TN. Cache.

G10, $550-$900
Parsons, TN. Rare blade form.

G9, $250-$400
Florence, AL. Unusual side-notched form. Note typical Cotaco pressure flaking on blade edges.

COTACO-WRIGHT - Woodland, 2500 - 1800 B.P.

(Also see Flint Creek and Little Bear Creek)

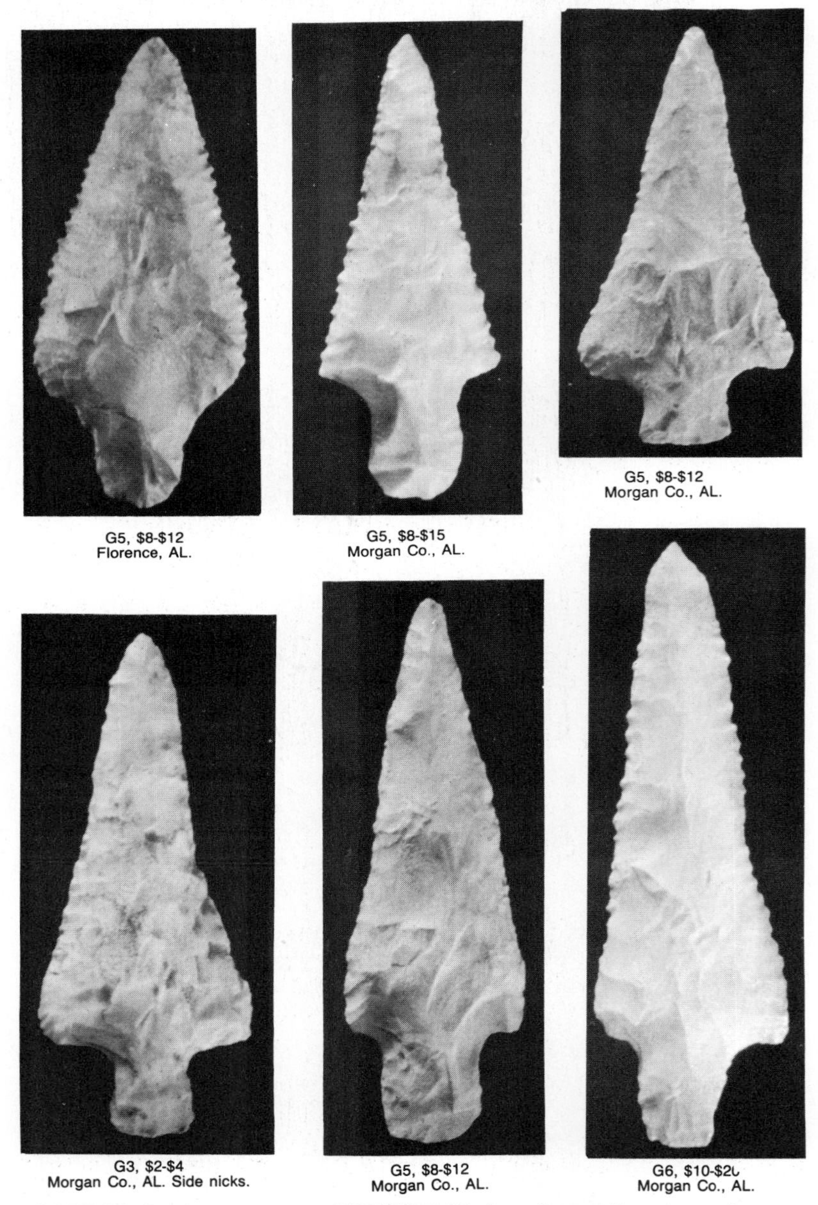

G5, $8-$12
Florence, AL.

G5, $8-$15
Morgan Co., AL.

G5, $8-$12
Morgan Co., AL.

G3, $2-$4
Morgan Co., AL. Side nicks.

G5, $8-$12
Morgan Co., AL.

G6, $10-$20
Morgan Co., AL.

LOCATION: Southeastern states. **DESCRIPTION:** A small to medium size, well made, narrow, triangular stemmed point with rounded to square shoulders. Blade edges are usually finely serrated and some have blunt tips.

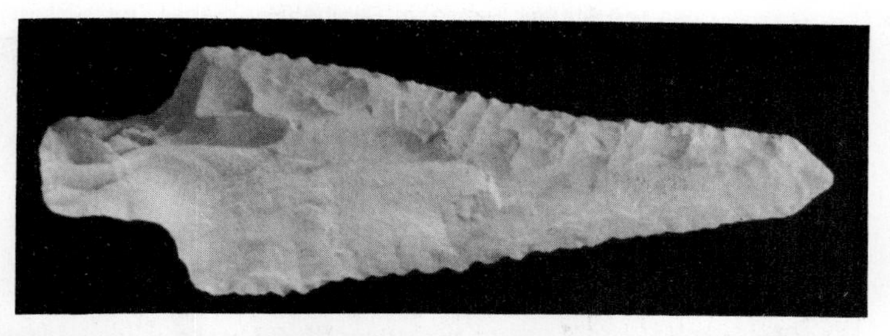

G8, $35-$50
Morgan Co., AL.

COTTONBRIDGE - Mid-Archaic, 6000 - 4000 B.P.

(Also see Abbey and Elora)

G8, $35-$60
Henry Co., AL.

LOCATION: Southern Gulf states. **DESCRIPTION:** A medium size, broad, stemmed point that is fairly thick and beveled on all four sides. Shoulders are tapered and blade edges are straight. Base is small and rounded with contracting sides.

COTTONWOOD TRIANGLE - Late Archaic, 4000 - 3000 B.P.

(Also see Papago and San Jose)

G3, $2-$3
Yavapai Co., AZ.

G1, .25-.50
Yavapai Co., AZ.

LOCATION: Southwestern states. **DESCRIPTION:** A small to medium size triangular point with very weak shoulders near the base which has rounded corners and is concave.

COVINGTON - Late Archaic, 4000 - 3000 B.P.

(Also see Friday, Gahagan, Sabine, San Saba, Texas Blade)

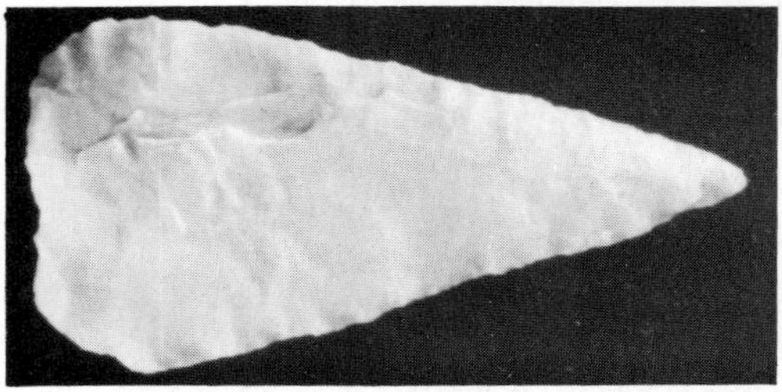

G5, $4-$6
Comanche Co., TX.

G6, $4-$6
Comanche Co., TX.

G4, $2-$5
Austin, TX.

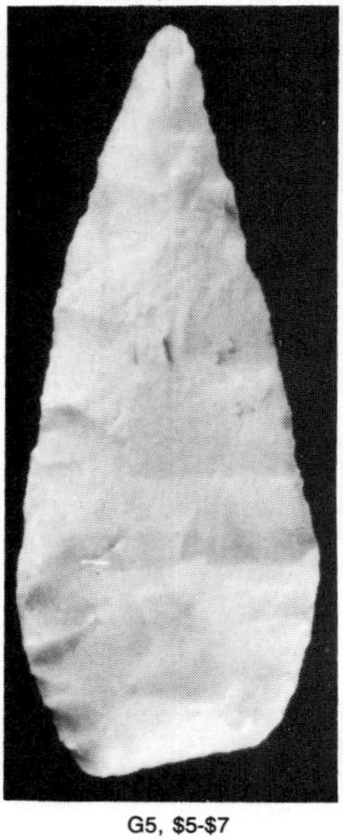

G5, $5-$7
Comanche Co., TX.

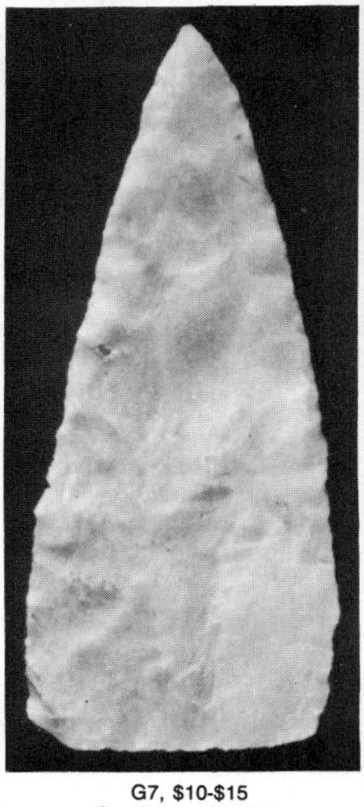

G7, $10-$15
Comanche Co., TX.

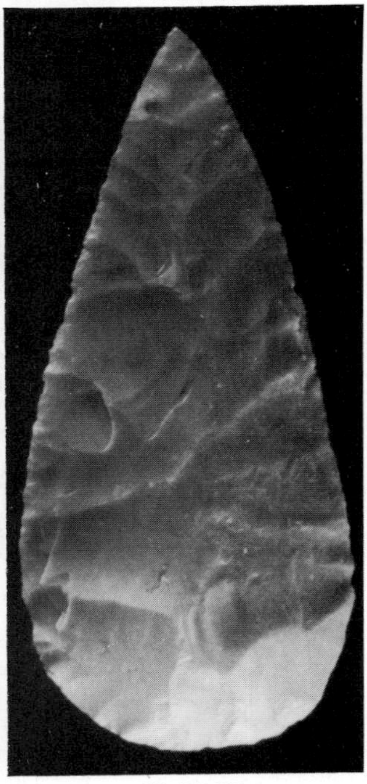

G9, $20-$35
Austin, TX.

LOCATION: Midwestern states. **DESCRIPTION:** A medium to large size, thin, lanceolate blade with a broad, rounded base.

COWHOUSE SLOUGH - Transitional Paleo, 10000 - 6000 B.P.

(Also see Angostura, Hardaway Blade and Paint Rock Valley)

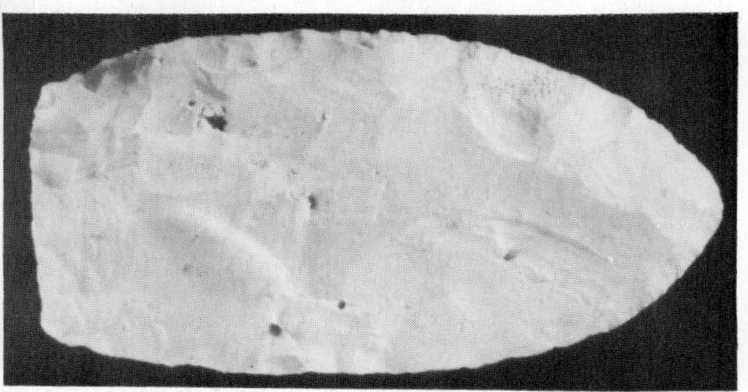

G7, $65-$90
Hillsborough Co., FL.

G6, $45-$70
Hillsborough Co., FL.

G8, $85-$150
Hillsborough Co., FL.

G5, $35-$50
Lawrence Co., AL.

LOCATION: Southern Southeastern states. **DESCRIPTION:** A medium to large size, broad, lanceolate blade with a contracting, straight to concave base which may be ground as well as fluted or thinned. **I.D. KEY:** Paleo flaking.

CRAWFORD CREEK - Early Archaic, 8000 - 5000 B.P.

(Also see Coosa, Mud Creek and White Springs)

G6, $6-$10
Limestone Co., AL.

G1, .50-$1
Hamilton Co., TN.

G5, $4-$6
Madison Co., AL.

G6, $6-$10
Morgan Co., AL.

G8, $25-$40
Limestone Co., AL.

G7, $8-$12
Limestone Co.. AL.

G6, $6-$10
Meigs Co., TN.

G5, $4-$6
Marshall Co., AL.

G4, $2-$5
Marshall Co., AL.

G3, $2-$3
Morgan Co., AL.

LOCATION: Southeastern states. **DESCRIPTION:** A small to medium size point that is usually serrated with a short, straight to expanding stem. Shoulders are square to tapered. Blade edges are straight to convex. **I.D. KEY:** Edgework.

CRESCENT KNIFE - Mid-Archaic, 7000 - 4000 B.P.

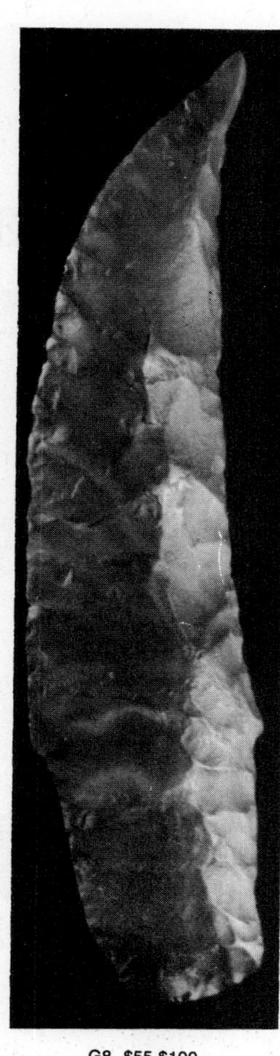

G8, $55-$100
Alaska

G8, $60-$110
Austin, TX.

LOCATION: Texas westward to Alaska. **DESCRIPTION:** A large size, thick, narrow, dagger shaped knife with a curved blade. Weak shoulders are usually present marking the beginning of the hafting area.

CRUMP LAKE STEMMED - Early to Mid Archaic, 8000 - 5000 B.P.

(Also see Kirk Serrated & Little Bear Creek)

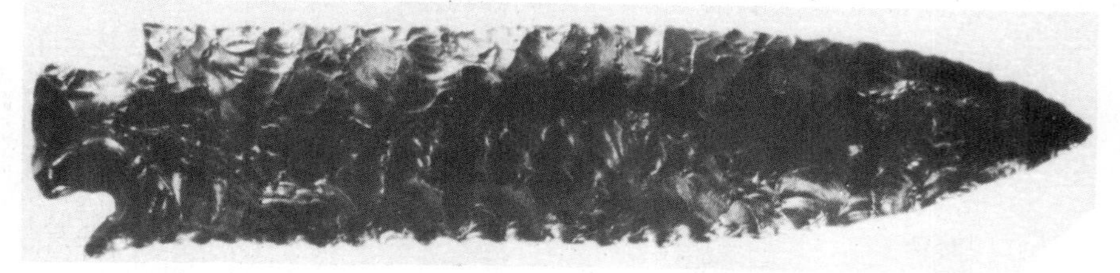

G9, $174-$300, Lake Co., OR, Crump Lake. Obsidian. Note diagonal, parallel flaking.

LOCATION: Northwestern states. **DESCRIPTION:** A large size, narrow, fairly thick, barbed, stemmed point. Oblique, parallel flaking is usually present on one or both blade faces. The stem is short and expanding.

CULBREATH - Late Archaic to Woodland, 5000 - 3000 B.P.

(Also see Citrus, Eva, Hernando, Lafayette & Wade)

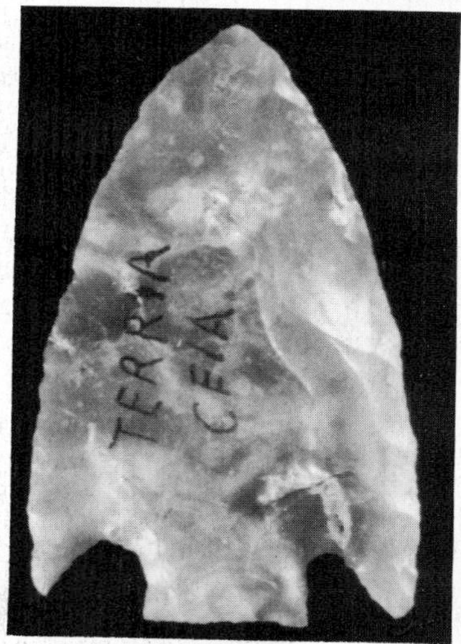

G7, $125-$225
Manatee Co., FL.

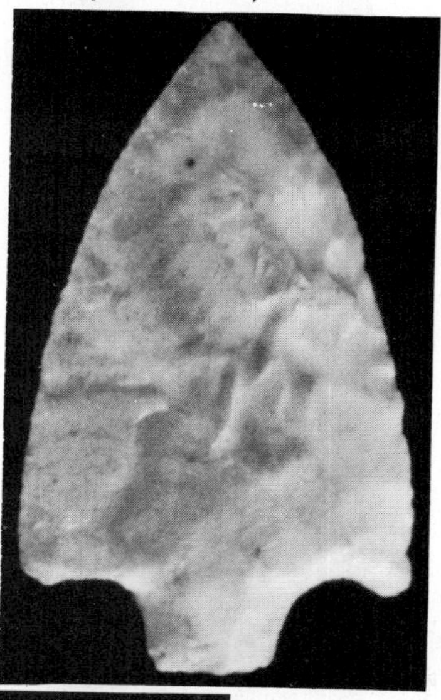

G6, $120-$200
Hillsborough Co., FL.

G4, $35-$50
Suwannee RV., FL.

CULBREATH (continued)

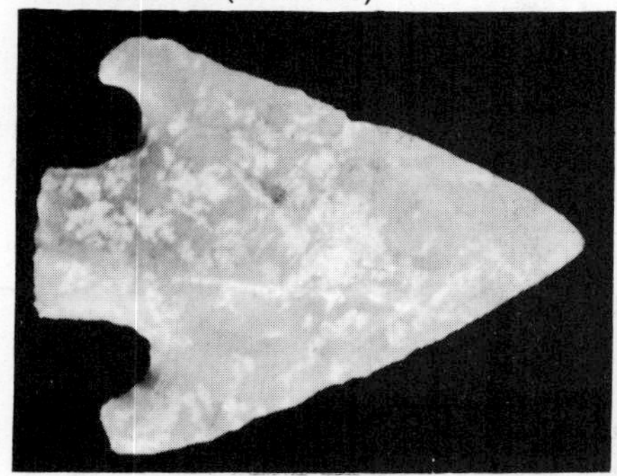

G5, $70-$100
Hillsborough Co., FL.

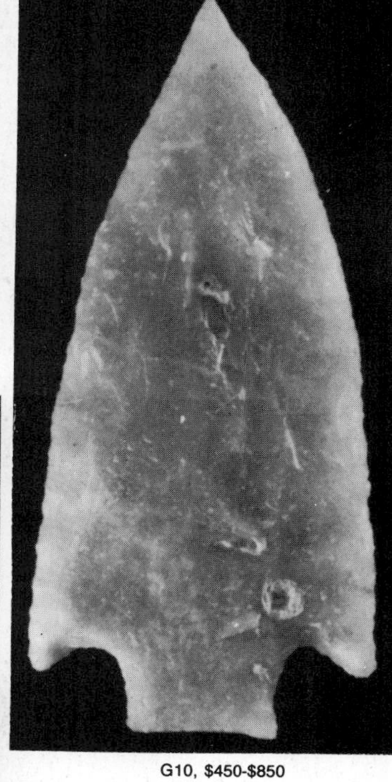

G10, $450-$850
Polk Co., FL.

G9, $250-$400
NW Cent. FL.

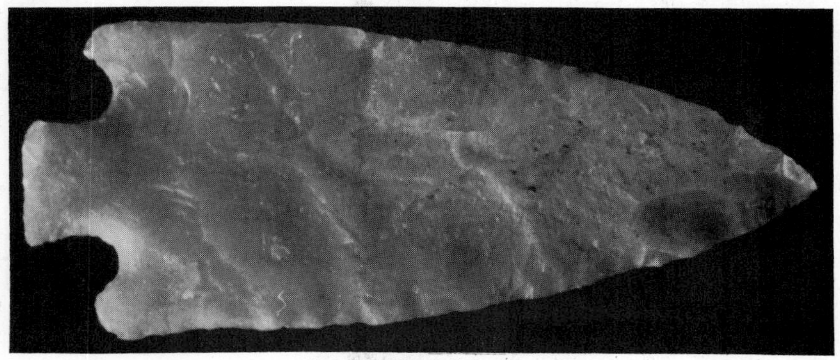

G10, $450-$800, Polk Co., FL.

LOCATION: Southern Gulf states. **DESCRIPTION:** A medium to large size, broad, basal notched point. Tangs are rounded and blade edges are convex. On some examples the tangs do not reach the base. The earlier *Eva* point found in Kentucky and Tennessee could be a Northern cousin. **I.D. KEY:** Notching.

CULBREATH-SNAPPED BASE - Late Archaic to Woodland, 5000 - 3000 B.P.

(Also see Citrus, Eva and Hernando)

G6, $20-$35
South GA.

G5, $20-$30
South GA. Sugar quartz.

LOCATION: Southern Gulf states. **DESCRIPTION:** A medium to large size, broad, basal notched point with a snapped or fractured base. It is interesting to note that its Northern cousin, *Eva* has also been found with a snapped base.

CULPEPPER (See Rice Lobbed)

CUMBERLAND - Paleo, 12000 - 8000 B.P.

(Also see Beaver Lake, Clovis, Copena Auriculate and Quad)

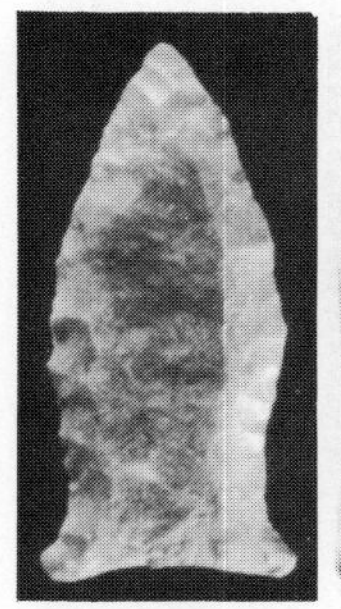

G1, $70-$90
Limestone Co., AL.

G2, $80-$150
Florence, AL.

G3, $150-$250
TN.

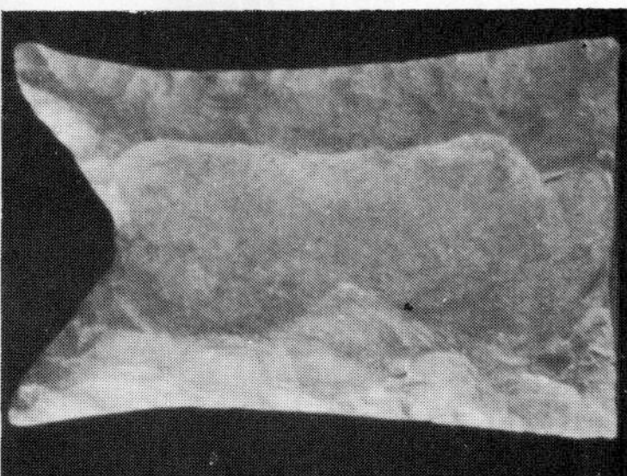

G1, $25-$35
Humphreys Co., TN. Rear half.

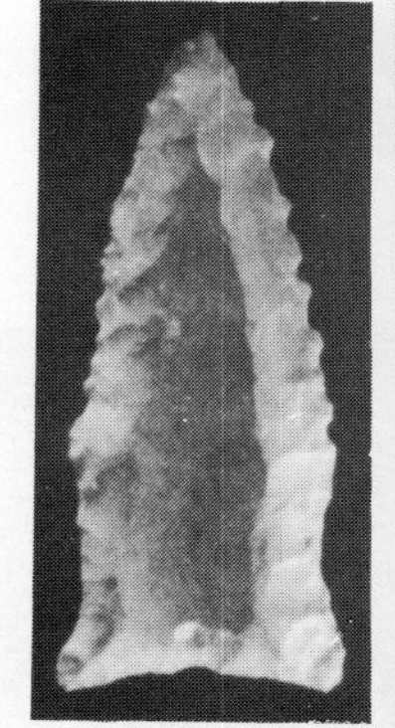

G1, $70-$100
Limestone Co., AL.

G5, $450-$600
Robertson Co., TN. Classic.

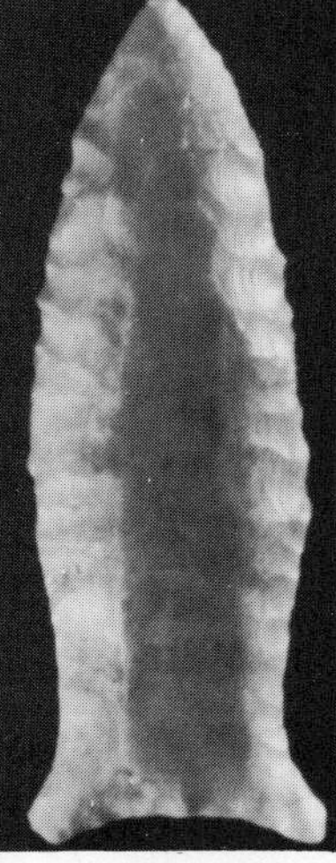

G5, $450-$600
Taylor Co., KY

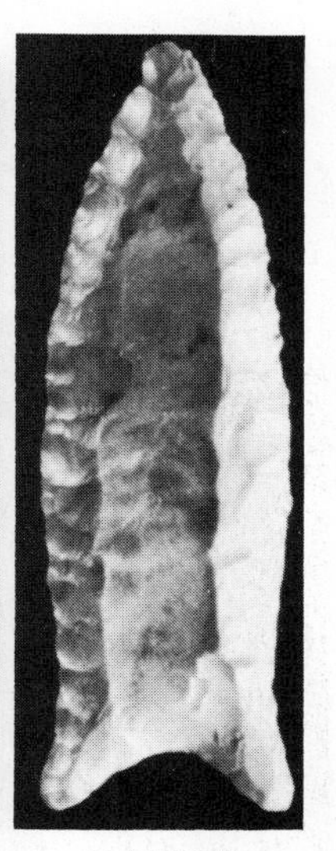

G5, $450-$650
Smith Co., TN. Classic.

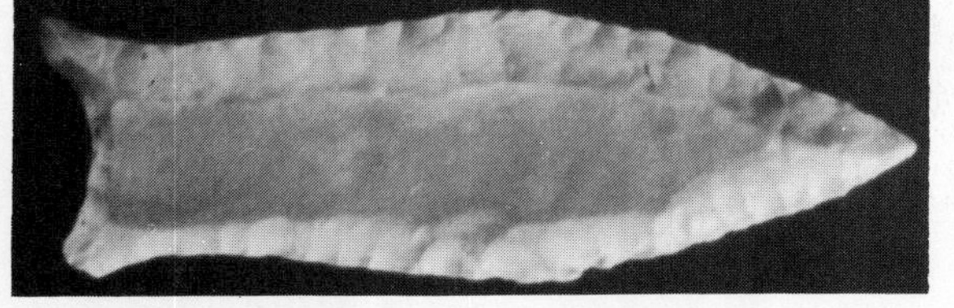

G5, $450-$600
Lauderdale Co., AL. Ear nick.

LOCATION: Southeastern states. **DESCRIPTION:** A medium to large size, lanceolate, eared form that is usually fluted on both faces. The fluting and flaking technique is an advanced form as in *Folsom*, with the flutes usually extending the entire length of the blade. Bases are ground on all examples. An unfluted variant which is thicker than *Beaver Lake* has been found. This point is scarce everywhere and has been reproduced in large numbers. **I.D. KEY:** Paleo flaking, indirect pressure fluted.

CUMBERLAND (continued)

G6, $500-$850
Lauderdale Co., AL. Classic.

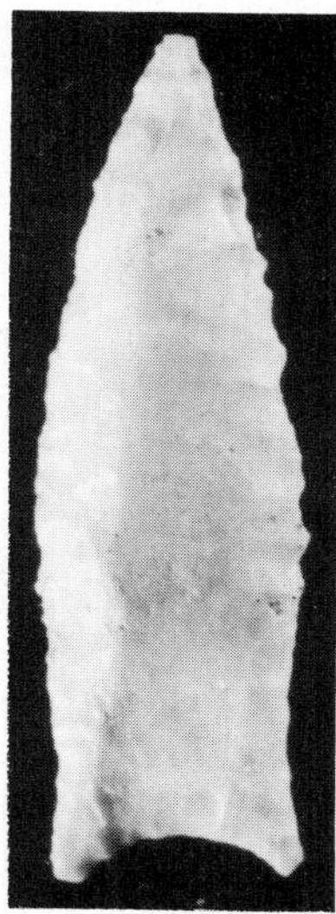

G4, $350-$500
Benton Co., TN.

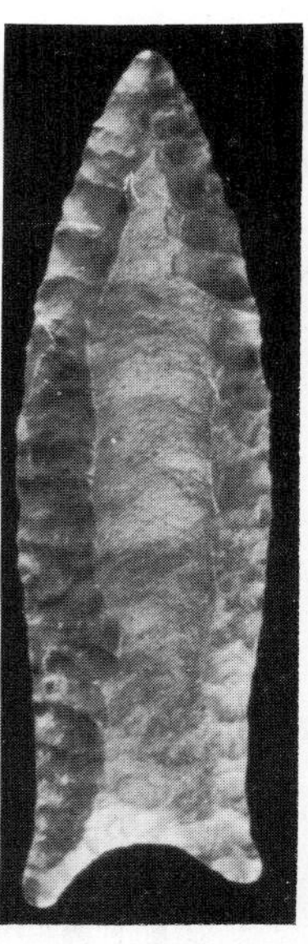

G7, $600-$1000
Benton Co., TN. Classic.

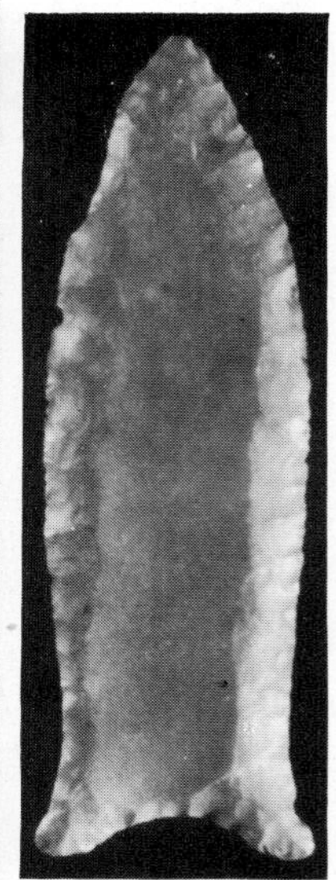

G4, $350-$550
Coffee Co., TN. Excellent fluting. Minor nicks.

G5, $400-$600
W. TN.

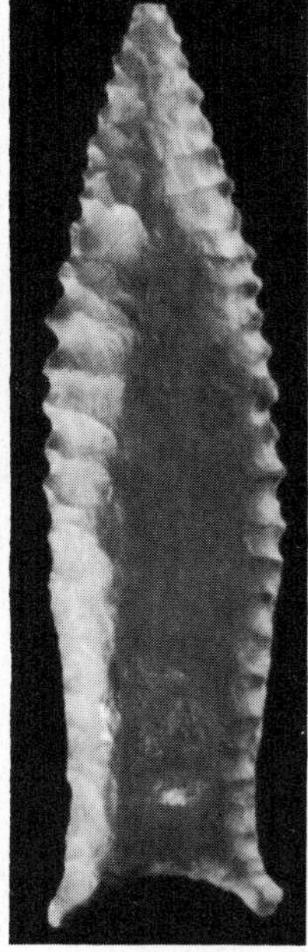

G8, $800-$1500
Humphreys Co., TN. Rare serrated form. Classic.

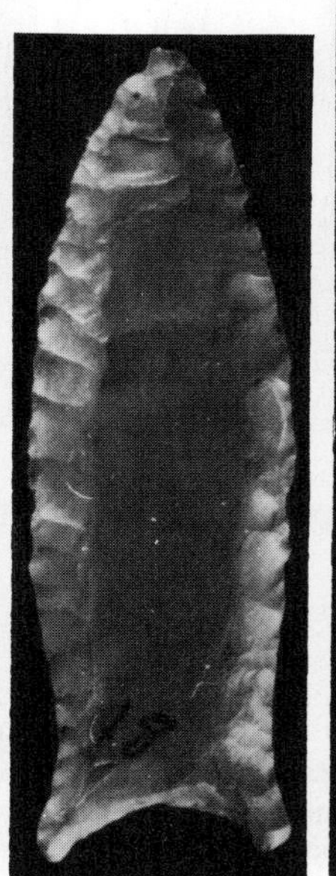

G6, $500-$800
W. TN.

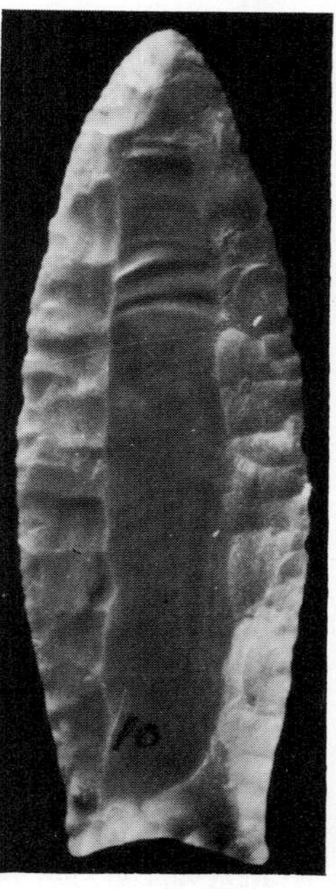

G7, $600-$1000
KY.

CUMBERLAND (continued)

G7, $750-$1350
Jackson Co., AL. Classic wide form. Minor tip nick.

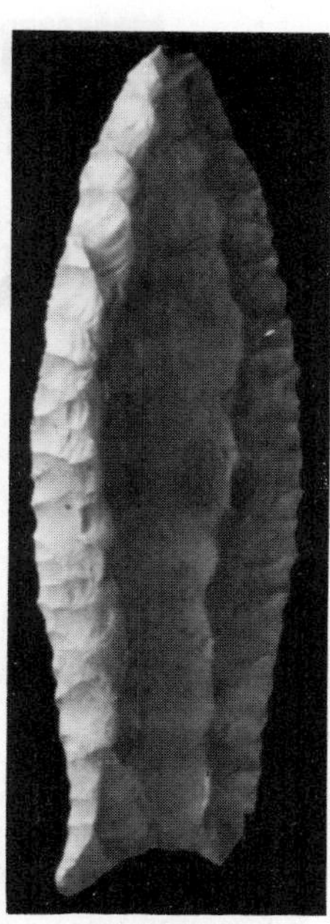

G3, $250-$350
W. TN. Excellent fluting. Tip and ear damage.

G4, $350-$500
Elk River, Giles Co., TN. Note impact repair on left side by Indian.

G7, $600-$1000
Mercer Co., KY.

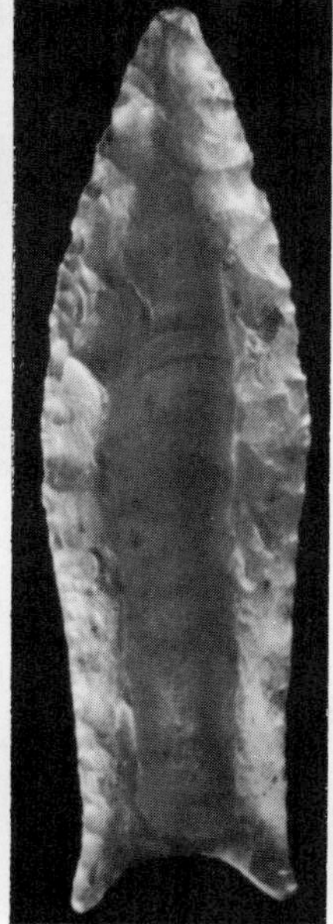

G8, $1200-$1800
Giles Co. TN. Deep fluting both sides. Excellent quality.

G8, $1000-$1600
Giles Co., TN.

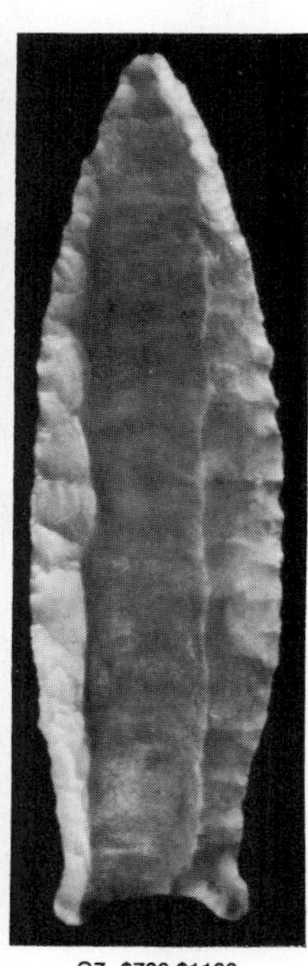

G7, $700-$1100
Transylvania Co., NC.

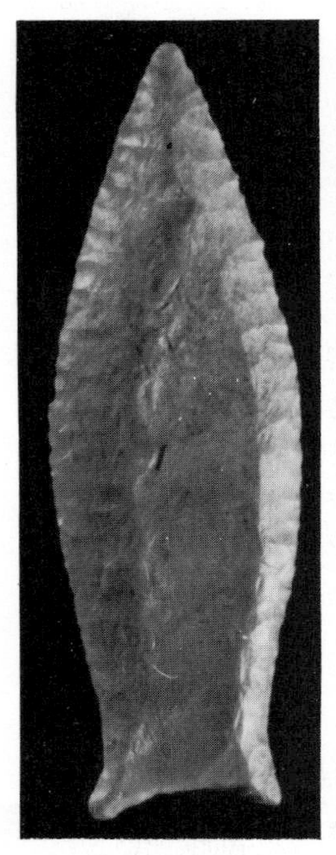

G10, $3500-$5000
Colbert Co., AL. Classic form. In Alabama type book.

G7, $550-$850
Hardin Co., TN. Heavy patina. Charred by fire.

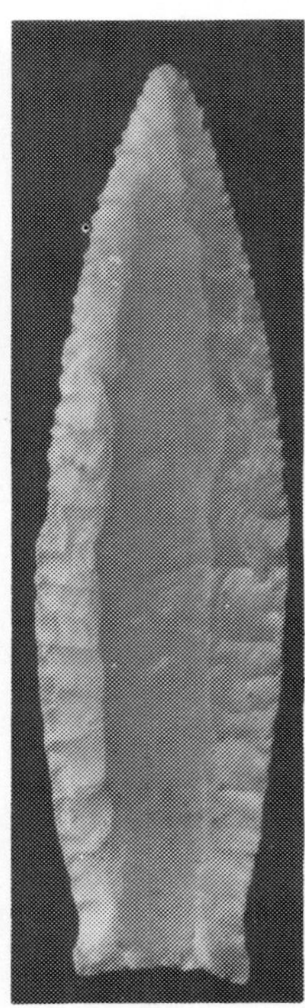

G7, $600-$1000
KY.

G9, $2000-$3500
Humphreys Co., TN.

G6, $500-$800
W. TN. Tip nick.

CUMBERLAND (continued)

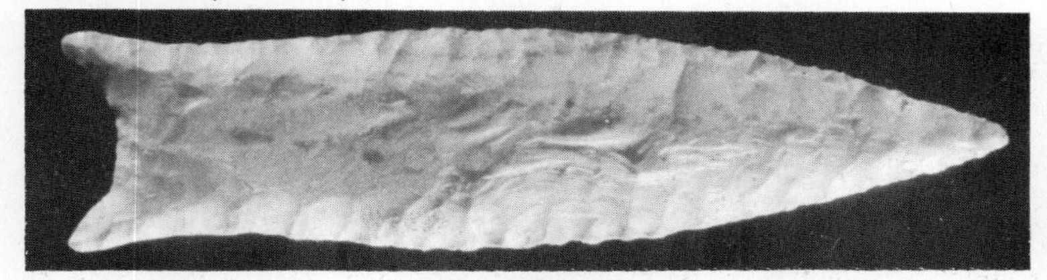

G9, $1500-$2500
Humphreys Co., TN. Buffalo River chert. Very thin, weak fluting.

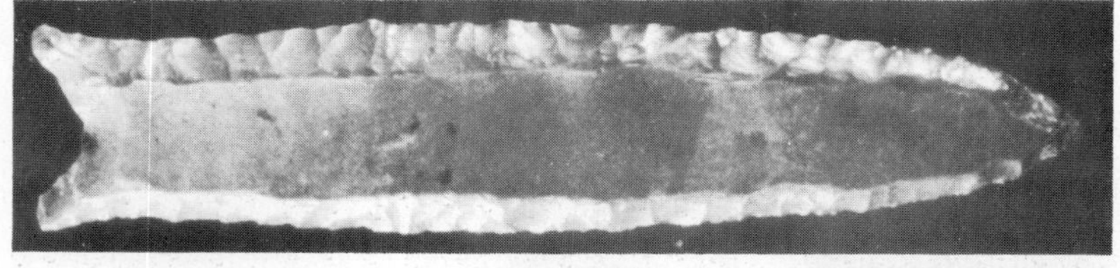

G5, $400-$600
Lake Champlain, VT.

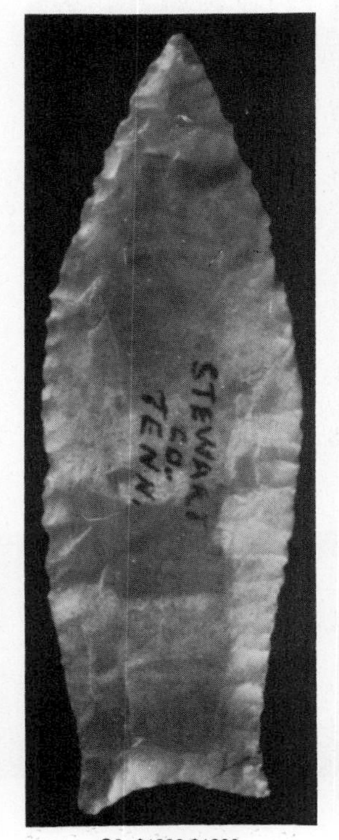

G8, $1200-$1800
Stewart Co., TN.

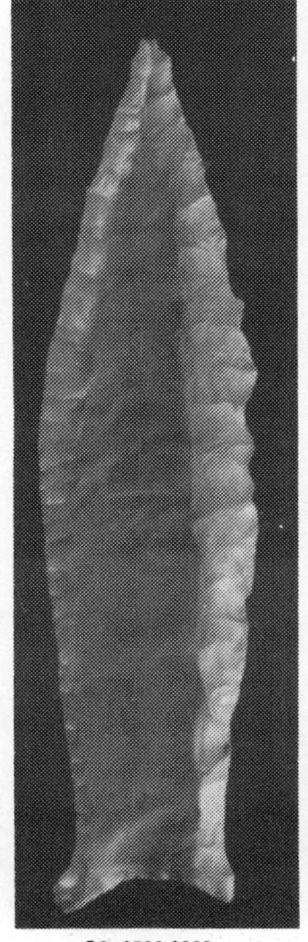

G6, $500-$800
Kingston, TN. Blade nicks.

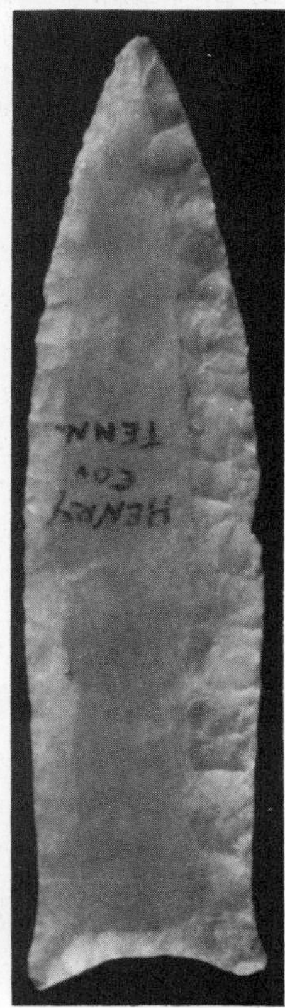

G8, $800-$1500
Henry Co., TN.

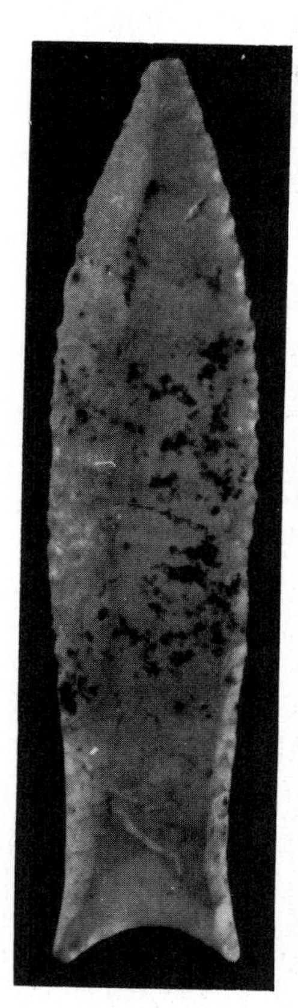

G8, $1700-$2500
Pike Co., IL.

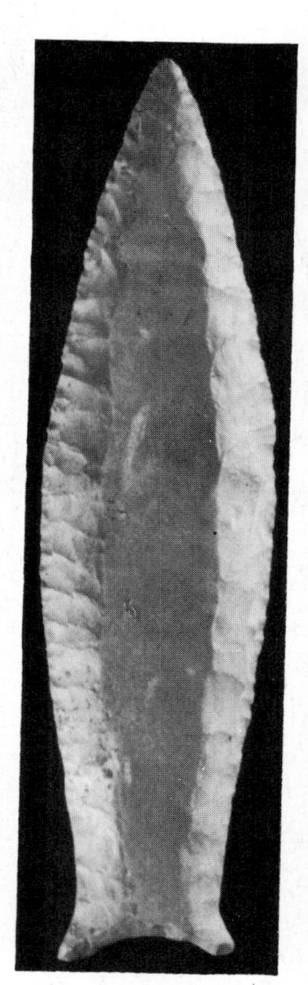

G10, $4500-$8000
Montgomery Co., TN. Outstanding quality and fluted to tip on both sides. Fort Payne chert.

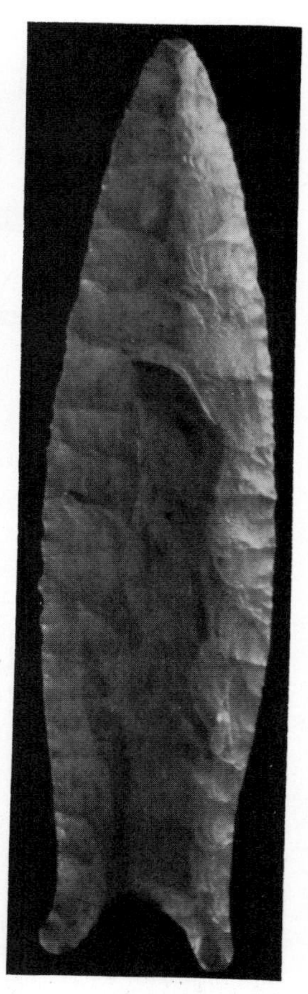

G9, $2500-$4000
Stewart Co., TN., Wells Creek. Used in Sun Circles & Human Hands. Fluted on one side only.

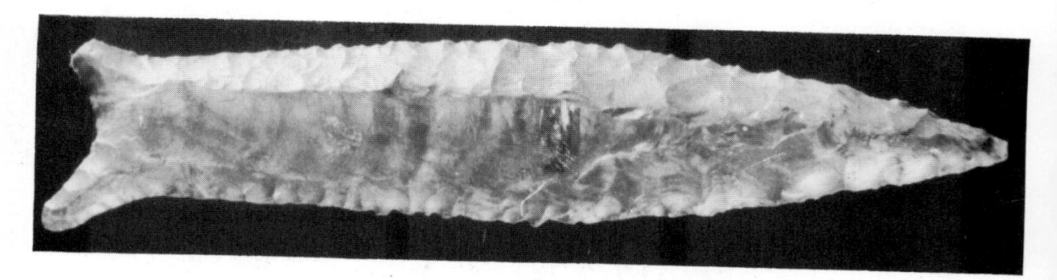

G6, $500-$850
Smith Co., TN. Ear nick.

G6, $550-$850
KY. Ear damage.

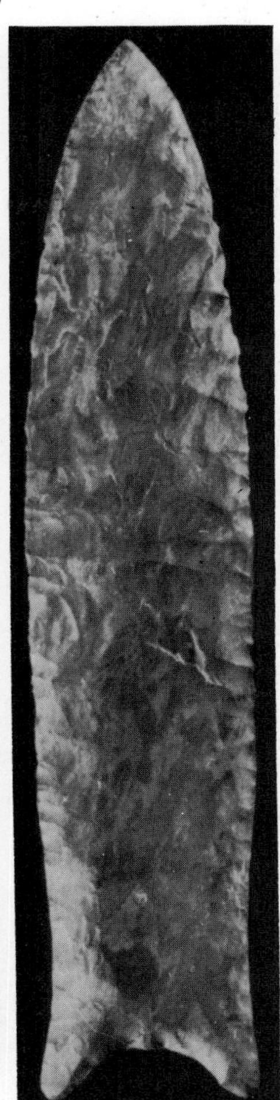

G9, $2500-$3500
Humphreys Co., TN.
Dover chert.

G10, $7500-$10,000
Dickson Co., TN. Excellent quality. Fluted to tip on both sides. Fort Payne chert. One of Tennessee's finest.

G10, $5000-$7500
Marsker Creek, N. of Nashville, TN. Classic form. Known as "Big Red." Made of pink chert.

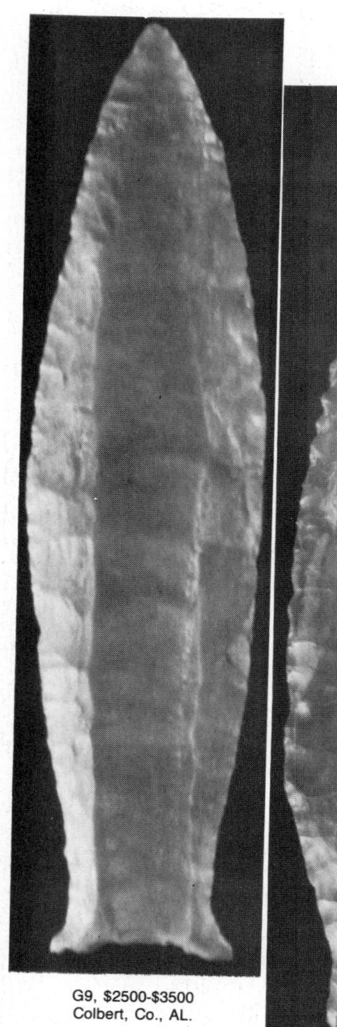

G9, $2500-$3500
Colbert, Co., AL.

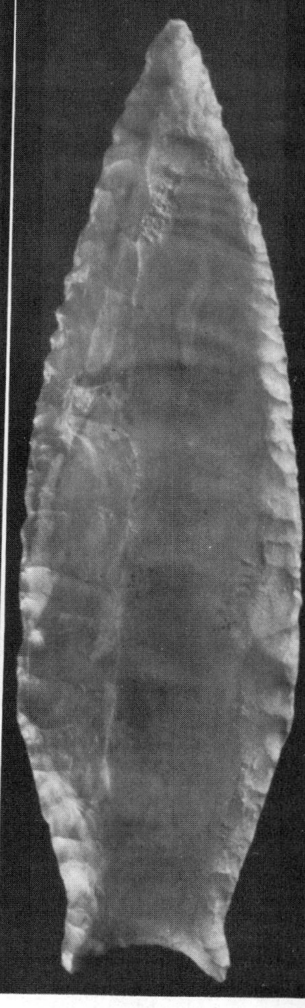

G9, $3000-$5000
Mouth of Flint Creek, AL.

G8, $1400-$2200
N. AL. Note serrated edges.

G7, $600-$1000
Lincoln Co., TN. Ears clipped.

G10, $15,000-$20,000
Florence, AL. This is one of the finest and largest Cumberlands you will ever see. Extremely rare and super.

CUNEY - Historic, 400 - 200 B.P.

(Also see Bonham, Fox Valley, Morris, Perdiz, Rockwall and Scallorn)

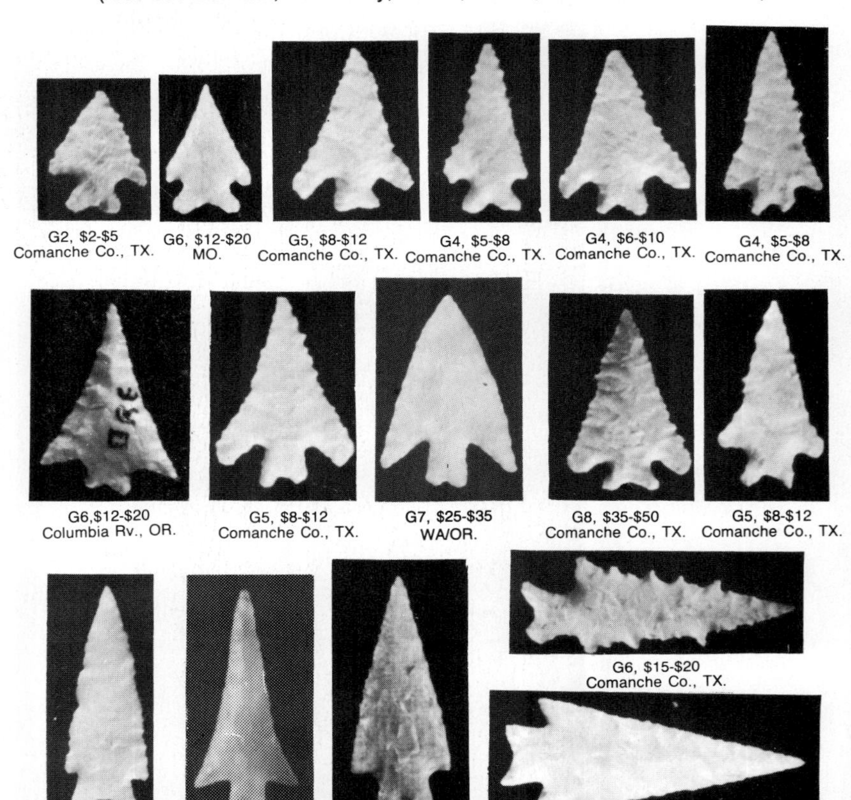

G2, $2-$5 Comanche Co., TX.

G6, $12-$20 MO.

G5, $8-$12 Comanche Co., TX.

G4, $5-$8 Comanche Co., TX.

G4, $6-$10 Comanche Co., TX.

G4, $5-$8 Comanche Co., TX.

G6,$12-$20 Columbia Rv., OR.

G5, $8-$12 Comanche Co., TX.

G7, $25-$35 WA/OR.

G8, $35-$50 Comanche Co., TX.

G5, $8-$12 Comanche Co., TX.

G6, $15-$20 Comanche Co., TX.

G3, $4-$6 Comanche Co., TX.

G6, $15-$20 Columbia Rv., WA.

G5, $8-$12 Columbia Rv., WA.

G9, $45-$80 Columbia Rv., WA.

LOCATION: Midwestern states. **DESCRIPTION:** A small size, well made, barbed, triangular point with a very short, small base that is bifurcated.

CUPP - Late Woodland to Mississippian, 1500 - 600 B.P.

(Also see Buck Creek, Epps, Hamilton, Motley, Smithsonia and Snyders)

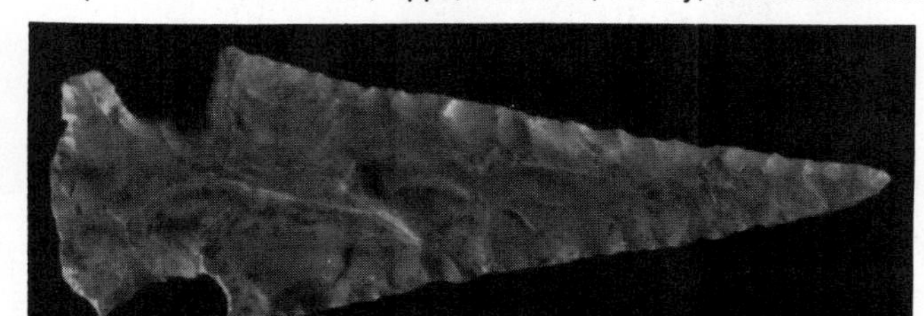

G5, $25-$45 MO.

CUPP (continued)

G10, $1200-$2000
Greene Co., MO. Excellent quality.

LOCATION: Eastern states. **DESCRIPTION:** A medium to large size, narrow point with wide corner notches, shoulder barbs and a convex base. Similar to *Motley*, but the base stem is shorter and broader. *Epps* has square to tapered shoulders, otherwise is identical.

CYPRESS CREEK - Mid-Archaic, 7000 - 3000 B.P.

(Also see Alachua, Hillsborough, Levy, Morrow Mountain, Putnam and Sumter)

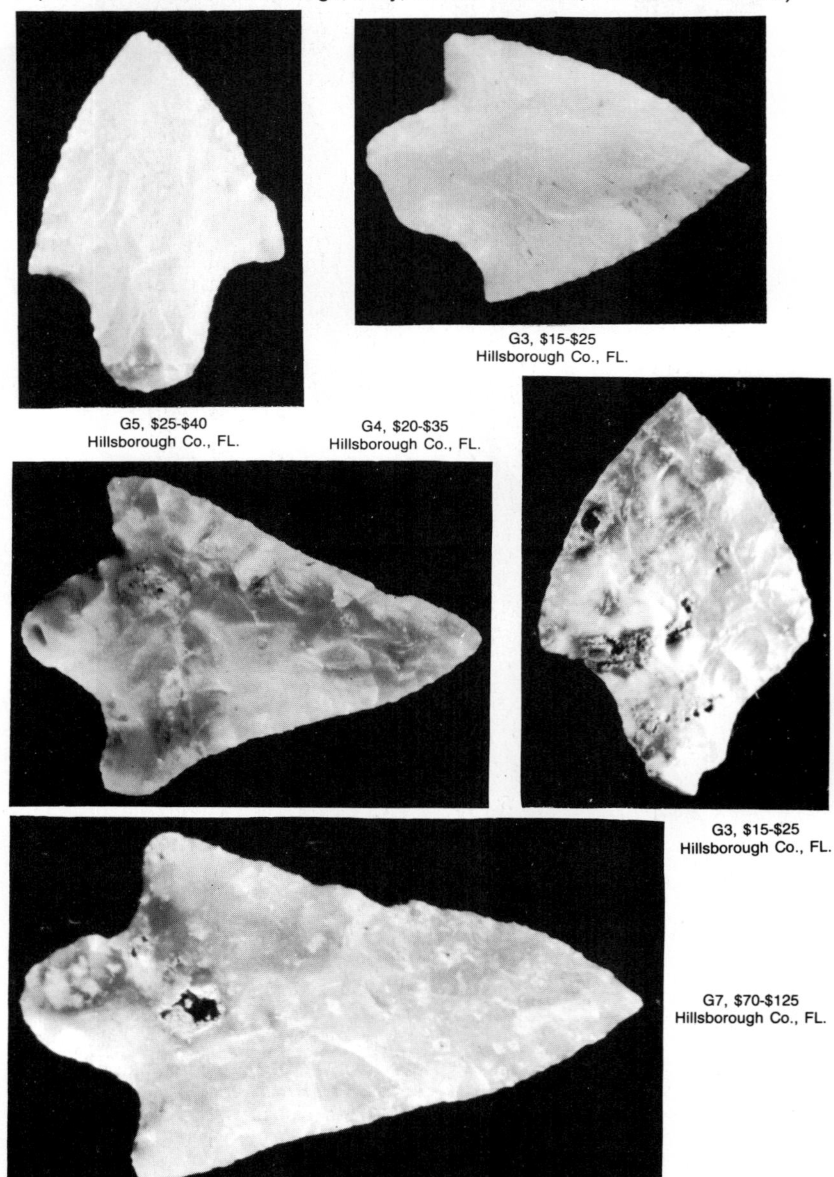

G3, $15-$25
Hillsborough Co., FL.

G5, $25-$40
Hillsborough Co., FL.

G4, $20-$35
Hillsborough Co., FL.

G3, $15-$25
Hillsborough Co., FL.

G7, $70-$125
Hillsborough Co., FL.

LOCATION: Southern Southeastern states. **DESCRIPTION:** A medium size point with a short, pointed to rounded contracting base. Shoulders have short barbs and can be asymmetrical with one barbed and the other tapered.

CYPRESS CREEK (continued)

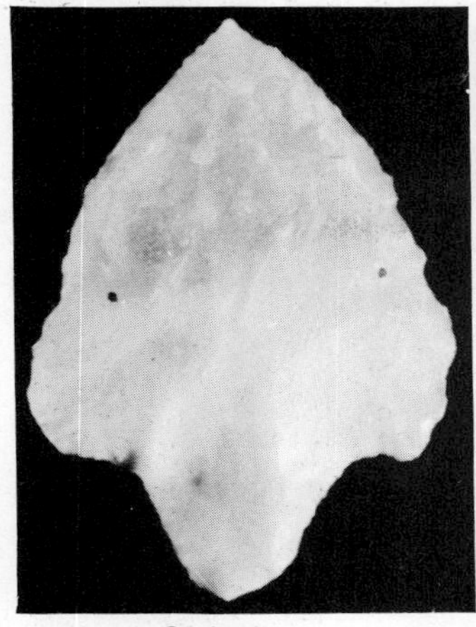

G5, $25-$40
Hillsborough Co., FL.

G4, $20-$35
Hillsborough Co., FL.

CYPRESS CREEK - Mid to late Archaic, 5000 - 3000 B.P.

(Also see Hardin, Kirk Corner-Notched and Lost Lake)

G8, $45-$70
Giles Co., TN.

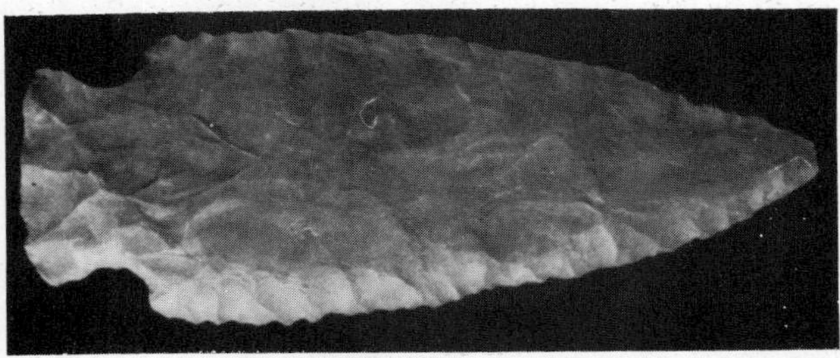

G4, $12-$20
Humphreys Co., TN. Weak shoulders.

LOCATION: Southeastern states. **DESCRIPTION:** A medium to large size, broad stemmed point with an expanded base and drooping "umbrella" shoulder tangs. A cross between *Lost Lake* and *Kirk Corner Notched*. The blade is beveled on all four sides. **I.D. KEY:** Archaic flaking, shoulders droop.

CYPRESS CREEK (continued)

G8, $50-$80
Humphreys Co., TN.

G6, $35-$50
Humphreys Co., TN. Note thinning strikes from base.

DALLAS (See Guntersville)

DALLAS - Late Archaic to Woodland, 4000 - 1500 B.P.

(Also see Adena-Wells, Buggs Island, Carrollton, Dawson, Elam, Rheems Creek and Ventana-Amargosa)

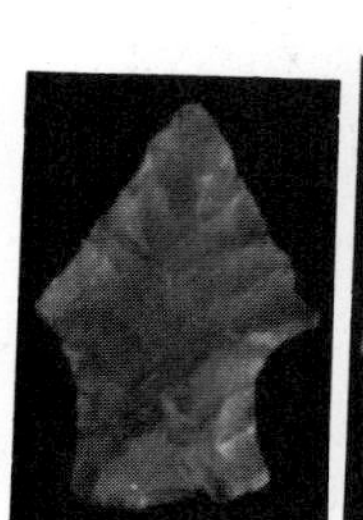

G2, $2-$4
Dallas, TX.

G1, $1-$2
Dallas, TX.

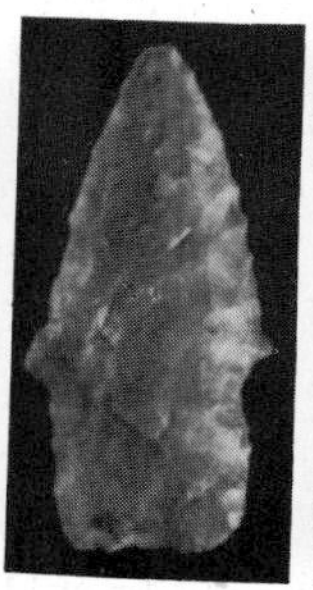

G4, $3-$5
Dallas, TX.

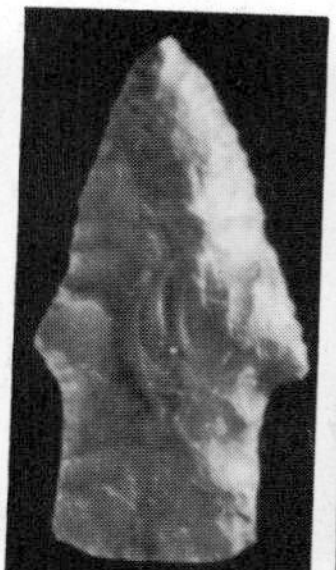

G5, $4-$6
Comanche Co., TX.

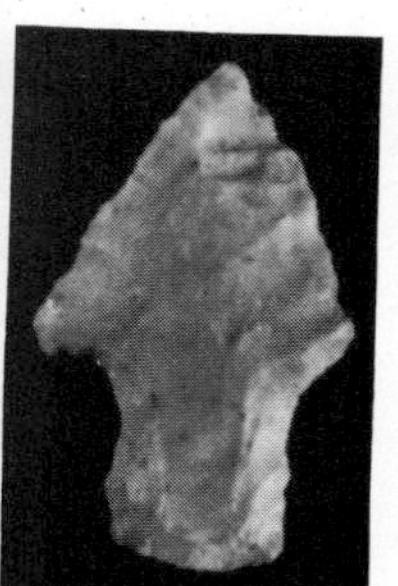

G2, $2-$3
Dallas, TX.

LOCATION: Midwestern states. **DESCRIPTION:** A small to medium size point with a short blade, weak shoulders, and a long squared stem. Stem can be half the length of the point. Basal area can be ground.

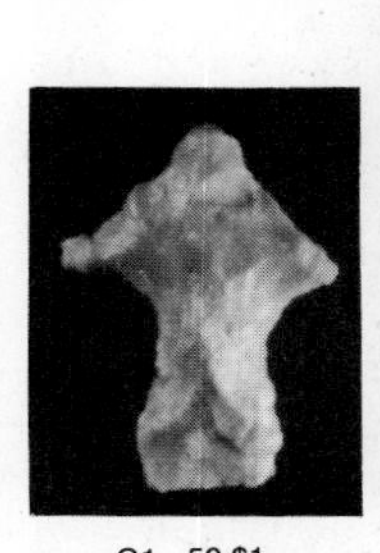

G1, .50-$1
Dallas, TX.

G1.50-$1
Dallas, TX.

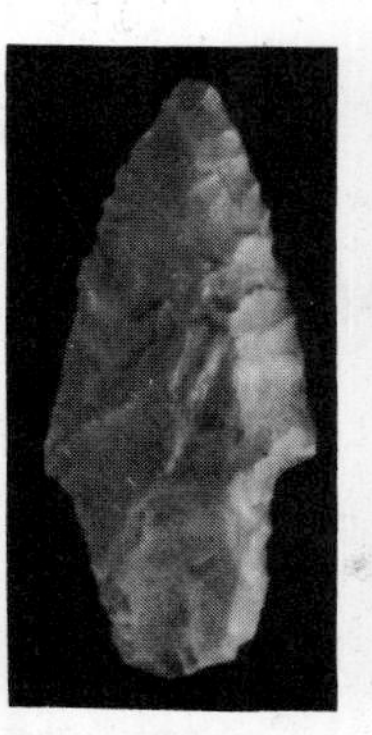

G5, $4-$6
Dallas, TX.

G4, $3-$5
Comanche Co., TX.

DALTON-BRECKENRIDGE - Late Paleo to Mid-Archaic, 10000 - 5000 B.P.

(Also see Meserve)

G3, $15-$25
Breckenridge, MO.

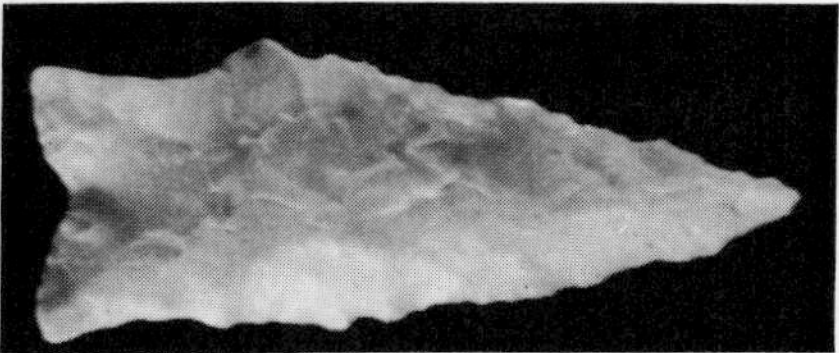

G4, $20-$35
AR.

LOCATION: Midwestern states. **DESCRIPTION:** A medium to large size, auriculate point with an obvious bevel extending the entire length of the point from tip to base. Similar in form to the *Dalton-Greenbrier*. Basal area is usually ground.

DALTON-CLASSIC - Late to Transitional Paleo, 10000 - 8000 B.P.

(Also see Alamance, Chipola, Dalton-Greenbrier, Debert, Golondrina, Plainview & San Patrice)

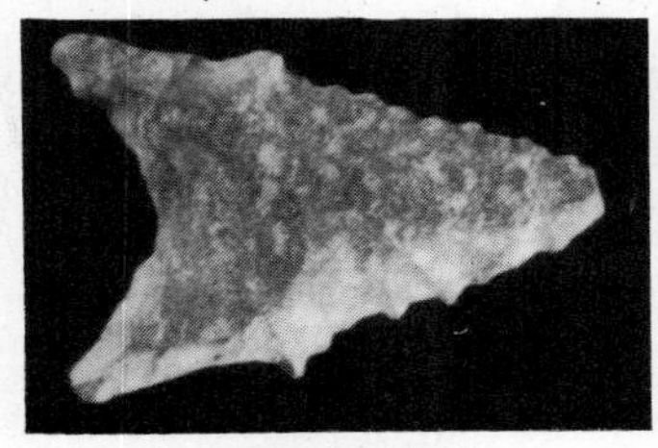

G2, $10-$15
Moore Co., NC. Tip nick.

G3, $15-$25
Humphreys Co., TN.

DALTON-CLASSIC (continued)

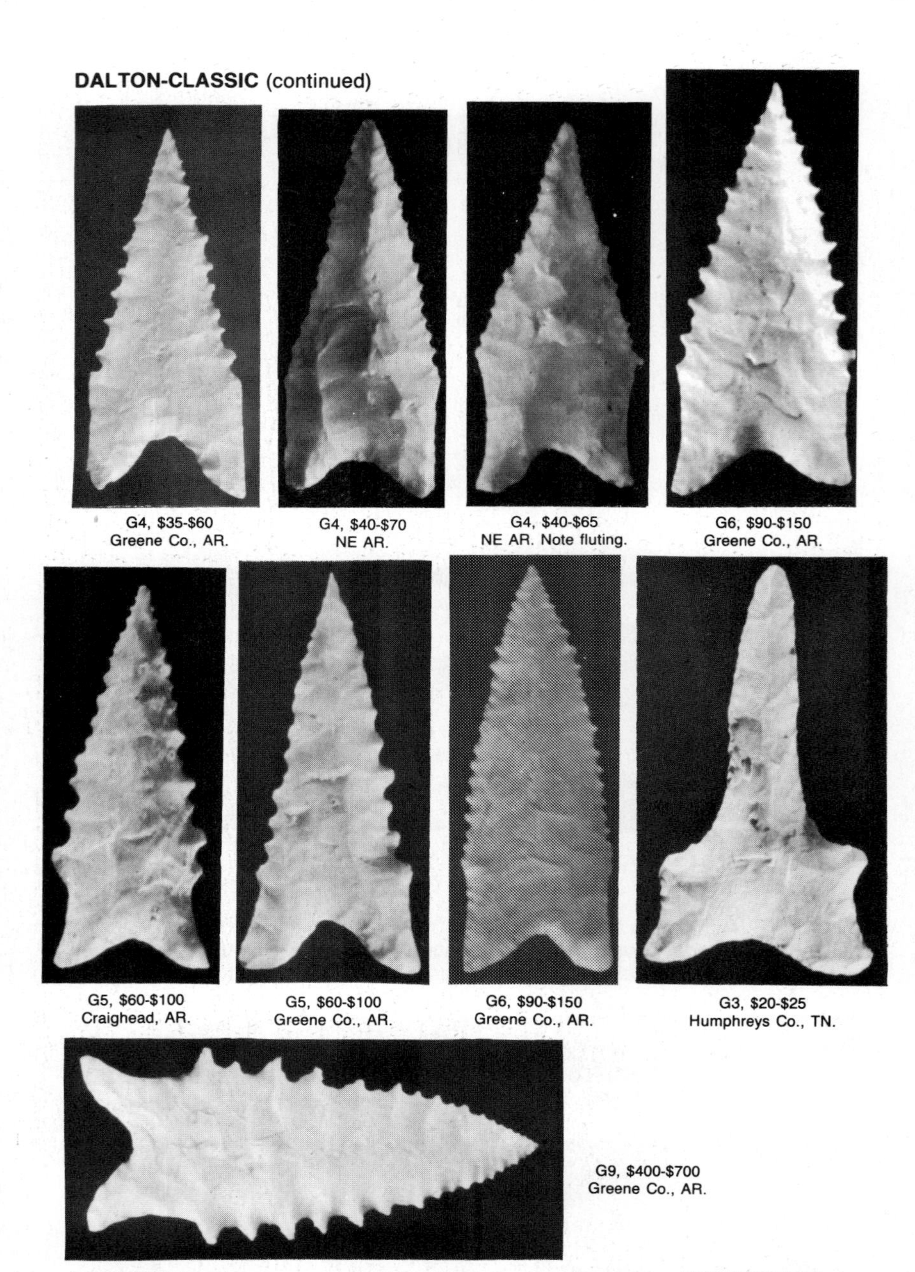

G4, $35-$60
Greene Co., AR.

G4, $40-$70
NE AR.

G4, $40-$65
NE AR. Note fluting.

G6, $90-$150
Greene Co., AR.

G5, $60-$100
Craighead, AR.

G5, $60-$100
Greene Co., AR.

G6, $90-$150
Greene Co., AR.

G3, $20-$25
Humphreys Co., TN.

G9, $400-$700
Greene Co., AR.

LOCATION: Midwestern states and extends into the Southeast. **DESCRIPTION:** A medium to large size, thin, auriculate, fishtailed point. Many examples are finely serrated and exhibit excellent flaking. Beveling may occur on one side of each face but is usually on the right side. All have basal grinding. This early type spread over most of the U.S. and strongly influenced many other types to follow. The narrow, longer forms were previously called *Yuma* points.

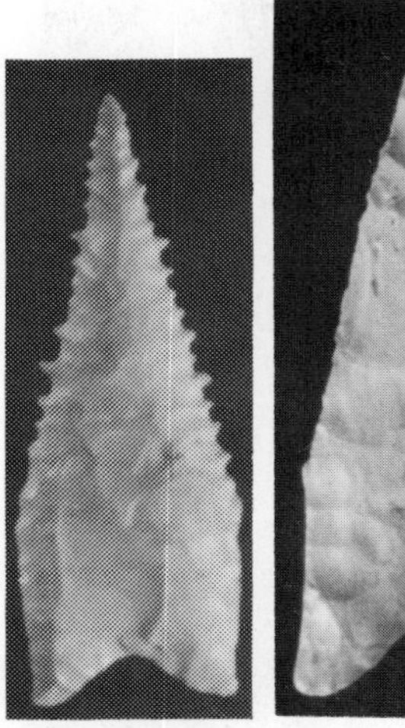

G5, $55-$100
Greene Co., AR.

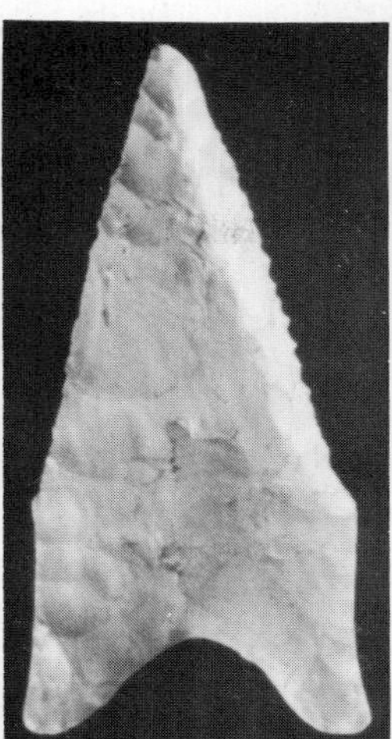

G6, $80-$140
Austin, TX.

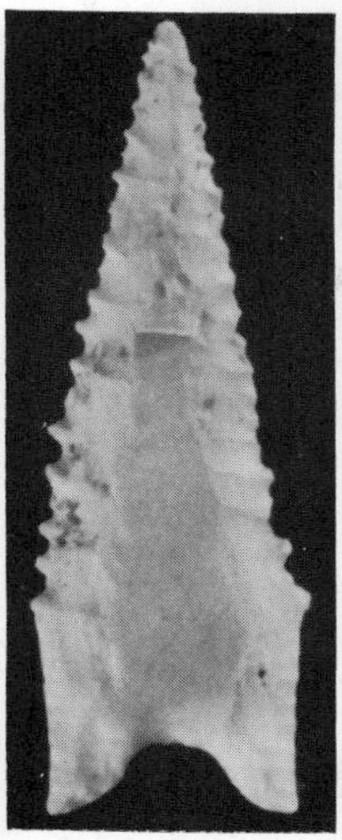

G8, $250-$400
Clay Co., AR.

G8, $250-$400
Greene Co., AR.

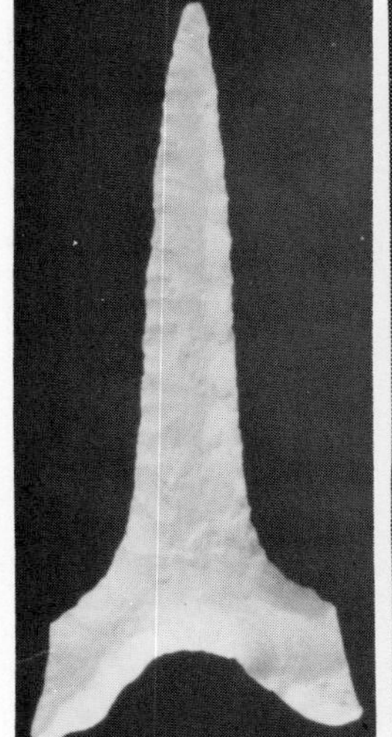

G8, $300-$500
Greene Co., AR.

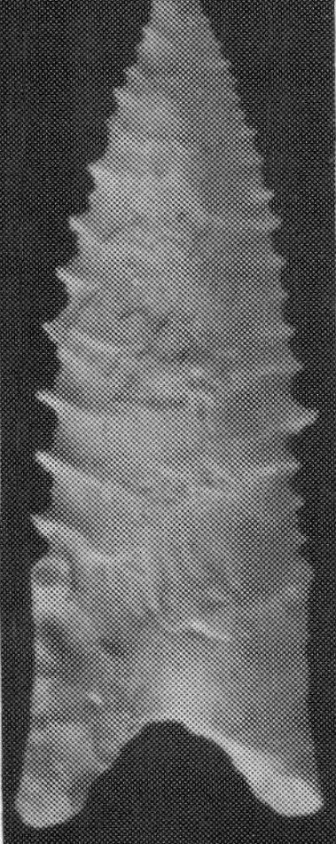

G7, $120-$200
MO.

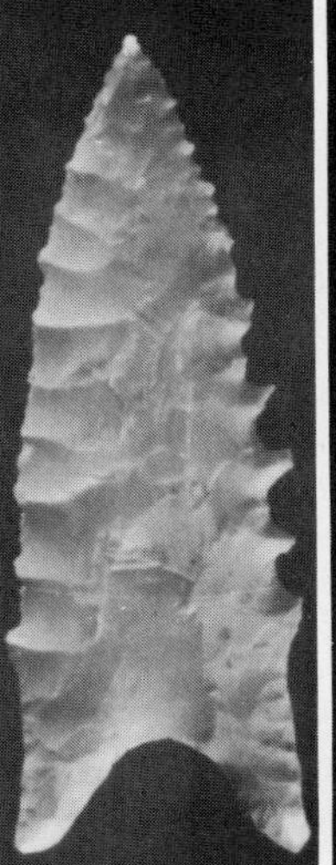

G6, $80-$130
Greene Co., AR.

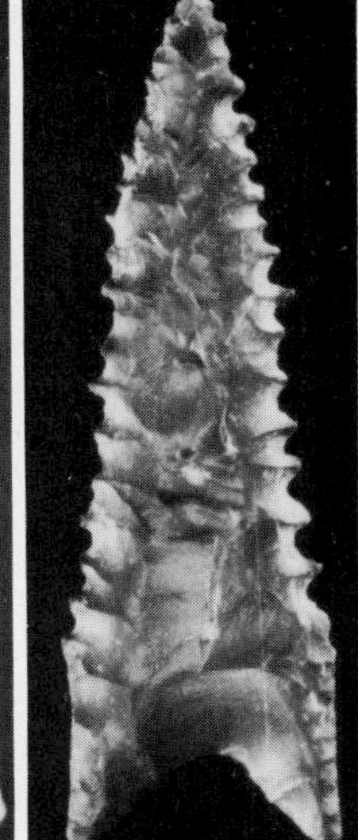

G7, $120-$200
Greene Co., AR.

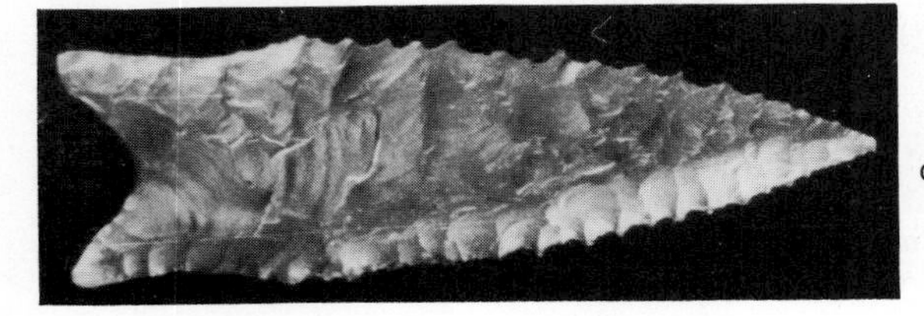

G8, $250-$400
Greene Co., AR.

G5, $60-$100
MO.

G6, $100-$180
Lafayette Co., MO.

G7, $150-$250
Greene Co., AR.

G6, $90-$150
Greene Co., AR.

G8, $280-$400
Greene Co., AR.

G8, $300-$500
MO. Drill form.

G6, $110-$200
Cole Co., MO.

G8, $350-$500
Greene Co., AR.

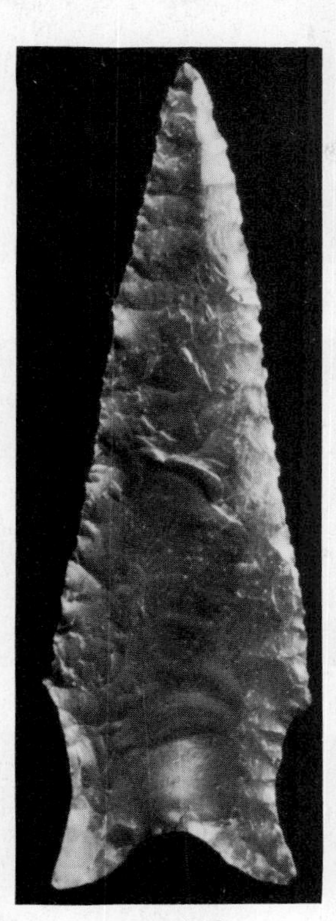

G8, $280-$400
Greene Co., AR.

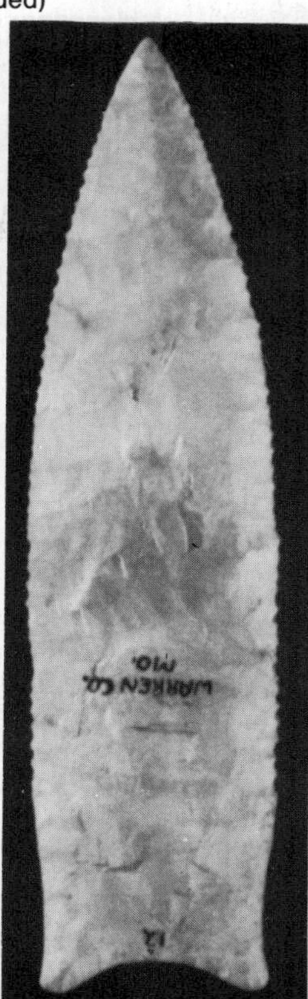

G10, $900-$1600
Warren Co., MO.

G8, $250-$400
Kansas City, MO.

G8, $450-$700
N. Cent. AR. A first state (unsharpened) form.

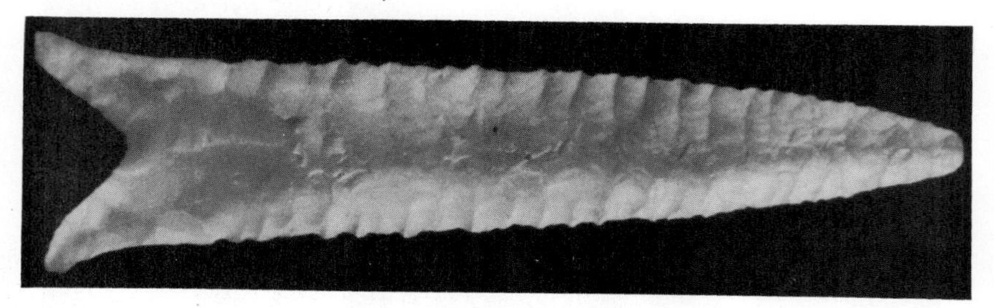

G8, $280-$400
Howard Co., MO.

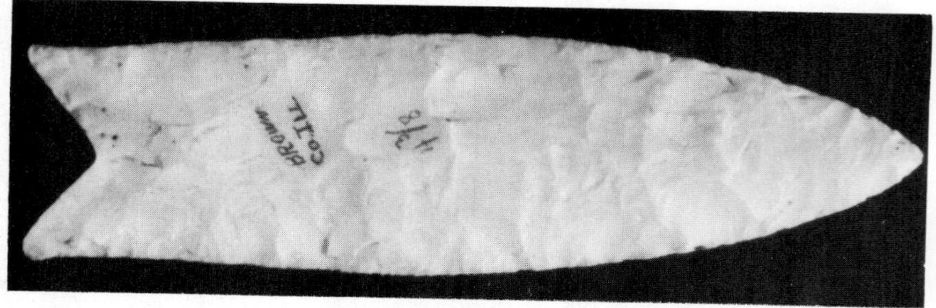

G10, $900-$1600
Brown Co., IL.

G10, $1200-$2000
Cooper Co., MO.

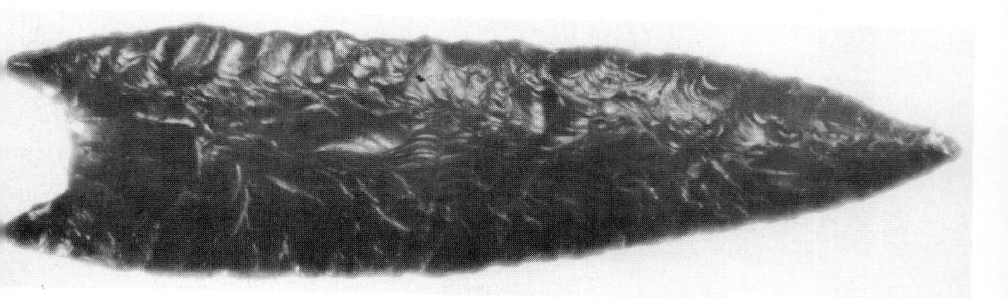

G9, $700-$1200
CA. Obsidian.

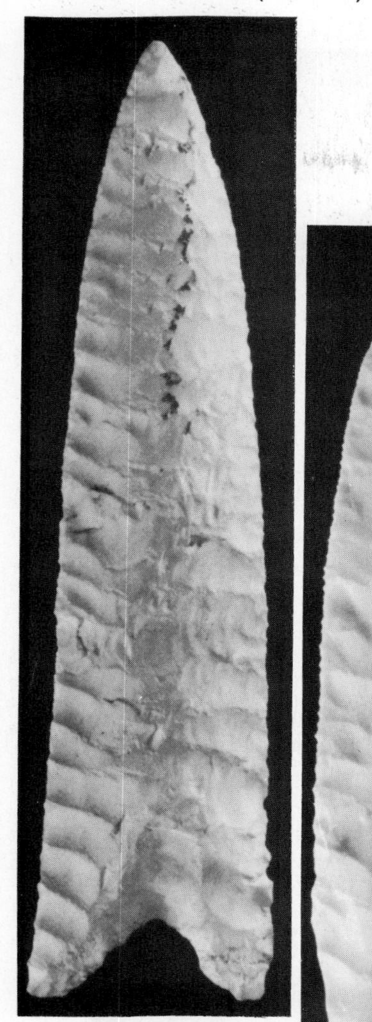

G9, $700-$1200
Franklin Co., MO. Note collateral flaking.

G8, $250-$400
Greene Co., AR.

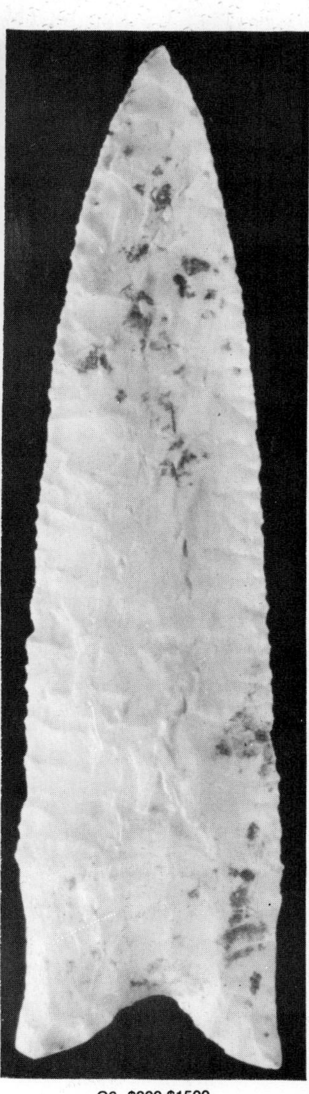

G9, $800-$1500
Greene Co., AR.

G10, $1500-$2500
Boone Co., MO.

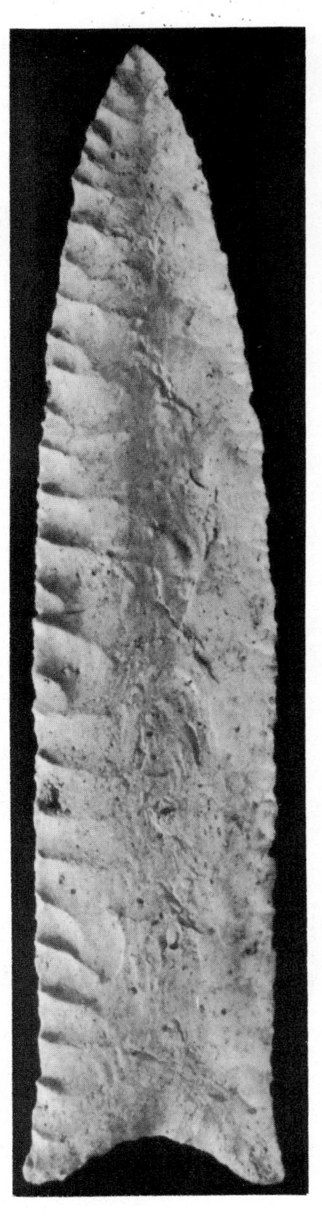

G9, $800-$1500
Boat Hill, MO.

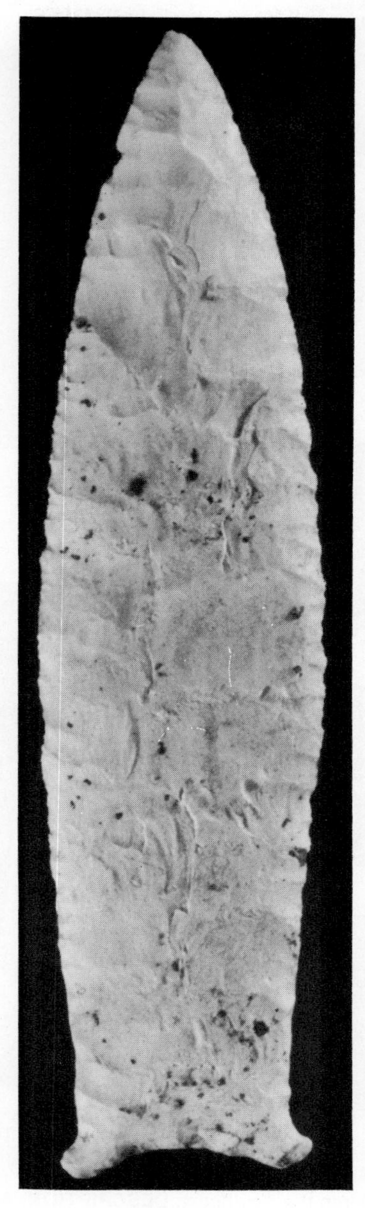

G9, $800-$1500
Vernon Co., MO. "Pike County" type.

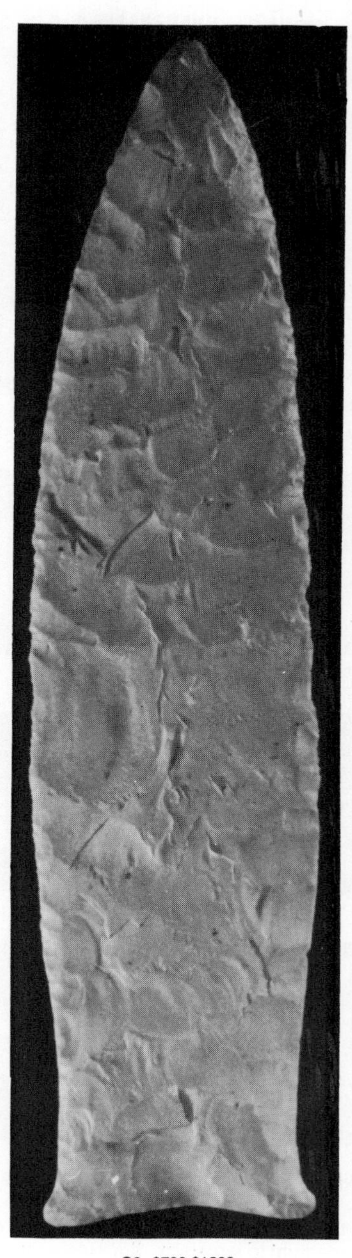

G9, $700-$1200
Pike Co., IL. "Pike County" type.

DALTON-COLBERT - Late Paleo to Mid-Archaic, 10000 - 5000 B.P.

(Also see Dalton-Nuckolls, Plainview and Searcy)

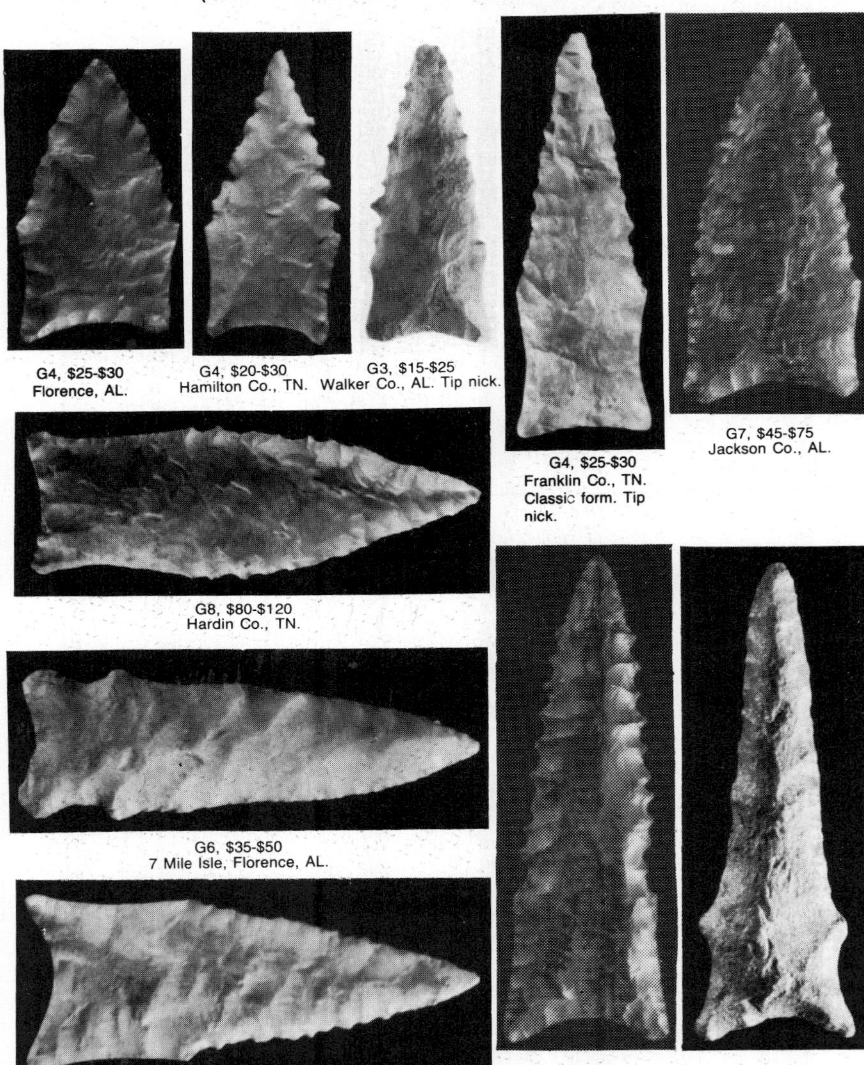

G4, $25-$30
Florence, AL.

G4, $20-$30
Hamilton Co., TN.

G3, $15-$25
Walker Co., AL. Tip nick.

G4, $25-$30
Franklin Co., TN.
Classic form. Tip nick.

G7, $45-$75
Jackson Co., AL.

G8, $80-$120
Hardin Co., TN.

G6, $35-$50
7 Mile Isle, Florence, AL.

G9, $250-$400, Lauderdale Co., AL. Outstanding example.

G8, $90-$150
Stewart Co., TN.
Dover chert.

G7, $45-$70
Humphreys Co., TN.
Quartzite.

LOCATION: Midwestern states and extends into the Southeast. **DESCRIPTION:** A medium to large size, auriculate form with a squared base and a weakly defined hafting area which is ground. Some examples are serrated and exhibit parallel flaking of the highest quality. **I.D. KEY:** Large shoulders.

DALTON-GREENBRIER - Late Paleo to early Archaic, 10000 - 6000 B.P.

(Also see Alamance, Breckenridge, Golondrina, Greenbrier, Hardaway, Haw River, Meserve, Pelican and Plainview)

G4, $20-$30
Walker Co., AL.

G3, $15-$25
Wilcox Co., AL.

G4, $25-$30
Huntsville, AL.

G6, $40-$60
Jackson Co., AL.

G6, $35-$50
Nickajack Lake, TN.

G3, $15-$20
Marion Co., TN. Tip nick.

G5, $25-$40
N. AL.

G6, $35-$55
Watts Bar Lake, TN.

G2, $10-$20
Jackson Co., AL. Tip nick.

G7, $45-$70
Dayton, TN.

LOCATION: Midwestern to Eastern states and Florida. **DESCRIPTION:** A medium to large size, auriculate form with a concave base and drooping to expanding auricles. Many examples are serrated, some are fluted on both sides, and all have basal grinding. Resharpened examples are usually beveled on the right side of each face although left side beveling does occur. Thinness and high quality flaking is evident on many examples. This early type spread over most of the U.S. and strongly influenced many other types to follow.

DALTON-GREENBRIER (continued)

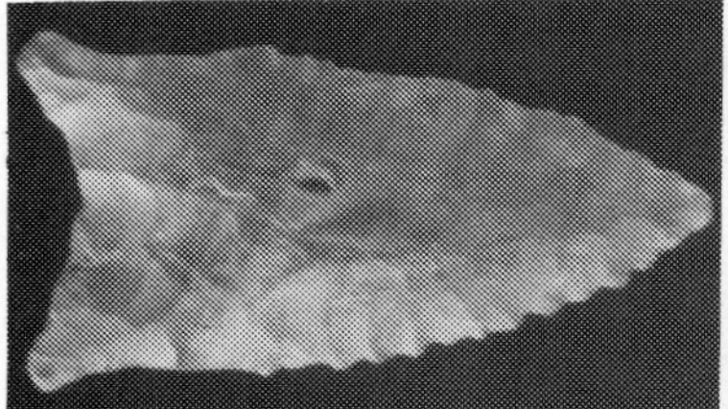

G6, $35-$55
Jackson Co., AL.

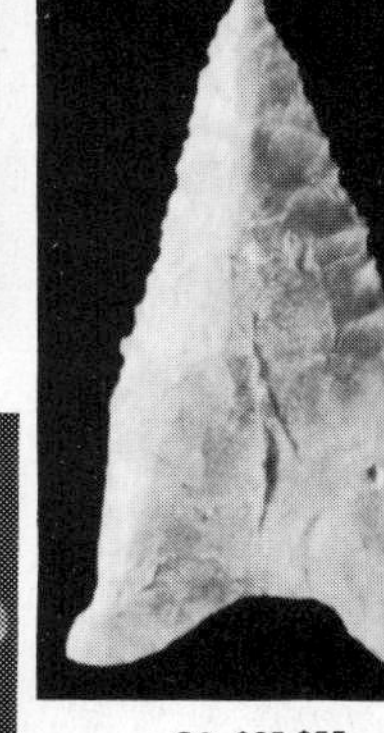

G6, $35-$55
Walker Co., AL.

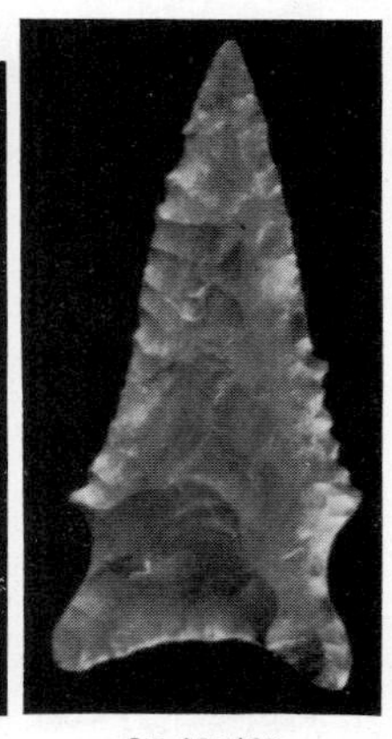

G5, $25-$35
Florence, AL. Red jasper.

G5, $25-$40
Jackson Co., AL.

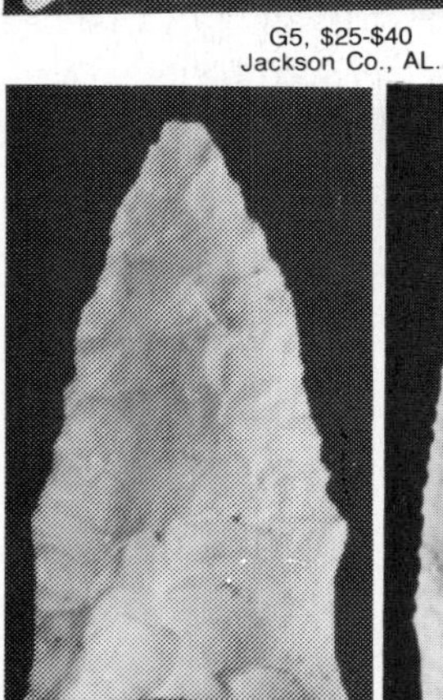

G6, $35-$55
Jackson Co., AL.

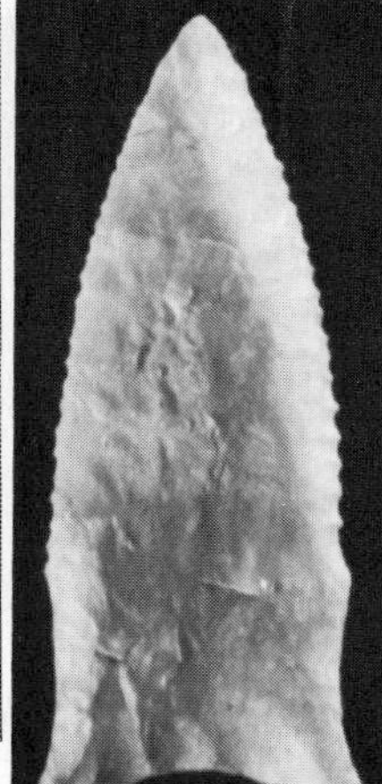

G9, $200-$350
NE AR.

G4, $15-$25
Edgefield Co., SC.

G7, $45-$70
Lauderdale Co., AL.

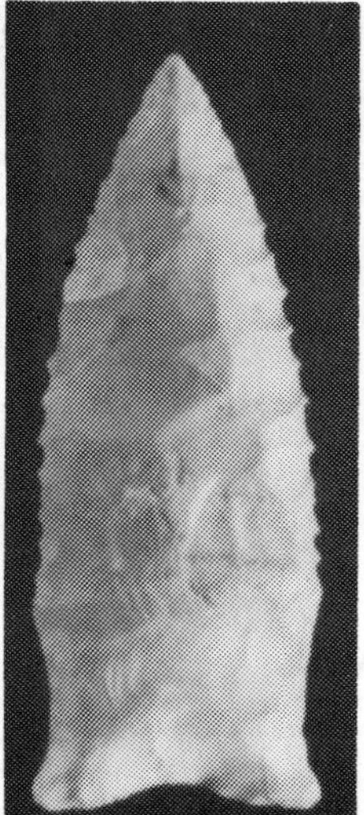

G8, $120-$220
NE AR.

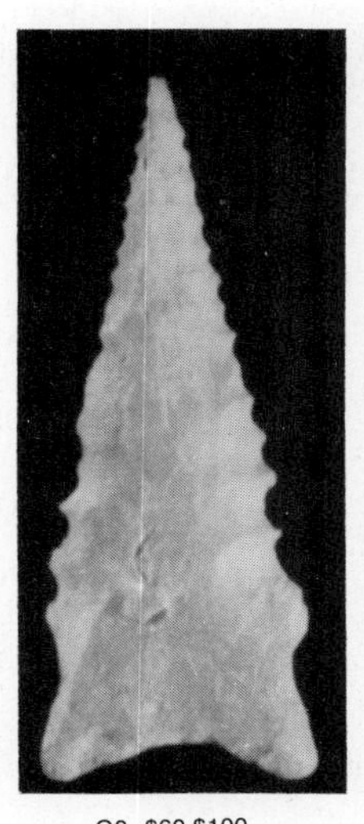

G8, $60-$100
NE AR.

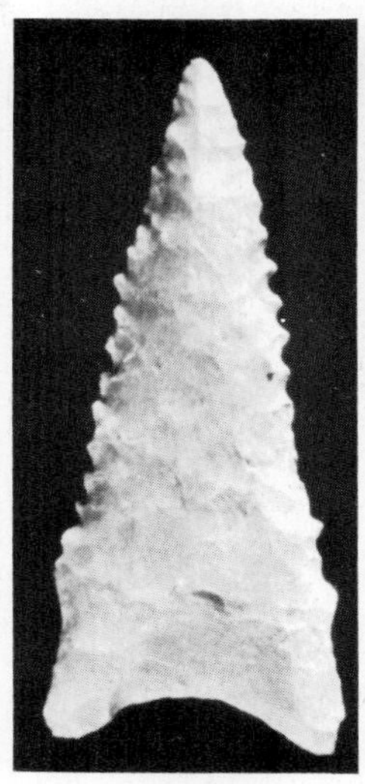

G4, $25-$35
Humphreys Co., TN.

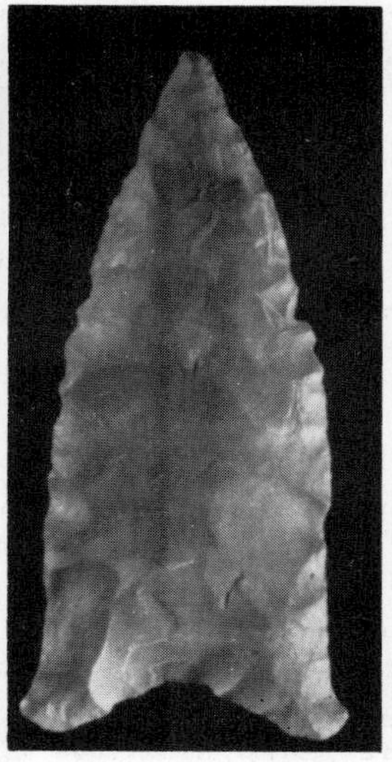

G6, $35-$55
NE AR.

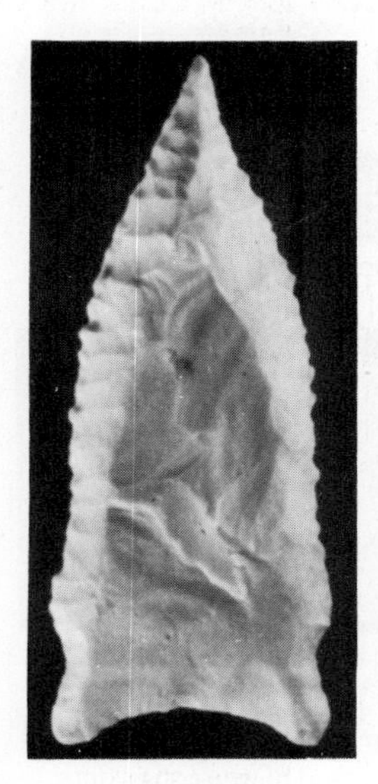

G8, $90-$150
Stewart Co., TN.

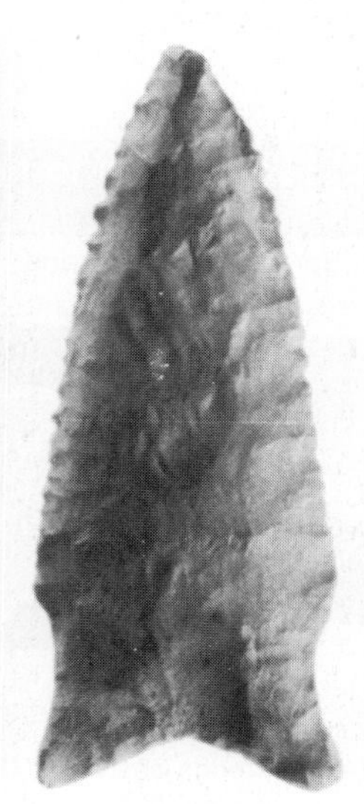

G6, $35-$55
Lyon Co., KY. Tip nick.

G7, $45-$70
Florence, AL.

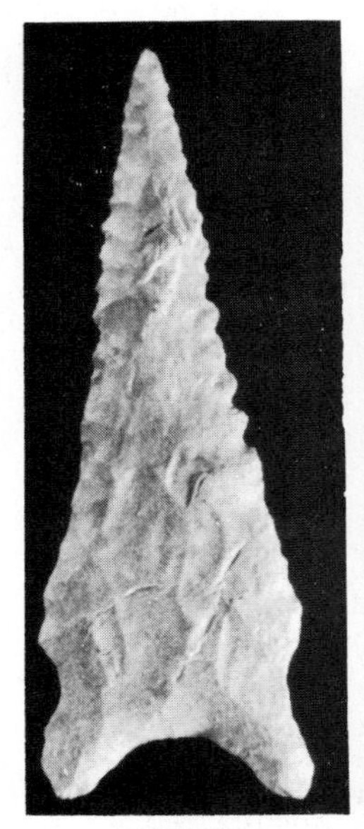
G7, $45-$75
Humphreys Co., TN.

G8, $120-$200
Humphreys Co., TN.

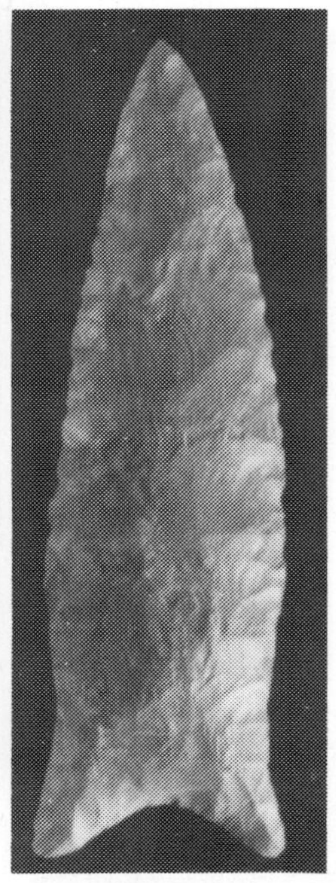
G8, $150-$250
AR.

DALTON-HEMPHILL - Late Paleo to mid-Archaic, 10000 - 6000 B.P.

(Also see Cave Spring, Hardaway and Holland)

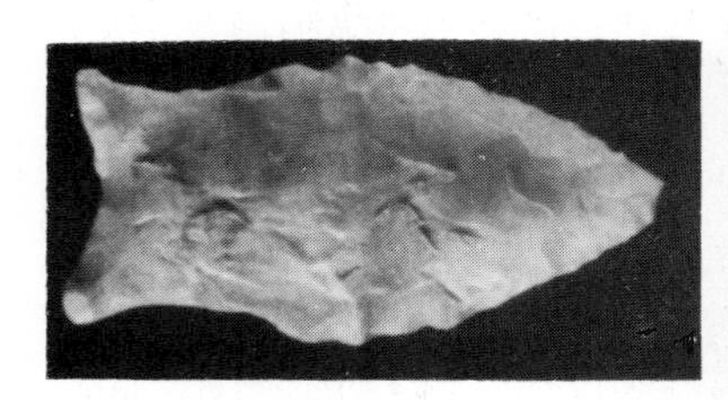
G3, $6-$10
Humphreys Co., TN.

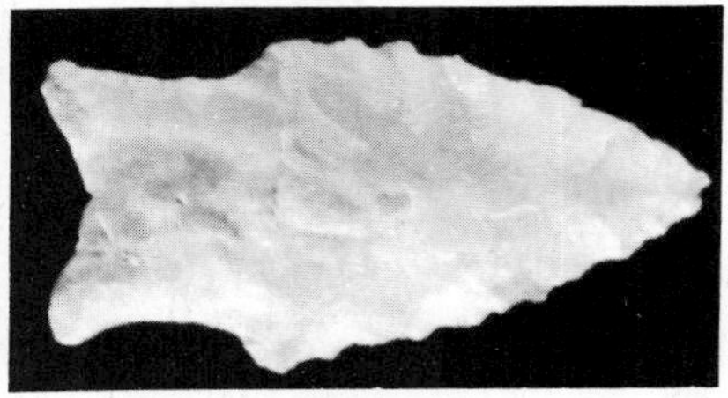
G4, $8-$15
Pemiscot, MO.

LOCATION: Midwestern states and extends eastward. **DESCRIPTION:** A medium to large size point with expanded auricles and horizontal, tapered to weak shoulders. Blade edges are usually serrated and bases are ground. In later times, this variant developed into the *Hemphill* point. **I.D. KEY:** Straightned extended shoulders.

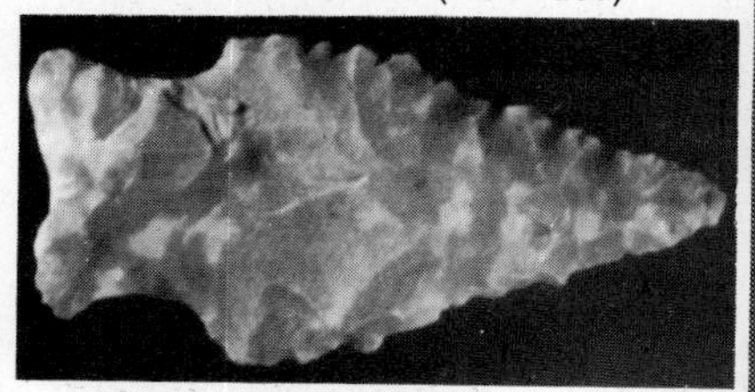

G4, $8-$15
Walker Co., AL.

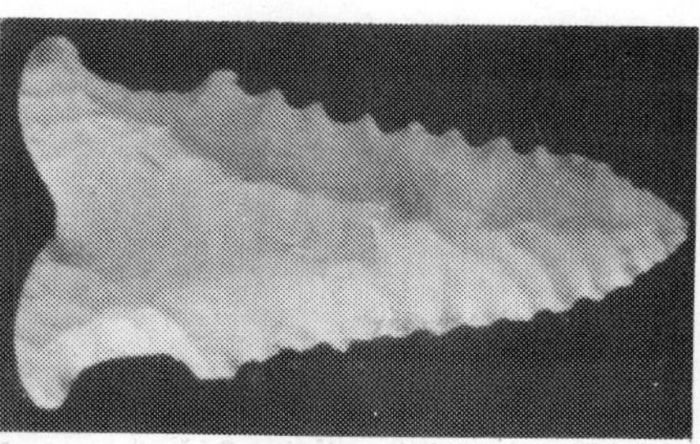

G7, $50-$85
Greene Co., AR.

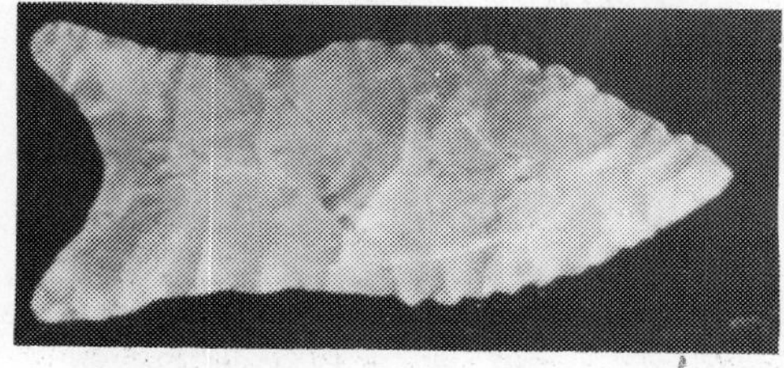

G6, $30-$50
KY. Oblique flaking.

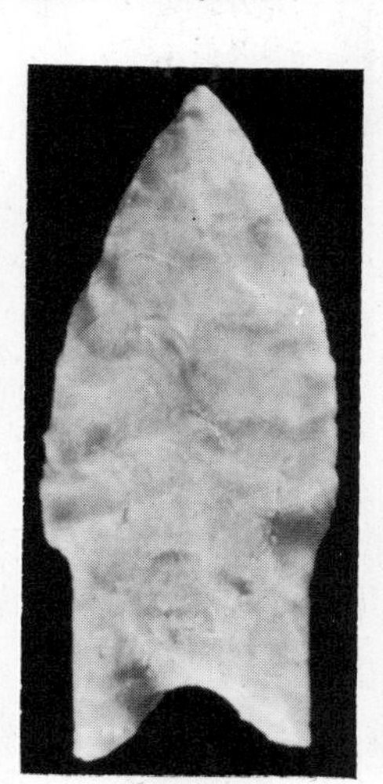

G7, $45-$80
Red River Parrish, LA.

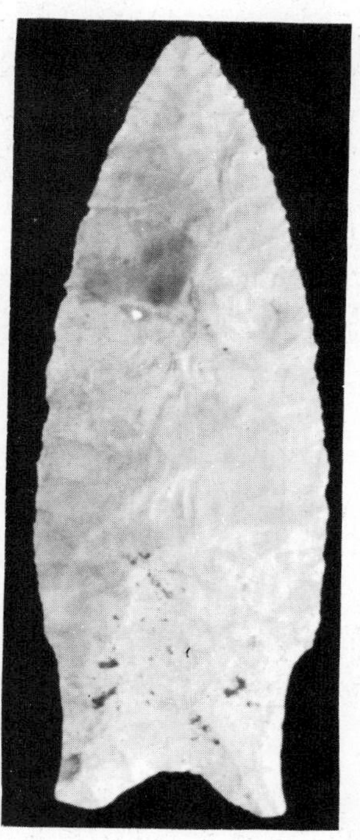

G8, $180-$250
Sou. IL.

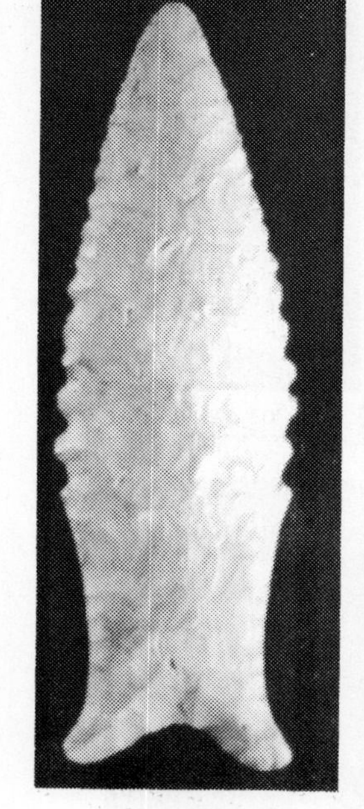

G9, $450-$800
Obion Co., IL.

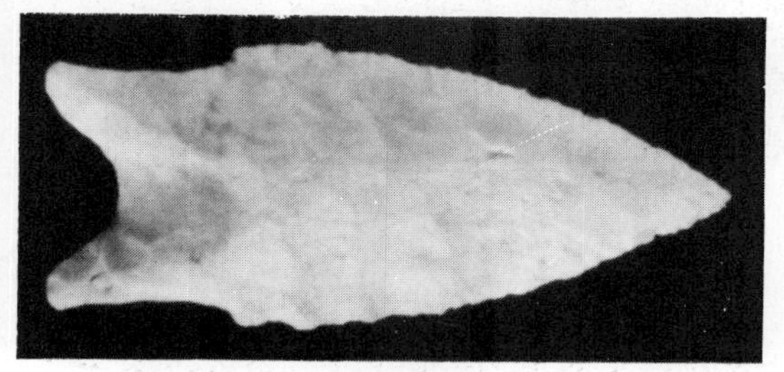

G7, $90-$150
Sou. Cent. IA.

G6, $25-$40
Florence, AL., Coffee Lake.

G6, $35-$60
SW KY. Tip damage.

G8, $150-$250
SW KY.

G9, $350-$650
MO.

G9, $300-$500
Ozark, AR. Excellent example.

DALTON-NUCKOLLS - Late Paleo, 10000 - 5000 B.P.

(Also see Dalton-Colbert and Hardaway)

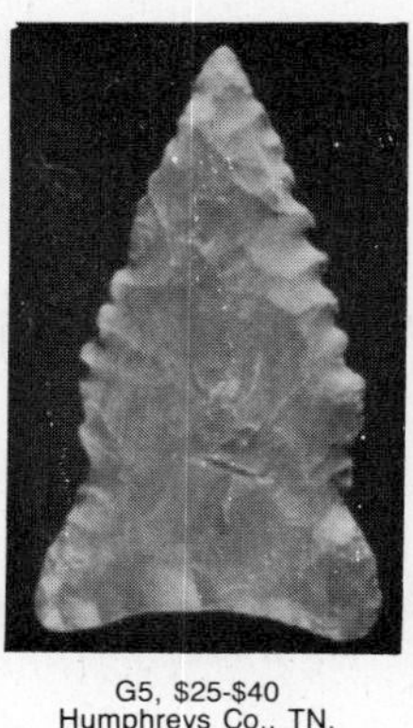

G5, $25-$40
Humphreys Co., TN.

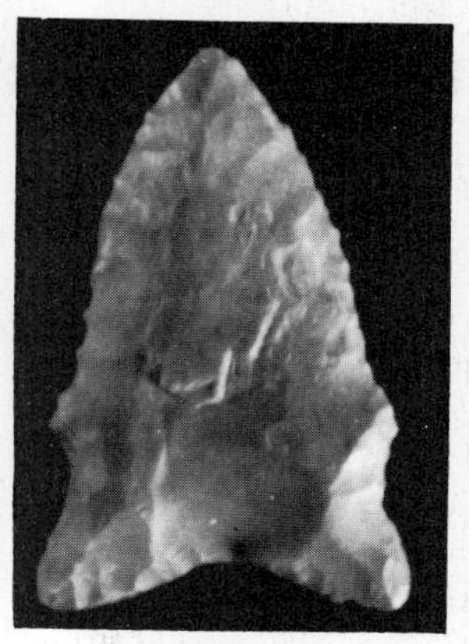

G5, $25-$40
Humphreys Co., TN.

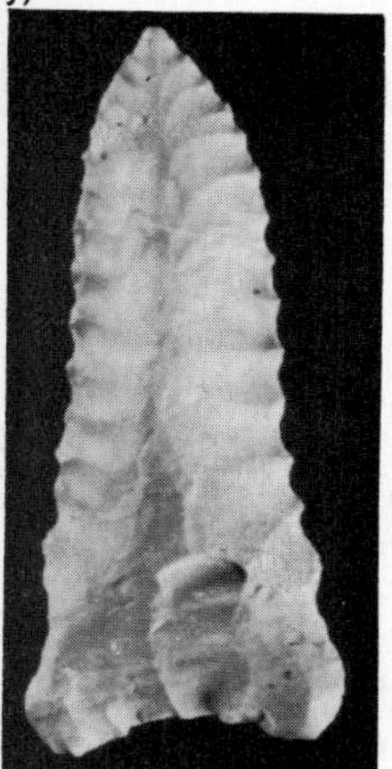

G5, $25-$45
Humphreys Co., TN. Collateral flaking.

G5, $25-$40
Humphreys Co., TN. Ground basal area.

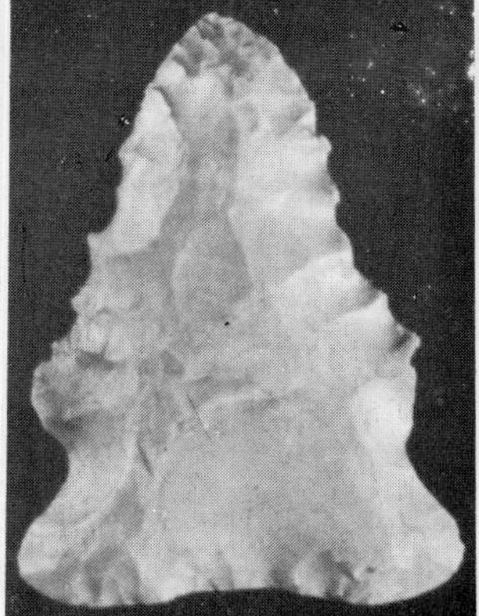

G3, $8-$15
Humphreys Co., TN. Fluted.

G5, $25-$45
Humphreys Co., TN.

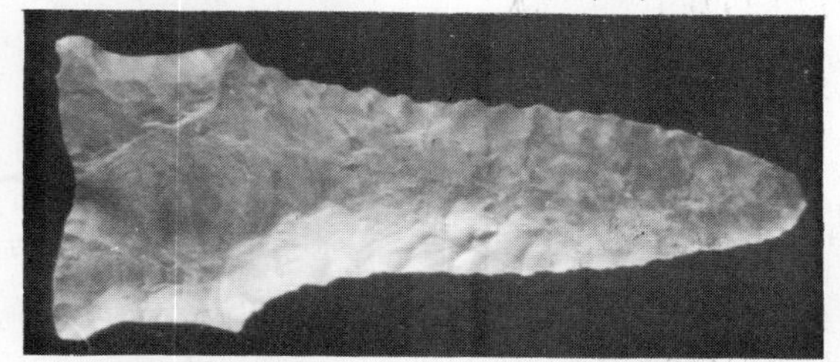

G6, $40-$60
Barkley Lake, KY. Fluted.

LOCATION: Midwestern to Southeastern states. Type site is in Humphreys Co. TN. **DESCRIPTION:** A medium to large size variant form, probably occuring from resharpening the *Greenbrier Dalton*. Bases are squared to lobbed to eared, and have a shallow concavity. **I.D. KEY:** Broad base and shoulders, flaking on blade.

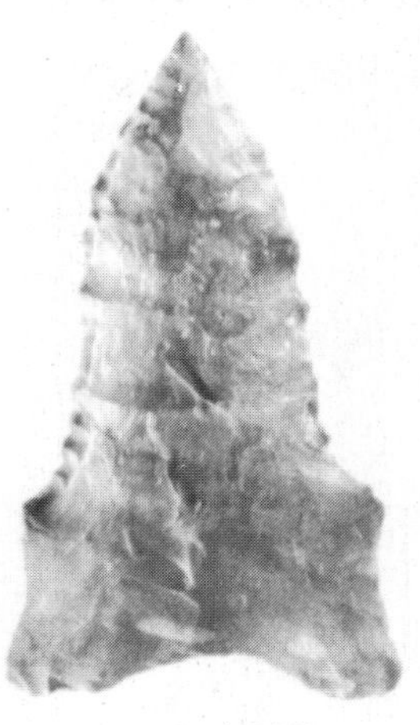

G5, $30-$50
W. TN.

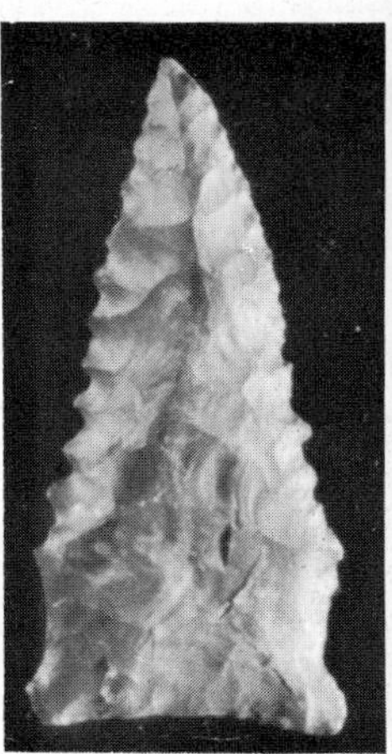

G5, $25-$40
Humphreys Co., TN.

G4, $20-$35
Humphreys Co., TN. Fluted.
Dover chert. Nuckolls site.

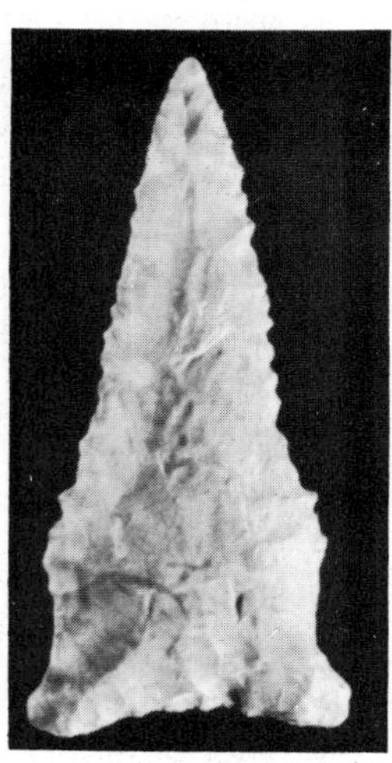

G7, $45-$80
Humphreys Co., TN.

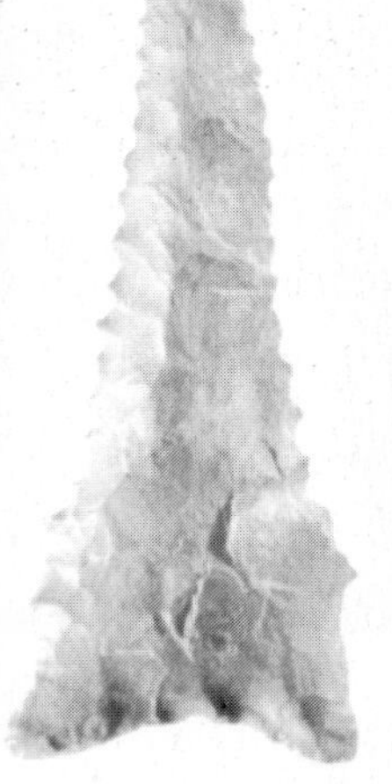

G7, $60-$90
Humphreys Co., TN.

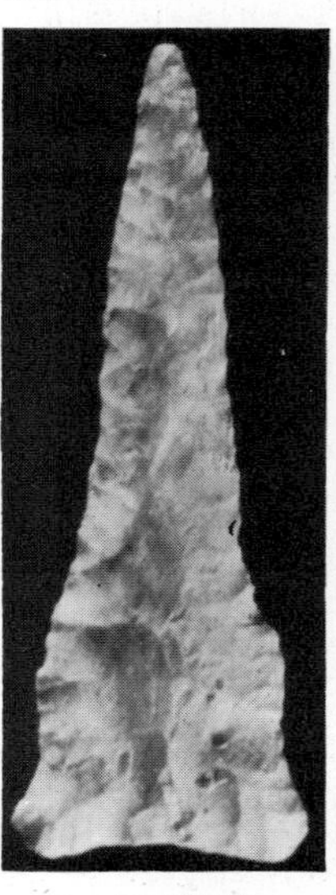

G6, $35-$50
Humphreys Co., TN.

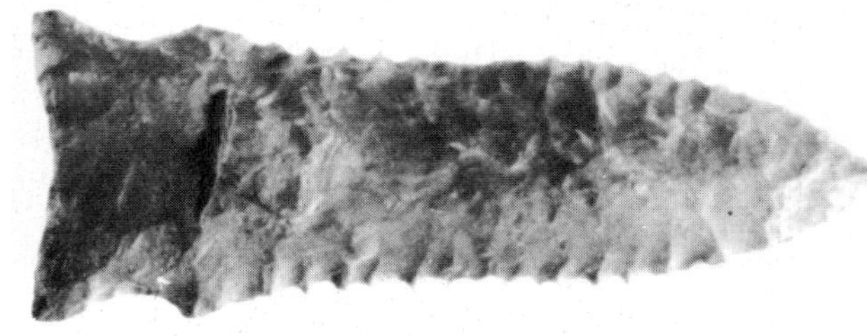

G9, $250-$400
Humphreys Co., TN. Fluted.
Dover chert.

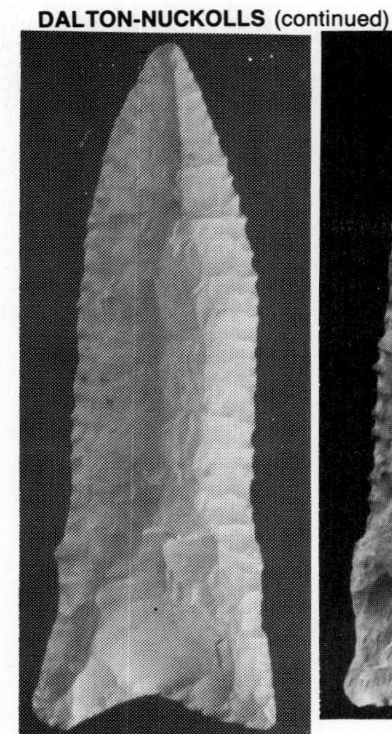

G8, $150-$250
Graves Co., MS. Note collateral flaking.

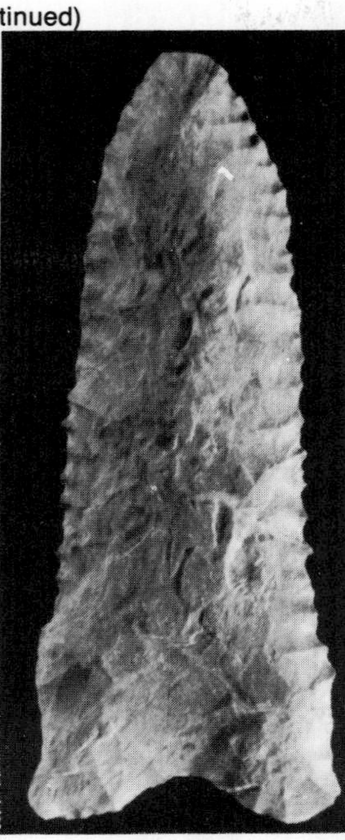

G5, $25-$40
Humphreys Co., TN. Tip nick. Dover chert.

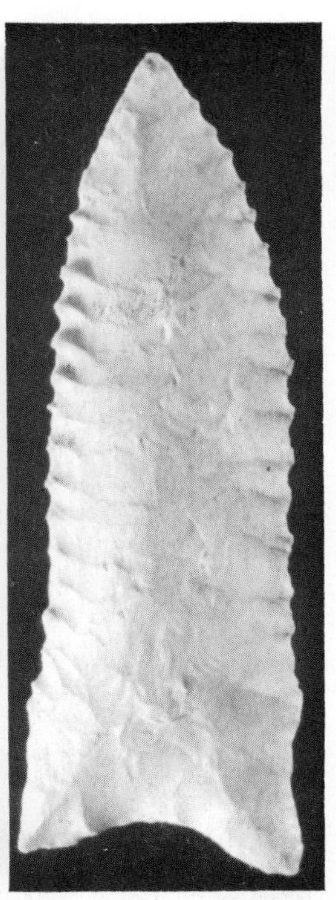

G8, $150-$220
Barkley Lake, KY.

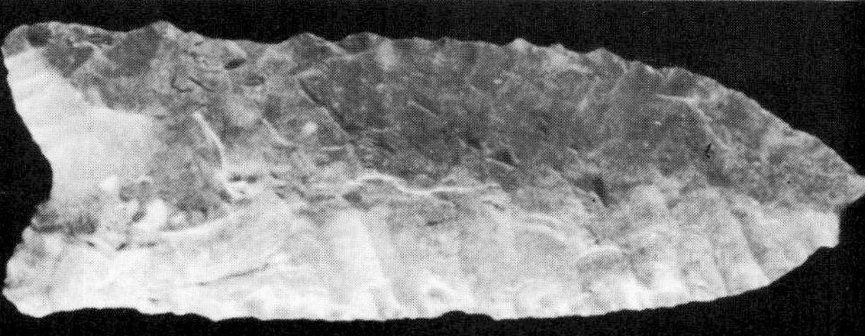

G3, $8-$15
Humphreys Co., TN. Tip nick.

G7, $45-$80
Humphreys Co., TN. Nuckolls site. Note left-hand bevel.

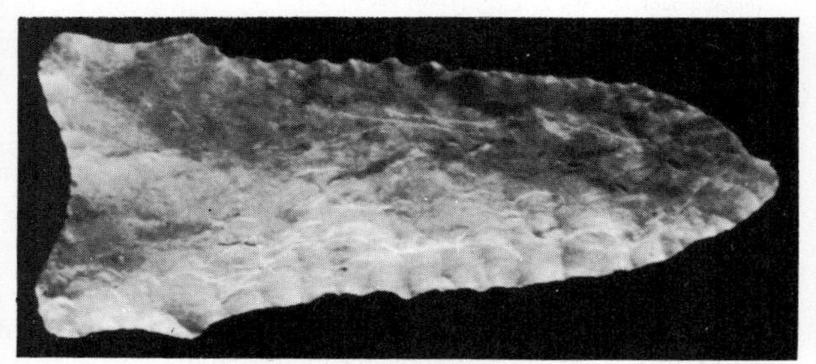

G5, $30-$50
Humphreys Co., TN. Nuckolls site. tip nick. Dover chert.

DALTON-SANTA FE - Late Paleo, 10000 - 8000 B.P.

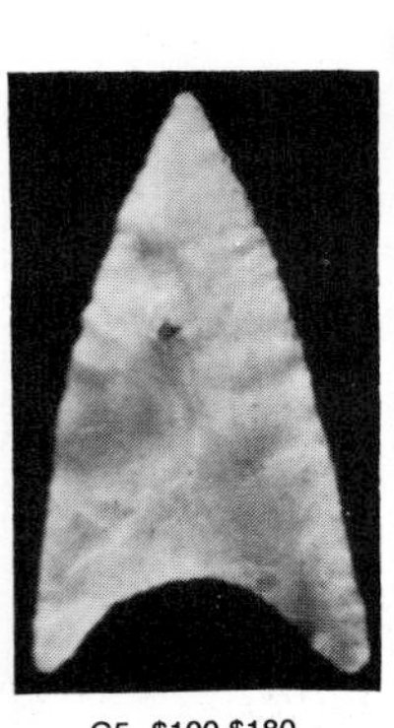
G5, $100-$180
Tift Co., GA.

G3, $30-$50
FL/GA. Vein quartz.

G3, $30-$50
Hillsborough Co., FL.
Ear Nick.

G3, $50-$80
Hillsborough Co., FL.

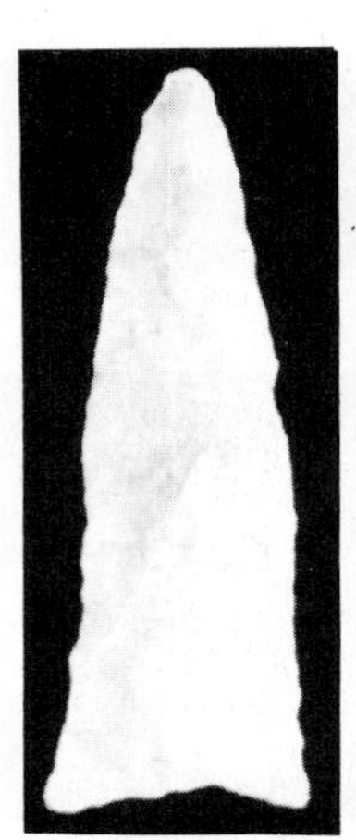
G3, $25-$40
Hillsborough Co., FL.

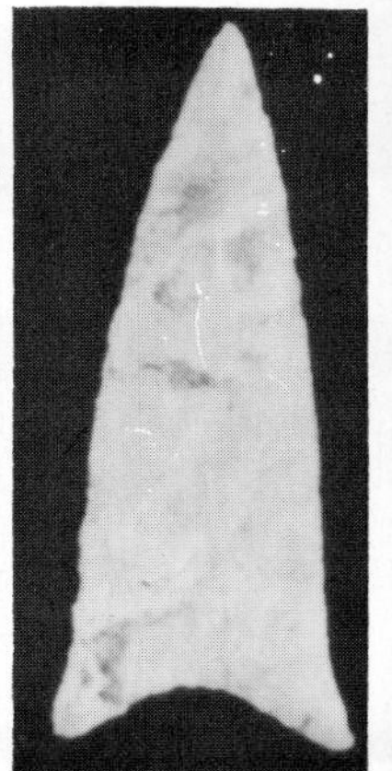
G5, $120-$200
NW Cent. FL.

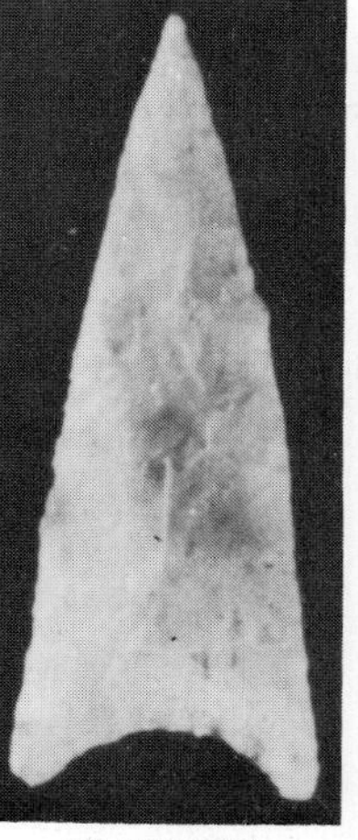
G6, $150-$250
NW Cent. FL.

G6, $150-$250
NW Cent. FL.

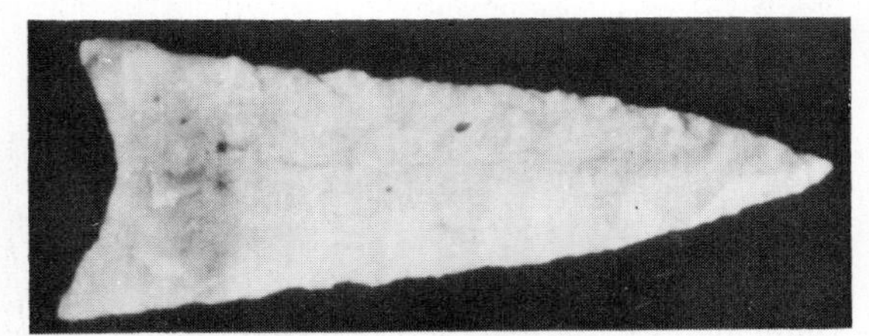
G7, $300-$500
NW Cent. FL.

LOCATION: Southern Southeastern states. **DESCRIPTION:** A medium to large size auriculate point with expanding auricules and a concave base. Hafting area is not well defined. Blade edges are usually not serrated as in *Tallahassee Dalton*. **I.D. KEY:** One sharper tang, symmetry.

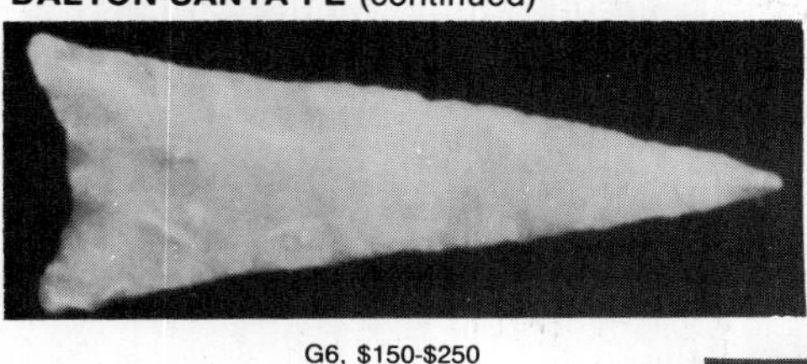

G6, $150-$250
NW Cent. FL.

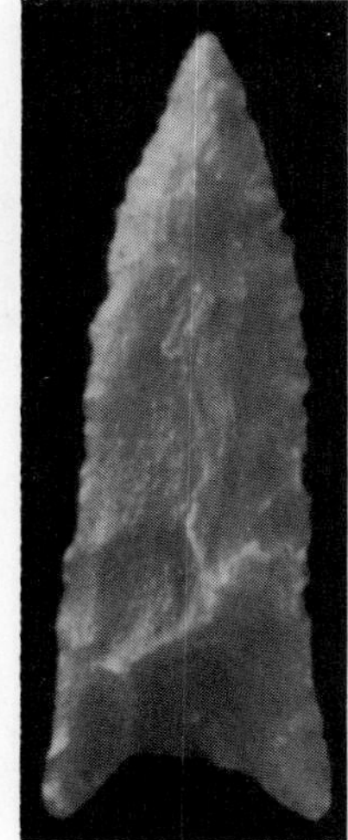

G5, $120-$200
NW Cent. FL.

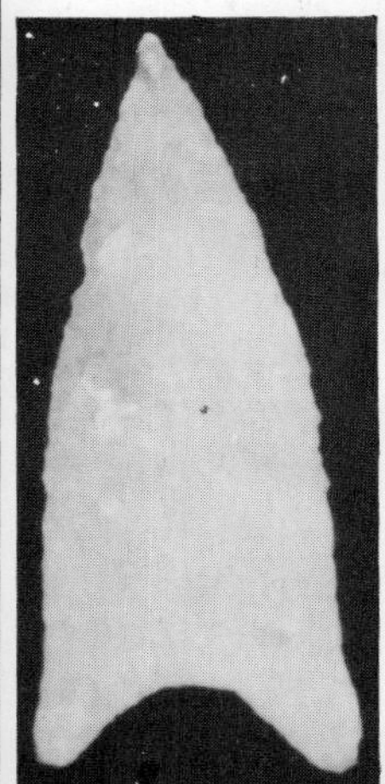

G6, $150-$250
NW Cent. FL.

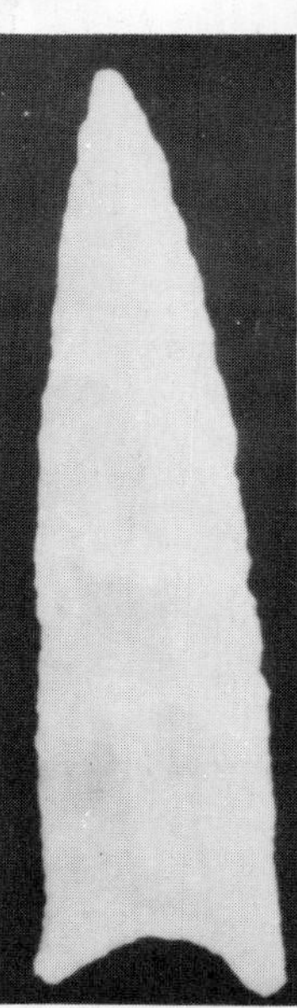

G7, $300-$500
NW Cent. FL.

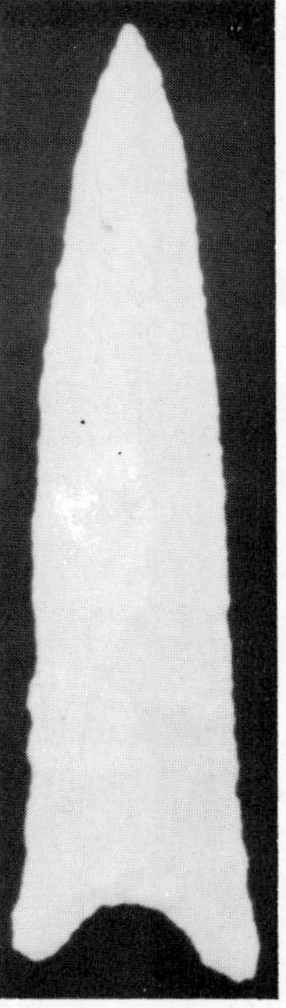

G8, $300-$500
NW Cent. FL.

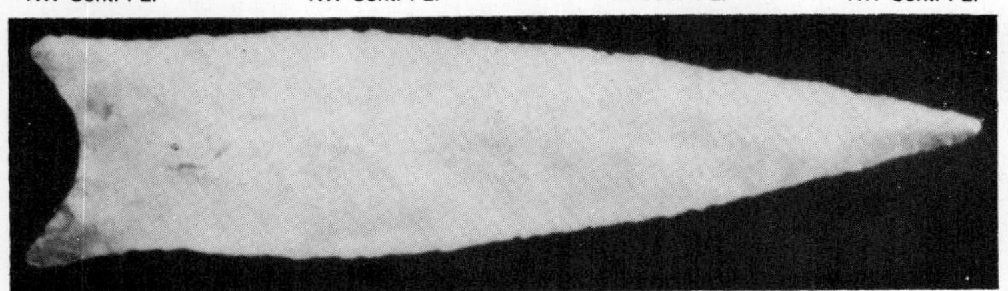

G9, $700-$1350
NW Cent. FL.

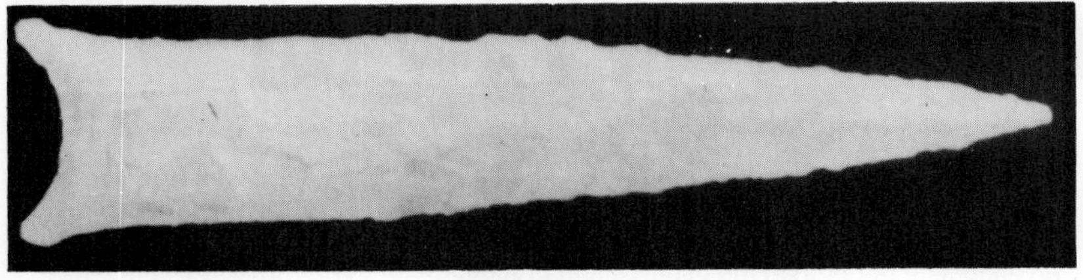

G10, $1200-$2000
NW Cent. FL.

DALTON-TALLAHASSEE - Late Paleo, 10000 - 8000 B.P.

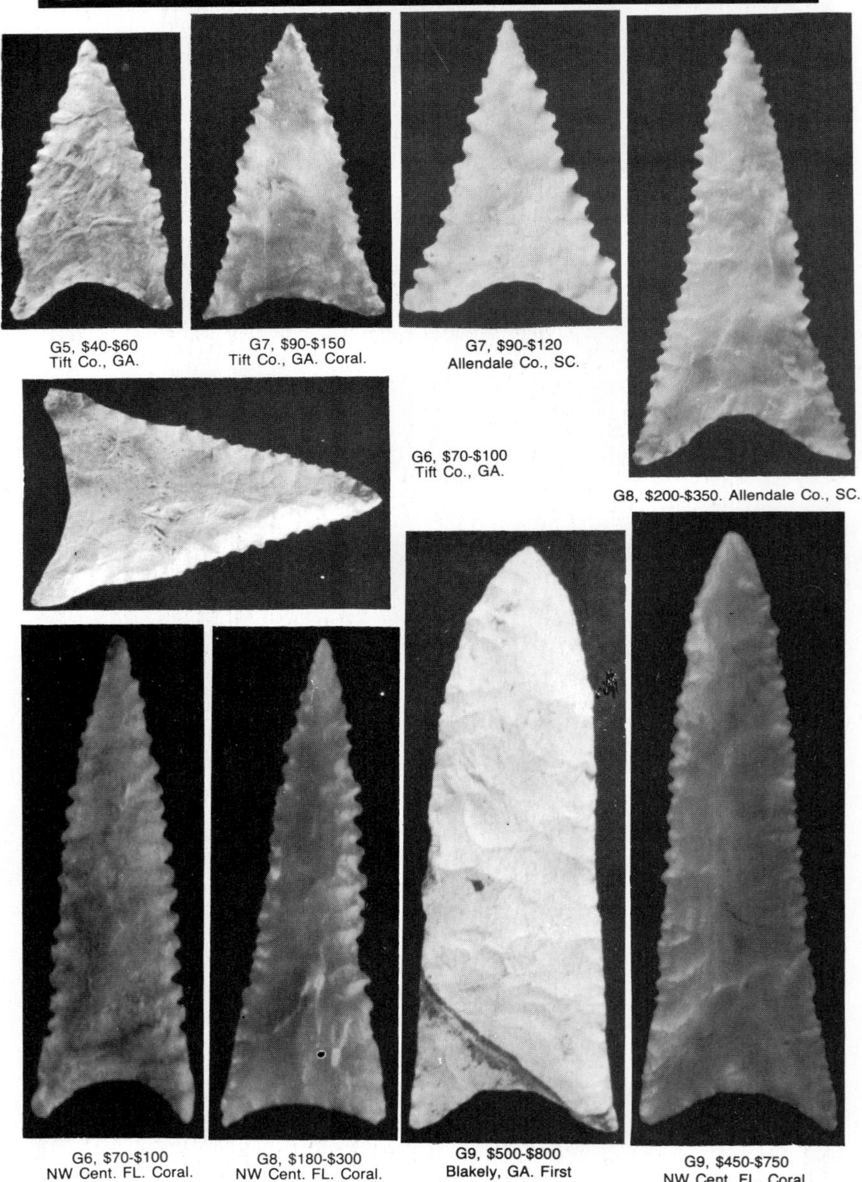

G5, $40-$60
Tift Co., GA.

G7, $90-$150
Tift Co., GA. Coral.

G7, $90-$120
Allendale Co., SC.

G6, $70-$100
Tift Co., GA.

G8, $200-$350. Allendale Co., SC.

G6, $70-$100
NW Cent. FL. Coral.

G8, $180-$300
NW Cent. FL. Coral.

G9, $500-$800
Blakely, GA. First stage form.

G9, $450-$750
NW Cent. FL. Coral.

LOCATION: Southern Southeastern states. **DESCRIPTION:** A medium to large size thin, triangular, serrated auriculate point with a concave base. The shoulders usually expand and are an extension of the blade itself. The blade edges are resharpened on each face rather than the usual *Dalton* proceedure of beveling on opposite faces. **I.D. KEY:** One tang sharper, edgework.

DAMRON - Early to mid-Archaic, 8000 to 4000 B.P.

(Also see Autauga, Dovetail, Ecusta, Gibson and Palmer)

G2, $1-$2
Dallas Isle, Hamilton Co., TN.

G3, $1-$3
SE TN.

G4, $3-$5
Citico, TN.

G7, $8-$12
SE TN.

G7, $8-$12
Hamilton Co., TN.
Brainerd.

G6, $5-$8
Sussex Co., VA.

G4, $3-$5
Humphreys Co., TN.

G8, $15-$25
Limestone Co., AL.

G6, $5-$8
Dunlap, TN.

G9, $40-$60
Florence, AL.

G5, $4-$6
Limestone Co., AL.

LOCATION: Southeastern states. **DESCRIPTION:** A small to medium size, triangular, side-notched point with a wide, prominent, convex to straight base. **I.D. KEY:** basal form.

DARDANELLE - Mississippian, 600 - 400 B.P.

(Also see Keota and Nodena)

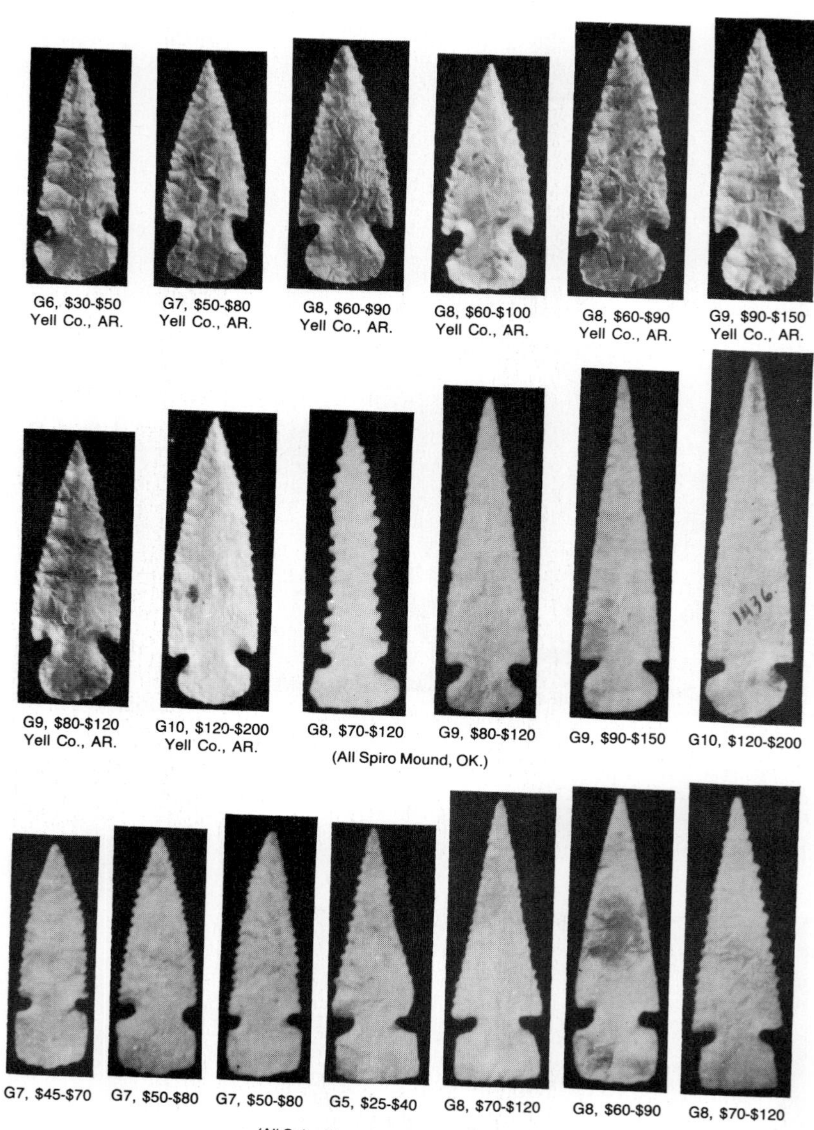

G6, $30-$50 Yell Co., AR. G7, $50-$80 Yell Co., AR. G8, $60-$90 Yell Co., AR. G8, $60-$100 Yell Co., AR. G8, $60-$90 Yell Co., AR. G9, $90-$150 Yell Co., AR.

G9, $80-$120 Yell Co., AR. G10, $120-$200 Yell Co., AR. G8, $70-$120 G9, $80-$120 G9, $90-$150 G10, $120-$200

(All Spiro Mound, OK.)

G7, $45-$70 G7, $50-$80 G7, $50-$80 G5, $25-$40 G8, $70-$120 G8, $60-$90 G8, $70-$120

(All Spiro Mound, OK, square base form)

LOCATION: Midwestern states. **DESCRIPTION:** A small to medium size, narrow, thin, serrated, corner or side notched arrow point. Bases can be rounded or square. A *Nodena* variant form with basal notches. This type has been bound in caches from the Spiro mound in Oklahoma and from Arkansas.

DARL - Woodland, 2500 - 1000 B.P.

(Also see Brazos, Dawson, Hoxie, Lampasos & Pandale)

G4, $4-$6 Austin, TX.

G5, $8-$15 Comanche Co., TX.

G5, $10-$20 Austin, TX.

G5, $10-$20 Austin, TX.

G2, $2-$4 Comanche Co., TX.

G8, $50-$80 Austin, TX.

G5, $10-$20 Austin, TX.

G7, $40-$70 Austin, TX.

G9, $120-$200 Austin, TX.

G8, $50-$80 Comanche Co., TX.

G7, $35-$60 Austin, TX.

LOCATION: Midwestern states. **DESCRIPTION:** A small to medium size, slender, triangular, expanded stemmed point. Some have a distinct bevel on one side of each face. Shoulders are tapered to weakly barbed.

DARL (continued)

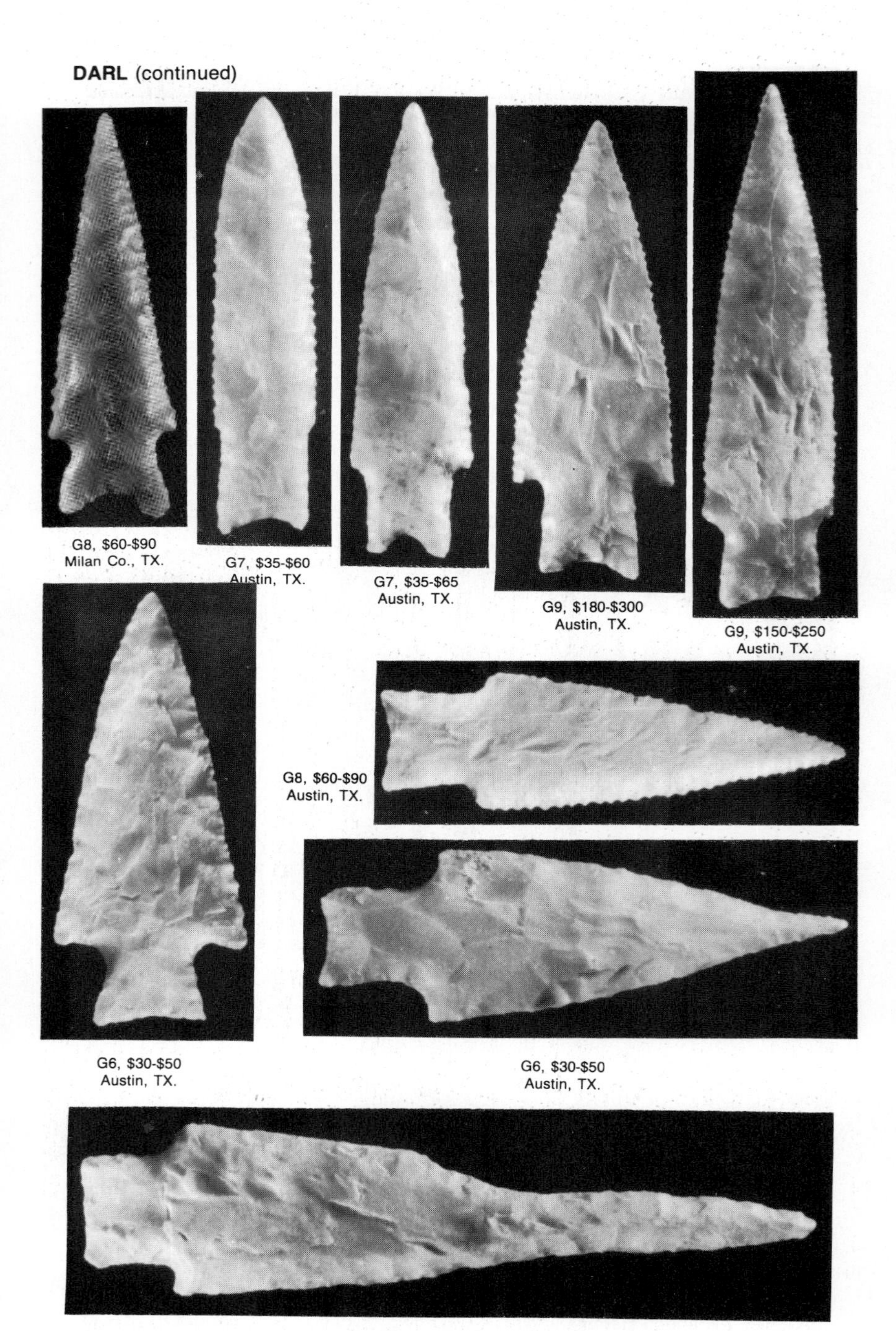

G8, $60-$90
Milan Co., TX.

G7, $35-$60
Austin, TX.

G7, $35-$65
Austin, TX.

G9, $180-$300
Austin, TX.

G9, $150-$250
Austin, TX.

G8, $60-$90
Austin, TX.

G6, $30-$50
Austin, TX.

G6, $30-$50
Austin, TX.

G6, $35-$60, Austin, TX. Drill form.

DARL BLADE - Woodland, 2500 - 1000 B.P.

(Also see Kinney)

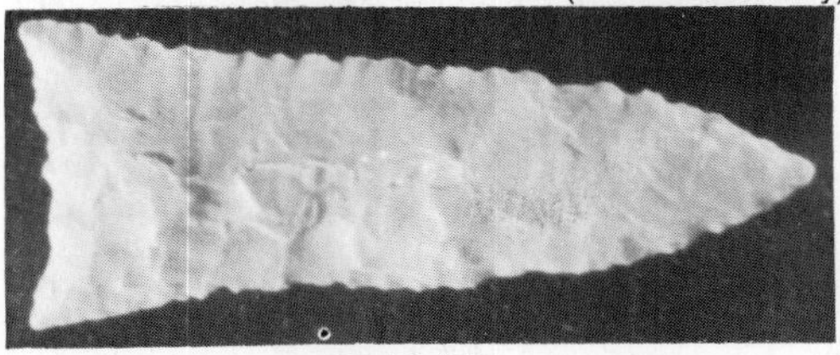

G5, $20-$35
Austin, TX.

G6, $45-$70
Little River Co., AR.

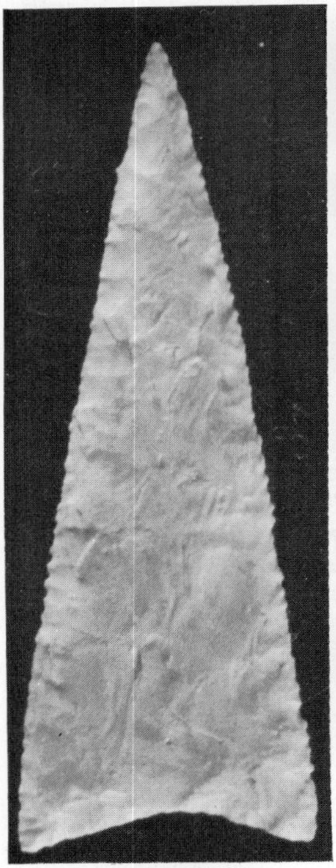

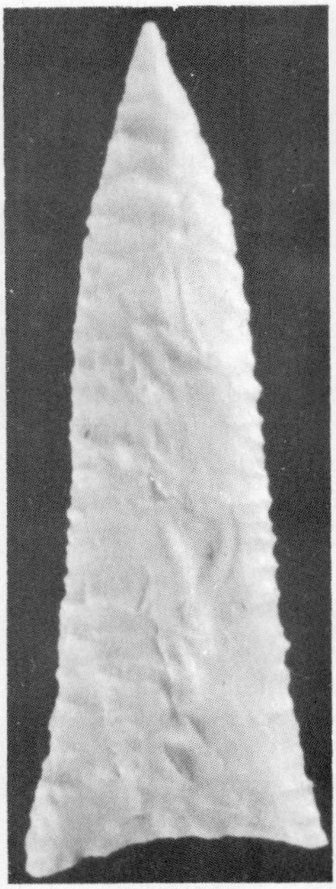

G8, $120-$220
Cent. TX.

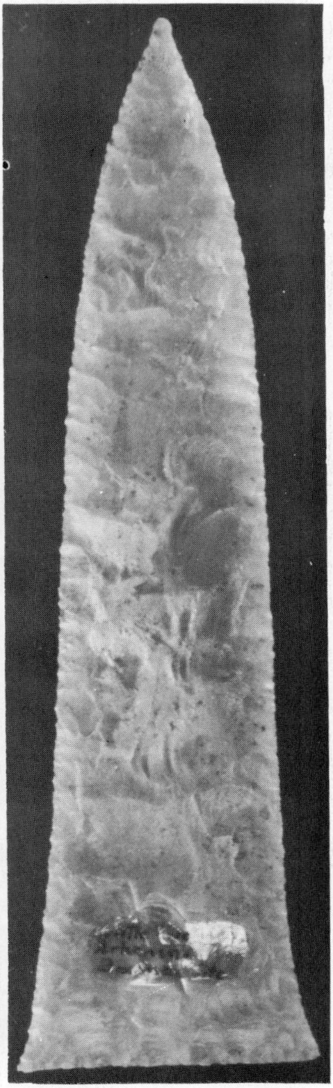

G10, $600-$1000
Little River Co., AR.

G9, $250-$400
Austin, TX.

LOCATION: Midwestern states. **DESCRIPTION:** A medium to large size, thin, lanceolate blade with typical *Darl* flaking, fine edgework and a concave to straight base.

DARL BLADE (continued)

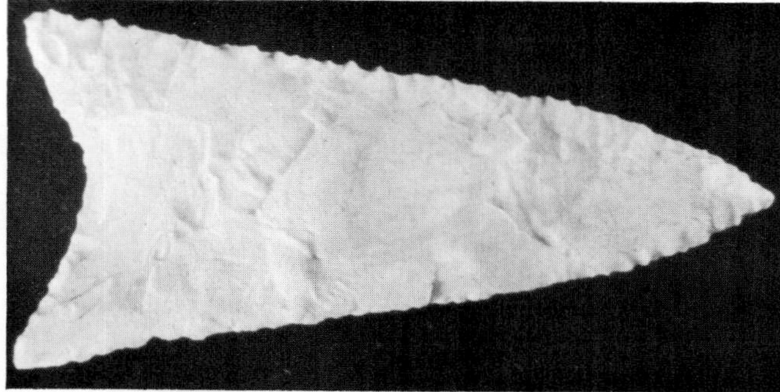

G8, $70-$100
Austin, TX.

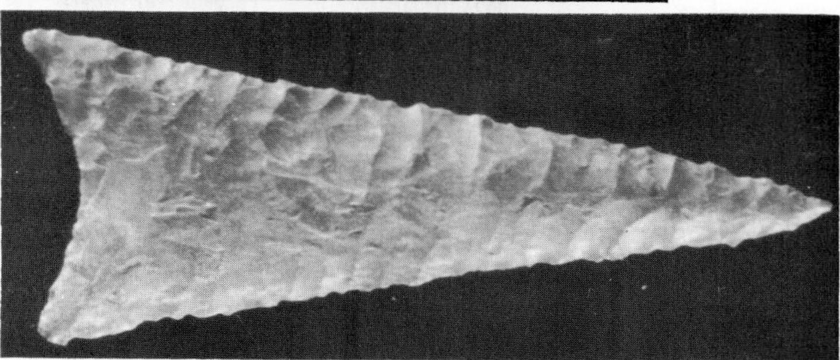

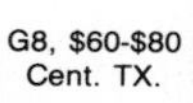

G8, $60-$80
Cent. TX.

DATIL - Early Archaic, 8000 - 6000 B.P.

G4, $1-$3
Yavapai Co., AZ.

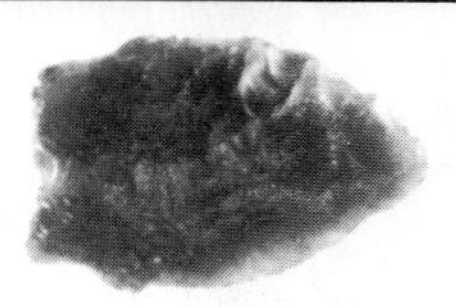

G6, $2-$5
Yavapai Co., AZ.

LOCATION: Southwestern states. **DESCRIPTION:** A small size point with a short base. Most examples are serrated. Shoulders are weak to absent.

DAWSON - Mid-Archaic, 7000 - 4000 B.P.

(Also see Adena Wells and Darl)

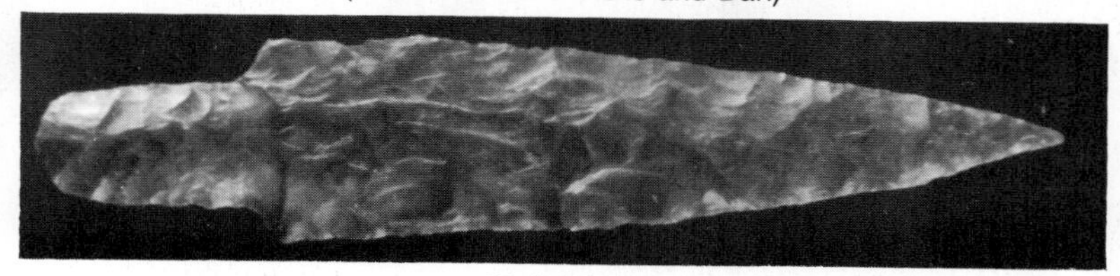

G9, $120-$200
Austin, TX. Very thin and excellent.

LOCATION: Midwestern states. **DESCRIPTION:** A medium size, narrow, stemmed point with strong, tapered shoulders. The base is rounded to square.

DEADMAN - Mississippian, 1000 - 500 B.P.

(Also see Gunther, Rockwall & Sabinal)

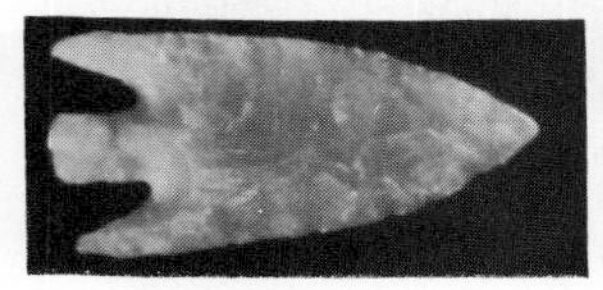

G9, $60-$100
WA/OR.

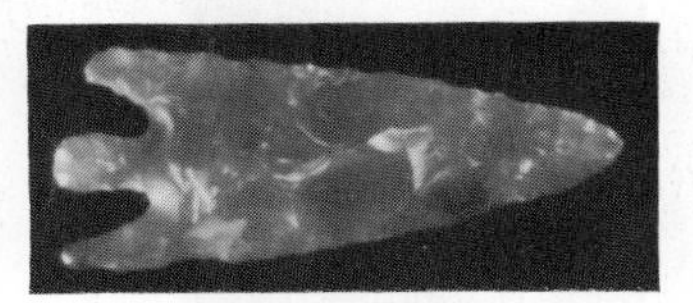

G7, $50-$80
WA/OR.

LOCATION: Northwestern states. **DESCRIPTION:** A small size, narrow, thin point with long barbs that usually reach the base. The base is parallel sided and narrow.

DEBERT - Paleo, 11000 - 9500 B.P.

(Also see Clovis and Dalton)

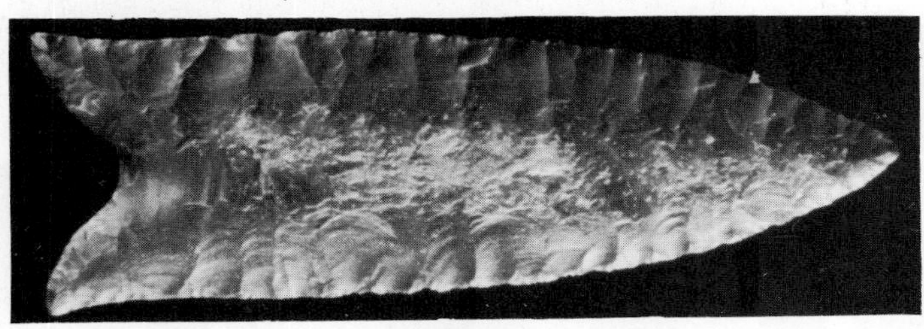

G9, $600-$1000
Greene Co., AR.

LOCATION: Midwestern to Eastern states. **DESCRIPTION:** A medium size, thin auriculate point with a deeply concave base that is ground. Fluting occurs on many examples. As in *Clovis*, blade edges gently curve into auricles with no shoulders visible.

DECATUR - Early Archaic, 9000 to 3000 B.P.

(Fractured base; see Cobbs Triangular)

G3, $5-$8
Walker Co., AL.

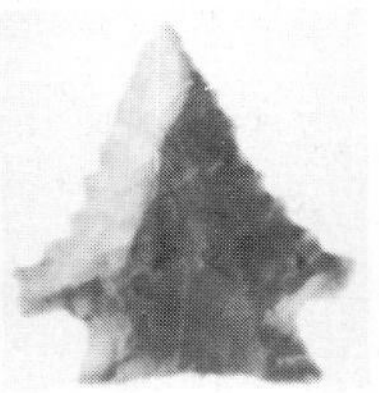

G4, $10-$20
Coffee Lake, AL.

G3, $6-$10
Nickajack Lake, TN.

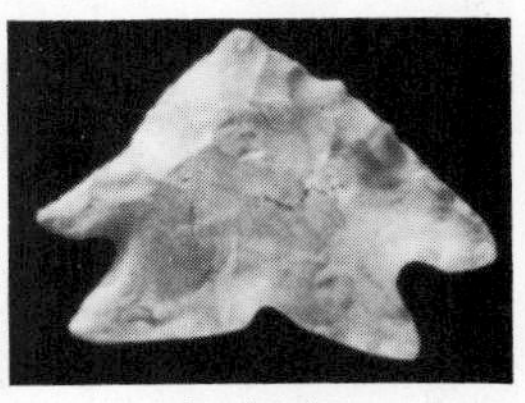

G4, $10-$20
Huntsville, AL.

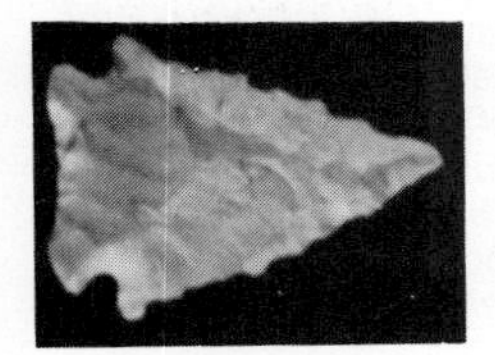

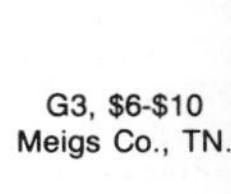

G3, $4-$6
Walker Co., AL.

G3, $6-$10
Meigs Co., TN.

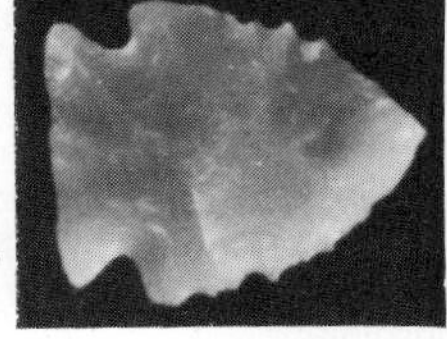

G7, $60-$80
Hamilton Co., TN.
Classic form.

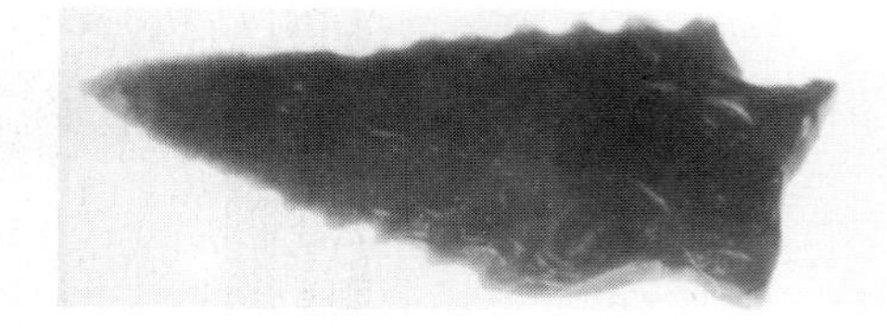

Above: Actual size photo of an excellent example found in Hamilton Co., TN. The oblique (out of scale) photos to the right illustrate the fractured tangs, stem sides and base that occur on this type.

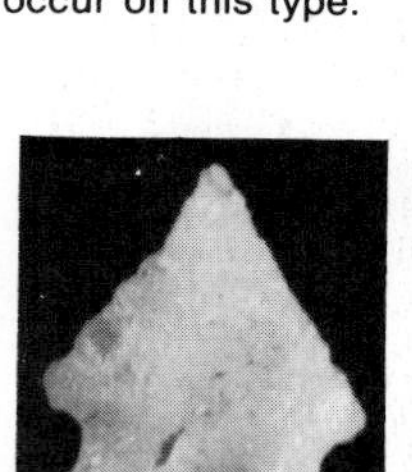

G2, $2-$4
Walker Co., AL.
Vein quartz.

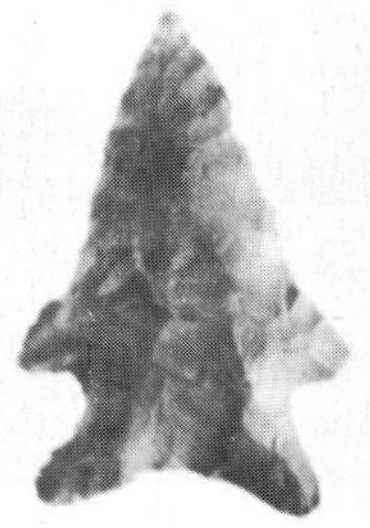

G4, $10-$20
Colbert Co., AL. Base
is unfractured.

G5, $20-$30
Walker Co., AL.

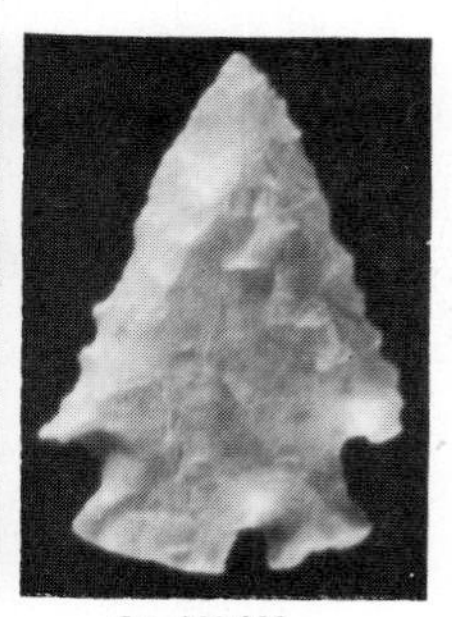

G5, $20-$30
Nickajack Lake, TN.
Note bifurcated base.

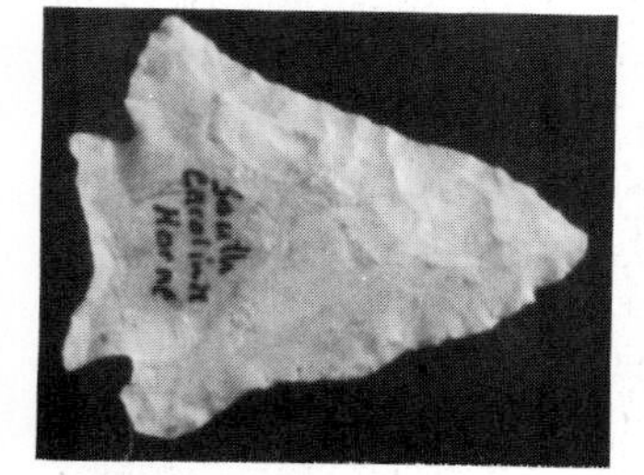

G5, $20-$30
SC.

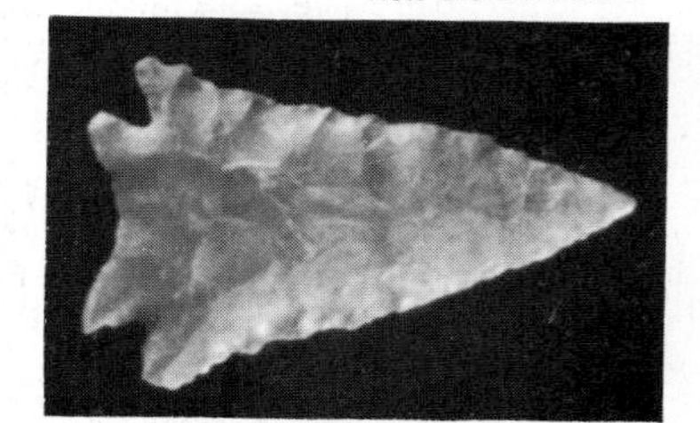

G7, $45-$70
Florence, AL. Coffee Lake.

LOCATION: Eastern states. **DESCRIPTION:** A small to medium size, serrated, corner notched point that is usually beveled on one side of each face. The base is usually broken off (fractured) by a blow inward from each corner of the stem. Sometimes the sides of the stem and backs of the tangs are also fractured, and rarely the tip may be fractured by a blow on each side directed towards the base. Bases are usually ground and flaking is of high quality. Basal fracturing also occurs in *Dovetail, Eva, Kirk, Motley* and *Snyders*. Unfractured forms are called *Angelico Corner-Notched* in Virginia.

DECATUR (continued)

G6, $35-$50
Elkmont, AL.

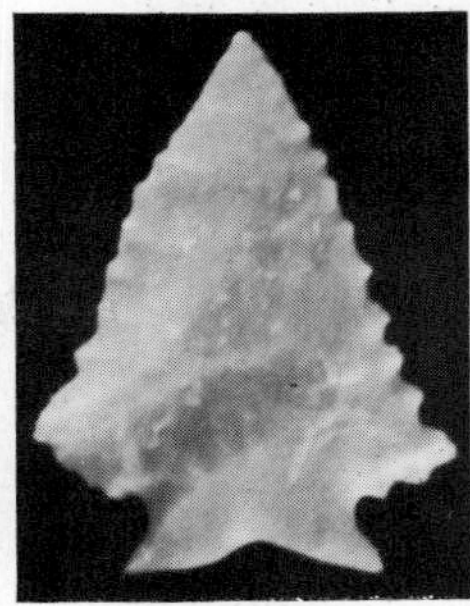
G9, $250-$350
Huntsville, AL. Excellent & thin. Clipped wing.

G7, $50-$80
Humphreys Co., TN. Base & basal sides are fractured.

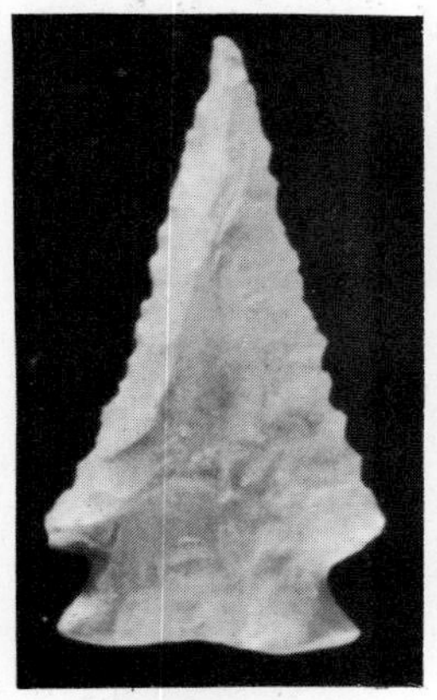
G7, $45-$70
Florence, AL. Coffee Lake.

G8, $80-$120
Florence, AL. Coffee Lake. Carter Cave flint.

G6, $40-$65
Florence, AL. Coffee Lake.

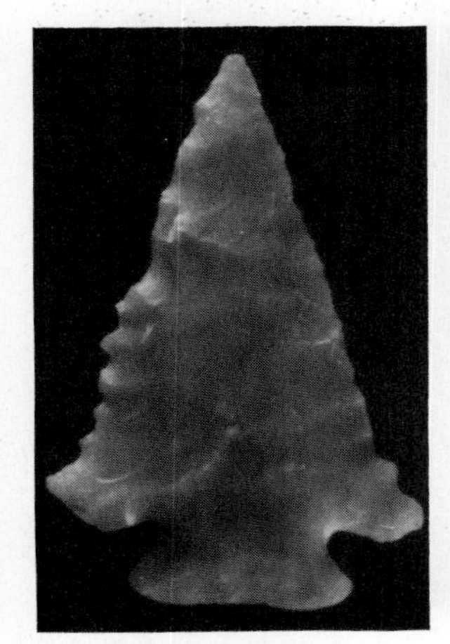
G8, $75-$110
Meigs Co., TN.

G7, $50-$80
Florence, AL. Coffee Lake.

G7, $50-$80
Florence, AL. Coffee Lake.

G7, $70-$120
W. TN.

G8, $150-$225
Florence, AL. Coffee Lake.
Left-hand bevel on blade.

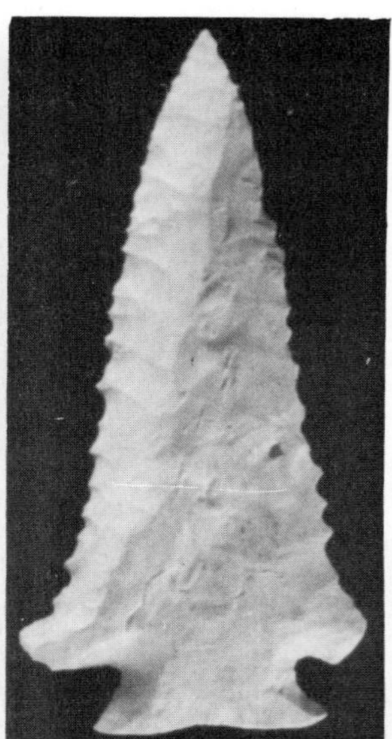

G8, $150-$225
Florence AL. Coffee Lake. Base, base sides and one shoulder are fractured.

G6, $40-$60
Fairfield Co., SC. Slate.

G9, $250-$450
MO/IL.

G8, $150-$250
Florence, AL. Coffee Lake. Note oblique flaking. Resembles *LeCroy* but was found on a *Decatur* chipping site. The base is fractured.

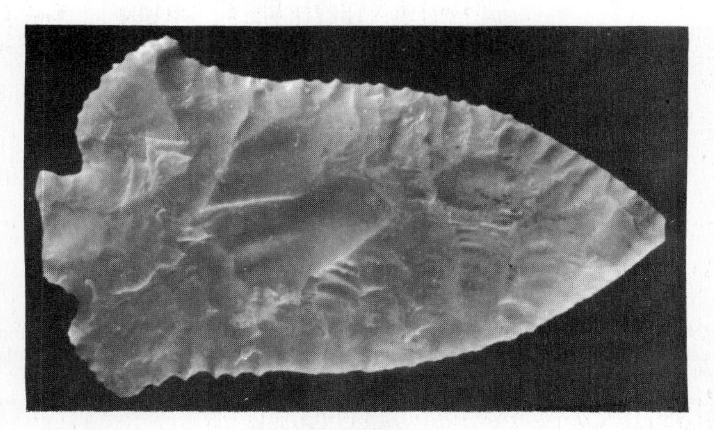

G8, $150-$250
Nashville, TN. Tip & base nicks.

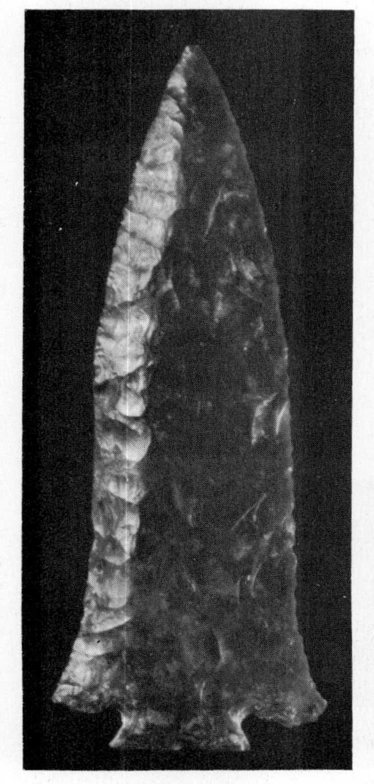

G10, $600-$1000
Jeff Co., KY.

G9, $350-$600
OH. Note unusual *Afton* type barbs on blade edges.

DECATUR BLADE - Early Archaic, 9000 - 3000 B.P.

(Also see Hardaway Blade)

G4, $3-$5
Florence, AL., Coffee Lake.

LOCATION: Eastern states. **DESCRIPTION:** A medium to large size, broad triangular blade with rounded corners and a straight base. A preform for *Decatur* points.

DELHI - Woodland, 3500 - 2000 B.P.

(Also see Bulverde, Kays and Pontchartrain)

G7, $25-$40
Comanche Co., TX.

G8, $35-$50
Comanche Co., TX. Leon River chert.

G9, $150-$280
Comanche Co., TX.

G9, $90-$150
Comanche Co., TX. Edwards Plateau chert.

LOCATION: Southern Midwestern states. **DESCRIPTION:** A medium to large size, narrow, expanded barbed point with a short, parallel sided base.

DELHI (continued)

G10, $220-$300, Austin, TX. Note caliche deposit on blade surface.

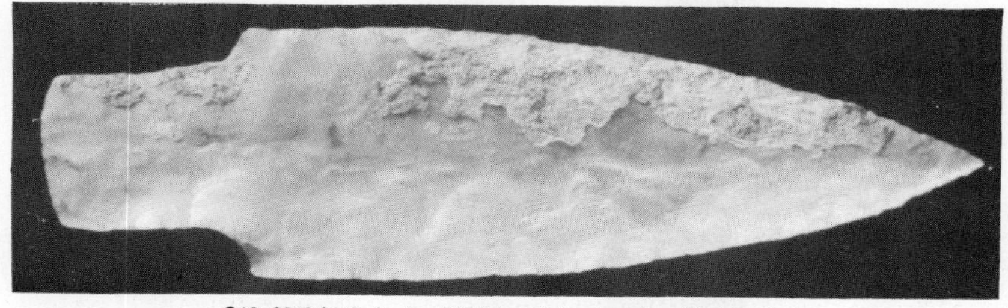

G10, $250-$400, Austin, TX. Note caliche deposit on blade surface.

DESERT CORNER NOTCHED - Woodland to Historic, 2500 - 400 B.P.

(also see Elko & Pinto)

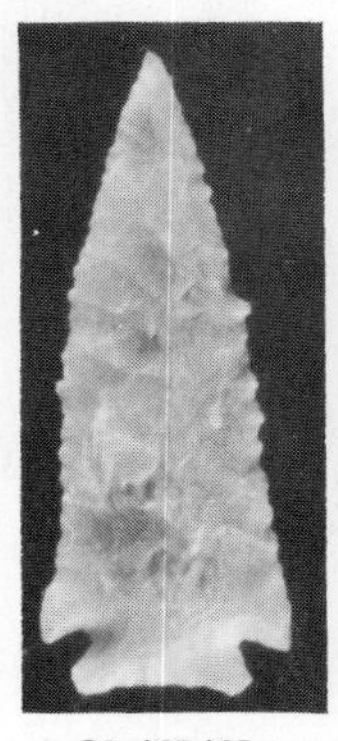

G6, $25-$35 WA/OR.

G8, $35-$50 WA/OR.

G5, $15-$25 WA/OR.

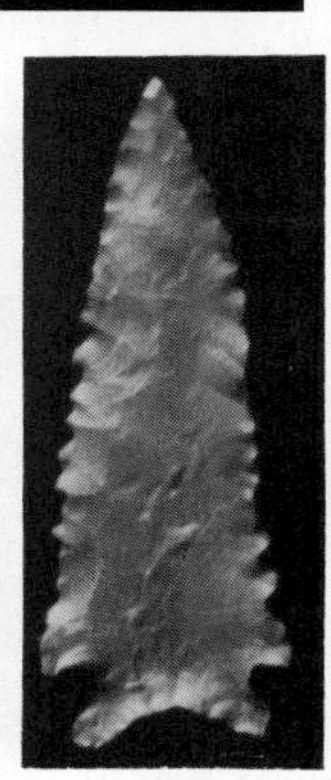

G5, $15-$25 WA/OR.

LOCATION: Northwestern states. **DESCRIPTION:** A small, thin, triangular point with corner notches and a concave base.

DESERT SIDE NOTCHED - Woodland to Historic, 2500 - 400 B.P.

(also see Black Rock, Cahokia, Harrell & Northern Side Notched)

LOCATION: Northwestern states. **DESCRIPTION:** A small, thin, side notched point with a concave base. Blade edges can be serrated. Some examples have a basal notch. Reported to have been used by the Shoshoni Indians of the historic period.

DESERT SIDE NOTCHED (continued)

G3, $4-$6
Comanche Co., TX.

G4, $6-$10
Comanche Co., TX.

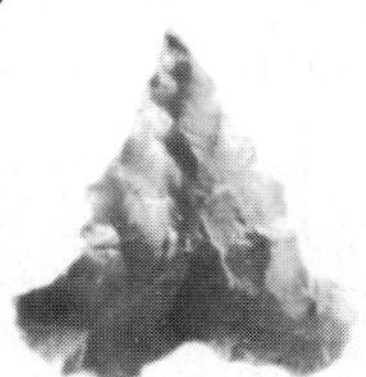
G2, $3-$5
Yavapai Co., AZ.

G3, $3-$5
Yavapai Co., AZ.

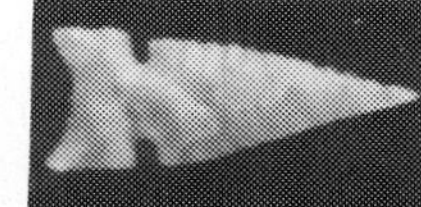
G8, $40-$60
Columbia Rv., WA.

G7, $15-$25
Cent. TX.

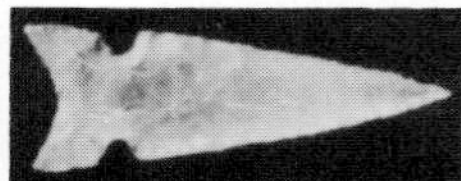
G5, $10-$15
Portland, OR.

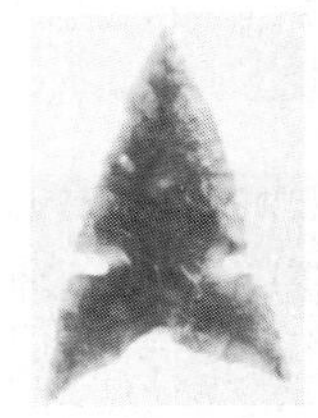
G5, $10-$15
Klamath Co., OR.

G5, $10-$15
Klamath Co., OR.

G6, $15-$20
Klamath Co., OR.
Obsidian

G6, $15-$20
Klamath Co., OR.
Obsidian

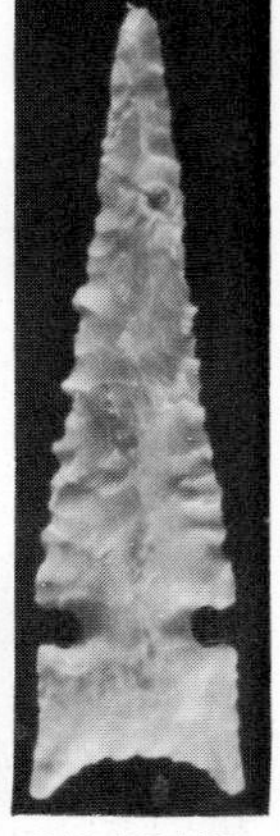
G10, $60-$100
WA/OR.

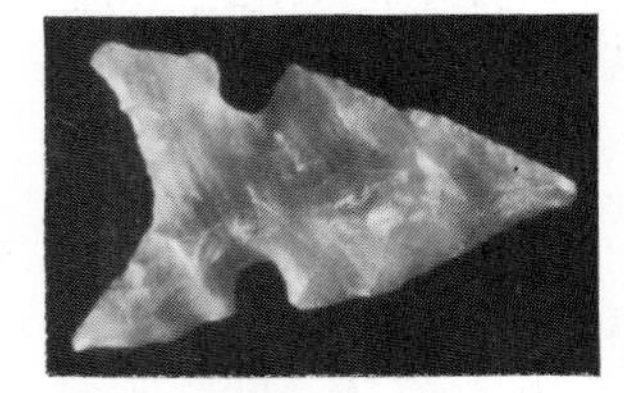
G8, $40-$60
WA/OR.

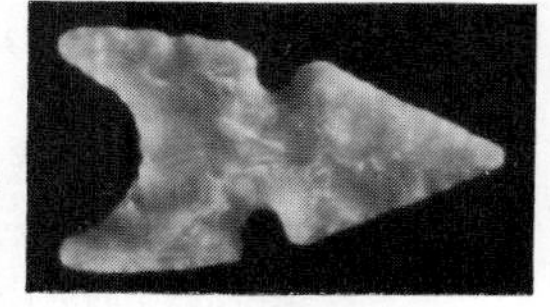
G5, $10-$15
WA/OR.

DICKSON (See Adena-Dickson)

DOUBLE TIP - Mississippian, 1000 - 500 B.P.

(Also see Perdiz)

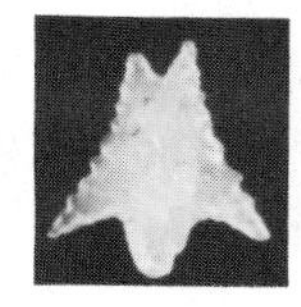
G9, $15-$25
Multnomah Co., OR. Agate.

LOCATION: Northwestern states. **DESCRIPTION:** A small size, barbed, contracted base point with two tips. Very rare in type area.

DOVETAIL - Early Archaic, 9000 - 5000 B.P.

(Also see Cobbs Triangular, Gibson, Lost Lake, St. Charles & Thebes)

G3, $15-$25
Hamilton Co., TN.

G2, $10-$15
KY.

G4, $25-$40
Walker Co., AL.

G5, $150-$250
Cent. NC. Patinated rhyolite.

G2, $10-$15
KY. Resharpened form.

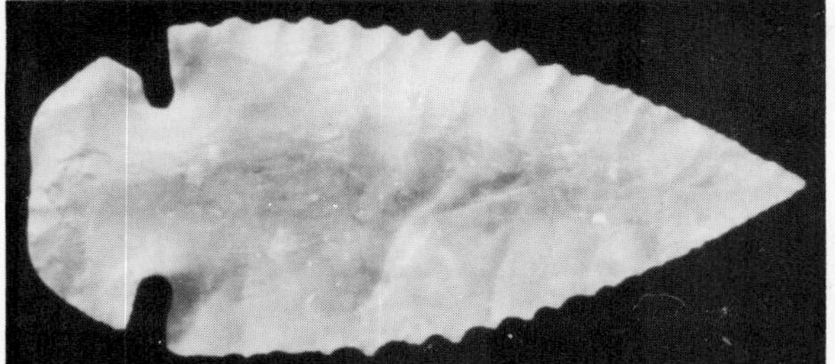

G8, $450-$750
Cynthiana, KY.

LOCATION: Southeastern states. **DESCRIPTION:** A medium to large size, corner notched, dovetailed base point. The blade is always beveled on one side of each face (usually the left side). Unbeveled examples would place the point into the *St. Charles* type. Bases are always convex. Straight bases would place a point into the *Lost Lake* type. Bases are ground and can be fractured on both sides or center notched on some examples. **I.D. KEY:** Dovetailed base and beveled sides.

DOVETAIL (continued)

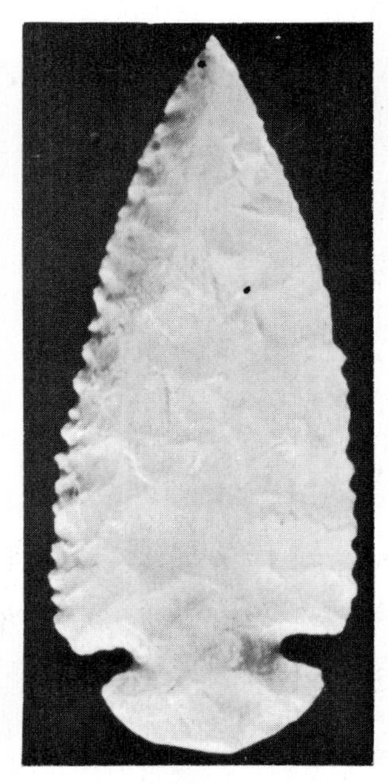

G4, $90-$150
Hamilton Co., TN. Evidence of hafting is still visible. Note unpatinated dark area on base at right notch where hafting remained for a long period of time while the rest of the point patinated. This dark area also appears on the reverse right side at notch.

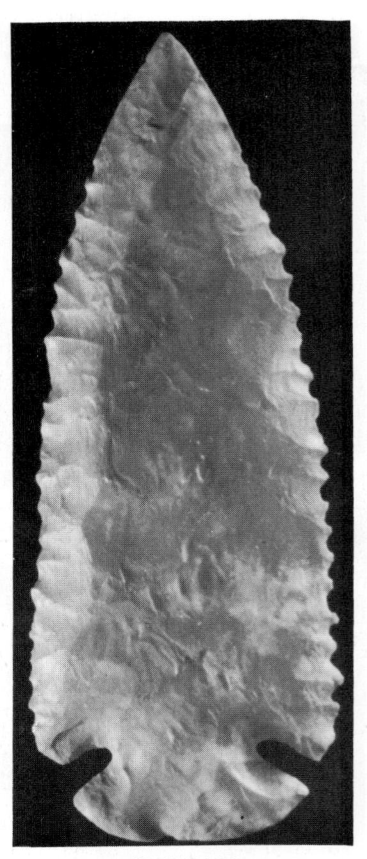

G7, $280-$350
Marion Co., KY.

G5, $150-$250
Benton Co., TN. Notched base form.

DOVETAIL (continued)

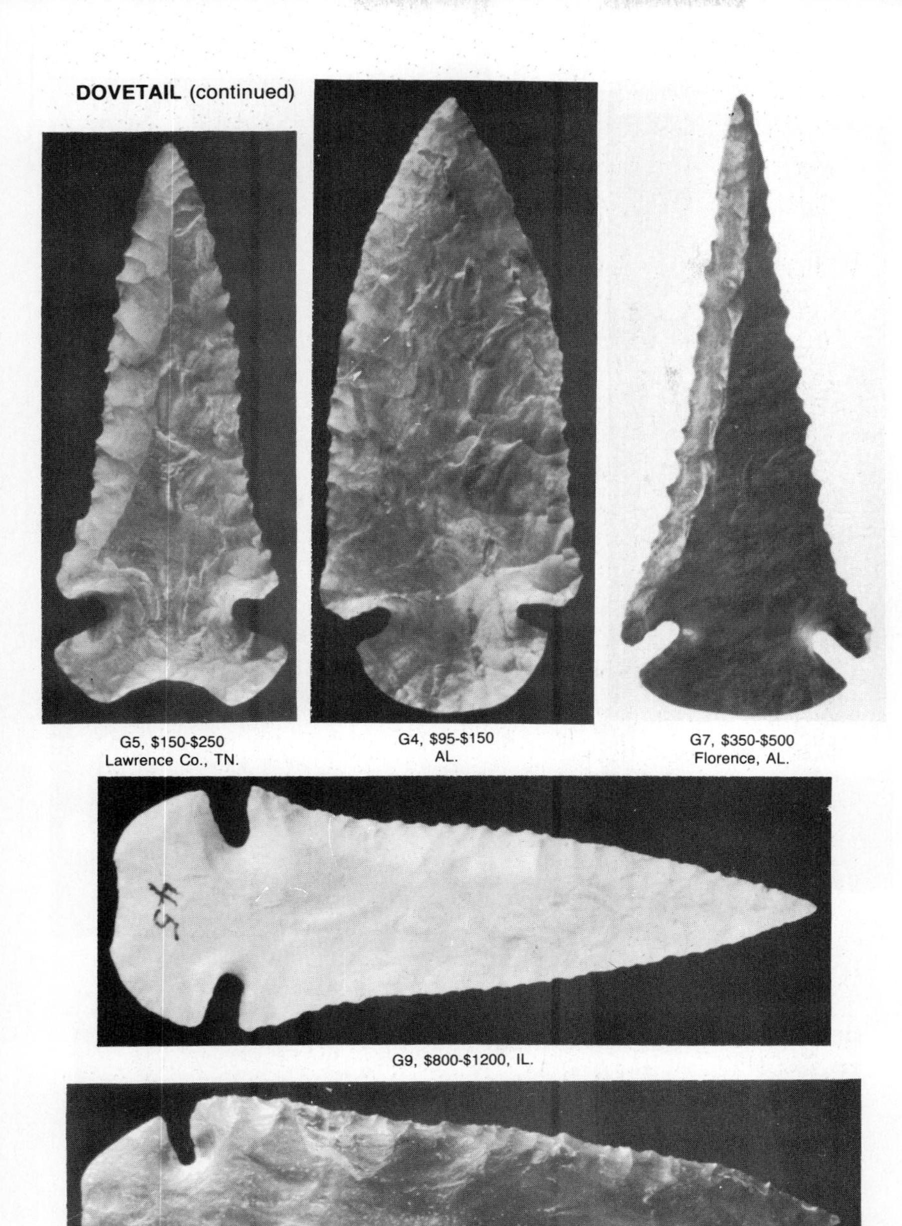

G5, $150-$250
Lawrence Co., TN.

G4, $95-$150
AL.

G7, $350-$500
Florence, AL.

G9, $800-$1200, IL.

G7, $300-$500, Warren Co., TN. Rare red, white and blue flint. Field find.

DOVETAIL (continued)

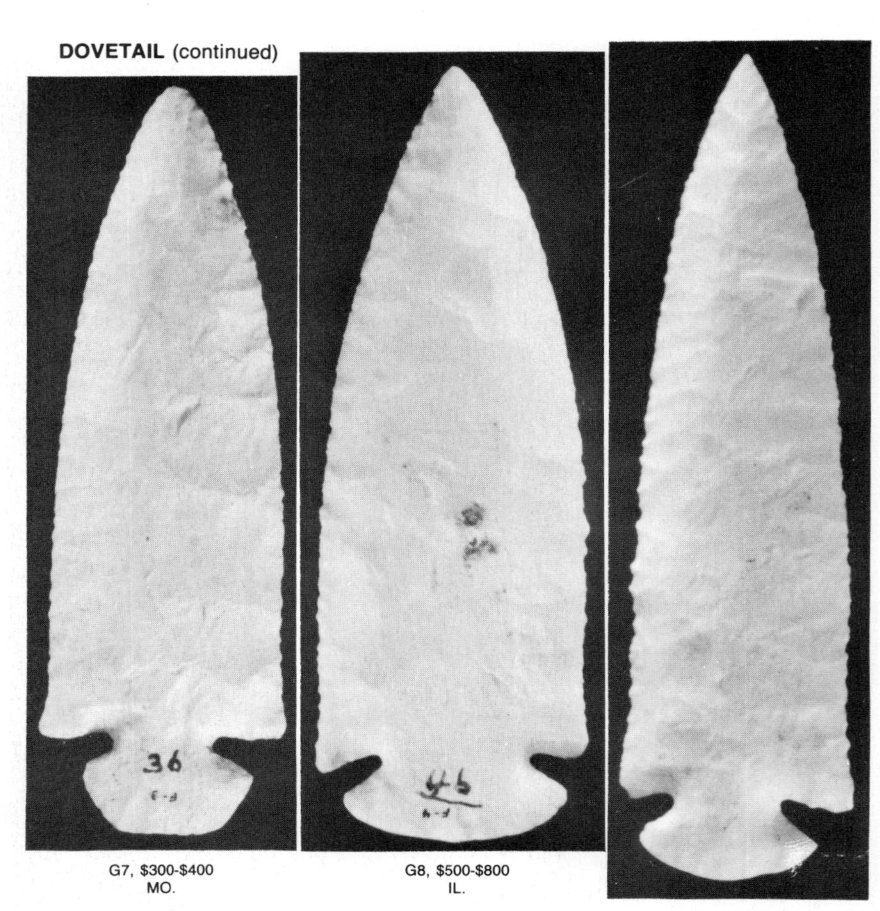

G7, $300-$400
MO.

G8, $500-$800
IL.

G7, $300-$500
Fulton, Co., IL.

G7, $300-$500
Boone Co., MO.

DOVETAIL (continued)

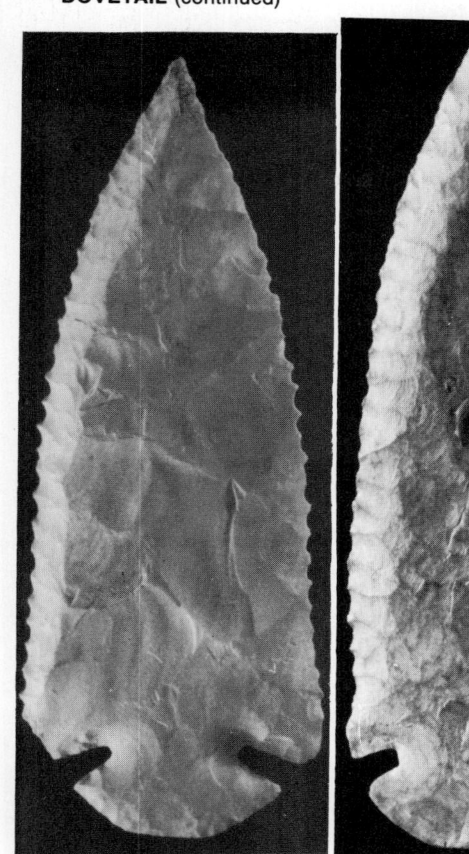

G5, $150-$250
Eva, TN., Kent Lake.

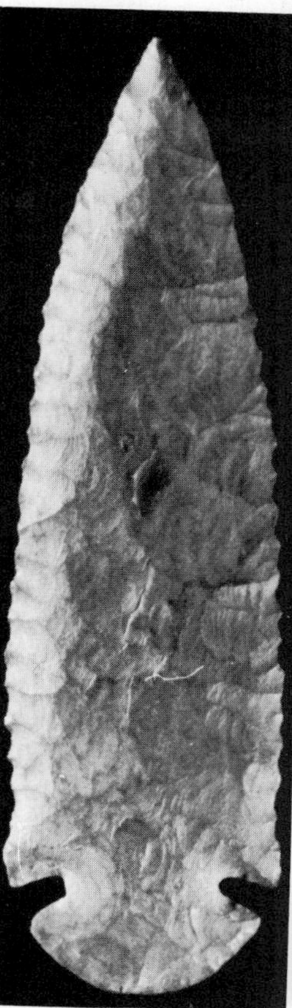

G9, $800-$1200
Humphreys Co., TN. Dover chert.
Heavy patina.

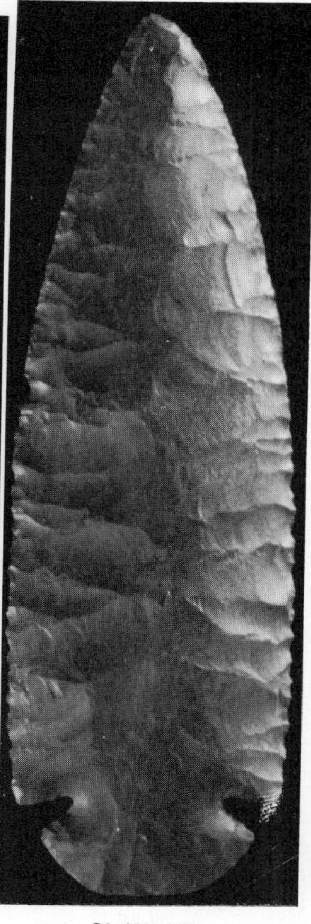

G8, $500-$800
MO/IL.

G7, $300-$400
Cumberland Co., TN.

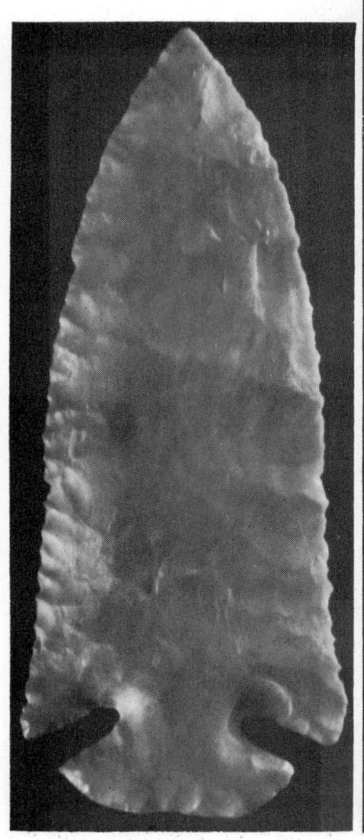

G9, $800-$1200
Sumner Co., TN.

G9, $800-$1200
Livingston Co., KY.

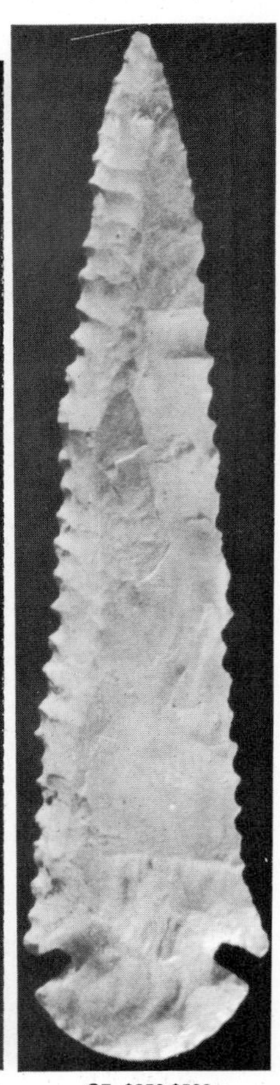

G7, $350-$500
Morgan Co., AL.

G8, $600-$900
Robertson Co., TN.

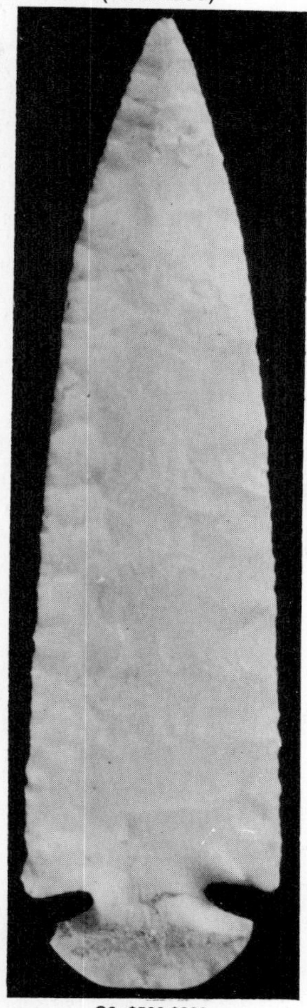

G8, $500-$800
IL.

G10, $1200-$2000
Sou. IN.

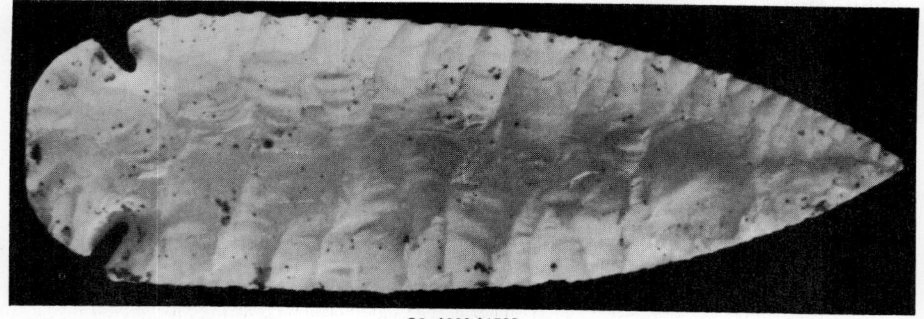

G9, $900-$1500
Clark Co., MO.

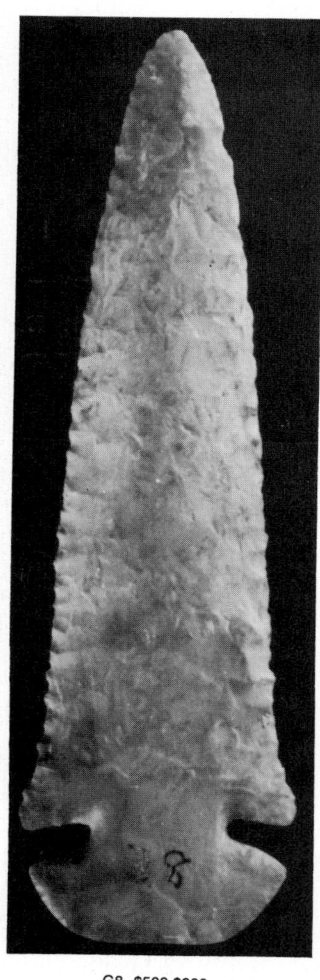

G8, $500-$800
Ohio.

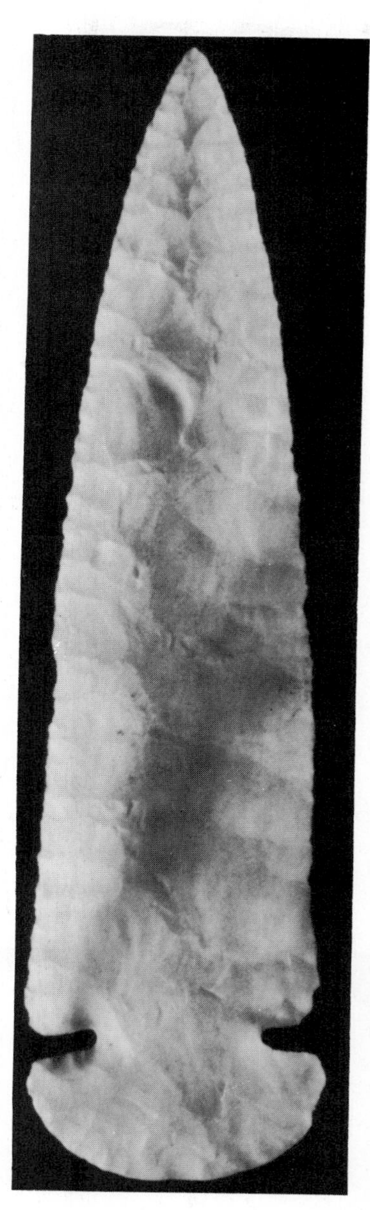

G7, $400-$750
Calhoun Co., IL. Shoulder nick.

DOVETAIL (continued)

G10, $1200-$2000
Putnam Co., IL.

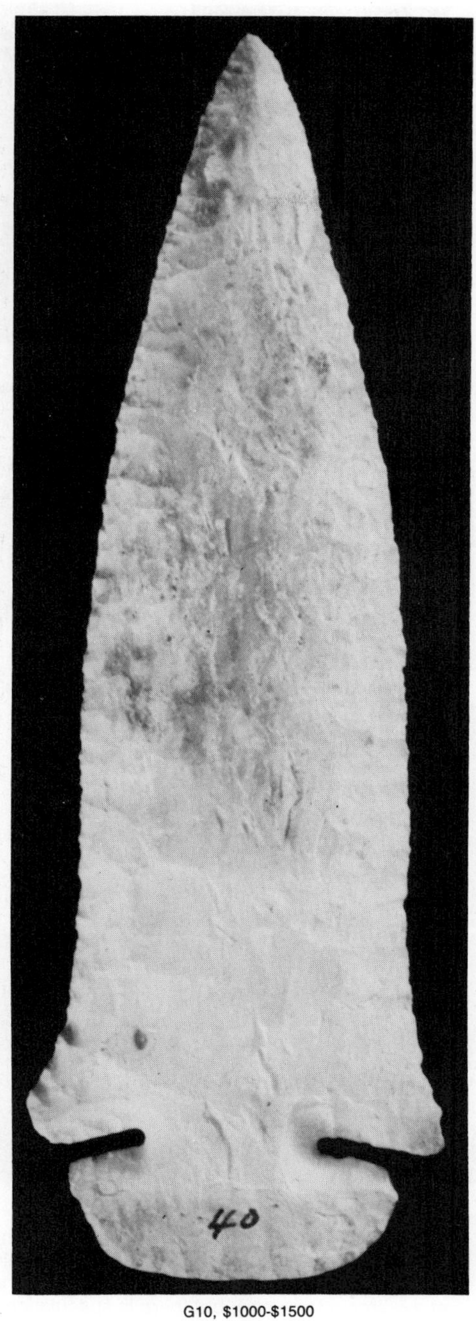

G10, $1000-$1500
Perry Co., MO.

DRILL - Paleo to Historic, 15000 - 200 B.P.

(Also see Addison Micro-Drill)

G2, $1-$3
Meigs Co., TN.
Mississippian.

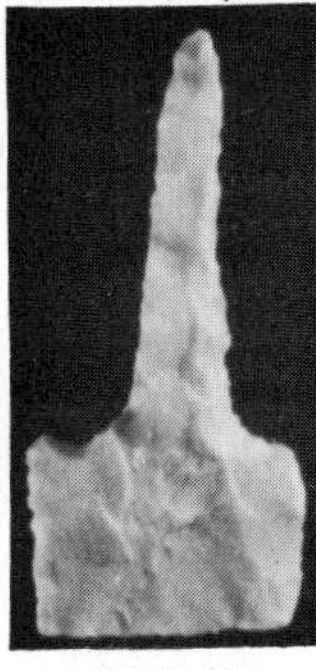
G3, $3-$5
Humphreys Co., TN.
Mississippian.

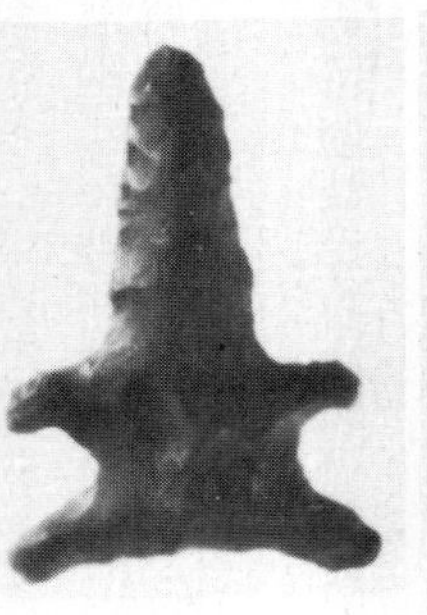
G4, $15-$20
Hamilton Co., TN.
Big Sandy form.

G2, $1-$2
MS. Red jasper.

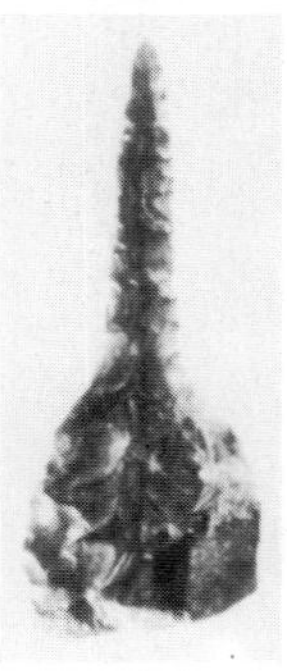
G3, $3-$5
Meigs Co., TN.
Mississippian.

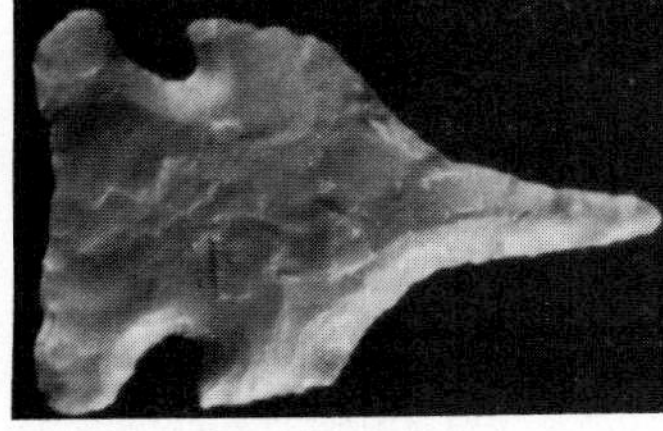
G4, $15-$20, Austin, TX.

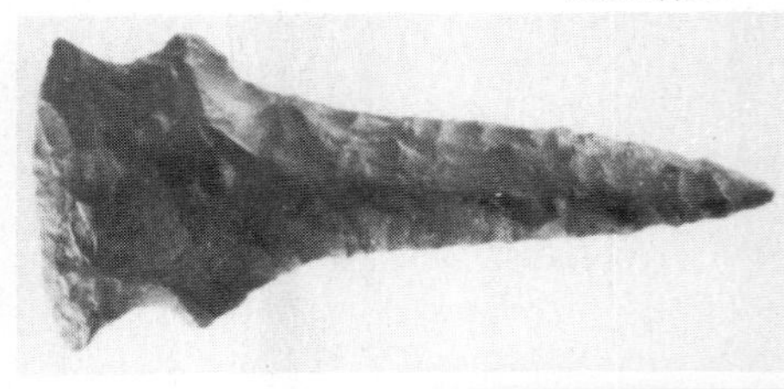
G4, $15-$20, AR.

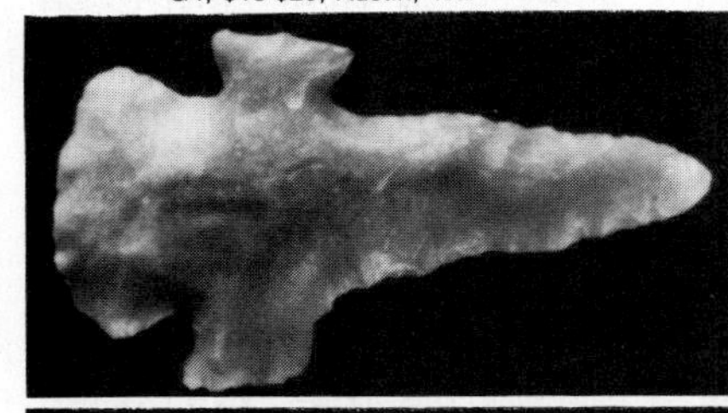
G3, $6-$10
Austin, TX. Castroville.

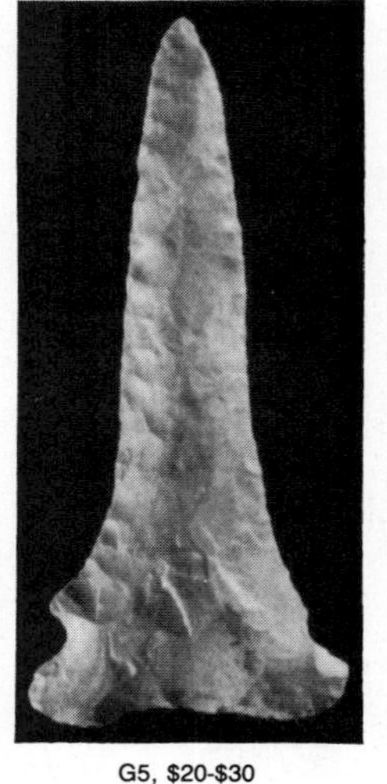
G5, $20-$30
Humphreys Co., TN. Greenbrier.

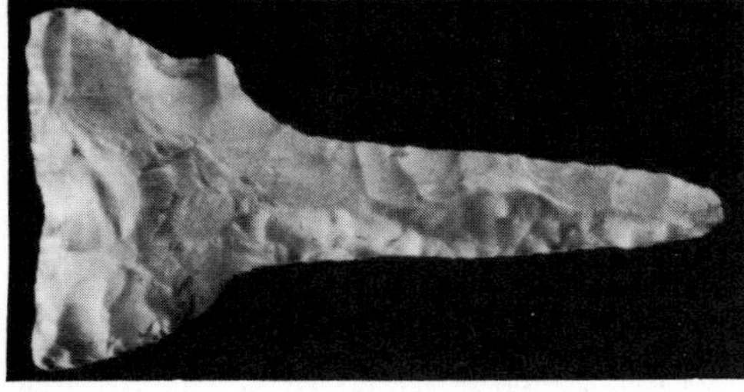
G3, $6-$10, Austin, TX.

LOCATION: Everywhere. **DESCRIPTION:** Although many drills were made from scratch, all point types were made into the drill form. Usually, broken points were salvaged and rechipped into drills. These objects were certainly used as drills (evidence of extreme edge wear), but there is speculation that some of these forms may have been used as pins for clothing, ornaments, ear plugs and other uses.

DRILL (continued)

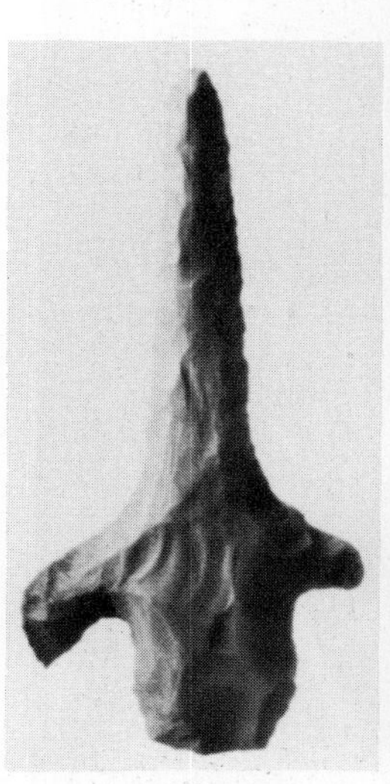

G5, $20-$30
W. TN.

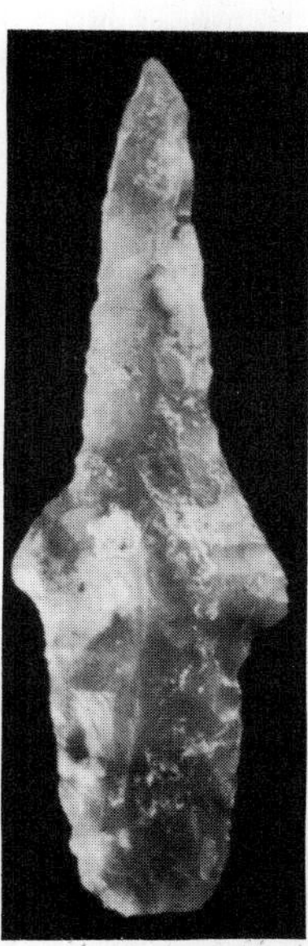

G4, $12-$20
Austin, TX. Wells Adena.

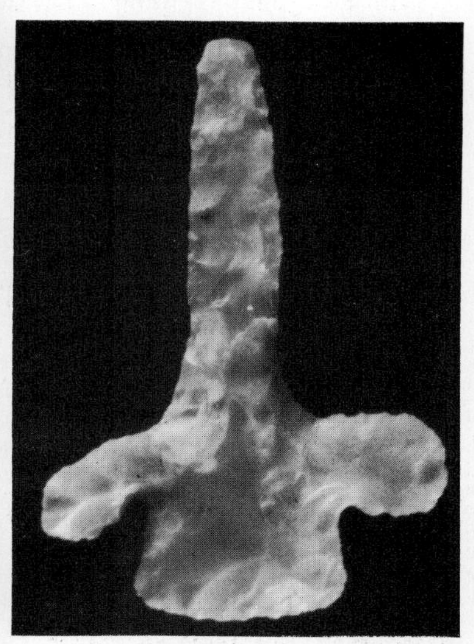

G5, $25-$40
Austin, TX. Castroville.

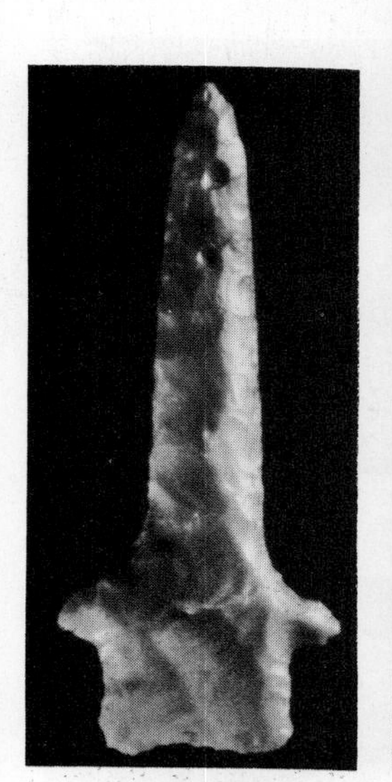

G5, $25-$40
Austin, TX.

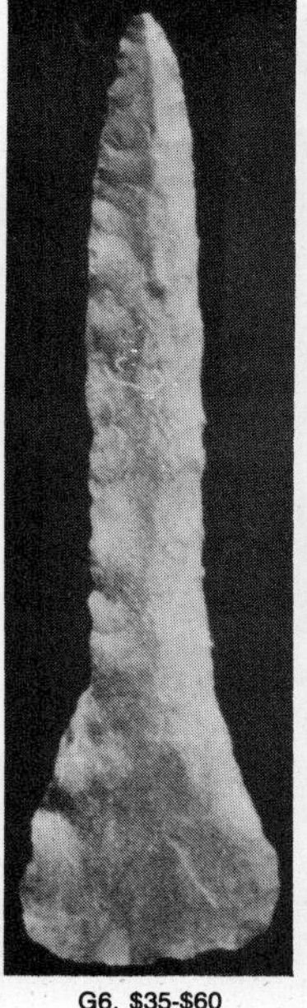

G6, $35-$60
TX/AR.

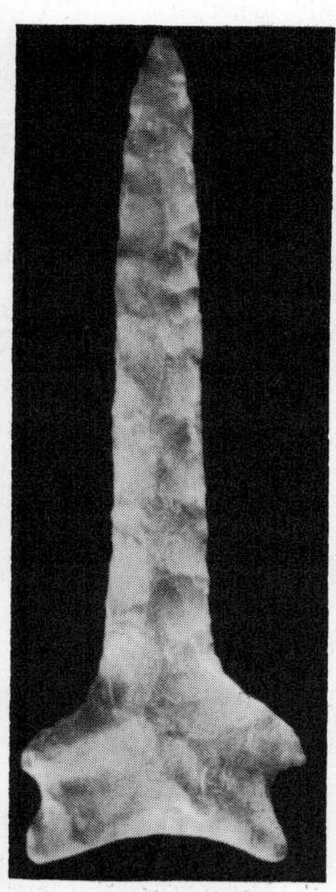

G7, $60-$90
Stokes Co., NC.

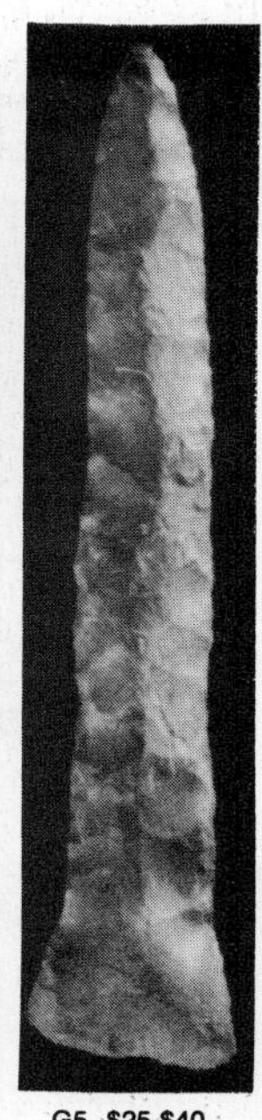

G5, $25-$40
TX/AR. Pencil drill.

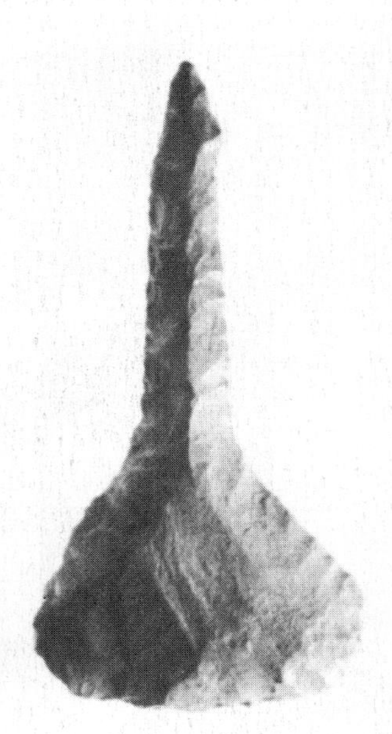

G6, $25-$40
W. TN.

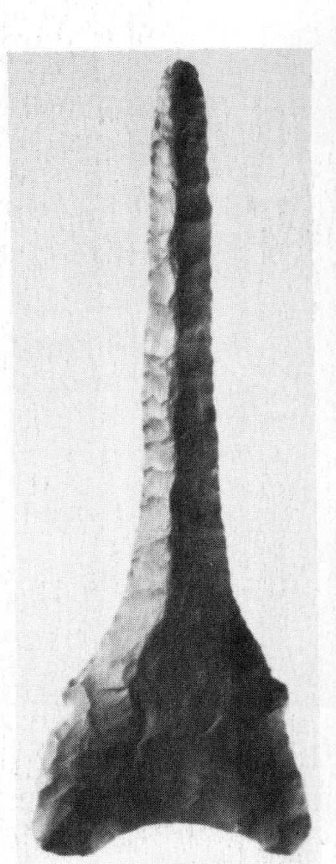

G7, $60-$100
Humphreys Co., TN.

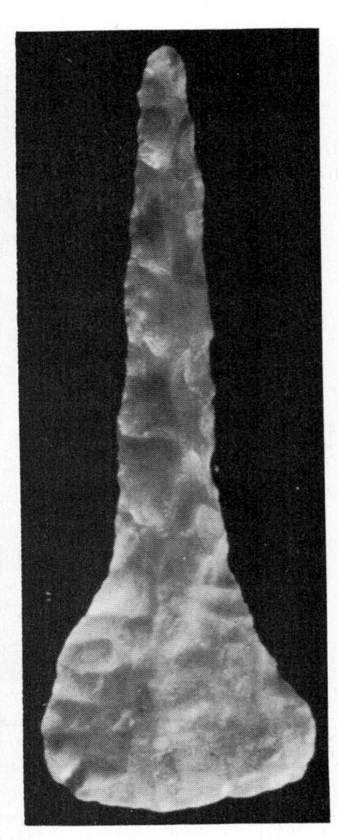

G6, $35-$45
Austin, TX.

G8, $90-$150
Austin, TX. Castroville

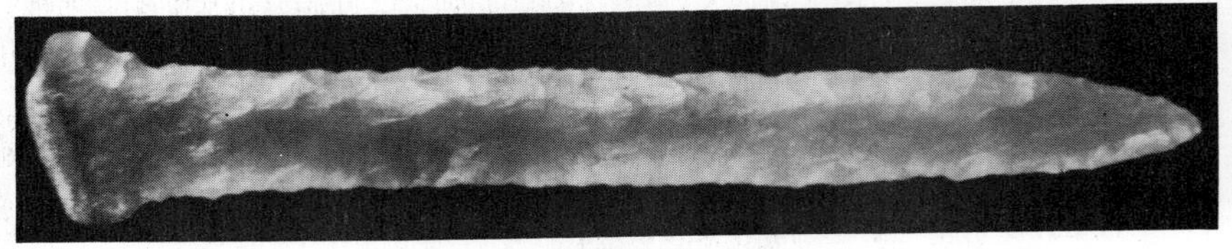

G8, $90-$150
Burke Co., GA.

DRILL (continued)

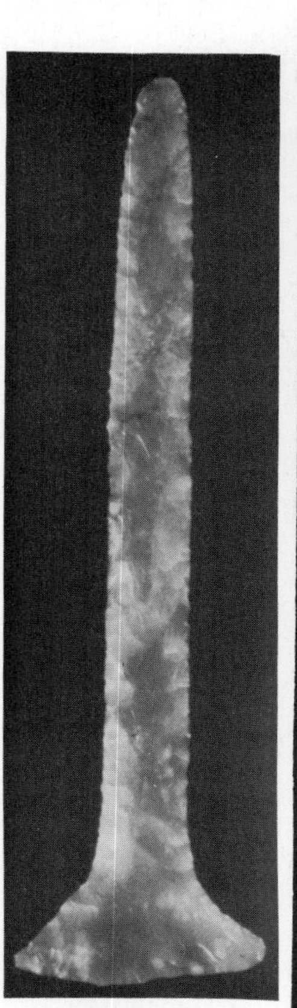

G10, $300-$500
Burke Co., GA.

G6, $25-$35
Austin, TX.

G8, $120-$220
Benton Co., TN.

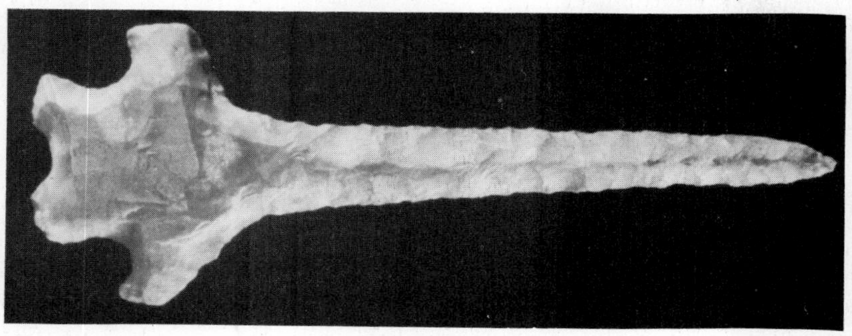

G9, $150-$250
Meigs Co., TN. Buzzard Roost.

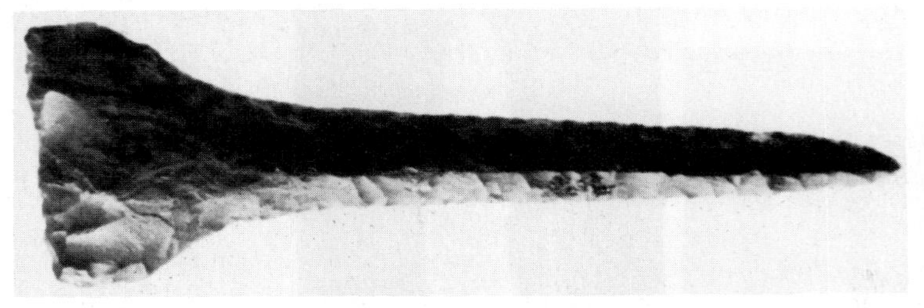

G7, $60-$100
Humphreys Co., TN.

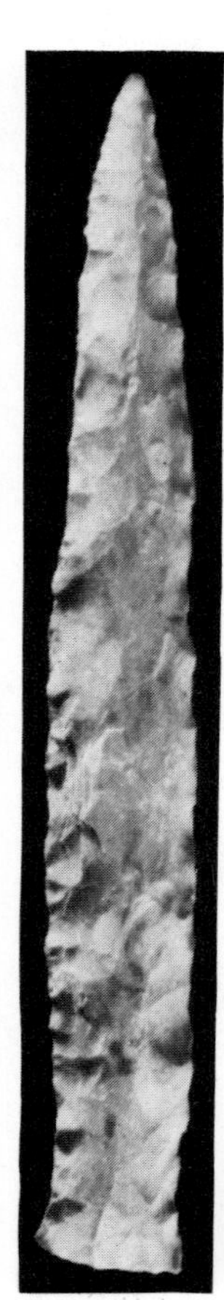

G9, $150-$250
Comanche Co., TX.
Pencil drill. Rare.

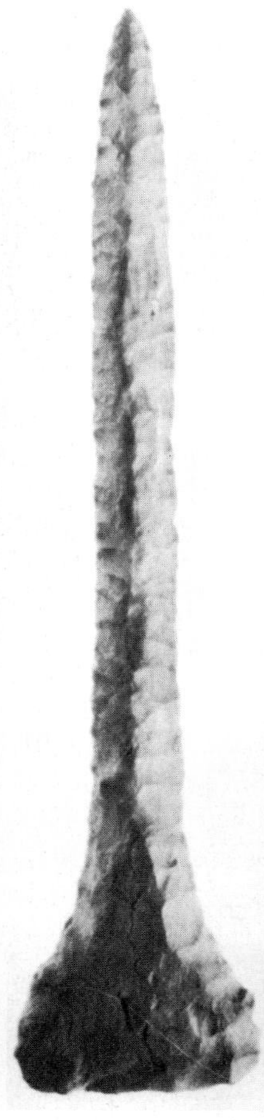

G10, $500-$800
Humphreys Co., TN.

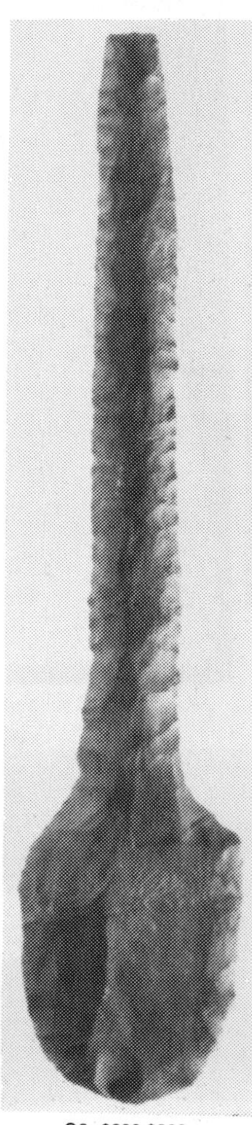

G9, $200-$300
Humphreys Co., TN. Lerma form.

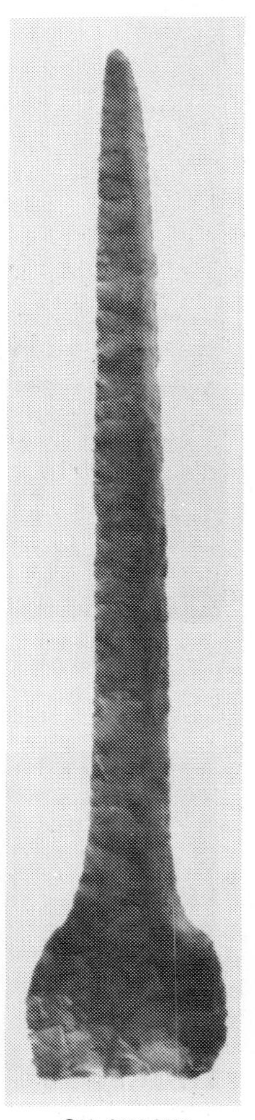

G10, $500-$800
Calloway Co., KY.

DUNCAN - Late Archaic to Woodland, 4500 - 2500 B.P.

(Also see Hanna, Patrick, Pinto Basin & SW Hanna)

G5, $8-$12
Yavapai Co., AZ.

G2, $2-$4
Yavapai Co., AZ.

G4, $4-$6
Yavapai Co., AZ.

LOCATION: Midwestern to Western states. **DESCRIPTION:** A small to medium size, narrow point with tapered shoulders and a bifurcated base. The stem can expand, contract or is parallel sided.

DURANT'S BEND - Woodland to Miss., 1600 - 1000 B.P.

(Also see Nova and Washington)

G1, .25-.50

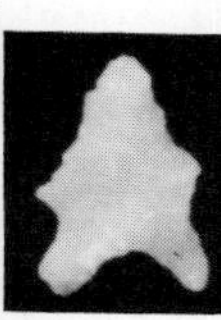
G2, .50-$1

G2, .50-$1

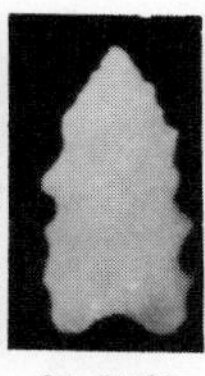
G2, .50-$1

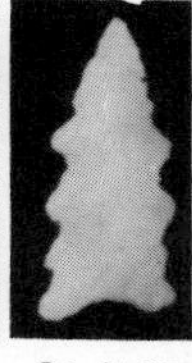
G3, $1-$2

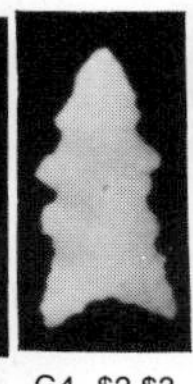
G3, $1-$2

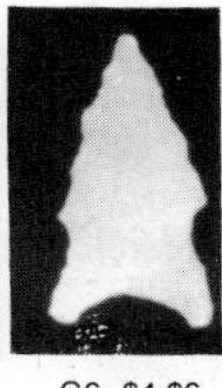
G4, $2-$3

G6, $4-$6

(All Dallas Co., AL.)

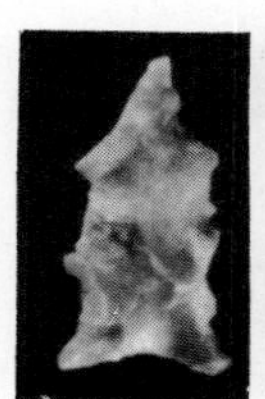
G4, $2-$3

G6, $5-$7

G6, $4-$6

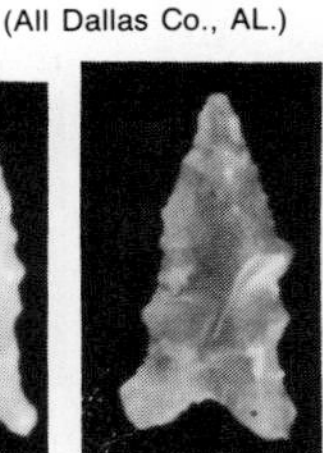
G4, $2-$4

G5, $3-$5

G7, $8-$12

LOCATION: Alabama. **DESCRIPTION:** A small size, narrow, triangular point with flaring ears and a serrated blade made from nodular black chert or milky quartz.

DURST - Woodland, 3000 - 2500 B.P.

(Also see Ellis, Godley, Holston, Macpherson, Mud Creek, San Pedro & Swan Lake)

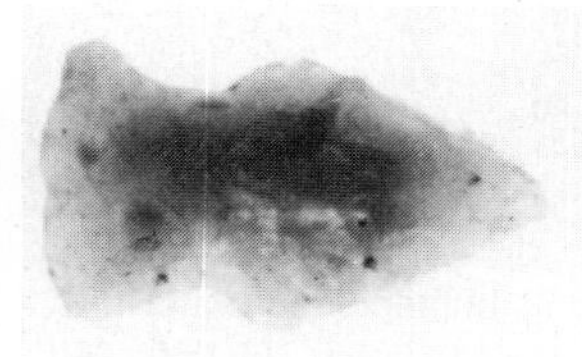
G4, $1-$3
Dunlap, TN.

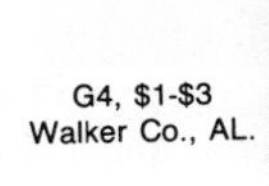
G4, $1-$3
Walker Co., AL.

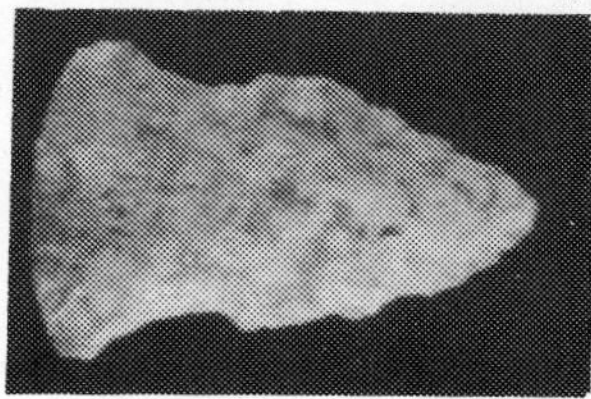

DURST (continued)

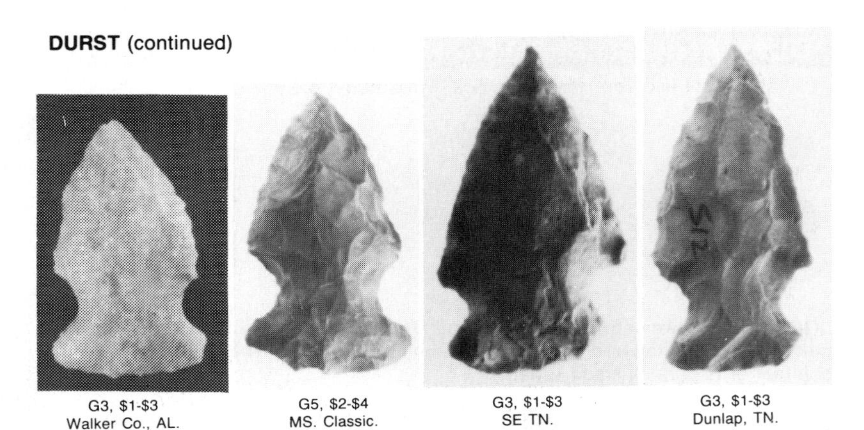

G3, $1-$3
Walker Co., AL.

G5, $2-$4
MS. Classic.

G3, $1-$3
SE TN.

G3, $1-$3
Dunlap, TN.

LOCATION: Midwestern to Southeastern states. **DESCRIPTION:** A small, thick, wide side-notched point with a large flaring and rounded base. Called *Holston Side-Notched* in Virginia.

DUVAL - Late Woodland, 2000 - 1000 B.P.

(Also see Bradley, Flint River & Schild Spike, Fishspear, Leon, Macpherson & Randolph)

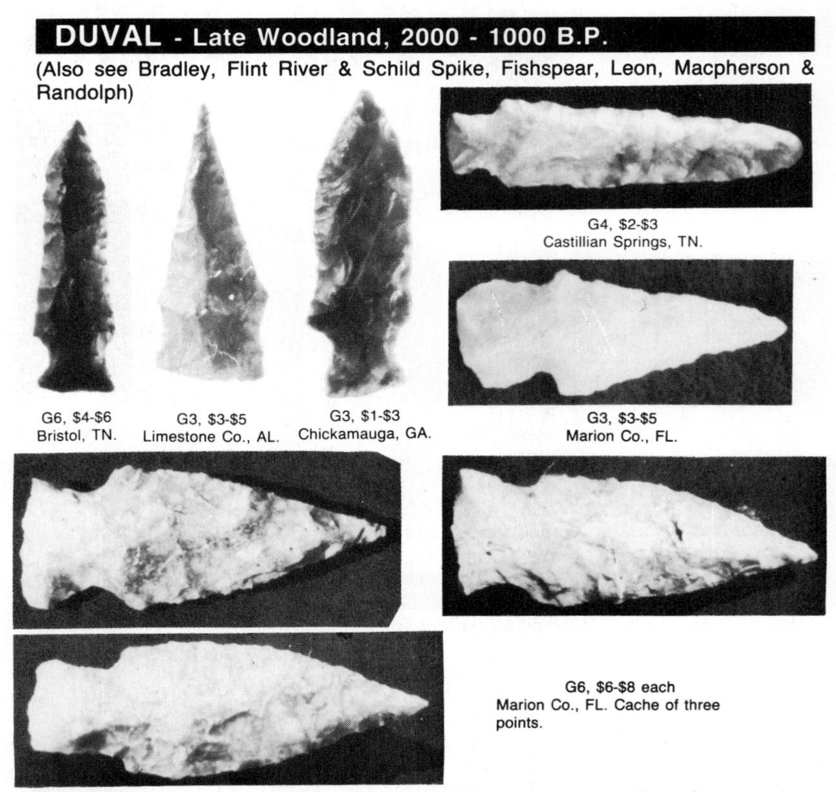

G4, $2-$3
Castillian Springs, TN.

G6, $4-$6
Bristol, TN.

G3, $3-$5
Limestone Co., AL.

G3, $1-$3
Chickamauga, GA.

G3, $3-$5
Marion Co., FL.

G6, $6-$8 each
Marion Co., FL. Cache of three points.

LOCATION: Southeastern states. **DESCRIPTION:** A small to medium size, narrow, spike point with shallow side notches and a straight to concave base. The base can be slight to moderate.

EBENEZER - Woodland, 2000 - 1500 B.P.

(Also see Buggs Island, Clifton, Gary, Montgomery and Morrow Mountain)

G3, $1-$2 Morgan Co., AL. | G3, $1-$2 Lawrence Co., AL. | G4, $1-$3 Dallas Co., AL. | G6, $3-$5 Dallas Co., AL.

G5, $2-$4 E. TN. | G3, $1-$2 Lawrence Co., AL. | G1, .50-$1 Madison Co., AL. | G1, .50-$1 Catoosa Co., GA.

LOCATION: Southeastern states. **DESCRIPTION:** A small size, broad, triangular point with a short, rounded stem. Some are round base triangles with no stem. Shoulders are tapered to square. Very similar to the earlier *Morrow Mountain Round Base* but with random Woodland chipping. Related to *Candy Creek, Camp Creek* and *Nolichucky*.

ECUSTA - Early Archaic, 8000 - 5000 B.P.

(Also see Autauga, Brewerton, Damron and Palmer)

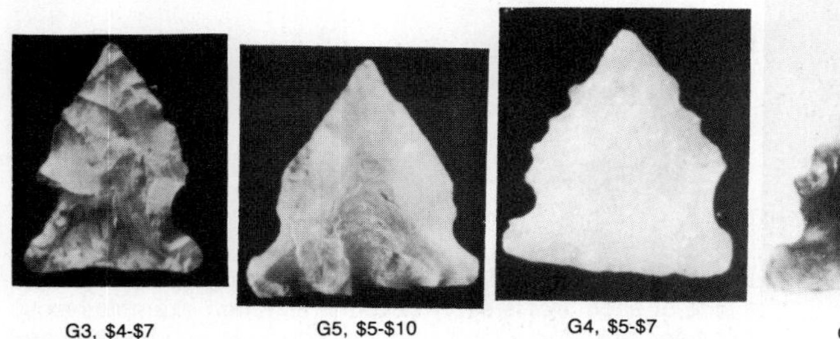

G3, $4-$7 Bethany WV. | G5, $5-$10 Bethany WV. | G4, $5-$7 Dalton, GA. Milky quartz. | G5, $8-$12 Hamilton Co., TN. High grade flint.

ECUSTA (continued)

G4, $5-$8
Bethany WV.

G7, $25-$40
Dunlap, TN.

G3, $2-$4
Stanly Co., NC.

G4, $5-$8
Dalton, GA.

G2, $2-$3
Dalton, GA.

G10, $50-$80
Meigs Co., TN. Hiwassee River.

G7, $20-$35
Perry Co., TN.

G6, $20-$25
Bethany WV.

G6, $15-$25
W. TN.

G9, $45-$70
Perry Co., TN. Crooked Cr.
Note collateral flaking.

G7, $20-$35
Walker Co., AL.

G9, $40-$60
Walker Co., AL. Basal thinning and collateral flaking.

LOCATION: Southeastern states. **DESCRIPTION:** A small size, serrated, side-notched point with usually one side of each face steeply beveled, although examples exist with all four sides beveled and flaked to a median ridge. The base and notches are ground. Very similar to *Autauga*, with the latter being corner-notched.

EDEN - Transitional Paleo to Early Archaic, 9500 - 7500 B.P.

(Also see Agate Basin, Angostura, Scottsbluff and Sedalia)

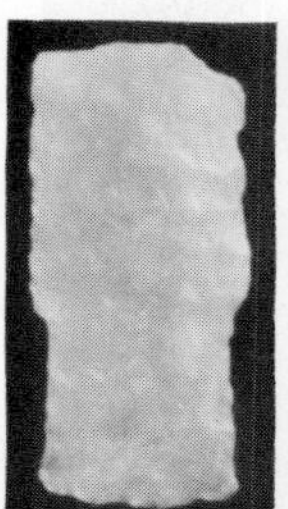

G1, $10-$20
CO/TX. Broken back.

G1, $10-$20
CO/TX. Broken back.

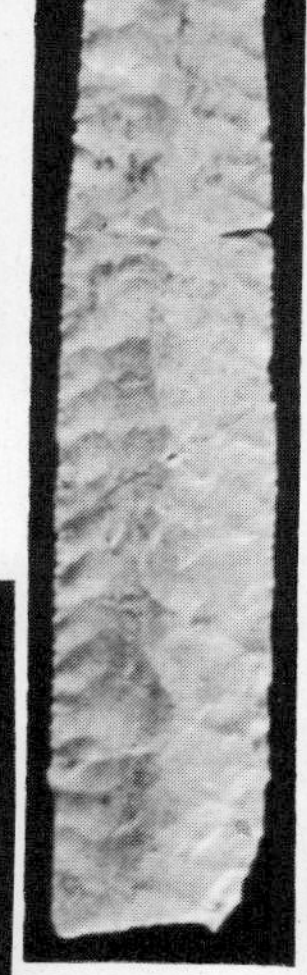

G1, $15-$30
CO. Glued. Note fine collateral flaking & very weak shoulders.

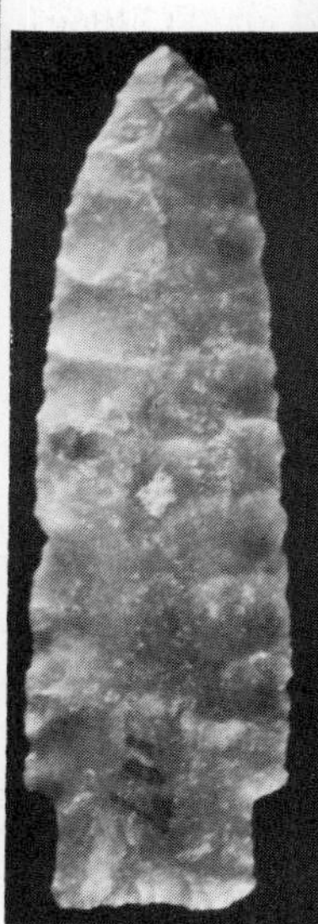

G5, $80-$120
W. MO. Collateral flaking.

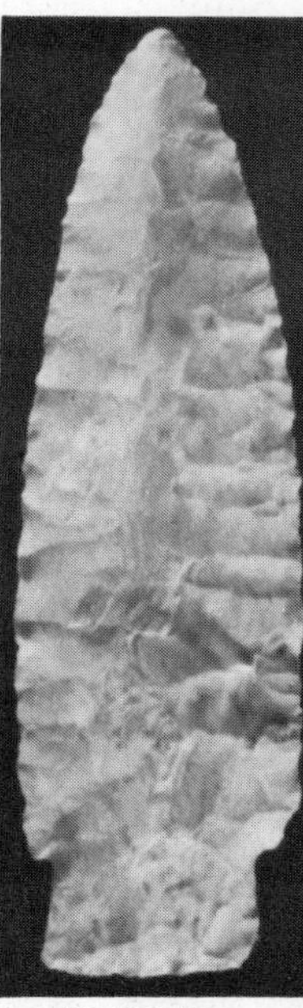

G8, $600-$800
N. Cent. MO. Note median ridge & collateral flaking.

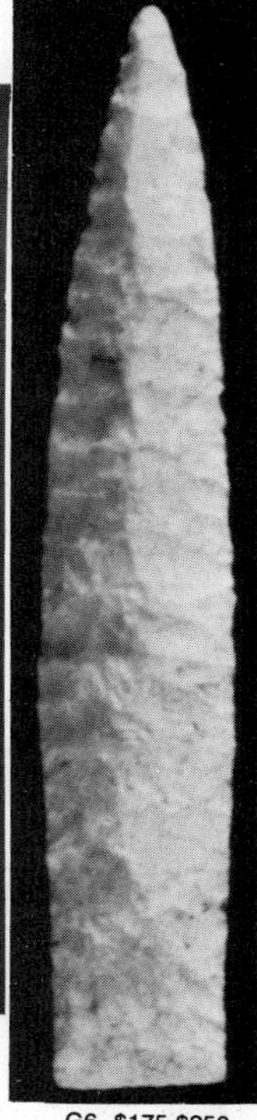

G6, $175-$250
Greene Co., AR.

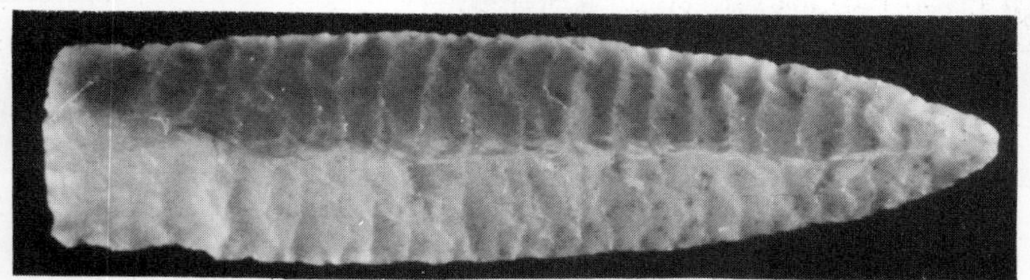

G9, $900-$1500, CO. Note collateral flaking.

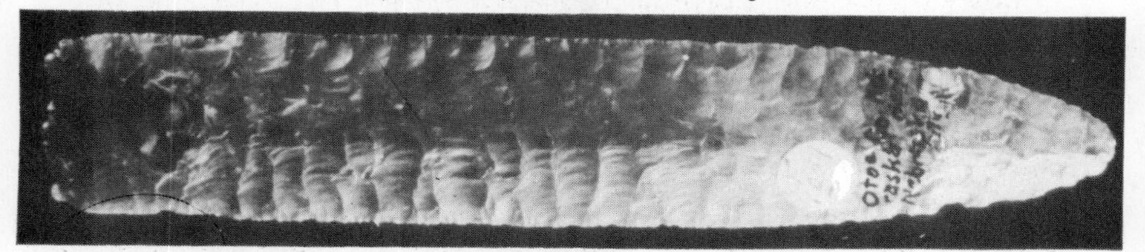

G9, $600-$1000, Otoe Co., NE. Note Collateral flaking.

LOCATION: Midwestern states. **DESCRIPTION:** A medium to large size, narrow, lanceolate blade with a straight to concave base. Many examples have a median ridge and collateral to oblique parallel flaking. Bases are usually gound. **I.D. KEY:** Paleo flaking.

EDGEFIELD SCRAPER - Early Archaic, 9000 - 6000 B.P.

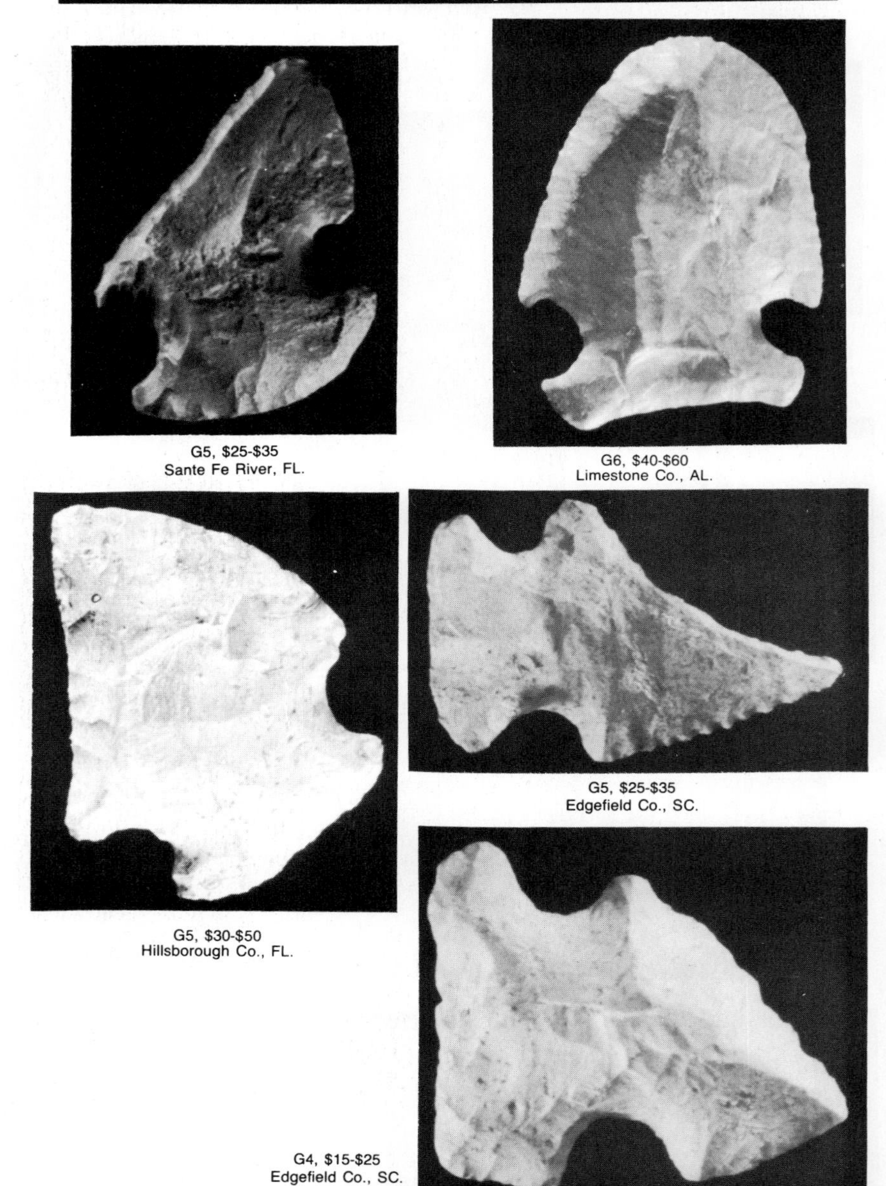

G5, $25-$35
Sante Fe River, FL.

G6, $40-$60
Limestone Co., AL.

G5, $30-$50
Hillsborough Co., FL.

G5, $25-$35
Edgefield Co., SC.

G4, $15-$25
Edgefield Co., SC.

LOCATION: Southern Atlantic coast states, especially South Carolina, Georgia, Alabama and Florida. **DESCRIPTION:** A medium to large size corner notched point that is asymmetrical. Many are uniface and usually steeply beveled along the diagonal side. The blade on all examples leans heavily to one side. Used as a scraper.

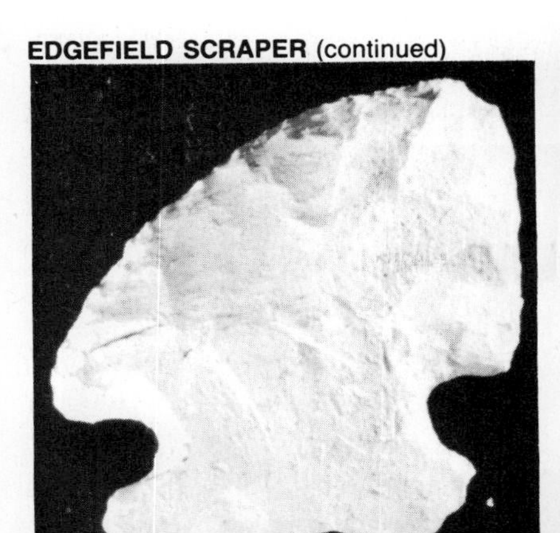

G5, $30-$50
Sou. GA. Not uniface, flaked on both sides.

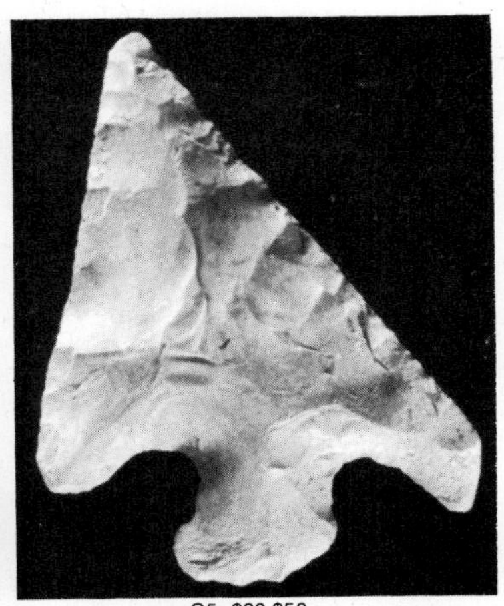

G5, $30-$50
Sou. GA. Not uniface, flaked on both sides.

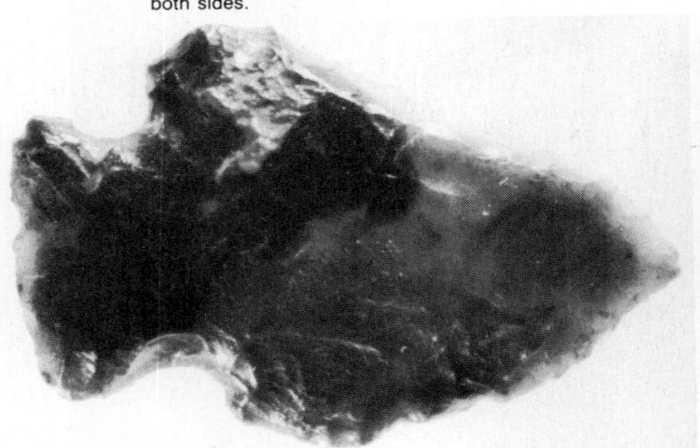

G4, $25-$40
Pea River, AL. Coral.

G7, $45-$70
Edgefield Co., SC.

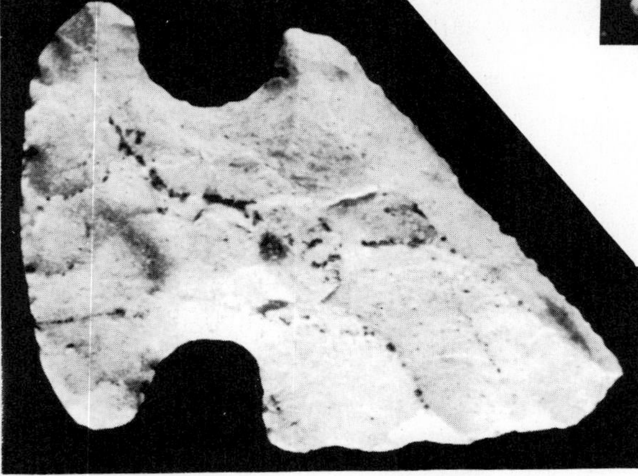

G7, $45-$70
Worth Co., GA.

EDGEFIELD SCRAPER (continued)

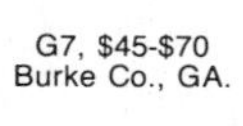

G7, $45-$70
Burke Co., GA.

G8, $250-$400, Sante Fe River, FL. Excellent quality.

G9, $350-$500, Suwannee River, FL. Excellent quality.

EDGEWOOD - Woodland, 3000 - 1500 B.P.

(Also see Bakers Creek, Ellis and Fairland)

G3, $2-$4
Waco, TX.

G5, $10-$12
Comanche Co., TX.

G6, $15-$25
Comanche Co., TX.

G5, $12-$15
Cent. TX.

G5, $8-$12
Comanche Co., TX.

G5, $10-$12
Austin, TX.

G6, $15-$25
McIntosh Co., OK.

G8, $25-$40
McIntosh Co., OK.

LOCATION: Midwestern states. **DESCRIPTION:** A small to medium size, expanded stem point with a concave base. Shoulders are barbed to tapered and the base is usually as wide as the shoulders.

EDWARDS - Woodland to Mississippian, 2000 - 1000 B.P.

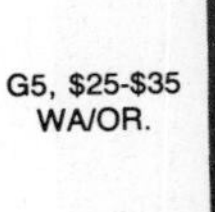

G5, $25-$35
WA/OR.

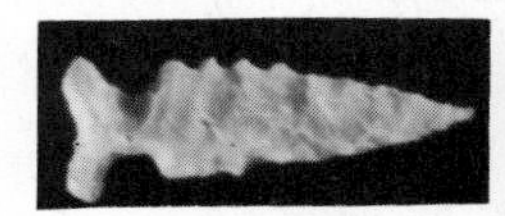

G3, $6-$10
Comanche Co., TX.

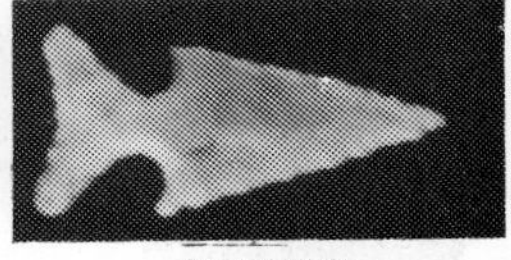

G5, $25-$35
Sou. IL.

LOCATION: Midwestern states. **DESCRIPTION:** A small size, thin, barbed point with long, flaring ears at the base. Some examples are finely serrated. **I.D. KEY:** Basal form and flaking.

G6, $45-$60
Spiro Mound, OK.

G6, $40-$60
Columbia Rv., WA.
Classic form.

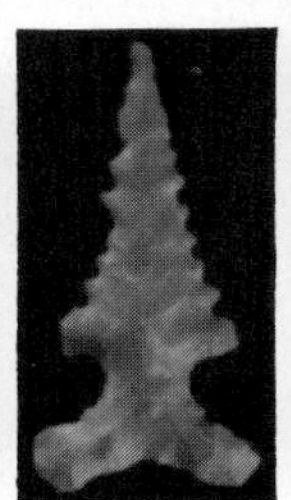
G7, $50-$80

G6, $45-$60

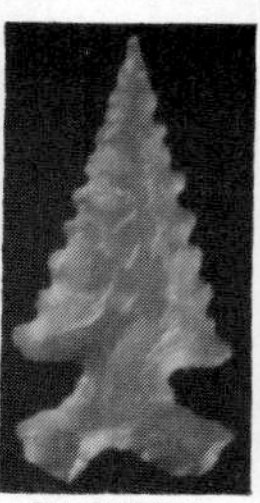
G7, $50-$70

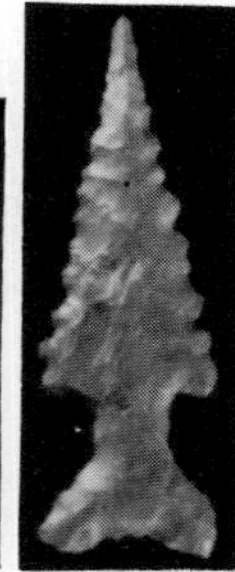
G5, $25-$40

(All Spiro Mound, OK.)

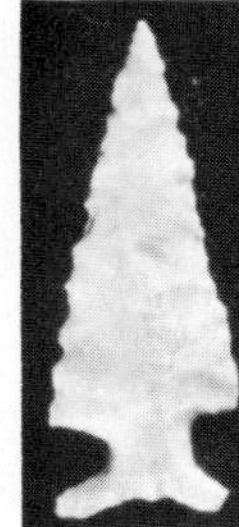
G6, $30-$45
Comanche Co., TX.

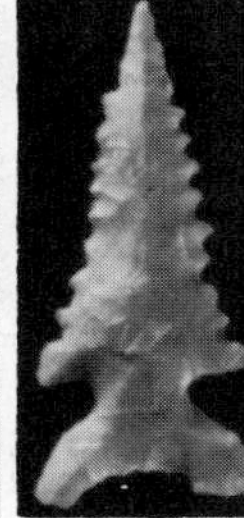
G8, $60-$90

G8, $60-$90

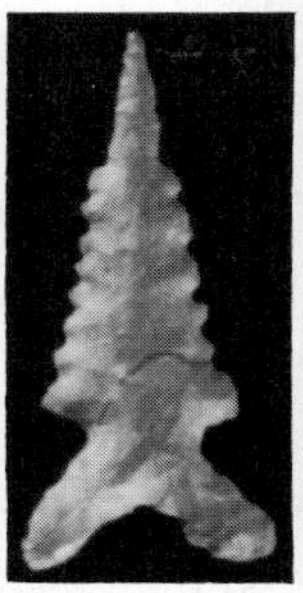
G8, $60-$90

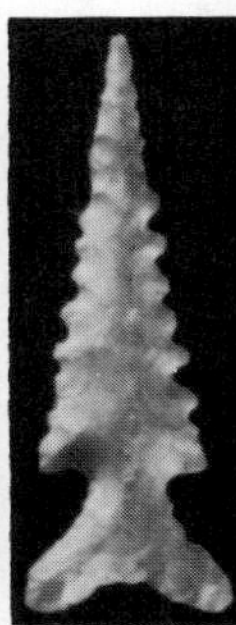
G8, $60-$100

(All Spiro Mound, OK.)

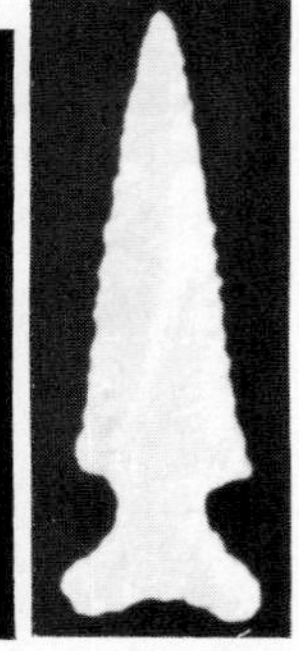
G8, $45-$70
Cent. IL.

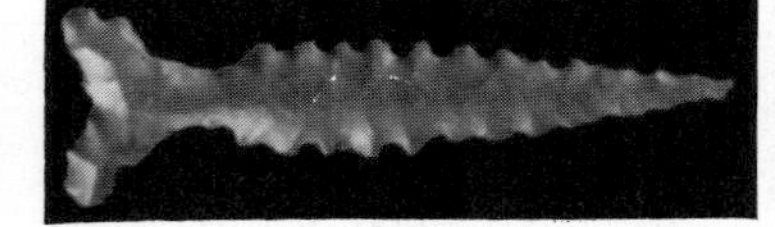
G9, $90-$150, Spiro Mound OK. Note unusual basal area and base notching.

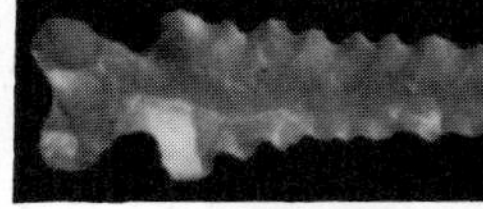
G10, $120-$200, Spiro Mound, OK.

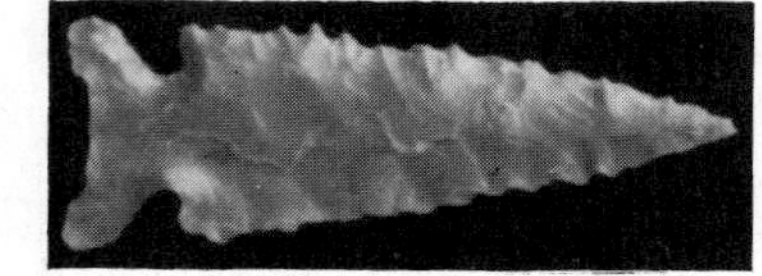
G9, $80-$120, Spiro Mound, OK.

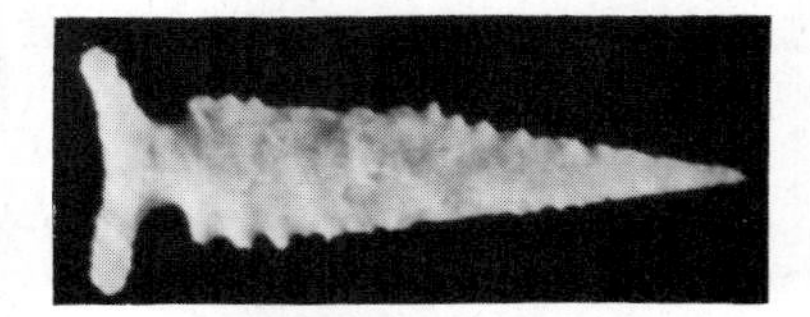
G10, $180-$300, Comanche Co., TX.

EIFFEL TOWER - Mississippian, 800 - 400 B.P.

(Also see Catahoula, John Day River & Rogue River)

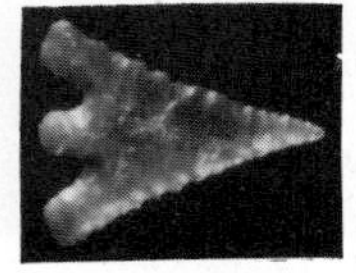
G8, $35-$50
Douglas Co., OR. Agate.

G9, $50-$85
Wakemap Mound, The Dalles, OR.

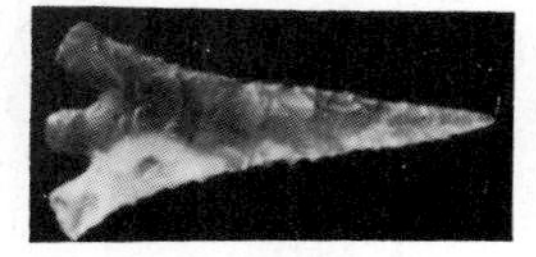
G10, $60-$100
Douglas Co., OR. Agate.

LOCATION: Northwestern states. **DESCRIPTION:** A small size, thin arrow point with expanding, squared barbs and a short, parallel sided base.

ELAM - Late Archaic to Woodland, 4000 - 2000 B.P.

(Also see Dallas, Halifax and Rheems Creek)

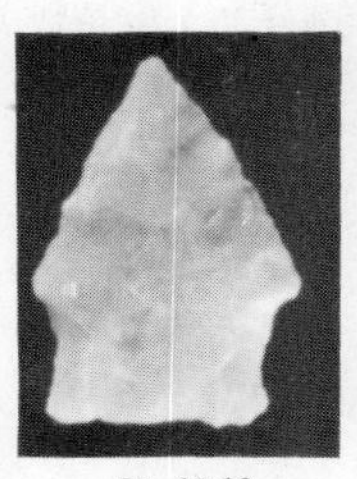

G4, $2-$3
Comanche Co., TX.

G5, $2-$4
Comanche Co., TX.

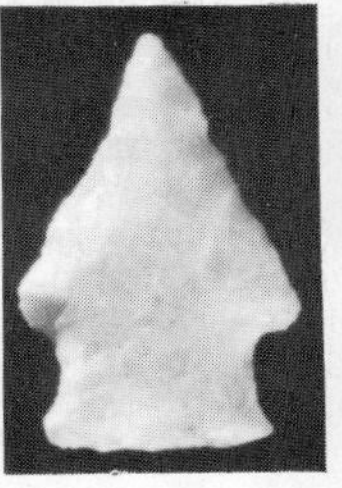

G6, $3-$5
Comanche Co., TX.

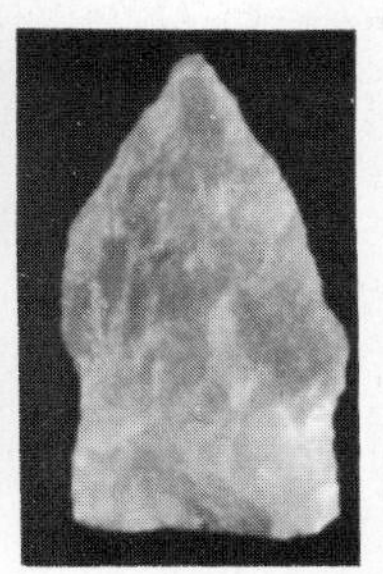

G4, $1-$3
Waco, TX.

LOCATION: Midwestern states. **DESCRIPTION:** A small size stubby point with a squared base and weak shoulders.

ELK RIVER - Early Archaic, 8000 - 5000 B.P.

(Also see Benton and Buzzard Roost Creek)

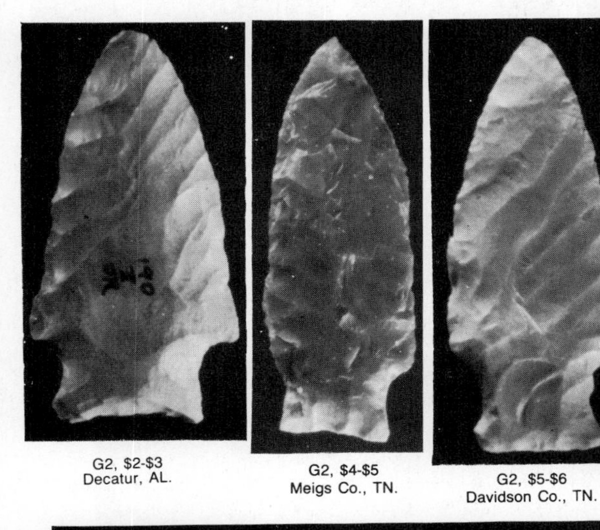

G2, $2-$3
Decatur, AL.

G2, $4-$5
Meigs Co., TN.

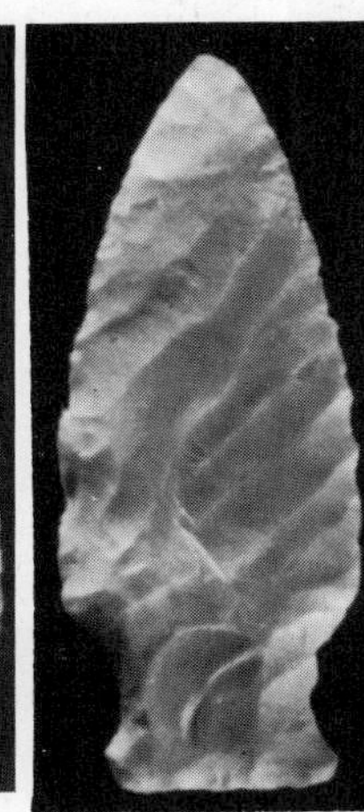

G2, $5-$6
Davidson Co., TN.

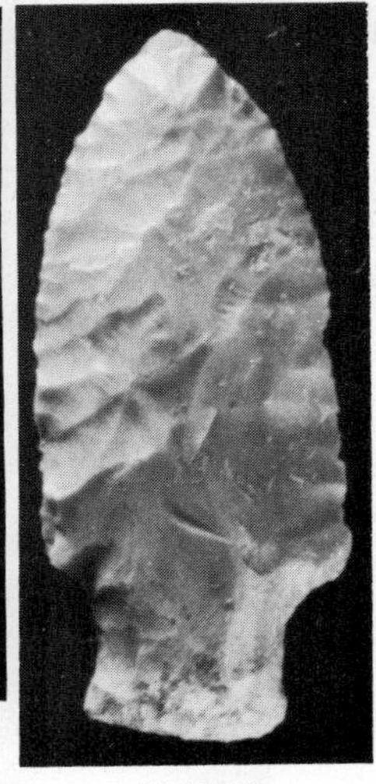

G3, $7-$10
Meigs Co., TN.

G5, $25-$40
Limestone Co., AL.

G4, $10-$15
Lauderdale Co., AL.

G5, $15-$25
Humphreys Co., TN.

G4, $10-$15
Lauderdale Co., AL.

G5, $20-$35
Florence, AL.

G6, $35-$45, Morgan Co., AL.

LOCATION: Southeastern states. **DESCRIPTION:** A medium to large size, narrow, stemmed blade with oblique parallel flaking. Shoulders are tapered, straight or barbed. Stems are parallel, contracting, expanding, bulbous or bifurcated. Believed to be related to *Benton* points. **I.D. KEY:** Squared base, parallel flaking.

G8, $120-$200
Humphreys Co., TN.

G6, $30-$50
Humphreys Co., TN. Note bifurcated base.

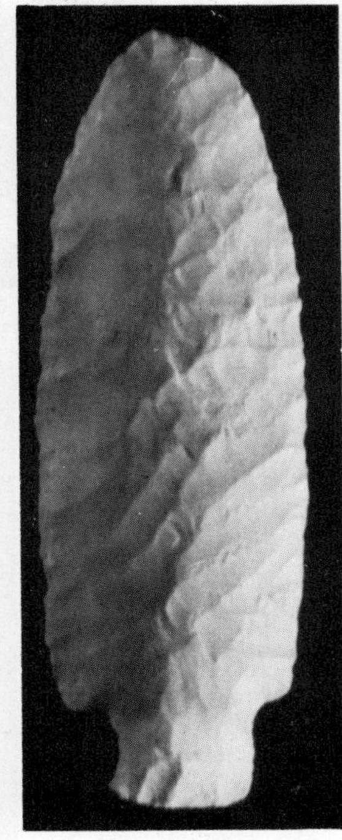

G5, $15-$25
Sevier Co., TN.

G6, $30-$50
Benton Co., TN.

G6, $30-$50
KY.

ELK RIVER (continued)

G7, $50-$80
Humphreys Co., TN. Dover chert.

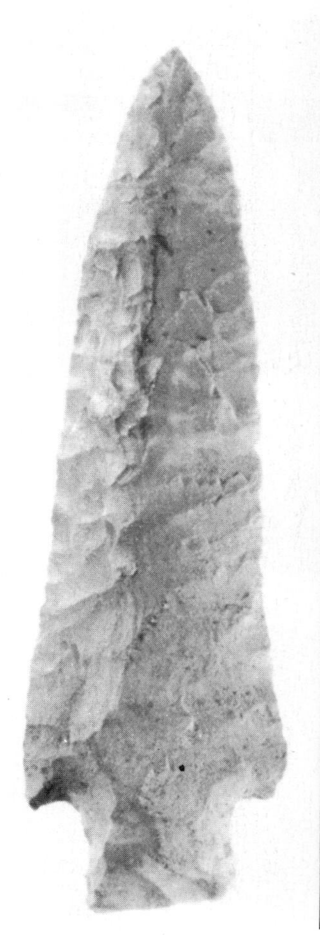

G7, $50-$80
Jackson Co., AL. Thick cross section.

G8, $120-$200
Ky. Classic form.

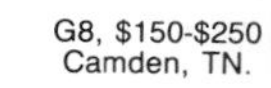

G8, $150-$250
Camden, TN.

ELK RIVER (continued)

G10, $600-$1000
Hardin Co., TN.

G9, $500-$800
Humphreys Co., TN.

ELLIS - Late Archaic, 4000 - 2000 B.P.

(Also see Bakers Creek, Durst, Edgewood, Ensor, Godley, Holmes, Scallorn & Swan Lake

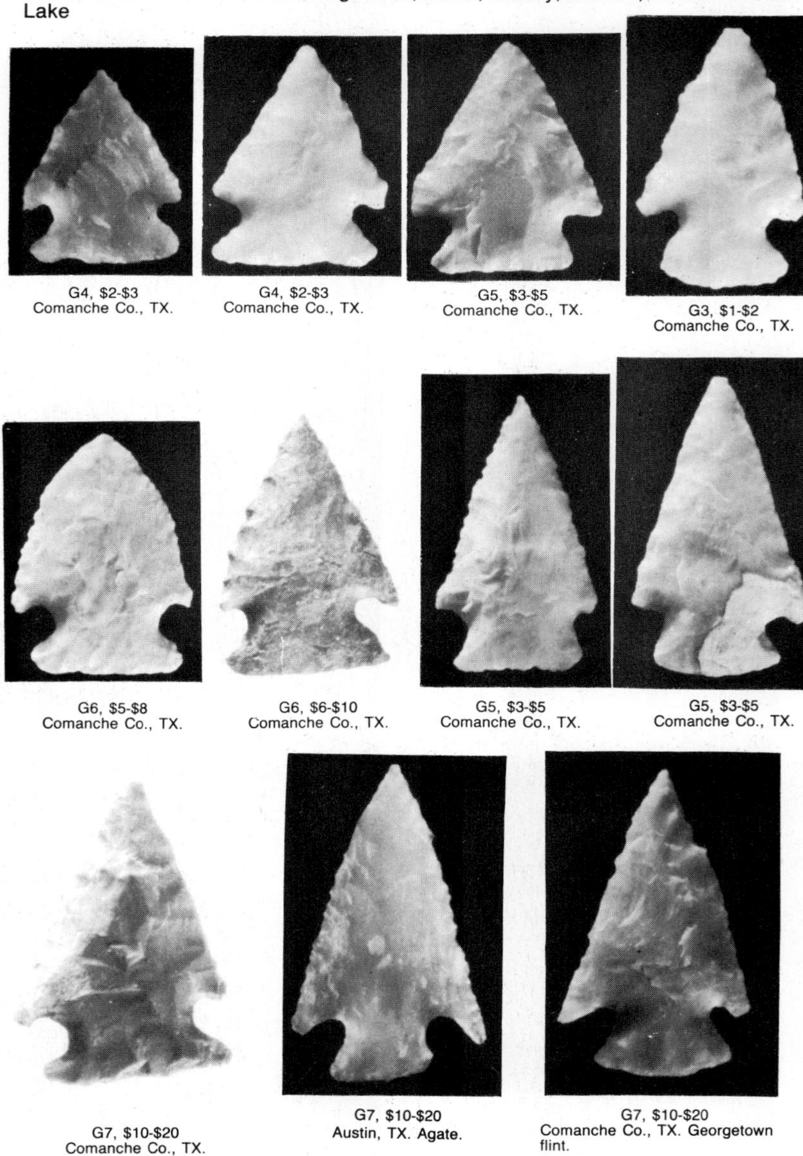

G4, $2-$3
Comanche Co., TX.

G4, $2-$3
Comanche Co., TX.

G5, $3-$5
Comanche Co., TX.

G3, $1-$2
Comanche Co., TX.

G6, $5-$8
Comanche Co., TX.

G6, $6-$10
Comanche Co., TX.

G5, $3-$5
Comanche Co., TX.

G5, $3-$5
Comanche Co., TX.

G7, $10-$20
Comanche Co., TX.

G7, $10-$20
Austin, TX. Agate.

G7, $10-$20
Comanche Co., TX. Georgetown flint.

LOCATION: Midwestern states. **DESCRIPTION:** A small to medium size, expanded stemmed to corner notched point with tapered to barbed shoulders. Bases are convex to straight.

ELKO - Woodland, 4000 - 2000 B.P.

(Also see Desert Corner Notched)

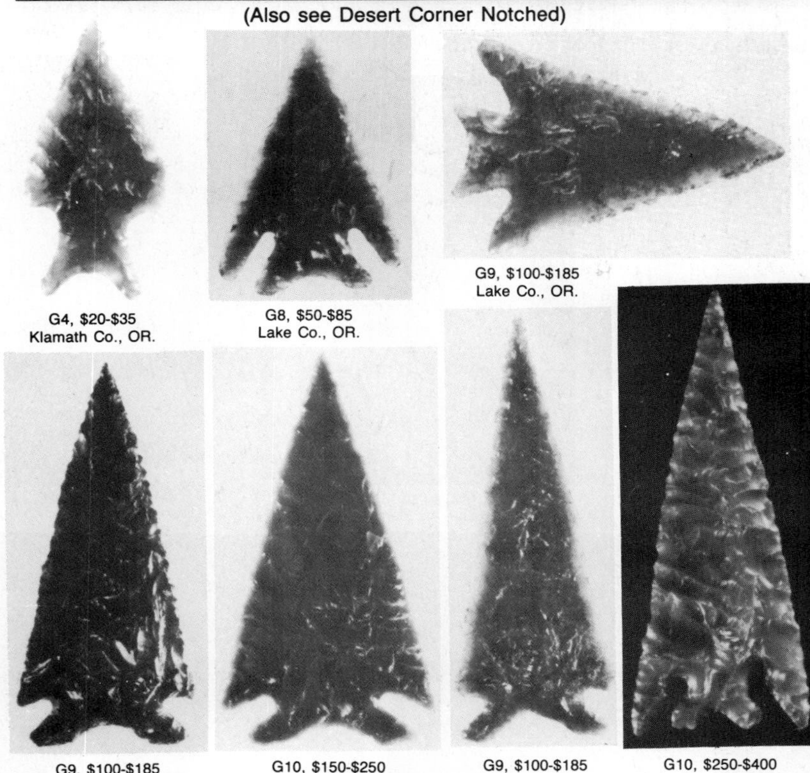

G4, $20-$35
Klamath Co., OR.

G8, $50-$85
Lake Co., OR.

G9, $100-$185
Lake Co., OR.

G9, $100-$185
Lake Co., OR. Obsidian.

G10, $150-$250
Lake Co., OR. Obsidian

G9, $100-$185
Lake Co., OR.

G10, $250-$400
Lake Co., OR. Agate.

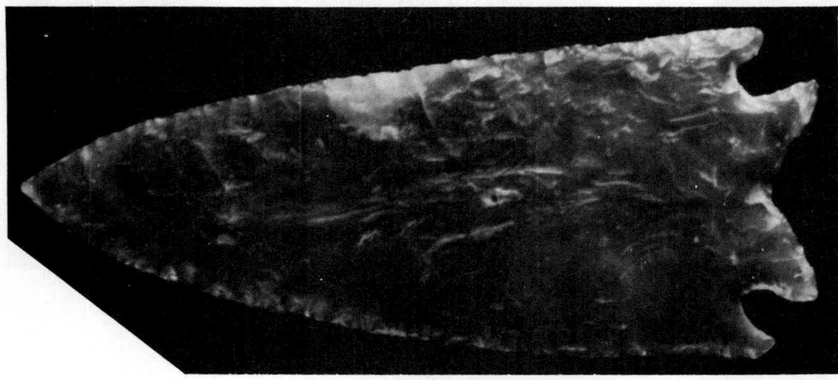

G10, $350-$600
Lake Tahoe, NV. Translucent agate.

LOCATION: Western states. **DESCRIPTION:** A medium to large size corner notched blade with shoulder tangs and a short, auriculate base.

ELORA - Mid to late Archaic, 6000 - 3000 B.P.

(Also see Abbey, Alachua, Cottonbridge, Levy, Maples, Newnan, Pickwick, Putnam, Savannah River, Six Mile Creek & South Prong Creek)

G5, $8-$12
SE TN.

G4, $4-$6
Dallas Co., AL. Hemitite.

G4, $4-$6
GA. Note fine serrations.

G3, $3-$5
Colbert Co., AL. Conglomerate.

G7, $25-$35
Worth Co., GA.

G5, $8-$15
Decatur, AL.

LOCATION: Southeastern states. **DESCRIPTION:** A medium size, broad, thick point with tapered shoulders and a short, contracting stem that is sometimes fractured or snapped off. However, some examples have finished bases. Early examples are serrated. **I.D. KEY:** One barb sharper, edgework.

G5, $8-$12
GA. Note fine serrations.
Rind base.

G5, $8-$12
Decatur, AL.

G6, $10-$20
Alexander City, AL.

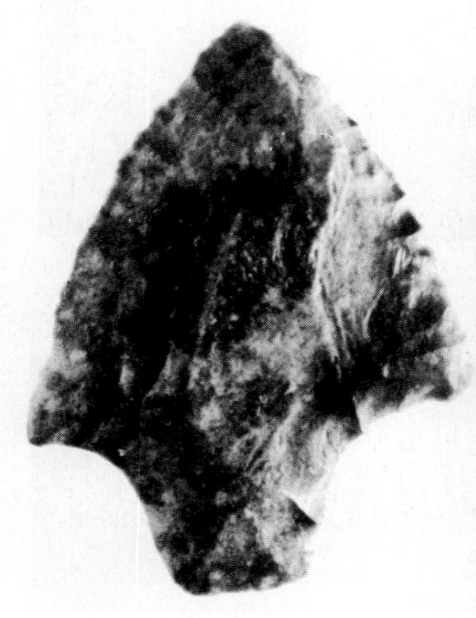

G5, $6-$10
Hillsborough Co., FL.

G9, $50-$80
Lee Co., GA.

ENSOR - Late Archaic to early Woodland, 4000 - 1500 B.P.

(Also see Ellis, Frio, Marcos and Marshall)

G4, $10-$15
Comanche Co., TX.

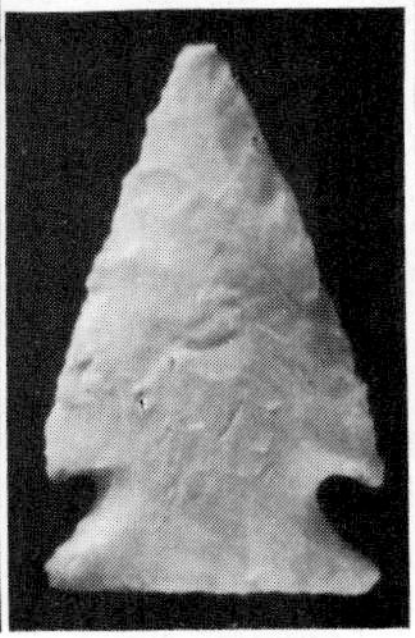

G2, .50-$1
Comanche Co., TX.

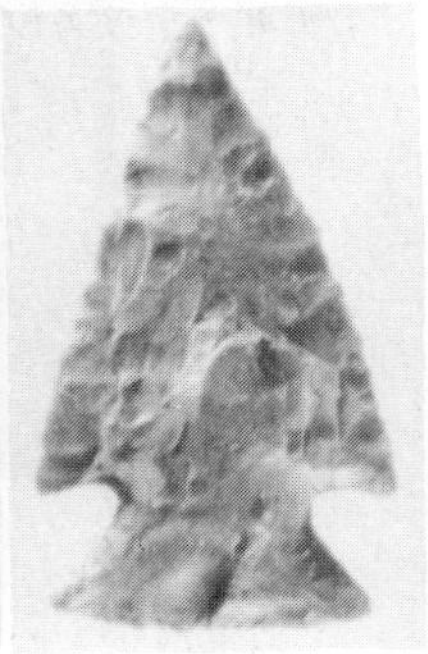

G5, $15-$25
Austin, TX.

G4, $10-$15
Austin, TX. Leon Rv. chert.

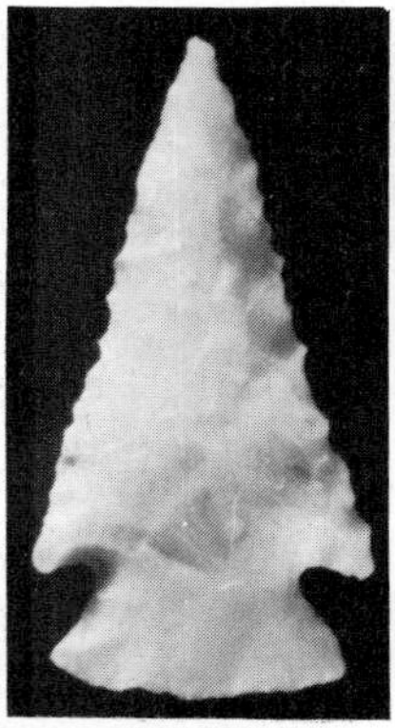

G6, $25-$40
Comanche Co., TX.

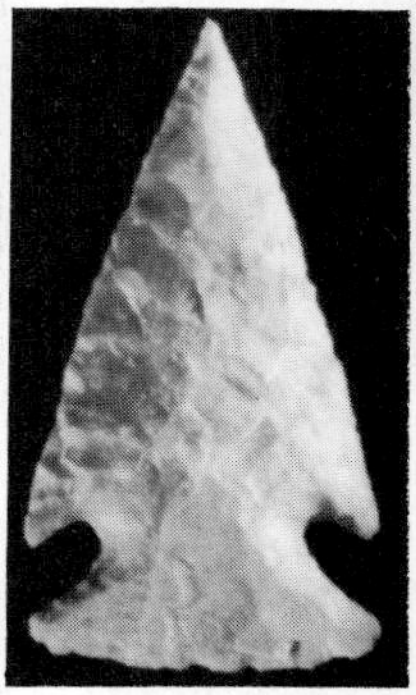

G6, $35-$45
Austin, TX.

G6, $35-$45
Austin, TX.

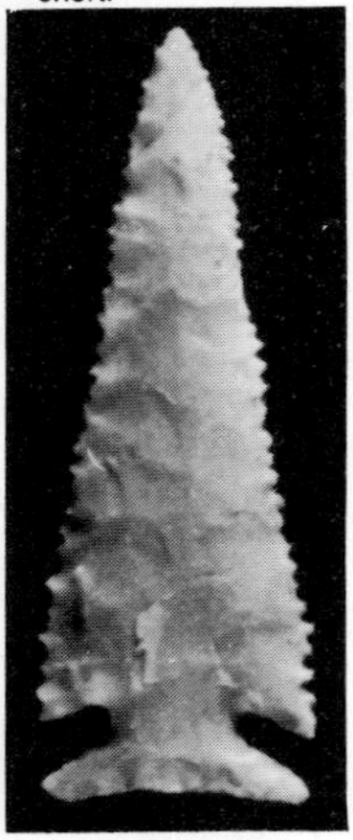

G8, $90-$150
Cent. TX.

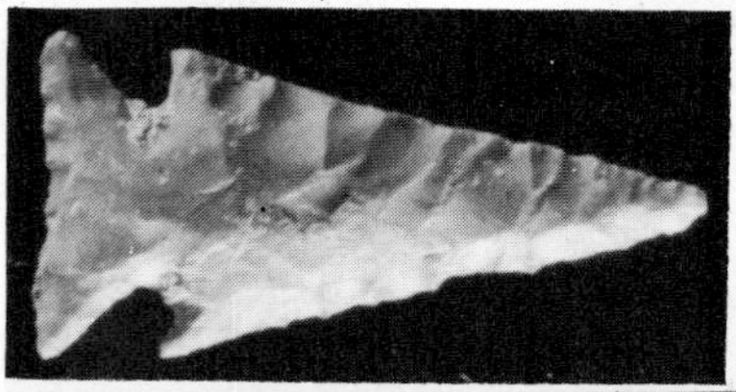

G4, $10-$15
Austin, TX.

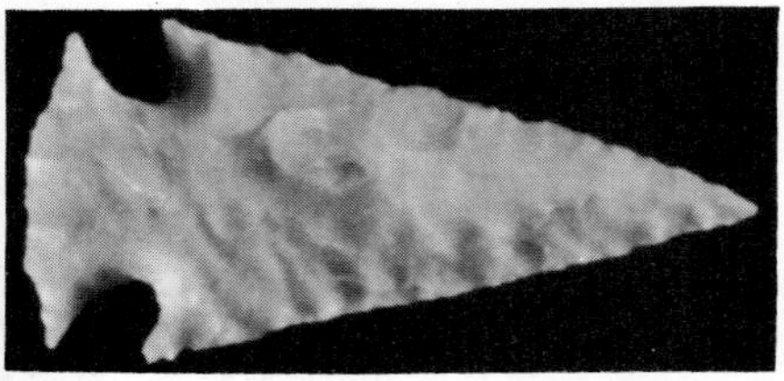

G7, $40-$60
Austin, TX. Note unusual base form.

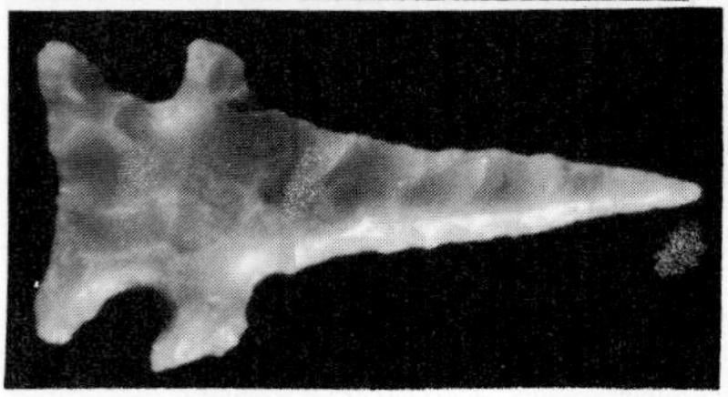

G6, $25-$40
Austin, TX. Drill.

LOCATION: Midwestern states. **DESCRIPTION:** A medium to large size, thin, well made corner-notched point with a concave, convex or straight base. Some examples are serrated and well barbed.

G8, $60-$90
Austin, TX.

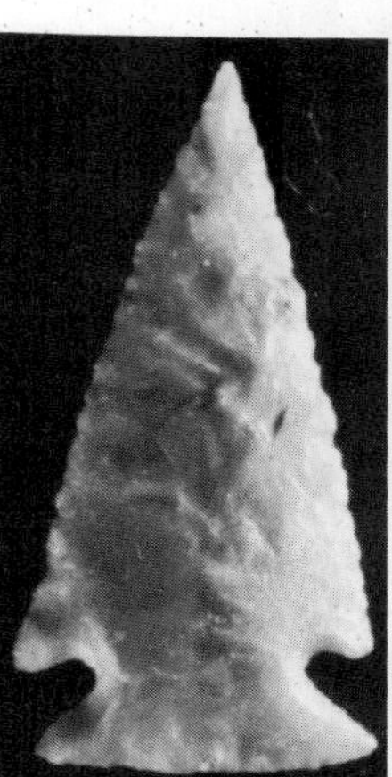

G7, $40-$65
Austin, TX.

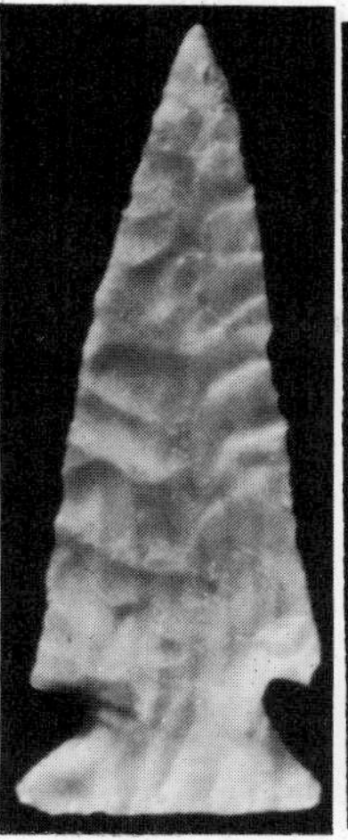

G6, $25-$40
Austin, TX. Banded chert.

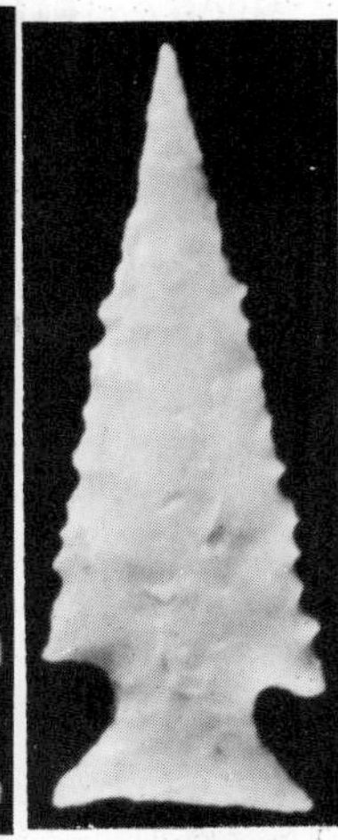

G8, $80-$120
Austin, TX.

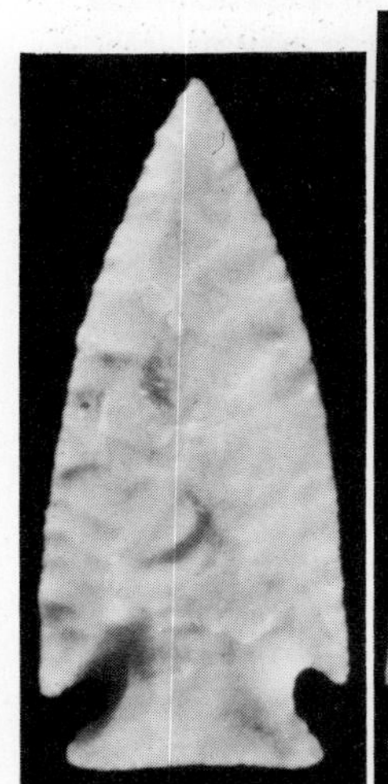

G8, $80-$120
Austin, TX.

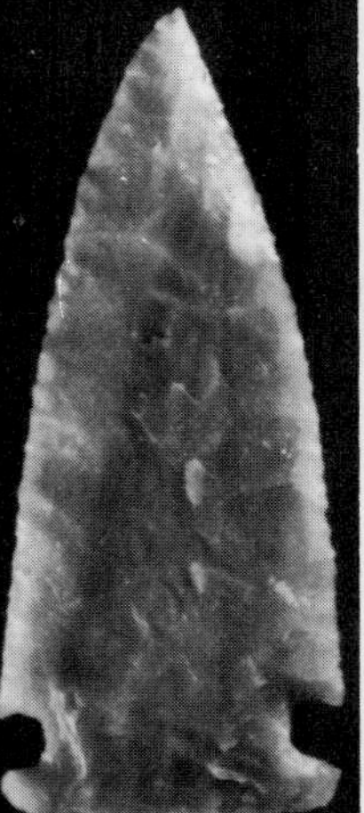

G8, $60-$90
Austin, TX.

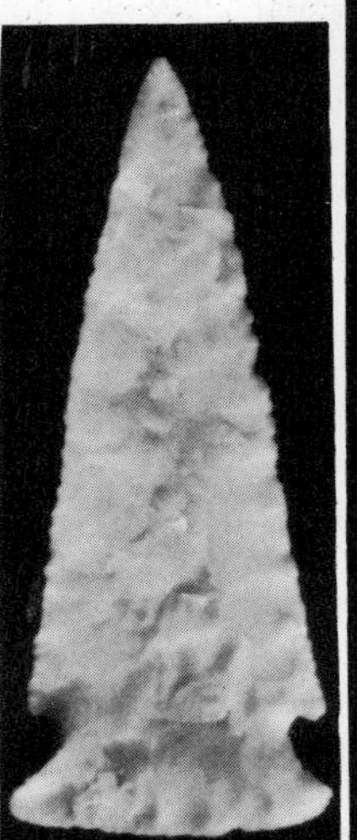

G8, $60-$90
Austin, TX.

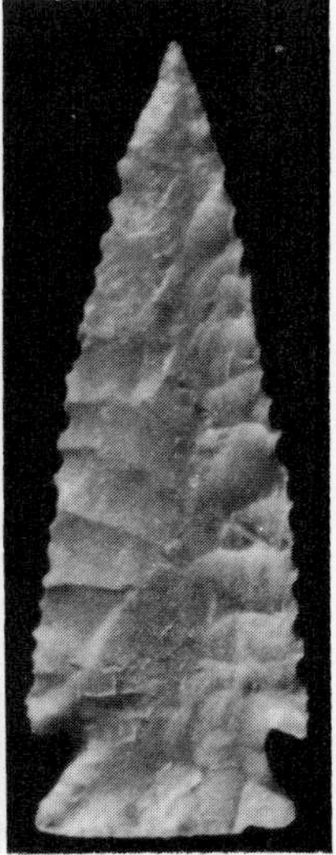

G8, $60-$90
Austin, TX.

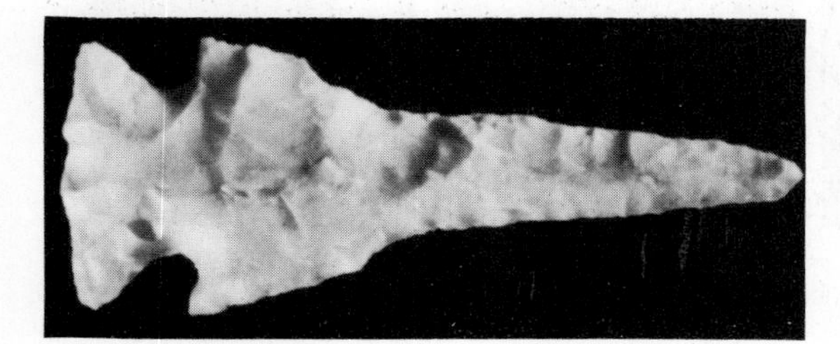

G6, $35-$45
Austin, TX., Drill.

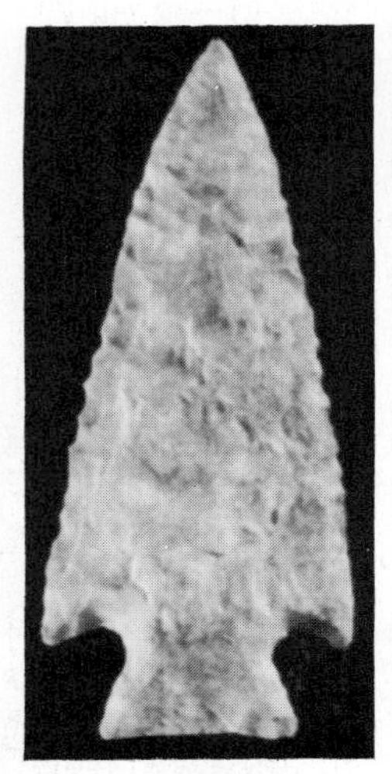

G7, $35-$50
Austin, TX.

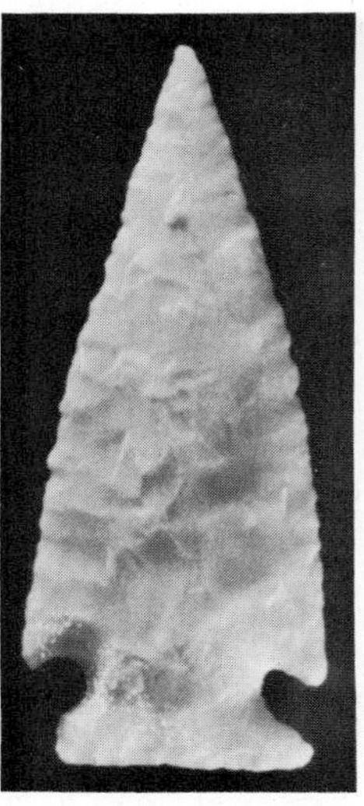

G6, $25-$40
Comanche Co., TX. Base nick.

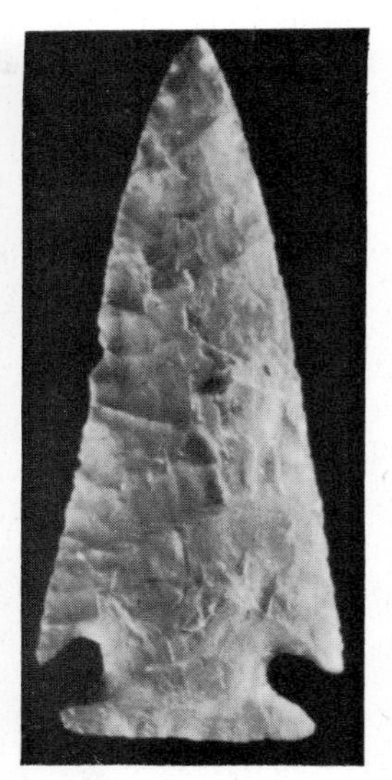

G8, $80-$120
Austin, TX.

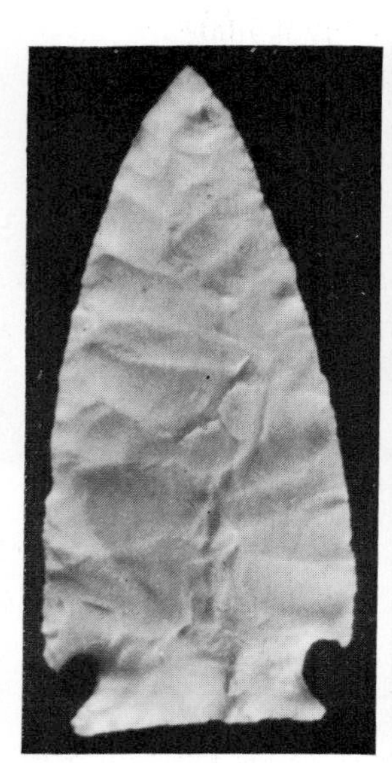

G6, $25-$45
Austin, TX.

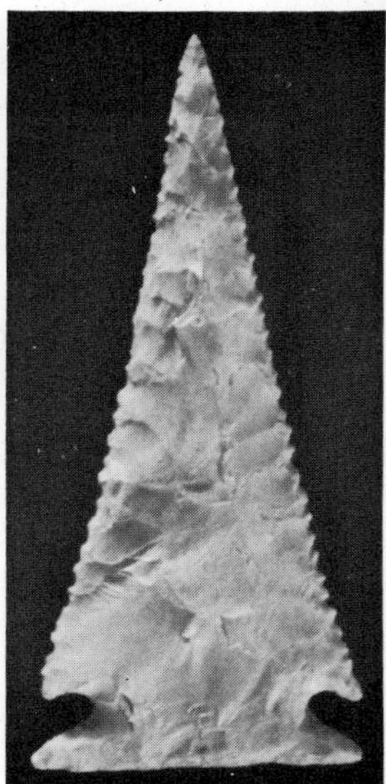

G9, $180-$300
Comanche Co., TX. Note fine edgework.

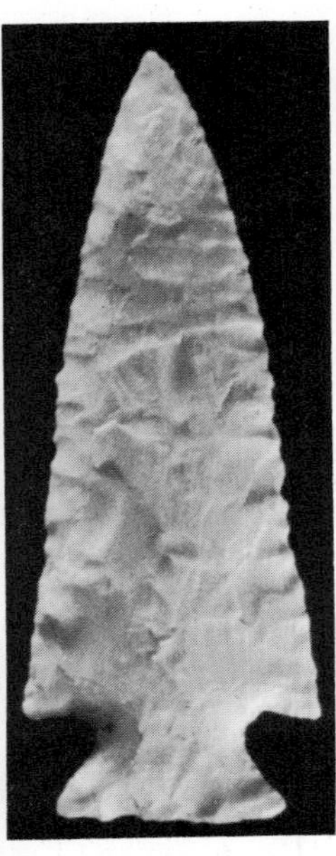

G8, $80-$120
Austin, TX.

ENSOR SPLIT-BASE - Late Archaic to early Woodland, 4000 - 1500 B.P.

(Also see Frio)

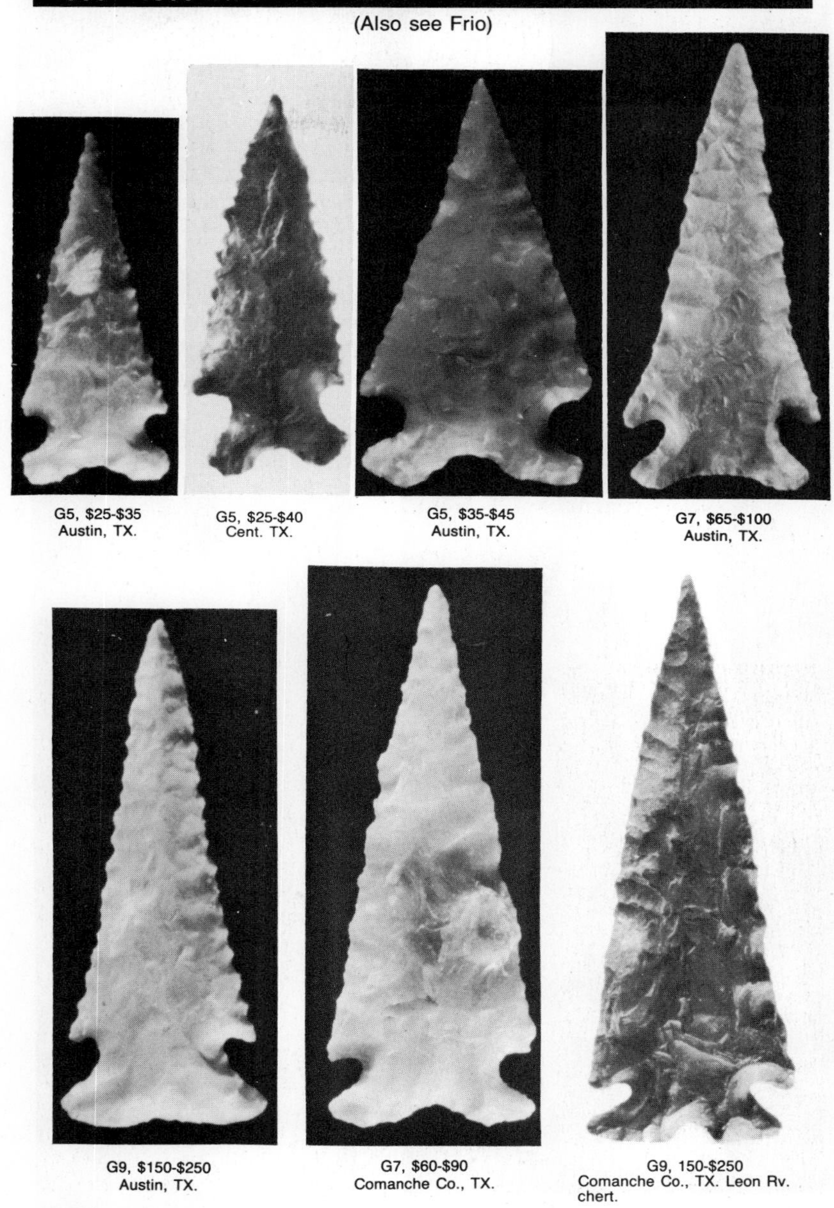

G5, $25-$35
Austin, TX.

G5, $25-$40
Cent. TX.

G5, $35-$45
Austin, TX.

G7, $65-$100
Austin, TX.

G9, $150-$250
Austin, TX.

G7, $60-$90
Comanche Co., TX.

G9, 150-$250
Comanche Co., TX. Leon Rv. chert.

LOCATION: Midwestern states. **DESCRIPTION:** Identical to *Ensor* except for the bifurcated base. Look for *Ensor* flaking style.

EPPS - Late Archaic to Woodland, 3500 - 2000 B.P.

(Also see Cupp and Motley)

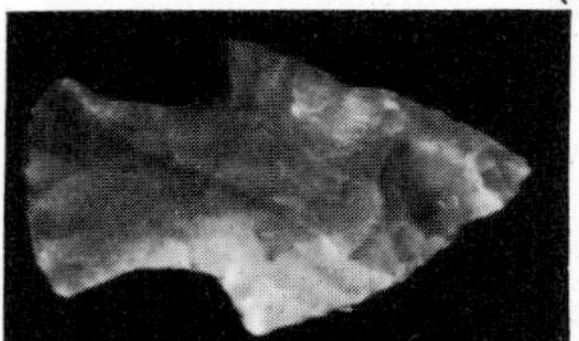

G2, .50-$1
Waco, TX.

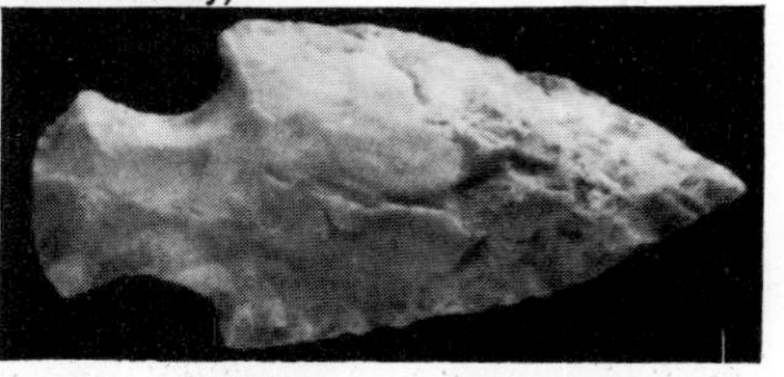

G5, $4-$6
Waco, TX.

LOCATION: Midwestern states. **DESCRIPTION:** A medium to large size point with wide corner notches, square to tapered shoulders and a convex base. *Cupp* has barbed shoulders. **I.D. KEY:** Square/tapered shoulders.

ETLEY - Late Archaic, 4000 - 2500 B.P.

(Also see Hardin, Stilwell and Stone Square Stem)

G7, $180-$300
MO.

G8, $200-$350
Greene Co., IL.

G7, $180-$300
Greene Co., IL.

G9, $350-$600
Saline Co., MO.

LOCATION: Midwestern states. **DESCRIPTION:** A large, narrow, blade with an angular point, recurved blade edges, an expanded stem and a straight base.

ETLEY (continued)

G10, $600-$1000
St. Clair Co., IL.

G8, $250-$350
Maries Co., MO.

ETLEY (continued)

G8, $250-$450
Craighead Co., AR.

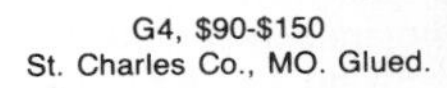

G4, $90-$150
St. Charles Co., MO. Glued.

EVA - Early to Mid-Archaic, 8000 - 5000 B.P.

(Also see Citrus, Culbreath, Hernando, Parowan, San Saba & Shumla)

G2, $4-$6
Humphreys Co., TN.

G3, $8-$12
Humphreys Co., TN.

G4, $15-$25
Humphreys Co., TN.

G6, $45-$70
Humphreys Co., TN.
Conglomerate.

G6, $45-$70
Florence, AL., Coffee Lake.

G7, $50-$80
KY. Note parallel flaking.

G6, $250-$400
Lauderdale Co., AL. Red, white and blue chert. Very rare.

LOCATION: West Tennessee to SW Kentucky. **DESCRIPTION:** A medium to large size, triangular point with shallow basal notches, recurved sides and sometimes flaring tangs. Early examples show parallel flaking. **I.D. KEY:** Notches, archaic flaking.

EVA (continued)

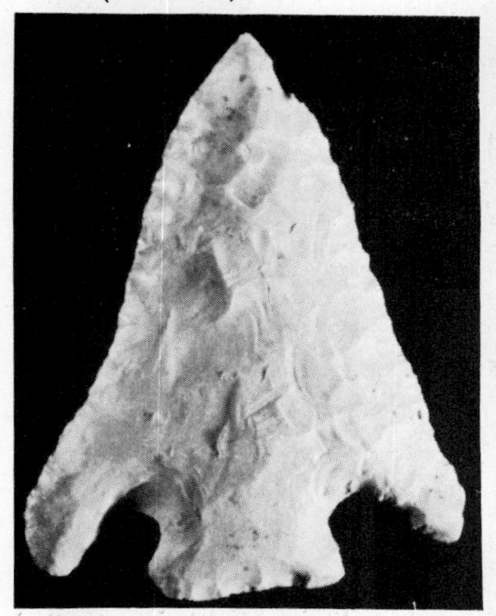

G4, $15-$25. Humphreys Co., TN. Note umbrella tangs.

G9, $180-$300
Humphreys Co., TN. Umbrella tangs.

G6, $60-$90
Florence, AL., 7 Mile Isle. Red jasper.

G7, $60-$90
Parsons, TN.

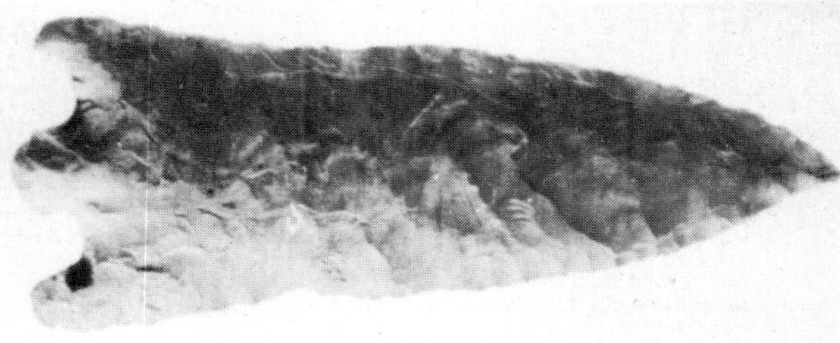

G7, $60-$90
Humphreys Co., TN.

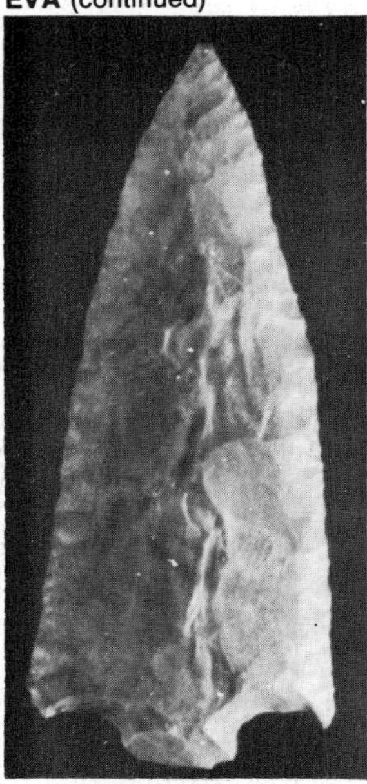

G5, $35-$50
Humphreys Co., TN. Snapped base.

G7, $50-$80
Humphreys Co., TN.

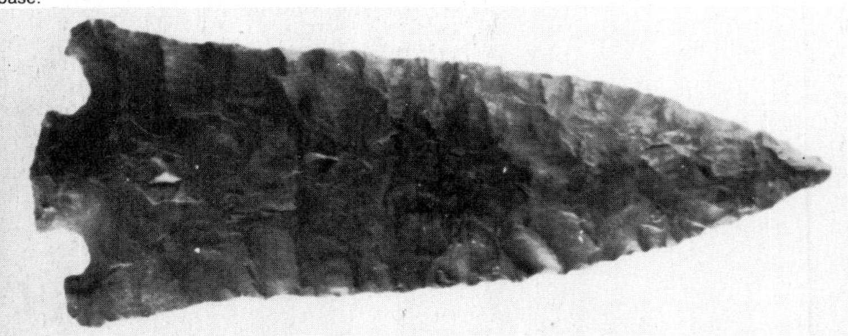

G9, $150-$250
Humphreys Co., TN. Dover chert.

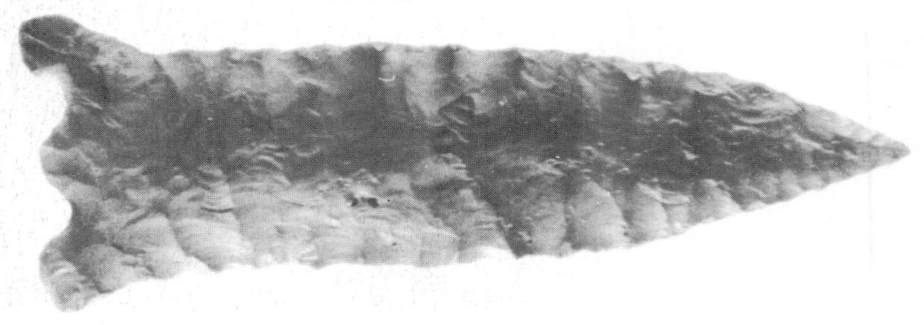

G10, $450-$750
Perry Co., TN. Outstanding early form with expanded (Paleo type) tangs. Note unusual fine oblique flaking. The central base prong could be the remnant or carry over of a striking platform from millinia past (Paleo times).

EVANS - Late Archaic to Woodland, 4000 - 2000 B.P.

(Also see Benton, Leighton, Ohio Double-Notched, Sinner & Turkeytail)

G3, $10-$20
Hamilton Co., TN.

G5, $35-$45
W. TN.

G8, $70-$100
Lincoln Co., MO.

G7, $45-$70
Choctaw Co., AL.

G6, $40-$60
KY.

G7, $50-$60
Granville, Co., NC.

G10, $100-$180
N. TN.

LOCATION: Midwestern to Southeastern states. **DESCRIPTION:** A medium to large size stemmed point that is notched on each side somewhere between the point and shoulders. A similar form is found in Ohio and called *Ohio Double-Notched*.

G6, $40-$50
Colbert Co., AL.

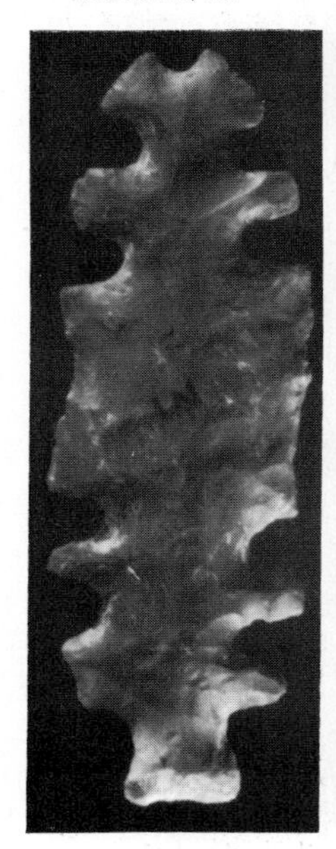

G10, $150-$250
N. TN.

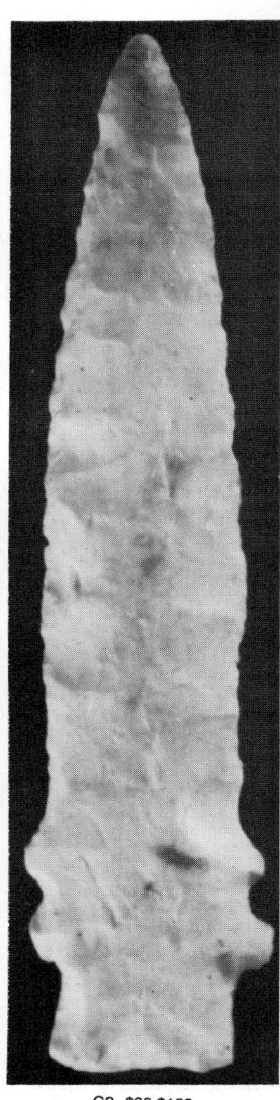

G9, $90-$150
KY.

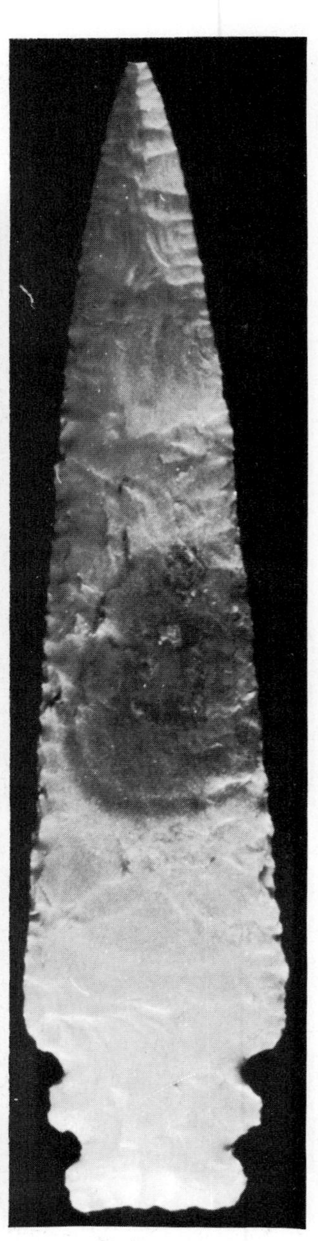

G9, $180-$300
KY. Tip damage.

EXOTIC FORMS -Woodland to Mississippian, 3000 - 1000 B.P.

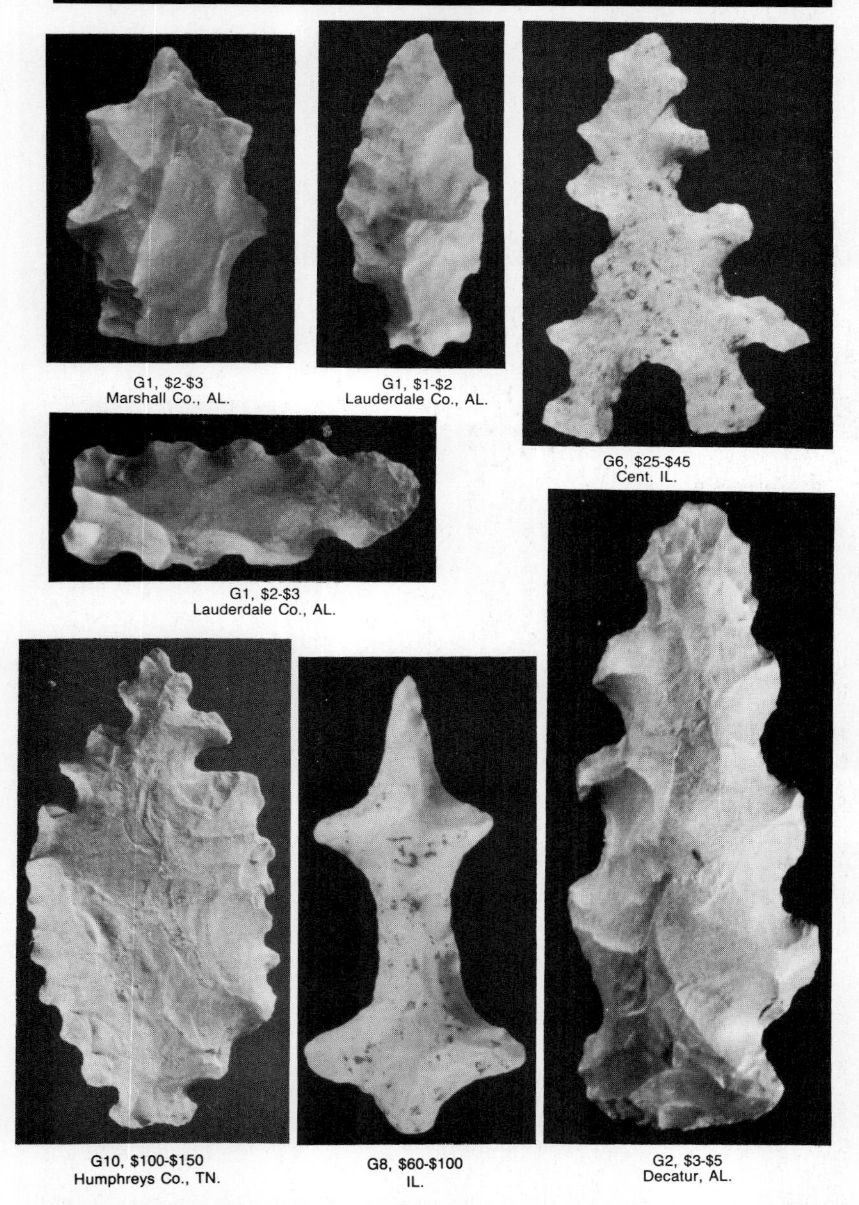

G1, $2-$3
Marshall Co., AL.

G1, $1-$2
Lauderdale Co., AL.

G6, $25-$45
Cent. IL.

G1, $2-$3
Lauderdale Co., AL.

G10, $100-$150
Humphreys Co., TN.

G8, $60-$100
IL.

G2, $3-$5
Decatur, AL.

LOCATION: Everywhere. **DESCRIPTION:** The forms illustrated on this and the following pages are very rare. Some are definitely effigy forms while others may be no more than unfinished and unintentional doodles.

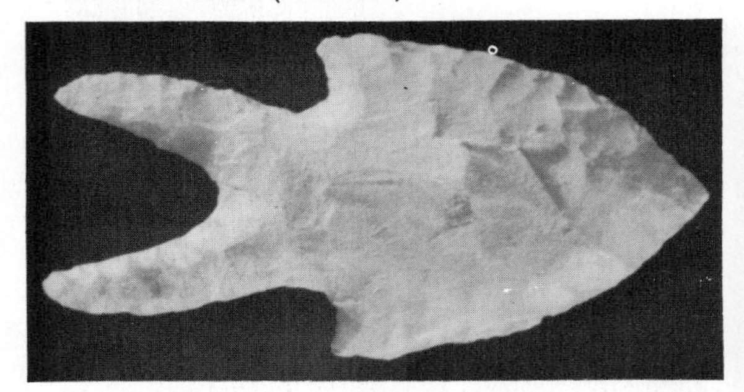

G3, $20-$30
Humphreys Co., TN. Restored
ear. New type?

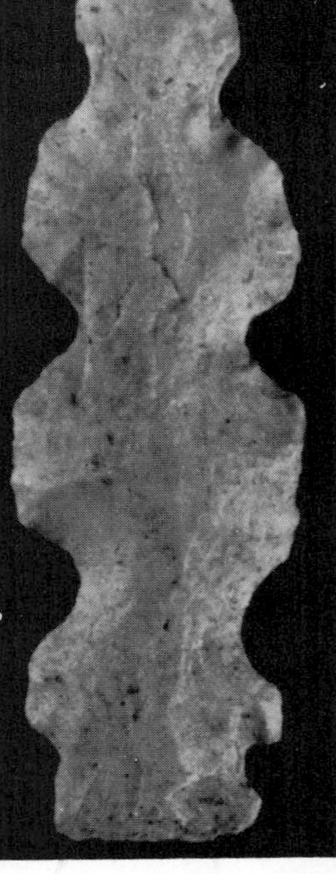

G7, $60-$90
Lauderdale Co., AL.

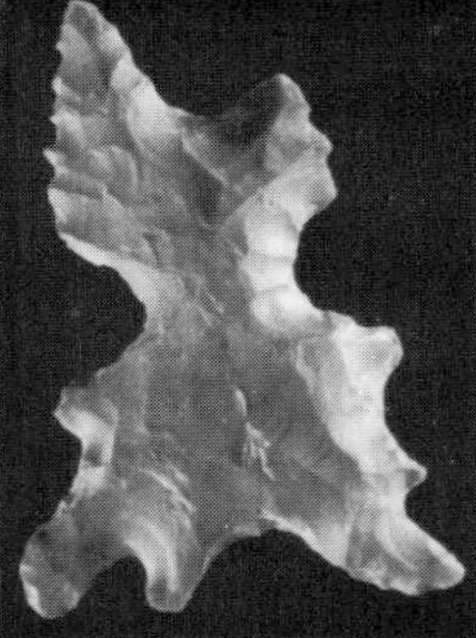

G7, $50-$80
Humphreys Co., TN.

G6, $25-$45
Boone Co., MO.

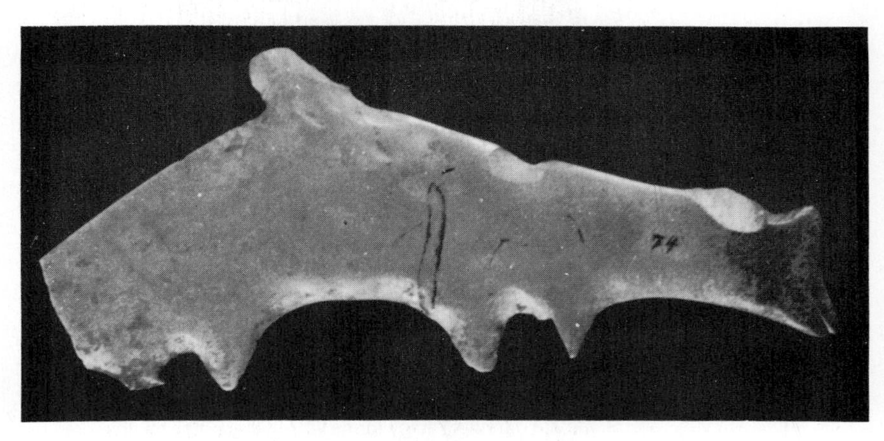

G6, $150-$250. Cent. IL. Effigy of animal (Buffalo? See hump on back).

EXOTIC FORMS (continued)

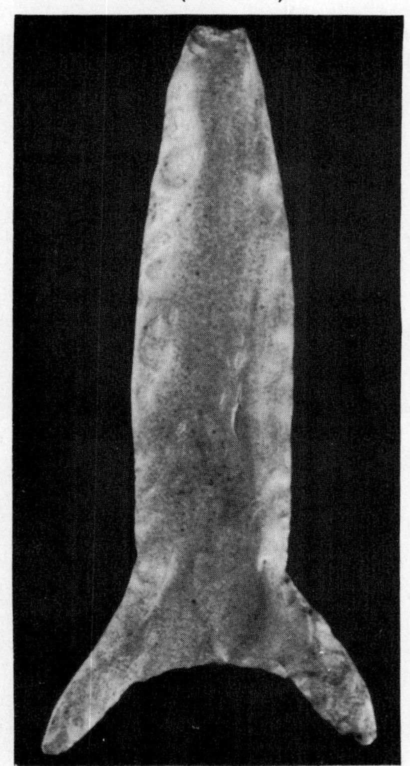

G5, $20-$30
Calhoun Co., IL.

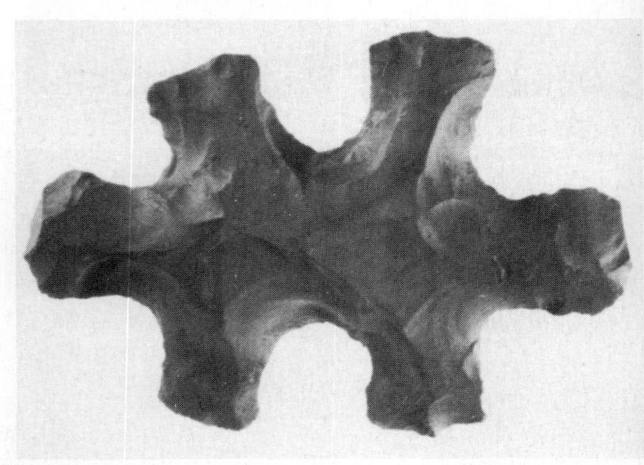

G8, $80-$120
Florence, AL. Turtle effigy?

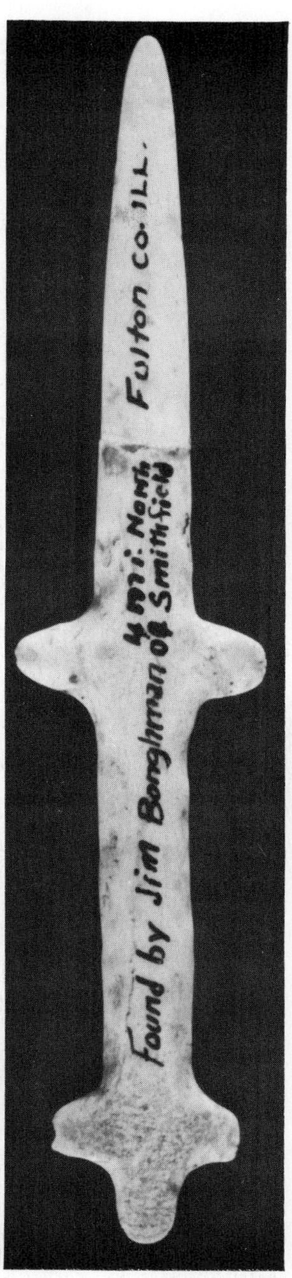

G10, $450-$600
Fulton Co., IL.

FAIRLAND - Woodland, 3000 - 1500 B.P.

(Also see Edgewood and Ellis)

G2, $2-$3
Comanche Co., TX.

G4, $3-$5
MS. Red jasper.

G6, $29-$35
Linden, TN.

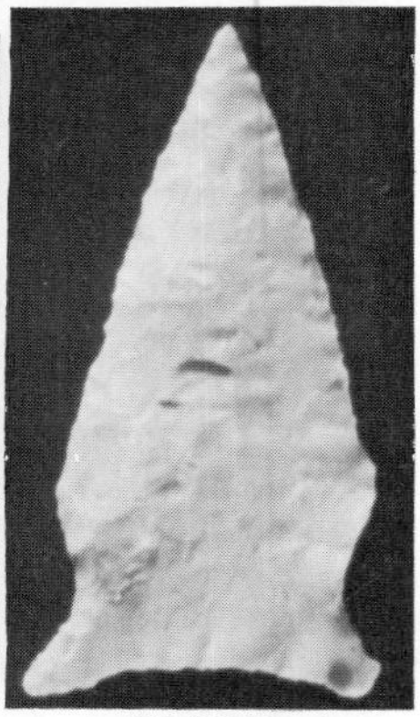

G7, $25-$40
Austin, TX.

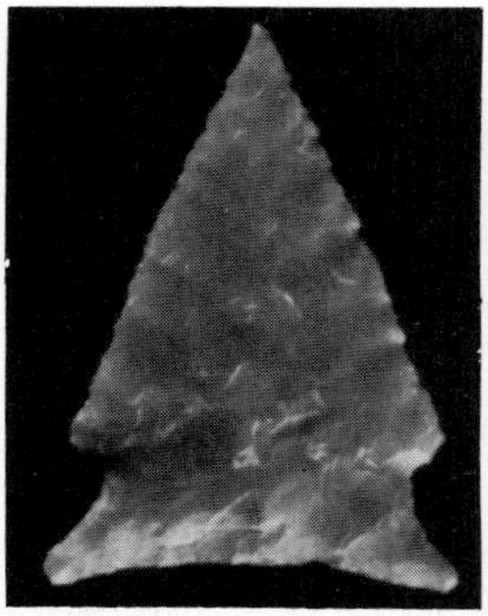

G7, $45-$60
Bell Co., TX. Classic.

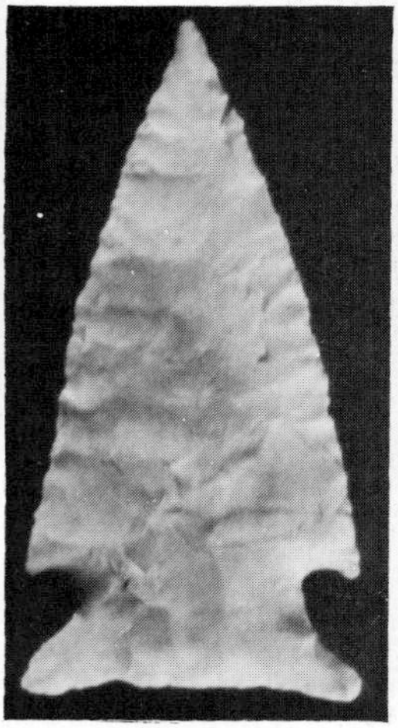

G8, $90-$120
Austin, TX. Classic.

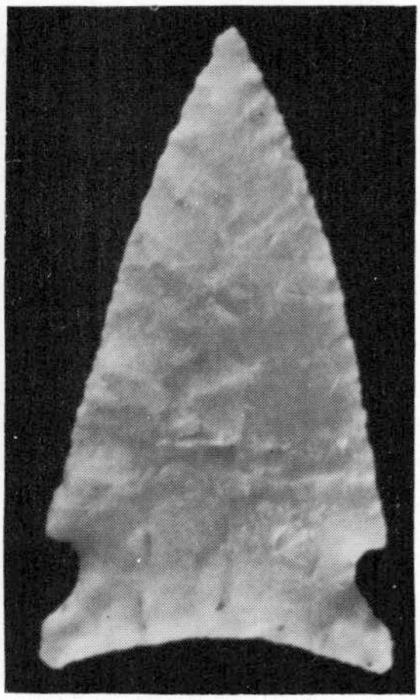

G8, $90-$120
Bell Co., TX. Classic.

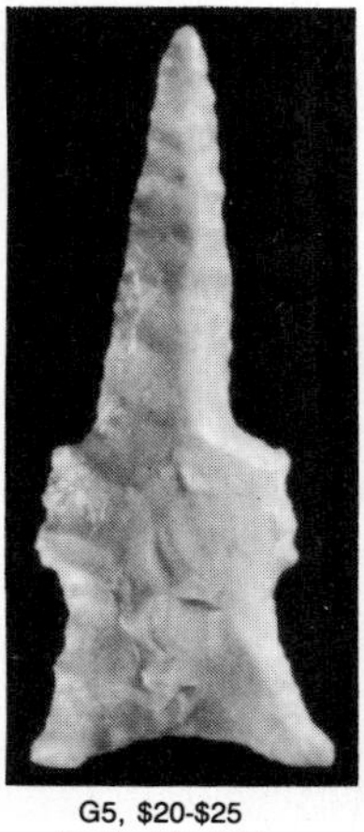

G5, $20-$25
Austin, TX. Drill.

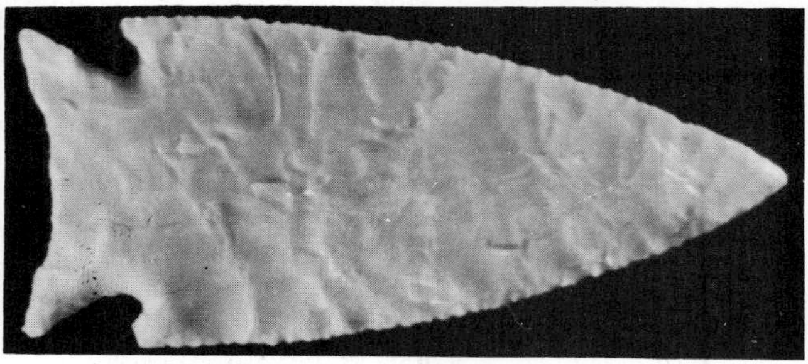

G10, $150-$250, Austin, TX. Outstanding, thin, well flaked point.

LOCATION: Midwestern states. **DESCRIPTION:** A small to medium size, expanded stem point with a concave that is usually thinned. Shoulders are weak and tapered. **I.D. KEY:** Basal form, systematic form of flaking.

FISHSPEAR - Early to mid-Archaic, 8000 - 6000 B.P.

(Also see Duval and Mantanzas)

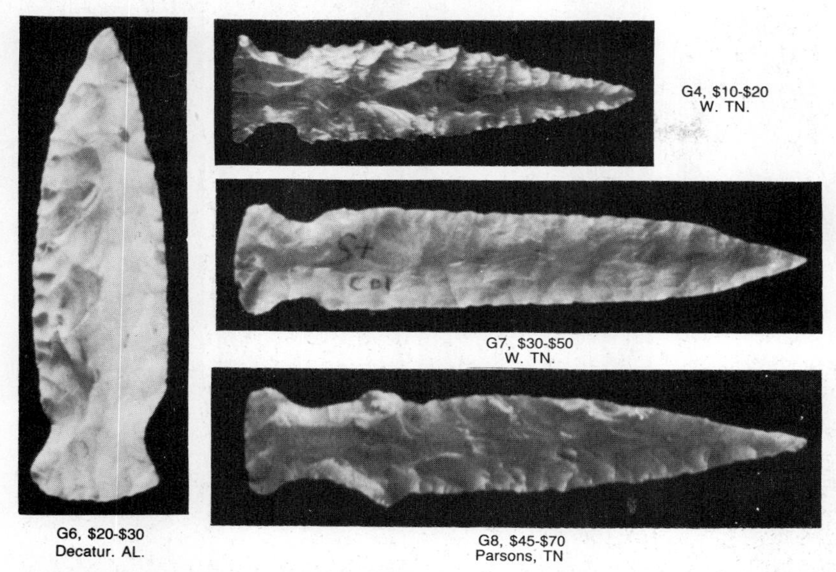

G4, $10-$20
W. TN.

G7, $30-$50
W. TN.

G6, $20-$30
Decatur. AL.

G8, $45-$70
Parsons, TN

LOCATION: Northeastern states. **DESCRIPTION:** A medium to large size, narrow, thick, point with wide side notches. Bases are usually ground and blade edges can be serrated. Named due to its appearnace that resembles a fish.

FLINT CREEK - Woodland, 3500 - 1000 B.P.

(Also see Cotaco, Lamoka, Mud Creek and Pontchartrain)

G4, $3-$5
Walker Co., AL.

G4, $3-$5
Walker Co., AL.

G4, $2-$4
Walker Co., AL.

G5, $7-$10
Walker Co., AL.

LOCATION: Southeastern & Gulf states. **DESCRIPTION:** A medium to large size, narrow, thick, serrated, expanded stem point. Shoulders can be horizontal, tapered or barbed. Base can be expanded, parallel sided or rounded. **I.D. KEY:** Thickness and flaking near point.

FLINT CREEK (continued)

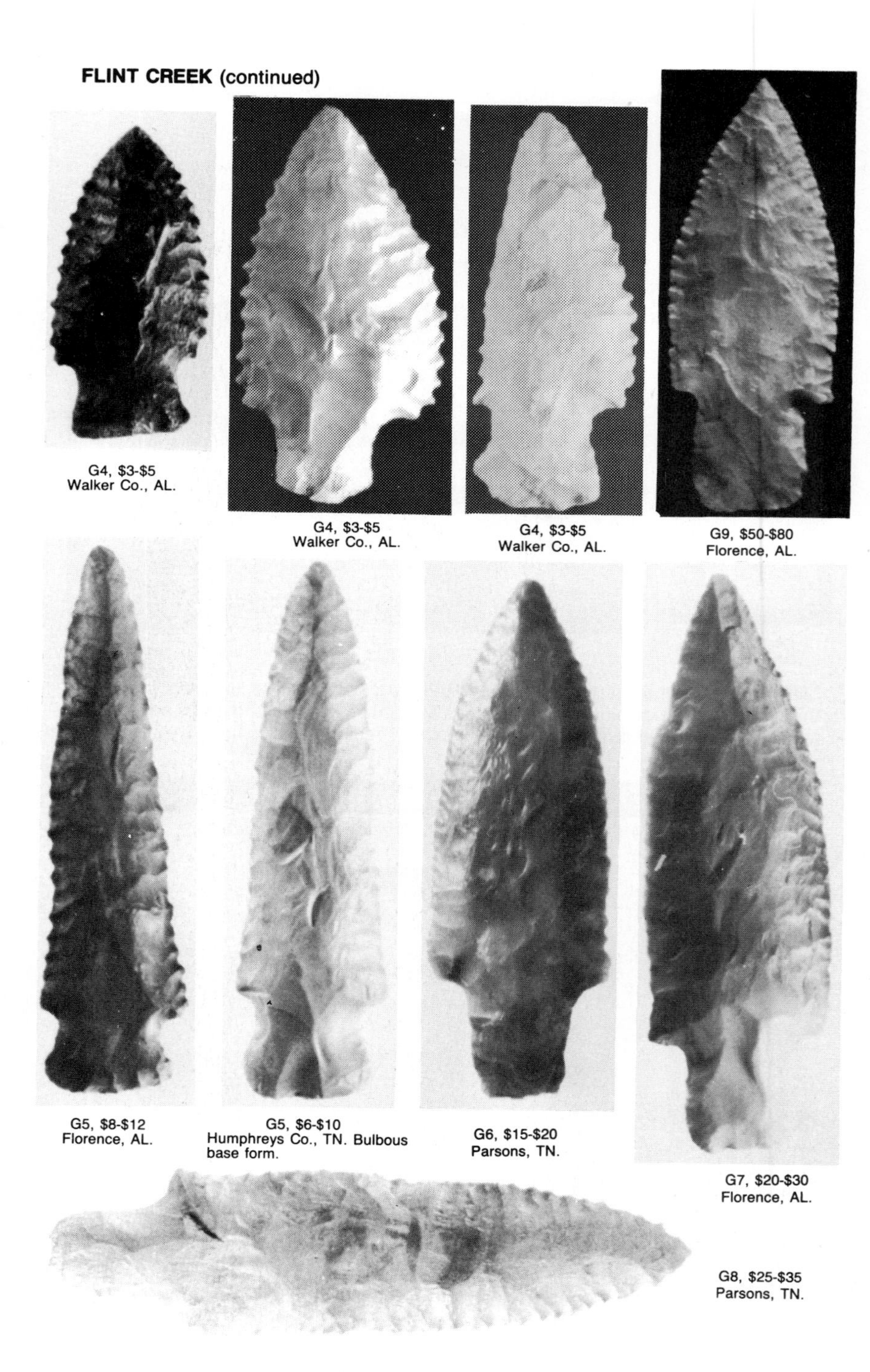

G4, $3-$5
Walker Co., AL.

G4, $3-$5
Walker Co., AL.

G4, $3-$5
Walker Co., AL.

G9, $50-$80
Florence, AL.

G5, $8-$12
Florence, AL.

G5, $6-$10
Humphreys Co., TN. Bulbous base form.

G6, $15-$20
Parsons, TN.

G7, $20-$30
Florence, AL.

G8, $25-$35
Parsons, TN.

G8, $45-$70
Walker Co., AL. Bulbous base form.

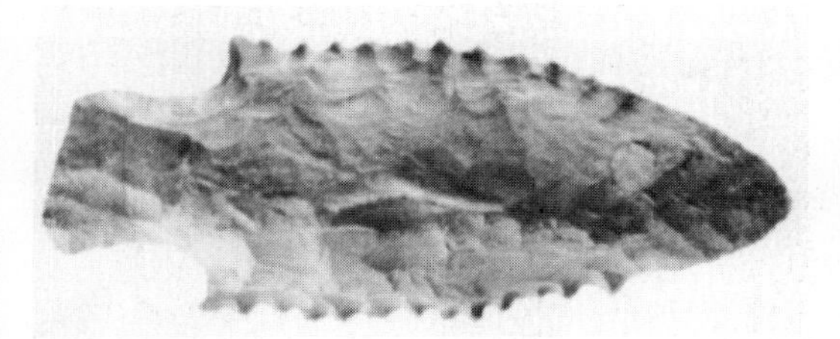

G6, $10-$20
Walker Co., AL.

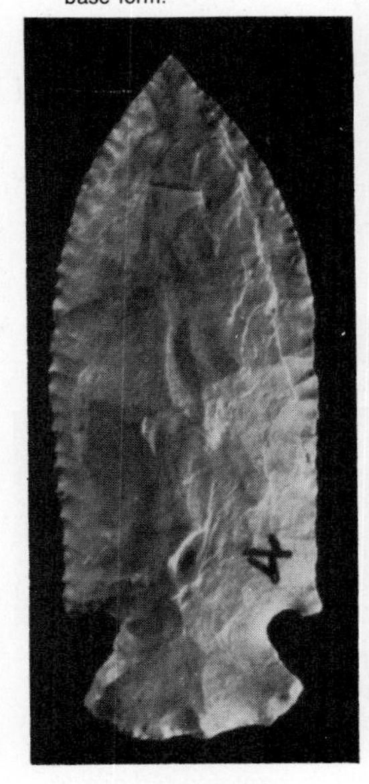

G10, $80-$120
7 Mile Isle, Florence, AL.

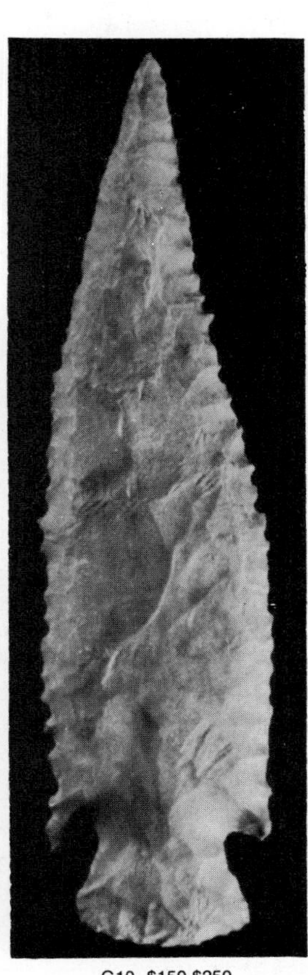

G10, $150-$250
7 Mile Isle, Florence, AL.

G9, $60-$85
Colbert Co., AL.

FLINT RIVER - Late Achaic, 4000 - 3000 B.P.

(Also see Pickwick)

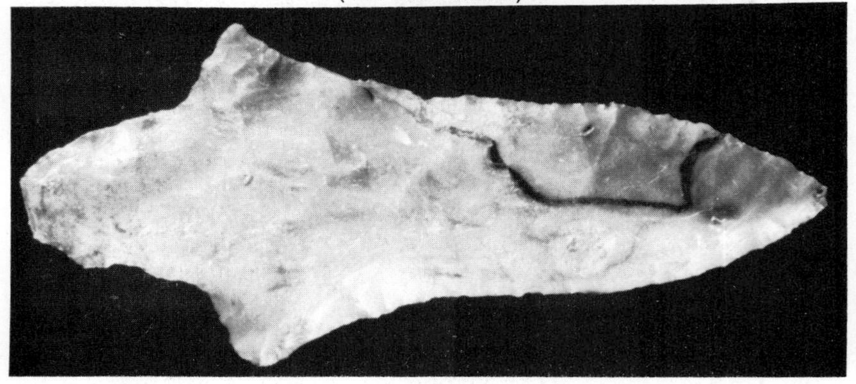

G7, $60-$100
Flint River, GA.

LOCATION: Southern GA, AL & northern FL. **DESCRIPTION:** A medium to large size, expanded shoulder, contracted stem point. A southern cousin to the *Pickwick* type.

FLINT RIVER SPIKE - Woodland, 4000 - 1800 B.P.

(Also see Bradley & Schild Spike, Duval and Randolph)

G2, $1-$3
SE TN.

LOCATION: Southeastern states. **DESCRIPTION:** A small to medium size, narrow, spike point with no stem or shoulders. Blade sides are usually convex and the base can be either straight or rounded.

FOLSOM - Paleo, 12000 - 9000 B.P.

(Also see Clovis, Cumberland, Midland, Redstone and Wheeler)

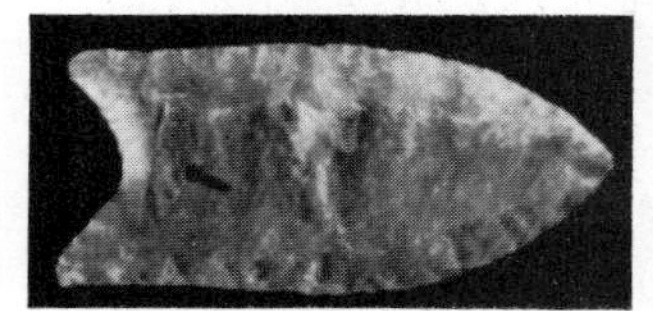

G6, $250-$300
TX.

G7, $300-$350
TX.

LOCATION: Midwestern to Western states. **DESCRIPTION:** A small to medium size, thin, high quality, fluted point with contracted, pointed auricles and a concave base. Fluting usually extends the entire length of each face. Blade flaking is extremely fine. The hafting area is ground. A very rare type, even in area of highest incidence. Modern reproductions have been made and extreme caution should be exercised in acquiring an original specimen. Usually found in association with extinct bison fossil remains. **I.D. KEY:** Flaking style (excessive secondary flaking).

FOLSOM (continued)

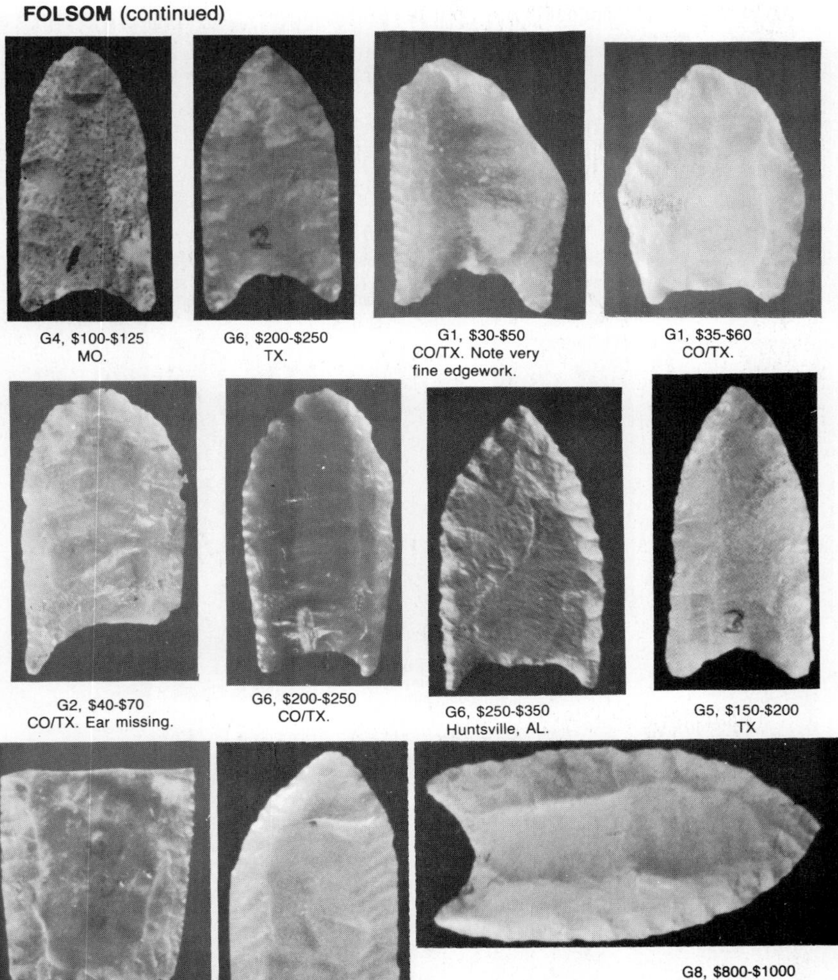

G4, $100-$125
MO.

G6, $200-$250
TX.

G1, $30-$50
CO/TX. Note very fine edgework.

G1, $35-$60
CO/TX.

G2, $40-$70
CO/TX. Ear missing.

G6, $200-$250
CO/TX.

G6, $250-$350
Huntsville, AL.

G5, $150-$200
TX

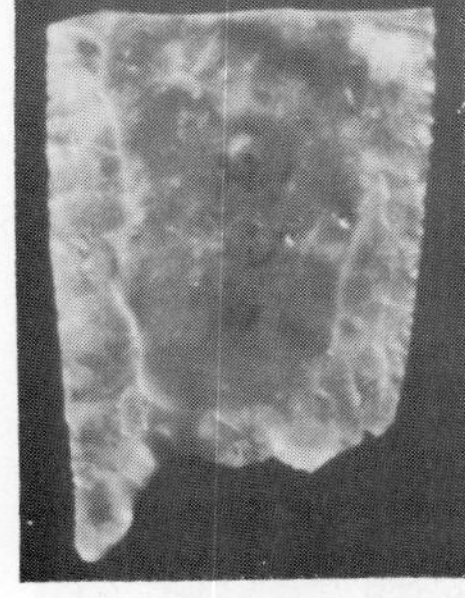

G1, $30-$50
CO/TX.

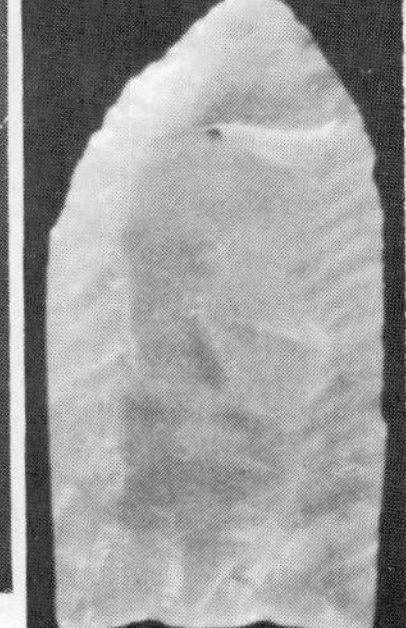

G8, $1500-$2500
Chaves Co., NM. Note very fine parallel flaking.

G8, $800-$1000
NE AR.

FORT ANCIENT - Mississippian to Historic, 800 - 400 B.P.

(Also see Fresno, Madison, Pinellas & Sand Mountain)

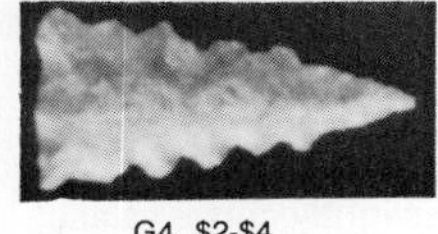

G4, $2-$4
KY/OH.

G4, $2-$4
N. AL.

G6, $5-$8
Marion Co., AL.

FORT ANCIENT (continued)

G4, $2-$4
N. AL.

G3, $2-$3
Kershaw Co., SC.
Slate.

G5, $4-$6
Ky/OH.

G6, $5-$8
Yadkin Co., NC.

G6, $5-$8
Rockingham Co., NC.

G5, $4-$6
KY/OH.

G7, $10-$15
KY.

G6, $6-$10
Stokes Co., NC.

G10, $180-$300
Humphreys Co., TN.
Best known.

G6, $10-$15
Humphreys Co., TN.

G7, $15-$25
KY.

G9, $30-$35
Decatur, AL.

G8, $20-$35
KY.

G9, $35-$50
SW VA.

G9, $30-$35
Sandersville, TN.

G9, $40-$65
KY.

G8, $20-$35
KY/OH

LOCATION: Southeastern states. **DESCRIPTION:** A small to medium size, thin, narrow, long, triangular point with concave sides and a straight to slightly convex base. Some examples are strongly serrated. **I.D. KEY:** Edgework.

FORT ANCIENT BLADE - Mississippian, 800 - 400 B.P.

(Also see Fox Creek Lanceolate)

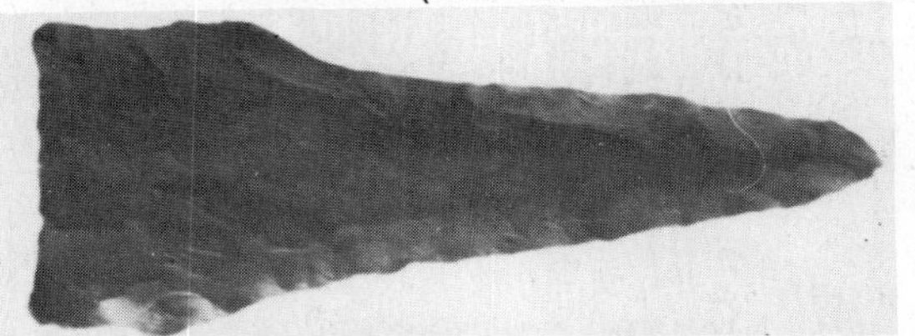

G6, $4-$6
Florence, AL.

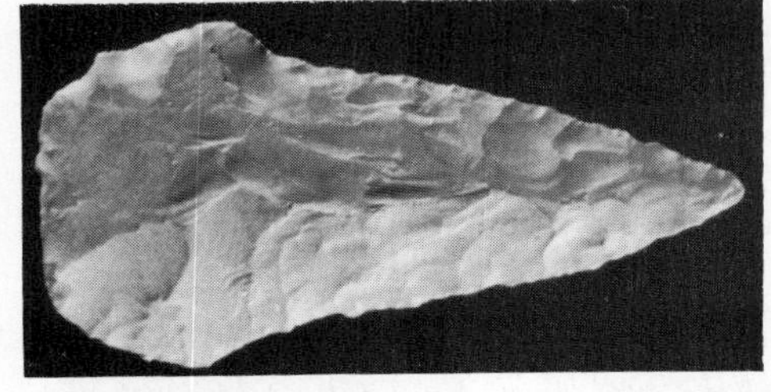

G7, $6-$10
Whitwell, TN.

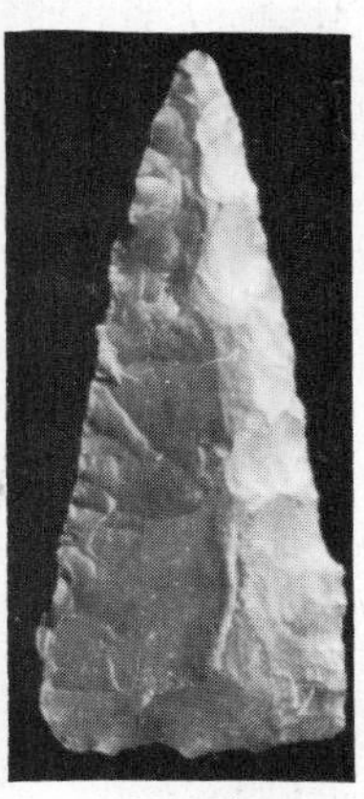

G3, $2-$4
NE AL.

LOCATION: Eastern to Southeastern states. **DESCRIPTION:** A medium size triangular blade with a squared base. Blade edges expand to meet the base which may be ground.

FORT ANCIENT KNIFE - Early Archaic, 9000 - 6000 B.P.

(Also see Mule Ear)

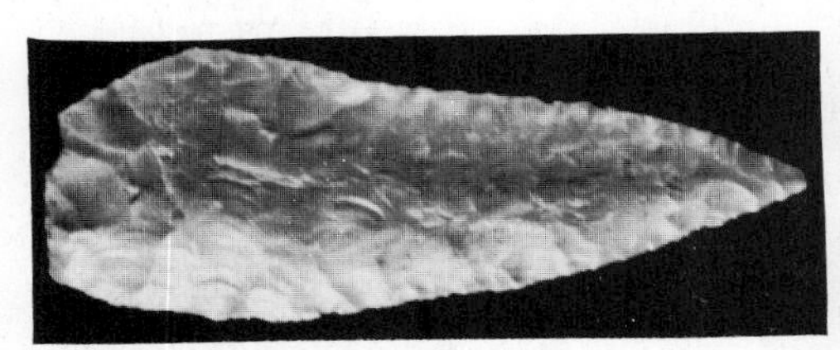

G3, $15-$20
Wasco Co., OR. The Dalles.

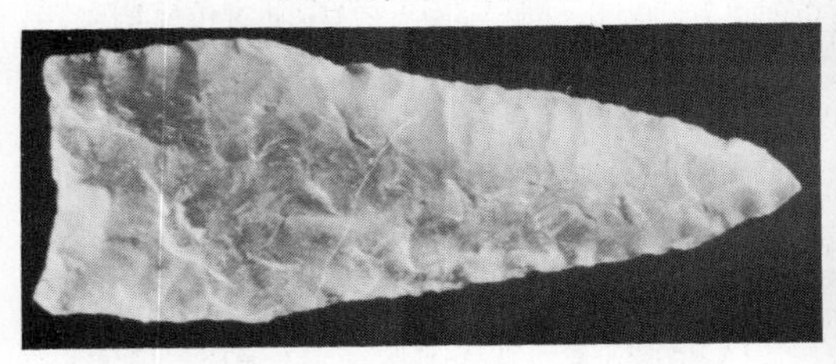

G8, $20-$35
Wasco Co., OR. The Dalles.

G9, $45-$55
Wasco Co., OR. The Dalles.

LOCATION: Mid to Northwestern states. **DESCRIPTION:** A medium to large size blade that expands into a broad, squarish to tapered base. Bases are usually ground. Some examples have been resharpened many times while still hafted creating very narrow blades. Blade faces show early parallel flaking. **I.D. KEY:** Early flaking.

FORT ANCIENT KNIFE (continued)

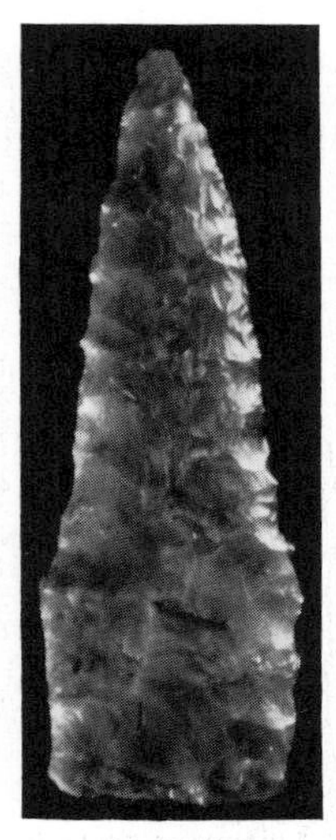

G3, $15-$20
Wasco Co., OR.

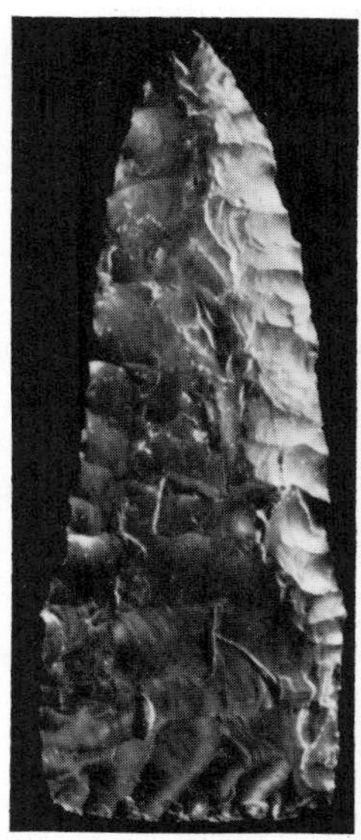

G8, $20-$30
Wasco Co., OR. Red Jasper.

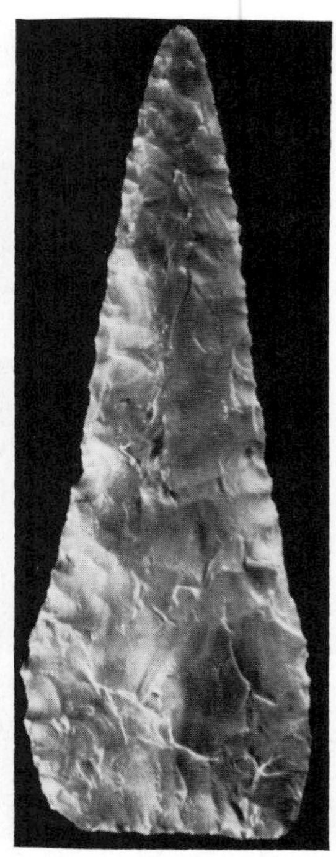

G9, $45-$65
Wasco Co., OR. The Dalles.

FOUNTAIN CREEK - Early Archaic, 9000 - 7000 B.P.

(Also see Boggy Branch and Kirk Serrated)

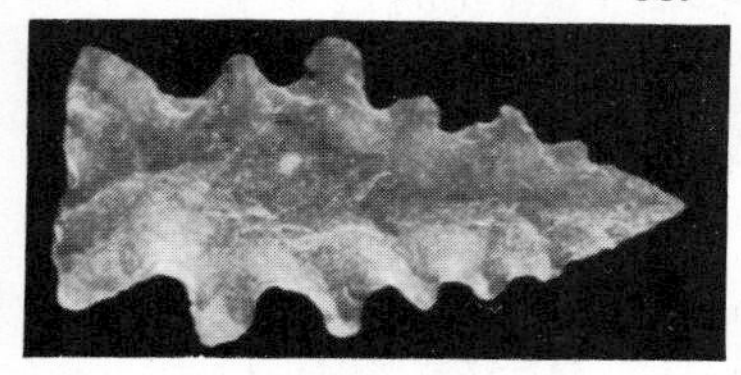

G7, $35-$50
Chatham Co., NC.

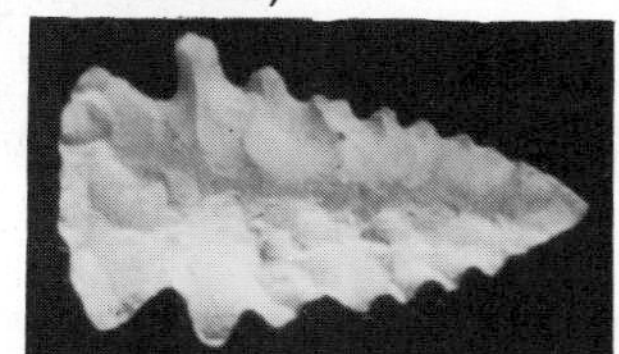

G6, $25-$30
Wayne Co., NC.

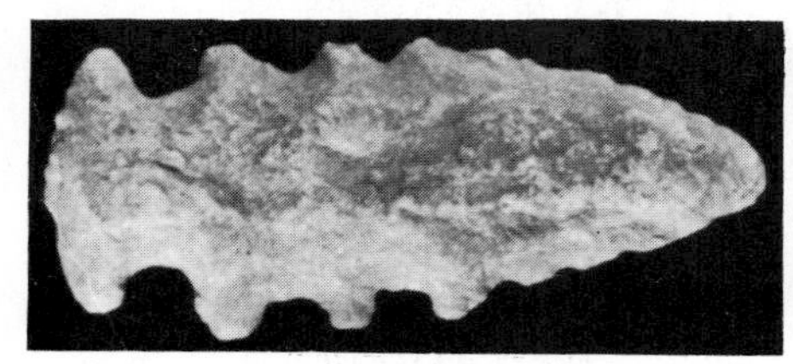

G4, $4-$8
Davidson Co., NC.

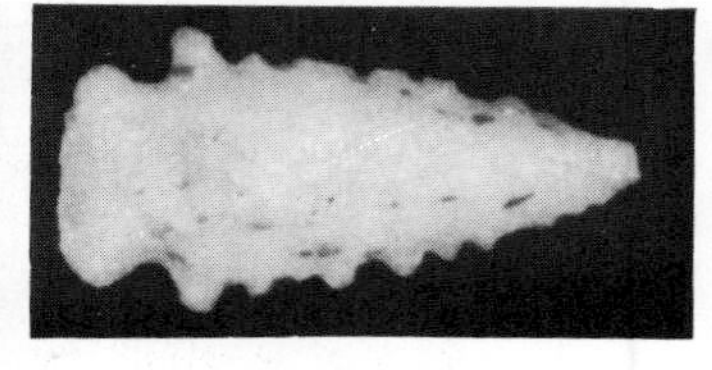

G3, $2-$4
Union Co., SC. Quartz.

LOCATION: Eastern states. **DESCRIPTION:** A medium size, narrow point with notched blade edges and a short, rounded base which is ground. **I.D. KEY:** Edgework.

FOX CREEK LANCEOLATE - Woodland, 3000 - 1200 B.P.

(Also see Fort Ancient Blade & Frazier)

G4, $10-$15
Cent. PA.

G8, $30-$35
Bethany, WV.

G2, $5-$8
Lane Co., PA. Augillite.

LOCATION: Northeastern states. **DESCRIPTION:** A medium size blade with a squarish to tapered hafting area and a straight base.

FOX EAR - Early Archaic, 9000 - 7000 B.P.

(Also see Desert & Northern Side Notched)

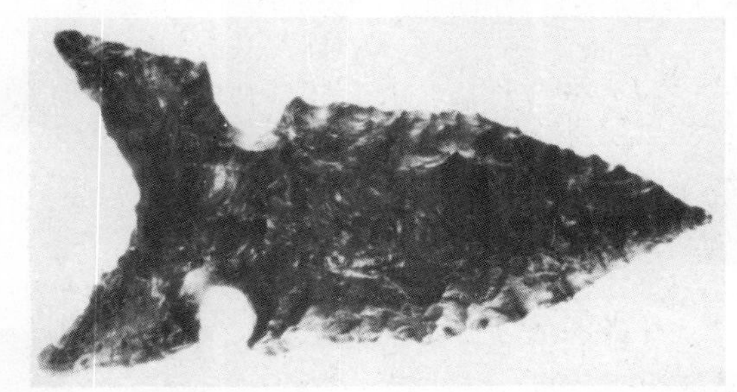

G9, $250-$400
Lake Co., OR. Crump Lake.
Obsidian.

G10, $350-$500
Lake Co., OR. Crump Lake.
Obsidian. Classic.

LOCATION: Northwestern states. **DESCRIPTION:** A medium to large size, narrow, auriculate point with side notches. Bases are deeply notched.

FOX VALLEY - Early to mid-Archaic, 9000 - 4000 B.P.

(Also see Garth Slough, Jude, Kanawha, Kirk, Lake Erie, LeCroy, Rice Lobbed and Stanly)

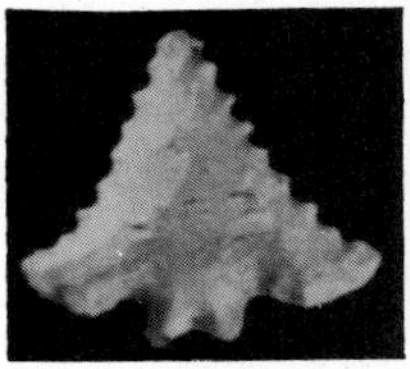

G4, $15-$25
IL.

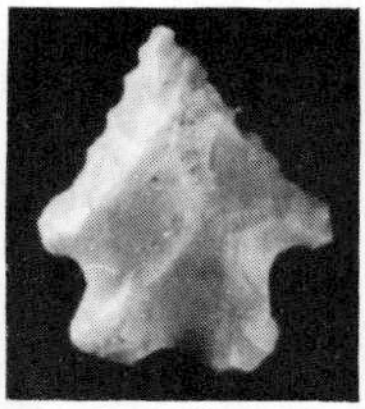

G2, $3-$4
Williams Isle,
Chattanooga, TN.

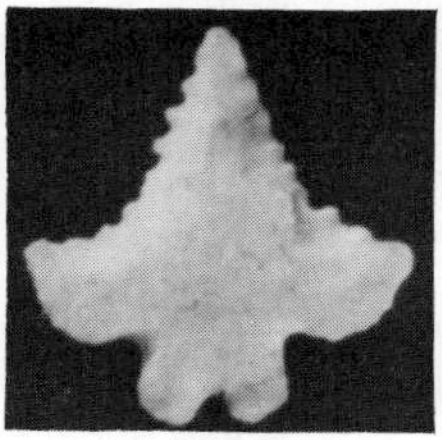

G8, $60-$90
IL.

G6, $25-$45
IL.

G4, $15-$25
IL.

G5, $20-$30
Warren Co., TN.

G6, $25-$45
IL.

G7, $30-$60
Will Co., IL.

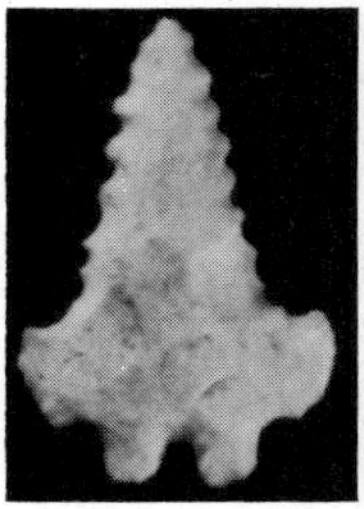

G6, $25-$45
IL.

G7, $45-$75
IL.

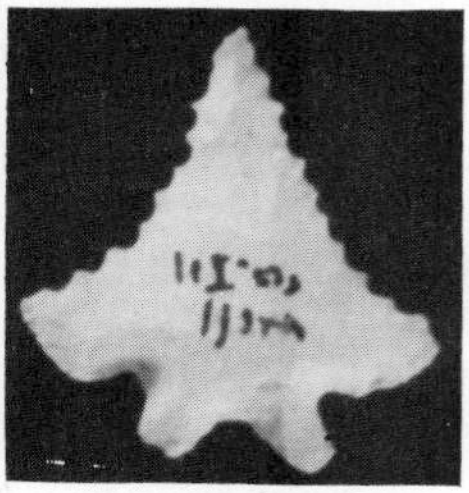

G8, $60-$90
Will Co., IL.

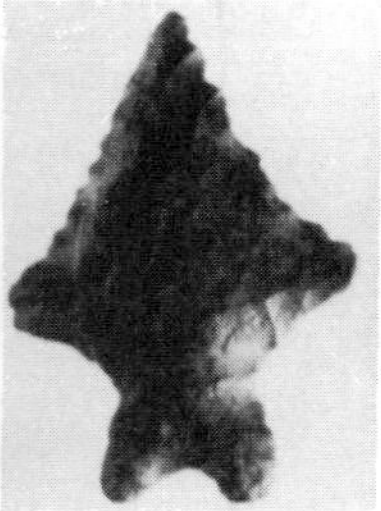

G6, $25-$40
Cookeville, TN.

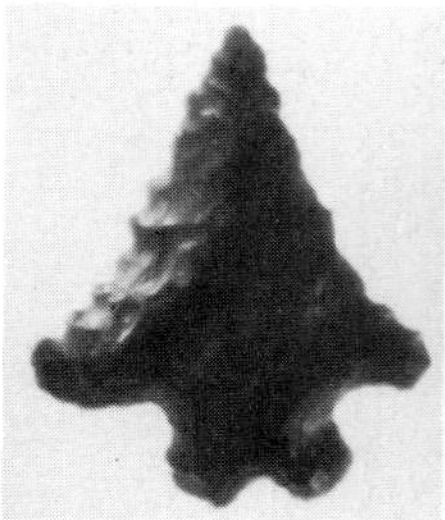

G5, $20-$35
Watts Bar, TN.

G8, $70-$110
Will Co., IL. Classic.

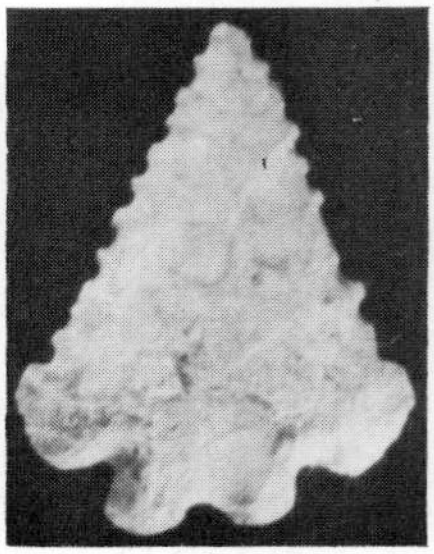

G6, $25-$45
IL.

G6, $25-$45
Will Co., IL.

LOCATION: Eastern states. **DESCRIPTION:** A small size, triangular point with flaring shoulders and a short bifurcated stem. Shoulders are sometimes clipped winged and have a tendency to turn towards the tip. Blade edges are usually serrated. **I.D. KEY:** Bifurcated base and barbs.

FOX VALLEY (continued)

G8, $50-$80
IL.

G7, $40-$60
IL.

G6, $25-$45
W. TN.

G6, $25-$45
IL.

G6, $25-$45
Mecklenburg Co., VA.
Black chert. Classic.

G7, $40-$60
IL.

G10, $100-$150
IL. Classic.

G7, $40-$60
Cumberland Co., KY.

G6, $25-$45
Monteray, TN.

G8, $50-$80
KY.

G3, $7-$12
IL.

G4, $15-$25
SE TN.

G4, $15-$25
IL. Tip nick.

FOX VALLEY (continued)

G8, $60-$90
IL.

G8, $65-$100
Wayne Co., KY.

FRAZIER - Mid to late Archaic, 7000 - 3000 B.P.

(Also see Big Sandy, Copena and Pandora)

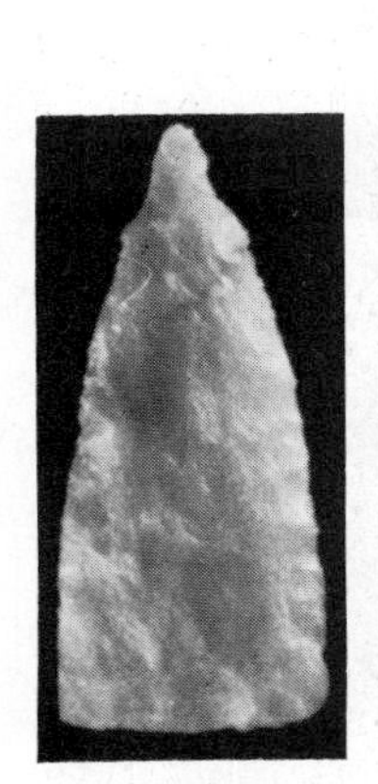

G4, $5-$6
Marion Co., TN.

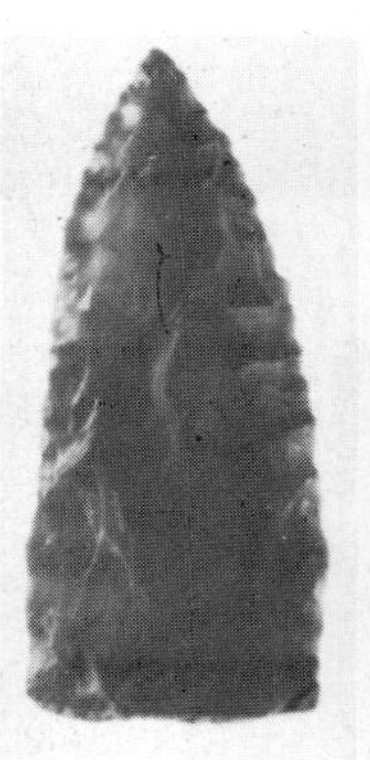

G4, $3-$5
SE TN.

G7, $10-$12
Decatur, AL.

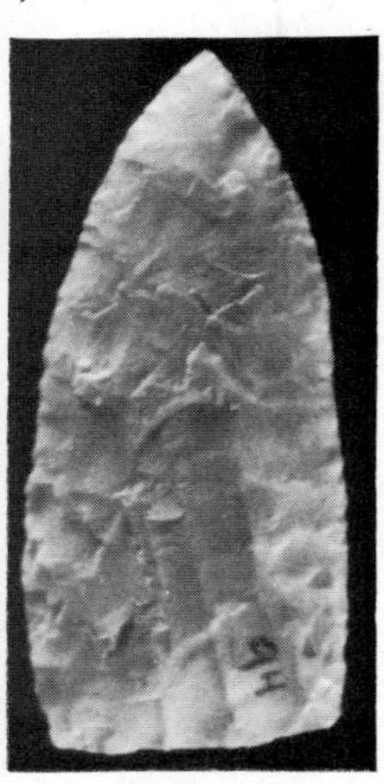

G7, $8-$15
Morgan Co., AL.

G7, $12-$20
W. TN.

LOCATION: Southeastern states. **DESCRIPTION:** A generally narrow, medium to large size lanceolate blade with a slightly concave to straight base. Flaking technique and shape is identical to that of *Big Sandy* points (minus the notches) and is found on *Big Sandy* sites. Could this type be unnotched *Big Sandy's*? **I.D. KEY:** Archaic flaking.

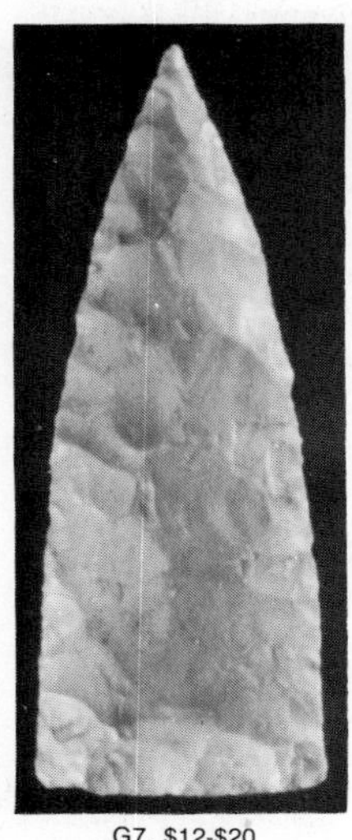
G7, $12-$20
W. TN.

G4, $3-$5
7 Mile Isle, Florence, AL.

G6, $6-$10
Lauderdale Co., AL.

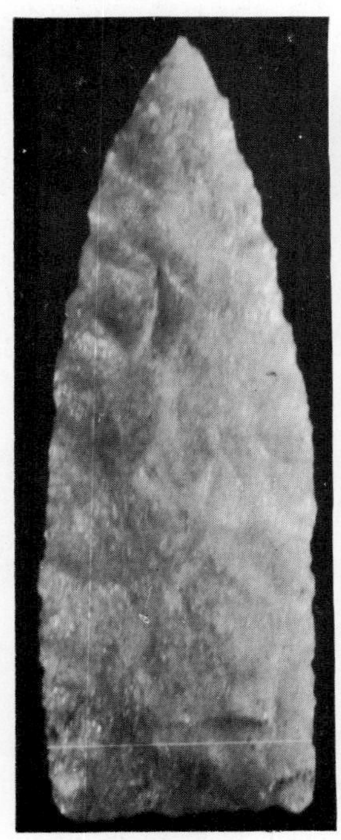
G8, $25-$40
Lawrence Co., AL.

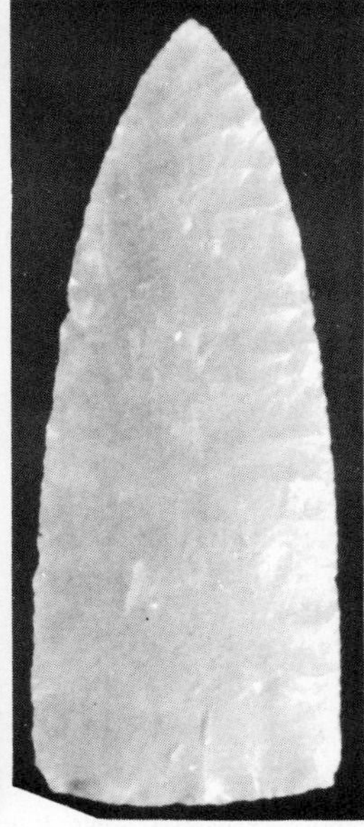
G9, $50-$80
Madison Co., IL.

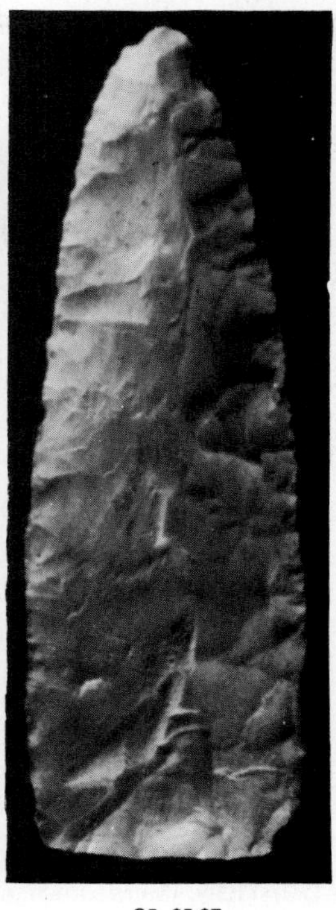
G5, $5-$7
Parsons, TN.

FRESNO - Mississippian, 1200 - 250 B.P.

(Also see Fort Ancient, Huffaker, Madison & Maud)

G6, $10-$20
Comanche Co., TX.

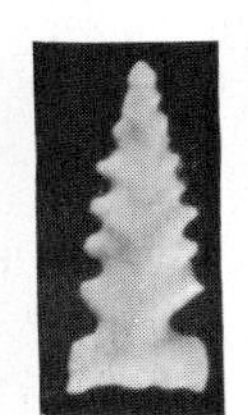

G5, $6-10
Comanche Co., TX.

G5, $8-$10
WA/OR.

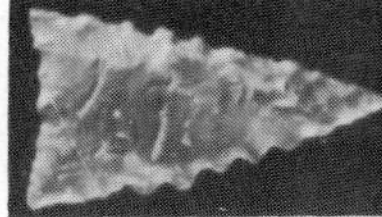

G7, $20-$30
Red Rv., TX.

G4, $5-$8
Comanche Co., TX.

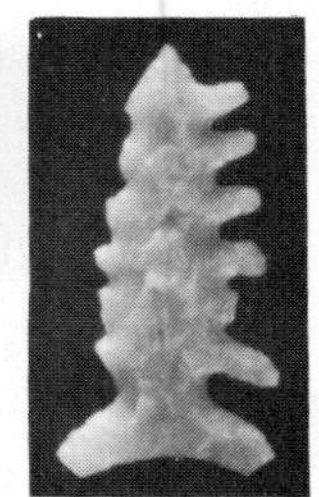

G7, $35-$50
Comanche Co., TX.

LOCATION: Midwestern to Southeastern states. **DESCRIPTION:** A small, thin, triangular point with convex to straight sides and a concave to straight base. Many examples are deeply serrated and some are side notched.

FRIDAY - Woodland, 4000 - 1500 B.P.

(Also see Copena, Covington, Gahagan, Sabine and Texas Blade)

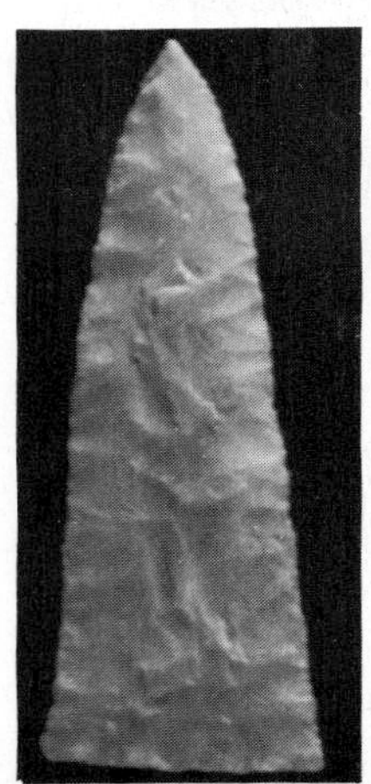

G8, $25-$35
Austin, TX.

G8, $25-$35
Waco, TX.

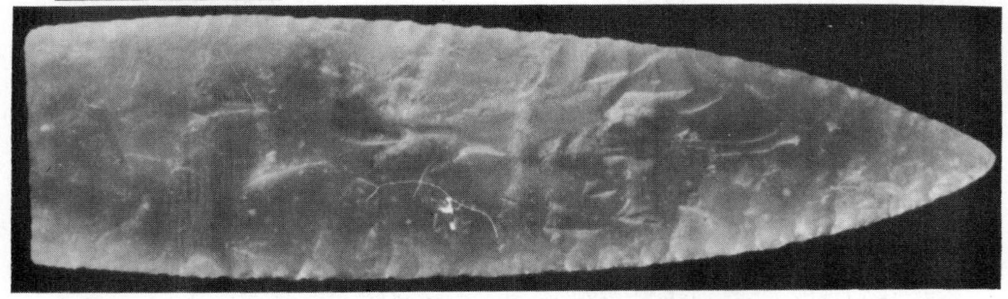

G10, $150-$250, Little River Co., AR. Classic.

LOCATION: Midwestern states. **DESCRIPTION:** A medium to large size, thin, lanceolate blade with recurved sides, sharp corners and a straight base. Flaking quality is excellent.

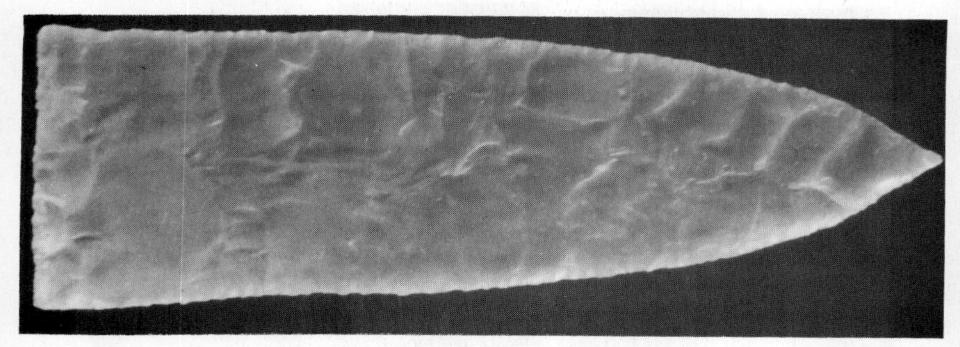

G10, $250-$400, Little River Co., AR. Classic.

FRILEY - Late Woodland, 1500 - 1000 B.P.

(Also see Steiner)

G3, $5-$7
Waco, TX.

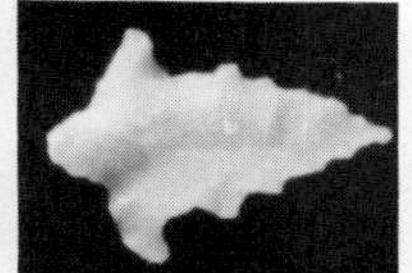

G5, $10-$20
Comanche Co., TX.

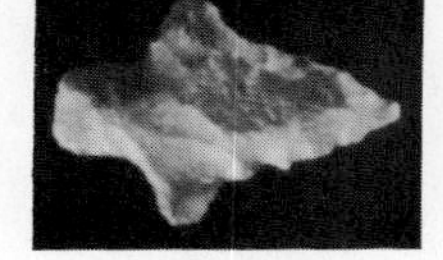

G4, $4-$6
Lincoln Parrish, LA.

G9, $50-$80
Comanche Co., TX.

G9, $60-$100
Comanche Co., TX.

LOCATION: Midwestern states. **DESCRIPTION:** A small size, thin, triangular point with exaggerated shoulders that flare outward and towards the tip. The base can be rounded to eared.

FRIO - Mid-Archaic to Woodland, 5000 - 1500 B.P.

(Also see Big Sandy, Ensor Split-Base, Fairland, MacCorkle, Montell & Uvalde)

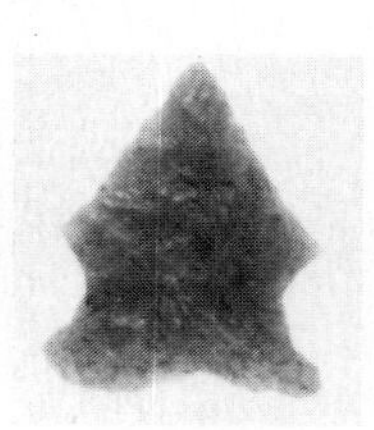

G3, $5-$10
Walker Co., GA.

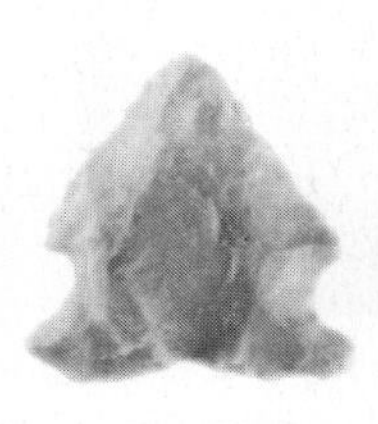

G2, $3-$5
SE TN.

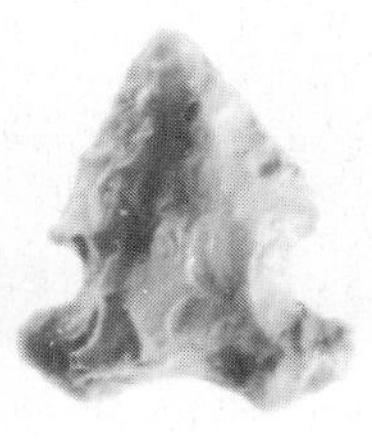

G4, $5-$10
SE TN.

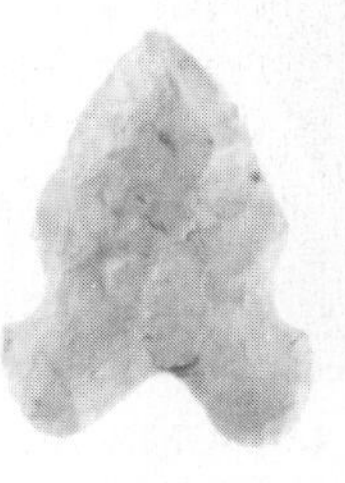

G2, $2-$4
SE TN.

FRIO (continued)

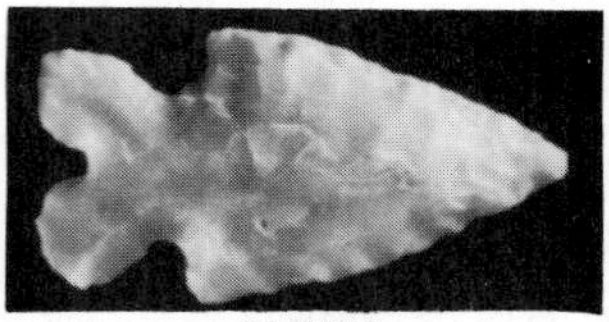

G3, $3-$5
Comanche Co., TX.

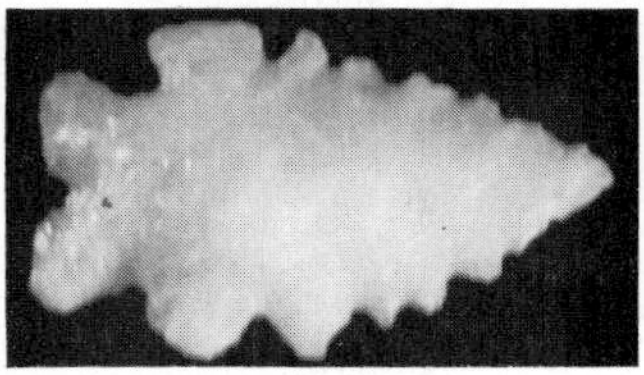

G7, $20-$25
Sevier Co., TN. Vein quartz.

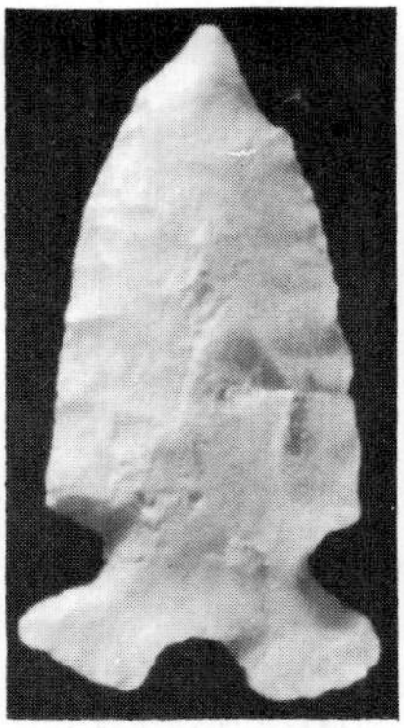

G6, $15-$20
Comanche Co., TX.

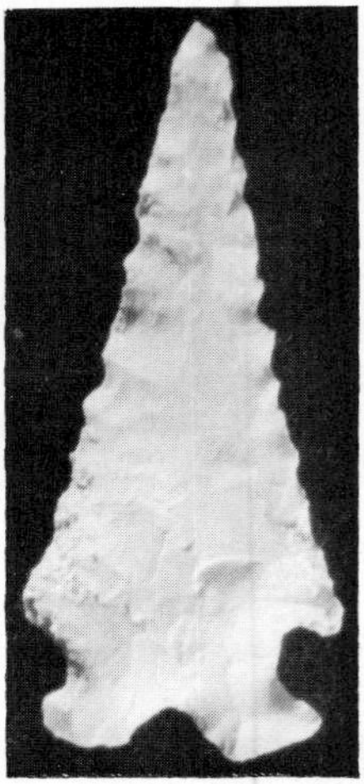

G6, $12-$20
Austin, TX.

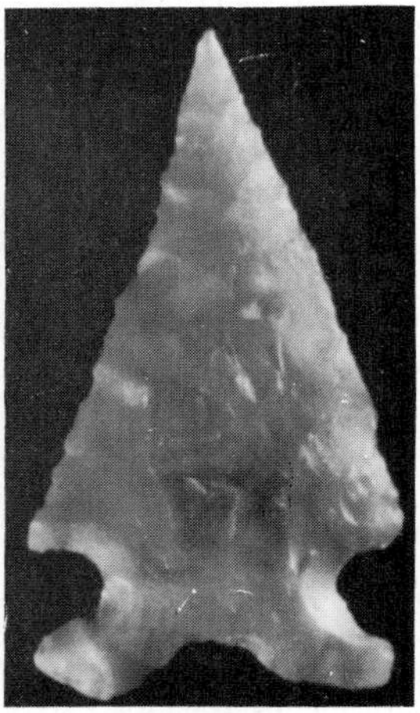

G7, $25-$40
Austin, TX.

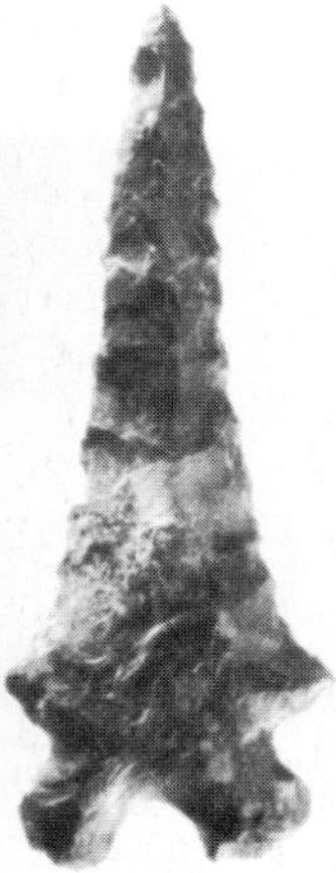

G7, $20-$30
Comanche Co., TX. Leon River chert.

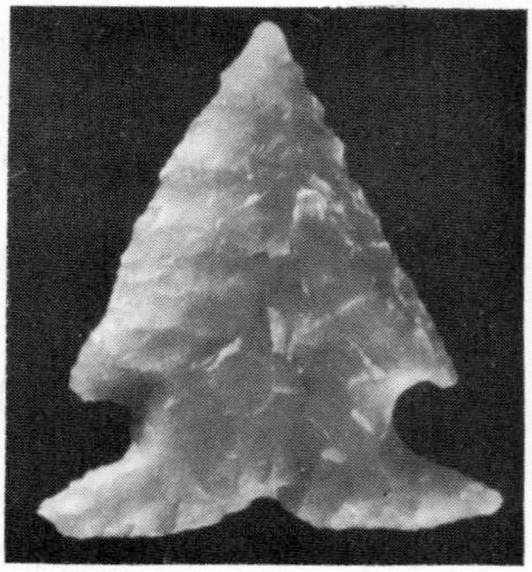

G8, $40-$60
Comanche Co., TX.

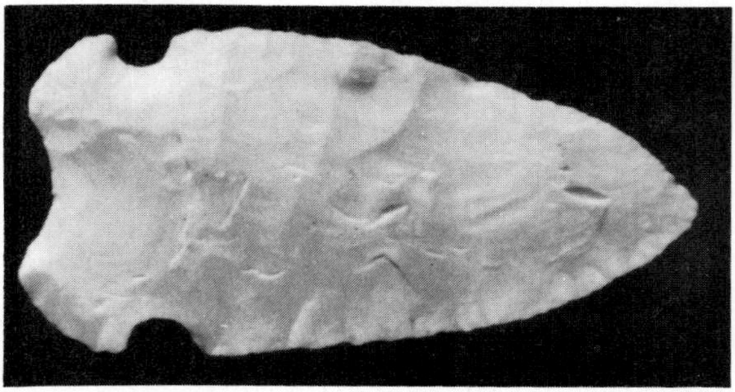

$35-$40
AR/TN.

LOCATION: Midwestern states. **DESCRIPTION:** A small to medium size, side to corner-notched point with a concave to notched base that has squared to flaring ears. Some examples can be confused with *Big Sandy Auriculate* forms.

GAHAGAN - Woodland, 4000 - 1500 B.P.

(Also see Covington, Darl Blade, Friday, Kinney, Sabine & Texas Blade)

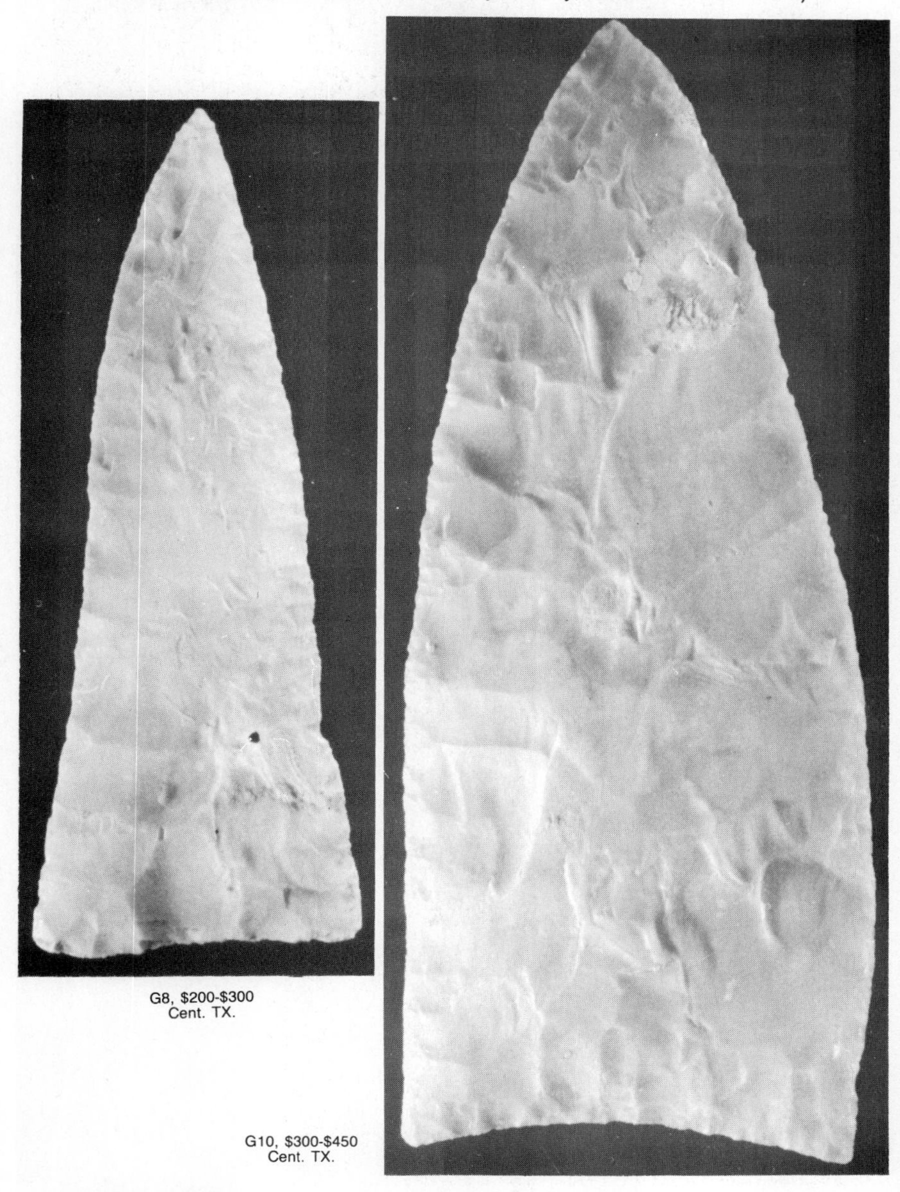

G8, $200-$300
Cent. TX.

G10, $300-$450
Cent. TX.

LOCATION: Midwestern states. **DESCRIPTION:** A large size, broad, thin, triangular blade with straight to convex sides and a straight to concave or shallowly v-shaped base.

G9, $250-$400
Cent. TX.

G10, $450-$600
Little River Co., AR. Excellent.

GARTH SLOUGH - Early Archaic, 9000 - 4000 B.P.

(Also see Catahoula, Fox Valley, Jude and Stanly)

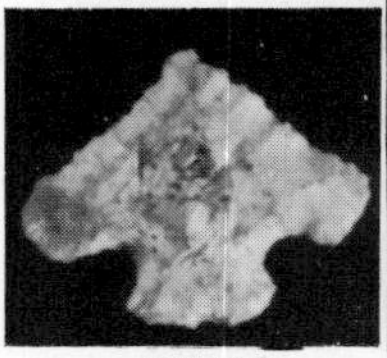

G2, $2-$3
Sevier Co., TN.
Classic form.

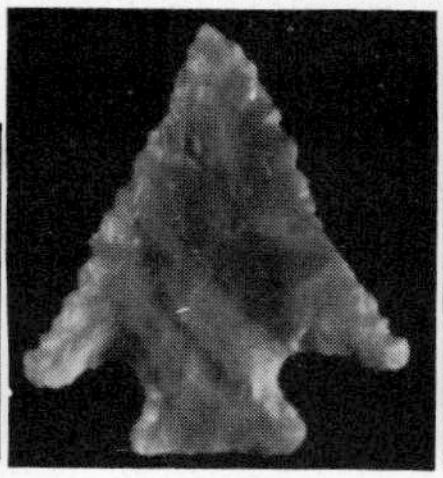

G6, $15-$25
Warren Co., TN.

G7, $25-$40
W. TN. Classic.

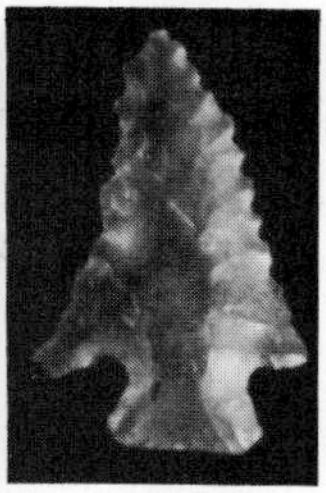

G3, $2-$4
Warren Co., TN.

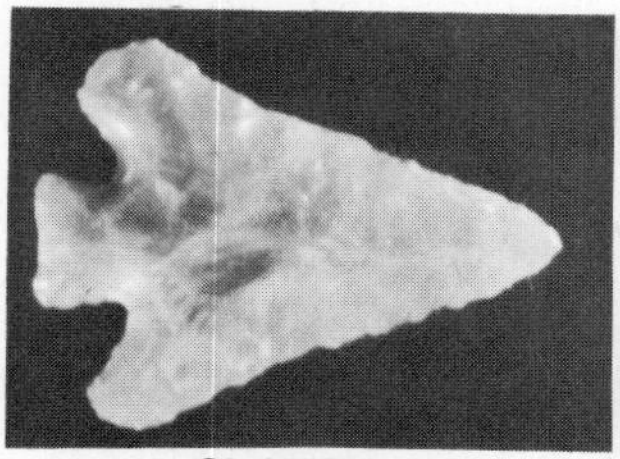

G8, $40-$70
Morgan Co., AL.

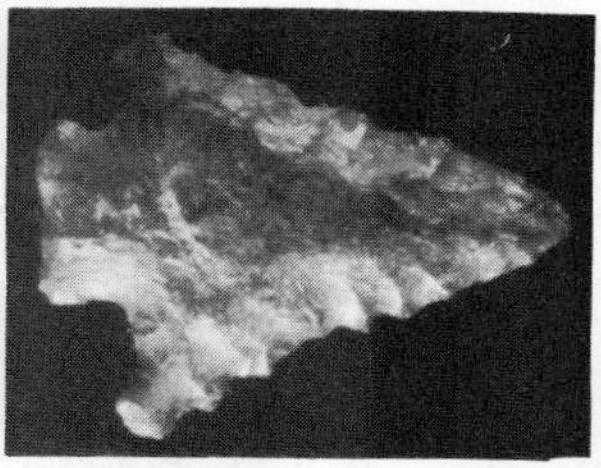

G7, $25-$35
Ft. Payne, AL.

G6, $15-$25
TN/KY.

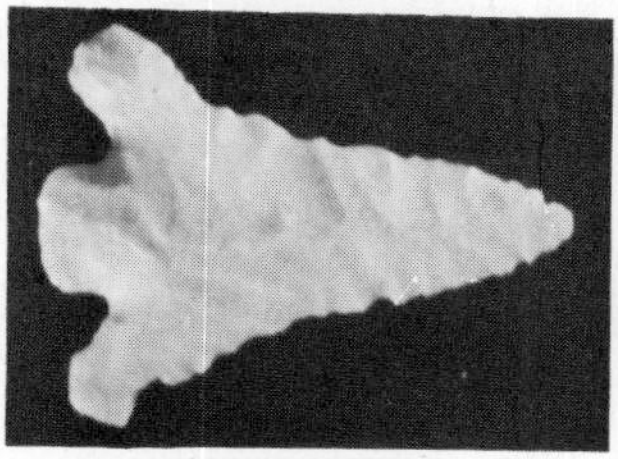

G5, $12-$20
Morgan Co., AL.

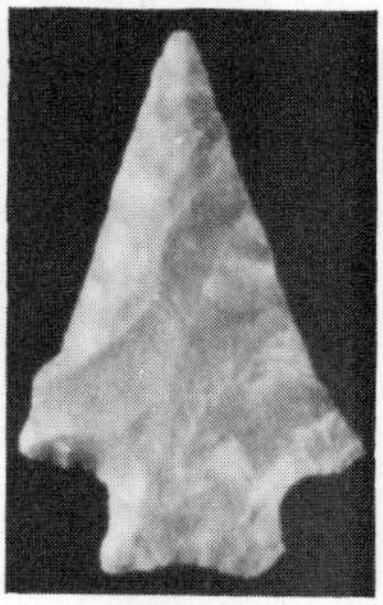

G3, $5-$8
Cumberland Co., KY.

G4, $8-$15
Marion Co., TN.
Broken wing.
color.

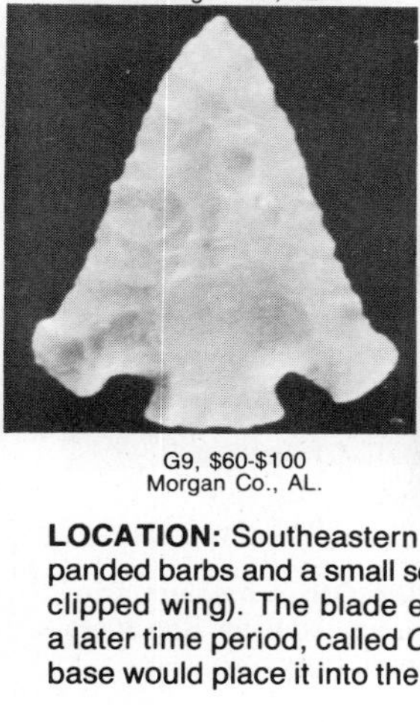

G9, $60-$100
Morgan Co., AL.

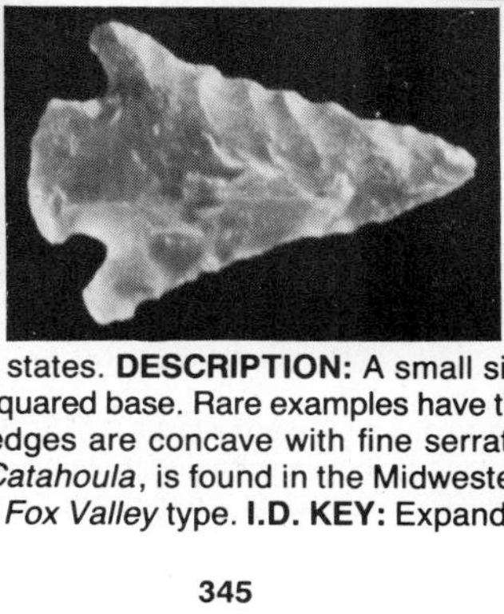

G6, $10-$20
Morgan Co., AL.

LOCATION: Southeastern states. **DESCRIPTION:** A small size point with wide, expanded barbs and a small squared base. Rare examples have the tangs clipped (called clipped wing). The blade edges are concave with fine serrations. A similar type of a later time period, called *Catahoula*, is found in the Midwestern states. A bifurcated base would place it into the *Fox Valley* type. **I.D. KEY:** Expanded barbs, early flaking.

GARTH SLOUGH (continued)

G10, $120-$200
Humphreys Co., TN. Classic form. Note "Umbrella" tangs.

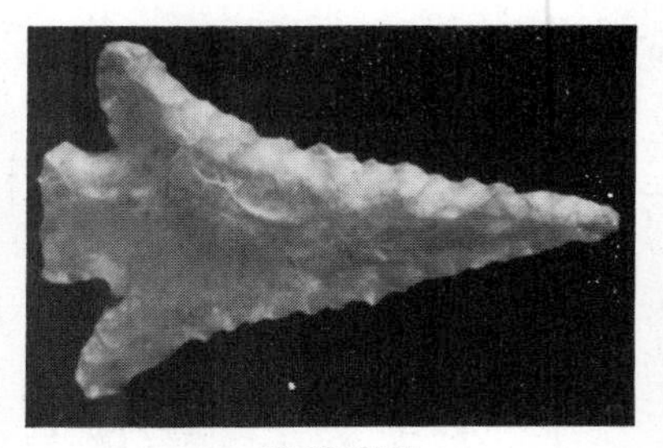
G9, $90-$150
Portland Lake, TN. Classic.

GARY - Late Archaic, 4000 - 1000 B.P.

(Also see Adena, Buggs Island, Ebenezer, Hidden Valley, Langtry and Morrow Mountain)

G1, .50-$100
Comanche Co., TX.

G2, $1-$2
Comanche Co., TX.

G2, $1-$2
Waco, TX.

G3, $2-$3
Waco, TX.

G3, $1-$3
Waco, TX.

G2, $1-$2
Comanche Co., TX.

G3, $2-$3
Meigs Co., TN.

LOCATION: Midwestern to Southeastern states. **DESCRIPTION:** A medium size, triangular point with a medium to long, contracted, pointed to rounded base. Shoulders are usually tapered. **I.D. KEY:** Similar to *Adena*, but thinned more.

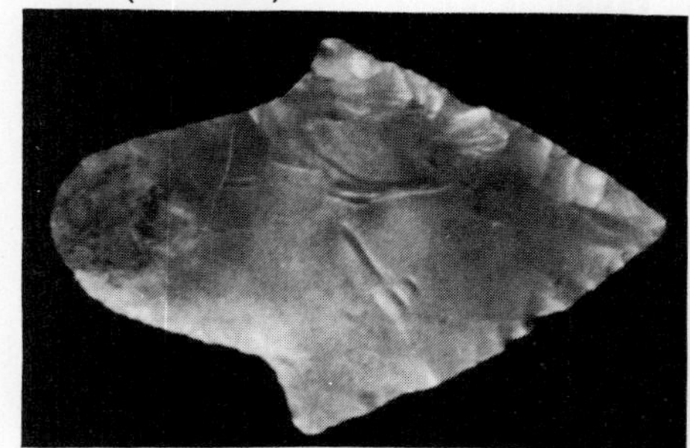

G5, $4-$6
AR.

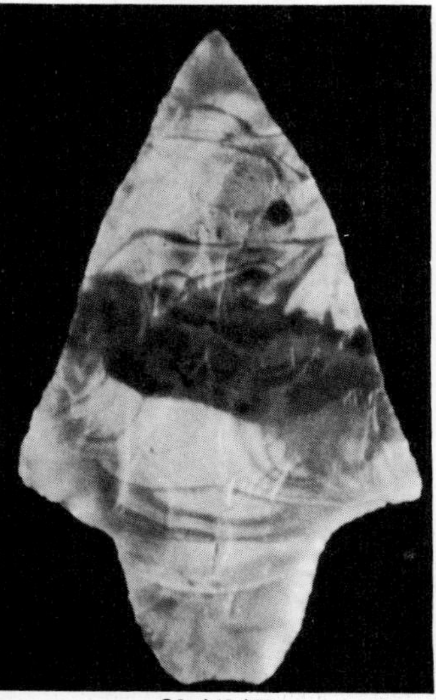

G8, $40-$70
St. Louis Co., MO.

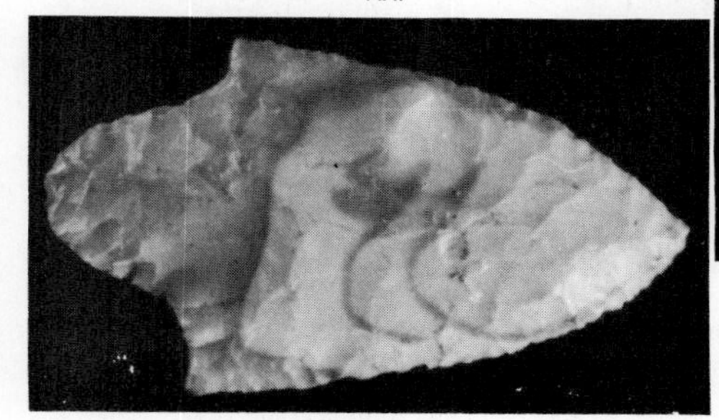

G5 $5$8
AR.

G4, $3-$5
McIntosh Co., OK.

G6, $15-$40
McIntosh Co., OK. Quartzite.

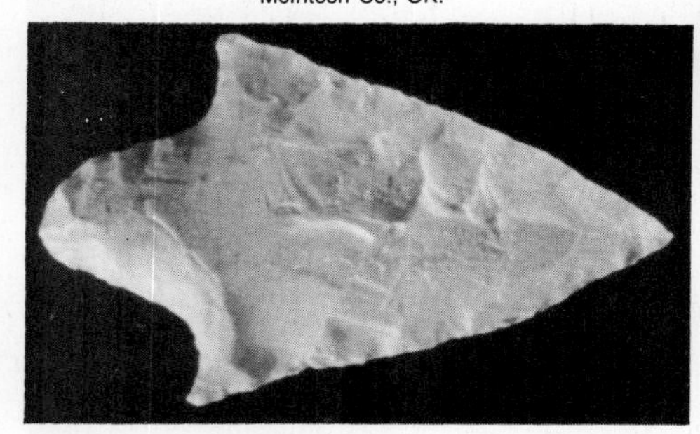

G5, $5-$8
McIntosh Co., OK.

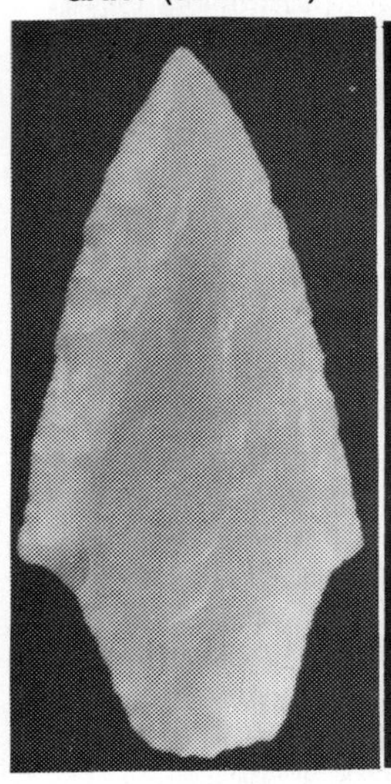

G7, $25-$40
AR. Novaculite.

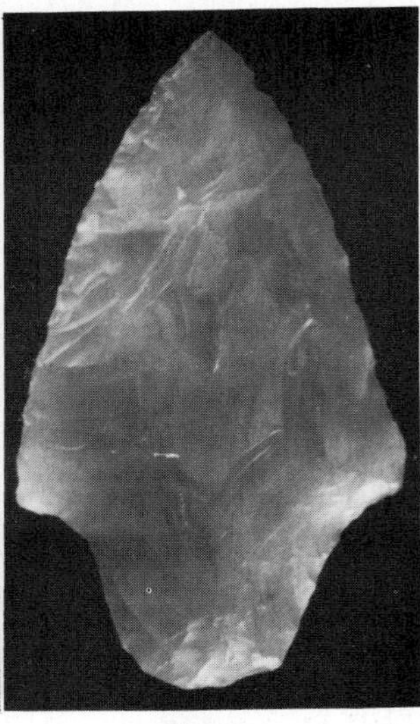

G6, $8-$12
Comanche Co., TX.

G7, $20-$35
Austin, TX.

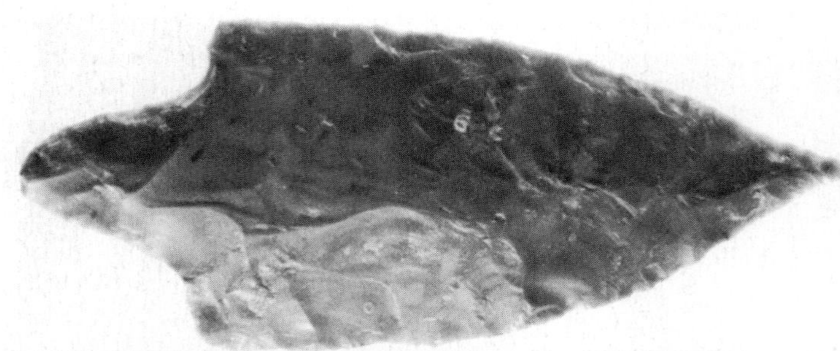

G9, $60-$100
Waco, TX.

G9, $60-$100. McIntosh Co., OK. Chickachock chert.

GARZA - Mississippian to Historic, 900 - 300 B.P.

(Also see Lott)

G1, $1-$2
Waco, TX.

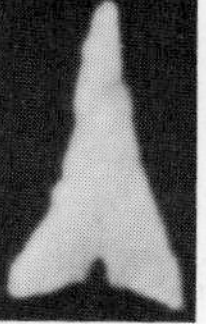

G3, $10-$15
Otero Co., NM.

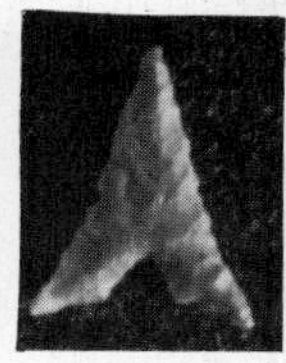

G7, $30-$40
Cent. TX.

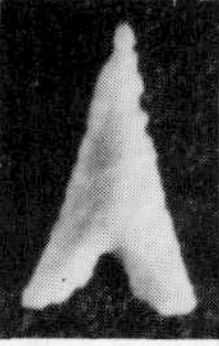

G5, $12-$20
Cent. TX.

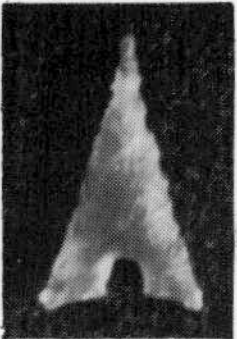

G7, $30-$40
Cent. TX.

G10, $90-$120
Spiro Mound, OK.

LOCATION: West to Midwestern states. **DESCRIPTION:** A small size, thin, triangular point with concave to convex sides and base that has a single notch in the center.

GIBSON - Woodland, 2000 - 1500 B.P.

(Also see Dovetail, Ocala and St. Charles)

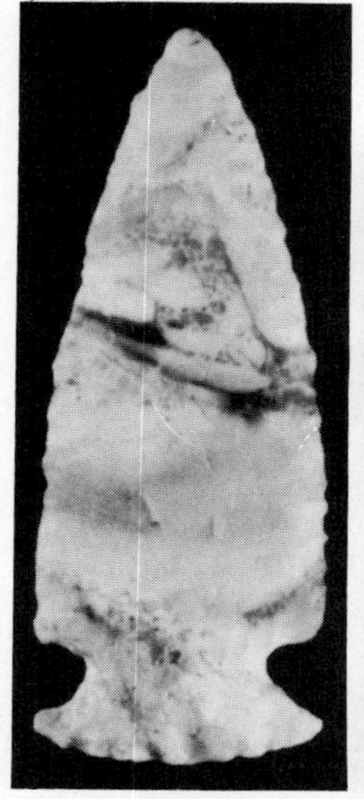

G5, $25-$40
AR.

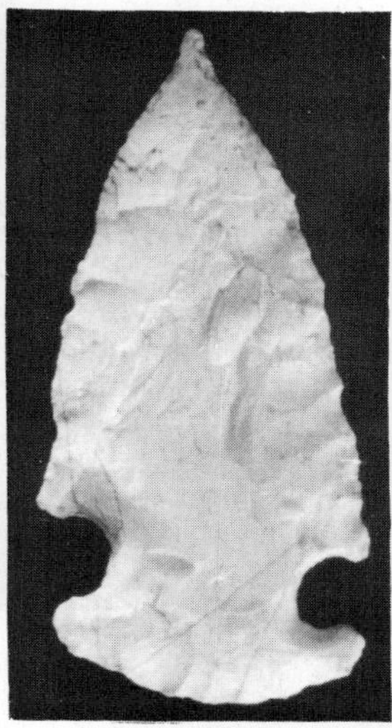

G7, $50-$80
Comanche Co., TX.

G10, $180-$300
Blackjack, MO.

LOCATION: Midwestern to Eastern states. **DESCRIPTION:** A medium to large size side to corner notched point with a large, convex base.

GIBSON (continued)

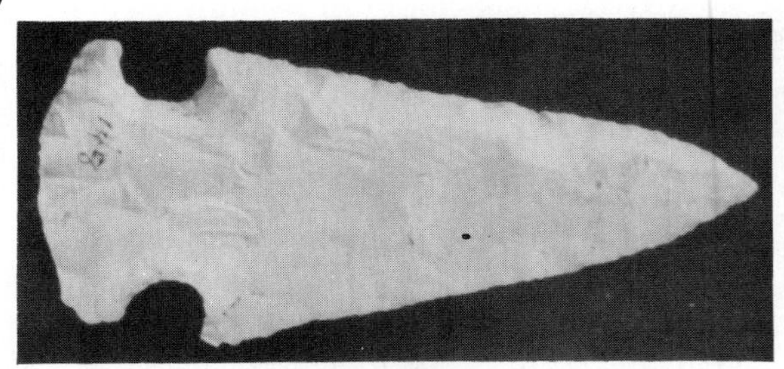

G8, $50-$85
IL.

G7, $40-$60
Walworth Co., WI.

GILCHRIST - Early Archaic, 10000 - 7000 B.P.

(Also see Buzzard Roost Creek, Coldwater and Taylor)

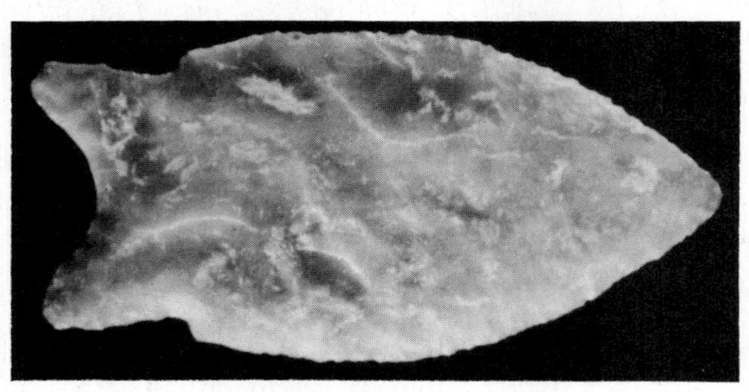

G10, $500-$800
Pasco Co., FL.

LOCATION: Southern Southeastern states. **DESCRIPTION:** A small to medium size, broad point with a short stem that is square, bifurcated or auriculate. Shoulders are weak and can be tapered, horizontal or slightly barbed. The base can be straight or concave and could be ground. Early forms may be related to *Suwanee*.

GODAR - Late Archaic, 4500 - 3500 B.P.

(Also see Big Sandy, Hemphill, Osceola, Otter Creek, Raddatz, Rowan & Savage Cave)

GODAR (continued)

G7, $45-$70
SW KY.

G4, $3-$5
Jonesboro, AR.

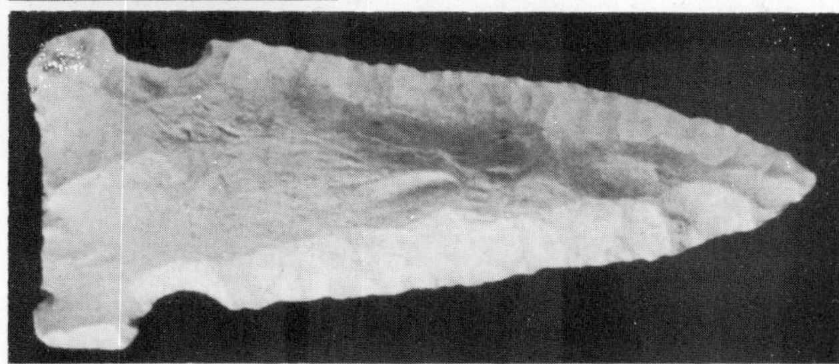

G6, $15-$25
Humphreys Co., TN.

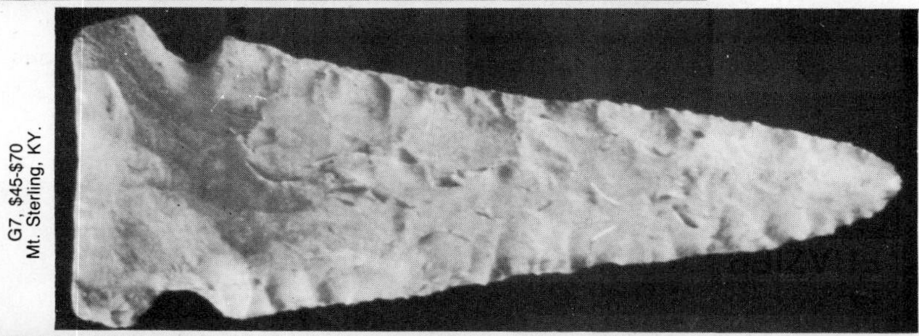

G7, $45-$70
Mt. Sterling, KY.

G7, $45-$70. WI. Note oblique flaking.

LOCATION: Midwestern states. **DESCRIPTION:** A medium to large size, narrow to wide, side-notched point with a straight to rounded base. Some examples show parallel flaking.

GODAR (continued)

G9, $150-$250, AR. Deep red chert.

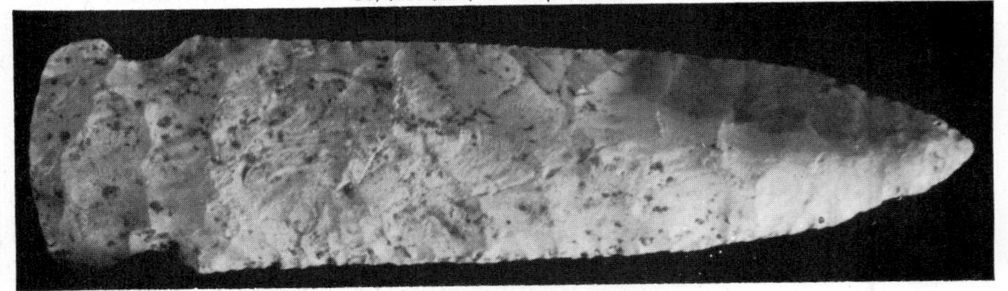

G8, $80-$120, Dyersburg, TN.

GODLEY - Late Archaic to Woodland, 4000 - 1500 B.P.

(Also see Durst, Ellis, Macpherson, San Pedro and Swan Lake)

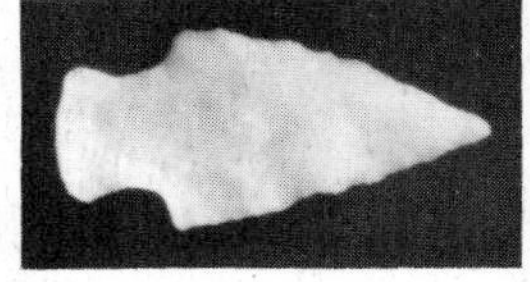

G2, $2-$3
Comanche Co., TX.

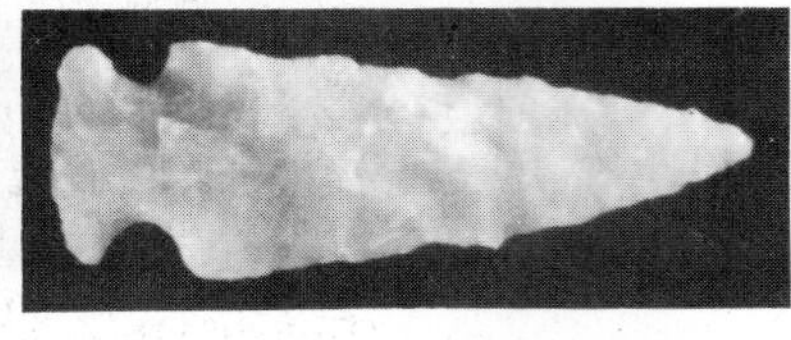

G3, $3-$5
Comanche Co., TX.

G5, $8-$12
Comanche Co., TX.

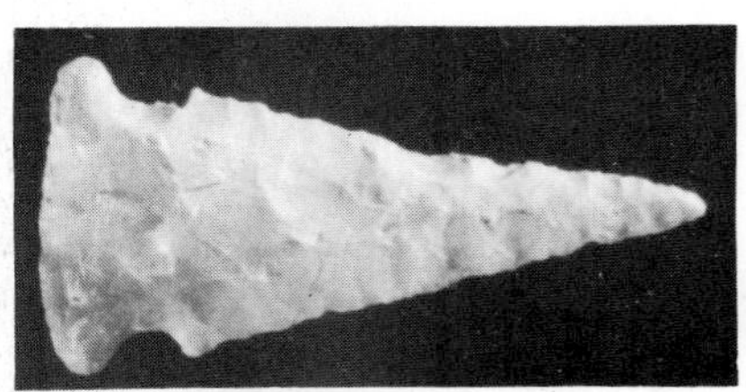

G4, $5-$8
Comanche Co., TX.

G3, $3-$5
Waco, TX. broken & Glued.

LOCATION: Midwestern to Southeastern states. **DESCRIPTION:** A small to medium size point with broad, expanding side-notches and a convex base.

GOLONDRINA - Transitional Paleo, 9000 - 7000 B.P.

(Also see Angostura, Beaver Lake, Clovis Unfluted, Dalton, Jeff, Midland, Simpson, Suwanee and Quad)

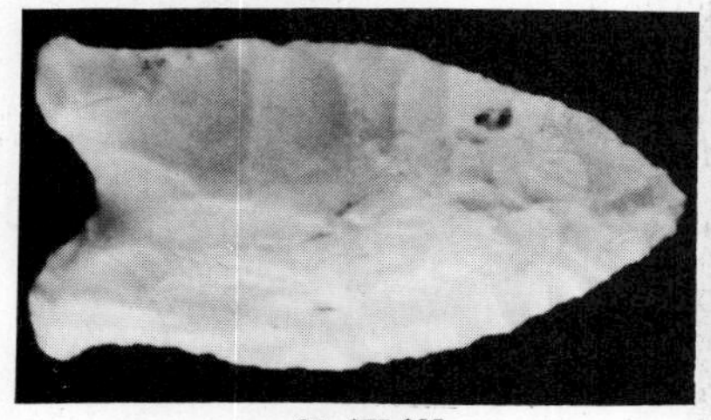

G5, $75-$85
TN/KY.

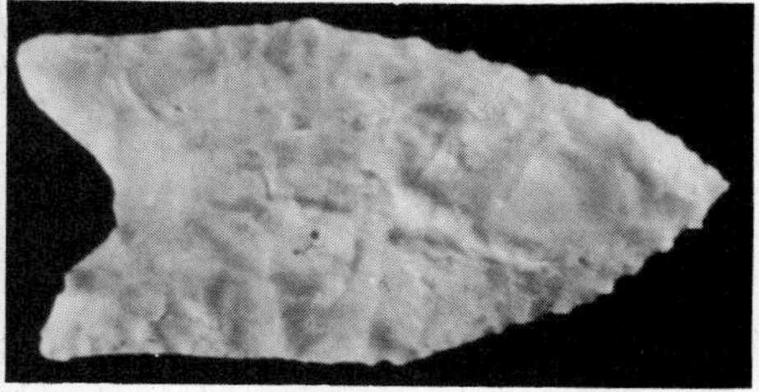

G7, $100-$125
Craighead, AR.

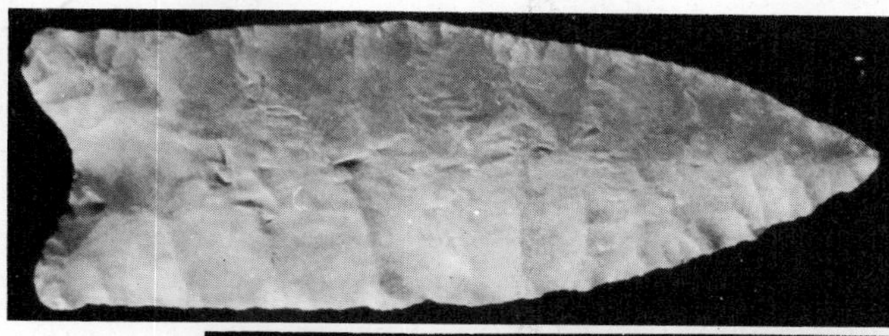

G8, $200-$250
Dyersburg, TN. Horizontal, transverse flaking.

G10, $350-$500
Adams Co., IL.

G10, $350-$500
Friendship Co., AR.

LOCATION: Midwestern states. **DESCRIPTION:** A medium to large size auriculate point with rounded ears and a deeply concave base. Believed to be related to *Dalton*. **I.D. KEY:** Expanded ears, paleo flaking.

GOWER - Early Archaic, 8000 - 5000 B.P.

(Also see Jetta, Pinto Basin & Uvalde)

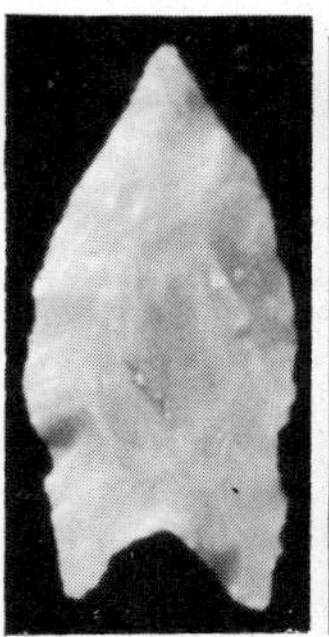

G4, $15-$25
Comanche Co., TX.

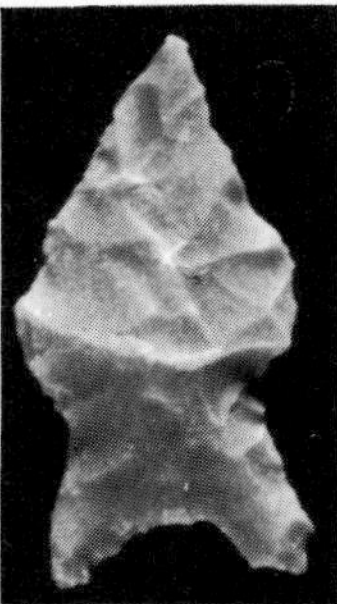

G4, $15-$25
Comanche Co., TX.

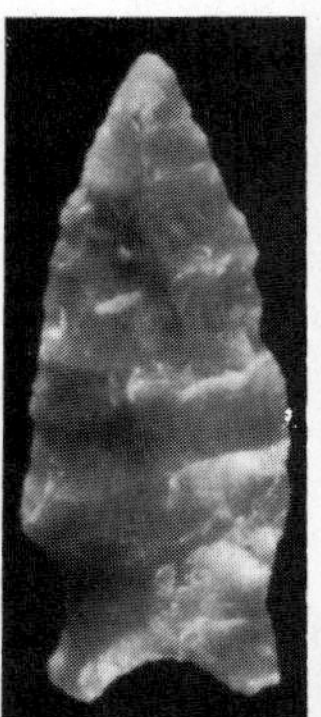

G6, $25-$40
Comanche Co., TX.

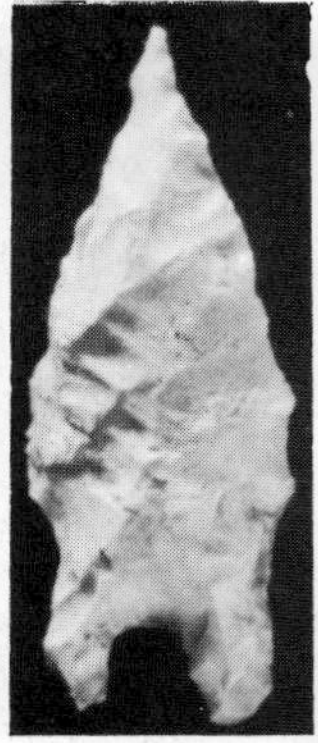

G5, $20-$30
Comanche Co., TX.

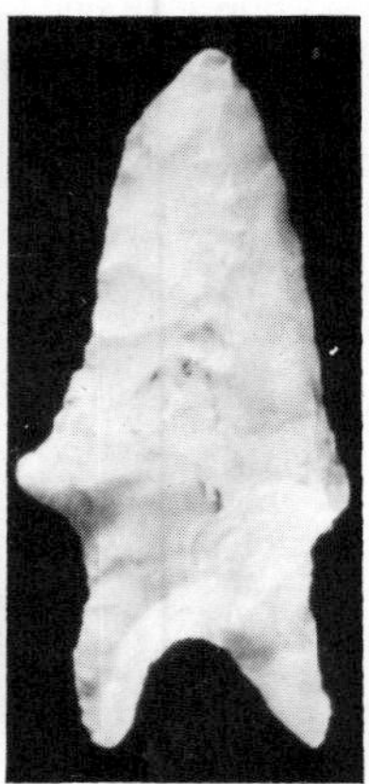

G6, $35-$45
Comanche Co., TX.

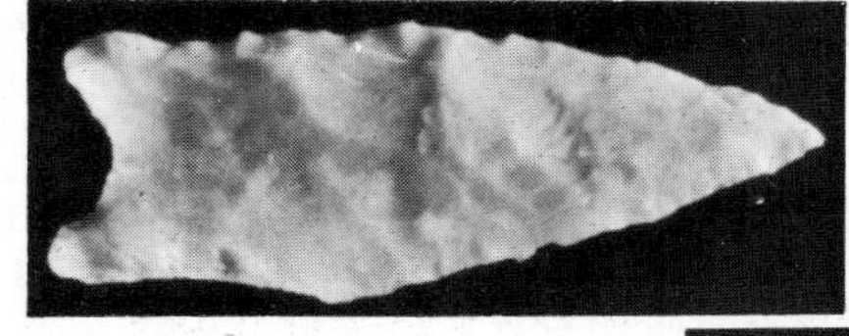

G6, $30-$50
Comanche Co., TX.

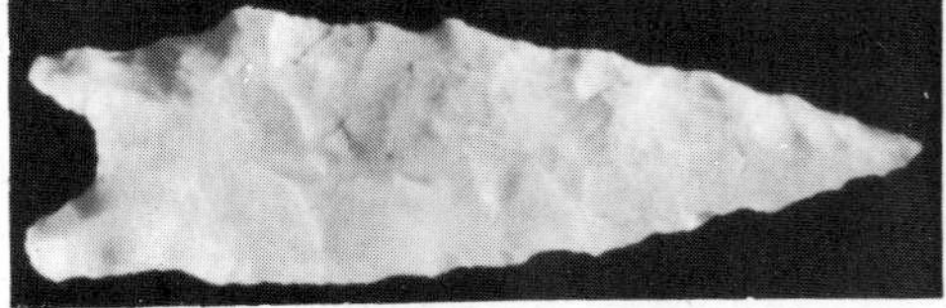

G7, $50-$80
Comanche Co., TX.

LOCATION: Midwestern states. **DESCRIPTION:** A medium size, narrow point with weak shoulders and a deeply bifurcated base. One or both Basal ears may turn inward.

GRAHAM CAVE - Transitional Paleo to mid-Archaic, 9000 - 5000 B.P.

(Also see Big Sandy, Oxbow, Raddatz and Rowan)

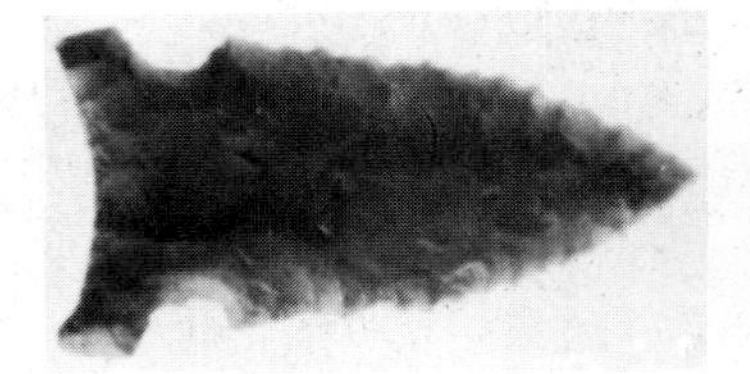

G6, $25-$40
Clarksville, TN.

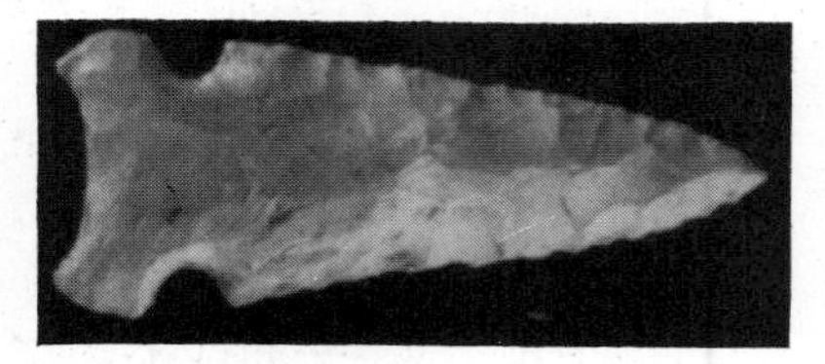

G6, $25-$40
Graham, MO.

LOCATION: Midwestern states. **DESCRIPTION:** A medium to large size, narrow, side-notched point with recurved sides, pointed auricles, and a concave base. Rarely, examples have been found fully fluted.

GRAHAM CAVE (continued)

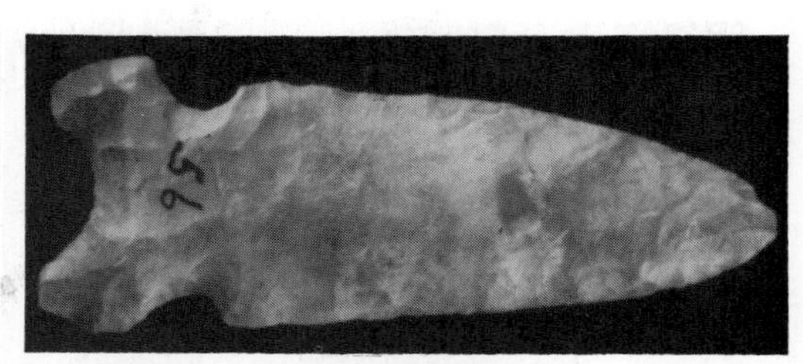

G5, $20-$25, IL.

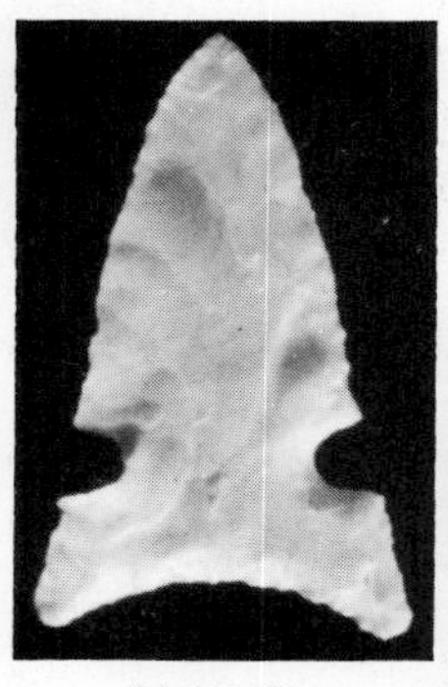

G4, $20-$30
TN.

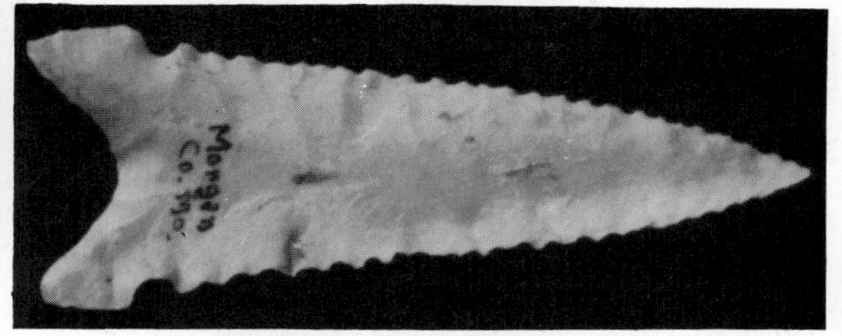

G9, $250-$400, Morgan Co., MO.

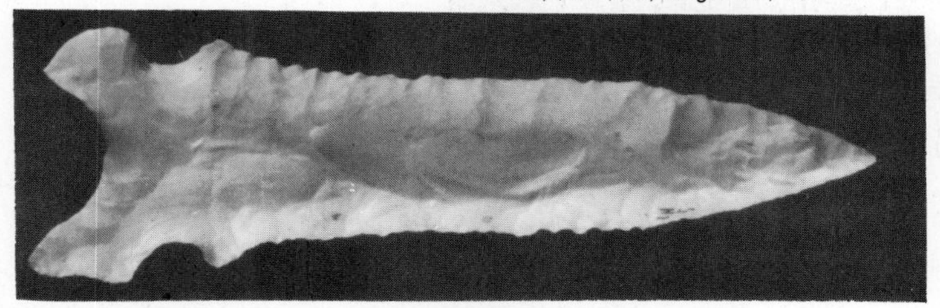

G8, $180-$300, Peoria, IL.

G9, $250-$400, McClean Co., IL.

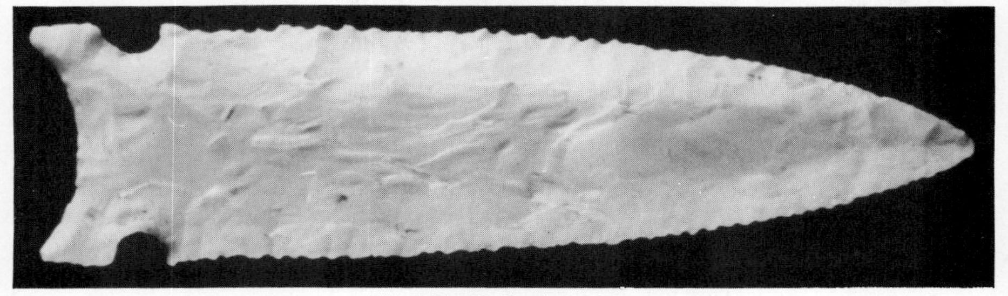

G10, $300-$500, Lincoln Co., MO.

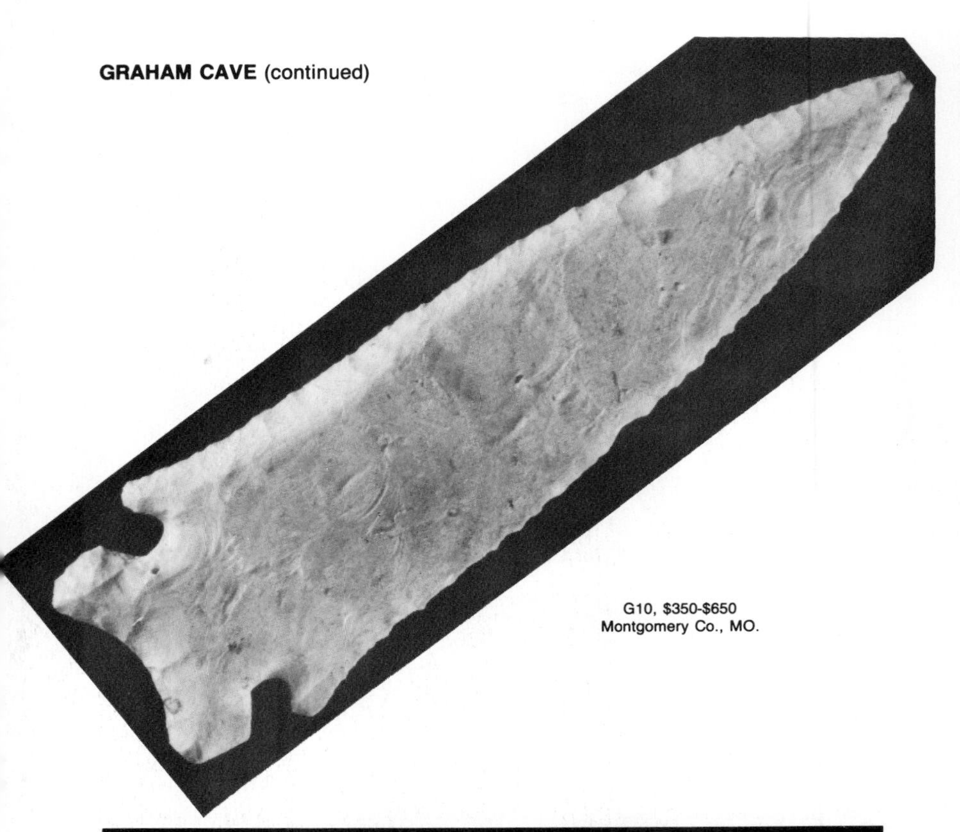

G10, $350-$650
Montgomery Co., MO.

GRAVER - Paleo to Archaic, 15000 - 4000 B.P.

(Also see Perforator and Scraper)

$2-$4
Dunlap, TN.

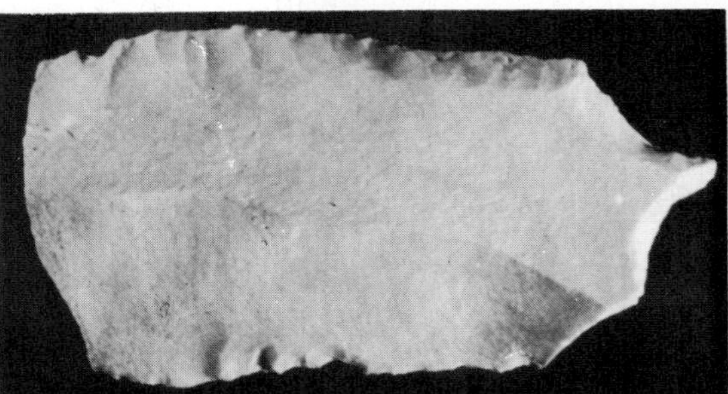

$4-$6
Humphreys Co., TN.

LOCATION: Found on Paleo and Archaic sites everywhere. **DESCRIPTION:** An irregular shaped uniface tool with sharp, pointed projections used for puncturing, incising, tatooing, etc. Some examples served a dual purpose for scraping as well. In later times, *Perforators* took the place of *Gravers*.

GRAVER (continued)

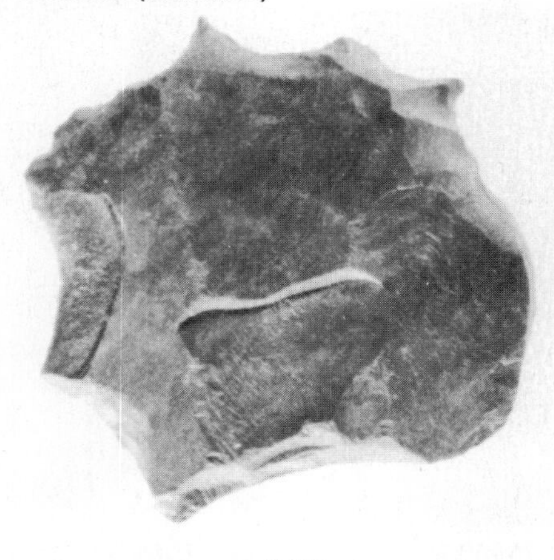

$8-$12
Humphreys Co., TN.

$8-$12
Humphreys Co., TN.

GREENBRIER- Transitional Paleo, 9500 - 6000 B.P.

(Also see Dalton-Greenbrier, Hardaway, Osceola-Greenbrier and Pine Tree)

G6, $80-$120
Parsons, TN. Fine quality & color. Buffalo River chert. Note basal thinning.

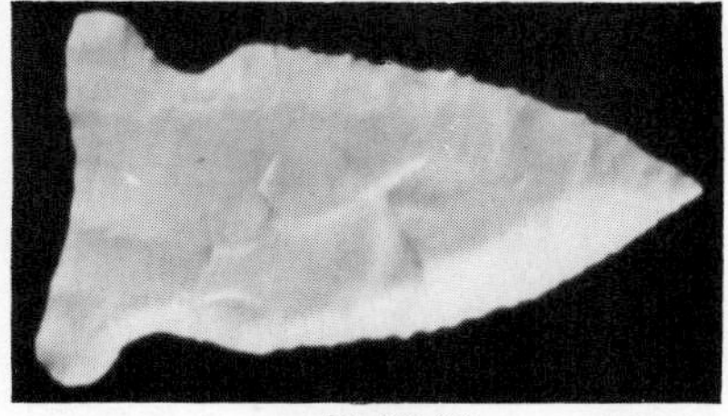

G4, $20-$35
Lauderdale Co., AL.

G5, $45-$60
Parsons, TN.

G5, $40-$65
MO. Nice color.

LOCATION: Southeastern states. **DESCRIPTION:** A medium to large size, Auriculate point with tapered shoulders and broad, weak side notches. Blade edges are usually finely serrated. The base can be concave, lobbed, eared, straight or bifurcated and is ground. Early examples can be fluted. This type developed from the *Dalton* point as well as directly from the *Clovis* point, and later evolved into other types such as the *Pine Tree* point. **I.D. KEY:** Heavy grinding in shoulders, good secondary edgework.

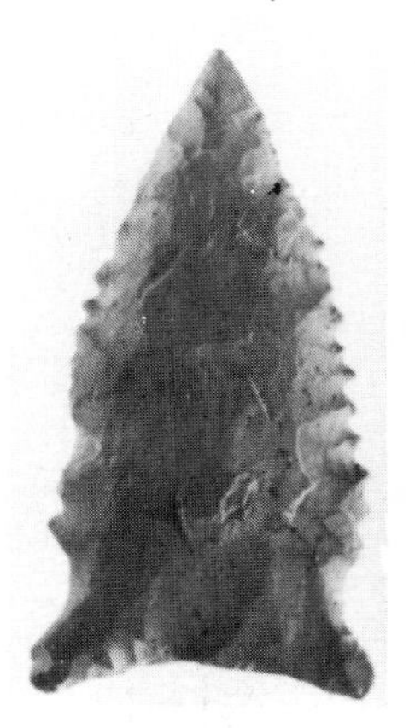

G3, $15-$20
Hardin Co., TN. Side nick.

G7, $70-$100
Hardin Co., TN. Note fine serrations.

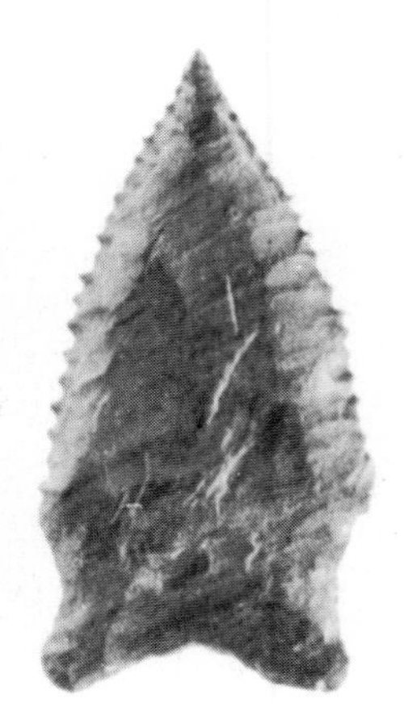

G5, $35-$60
Humphreys Co., TN.
Dover chert.

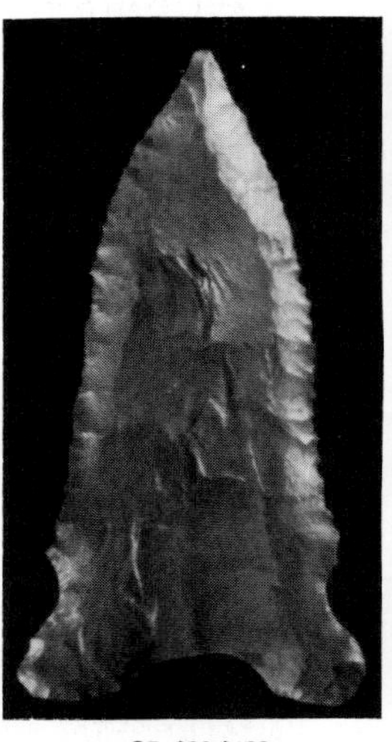

G7, $80-$120
Florence, AL. Coffee Lake.

G6, $60-$100
Saltillo, TN. Vertical yellow stripe.

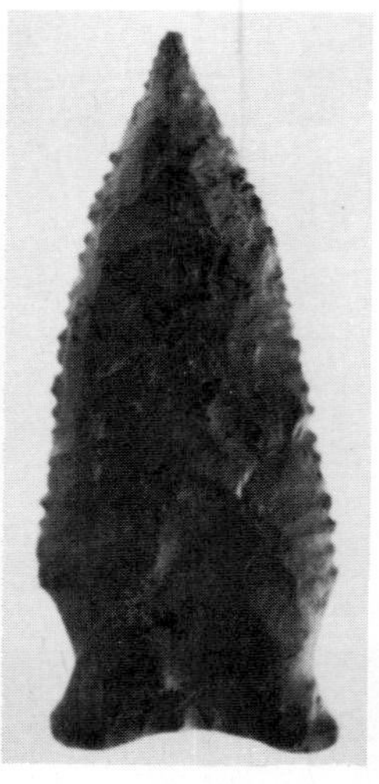

G6, $50-$80
Florence, AL. Coffee Lake.

G8, $150-$250
Florence, AL. Coffee Lake. Outstanding quality with fine serrations and a needle tip. Fort Payne chert.

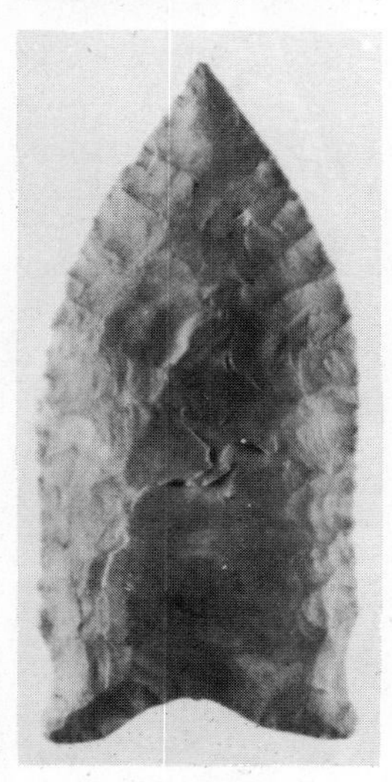

G8, $250-$400
W. TN. Fluted & excellent.

G7, $80-$120
Humphreys Co., TN. Dover chert.

G7, $90-$150
Humphreys Co., TN. Needle tip, excellent quality.

G8, $200-$300
Parsons, TN. High quality dark Dover chert.

G9, $350-$600
Perry Co., TN. Excellent.

G7, $100-$150
Humphreys Co., TN.

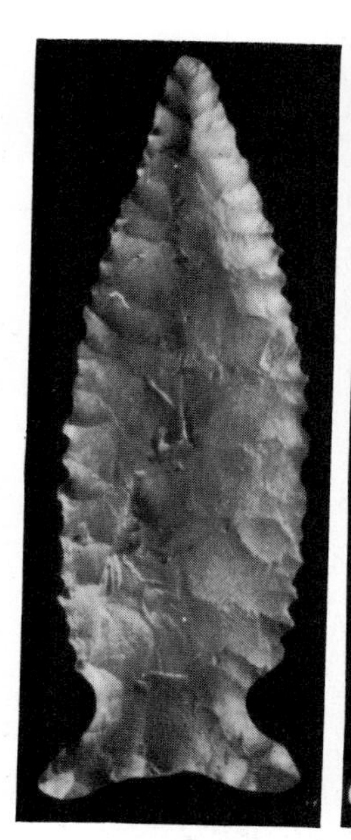

G7, $90-$160
Florence, AL. Coffee Lake.

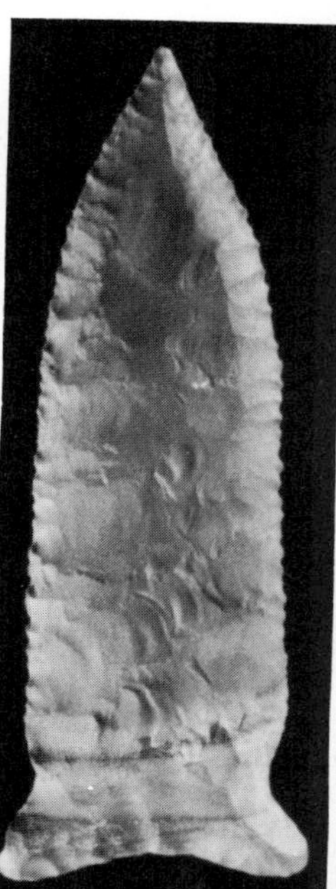

G10, $600-$1000
Hardin Co., TN. Color.

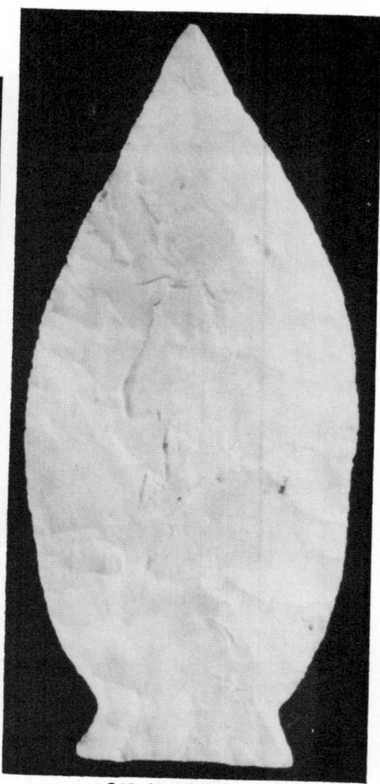

G10, $800-$1200
Saltillo, TN. 1st stage form.

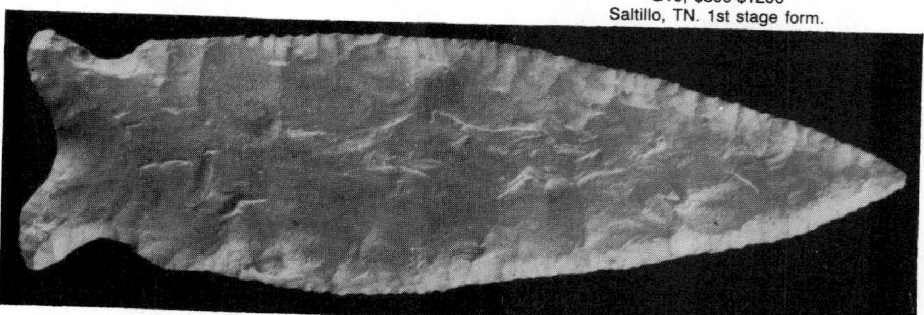

G10, $1200-$2000, Hardin Co., TN Note fine edgework. Classic.

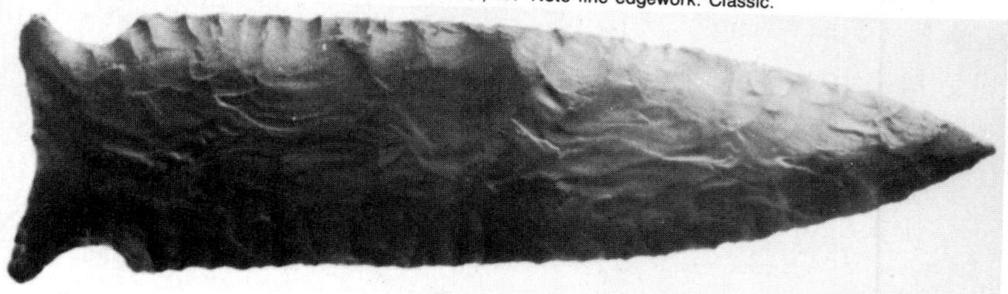

G10, $750-$1000, Parsons, TN. Very rare in this size. Classic form and excellent quality. Pink chert.

G10, $1200-$2000
Hardin Co., TN.

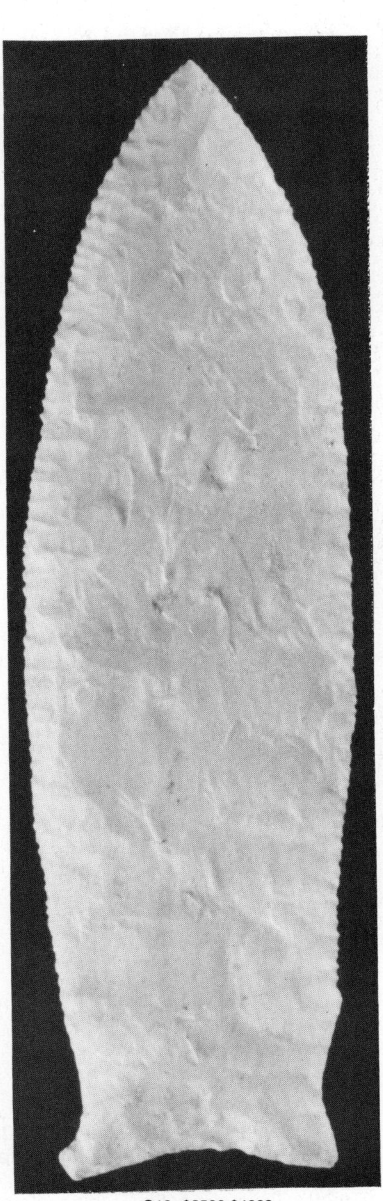
G10, $2500-$4000
Nebo, IL. Very rare size.

GREENEVILLE - Woodland, 3000 - 1500 B.P.

(Also see Camp Creek, Guntersville, Madison, Maud, Nolichucky & Shetley)

G4, $4-$6
SE TN.

G6, $6-$10
Humphreys Co., TN.

G7, $12-$20
Parsons, TN.

G6, $6-$10
Davidson Co., NC.

G8, $20-$35
Bristol, TN.

G5, $5-$8
Coffee Lake, AL.

G8, $20-$35
Florence, AL.

G10, $45-$70
Humphreys Co., TN. Classic.

G9, $50-$70
Dayton, TN.

LOCATION: Southeastern states. **DESCRIPTION:** A small to medium size lanceolate point with convex sides becoming contracting to parallel at the base. The basal edge is slightly concave, convex or straight. This point is usually wider and thicker than *Guntersville*, and is believed to be related to *Camp Creek, Ebenezer* and *Nolichucky points.*

GUERRERO - Historic, 300 - 100 B.P.

(Also see Greeneville and Guntersville)

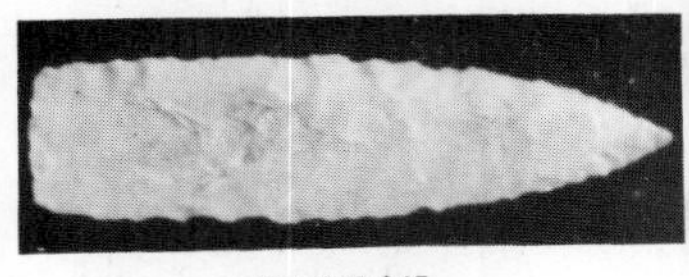

G8, $30-$45
Comanche Co., TX.

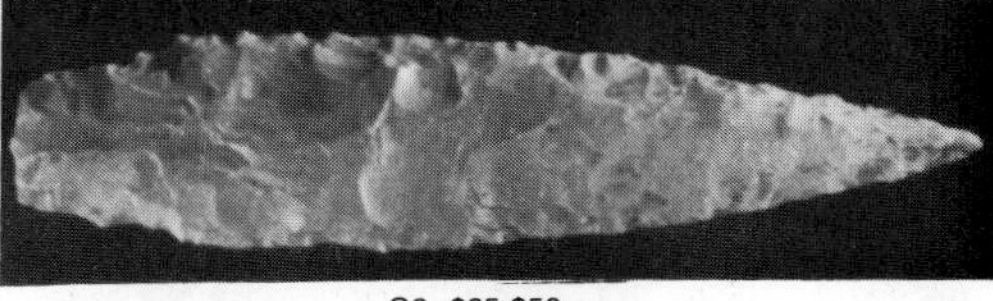

G9, $35-$50
Comanche Co., TX.

LOCATION: Texas. **DESCRIPTION:** A small to medium size, narrow, thin, lanceolate point with a straight base. Similar to the Eastern *Guntersville* point.

GUILFORD-ROUND BASE - Mid-Archaic, 6500 - 5000 B.P.

(Also see Agate Basin, Angostura, Browns Valley, Lerma, Pelona, Plainview and Sedalia)

G2, $1-$2
Spartanburg Co., SC. Crystal.

G3, $1-$3
Fairfield Co., SC. Vein quartz.

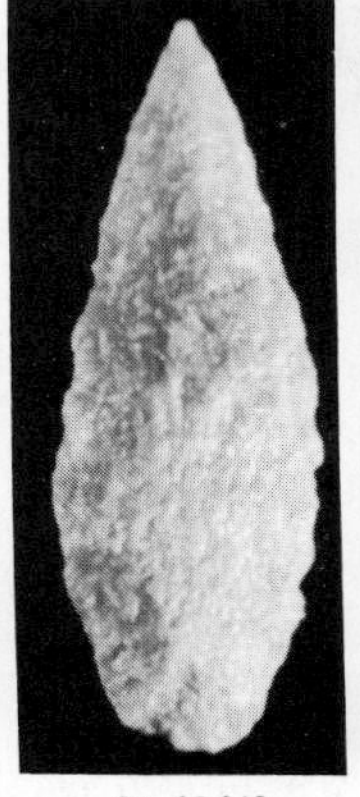

G5, $6-$10
Sussex Co., VA. Quartzite.

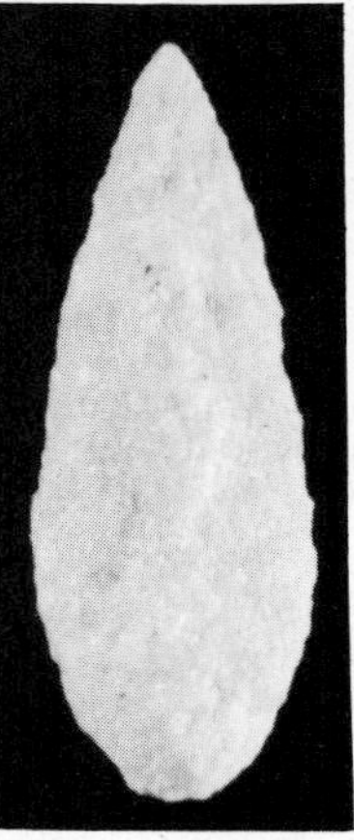

G7, $10-$15
Sussex Co., VA.

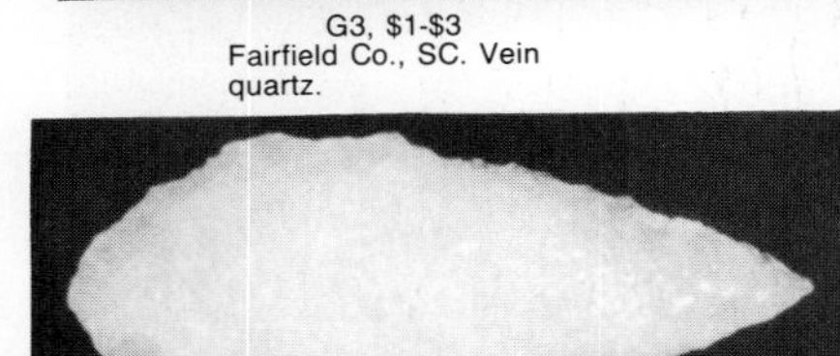

G4, $2-$4
Union Co., SC. Milky quartz.

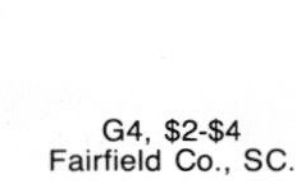

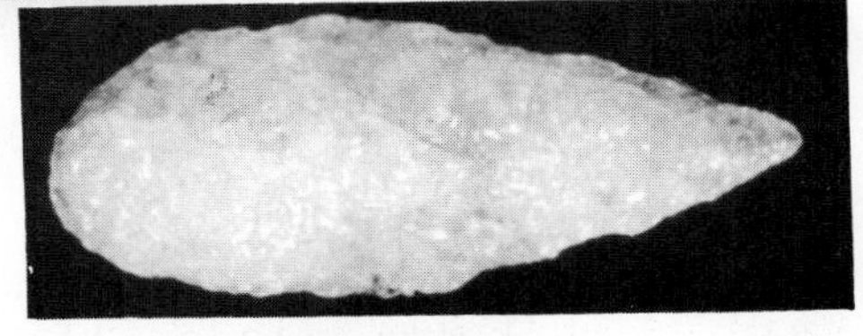

G4, $2-$4
Fairfield Co., SC.

LOCATION: North Carolina and surrounding area. **DESCRIPTION:** A medium to large size, thick, narrow, lanceolate point with a convex, contracting base. This type is usually made of quartzite or other poor quality flaking material which results in a more crudely chipped form than *Lerma* (its ancestor). **I.D. KEY:** Thickness, Archaic blade flaking.

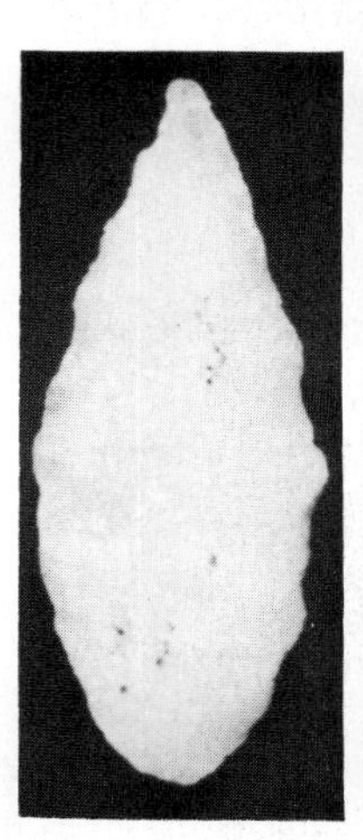

G4, $2-$4
Newberry Co., SC. Milky quartz.

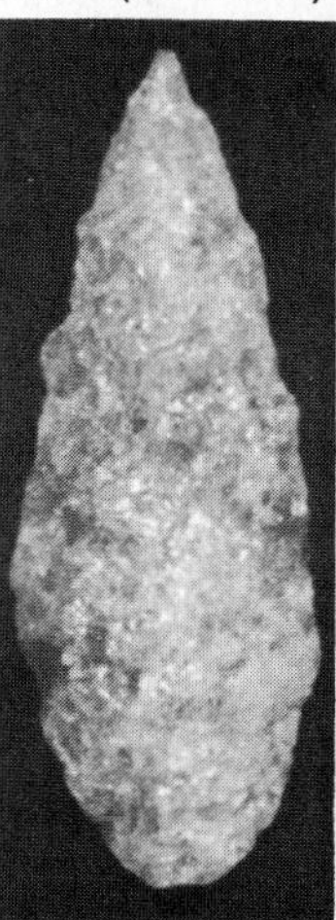

G4, $2-$4
Newberry Co., SC. Sugar quartz.

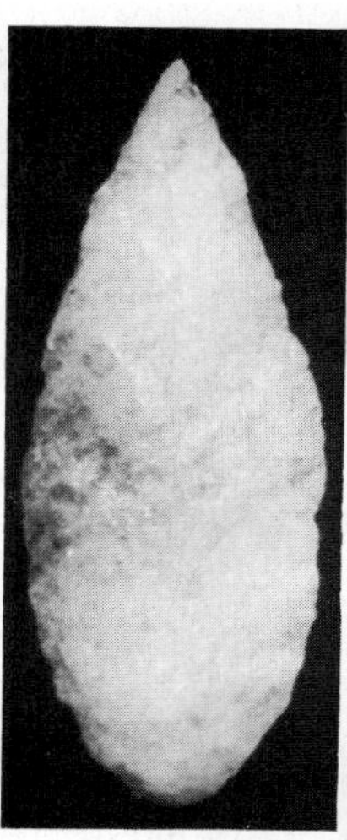

G5, $6-$10
Fairfield Co., SC.

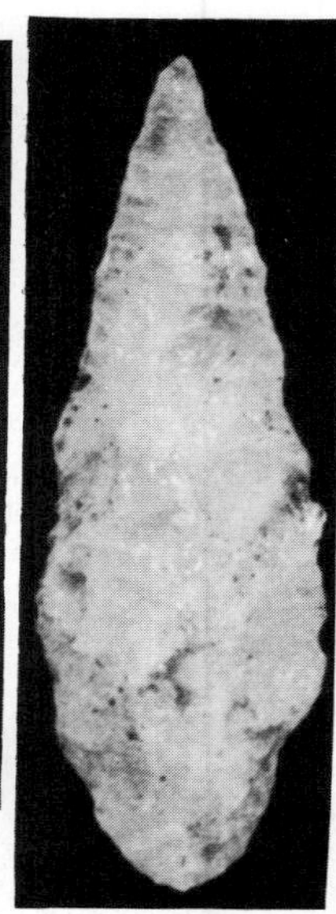

G6, $8-$12
Fairfield Co., SC.
Vein quartz.

G6, $8-$12
Chester Co., SC. Slate with quartz vein. Tip nick.

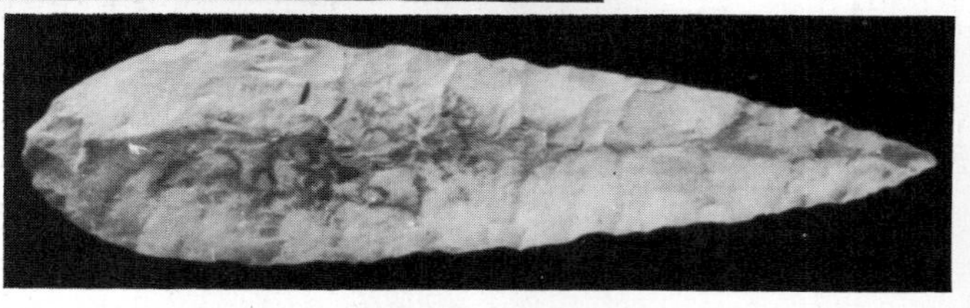

G9, $20-$30
Anderson Co., SC.

GUILFORD-STEMMED - Mid-Archaic, 6500 - 5000 B.P.

(Also see Angostura and Pinto Basin)

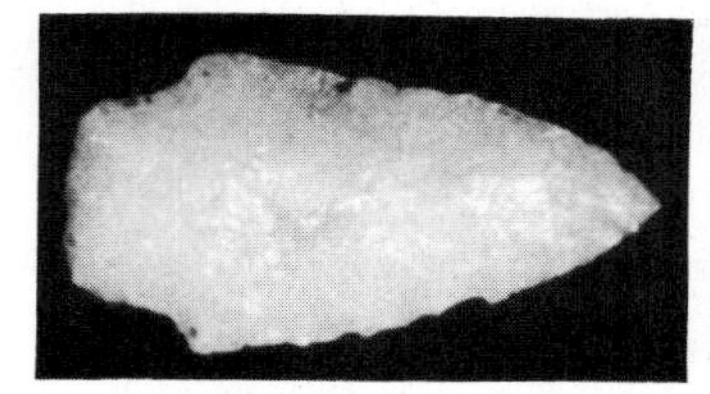

G2, $1-$2
Newberry Co., SC. Quartz.

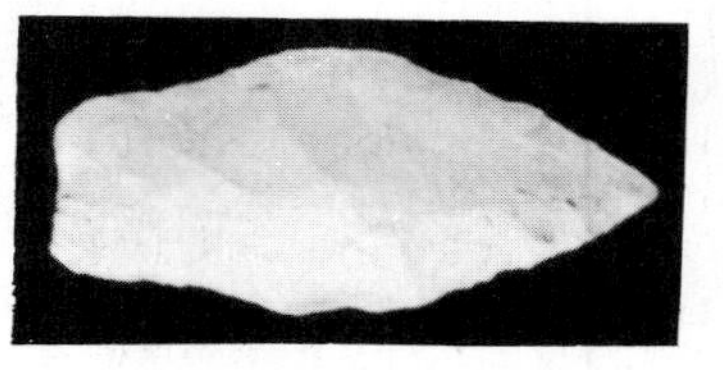

G3, $1-$3
Sussex Co., VA.

GUILFORD-STEMMED (continued)

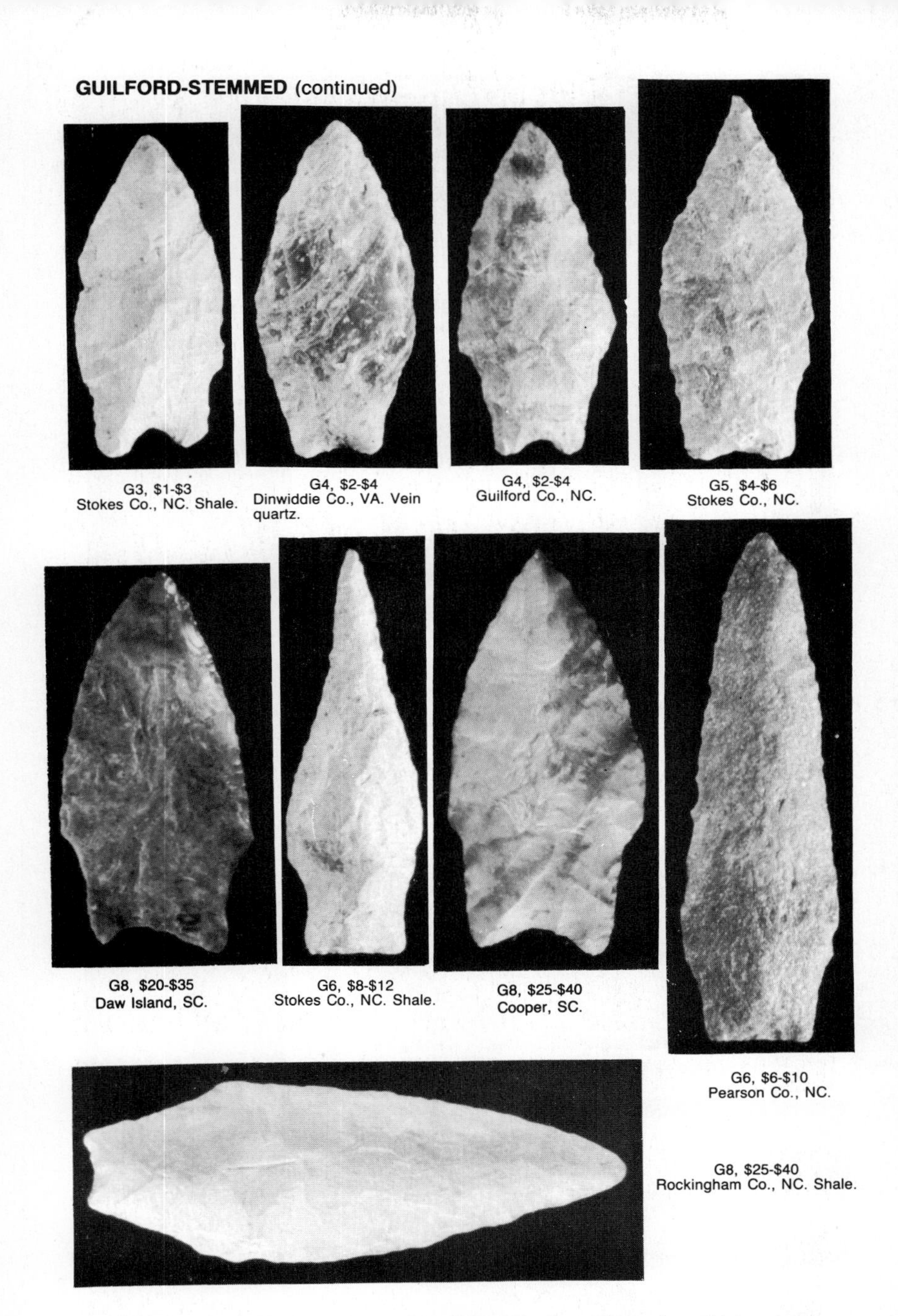

G3, $1-$3
Stokes Co., NC. Shale.

G4, $2-$4
Dinwiddie Co., VA. Vein quartz.

G4, $2-$4
Guilford Co., NC.

G5, $4-$6
Stokes Co., NC.

G8, $20-$35
Daw Island, SC.

G6, $8-$12
Stokes Co., NC. Shale.

G8, $25-$40
Cooper, SC.

G6, $6-$10
Pearson Co., NC.

G8, $25-$40
Rockingham Co., NC. Shale.

LOCATION: Far Eastern states. **DESCRIPTION:** A medium size, thick, narrow, lanceolate point with a straight to concave, contracting base. All examples have weak shoulders. Some bases are ground. Called *Briar Creek* in Georgia.

GUILFORD-STRAIGHT BASE - Mid-Archaic, 6500 - 5000 B.P.

(Also see Agate Basin, Angostura, Lerma and Pelona)

G5, $2-$4
Fairfield Co., SC. Milky quartz.

G9, $20-$30
Stokes Co., NC. Milky quartz.

G2, $1-$2
Newberry Co., SC. Vein quartz.

G7, $6-$10
Rowan Co., NC. Shale.

G8, $8-$15, Edgecombe Co., NC.

G9, $35-$45
Randolph Co., NC.

G8, $8-$12
Rockingham Co., NC.

LOCATION: Far Eastern states. **DESCRIPTION:** A medium size, thick, narrow, lanceolate point with a contracting stem and a straight base. This point is similar to *Greene* points, a later period New York Woodland type.

GUILFORD-STRAIGHT BASE (continued)

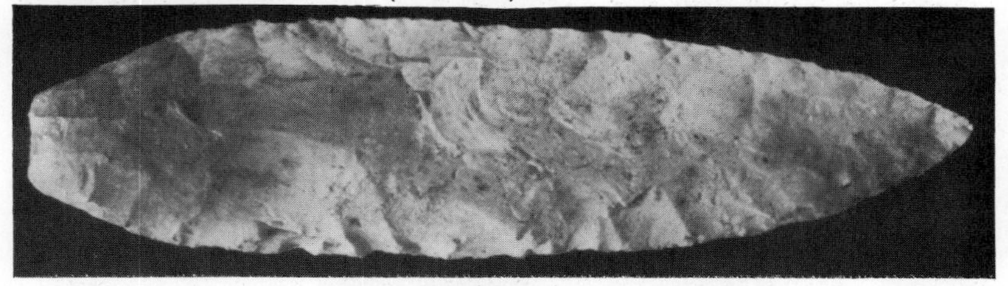

G10, $120-$220, Edgefield Co., SC. Excellent example.

GUILFORD-YUMA - Early Archaic, 7500 - 5000 B.P.

(Also see Agate Basin, Angostura, Conerly, Lerma, Plainview & Sedalia)

G3, $2-$4
Stokes Co., NC. Shaie.

G5, $6-$10
Randolph Co., NC.

G6, $10-$20
Allen Co., NC. Milky quartz.

G7, $20-$35
Stokes Co., NC. Milky quartz.

G9, $100-$150
Orangeburg Co., SC.

G10, $200-$300
Lake Marion, SC.

LOCATION: Far Eastern states. **DESCRIPTION:** A medium to slightly large size, thick, narrow, lanceolate point with a contracting stem and a concave base. Quality of flaking is governed by the type of material, usually quartzite, slate, rhyolite and shale. Bases can be ground. Believed to be an early form for the type and may be related to the *Conerly* type.

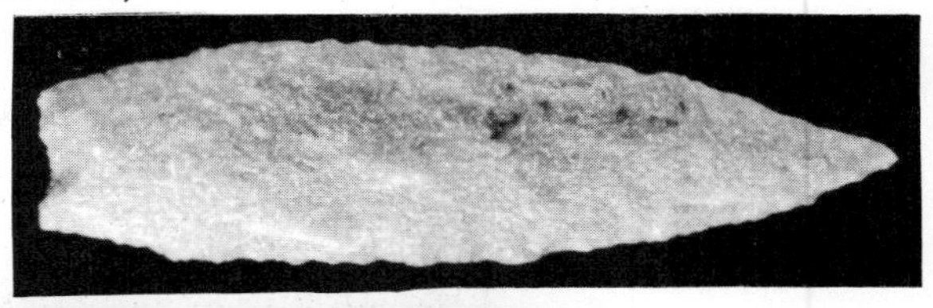

G8, $30-$50
Pearson Co., NC. Quartzite.

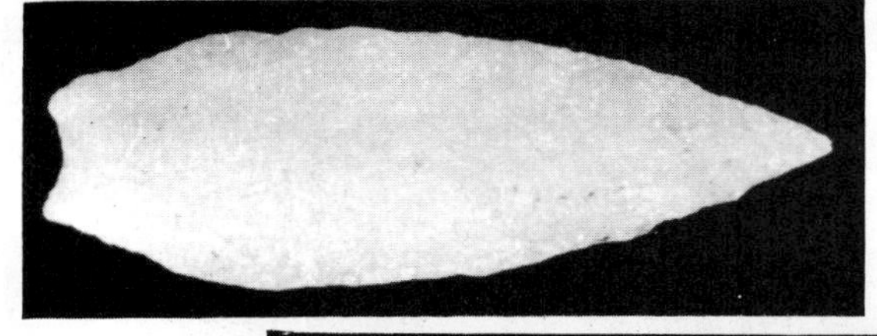

G7, $20-$35
Pearson Co., NC. Milky quartz.

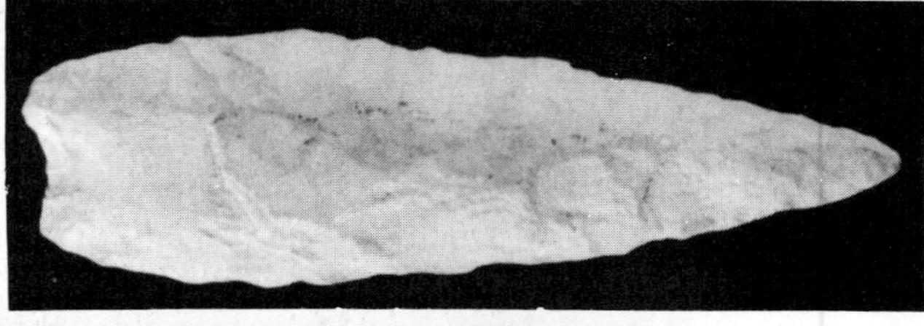

G7, $20-$35
Rowan Co., NC. Shale.

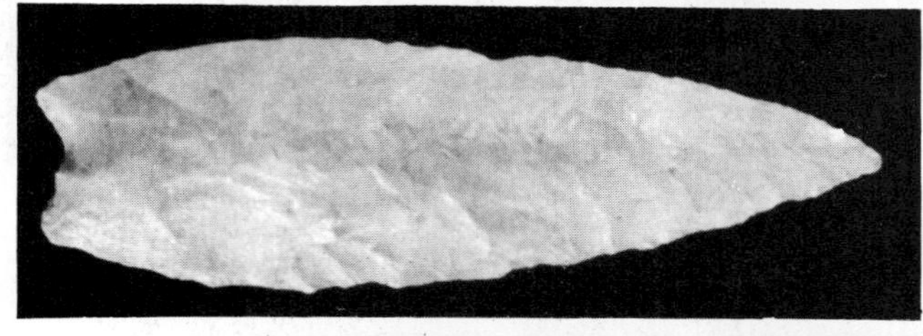

G8, $30-$50
NW NC.

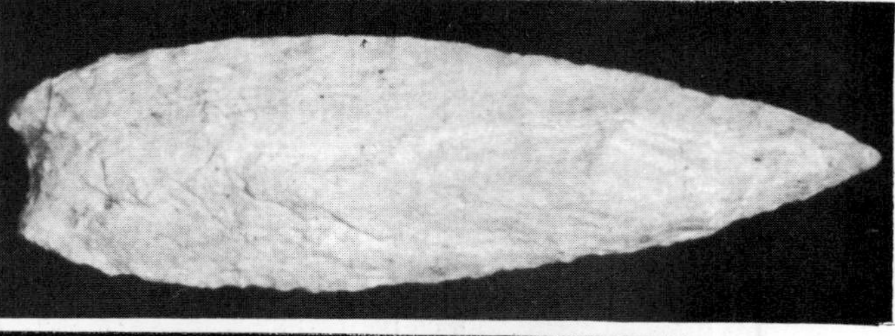

G8, $30-$50
Fairfield Co., SC. Banded shale.

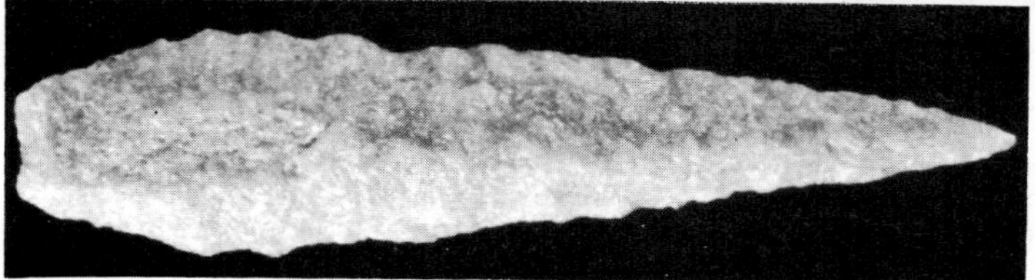

G9, $80-$120
Pearson Co., NC. Quartzite.

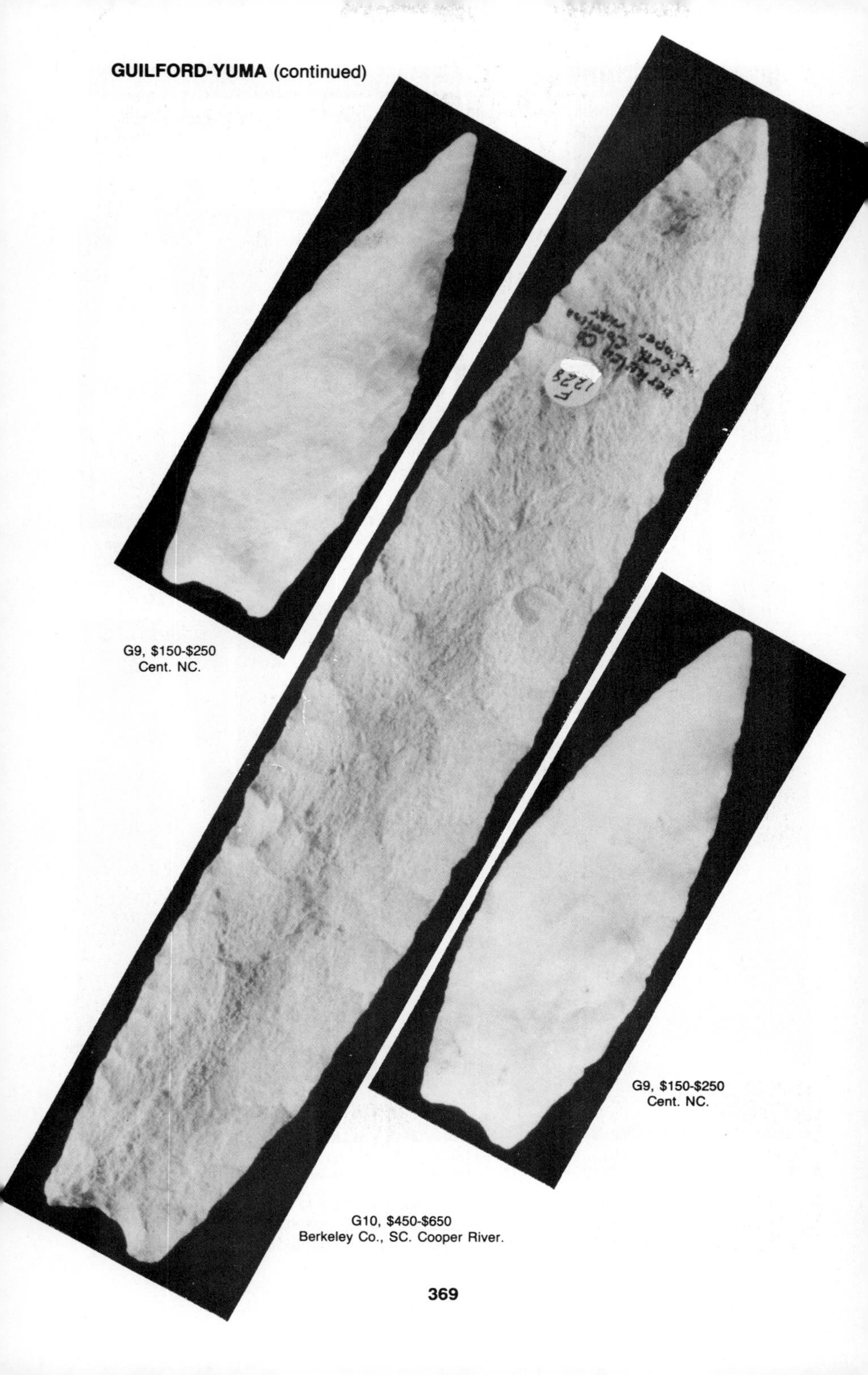

G9, $150-$250
Cent. NC.

G10, $450-$650
Berkeley Co., SC. Cooper River.

G9, $150-$250
Cent. NC.

GUNTERSVILLE - Mississippian to Historic, 700 - 200 B.P.

(Also see Camp Creek, Greeneville, Guerrero, Madison, Nodena and Shetley)

G3, $5-$8
Meigs Co., TN.

G5, $10-$20
Cherokee Co., AL.

G7, $35-$50
Cherokee Co., AL.

G7, $25-$40
Miss. Co., AR.

G7, $25-$40
Henry Co., AL.

G7, $20-$30
Marion Co., TN.

G9, $50-$80
Hamilton Co., TN.

G9, $50-$90
Humphreys Co., TN.

G10, $80-$120
Cherokee Co., AL.

G9, $35-$50
New Era, TN.

G9, $40-$60
Dayton, TN.

G6, $15-$25
Dayton, TN.

G7, $25-$40
Dayton, TN.

G9, $70-$100
Huntsville, AL.

LOCATION: Southeastern states. **DESCRIPTION:** A small to medium size, thin, narrow, lanceolate point with usually a straight base. Flaking quality is excellent. Formerly called *Dallas* points. **I.D. KEY:** Narrowness & blade expansion.

GUNTHER - Woodland to Historic, 2000 - 200 B.P.

(Also see Bonham, Deadman, John Day River, Rockwall & Sabinal)

G3, $5-$8
Columbia Rv., WA.

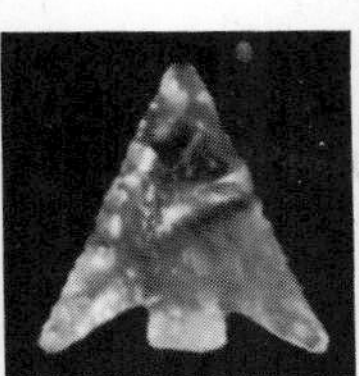
G2, $3-$5
Col. Rv., WA.

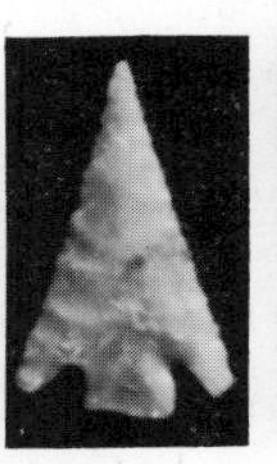
G4, $6-$10
OR.

G6, $25-$40
Col. Rv., WA.

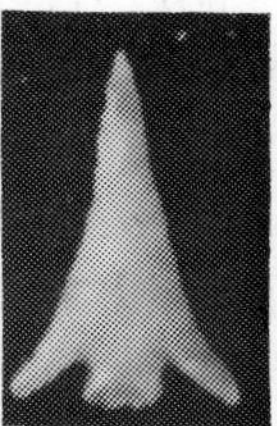
G6, $20-$30
Col. Rv., WA.

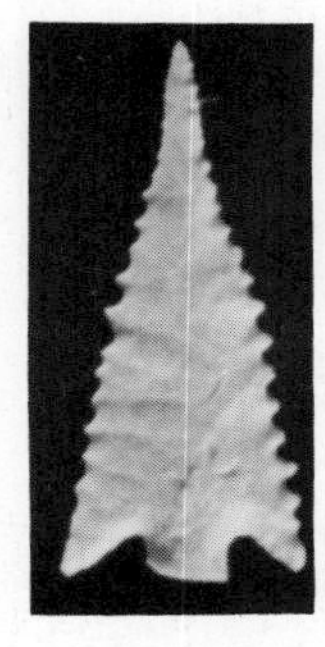
G6, $25-$40
Comanche Co., TX.
Snapped base.

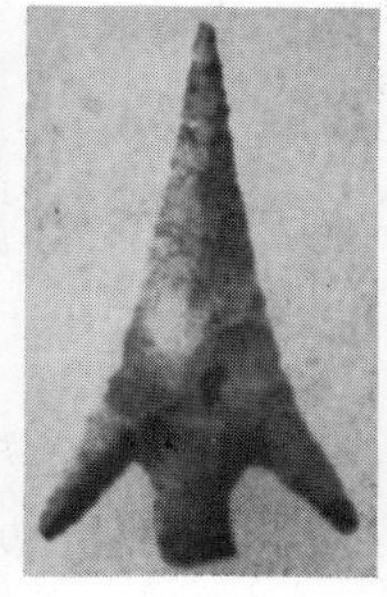
G6, $25-$40
Otero Co., NM.

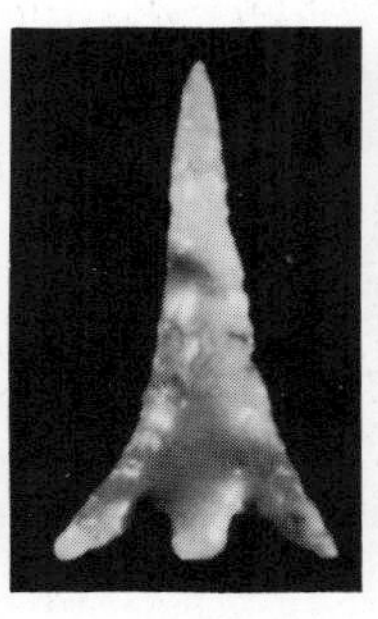
G6, $25-$40
Columbia Rv., WA.

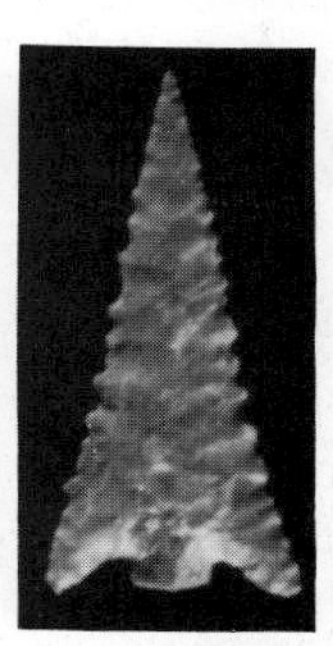
G6, $25-$40
Comanche Co., TX.
Snapped base.

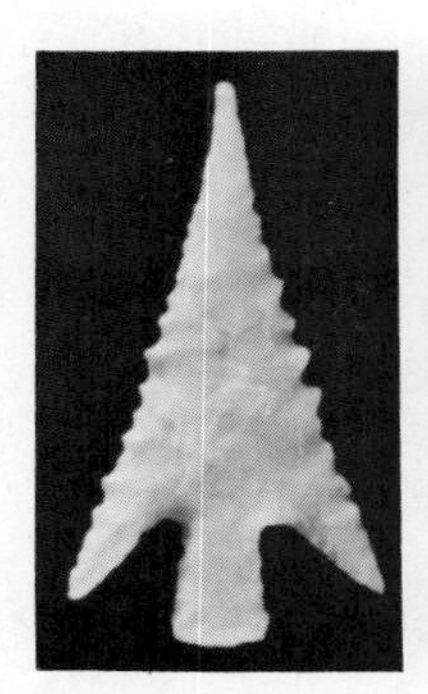
G10, $150-$250
Comanche Co., TX.

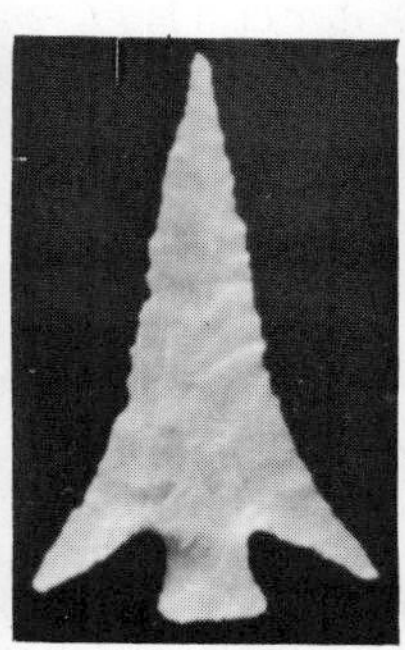
G10, $90-$150
Comanche Co., TX.

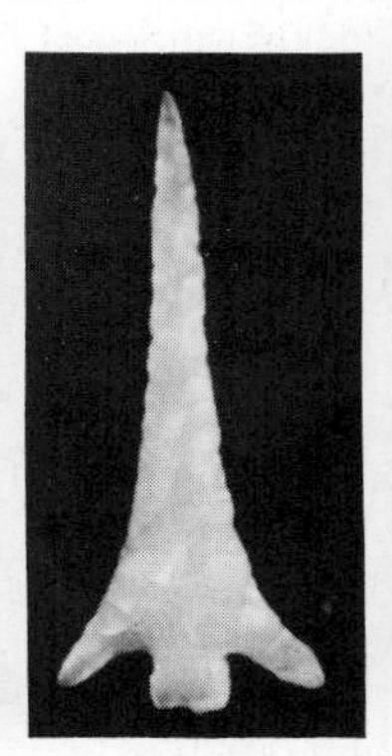
G9, $70-$100
Col. Rv., WA.

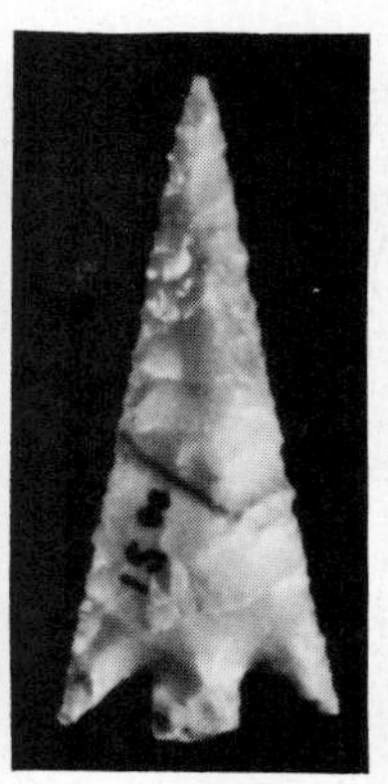
G7, $30-$50
Col. Rv., WA.

LOCATION: Western to Midwestern states. **DESCRIPTION:** A small to medium size, thin, broad, triangular point with long barbs that extend almost to the base. The blade sides are straight to concave and the stem is parallel sided to slightly expanding. These points exhibit high quality flaking.

GYPSUM CAVE - Early Archaic, 8000 - 5000 B.P.

(Also see Augustin, Gary, Kalapuyan, Morrow Mountain & Santa Cruz)

G4, $10-$12
WA/OR.

G7, $30-$50
OR. Agate.

G5, $15-$25
Mexico. Obsidian. Note collateral flaking.

G9, $75-$125
WA/OR. Note diagonal flaking.

G4, $10-$20
OR.

LOCATION: Western states. **DESCRIPTION:** A medium size, thin, triangular point with a contracting, pointed to rounded stem. Blade edges on some examples are concave and serrated. Both age and form are similar to *Morrow Mountain Rounded Base* points.

HALIFAX - Mid to Late-Archaic, 6000 - 3000 B.P.

(Also see Bakers Creek, Elam, Jude, Rheems Creek, Swan Lake and Trinity)

G1, .50-$1
Hinds Co., MS.

G1, .50-$1
Hinds Co., MS.

G2, $1-$2
Hinds Co., MS.

G4, $3-$5
Pearson Co., NC.

G2, $1-$2
Leflore Co., MS.

G2, $2-$3
Itawamba Co., MS.

G2, $1-$2
Southampton Co., VA.

G1, .25-.50
Walker Co., AL.

G2, $1-$2
Fairfield Co., SC.
Striped slate.

LOCATION: Southeastern states. **DESCRIPTION:** A small to medium size, narrow, side notched to expanded stemmed point. Shoulders can be weak to strongly tapered. Typically one shoulder is higher than the other. North Carolina examples are made of quartz, ryolite and shale.

HALIFAX (continued)

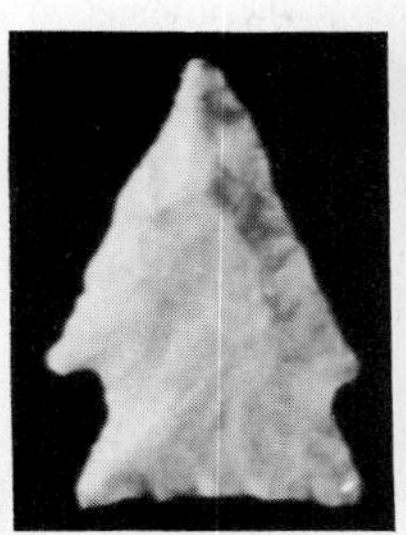
G3, $2-$3
Walker Co., AL.

G4, $5-$6
Meigs Co., TN.

G6, $6-$10
Sussex Co., VA.

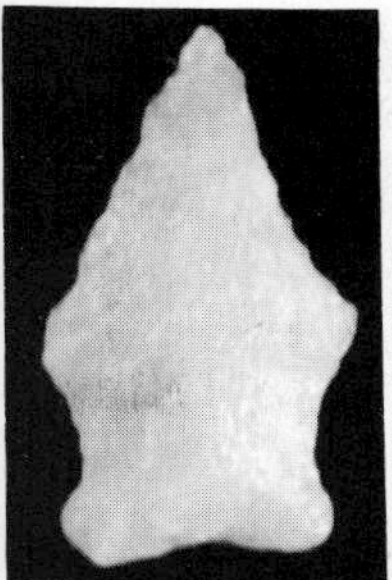
G3, $2-$3
Sussex Co., VA.
Milky quartz.

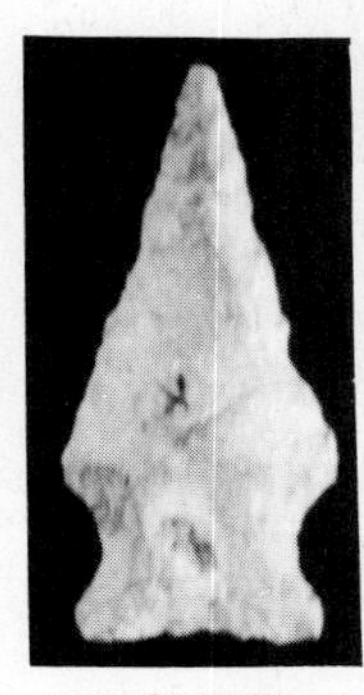
G4, $3-$5
Southampton Co., VA.

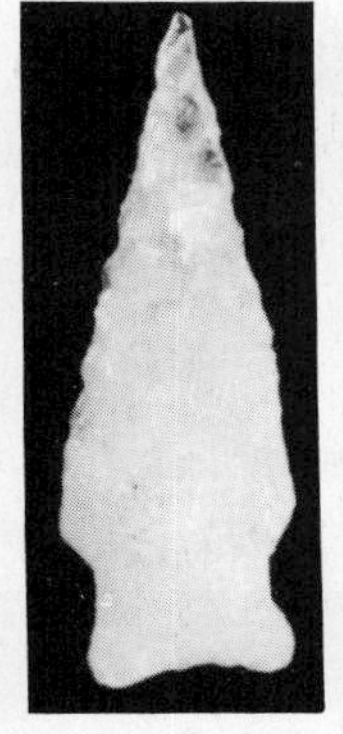
G7, $10-$20
Sussex Co., VA. Milky quartz.

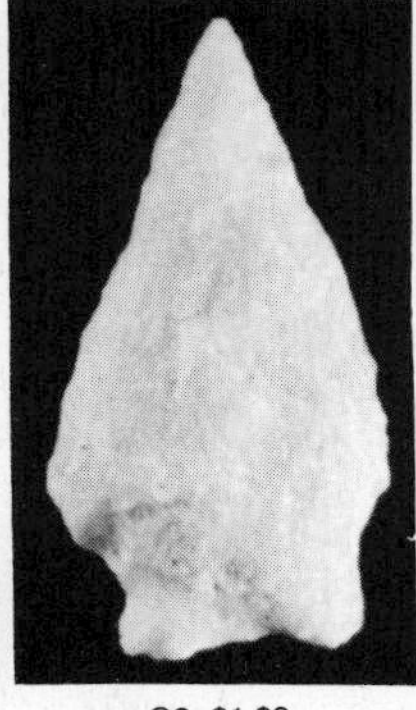
G2, $1-$2
Albermarle Co., VA.
Quartzite.

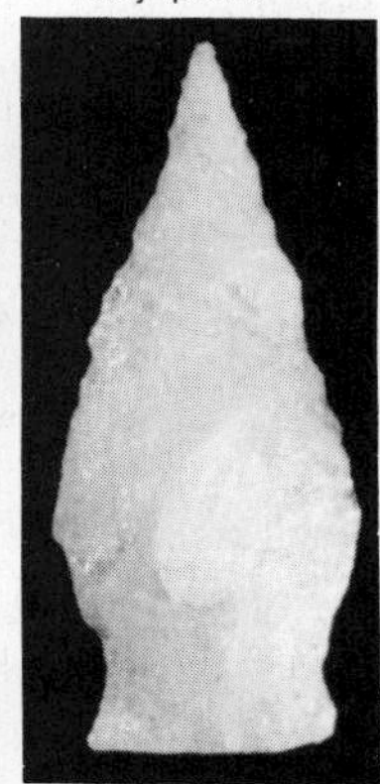
G6, $6-$10
Sussex Co., VA. Milky quartz.

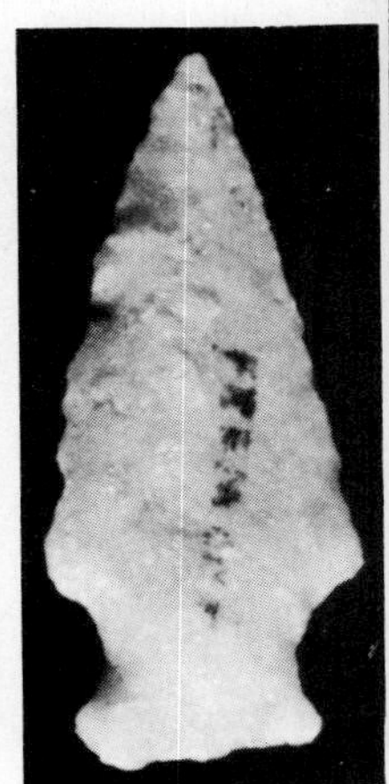
G5, $5-$7
Fremont, GA.

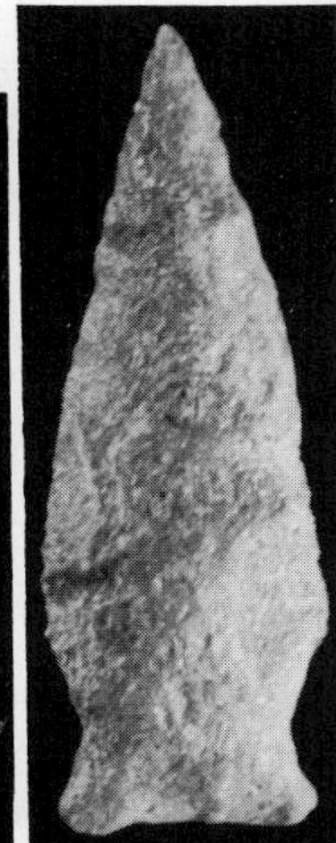
G9, $20-$35
Southampton Co., VA.
Quartzite.

G8, $15-$25
Sussex Co., VA. Quartzite.

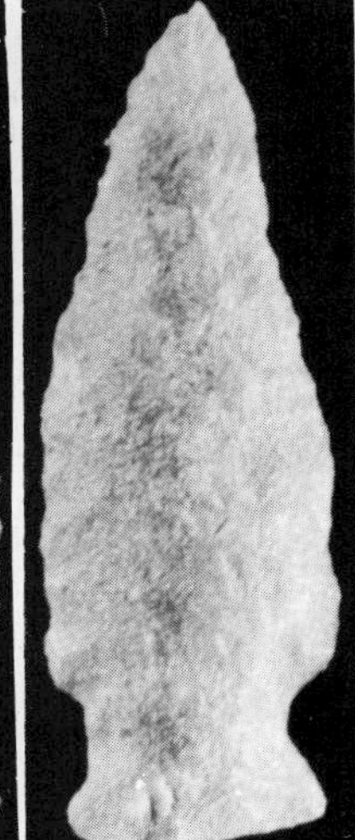
G8, $15-$25
Dinwiddie Co., VA. Quartzite.

HAMILTON - Early Archaic, 8000 - 5000 B.P.

(Also see Appalachian, Columbia, Kirk, Savannah River, Seminole & Thonotosassa)

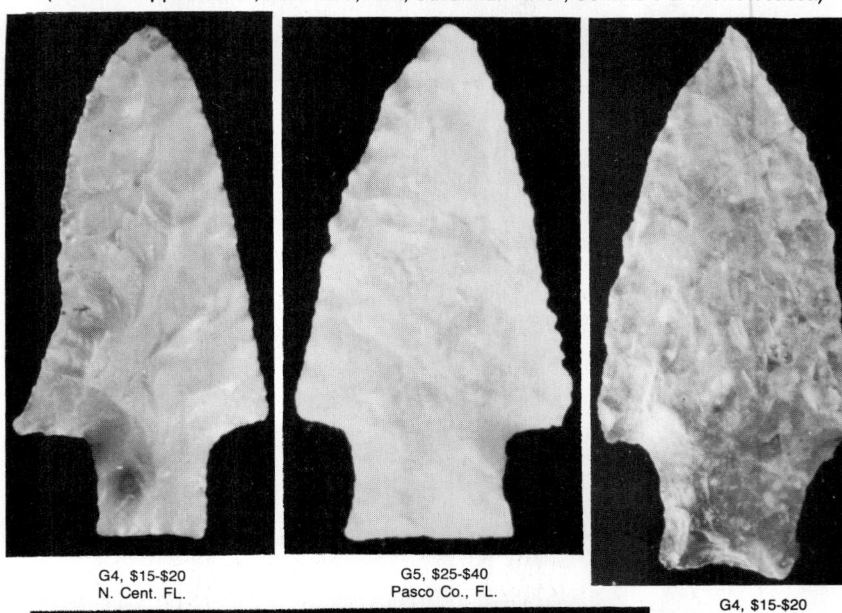

G4, $15-$20
N. Cent. FL.

G5, $25-$40
Pasco Co., FL.

G4, $15-$20
Beaufort Co., SC. Daw Isle.

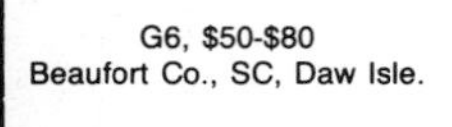

G6, $50-$80
Beaufort Co., SC, Daw Isle.

G8, $80-$120
Burke Co., GA. Nice color.

LOCATION: Southern Southeastern states. **DESCRIPTION:** A large size, thick, broad stemmed point with a concave base. Shoulders are horizontal to slightly tapering.

G8, $90-$150
Suwannee Rv., FL.

G10, $200-$300
Hillsborough Co., FL.

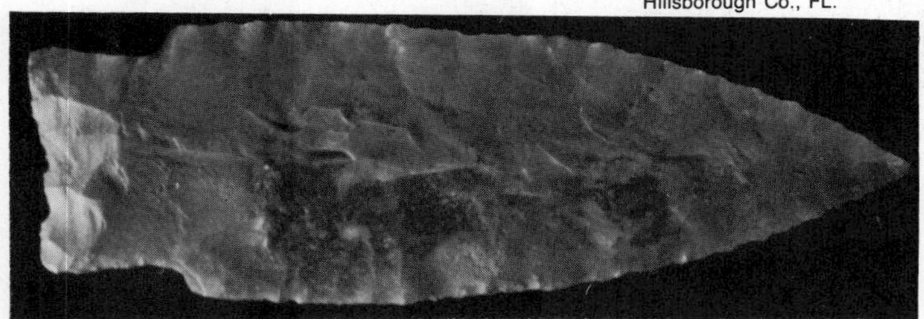

G10, $250-$400, Lerig Co., FL.

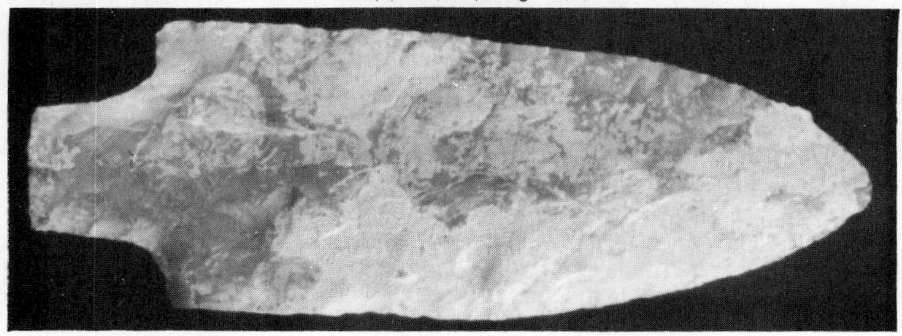

G8, $90-$150, Crystal Co., FL.

HAMILTON - Woodland to Mississippian, 1600 - 1000 B.P.

(Also see Camp Creek, Fresno, Madison, Talco and Yadkin)

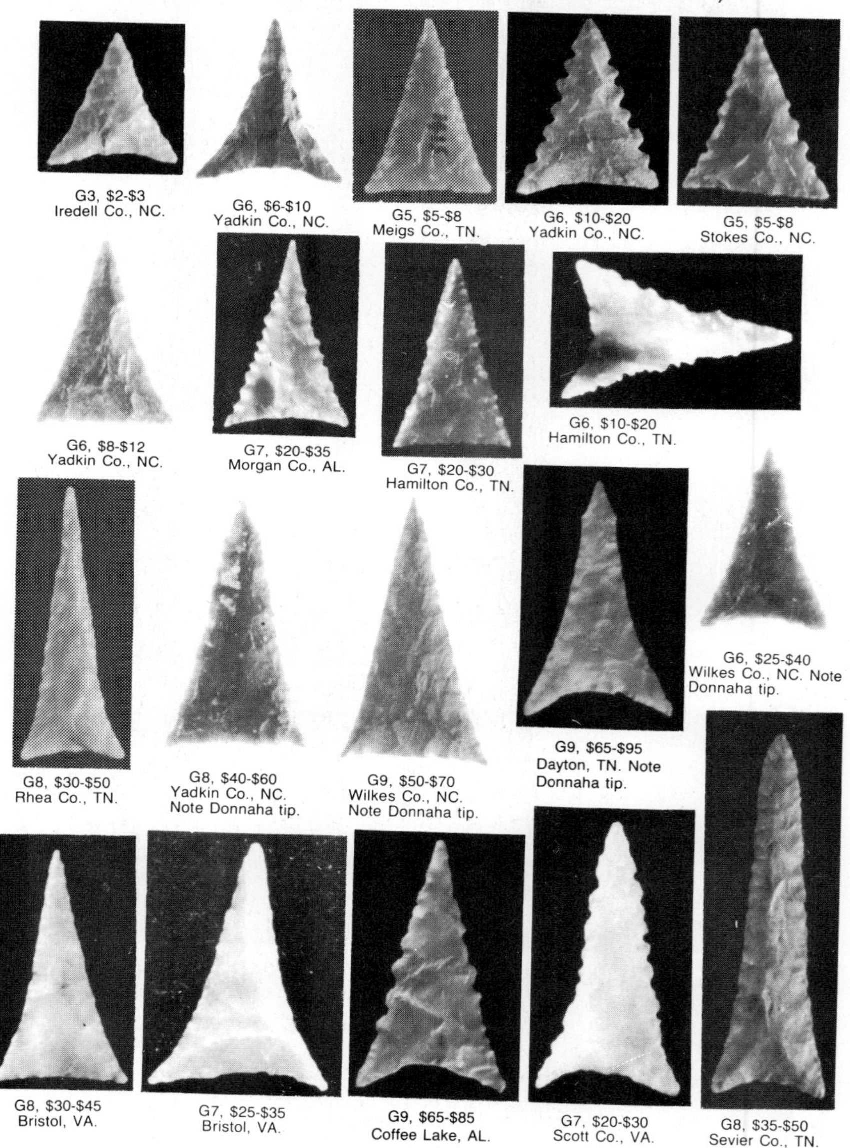

G3, $2-$3 Iredell Co., NC.

G6, $6-$10 Yadkin Co., NC.

G5, $5-$8 Meigs Co., TN.

G6, $10-$20 Yadkin Co., NC.

G5, $5-$8 Stokes Co., NC.

G6, $8-$12 Yadkin Co., NC.

G7, $20-$35 Morgan Co., AL.

G7, $20-$30 Hamilton Co., TN.

G6, $10-$20 Hamilton Co., TN.

G8, $30-$50 Rhea Co., TN.

G8, $40-$60 Yadkin Co., NC. Note Donnaha tip.

G9, $50-$70 Wilkes Co., NC. Note Donnaha tip.

G9, $65-$95 Dayton, TN. Note Donnaha tip.

G6, $25-$40 Wilkes Co., NC. Note Donnaha tip.

G8, $30-$45 Bristol, VA.

G7, $25-$35 Bristol, VA.

G9, $65-$85 Coffee Lake, AL.

G7, $20-$30 Scott Co., VA.

G8, $35-$50 Sevier Co., TN.

LOCATION: Southeastern states. **DESCRIPTION:** A small to medium size triangular point with concave sides and base. Many examples are very thin, of the highest quality, and with serrated edges. Side edges can also be straight. This type is believed to have evolved from *Camp Creek* points. Called *Uwharrie* in North Carolina. Some North Carolina examples have special constricted tips called *Donnaha Tips*.

HAMILTON-STEMMED - Late Woodland to Mississippian, 3000 - 1000 B.P.

(Also see Buck Creek, Motley, Smithsonia and Wade)

G5, $6-$10
Putnam Co., TN.

G2, $1-$2
White Co., TN. Blade nick.

G6, $10-$20
Meigs Co., TN.

G6, $10-$20
Meigs Co., TN.

G8, $25-$40
White Co., TN.

G8, $30-$35
Meigs Co., TN.

G6, $10-$20
Dayton, TN. Base nick.

LOCATION: Southeastern states. **DESCRIPTION:** A medium to large size, barbed, expanded stem point. Most examples have a sharp needle like point, and the blade edges are convex to recurved. Called *Rankin* in Northeast Tenn.

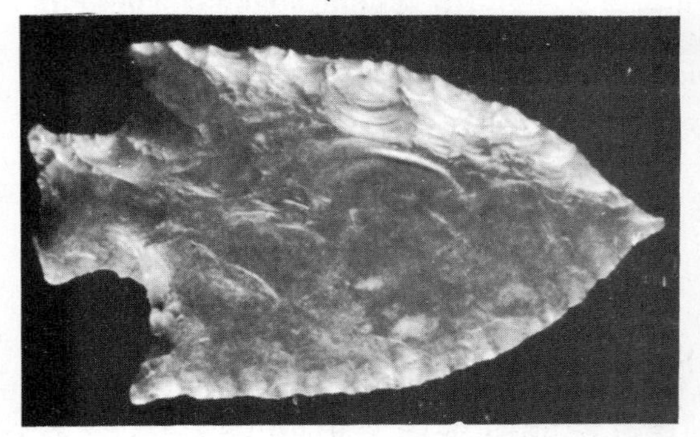

G5, $12-$20
Bakewell, TN.

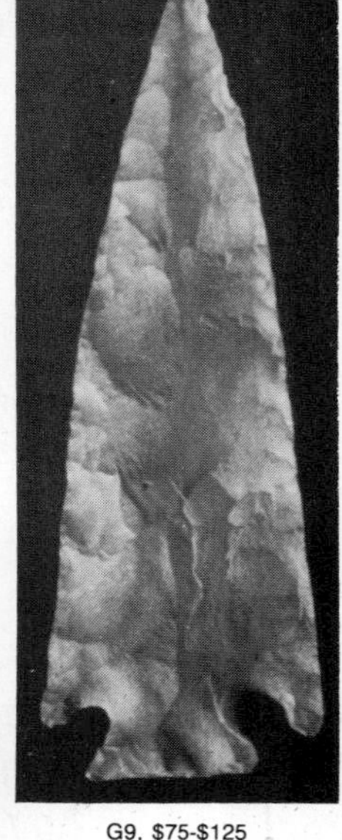

G9, $75-$125
Meigs Co., TN.

G6, $15-$25
Fentress Co., TN.

G9, $60-$100
Meigs Co., TN.

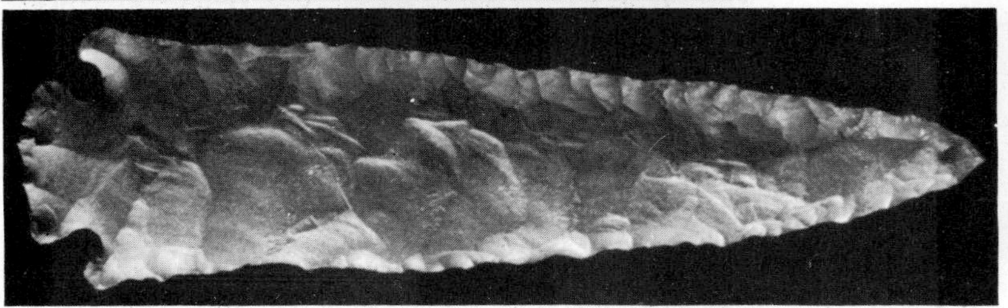

G7, $25-$40
Hamilton Co., TN.

HANNA - Late Archaic to Woodland, 4500 - 3000 B.P.

(Also see Cave Spring, Duncan, Patrick, Pinto Basin, SW Hanna & Wheeler Recurvate)

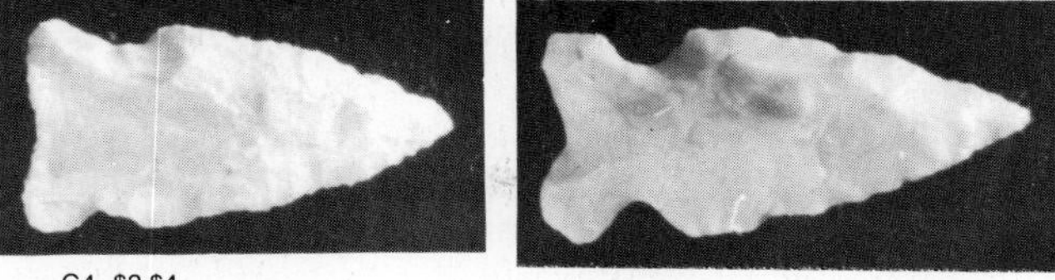

G6, $6-$10
Comanche Co., TX.

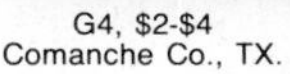

G4, $2-$4
Comanche Co., TX.

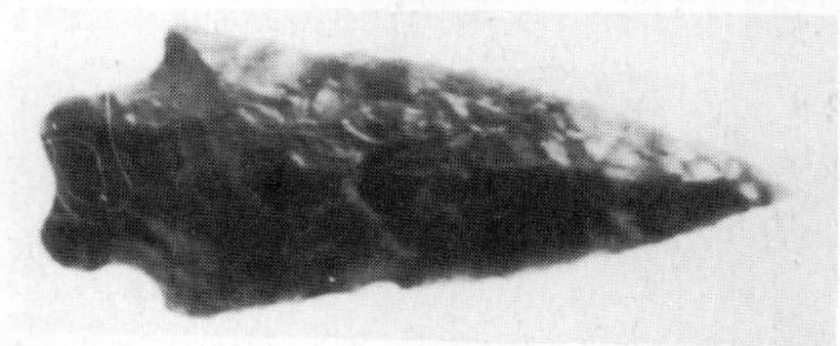

G5, $5-$8
Whitwell, TN.

LOCATION: Northwest spreading to the Southeastern states. **DESCRIPTION:** A small size, narrow, bifurcated stemmed point with tapered to horizontal shoulders.

HARAHEY - Mississippian, 700 - 350 B.P.

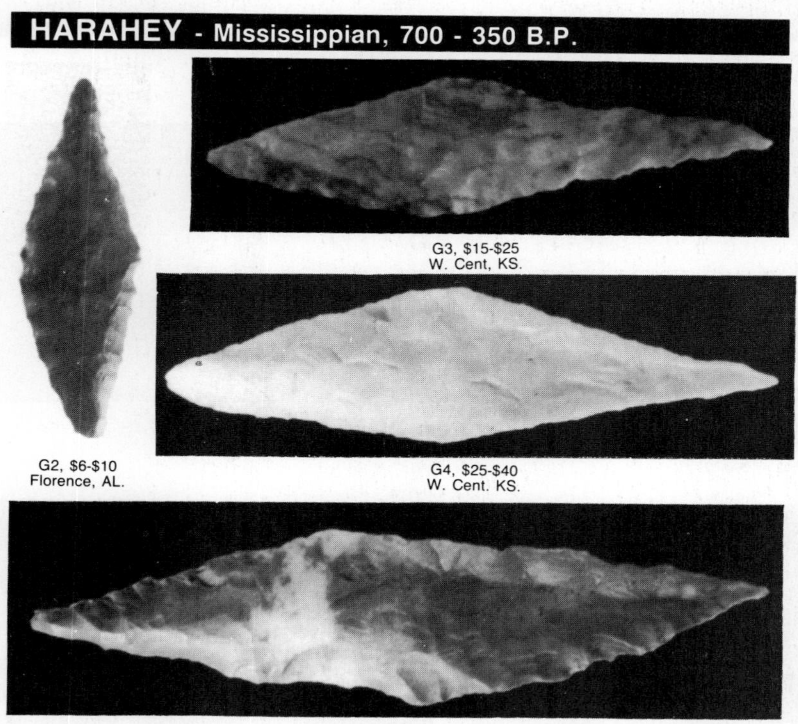

G3, $15-$25
W. Cent, KS.

G2, $6-$10
Florence, AL.

G4, $25-$40
W. Cent. KS.

G3, $15-$25
W. Cent. KS.

LOCATION: Midwestern states. **DESCRIPTION:** A large size, double pointed knife that is usually beveled on one side of each face. The cross section is rhomboid.

HARAHEY (continued)

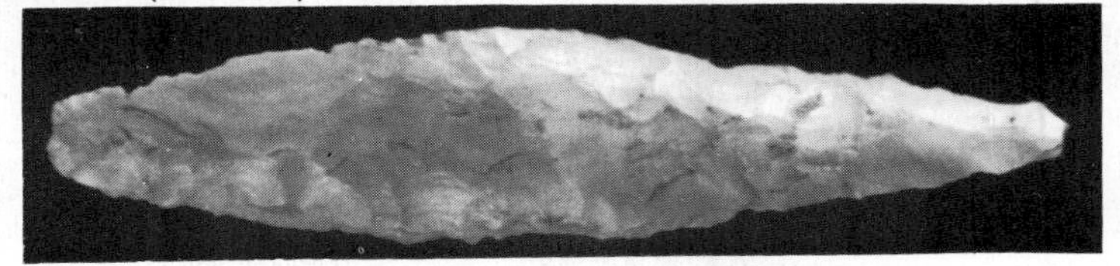

G2, $6-$10
Waco, TX.

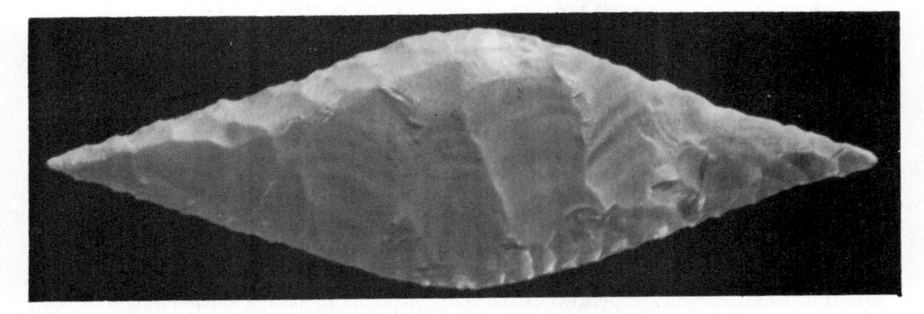

G8, $150-$250
E. CO.

G8, $150-$250
Brown Co., IL.

G6, $80-$120
KY.

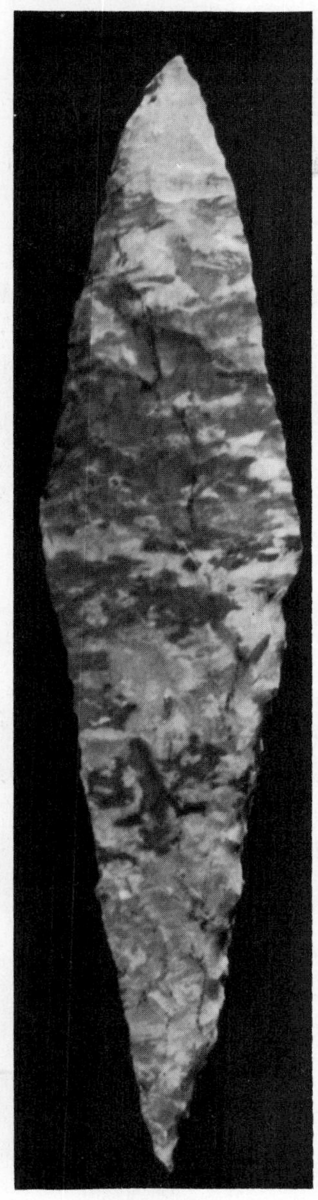

G9, $180-$300
NE OK.

G10, $350-$650
W. Cent. KS.

HARDAWAY - Late Paleo, 10000 - 8000 B.P.

(Also see Alamance, Dalton-Greenbrier, Haw River, Russell Cave, San Patrice, Taylor & Wheeler)

G2, $15-$25
Union Co., SC. Crystal.

G3, $60-$100
Southampton Co., VA.

G4, $60-$100
Moore Co., NC. Milky quartz.

G3, $15-$25
Lee Co., AL. Crystal.

G5, $80-$125
Cent. NC.

G4, $60-$80
Marion Co., TN.

G7, $180-$300
Lake Seminole, GA.

G5, $125-$200
Moore Co., NC.

G5, $100-$175
Southampton Co., VA.
Vein quartz.

G4, $150-$200
Moore Co., NC. Milky quartz.

G4, $75-$125
Sussex Co., VA.

G5, $70-$120
Lexington Co., SC.

G7, $200-$300
Moore Co., NC.

LOCATION: Southeastern states, especially North Carolina. Type site is Stanly Co., NC., Yadkin River. **DESCRIPTION:** A small to medium size point with shallow side notches and expanded auricles forming a wide deeply concave base. Wide specimens are called *Cow Head Hardaways* in North Carolina. Ears and base are usually heavily ground. This type evolved from the *Dalton* point. **I.D. KEY:** Heavy grinding in shoulders, paleo flaking.

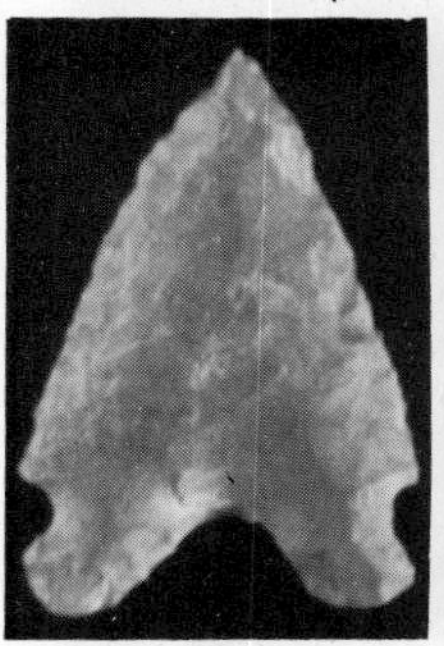

G5, $80-$125
Charles Co., VA.

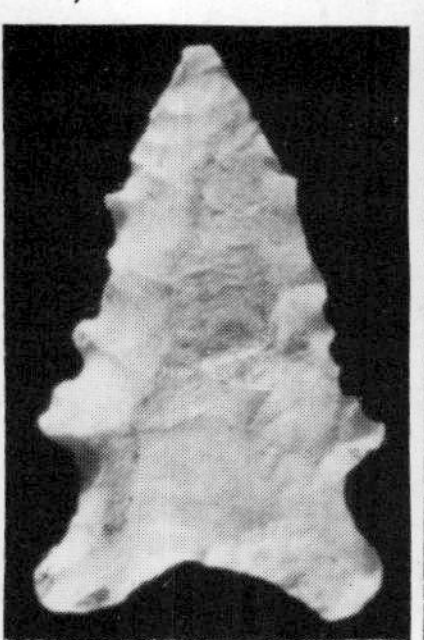

G3, $60-$70
Marion Co., TN.

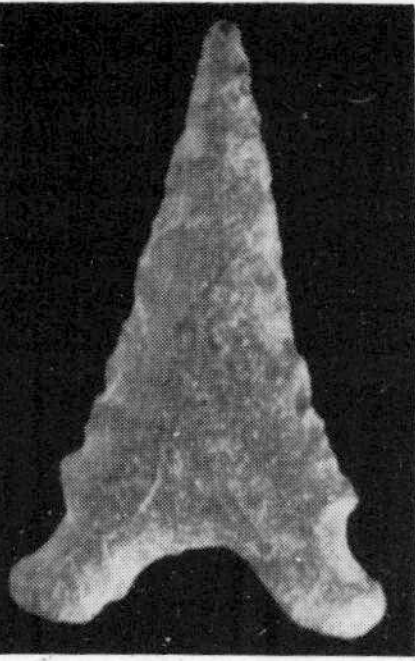

G6, $125-$225
Randolph Co., NC.

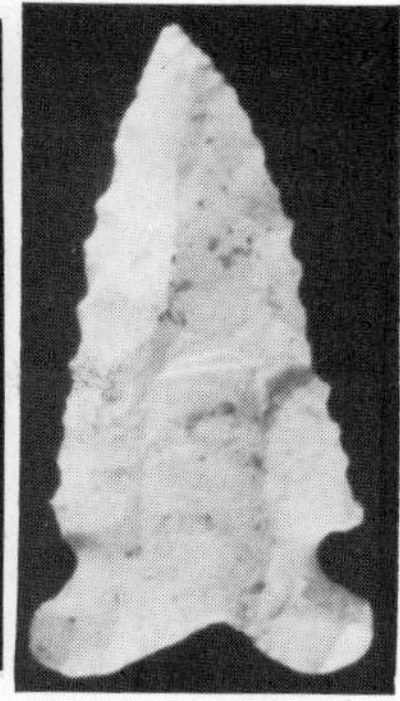

G4, $50-$75
Lexington Co., SC.
Fluted.

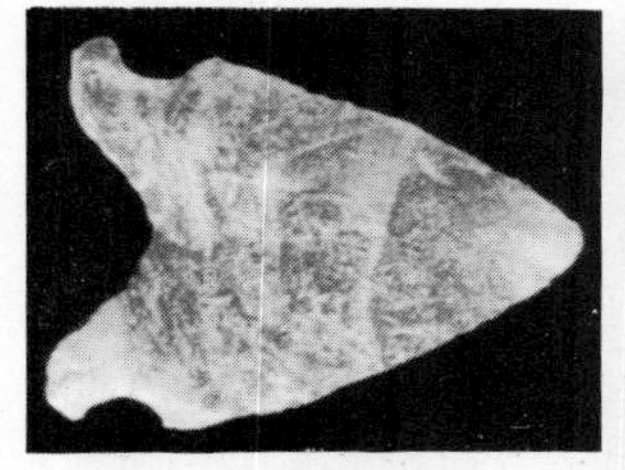

G5, $80-$125
Chatham Co., NC. Cowhead form.

G5, $60-$100
Cent. NC. Cowhead form.

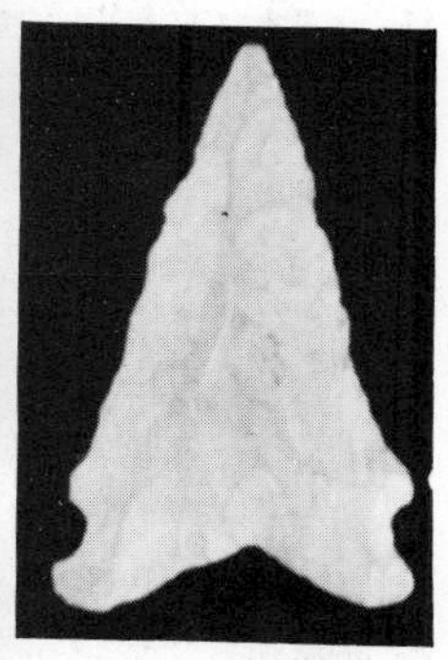

G4, $60-$85
Pilot Mtn., NC.

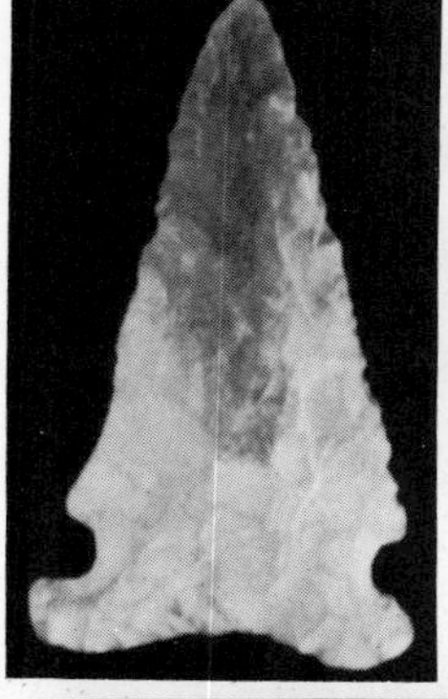

G5, $80-$125
Humphreys Co., TN.

G5, $100-$150
Moore Co., NC. Shale.

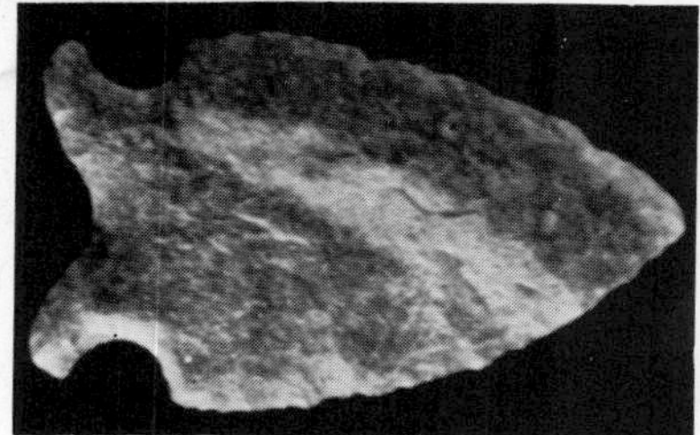

G9, $500-$800
VA.

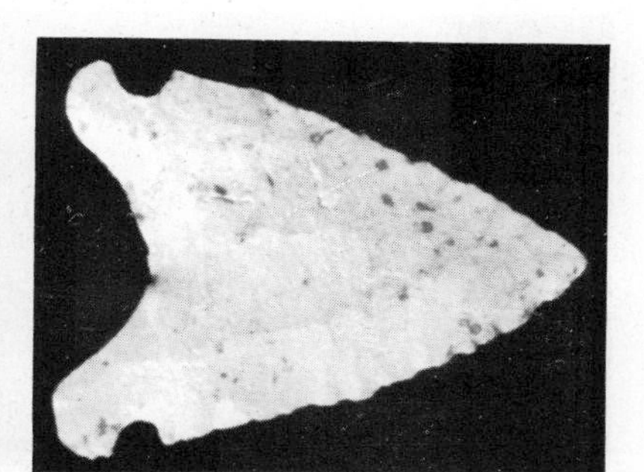

G8, $300-$450
Caswell Co., NC.

HARDAWAY (continued)

G7, $180-$300
Union Co., NC. Hardaway site. Cowhead form.

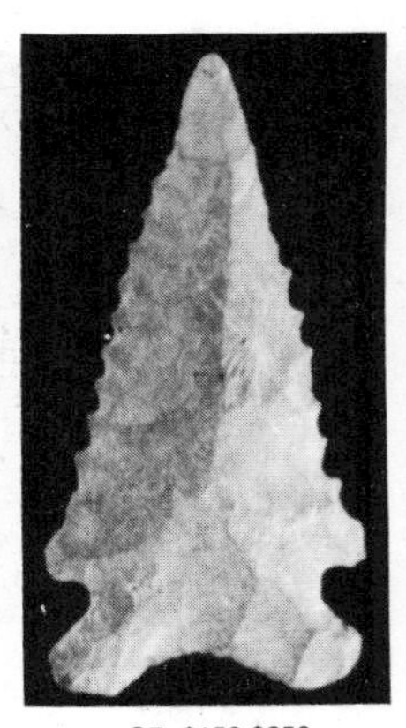

G7, $150-$250
Richmond Co., NC.

G8, $250-$400
Rowan Co., NC.

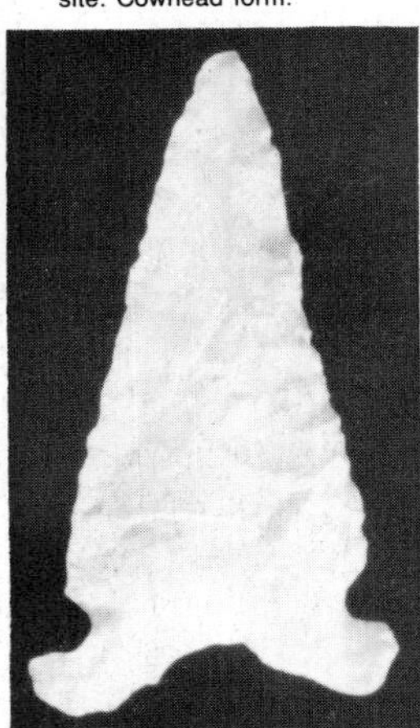

G6, $125-$225
Chatham Co., NC.

G7, $220-$400
Montgomery Co., NC.

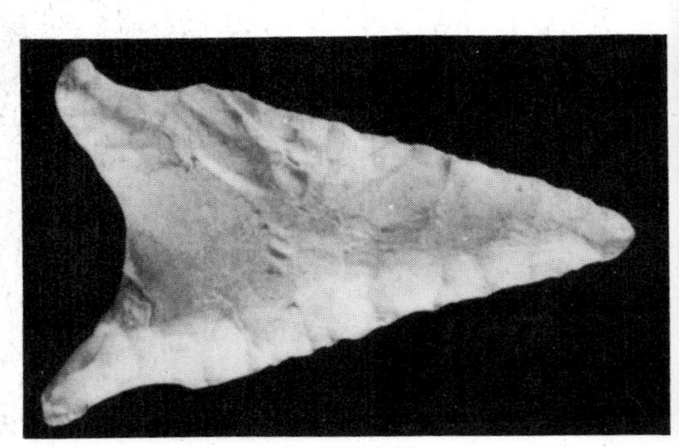

G8, $300-$450
Johnston Co., NC.

G9, $600-$900
Davidson Co., NC. Rhyolite.

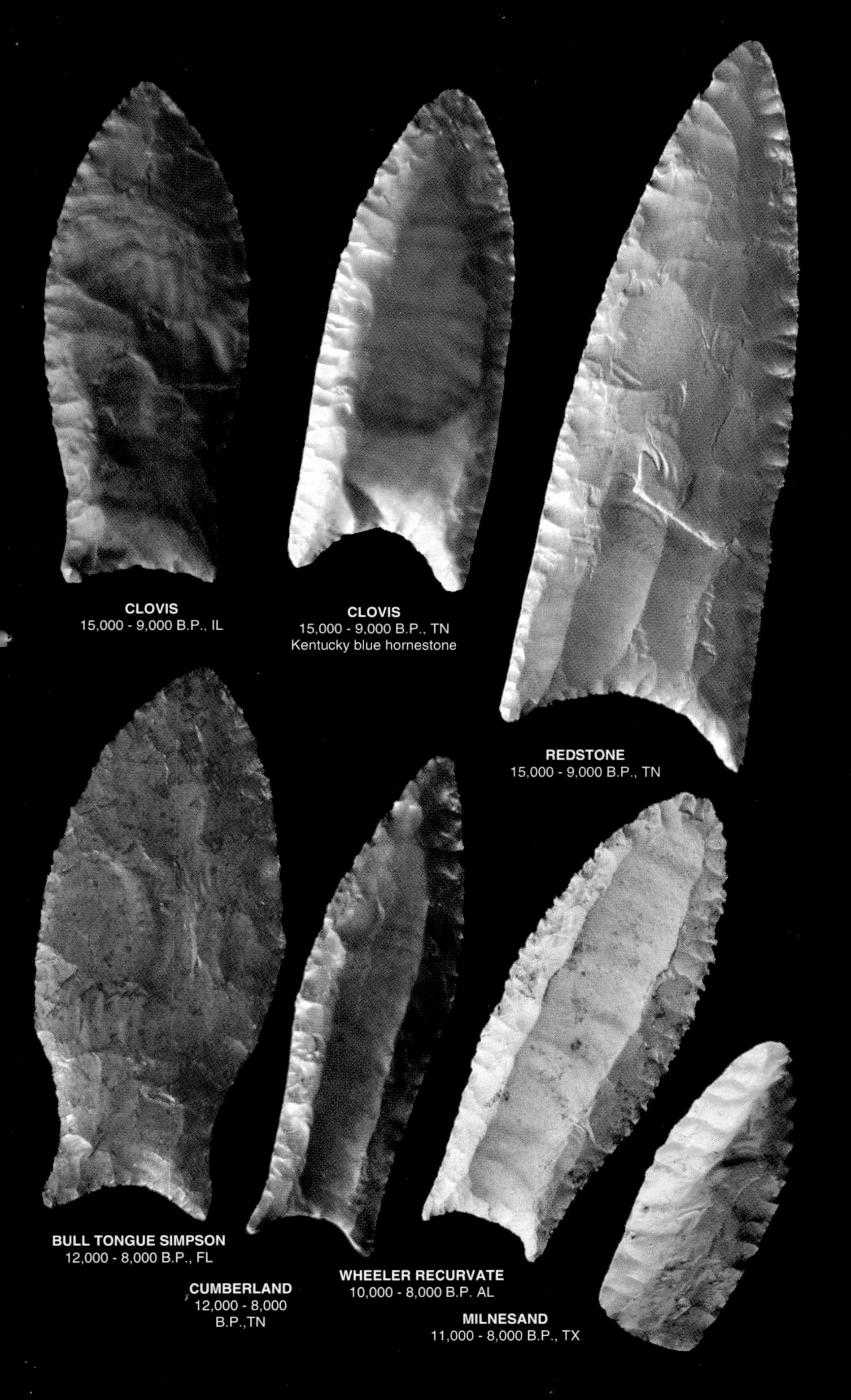

CLOVIS
15,000 - 9,000 B.P., IL

CLOVIS
15,000 - 9,000 B.P., TN
Kentucky blue hornestone

REDSTONE
15,000 - 9,000 B.P., TN

BULL TONGUE SIMPSON
12,000 - 8,000 B.P., FL

CUMBERLAND
12,000 - 8,000
B.P.,TN

WHEELER RECURVATE
10,000 - 8,000 B.P. AL

MILNESAND
11,000 - 8,000 B.P., TX

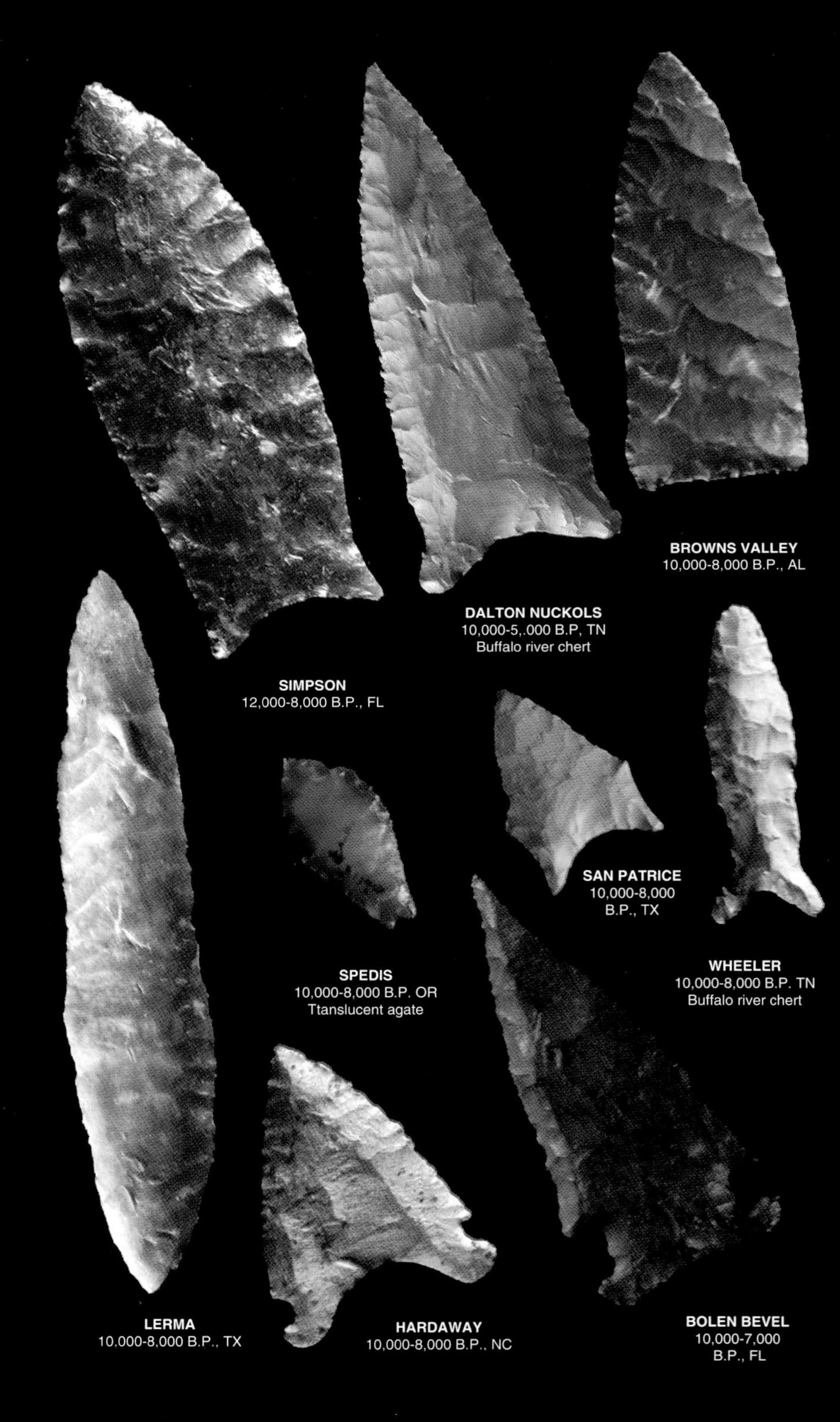
BROWNS VALLEY
10,000-8,000 B.P., AL
DALTON NUCKOLS
10,000-5,.000 B.P, TN
Buffalo river chert
SIMPSON
12,000-8,000 B.P., FL
SAN PATRICE
10,000-8,000
B.P., TX
WHEELER
10,000-8,000 B.P. TN
Buffalo river chert
SPEDIS
10,000-8,000 B.P. OR
Ttanslucent agate
LERMA
10,000-8,000 B.P., TX
HARDAWAY
10,000-8,000 B.P., NC
BOLEN BEVEL
10,000-7,000
B.P., FL

DALTON SANTE FE
10,000-8,000 B.P., GA
CHIPOLA
10,000-8,000 B.P., FL
PAINT ROCK VALLEY
10,000-6,000 B.P., AL
BIG SANDY
10,000-3,000 B.P., AL
GREENBRIER
9,500-6,000 B.P., TN
GREENBRIER
9,500-6,000 B.P., TN
ROWAN
9,500-8,000 B.P. NC
GARTH SLOUGH
9,000-4,000 B.P., TN
STOCTON
9,000-5,000 B.P., OR
GREENBRIER
9,500-6,000 B.P., TN

KIRK CORNER NOTCHED
9,000-6,000 B.P., TN
KIRK SERRATED
9,000-6,000 B.P., TN
LAMPASOS
9,000-6,000 B.P., TX
FORT ANCIENT
9,000-6,000 B.P., OR
HARPETH RIVER
9,000-8,000 B.P., TN
RUSSELL CAVE
9,000-7,000 B.P., TN
WACISSA
9,000-6,000 B.P., FL
DOVETAIL
9,000-5,000 B.P., TN

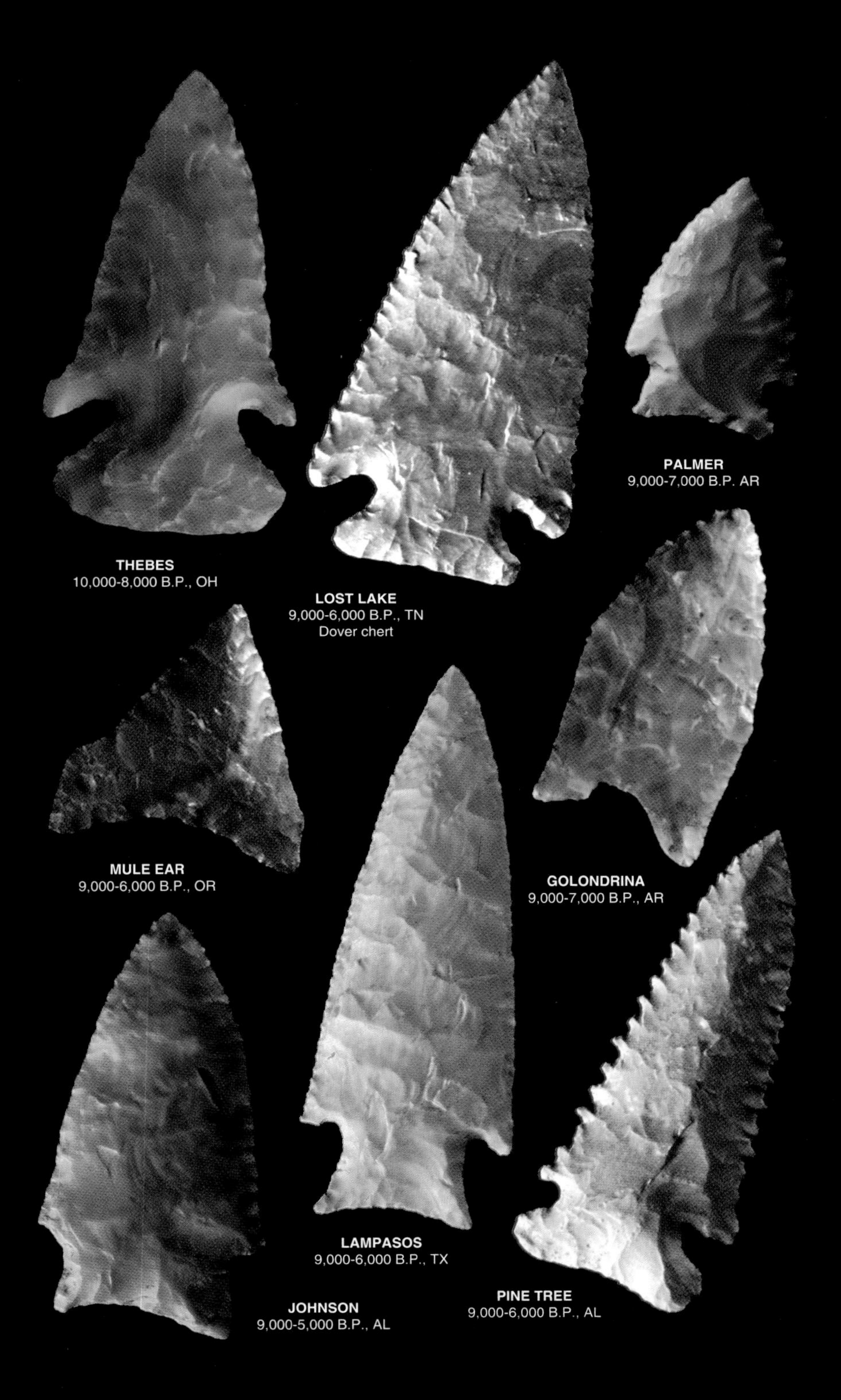
THEBES
10,000-8,000 B.P., OH
LOST LAKE
9,000-6,000 B.P., TN
Dover chert
PALMER
9,000-7,000 B.P. AR
MULE EAR
9,000-6,000 B.P., OR
GOLONDRINA
9,000-7,000 B.P., AR
LAMPASOS
9,000-6,000 B.P., TX
JOHNSON
9,000-5,000 B.P., AL
PINE TREE
9,000-6,000 B.P., AL

DECATUR
9,000-3,000 B.P.. AL
PELICAN
10,000-6,000 B.P., TN
STANLY
8,000-5,000 B.P., KY
ECUSTA
8,000-5,000
B.P., TN
LEIGHTON
8,000-5,000 B.P., AL
LECROY
9,000-5,000, TN
MARTINDALE
8,000-5,000 B.P., TX
THONOTOSASSA
8,000-6,000 B.P., FL
BRAZOS
8,000-5,000 B.P., TX
ELK RIVER
8,000-5,000 B.P., TN

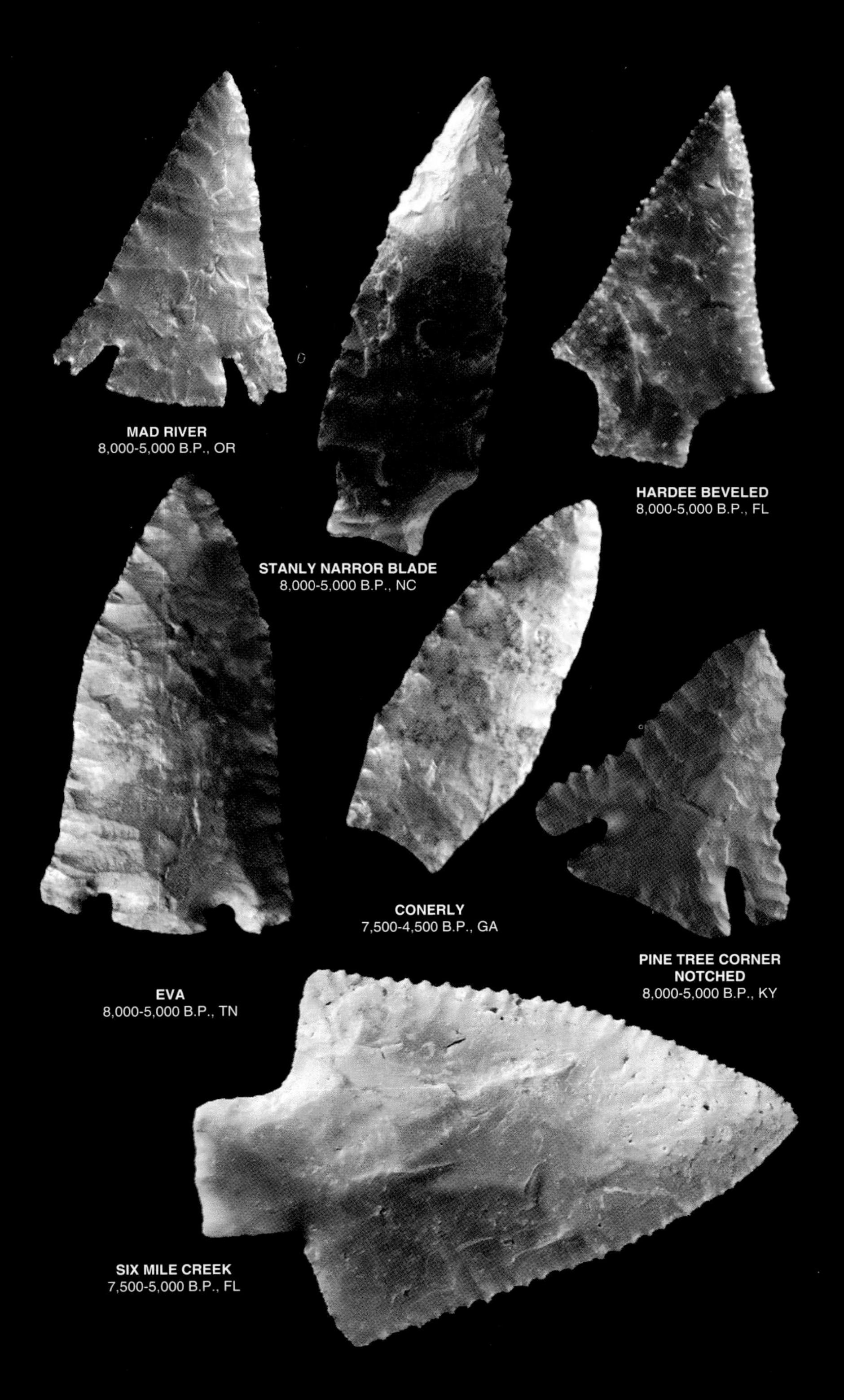

MAD RIVER
8,000-5,000 B.P., OR

STANLY NARROR BLADE
8,000-5,000 B.P., NC

HARDEE BEVELED
8,000-5,000 B.P., FL

EVA
8,000-5,000 B.P., TN

CONERLY
7,500-4,500 B.P., GA

PINE TREE CORNER NOTCHED
8,000-5,000 B.P., KY

SIX MILE CREEK
7,500-5,000 B.P., FL

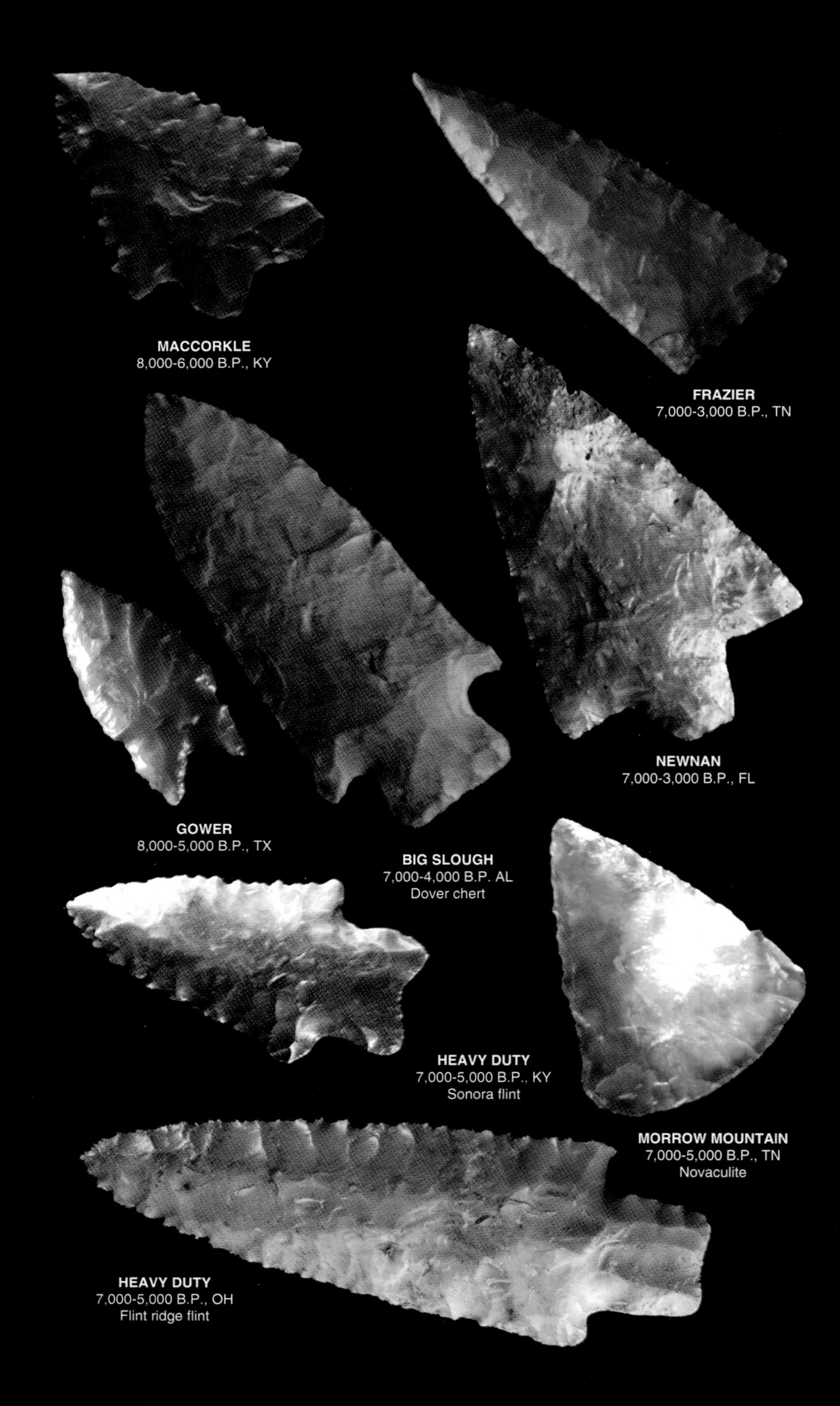

MACCORKLE
8,000-6,000 B.P., KY

FRAZIER
7,000-3,000 B.P., TN

NEWNAN
7,000-3,000 B.P., FL

GOWER
8,000-5,000 B.P., TX

BIG SLOUGH
7,000-4,000 B.P. AL
Dover chert

HEAVY DUTY
7,000-5,000 B.P., KY
Sonora flint

MORROW MOUNTAIN
7,000-5,000 B.P., TN
Novaculite

HEAVY DUTY
7,000-5,000 B.P., OH
Flint ridge flint

SAVAGE CAVE
7,000-4,000 B.P., AR
HILLSBORO
7,000-5,000 B.P., FL
GUILFORD STEMMED
6,500-5,000 B.P., SC
GUILFORD YUMA
6,500-5,000 B.P., SC
LANGE
6,000-1,000 B.P., TX
BENTON
6,000-4,000 B.P., TN
Red, white & blue flint
TURKEYTAIL
6,000-2,500 B.P., TN
PANDALE
6,000-3,000 B.P., TX
HALIFAX
6,000-3,000 B.P., VA
Vein quartz

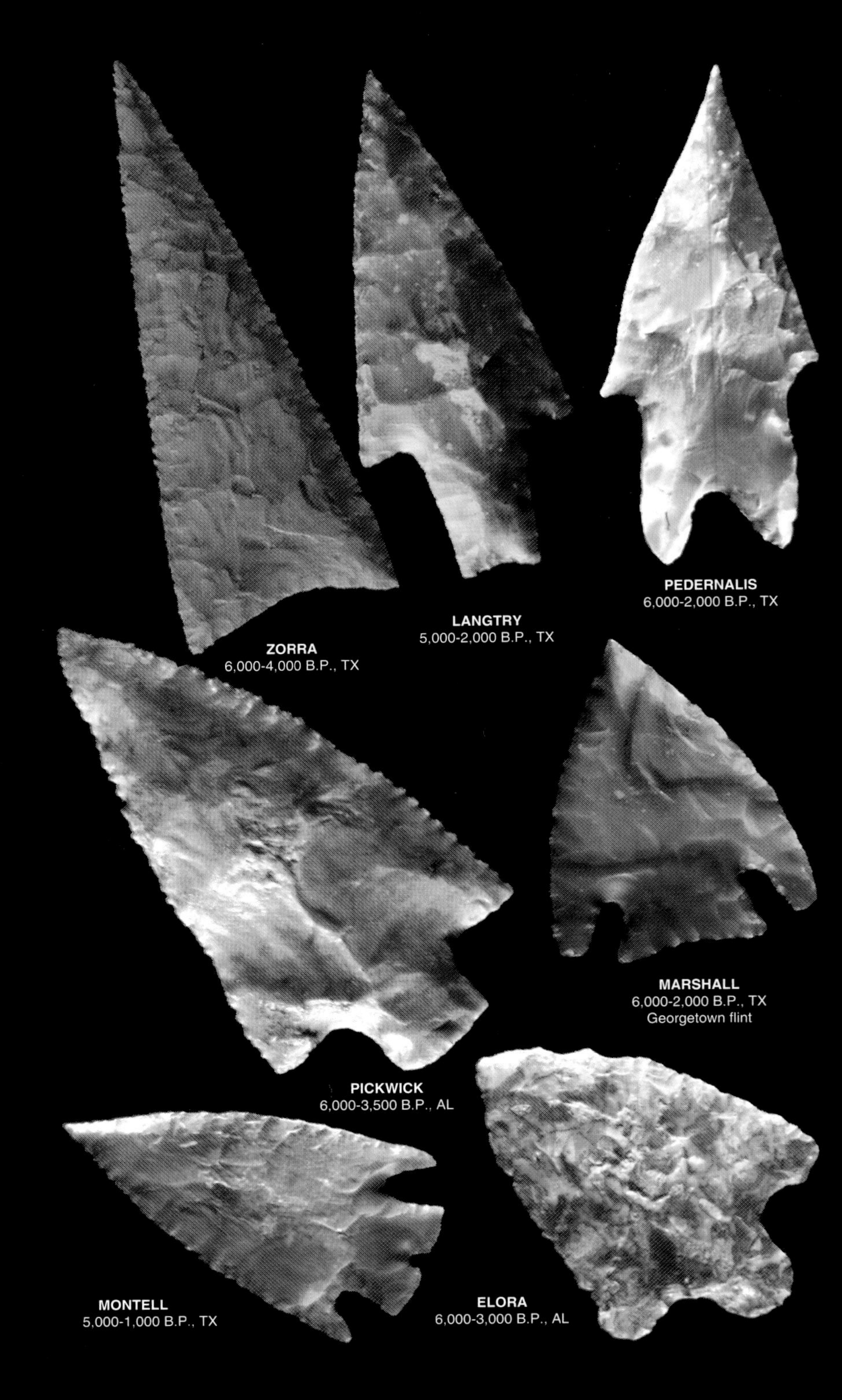
PEDERNALIS
6,000-2,000 B.P., TX
LANGTRY
5,000-2,000 B.P., TX
ZORRA
6,000-4,000 B.P., TX
MARSHALL
6,000-2,000 B.P., TX
Georgetown flint
PICKWICK
6,000-3,500 B.P., AL
MONTELL
5,000-1,000 B.P., TX
ELORA
6,000-3,000 B.P., AL

TORTUGAS
6,000-1,000 B.P. AL
Jasper

HIDDEN VALLEY
5,000-3,000 B.P., AR

LAFAYETTE
5,000-3,500 B.P., FL

LANGTRY
5,000-2,000 B.P., TX

COPENA AURICULATE
5,000-2,500 B.P., TN

KAYS
5,000-2,000 B.P., AL

AFTON
5,000-2,000 B.P.,
TN
Heat treated buffalo

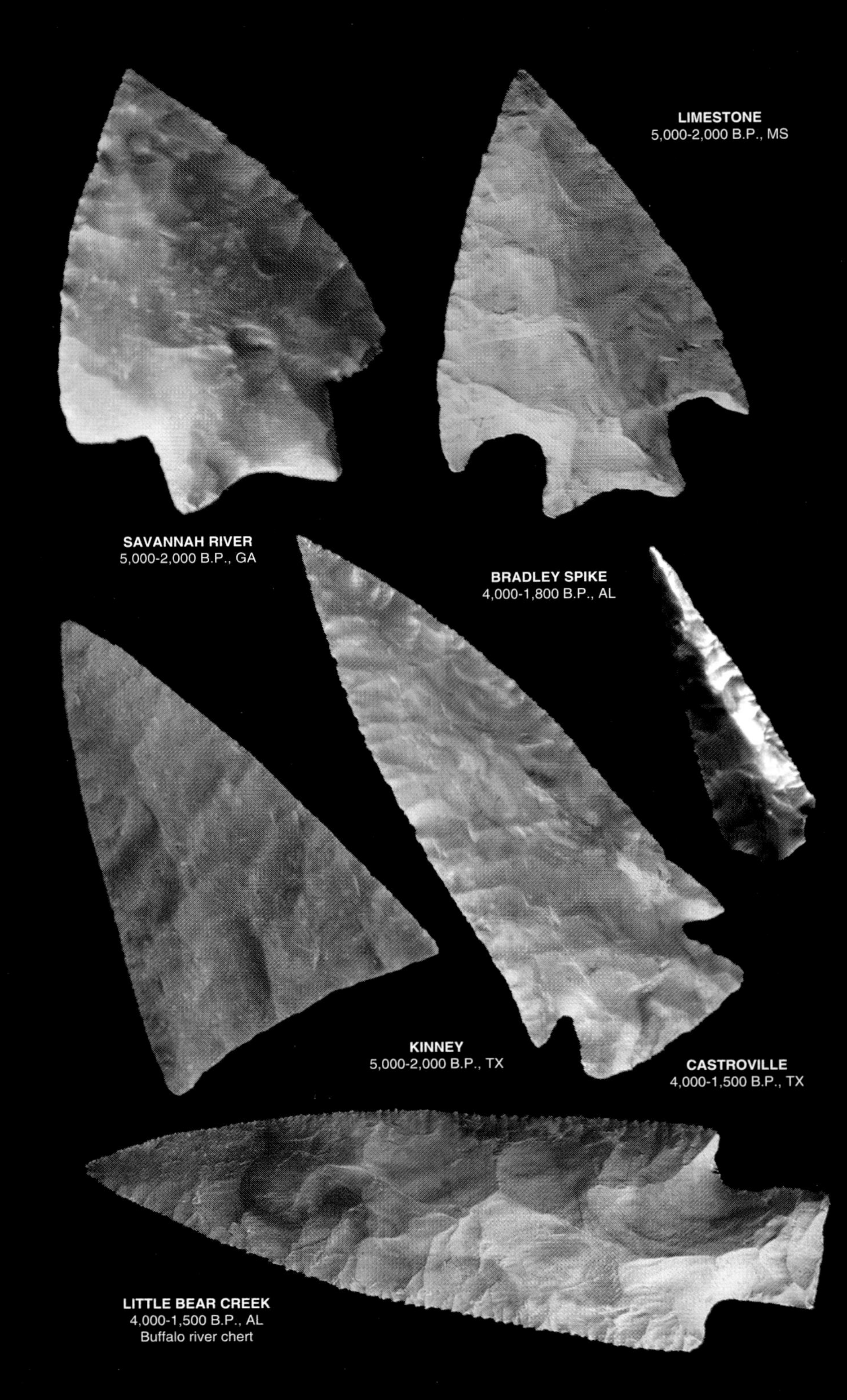
LIMESTONE
5,000-2,000 B.P., MS
SAVANNAH RIVER
5,000-2,000 B.P., GA
BRADLEY SPIKE
4,000-1,800 B.P., AL
KINNEY
5,000-2,000 B.P., TX
CASTROVILLE
4,000-1,500 B.P., TX
LITTLE BEAR CREEK
4,000-1,500 B.P., AL
Buffalo river chert

ALACHUA
4,000-2,500 B.P., GA
Banded chert

CASTROVILLE
4,000-1,500 B.P., TX
Banded georgetown flint

COPENA CLASSIC
4,000-1,200 B.P., AL

COPENA CLASSIC
4,000-1,200 B.P., AL

TABLE ROCK
4,000-3,000 B.P., TN

MARCOS
3,500-1,200 B.P., TX

BAKERS CREEK
4,000-1,300 B.P., TN
Dover chert

LITTLE BEAR CREEK
4,000-1,500 B.P., TN

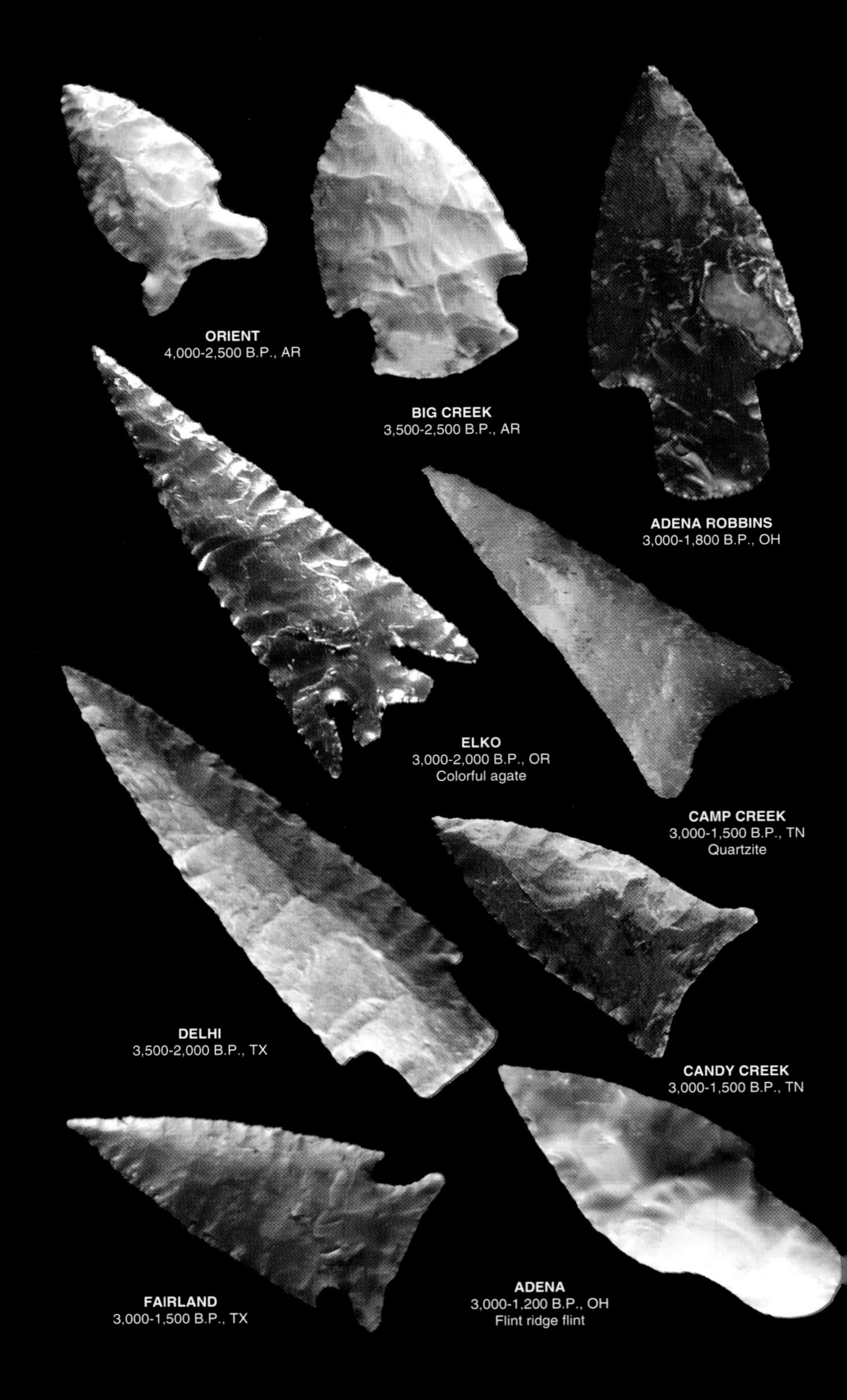
ORIENT
4,000-2,500 B.P., AR
BIG CREEK
3,500-2,500 B.P., AR
ADENA ROBBINS
3,000-1,800 B.P., OH
ELKO
3,000-2,000 B.P., OR
Colorful agate
CAMP CREEK
3,000-1,500 B.P., TN
Quartzite
DELHI
3,500-2,000 B.P., TX
CANDY CREEK
3,000-1,500 B.P., TN
FAIRLAND
3,000-1,500 B.P., TX
ADENA
3,000-1,200 B.P., OH
Flint ridge flint

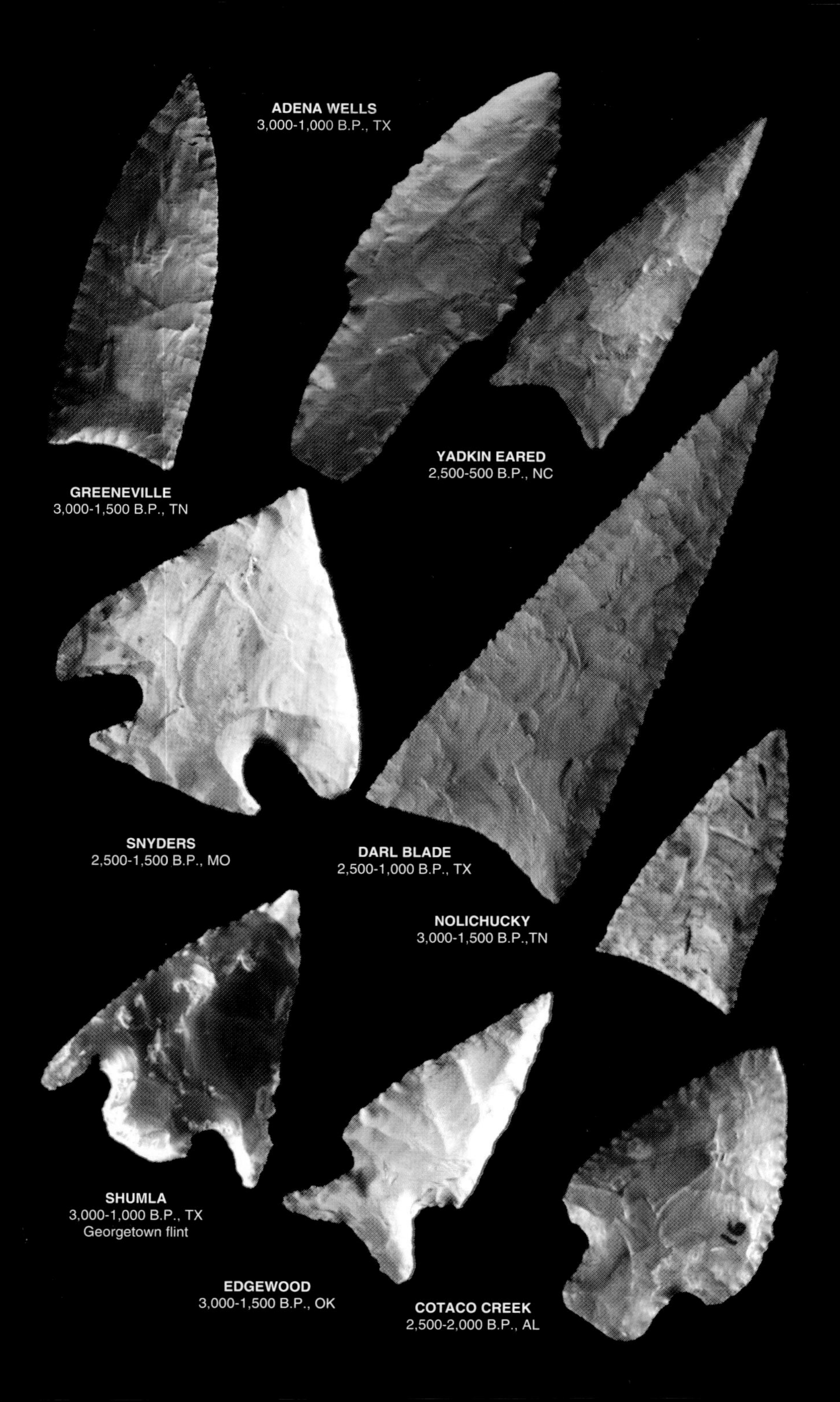
ADENA WELLS
3,000-1,000 B.P., TX
YADKIN EARED
2,500-500 B.P., NC
GREENEVILLE
3,000-1,500 B.P., TN
SNYDERS
2,500-1,500 B.P., MO
DARL BLADE
2,500-1,000 B.P., TX
NOLICHUCKY
3,000-1,500 B.P.,TN
SHUMLA
3,000-1,000 B.P., TX
Georgetown flint
EDGEWOOD
3,000-1,500 B.P., OK
COTACO CREEK
2,500-2,000 B.P., AL

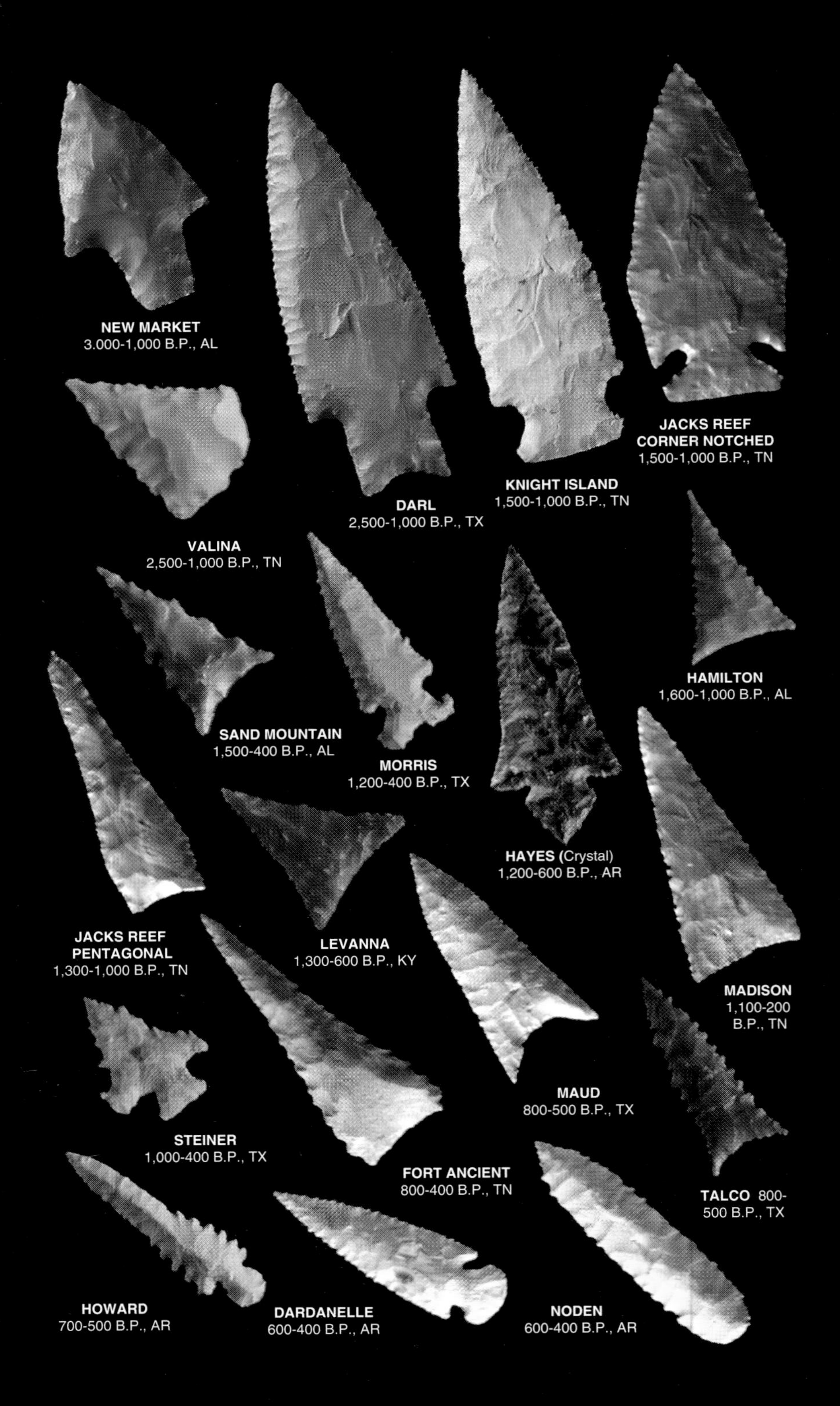
NEW MARKET
3.000-1,000 B.P., AL
VALINA
2,500-1,000 B.P., TN
DARL
2,500-1,000 B.P., TX
KNIGHT ISLAND
1,500-1,000 B.P., TN
JACKS REEF
CORNER NOTCHED
1,500-1,000 B.P., TN
HAMILTON
1,600-1,000 B.P., AL
SAND MOUNTAIN
1,500-400 B.P., AL
MORRIS
1,200-400 B.P., TX
HAYES (Crystal)
1,200-600 B.P., AR
JACKS REEF
PENTAGONAL
1,300-1,000 B.P., TN
LEVANNA
1,300-600 B.P., KY
MADISON
1,100-200
B.P., TN
MAUD
800-500 B.P., TX
STEINER
1,000-400 B.P., TX
FORT ANCIENT
800-400 B.P., TN
TALCO 800-
500 B.P., TX
HOWARD
700-500 B.P., AR
DARDANELLE
600-400 B.P., AR
NODEN
600-400 B.P., AR

HARDAWAY BLADE - Late Paleo, 10000 - 9000 B.P.

(Also see Cowhouse Slough, Decatur Blade, Hi-Lo and Paint Rock Valley)

G3, $3-$5
Cent. NC.

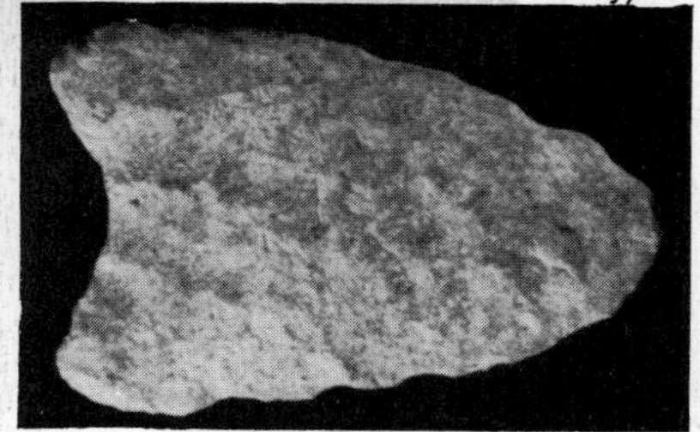

G5, $6-$10
Cent. NC.

LOCATION: North Carolina. **DESCRIPTION:** A small to medium size, thin, broad, blade with a concave base. The base usually is ground and has thinning strikes. A preform for the *Hardaway* point.

HARDAWAY-DALTON - Late Paleo, 10000 - 8000 B.P.

(Also see Alamance and Dalton)

G5, $35-$50
Dayton, TN. Flint.

G6, $45-$65
Guilford Co., NC.
Milky quartz.

G3, $20-$25
Lake Marion, SC.

G8, $120-$200
Dayton, TN.

G8, $120-$200
Coffee Lake, AL.

G7, $80-$120
Harnett Co., NC.

LOCATION: Southeastern states. **DESCRIPTION:** A small to medium size, serrated, auriculate point with a concave base. Basal Fluting or thinning is common. Bases are gound. Ears turn outward or are parallel sided. A cross between *Hardaway* and *Dalton*. **I.D. KEY:** Width of base, location found.

G7, $80-$120
Humphreys Co., TN.

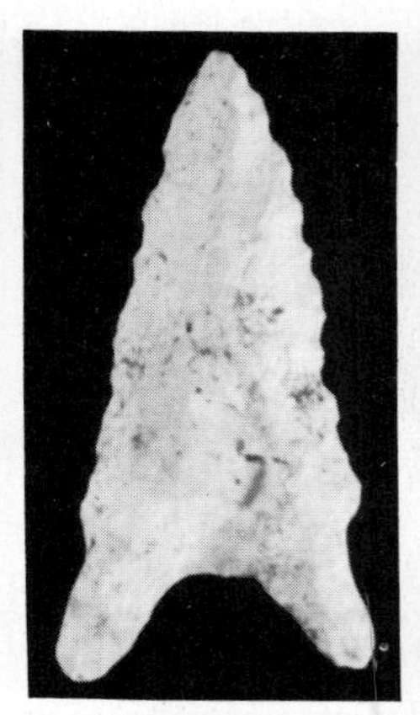

G7, $120-$225
Union Co., NC.

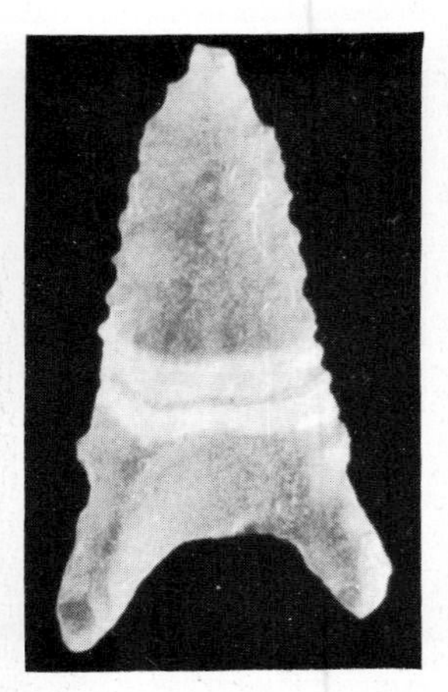

G6, $100-$150
Randolph Co., NC.

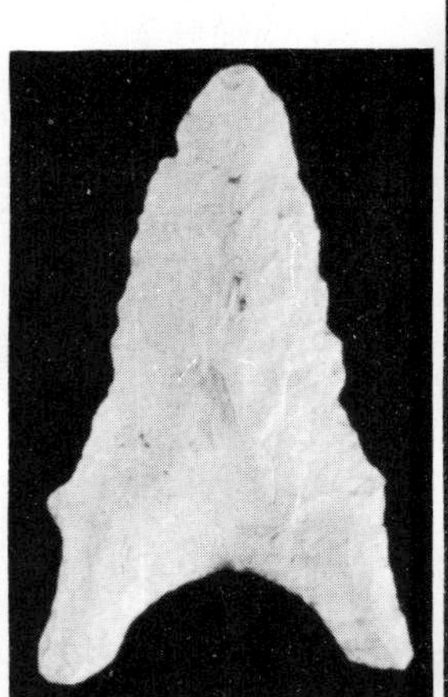

G6, $60-$100
Cent. NC.

G6, $150-$200
Moore Co., NC. Shale.

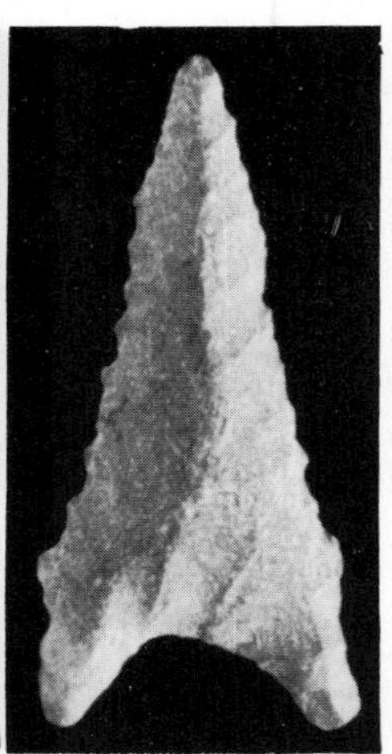

G7, $125-$225
Cent. NC.

G7, $100-$120
Humphreys Co., TN.

G4, $25-$40
Alexander Co., NC.

G9, $250-$400
Davidson Co., NC.

G7, $150-$200
Richmond Co., NC.

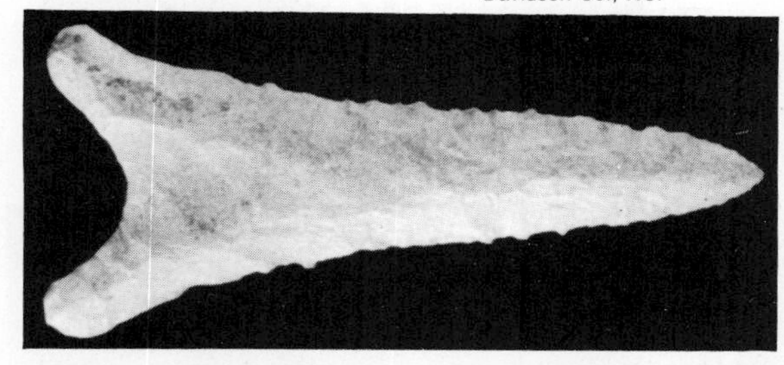
G9, $250-$350
Montgomery Co., NC.

HARDAWAY PALMER - Transitional Paleo, 10000 - 8000 B.P.

(Also see Palmer)

G6, $25-$40
Alleghany Co., NC.

G4, $15-$20
Randolph Co. NC.

G6, $25-$40
Randolph Co., NC.

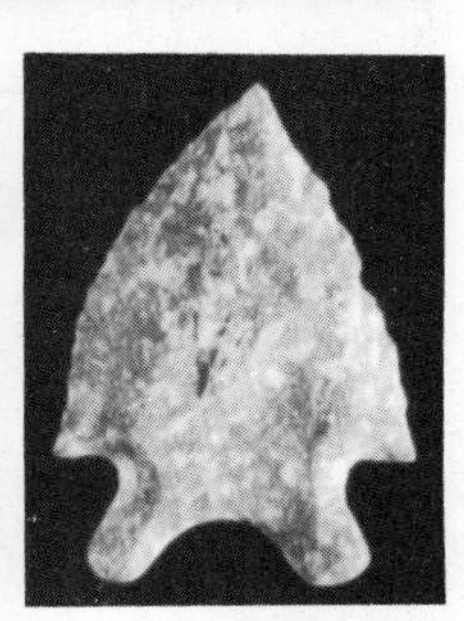
G9, $150-$250
Montgomery Co., NC.

LOCATION: Southeastern states. **DESCRIPTION:** A cross between *Hardaway* and *Palmer* with expanded auricles and a concave base that is ground.

HARDEE BEVELED - Early to mid-Archaic, 8000 - 5000 B.P.

(Also see Alachua, Levy, Marion and Putnam)

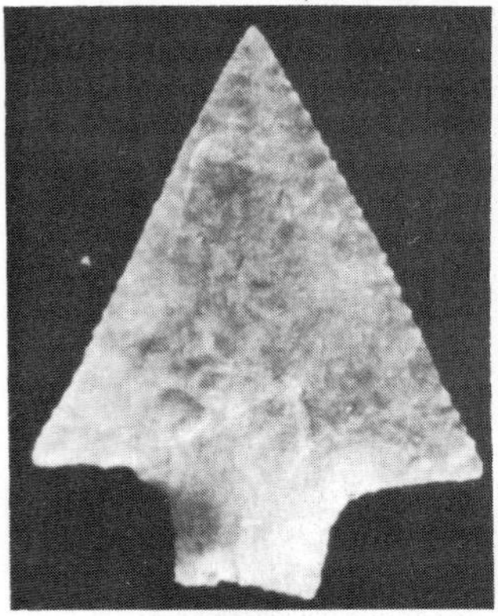

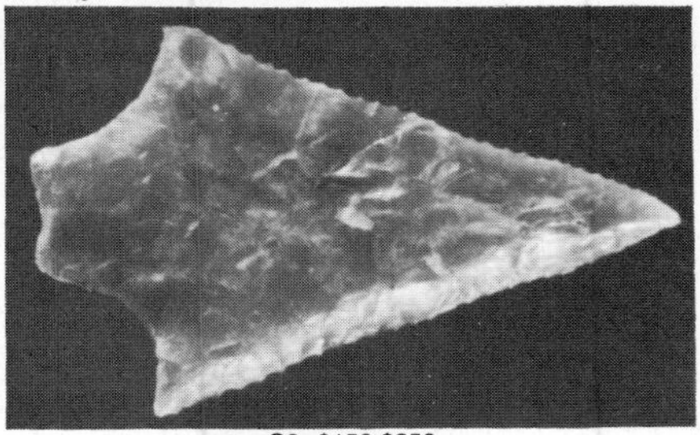

G9, $150-$250
Hillsborough Co., FL.

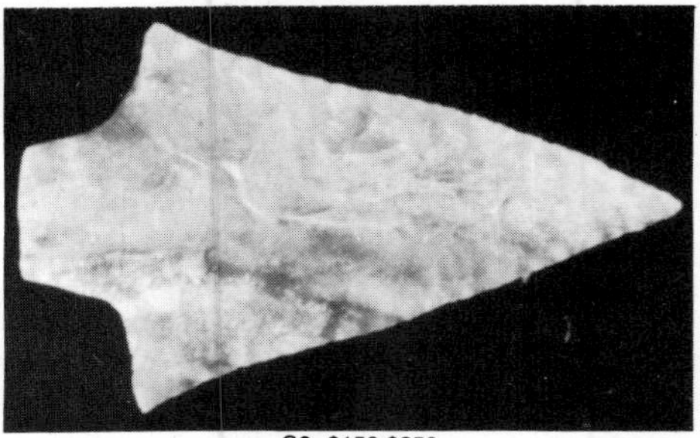

G10, $250-$350
Pasco Co., FL.

G9, $150-$250
Pasco Co., FL.

G9, $120-$200
Hillsborough Co., FL.

G9, $150-$250
Citrus Co., FL. Silver Lake.

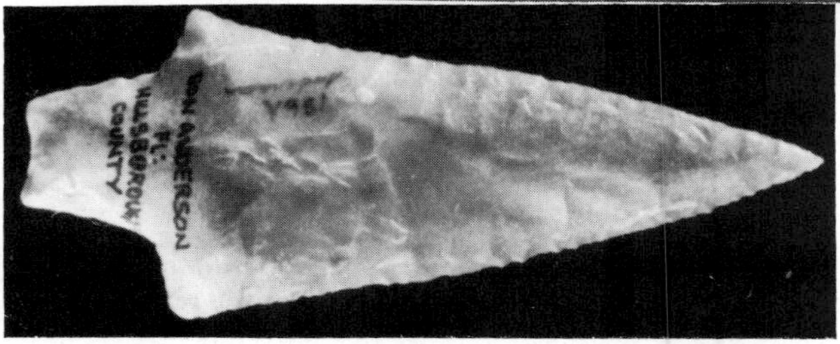

G10, $250-$400
Hillsborough Co., FL.

LOCATION: Southern Southeastern states. **DESCRIPTION:** A medium to large size stemmed point that occurs in two forms. One has a distinct bevel on one side of each face. The other has the typical bifacial beveling. Shoulders are tapered to horizontal. This type resembles the other Florida Archaic stemmed points (see above) except for the bevel and may be their ancestor. **I.D. KEY:** Beveling and one ear is higher.

HARDIN - Early Archaic, 9000 - 6000 B.P.

(Also see Buck Creek, Cypress Creek, Kirk, Lost Lake, Scottsbluff and Stilwell)

G3, $20-$30
Cent. IL. Tang nick.

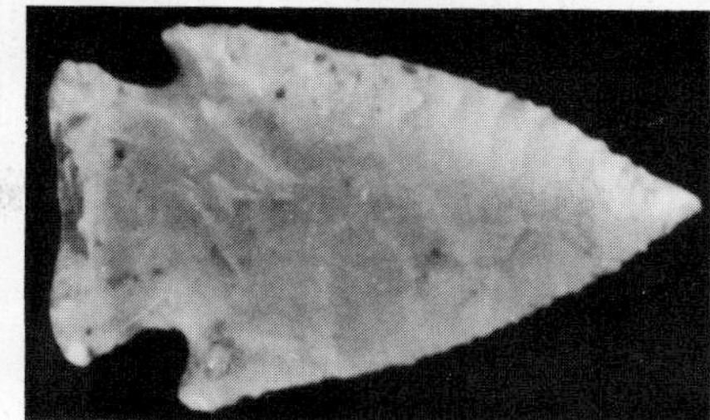

G4, $35-$60
MO.

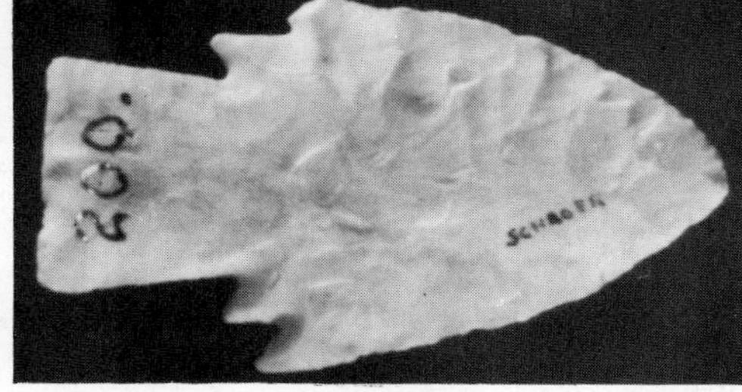

G5, $90-$160
Montgomery Co., MO. Tang nick.

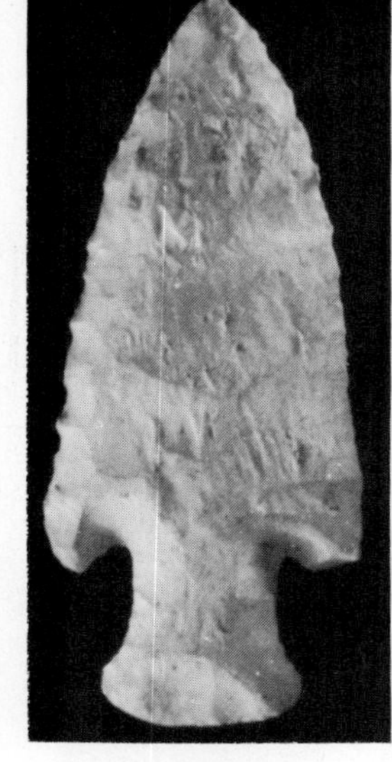

G4, $30-$45
SC. Tang nick.

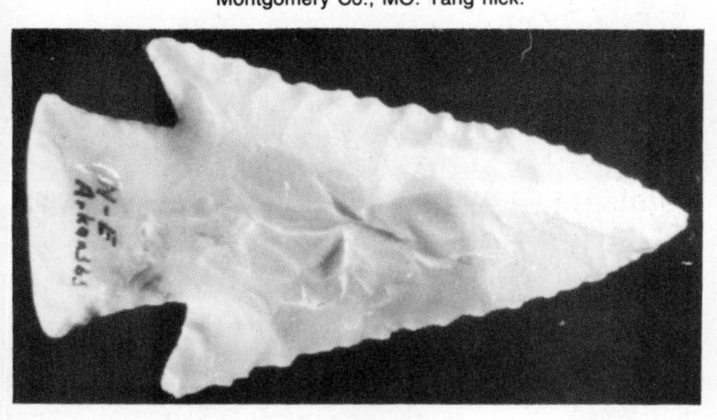

G7, $250-$400
NE AR.

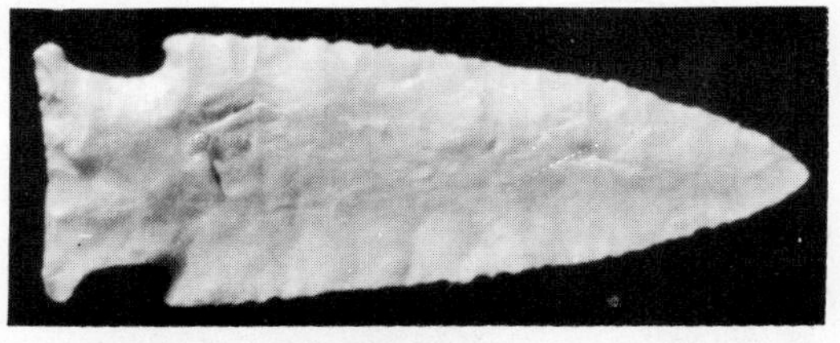

G5, $90-$160
Austin, TX.

LOCATION: Midwestern to Eastern states. **DESCRIPTION:** A large size, well made triangular barbed point with an expanded base that is usually ground. Resharpened examples have one beveled edge on each face. This type is believed to have evolved from the *Scottsbluff* type. **I.D. KEY:** Notches.

HARDIN (continued)

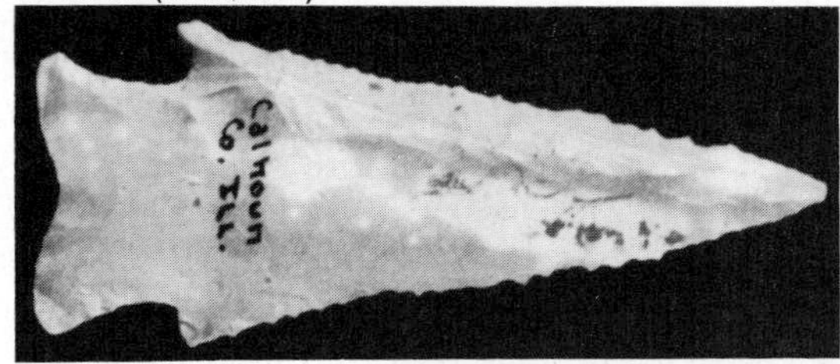

G4, $35-$65
Calhoun Co., IL.

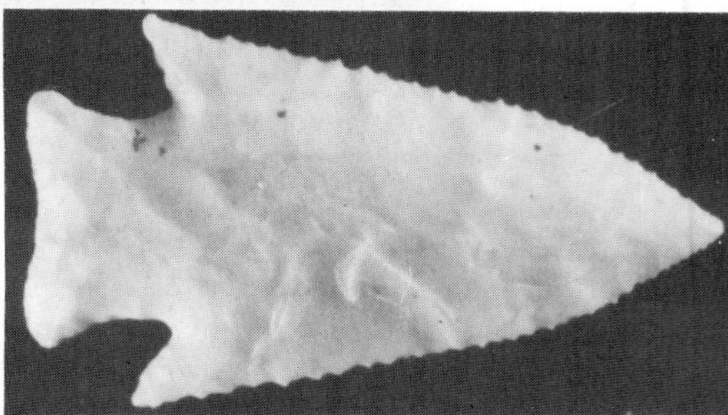

G7, $250-$350
MO.

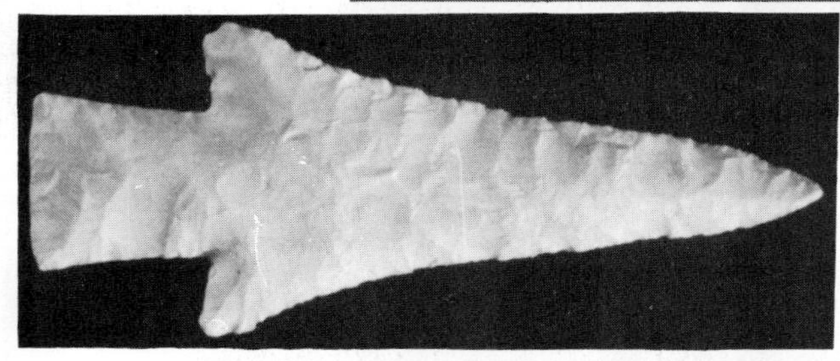

G5, $90-$160
NE AR.

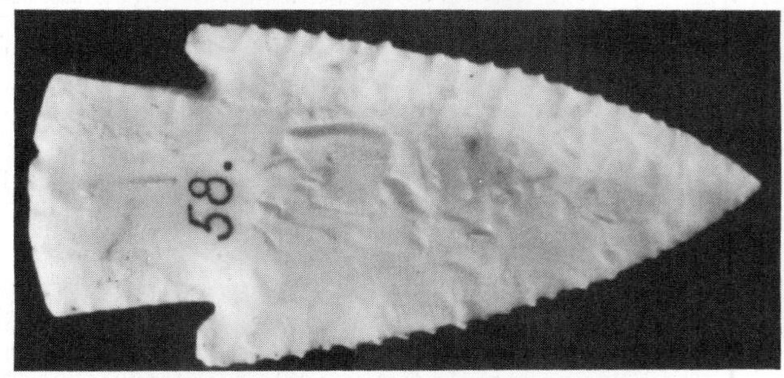

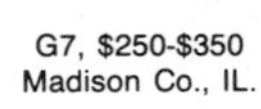

G7, $250-$350
Madison Co., IL.

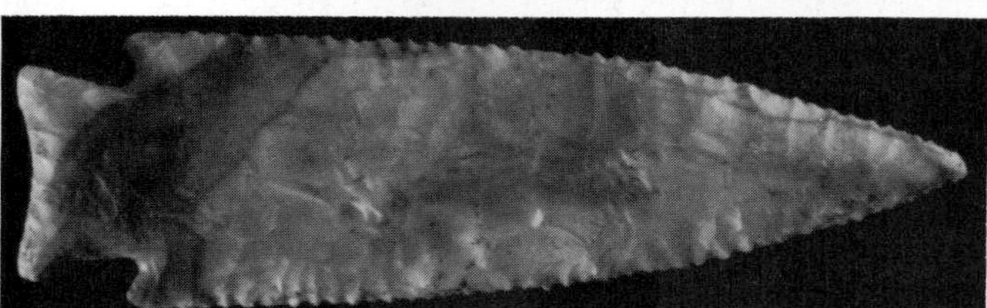

G7, $250-$380
Benton Co., MO.

HARDIN (continued)

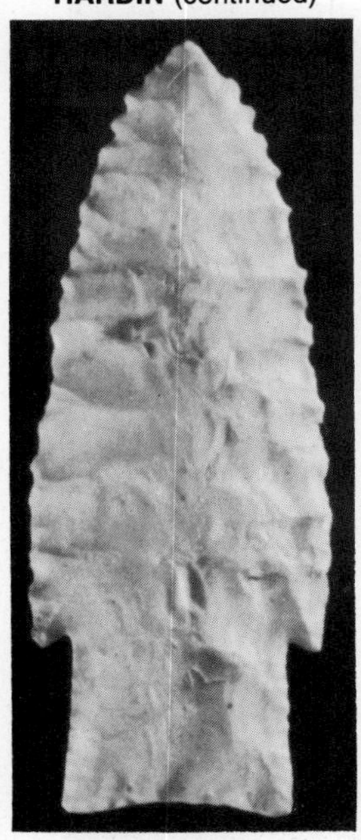

G6, $150-$280
Greene Co., AR.

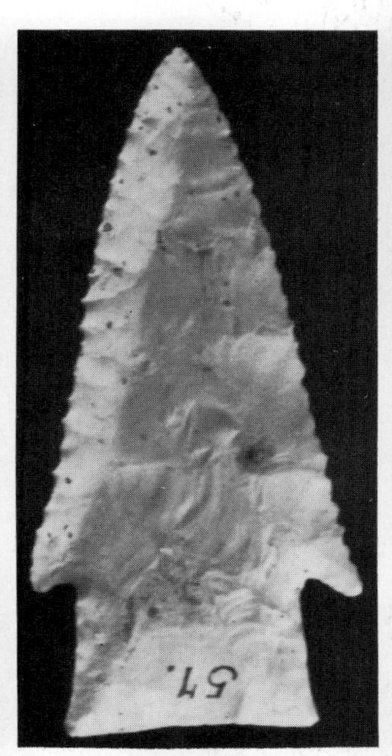

G7, $250-$450
Jersey Co., IL.

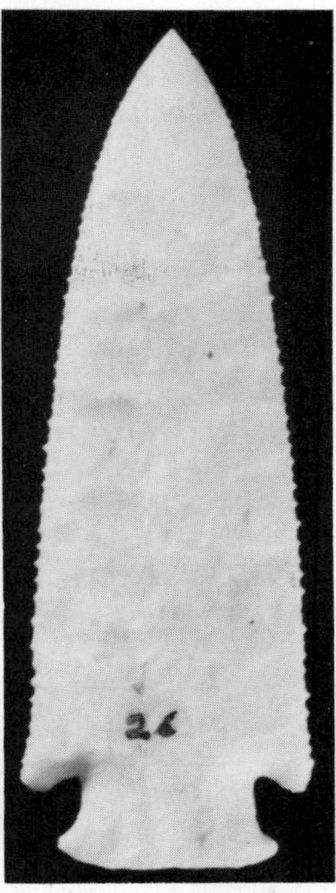

G9, $450-$800
IL.

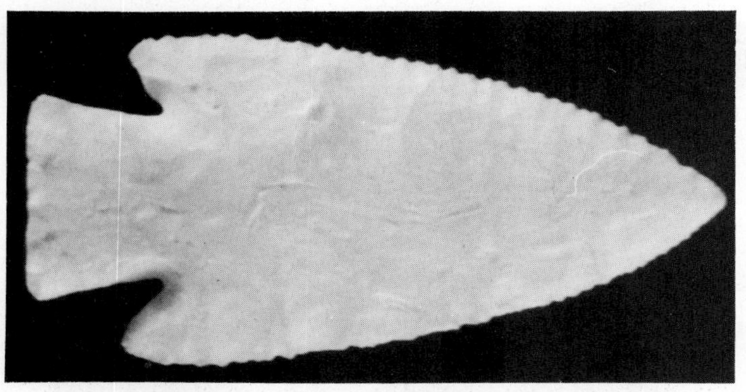

G8, $350-$600
Pike Co., IL.

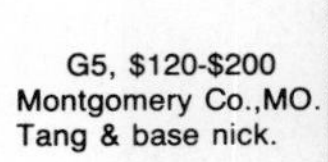

G5, $120-$200
Montgomery Co.,MO.
Tang & base nick.

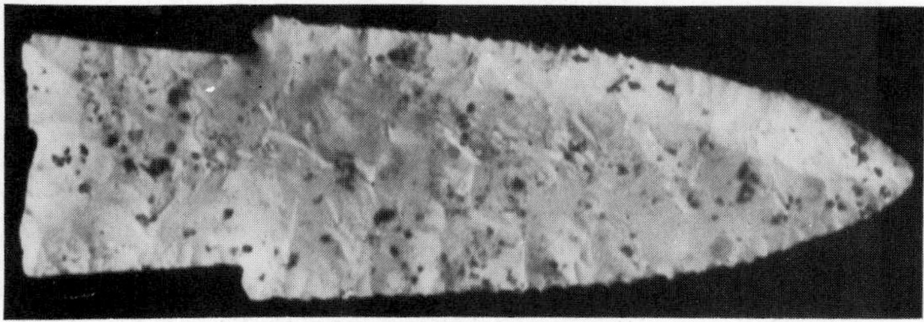

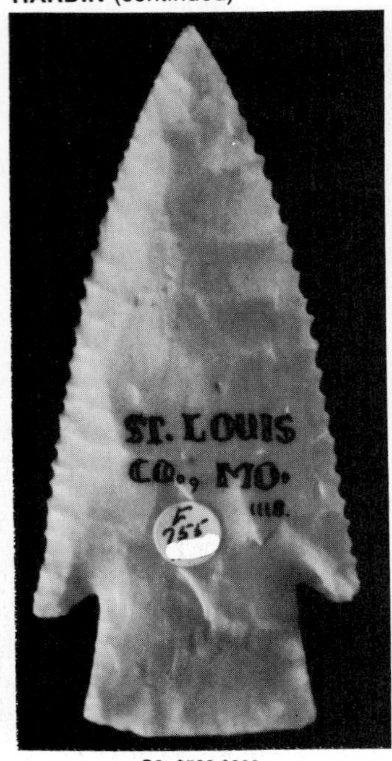

G9, $500-$800
St. Louis Co., MO.

G9, $500-$800
Scott Co., IL.

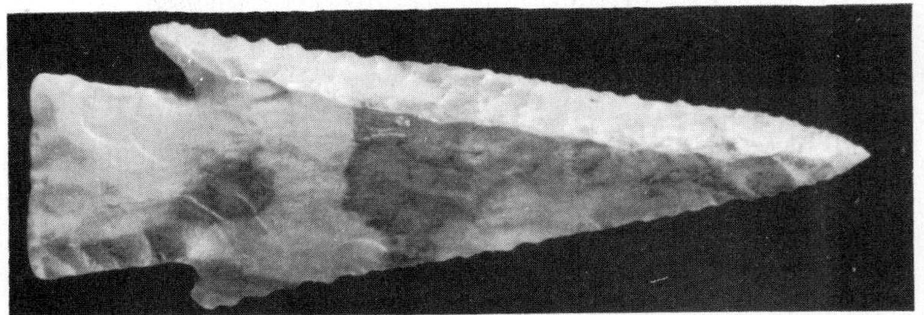

G7, $250-$350, KY. Bevel on left side.

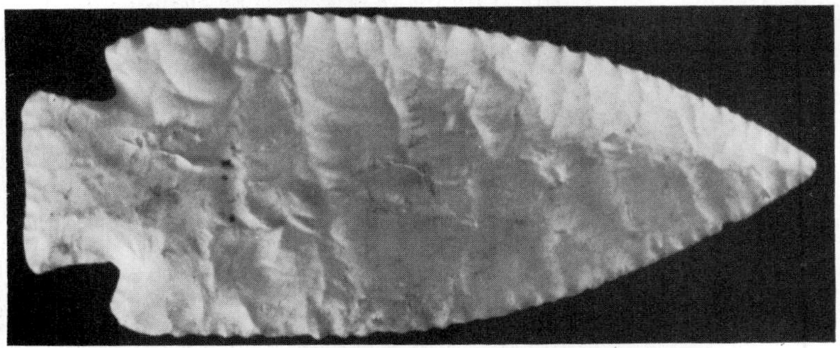

G8, $350-$600, Boone Co., MO.

HARDIN (continued)

G7, $250-$450
IL.

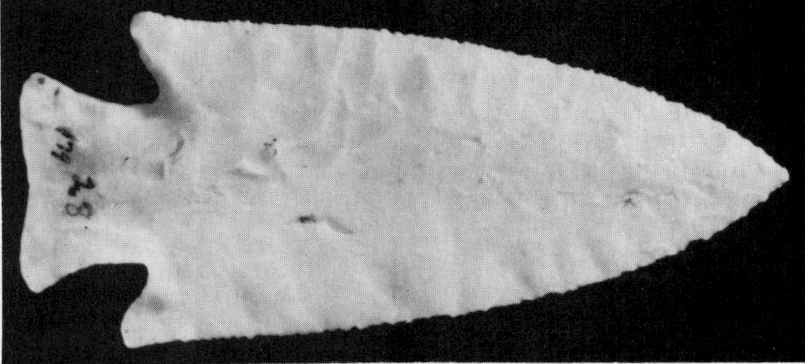

G10, $700-$1200
MO.

G5, $120-$200
Pike Co., IL.
Tang nick.

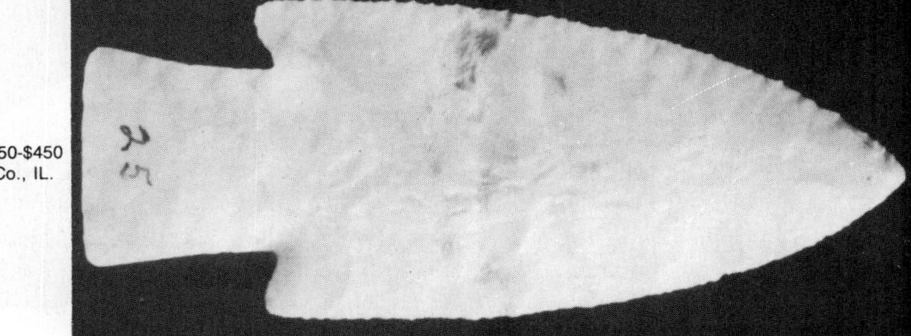

G7, $250-$450
Pike Co., IL.

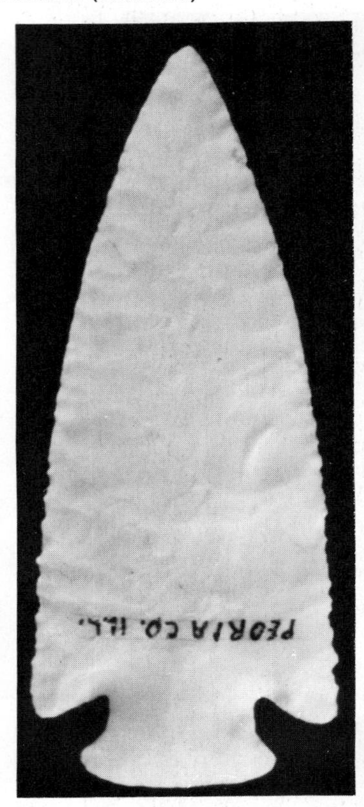

G8, $350-$500
Peoria Co., IL.

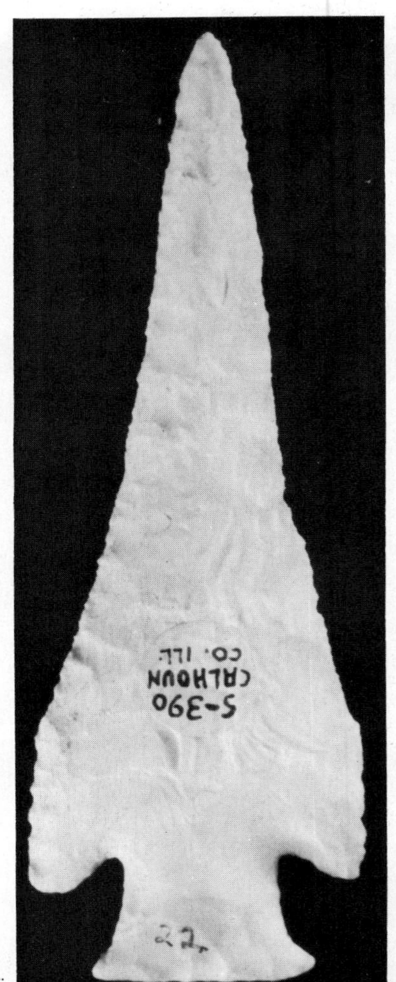

G9, $400-$700
Calhoun Co., IL.

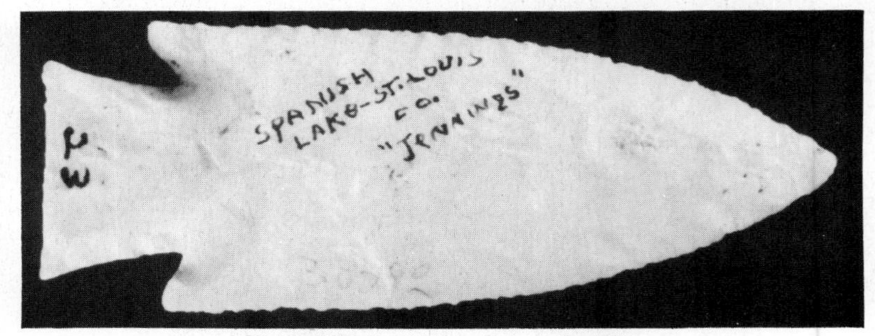

G9, $500-$950, Spanish Lake, St. Louis Co., MO.

G10, $800-$1500
IL.

G9, $450-$700
Pike Co., MO.

G8, $350-$600
MO.

G10, $5000-$8000
Ohio Co., KY. "Knobbed" Hardin.
One of the finest known.

G10, $1000-$1800
Clay Co., AR.

HARPETH RIVER - Transitional Paleo, 9000 - 8000 B.P.

(Also see Bakers Creek, Dalton-Nuckolls, Mud Creek, Russell Cave and Searcy)

G2, $2-$4
Humphreys Co., TN.

G5, $25-$40
Washington Co., VA.

G5, $25-$40
Clarksville, TN.

G6, $50-$80
Humphreys Co., TN.

G7, $80-$120
Davidson Co., TN. Cache point.

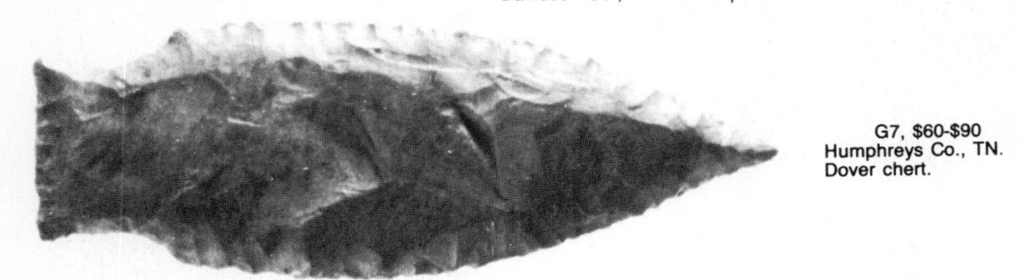

G7, $60-$90
Humphreys Co., TN.
Dover chert.

LOCATION: Southwestern Kentucky into the Southeastern states. **DESCRIPTION:** A medium to large size, narrow, thick, serrated stemmed point that is steeply beveled on all four sides. The hafting area either has shallow side notches or an expanding stem. The base is usually thinned and ground. Rarely, the base is birfurcated. **I.D. KEY:** Weak notches, edgework.

G8, $200-$300
Davidson Co., TN. Cache point.
Note bifurcated base.

G6, $50-$80
Humphreys Co., TN. Dover chert.
Thick cross section. Excellent.

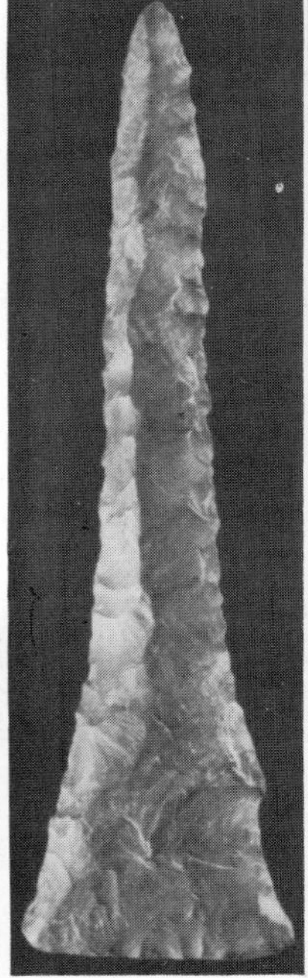

G8, $100-$180
Humphreys Co., TN.

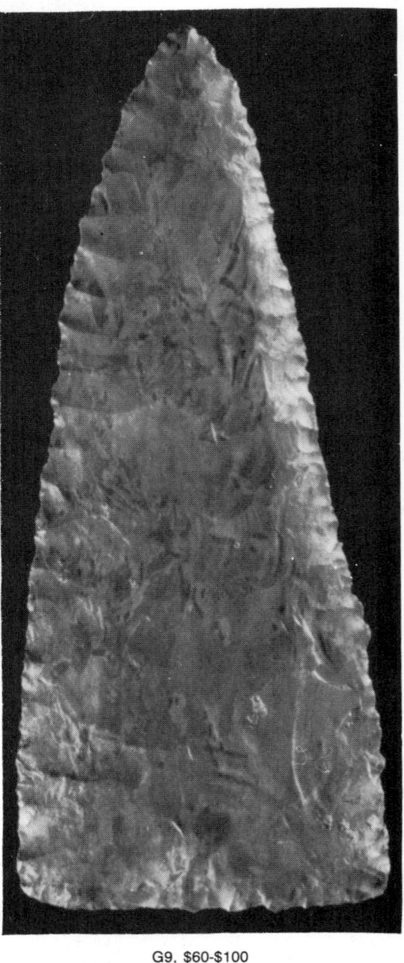

G9, $60-$100
Davidson Co., TN., Harpeth River
site. Preform for the type.

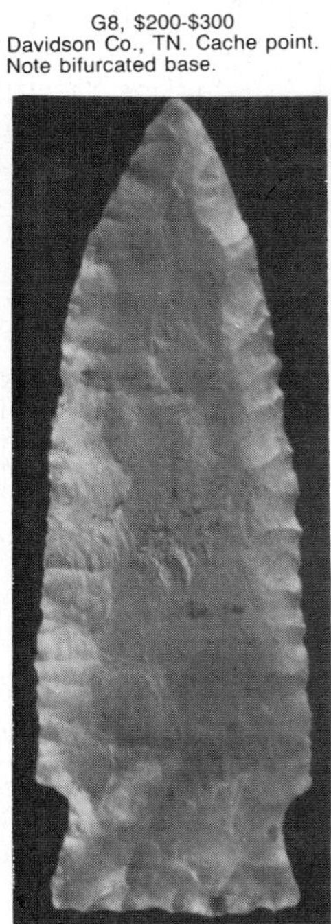

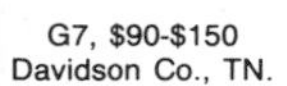

G7, $90-$150
Davidson Co., TN.

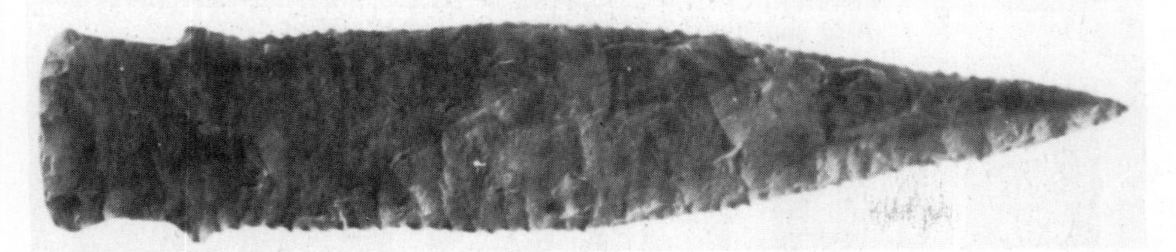

G10, $1500-$2500, Humphreys Co., TN. Thin and outstanding edgwork. Dover chert.

G8, $100-$180
Humphreys Co., TN. Buffalo River chert.

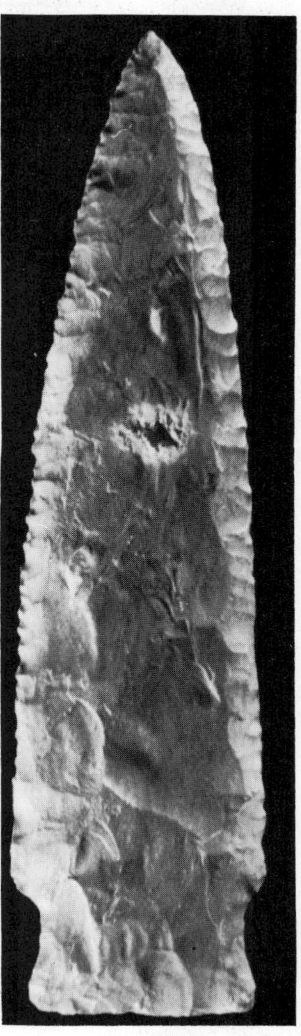

G9, $450-$600
Davidson Co., TN. Lacks the fine edgework or would grade a 10.

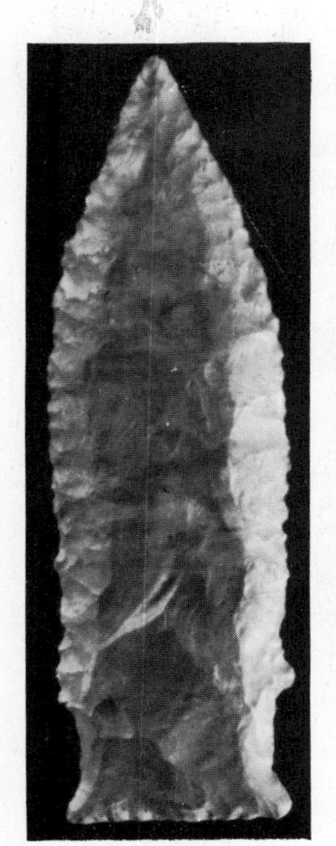

G9, $350-$450
Humphreys Co., TN. Dover chert.

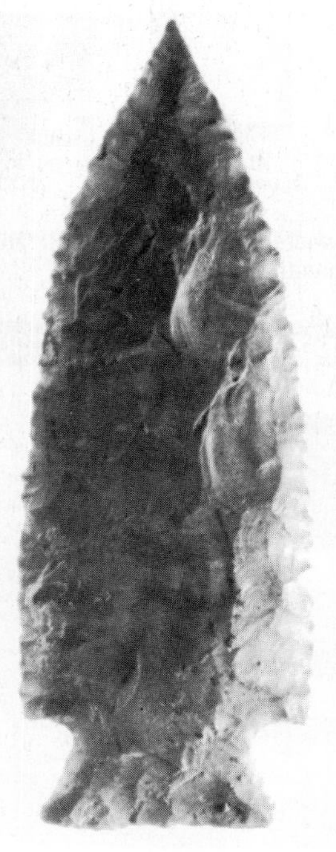

G9, $350-$450
Davidson Co., TN. Cache point.

HARRELL - Mississippian to Historic, 900 - 500 B.P.

(Also see Cahokia, Desert, Toyah and Washita)

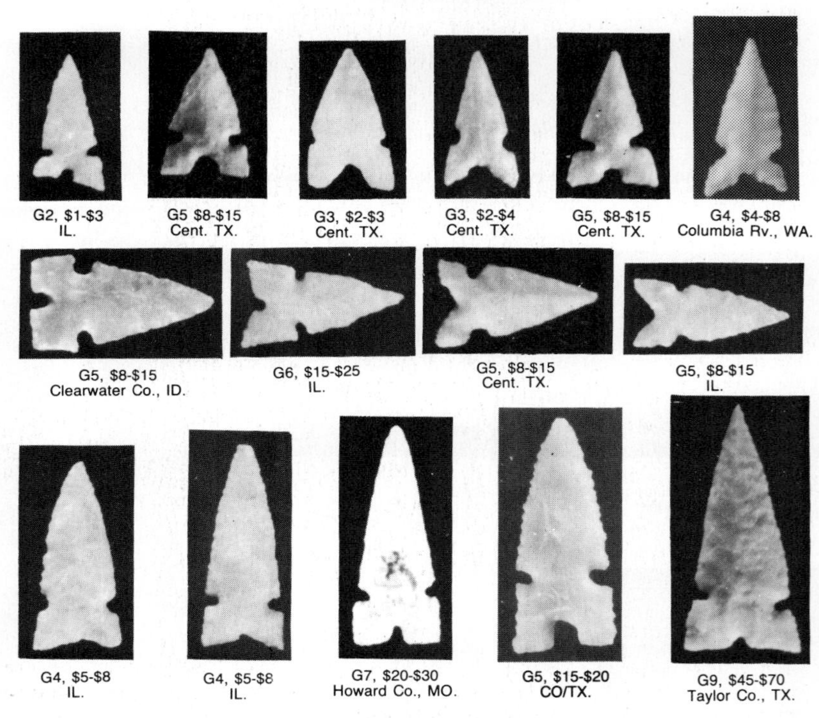

G2, $1-$3 IL. — G5 $8-$15 Cent. TX. — G3, $2-$3 Cent. TX. — G3, $2-$4 Cent. TX. — G5, $8-$15 Cent. TX. — G4, $4-$8 Columbia Rv., WA.

G5, $8-$15 Clearwater Co., ID. — G6, $15-$25 IL. — G5, $8-$15 Cent. TX. — G5, $8-$15 IL.

G4, $5-$8 IL. — G4, $5-$8 IL. — G7, $20-$30 Howard Co., MO. — G5, $15-$20 CO/TX. — G9, $45-$70 Taylor Co., TX.

LOCATION: Northwest to Midwestern states. **DESCRIPTION:** A small size, thin, triangular point with side and basal notches.

HASKELL - Mississippian to Historic, 800 - 600 B.P.

(Also see Desert and Toyah)

G4, $5-$8 Comanche Co., TX. — G8, $45-$70 Spiro Mound, OK. — G9, $60-$100 Pike Co., AR. Davis site. — G7, $25-$40 AR. — G4, $4-$6 Comanche Co., TX. — G10, $150-$250 Spiro Mound, OK. Note unusual double notch.

LOCATION: Northwest to Midwestern states. **DESCRIPTION:** A small size, thin, narrow, triangular, side-notched point with a concave base.

HAW RIVER - Transitional Paleo, 13000 - 8000 B.P.

(Also see Barber and Kinney)

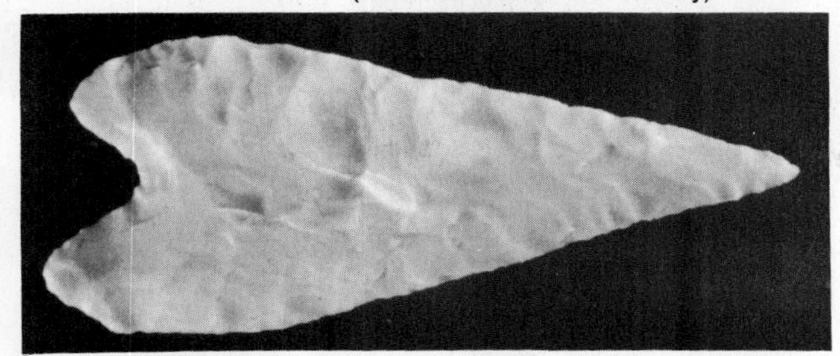

G6, $25-$40
Comanche Co., TX.

G8, $45-$70
Florence, AL., Coffee Lake.

LOCATION: Southeastern states, esp. North Carolina. **DESCRIPTION:** A medium to large size, thin, broad, elliptical blade with a basal notch and usually, rounded tangs that turn inward. Believed to be ancestor to the *Alamance* point.

HAYES - Mississippian, 1200 - 600 B.P.

(Also see Alba, Blevins, Homan, Howard, Klickatat Dagger, Perdiz & Sequoyah)

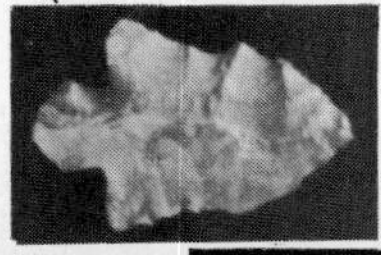

G2, $2-$4
Lincoln Parrish, LA.

G4, $20-$35
Sou. AR.

G7, $50-$80
Sou. AR.

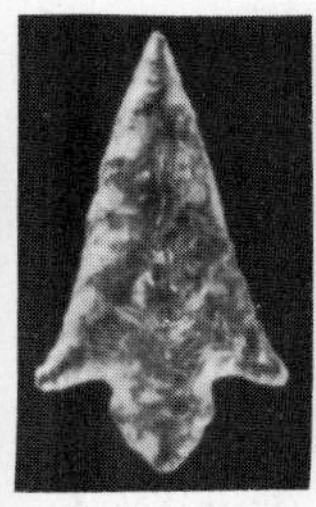

G7, $100-$200
Little Rv. Co., AR.
Crystal.

G6, $36-$60
Sou. AR.

G4, $25-$45
Little Rv. Co., AR.

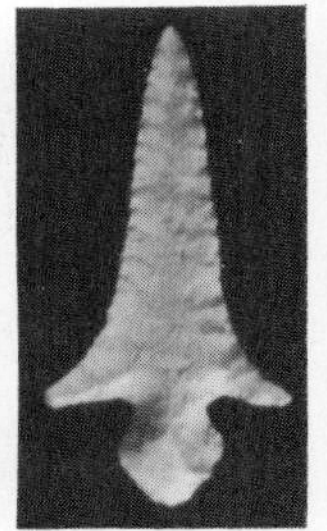

G8, $80-$140
Little Rv. Co., AR.

LOCATION: Midwestern states. **DESCRIPTION:** A small to medium size, narrow, expanded tang point with a turkeytail base. Blade edges are usually strongly recurved forming sharp pointed tangs. Some examples are serrated. **I.D. KEY:** Pointed base and flaking style.

HAYES (continued)

G8, $120-$220
Little Rv., Co., AR. Crystal.

G7, $60-$90
IL.

G7, $50-$80
Cent. MO.

G5, $30-$50
Comanche Co., TX.

G9, $100-$200
Sou. AR.

G8, $90-$150
Little Rv. Co., AR.

G8, $100-$175
Sou. AR.

G9, $120-$200
Sou. AR.

G8, $120-$200
Sou. AR. Crystal.

G8, $90-$150
Little Rv. Co., AR.

G10, $180-$300
Sou. AR.

G9, $100-$160
Little Rv. Co., AR.

G8, $70-$120
Little Rv. Co., AR.

G10, $250-$450
Little Rv. Co., AR.
Crystal

G10, $250-$450
Sou. AR.

G10, $200-$350
Sou. AR.

G8, $100-$180
Little Rv. Co., AR.

G9, $120-$200
Sou. AR.

G8, $90-$150
Little Rv. Co., AR.

G10, $180-$300
Sou. AR.

G9, $100-$180
Little Rv. Co., AR.

G9, $120-$200
Little Rv. Co. AR.

HEAVY DUTY - Early to mid-Archaic, 7000 - 5000 B.P.

(Also see Kirk Serrated and Stone Square Stem)

G3, $30-$40
Hardin Co., KY.
Sonora flint.

G5, $30-$40
Fayette Co., KY.

G3, $20-$30
Bethany, WV.

G4, $40-$60
Hardin Co., KY.
Sonora flint.

G5, $40-$70
Russell Co., KY.

LOCATION: Eastern states. **DESCRIPTION:** A medium to large size, thick, serrated point with a parallel stem and a straight to slightly concave base. A variant of *Kirk Serrated* found in the Southeast. **I.D. KEY:** Base, thickness, flaking.

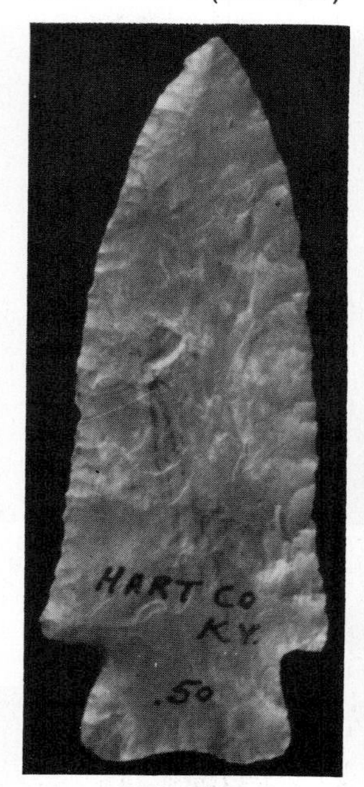

G7, $120-$200
Hart Co., KY.

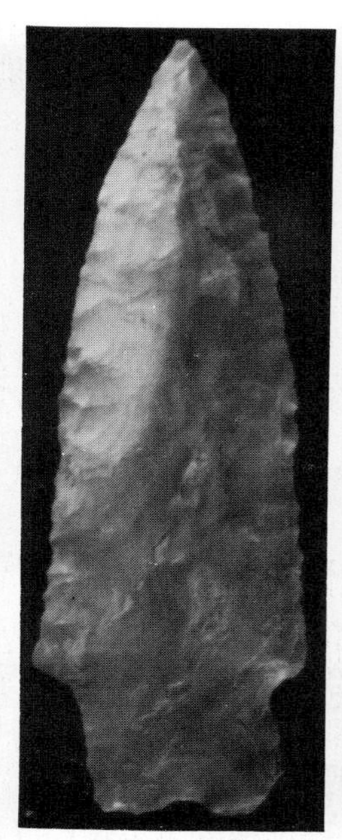

G6, $120-$200
Clark Co., KY. Carter
Cave flint.

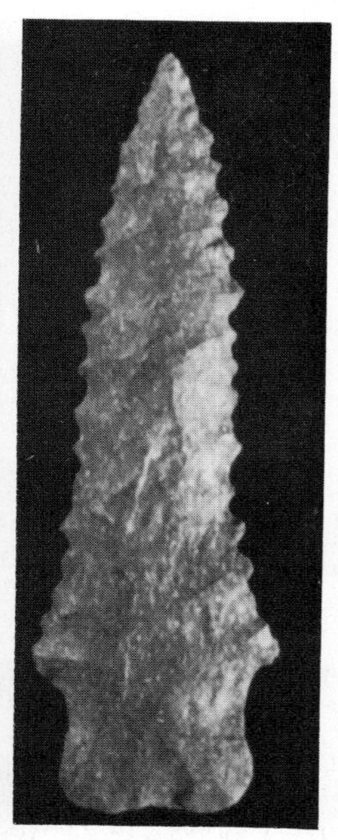

G6, $50-$80
KY.

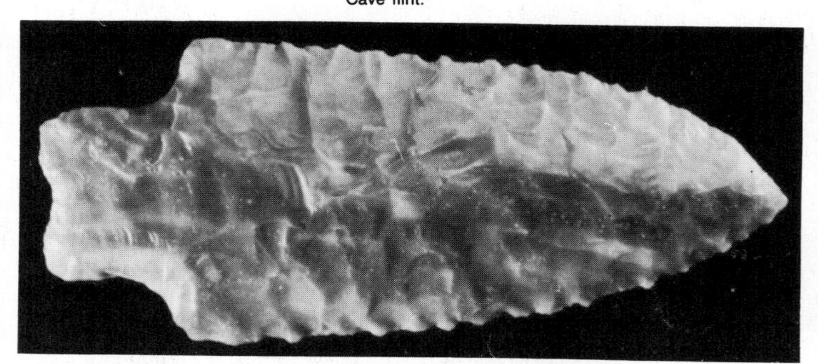

G7, $125-$200, Marion Co., KY.

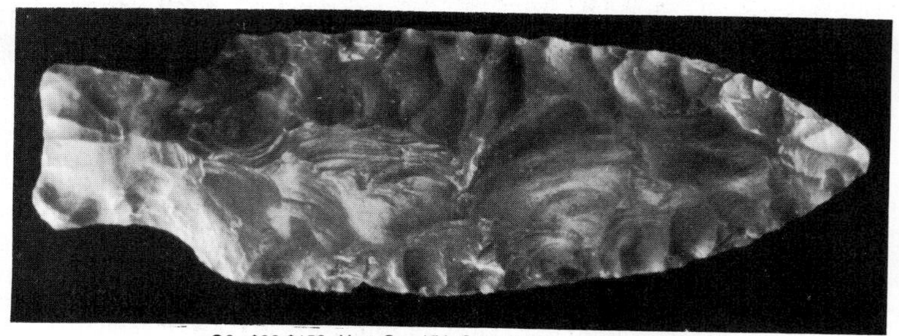

G6, $90-$150, Hart Co., KY. Sonora flint. Lacks edgework.

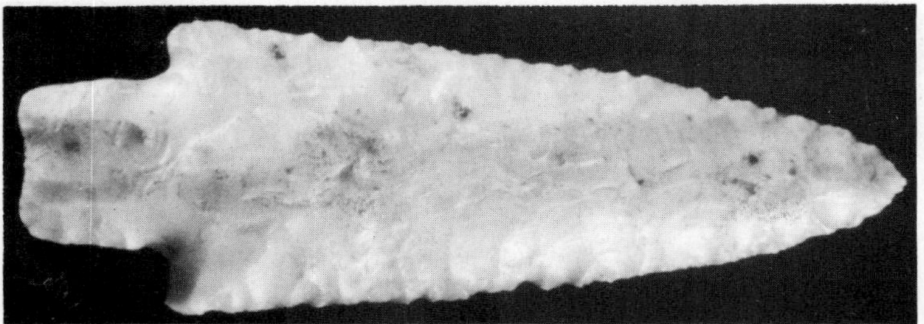

G8, $180-$300
Ohio

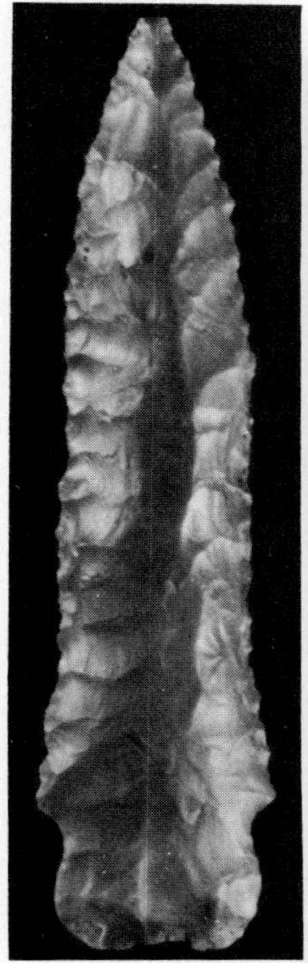

G5, $50-$80
Stewart Co., TN.

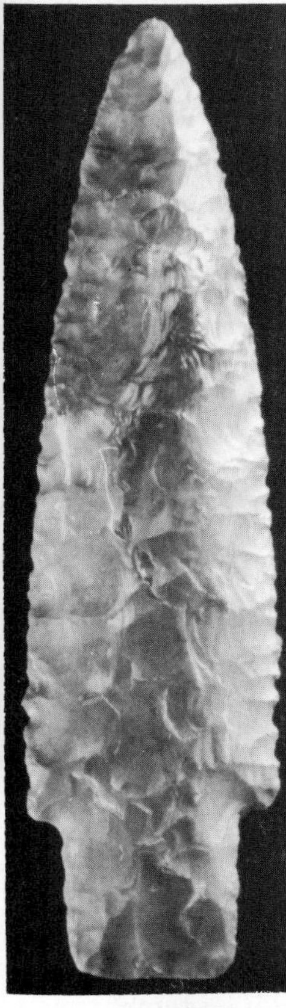

G8, $180-$300
Ohio.

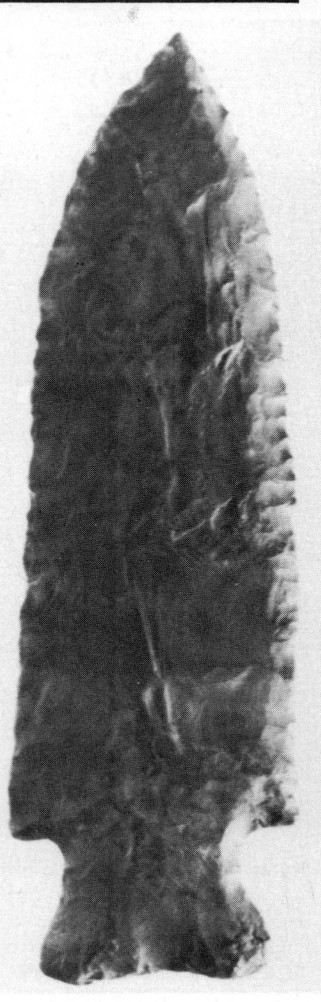

G9, $250-$400
Parsons, TN. Not classic form
but excellent quality.

HEBRON (See Turkeytail)

HELL GAP - Late Paleo, 12000 - 9000 B.P.

(Also see Agate Basin, Lake Mohave, Pelican and Rio Grande)

G3, $20-$35
Humphreys Co., TN.

G5, $45-$70
Lamar Co., AL.

G8, $250-$450
Benton Co., MO.

LOCATION: Midwestern to Western states. **DESCRIPTION:** A medium to large size lanceolate point with a long, contracting stem. The widest part of the blade is above mid-section. The base is straight to slightly concave and the stem edges are usually ground.

HELL GAP (continued)

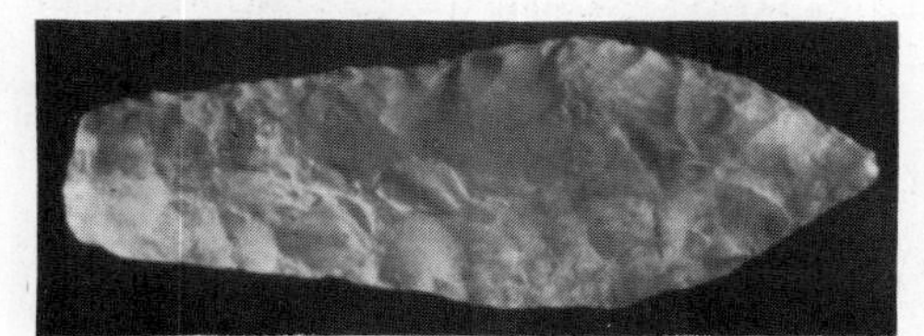

G6, $80-$120
MO.

G5, $45-$70
Comanche Co., TX.
Tip nick.

HEMPHILL - Early to mid-Archaic, 7000 - 4000 B.P.

(Also see Big Sandy, Dalton-Hemphill, Osceola)

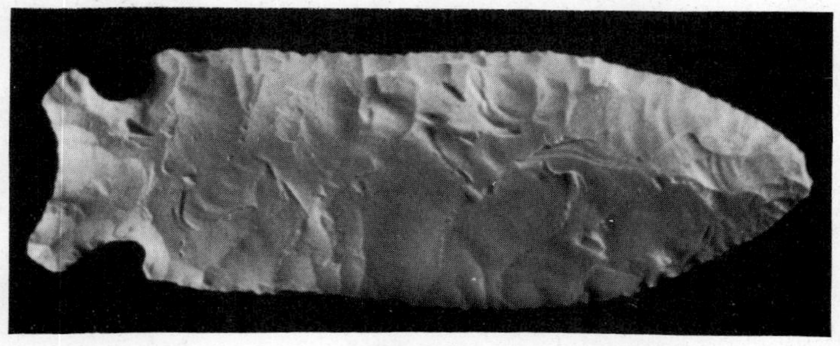

G7, $50-$80
Florence, AL., Coffee Lake. Similar to *Dalton-Hemphill*, and early form for the type. (Transitional).

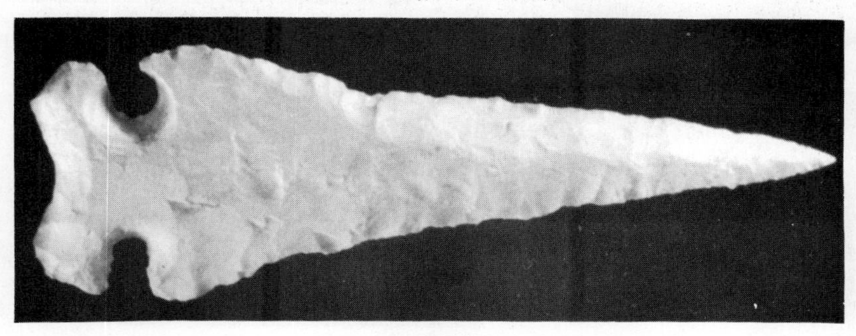

G9, $250-$400
Jackson Co., AL. Resharpened form. Left-hand bevel.

LOCATION: Midwestern to Northeastern states. **DESCRIPTION:** A medium to large size side-notched point with a concave base and parallel to convex sides. These points are usually thinner and of higher quality than the similar *Osceola* type.

HERNANDO - Late Archaic, 4000 - 2500 B.P.

(Also see Citrus, Culbreath, Eva, Parowan and San Saba)

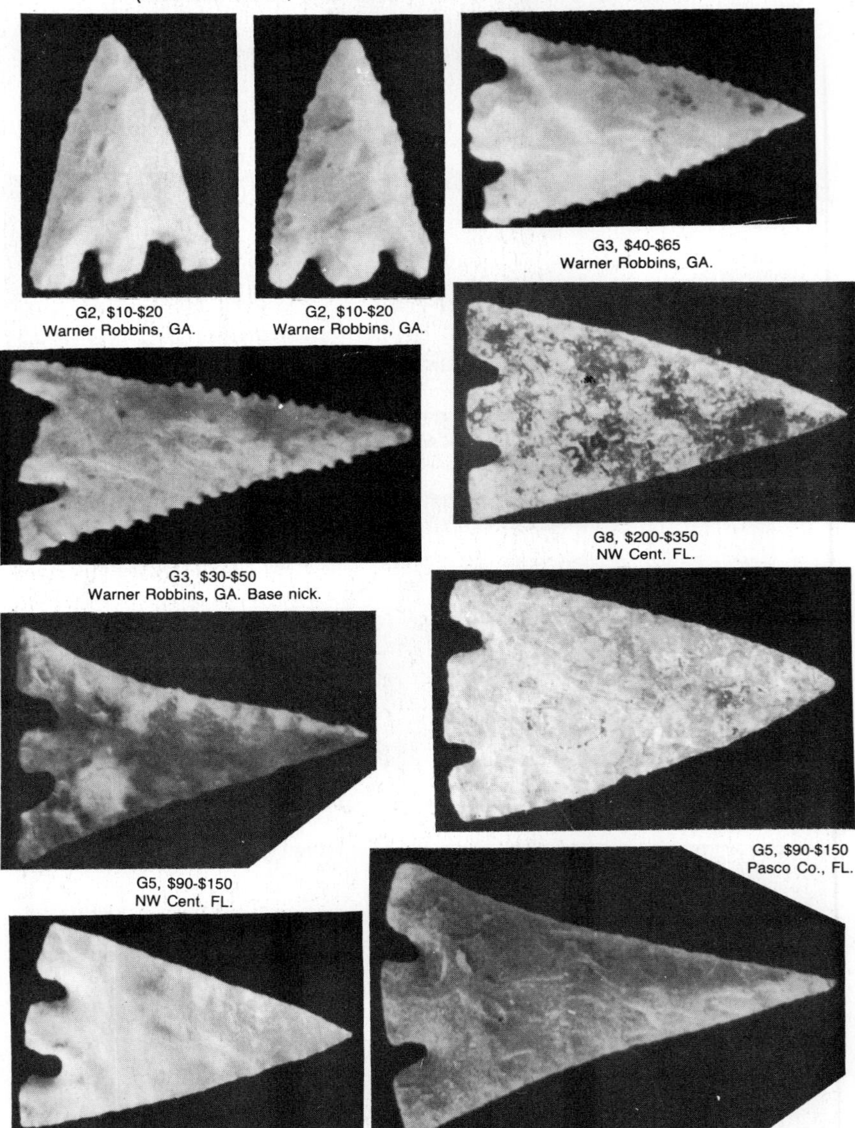

G2, $10-$20
Warner Robbins, GA.

G2, $10-$20
Warner Robbins, GA.

G3, $40-$65
Warner Robbins, GA.

G8, $200-$350
NW Cent. FL.

G3, $30-$50
Warner Robbins, GA. Base nick.

G5, $90-$150
NW Cent. FL.

G5, $90-$150
Pasco Co., FL.

G4, $60-$100
Jefferson Co., FL.

G9, $350-$500
NW Cent. FL.

LOCATION: Georgia, Alabama and Florida. **DESCRIPTION:** A medium to large size, basal notched, triangular point with wide flaring tangs that may extend beyond the base. Side edges are straight to concave. Similar in outline only to the much earlier *Eva* type. Has been found in same layer with Dalton-Tallhassee. **I.D. KEY:** Early flaking and base form.

HERNANDO (continued)

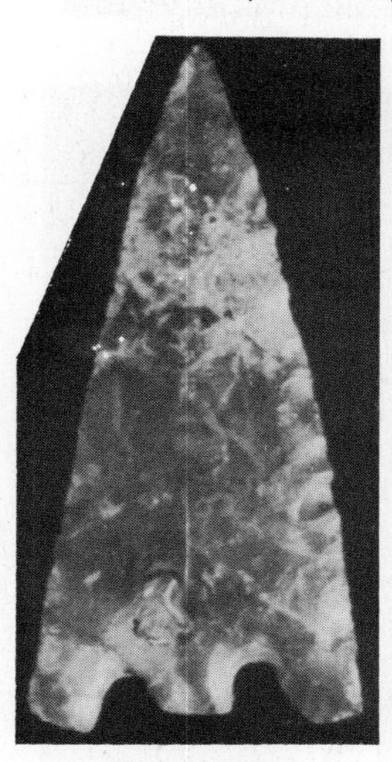

G8, $250-$400
NW Cent. FL. Coral.

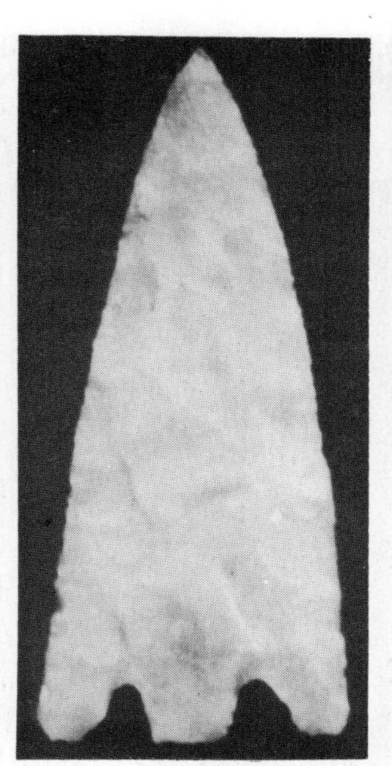

G7, $180-$300
NW Cent. FL.

G10, $400-$750
NW Cent. FL.

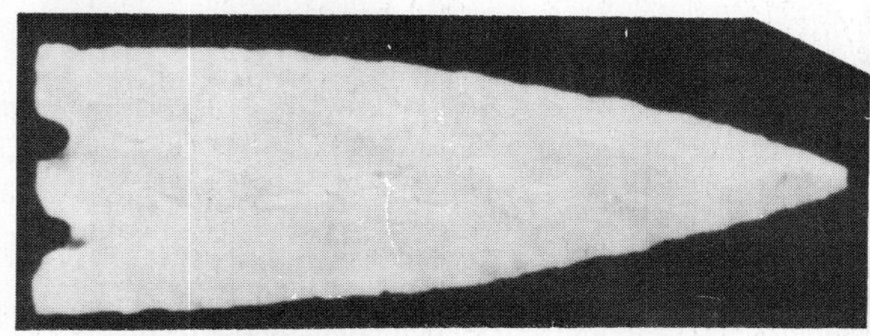

G6, $150-$250, NW Cent. FL.

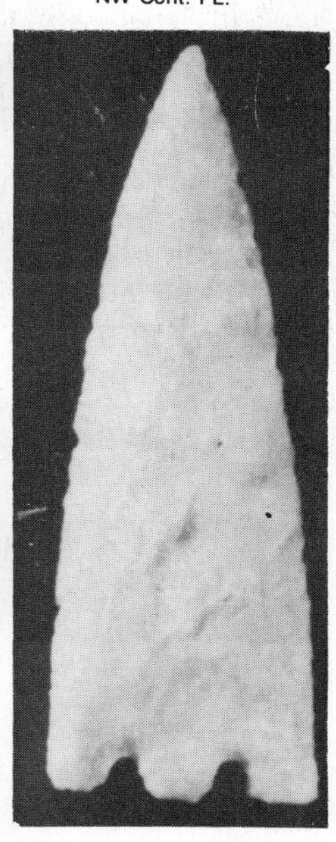

G8, $250-$400
NW Cent. FL.

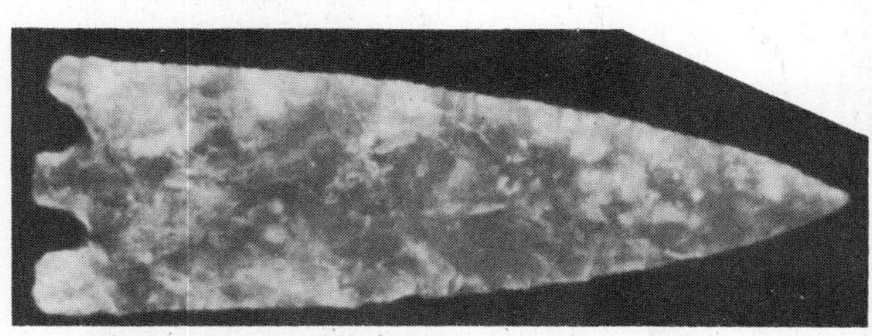

G8, $250-$400, NW Cent. FL.

G9, $350-$500, NW Cent. FL.

HIDDEN VALLEY - Mid to late Archaic, 5000 - 3000 B.P.

(Also see Gary, Langtry and Morrow Mountain)

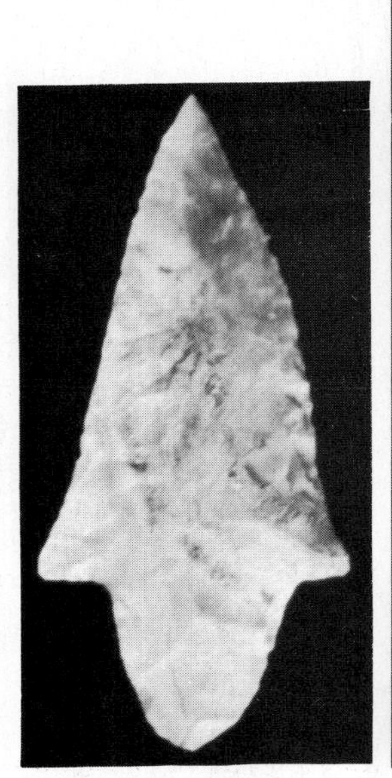

G7, $60-$90
Craighead, AR.

G6, $35-$65
Craighead, AR.

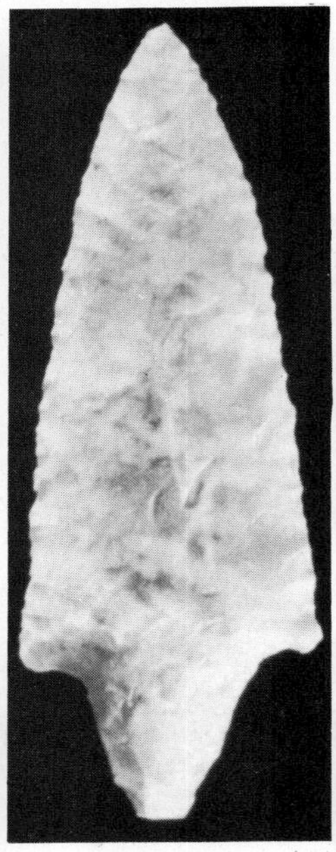

G6, $40-$75
Craighead AR.

LOCATION: Midwestern states. **DESCRIPTION:** A medium size point with square to tapered shoulders and a contracting base that can be pointed to straight. Flaking is earlier and more parallel than on *Gary* points. Called *Rice Contracted Stemmed* in Missouri.

HILLSBOROUGH - Mid-Archaic, 7000 - 5000 B.P.

(Also see Newnan)

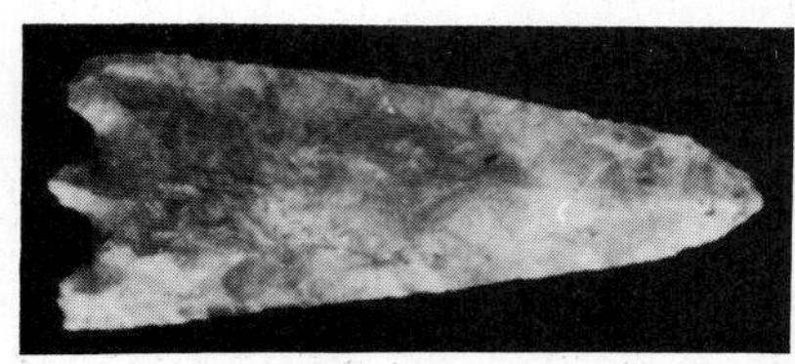

G2, $6-$10
Hillsborough Co., FL.

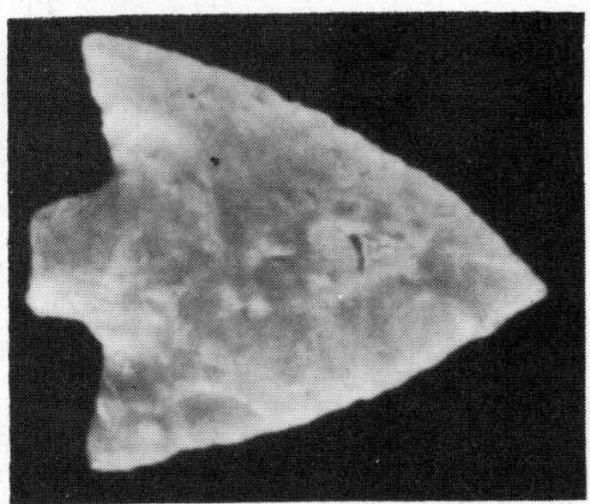

G3, $25-$45
NW FL.

LOCATION: Southern Southeastern states. **DESCRIPTION:** A medium to large size, broad, triangular point with a small contracting base. Shoulders are barbed and can expand beyond the base.

HILLSBOROUGH (continued)

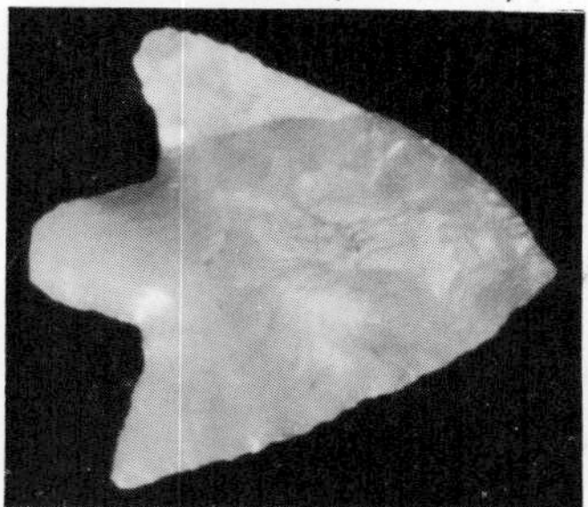

G3, $25-$45
Alachua Co., FL.

G3, $25-$40
Buddy Lake, FL.

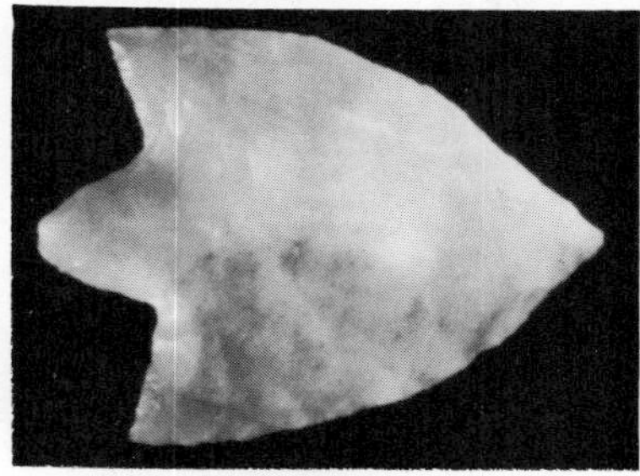

G4, $35-$60
Pasco, Co., FL.

G5, $60-$100
Hillsborough Co., FL.

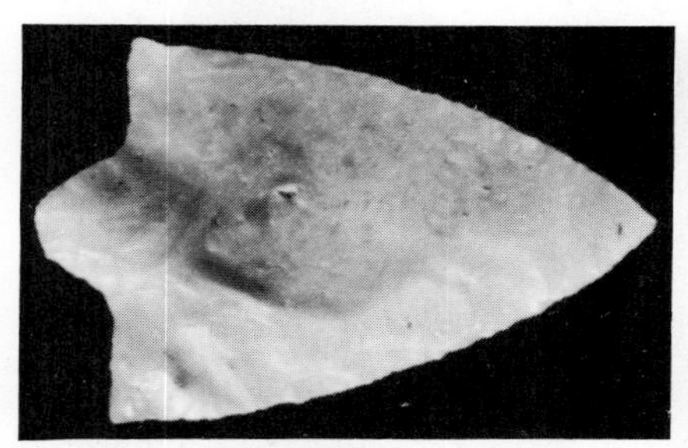

G5, $60-$100
Hillsborough Co., FL.

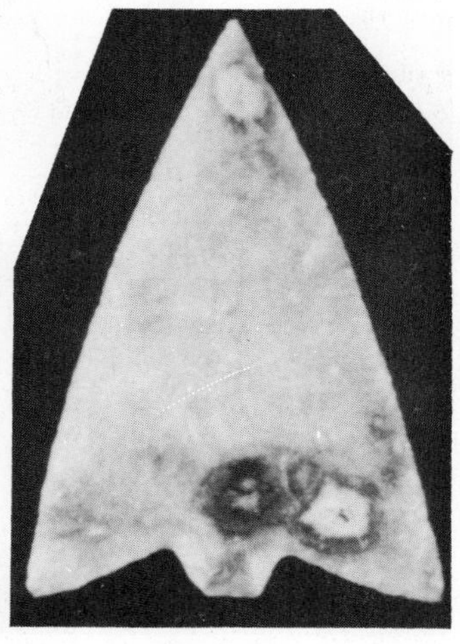

G7, $250-$450
NW Cent. FL.

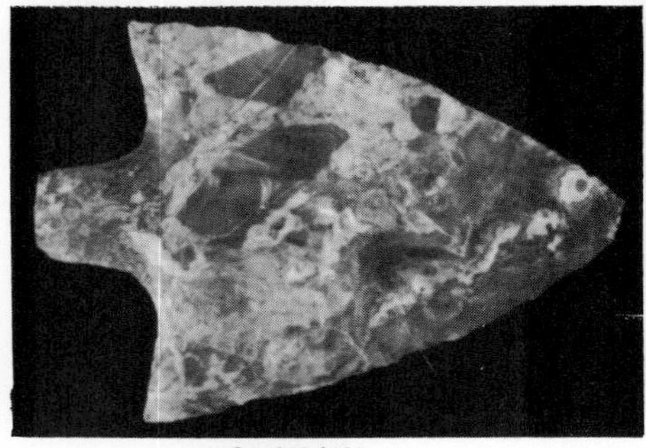

G5, $60-$100
Hillsborough Co., FL.

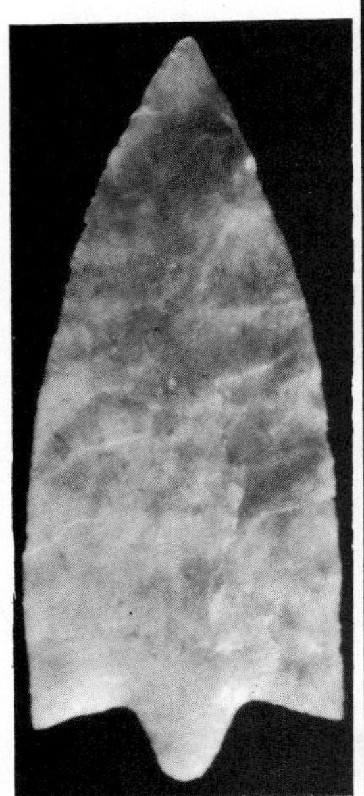

G8, $450-$700
Hillsborough Co., FL.

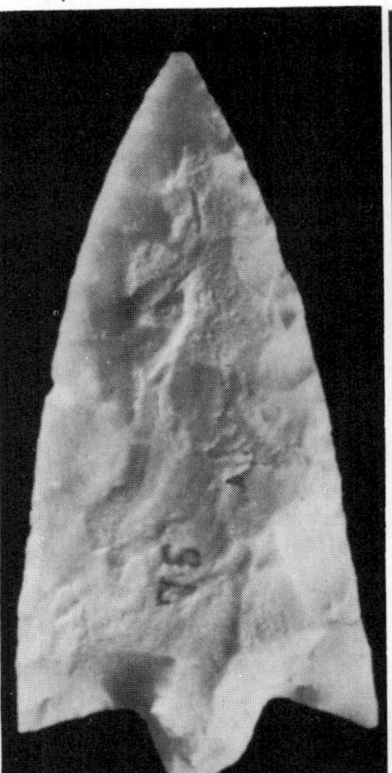

G7, $200-$350
Gainesville, FL., 43rd St.

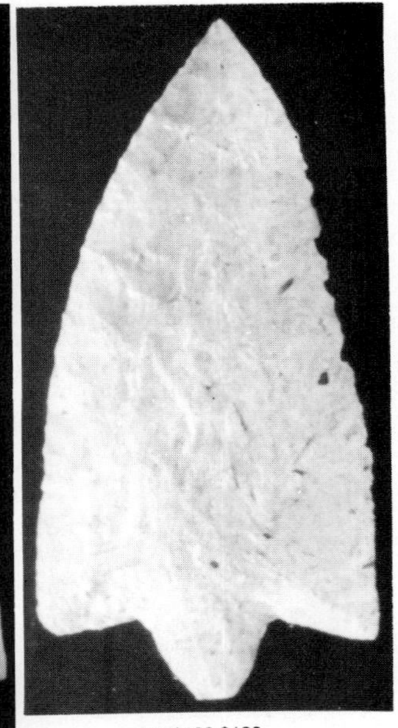

G6, $100-$180
Alachua Co., FL.

G9, $600-$1000
Hillsborough Co., FL. Color.

G8, $350-$550
NW Cent. FL.

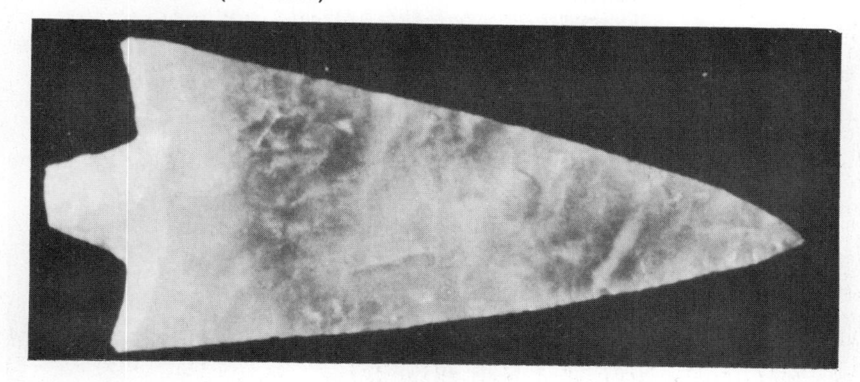

G9, $600-$1000
NW Cent. FL.

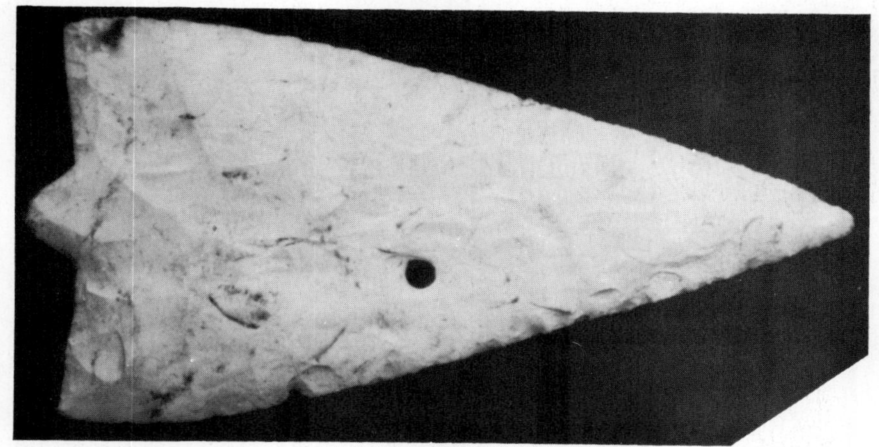

G8, $450-$600
Marion Co., FL.

G10, $1200-$1800
Pasco Co., FL.

G9, $600-$1000
NW Cent. FL.

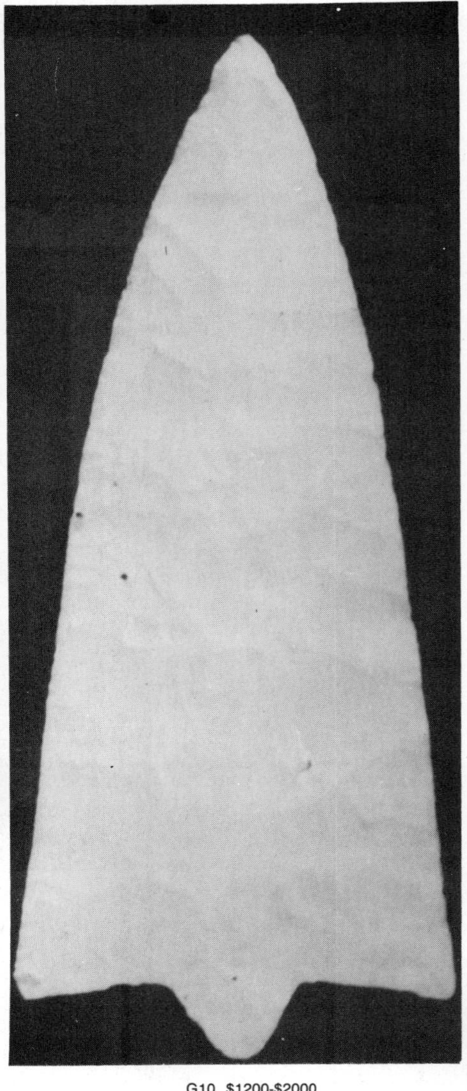

G10, $1200-$2000
NW Cent. FL.

HI-LO - Late Paleo, 10000 - 8000 B.P.

(Also see Angostura, Cowhouse Slough, Golondrina, Hardaway Blade, Jeff and Paint Rock Valley)

G5, $40-$50
Barren Co., KY.
Blade nicks.

G3, $12-$15
AR.

G7, $65-$75
MO.

LOCATION: Midwestern states. **DESCRIPTION:** A medium to large size, broad, eared, lanceolate point with a concave base. Believed to be related to *Plainview* and *Dalton* points.

HOLLAND - Transitional Paleo, 9500 - 7500 B.P.

(Also see Dalton, Hardin and Scottsbluff)

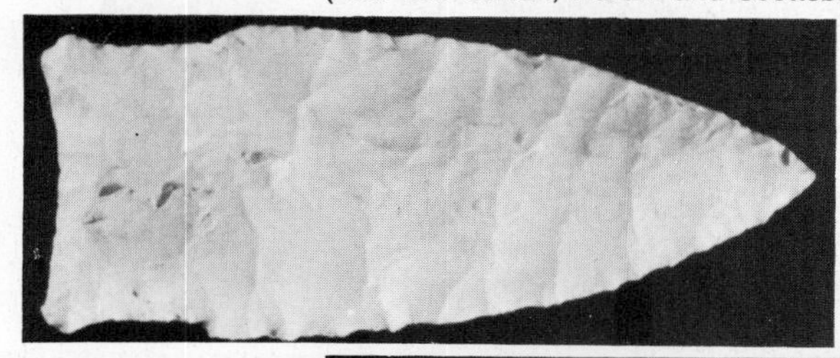

G5, $120-$220
W. Memphis, TN. Knobbed base. Oblique flaking.

G6, $150-$250
Anglum, MO.

LOCATION: Midwestern states. **DESCRIPTION:** A medium to large size lanceolate blade that is very well made. Shoulders are weak to nonexistant. Bases can be knobbed to auriculate and are usually ground. Some examples have horizontal to oblique transverse flaking. **I.D. KEY:** Weak notches, early flaking.

HOLLAND (continued)

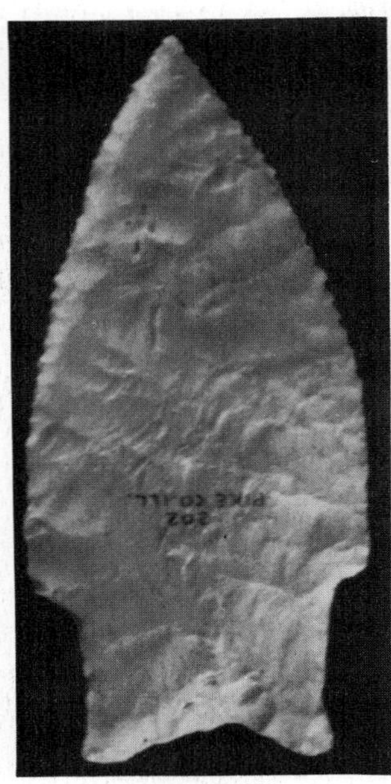

G8, $300-$500
Pike Co., IL.

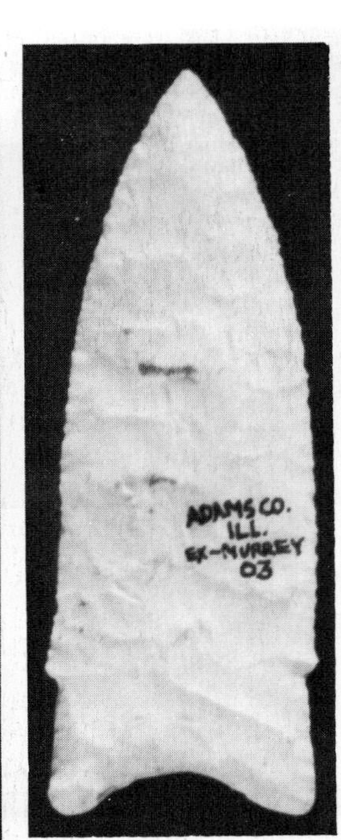

G7, $250-$400
Adams Co., IL.

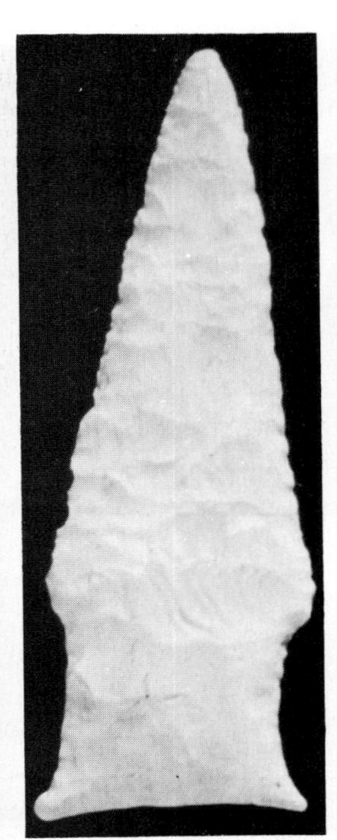

G7, $200-$300
Warnerd, KS.

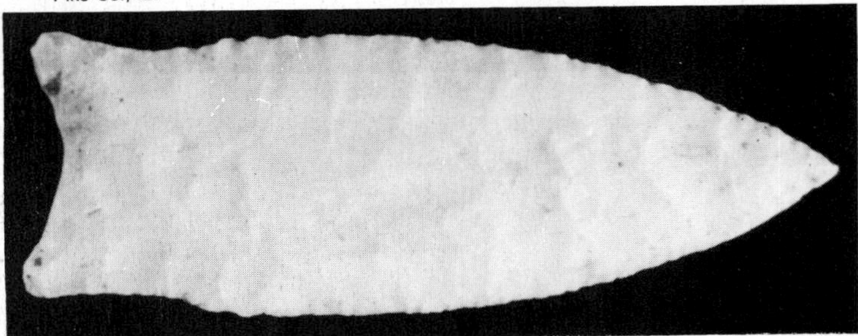

G8, $350-$600
Cent. IA.

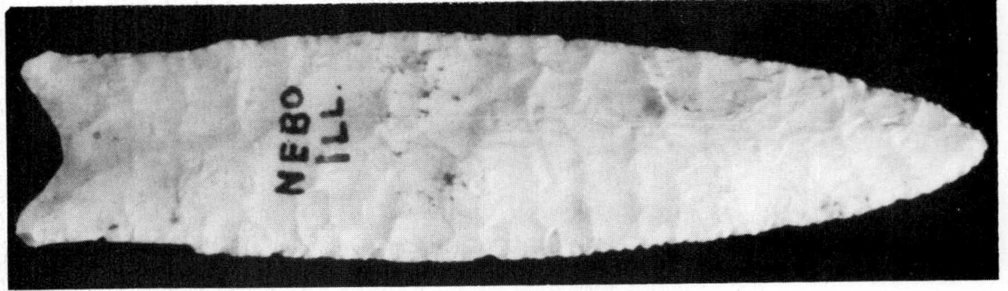

G7, $250-$400
Nebo, IL.

G10, $2500-$4000
St. Louis Co., MO. Note oblique parallel flaking. Very thin and excellent quality.

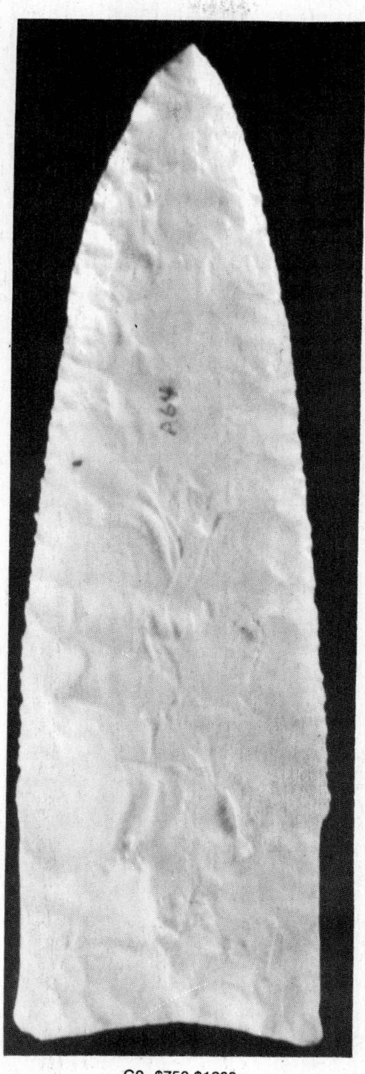

G9, $750-$1200
St. Louis Co., MO.

HOLLAND (continued)

G9, $1500-$2500
Calhoun Co., IL.

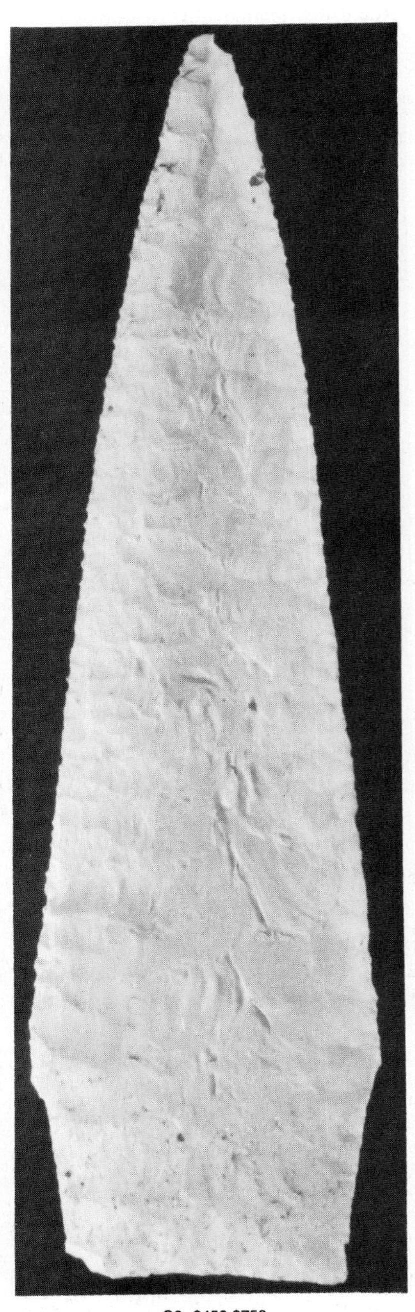

G9, $450-$750
Cooper, MO. Base & tip nick.

HOLMES - Late Archaic, 4000 - 3000 B.P.

(Also see Savannah River)

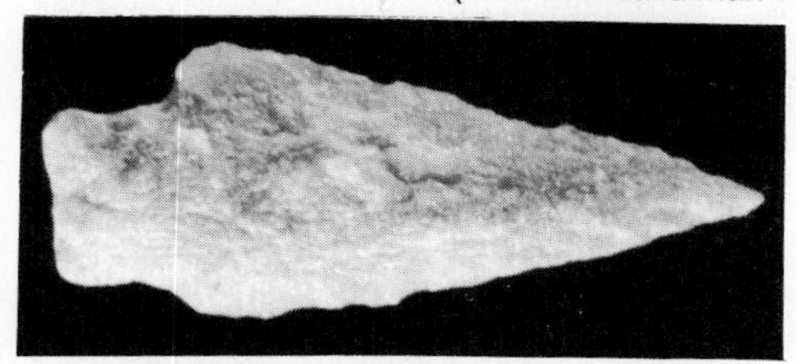

G5, $5-$8
Sussex Co., VA. Quartzite.

LOCATION: Far Eastern states. **DESCRIPTION:** A medium size, narrow point with weak, tapered shoulders and a weakly concave base.

HOLSTON - Mid-Archaic, 6500 - 3500 B.P.

(Alse see Durst, Ellis and Swan Lake)

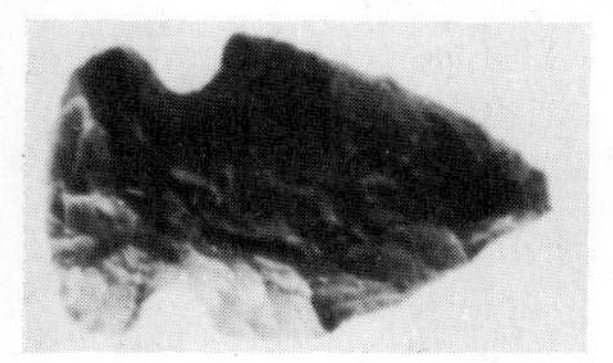

G4, $2-$3
E. TN.

LOCATION: Eastern to Southeastern states. **DESCRIPTION:** A small size point with wide side notches and a rounded to convex base.

HOMAN - Mississippian, 1000 - 700 B.P.

(Also see Agee, Alba, Hayes, Keota, Perdiz & Scallorn)

G5, $15-$25
Columbia Rv., WA.

G4, $8-$12
Col. Rv., WA.

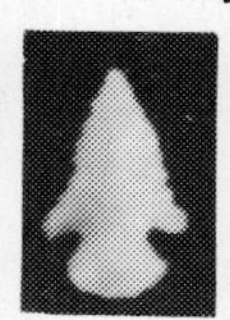

G5, $10-$20
Col. Rv., WA.

G4, $8-$12
Lincoln Parrish, LA.

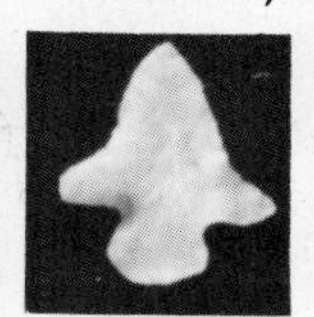

G4, $8-$12
Lincoln Parrish, LA.

G6, $25-$35
Col. Rv., WA.

G5, $15-$35
Columbia Rv., WA.

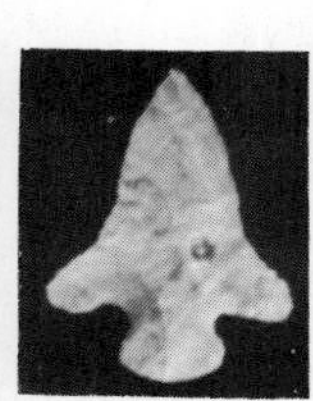

G7, $30-$40
Lincoln Parrish, LA.

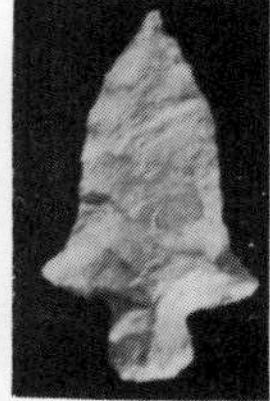

G7, $30-$40
Lincoln Parrish, LA.

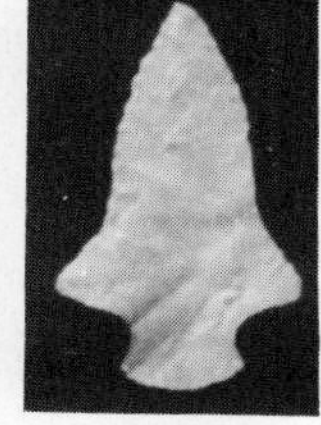

G6, $25-$35
Lincoln Parrish, LA.

G9, $60-$90
IL.

LOCATION: Northwest to Midwestern states. **DESCRIPTION:** A small size expanded barb point with a bulbous stem.

HOPEWELL - Woodland, 2500 - 1500 B.P.

(Also see North, Ross and Snyders)

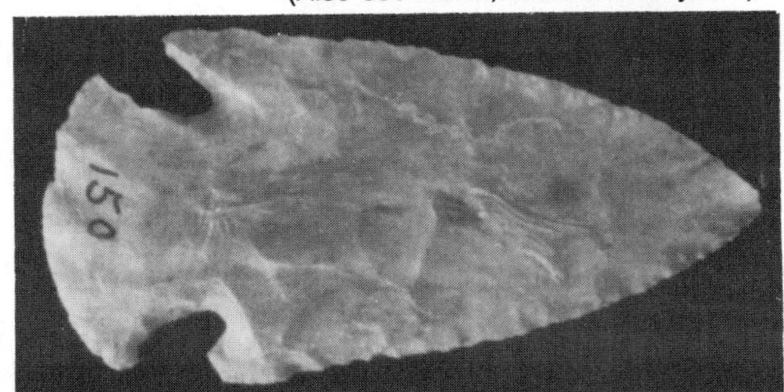

G6, $45-$80
MO/IL.

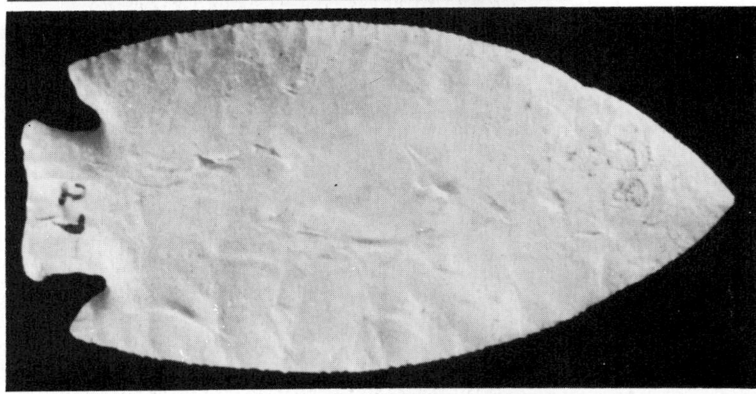

G8, $350-$600
Adams Co., IL.

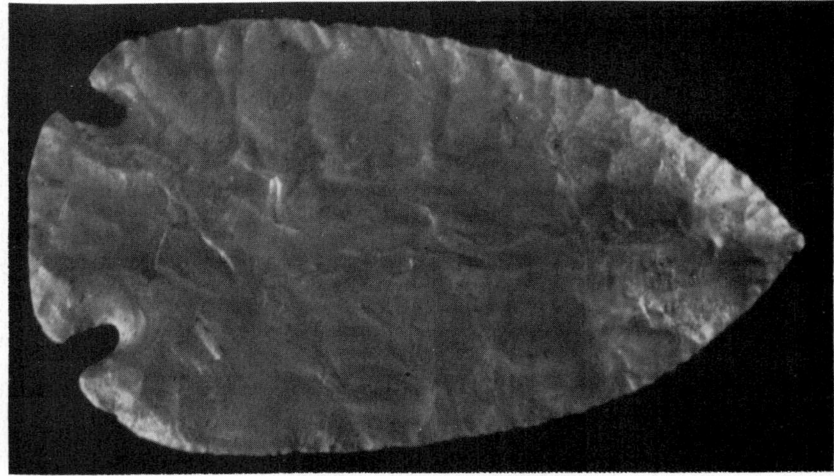

G7, $175-$200, KY.

LOCATION: Midwestern to Eastern states. **DESCRIPTION:** A large size, broad, corner notched point that is similar to *Snyders*.

G7, $175-$200
Boone Co., MO.

G9, $450-$550
Pettis Co., MO.

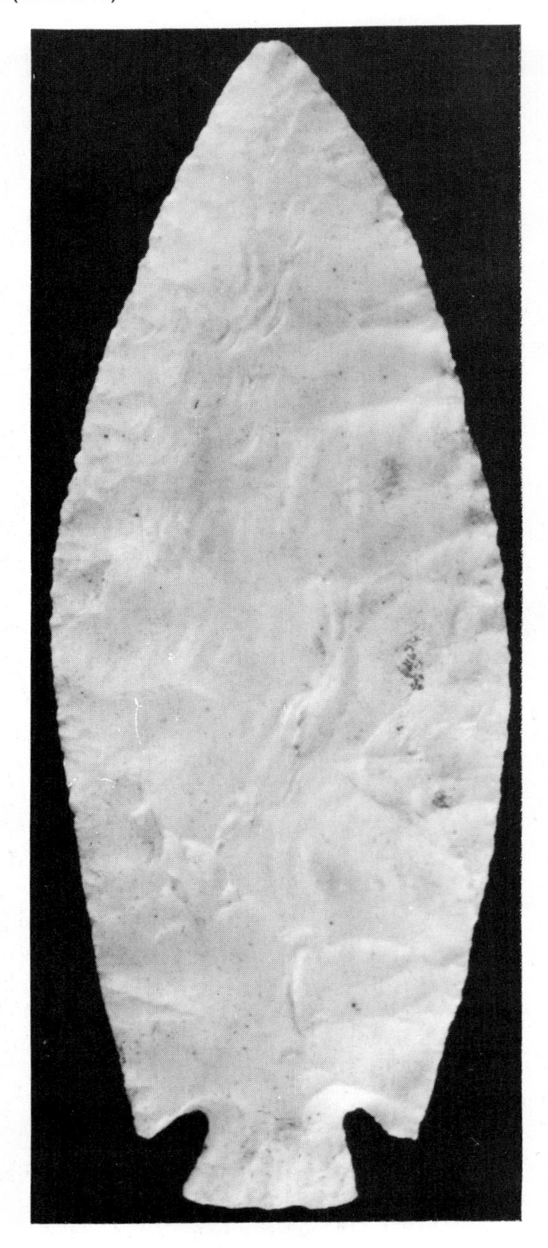

G10, $750-$1200
La Crosse Co., WI.

HOWARD - Mississippian, 700 - 500 B.P.

(Also see Blevins & Hayes)

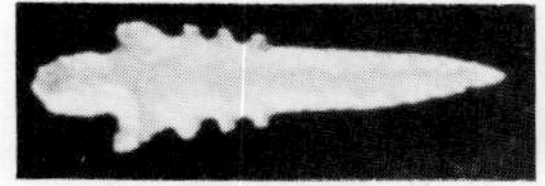
G8, $40-$70
OR.

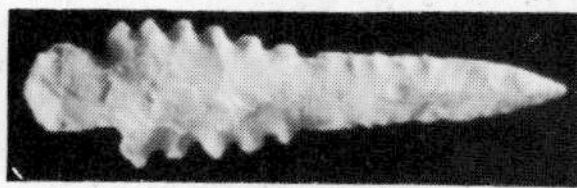
G9, $90-$150
W. AR.

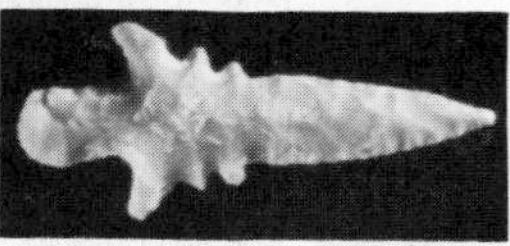
G10, $120-$200
W. AR.

LOCATION: Midwestern states. **DESCRIPTION:** A small size, narrow, spike point with two or more barbs on each side.

HOXIE - Early Archaic, 8000 - 5000 B.P.

(Also see Bulverde, Darl, Brazos, Gower and Lampasos)

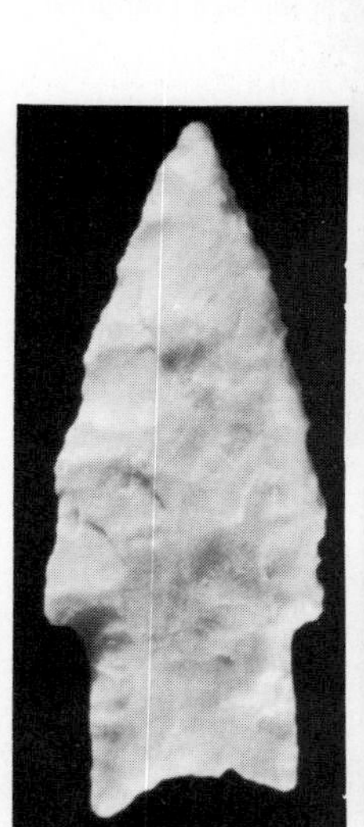
G6, $10-$20
Comanche Co., TX.

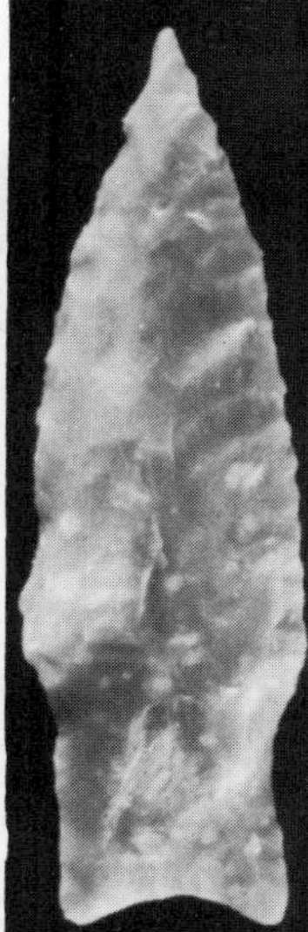
G7, $25-$35
Comanche Co., TX.

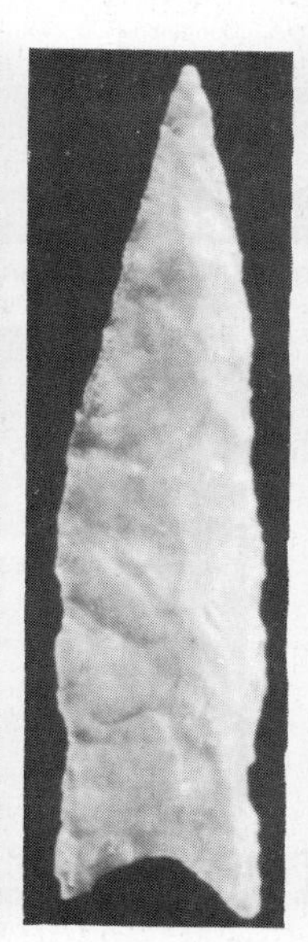
G8, $40-$60
Comanche Co., TX.

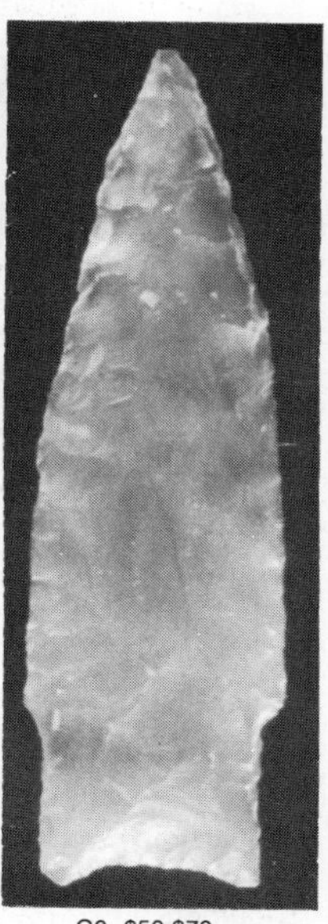
G9, $50-$70
Austin, TX. Translucent flint.

G10, $100-$150
Austin, TX. Note caliche deposit on blade surface.

LOCATION: Midwestern states. **DESCRIPTION:** A medium to large size, narrow point with weak shoulders and a parallel sided, concave base that is ground. Believed to be an early form of *Darl*.

HUFFAKER - Mississippian, 1000 - 500 B.P.

(Also see Evans, Fresno, Leighton and Ohio Double-Notched)

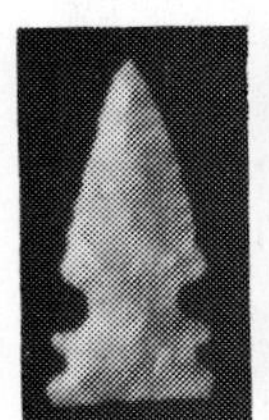

G7, $30-$40
Columbia Rv., WA.

G6, $25-$35
Columbia Rv., WA.

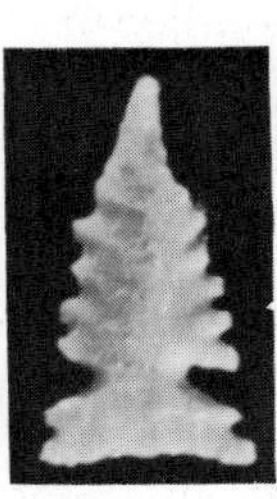

G7, $30-$40
Comanche Co., TX.

G5, $20-$30
Comanche Co., TX.

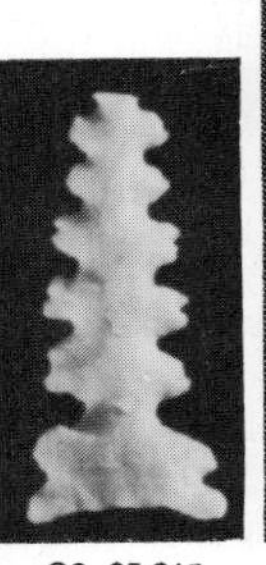

G3, $5-$10
CO/TX. Tip nick.

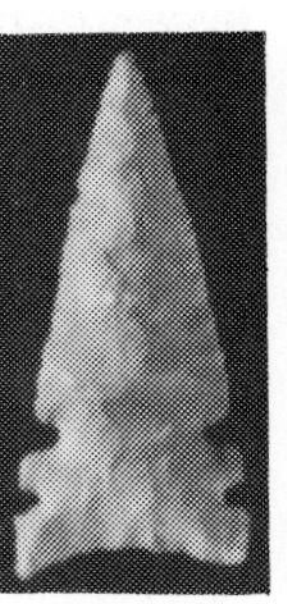

G8, $50-$80
Columbia Rv., WA.

LOCATION: Northwest to Midwestern states. **DESCRIPTION:** A small size triangular point with a straight to concave base and double side notches.

HUMBOLDT - Woodland, 2000 - 1500 B.P.

(Also see Allen, Angostura, McKean and Wheeler)

G5, $4-$6
Mexico. Obsidian.

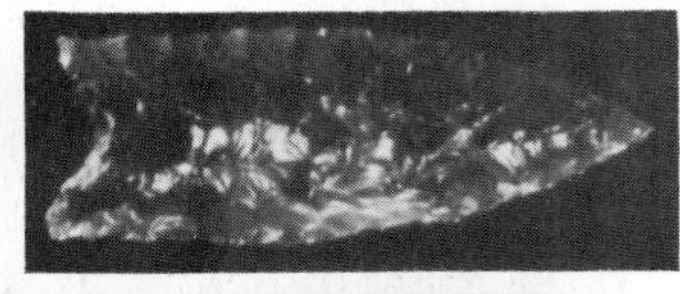

G8, $50-$75
WA/OR. Obsidian.

G6, $20-$25
WA/OR.

LOCATION: Western states. **DESCRIPTION:** A small to medium size, narrow, lanceolate point with a constricted, concave base. Some examples have faint shoulders.

JACKS REEF CORNER NOTCHED - Late Woodland to Mississippian, 1500 - 1000 B.P.

(Also see Afton and Knight Island)

G2, $1-$3
SE TN.

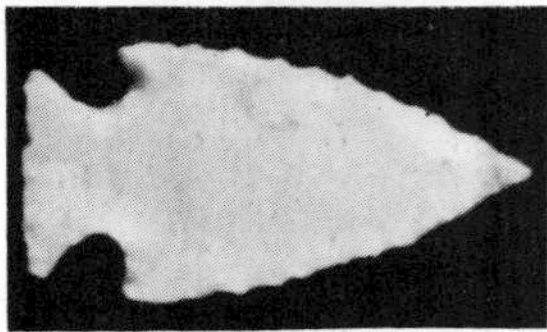

G4, $10-$15
Wellston, MO.

LOCATION: Southeastern states. **DESCRIPTION:** A small to medium size, very thin, corner notched point that is well made. The blade is convex to pentagonal. Some examples are widely corner notched and appear to be expanded stem points with barbed shoulders. Rarely, they are basal notched. **I.D. KEY:** Thinness, made by the birdpoint people.

G6, $15-$20
NE AL.

G4, $10-$15
Humphreys Co., TN.

G4, $10-$15
Decatur, AL.

G5, $6-$10
MO.

G5, $6-$10
Fulton, KY.

G6, $15-$20
New Era, TN.

G7, $15-$25
Florence, AL.

G8, $40-$60
OH.

G7, $25-$30
Colbert Co., AL.

G9, $80-$120
OH.

G7, $15-$25
Morgan Co., AL.

G6, $10-$20
Morgan Co., AL.

G10, $125-$240
Savannah, TN.

G5, $6-$10
Morgan Co., AL.

G6, $10-$20
Florence, AL.

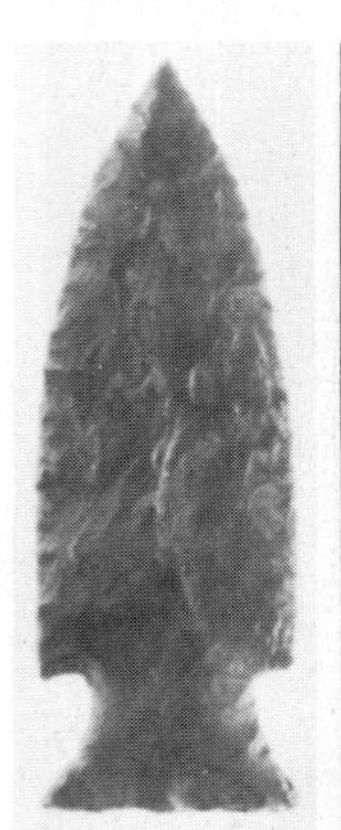
G10, $120-$200
Florence, AL. Excellent.

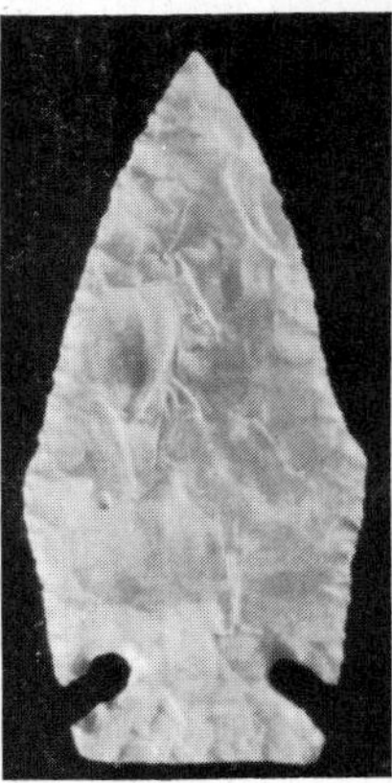
G10, $350-$600
Savannah, TN.

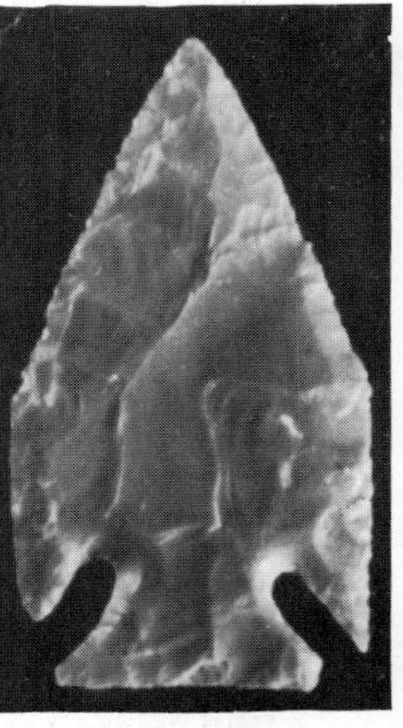
G10, $150-$200
Meade Co., KY. Base nick.

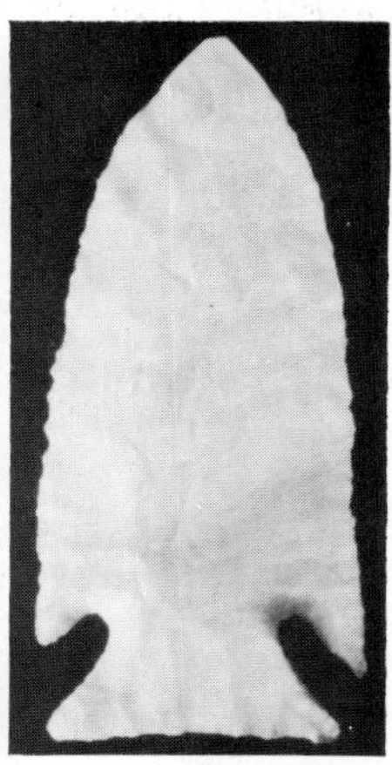
G9, $100-$150
Savannah, TN.

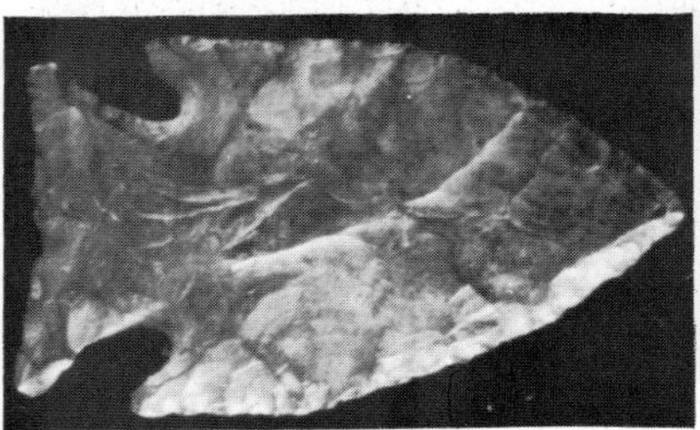
G9, $100-$150
Ripley, NY.

G10, $150-$250
Savannah, TN.

G10, $150-$260
Humphreys Co., TN.

G7, $15-$25
Lauderdale Co., AL.

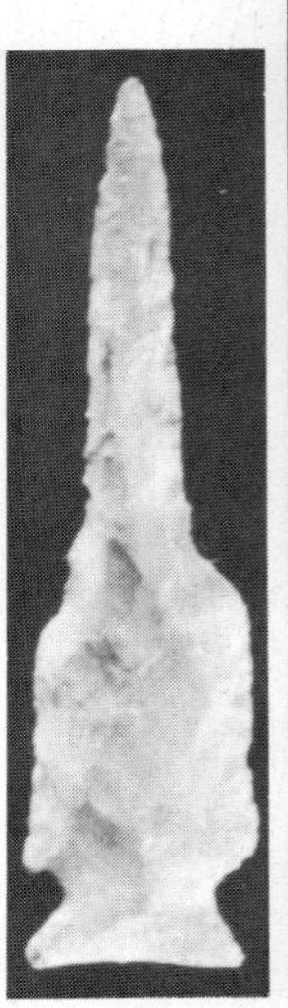
G6, $10-$20
Morgan Co., AL. Drill.

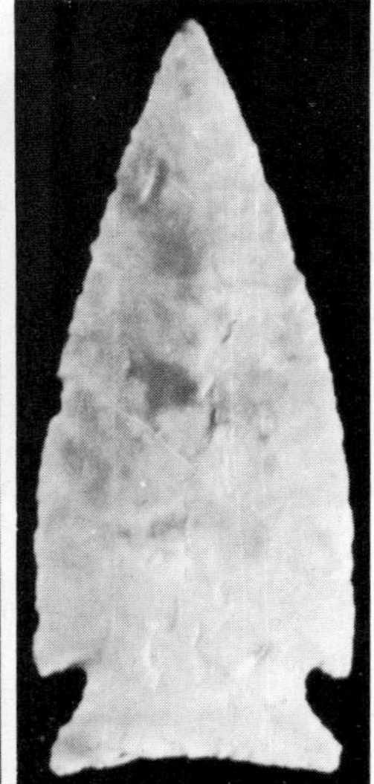
G9, $80-$120
Humphreys Co., TN.

JACKS REEF PENTAGONAL - Late Woodland to Mississippian, 1500 - 1000 B.P.

(Also see Mouse Creek)

G2, $1-$2 Meigs Co., TN.
G2, .50-$1 SE TN.
G1, .25-.50 Smyth Co., VA.
G3, $2-$3 Yadkin Co., NC.
G4, $2-$4 Smyth Co., VA.

G3, $1-$3 Wilkes Co., NC.
G4, $3-$5 Randolph Co., NC.
G4, $5-$7 Decatur, AL.
G4, $3-$5 NE AL.
G5, $5-$8 Bristol, TN.

G3, $2-$3 Florence, AL.
G4, $3-$5 Florence, AL.
G3, $2-$3 Dallas Co., AL.
G6, $15-$25 Dayton, TN.
G5, $6-$10 Limestone Co., AL.

G5, $6-$10 Humphreys Co., TN. Drill form.
G7, $25-$40 Huntsville, AL.
G5, $6-$10 Morgan Co., AL.
G6, $10-$20 Wilkes Co., NC.
G7, $25-$40 OH.

LOCATION: Southeastern states. **DESCRIPTION:** A small to large size, very thin, five sided point with a sharp tip. The hafting area is usually contracted with a slightly concave to straight base. This type is called *Pee Dee* in North and South Carolina.

G6, $10-$20
Randolph Co., NC.

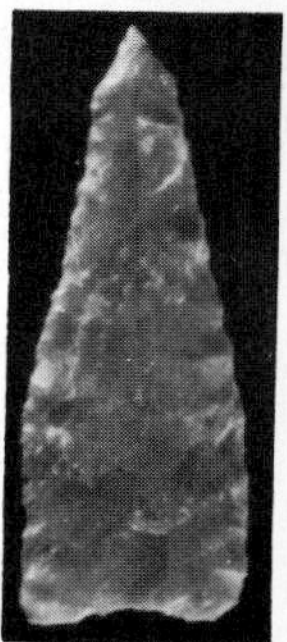

G6, $15-$25
Morgan Co., AL.
Donnaha tip.

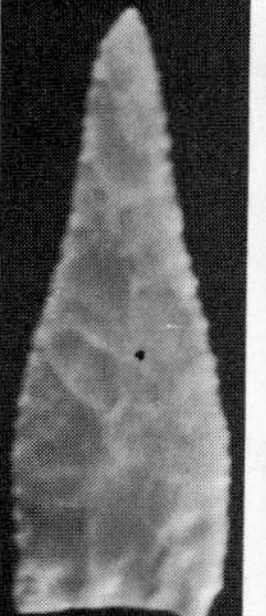

G6, $10-$20
Morgan Co., AL.

G8, $30-$50
Jackson Co., AL.

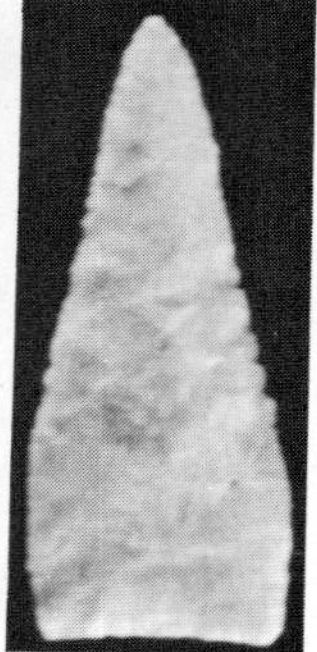

G6, $15-$20
Morgan Co., AL.

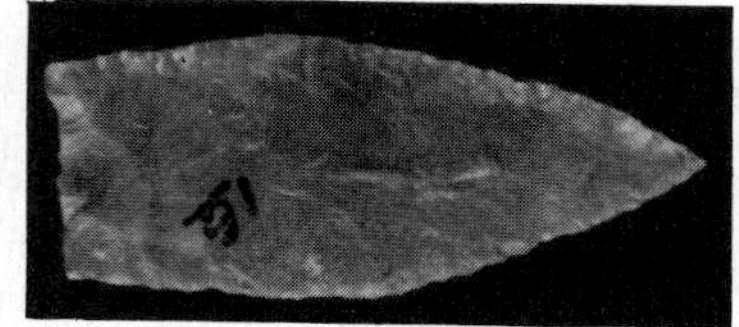

G8, $30-$50
Florence, AL.

G7, $25-$40
Humphreys Co., TN. Note unusual fine blade serrations.

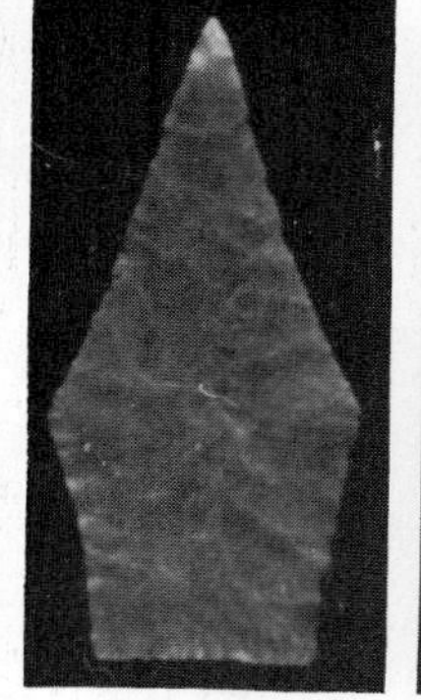

G10, $150-$250
Warren Co., TN.

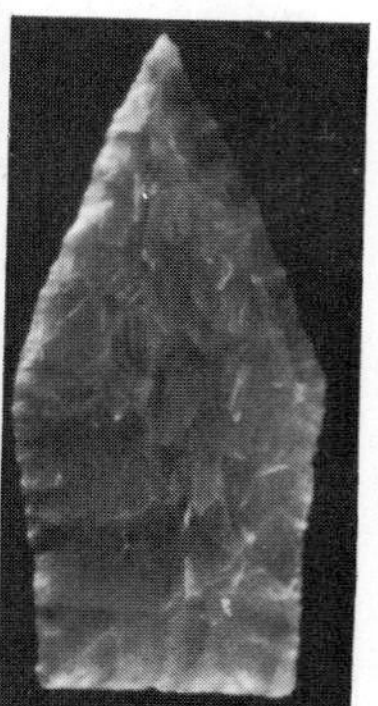

G9, $80-$125
Morgan Co., AL.

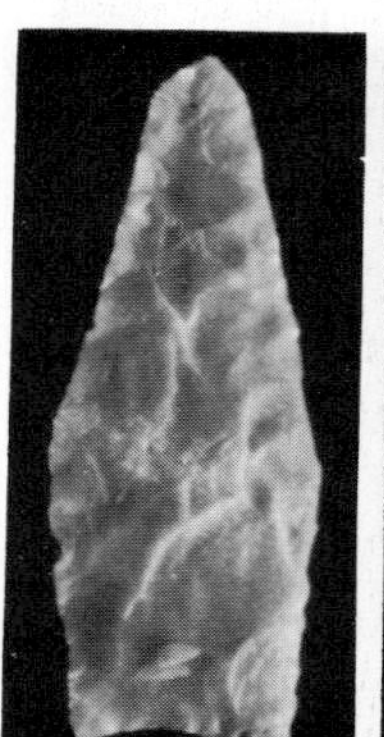

G4, $3-$5
Madison Co., AL.

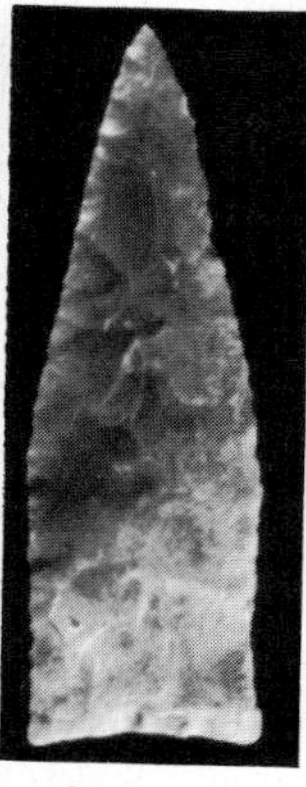

G9, $60-$100
Morgan Co., AL.

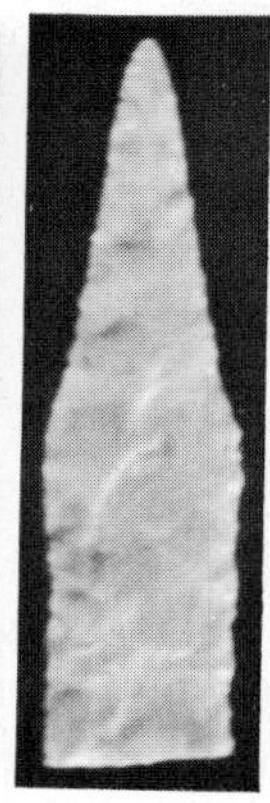

G8, $30-$50
Morgan Co., AL.

$30-$35
KY.

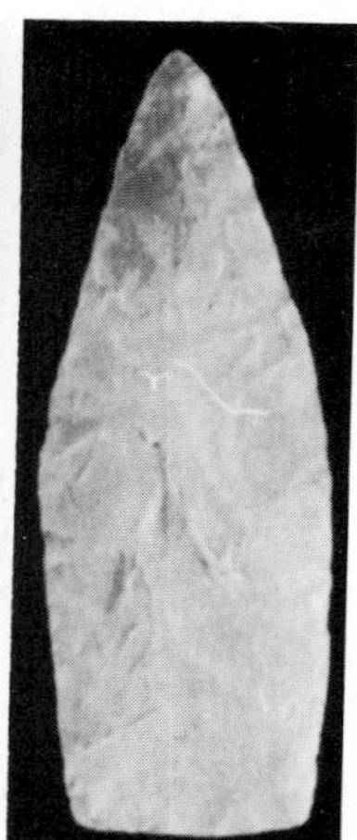

$30-$35
Humphreys Co., TN.

JACKSON (See Swan Lake)

JEFF - Late Paleo, 10000 - 8000 B.P.

(Also see Angostura, Browns Valley, Golondrina, Hi-Lo, Paint Rock Valley and Quad)

G9, $80-$120
Jackson Co., AL. Black chert.

G5, $30-$45
Florence, AL.

G2, $3-$5
Marion Co., AL.

G9, $80-$120
Huntsville, AL. Classic form.

G9, $80-$120
W. KY.

G9, $90-$150
Limestone Co., AL.

LOCATION: Southeastern states. **DESCRIPTION:** A medium sized, wide, lanceolate point with expanded auricles. The base is straight to slightly concave, is usually beveled or thinned, and may be ground. Auricles can either extend downward or out to the side. Some examples show fine pressure flaking on the blade edges. **I.D. KEY:** One shoulder stronger.

JEROME - Mississippian, 600 - 400 B.P.

(Also see Augustin, Morrow Mountain and Santa Cruz)

G2, $2-$4
Yavapai Co., AZ.

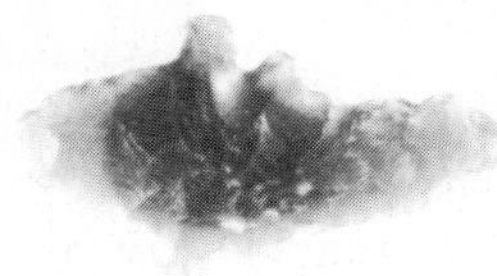

G4, $6-$10
Yavapai Co., AZ.

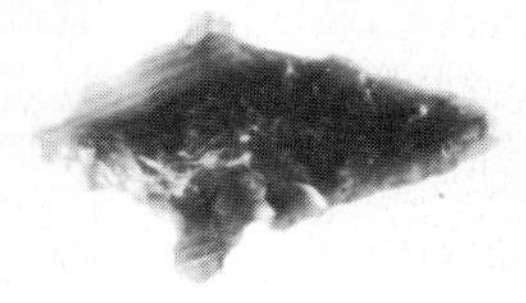

G2, $2-$4
Yavapai Co., AZ.

LOCATION: Southwestern states. **DESCRIPTION:** A medium size contracted base point with weak shoulders. Blade edges are usually serrated.

JETTA - Early Archaic, 8000 - 5000 B.P.

(Also see Gower, Pedernalis & Uvalde)

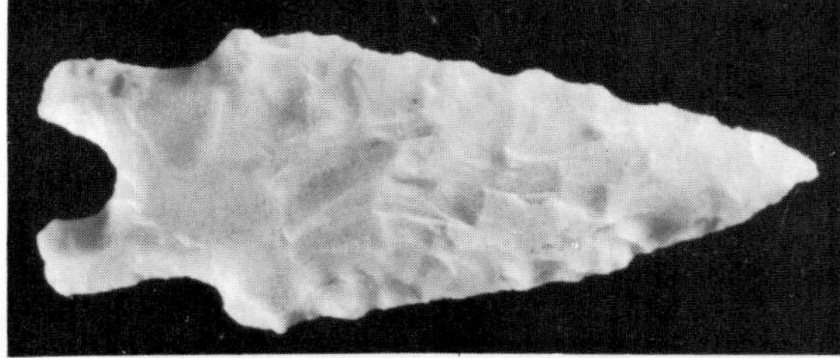

G8, $45-$70
Comanche Co., TX.

G10, $250-$400
Three Rivers, TX.

LOCATION: Midwestern states. **DESCRIPTION:** A medium size point with flaring barbs and a deeply notched base. Basal tangs are squared and wider than *Pedernalis*.

JOHN DAY RIVER - Mississippian, 1000 - 500 B.P.

(Also see Catahoula, Eiffel Tower, Gunther & Rogue River)

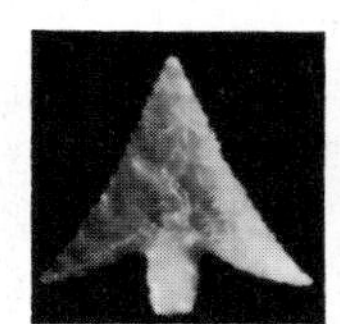

G10, $100-$125
Sherman Co., OR.

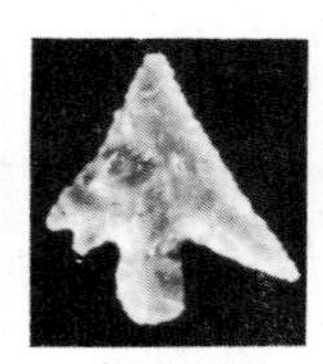

G8, $50-$80
Lane Co., OR. Rare notched shoulder.

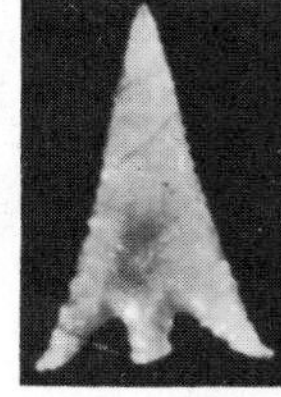

G7, $40-$50
Sherman Co., OR.

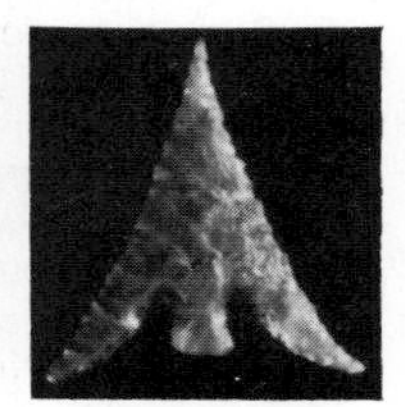

G10, $100-$125
Sherman Co., OR.

LOCATION: Northwestern states. **DESCRIPTION:** A small size, thin point with expanding barbs that can extend beyond the base. Shoulders are pointed. The stem is short and parallel sided. Some examples have an unusual notched shoulder.

JOHNSON - Early to mid-Archaic, 9000 - 5000 B.P.

(Also see Savannah River)

G5, $4-$7
NE AL.

G6, $8-$12
Coffee Lake, AL.

G7, $10-$20
Coffee Lake, AL.

G7, $10-$20
Huntsville, AL.

G9, $45-$70
Parsons, TN.

G8, $20-$30
Coffee Lake, AL.

LOCATION: Midwestern to Southeastern states. **DESCRIPTION:** A medium size, thick, well made, expanded stem point with a concave base. Shoulders can be slightly barbed, straight or tapered. Basal corners are rounded to pointed to auriculate. Bases are thinned and ground. **I.D. KEY:** Pointed ears and thickness.

JUDE - Early Archaic, 9000 - 6000 B.P.

(Also see Cave Spring, Fox Valley, Garth Slough, Halifax, LeCroy, McIntire and Rheems Creek)

G3, $2-$4
SE TN.

G3, $2-$3
SE TN.

G4, $4-$6
Walker Co., AL.

G4, $4-$6
SE TN.

G6, $8-$15
Pulaski, KY.

G4, $4-$6
Marion Co., TN.

G6, $8-$12
Huntsville, AL.

G5, $5-$8
Christian Co., KY.

G4, $4-$6
Morgan Co., AL.

G6, $12-$15
Humphreys Co., TN.

G8, $30-$50
Colbert Co., AL. Classic form.

G6, $25-$45
Marion Co., KY. Colorful Carter Cave flint.

LOCATION: Southeastern states. **DESCRIPTION:** A small size, short, barbed, expanded to parallel stemmed point with straight to convex blade edges. Stems are usually as large or larger than the blade. Bases are straight, concave, convex or bifurcated. Shoulders are either square, tapered or barbed. This is one of the earliest stemmed points along with *Pelican*. Some examples have serrated blade edges that may be beveled on one side of each face. **I.D. KEY:** Base form and flaking.

KALAPUYAN - Woodland to Mississippian, 4000 - 400 B.P.

(See Gypsum Cave)

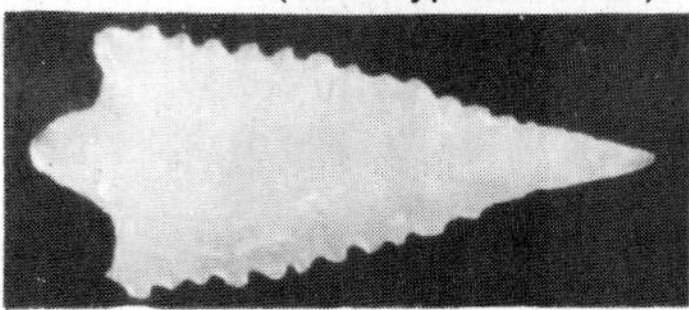

G9, $35-$50
WA/OR.

LOCATION: Northwestern states. **DESCRIPTION:** A medium size barbed point with a small contracting stem. Blade edges are usually serated.

KANAWHA - Early Archaic, 9000 - 5000 B.P.

(Also see Fox Valley, Jude, Kirk-Bifurcated, Lake Erie, LeCroy, St. Albans, Southampton and Stanly)

G2, .50-$1 Catoosa Co., GA.

G3, $1-$2 Catoosa Co., GA.

G4, $2-$3 SE TN.

G5, $3-$5 Catoosa Co., GA.

G8, $15-$25 SE TN.

G6, $4-$7 SE TN.

G5, $2-$4 Sussex Co., VA.

G5, $3-$5 Chilhowie, VA.

G4, $2-$3 Bristol, VA. Crystal.

G4, $1-$3 Dunlap, TN.

G5, $2-$4 Ft. Payne, AL.

G3, $1-$2 Catoosa Co., GA. Milky quartz.

G6, $4-$7 Christian Co., KY.

G3, $1-$2 Meigs Co., TN. Milky quartz.

G5, $3-$5 NJ.

G4, $2-$3 Sussex Co., VA.

LOCATION: Eastern to Southeastern states. **DESCRIPTION:** A small to medium size, fairly thick, shallowly-bifurcated stemmed point. The basal lobes are usually rounded and the shoulders tapered. Believed to be the ancestor to the *Stanly* type.

KAYS - Mid-Archaic to Woodland, 5000 - 2000 B.P.

(Also see Delhi, Kramer. Little Bear Creek. McIntire & Stone Square Stem)

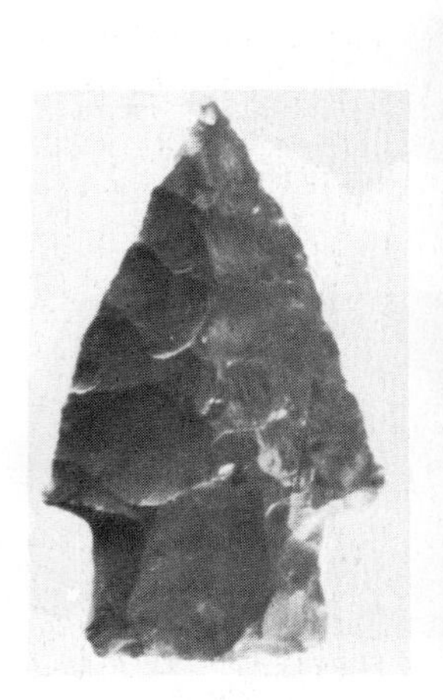

G4, $4-$6
Meigs Co., TN.

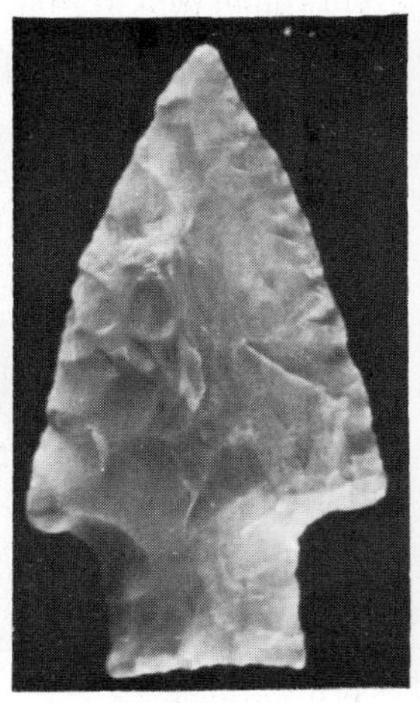

G5, $5-$8
Morgan Co., AL.

G5, $5-$8
Limestone Co., AL.

G4, $4-$6
Limestone Co., AL.

G5, $7-$15
Morgan Co., AL.

G7, $15-$25
Decatur, AL.

LOCATION: Southeastern states. **DESCRIPTION:** A medium to large size, narrow, parallel sided stemmed point with a straight base. Shoulders are tapered to square. The blade is straight to convex. **I.D. KEY:** One barb is higher.

KAYS (continued)

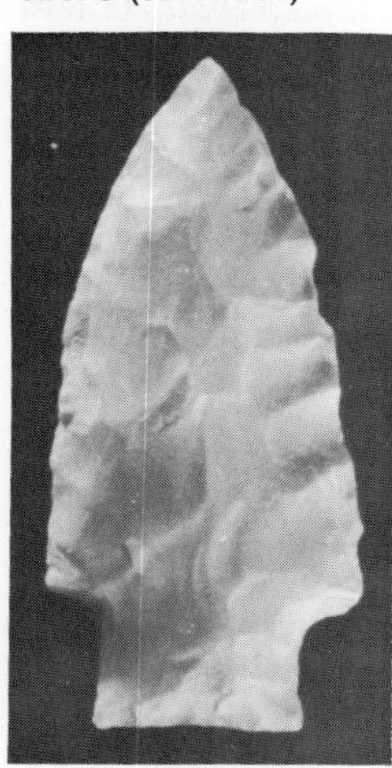

G5, $5-$8
Morgan Co., AL.

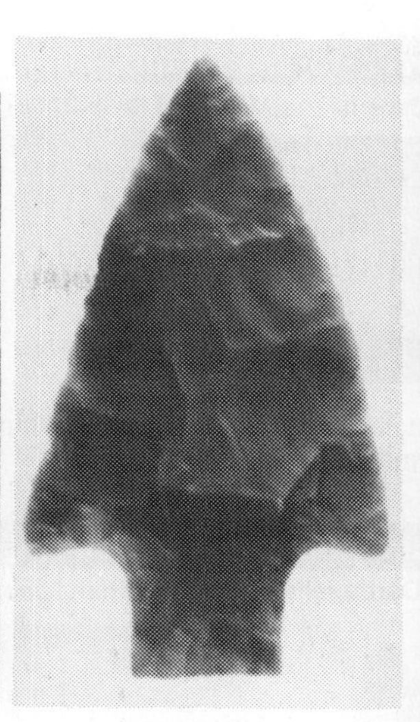

G7, $20-$35
Decatur, AL.

G6, $10-$20
Decatur, AL.

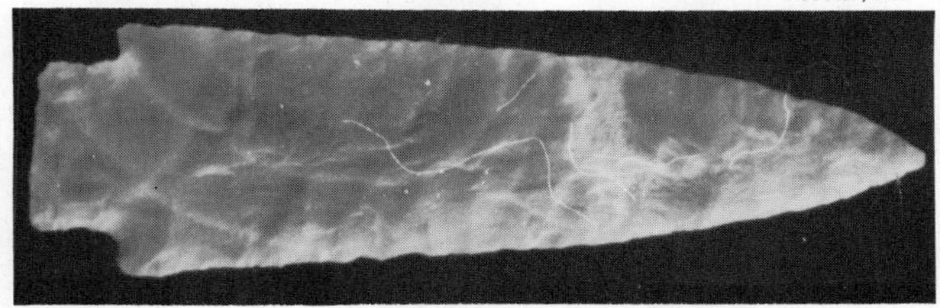

G7, $20-$35, E. TN.

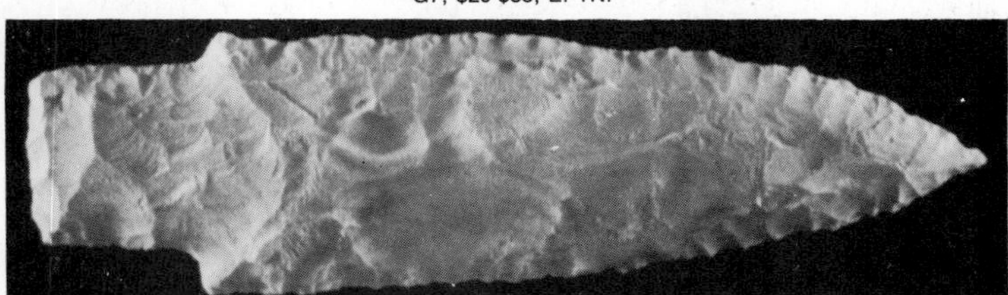

G9, $50-$60, Parsons, TN. Classic.

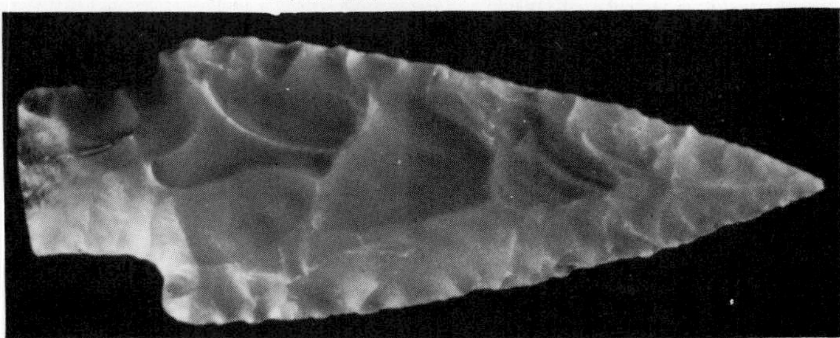

G7, $15-$30, Decatur, AL.

KENT - Late Archaic to Woodland, 4000 - 1000 B.P.

(Also see Bare Island, Nolan, Travis and Yarbrough)

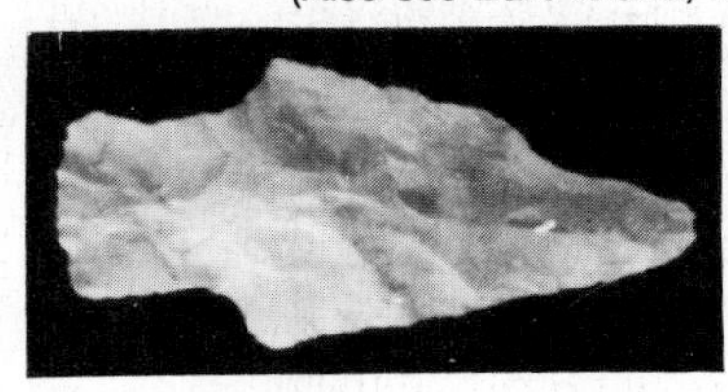

G2, $2-$3
Waco, TX.

LOCATION: Midwestern states. **DESCRIPTION:** A medium size, low quality stemmed point with tapered asymmetrical shoulders.

KEOTA - Mississippian, 800 - 600 B.P.

(Also see Agee, Alba, Dardanelle, Hayes, Homan, Leon, Merom & Sequoyah)

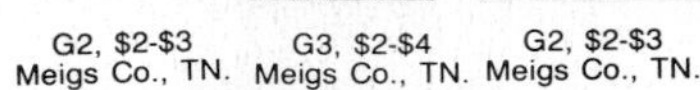

G2, $2-$3
Meigs Co., TN.

G3, $2-$4
Meigs Co., TN.

G2, $2-$3
Meigs Co., TN.

G6, $20-$30
Columbia Rv., WA.

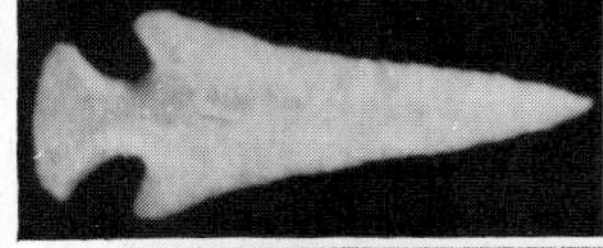

G9, $75-$130
Spiro Mound, OK.

G8, $35-$60
Spiro Mound, OK.

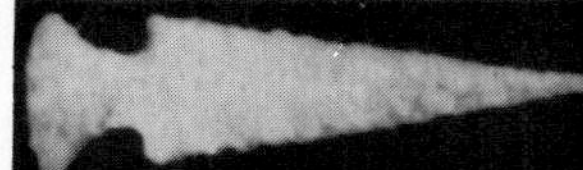

G8, $35-$60
Spiro Mound, OK.

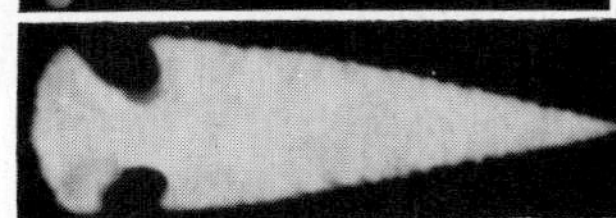

G9, $60-$100
Spiro Mound, OK.

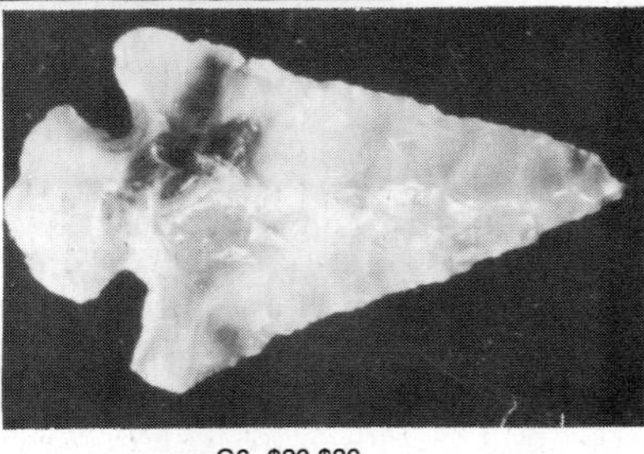

G6, $20-$30
WA/OR.

LOCATION: Midwestern states. **DESCRIPTION:** A small size, thin, triangular, side to corner-notched point with a rounded base.

KINNEY - Mid-Archaic, 5000 - 2000 B.P.

(Also see Copena, Darl Blade, Gahagan and Tortugas)

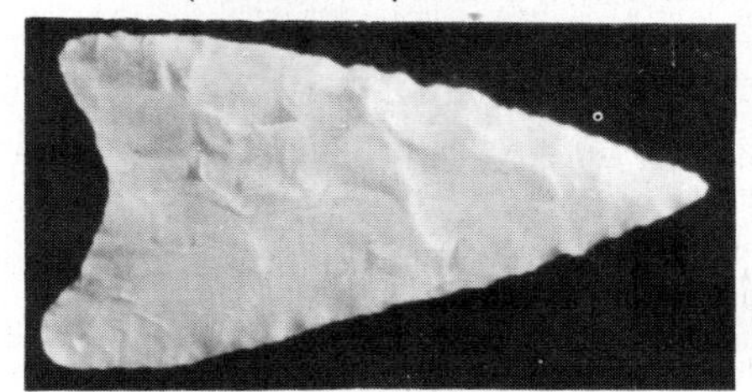

G3, $8-$15
Comanche Co., TX.

KINNEY (continued)

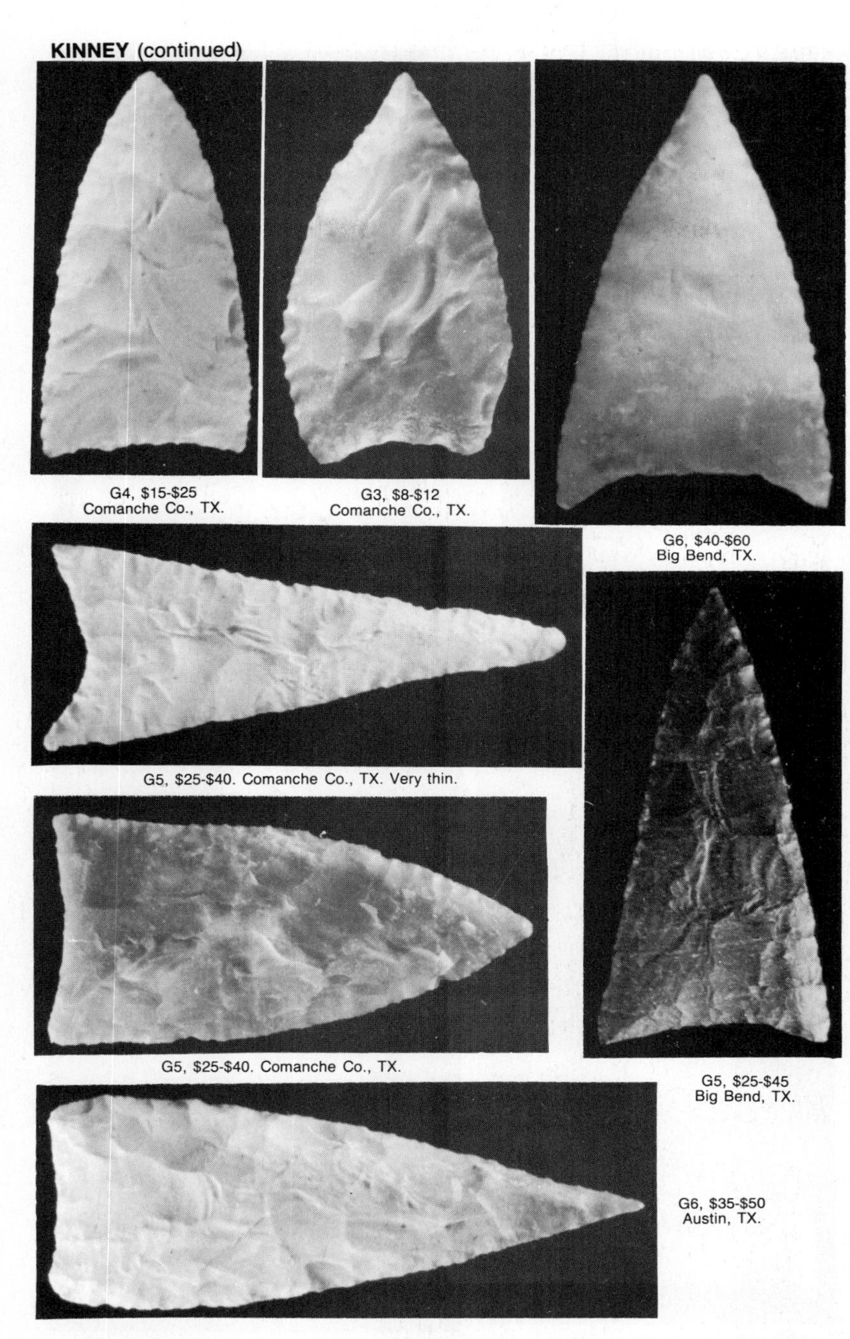

G4, $15-$25
Comanche Co., TX.

G3, $8-$12
Comanche Co., TX.

G6, $40-$60
Big Bend, TX.

G5, $25-$40. Comanche Co., TX. Very thin.

G5, $25-$40. Comanche Co., TX.

G5, $25-$45
Big Bend, TX.

G6, $35-$50
Austin, TX.

LOCATION: Midwestern states. **DESCRIPTION:** A medium to large size, thin, lanceolate, well made blade with convex to straight blade edges and a concave base.

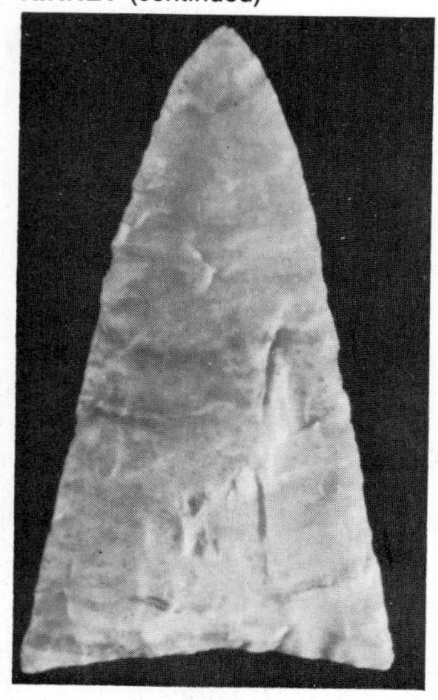

G6, $35-$50
Cent. OK.

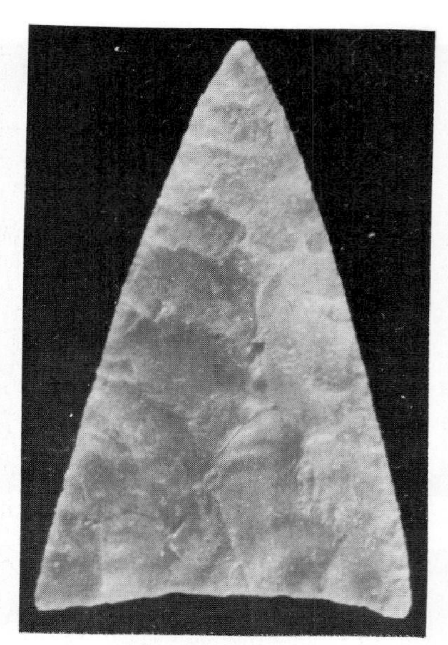

G7, $50-$80
Austin, TX.

G7, $50-$80
Big Bend, TX.

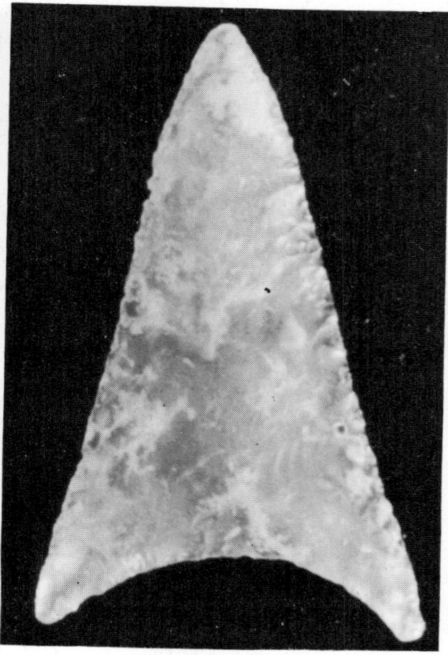

G7, $50-$80
Big Bend, TX. Agate.

KINNEY (continued)

G8, $80-$120
Cent. TX.

G10, $400-$600
Waco, TX.

KIRK CORNER NOTCHED - Early to mid-Archaic, 9000 - 6000 B.P.

(Also see Bolen, Cypress Creek, Dovetail, Lafayette, Lost Lake, Pine Tree and St. Charles)

G3, $10-$20
Meigs Co., TN.

G3, $10-$20
Surry Co., NC.

G5, $30-$45
Meigs Co., TN.

G3, $8-$12
Guilford Co., NC. Rhyolite.

G9, $180-$300
Harrison Co., IN.

G5, $30-$50
Spencer Co., OH.

G3, $10-$20
Florence, AL. Note unusual mucronate distal end.

G8, $150-$250
Coffee Lake, AL. Needle tip.

LOCATION: Southeastern states. **DESCRIPTION:** A medium to large size, corner notched point. Blade edges can be convex to recurved and are finely serrated on many examples. The base can be convex, concave, straight or auriculate. Points that are beveled on one side of each face would fall under the *Lost Lake* type. **I.D. KEY:** Secondary edgework.

G5, $30-$45
Chester Co., SC.

G4, $20-$30
IL.

G5, $35-$50
Wayne Co., NC.

G7, $90-$150
Humphreys Co., TN.

G5, $35-$50
Meigs Co., TN.

G6, $45-$70
Hiwassee Isle, Meigs Co., TN.

G8, $120-$220
Harrison Co., IN. Swan Landing.

G5, $30-$45
Wilson Co., NC.

G7, $60-$100
MO.

G5, $35-$50
Surry Co., NC.

G9, $200-$350
Lincoln Co., GA.

G7, $90-$150
Humphreys Co., TN.

G6, $45-$70
Davidson Co., TN.

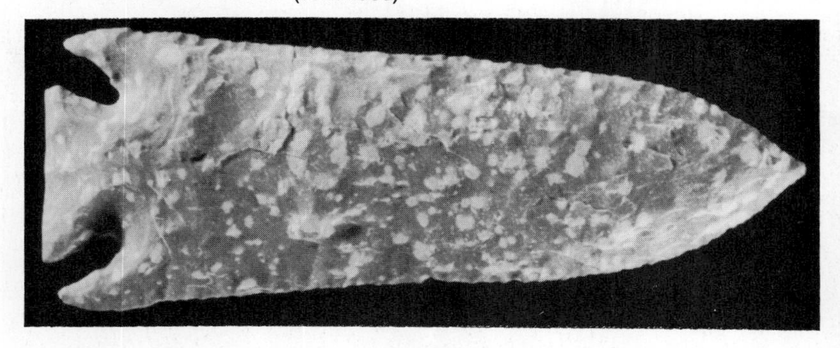

G10, $1500-$3000, Surry Co., NC. Green rhyolite with white spots. One of North Carolina's finest.

G9, $250-$400, Calhoun Co., IL.

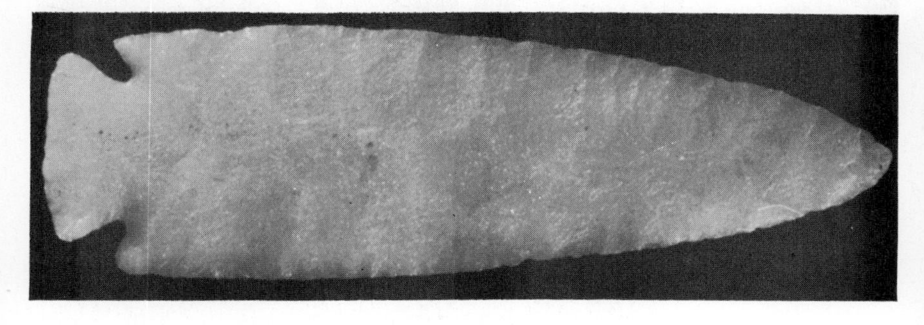

G9, $250-$400, Upper midwest. Sugar quartz.

KIRK CORNER NOTCHED (continued)

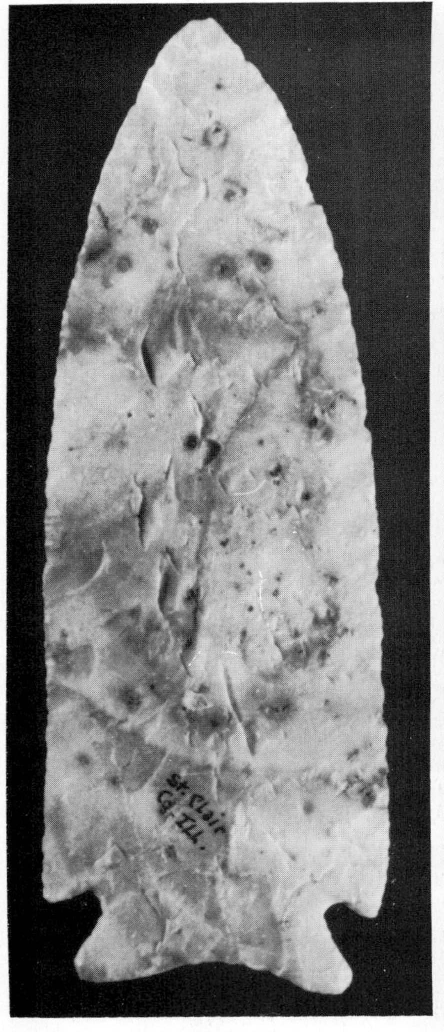

G9, $350-$600
Humphreys Co., TN.

G8, $300-$500
St. Clair Co., IL.

KIRK SERRATED - Early to mid-Archaic, 9000 - 6000 B.P.

(Also see Arrendondo, Boggy Branch, Bolen, Crump Lake Stemmed, Fountain Creek, Hamilton, Heavy Duty, Six Mile Creek & Stanly)

G2, $4-$8
Cent. NC.

G3, $30-$50
Moore Co., NC. Crystal.

G2, $4-$8
Bethany, WV.

G3, $6-$10
Bethany, WV.

G4, $8-$15
Bethany, WV.

G8, $80-$100
Humphreys Co., TN.

G3, $8-$15
Walker Co., AL.

G4, $10-$20
Cent. NC.

G4, $25-$40
Sante Fe River, FL.

LOCATION: Southeastern to Eastern states. **DESCRIPTION:** A medium to large size, barbed, stemmed point with deep notches or fine serrations along the blade edges. The stem is parallel to expanding. The stem sides may be steeply beveled on opposite faces. Some examples also have a distinct bevel on the right side of each blade edge. The base can be concave, convex or straight, and can be very short. The shoulders are usually strongly barbed. Believed to have evolved into *Stanly* and other types. **I.d. KEY:** Serrations.

KIRK SERRATED (continued)

G5, $25-$40
Wilson Co., NC.

G5, $20-$35
Cent. NC.

G6, $35-$60
Marshall Co., KY.

G6, $35-$60
Coffee Lake, AL.

G5, $25-$40
Coffee Lake, AL.

G10, $300-$500
Colbert Co., AL.

G6, $30-$50
Humphreys Co., TN.

G9, $150-$250
Humphreys Co., TN. Excellent quality.

G6, $35-$60
Lee Co., GA.

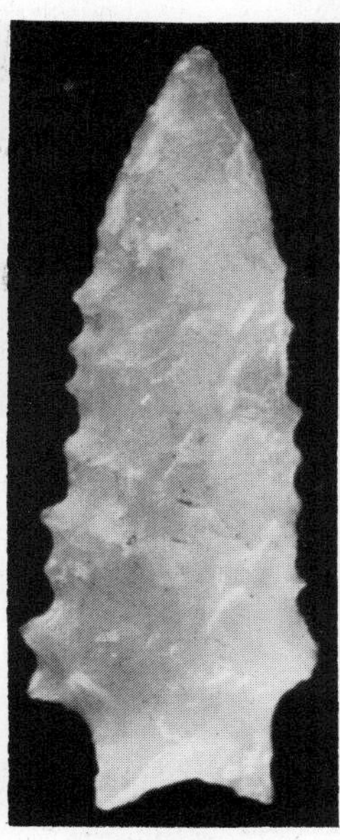
G6, $35-$60
Davidson Co., TN.

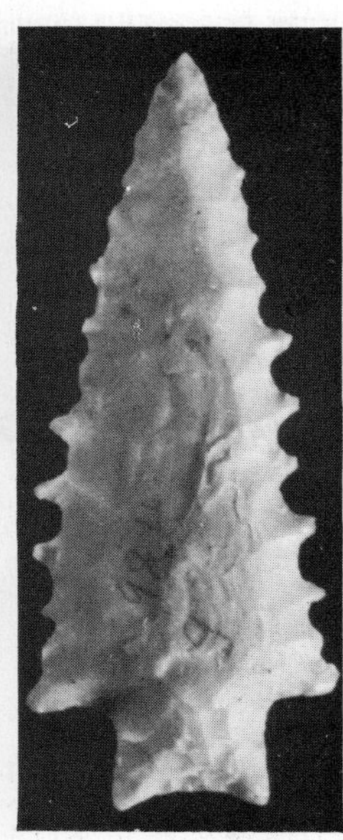
G10, $280-$450
Pasco Co., FL.

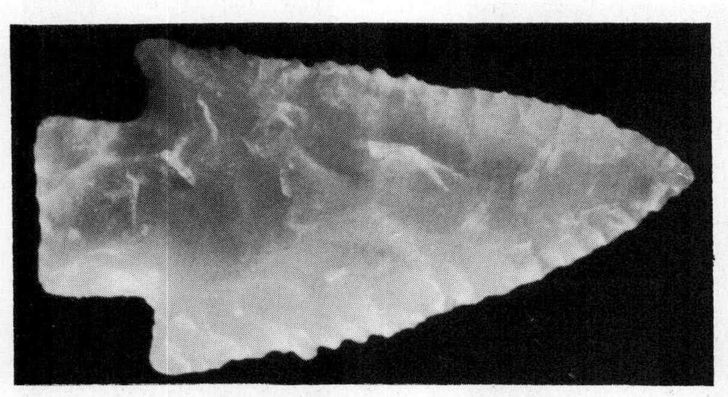
G7, $50-$80
Pasco Co., FL.

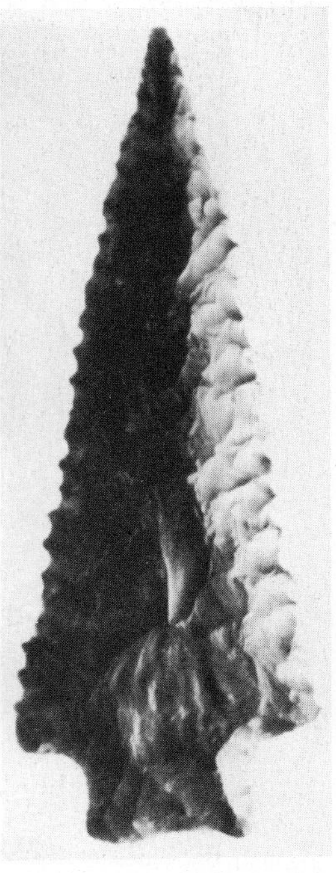
G9, $150-$250
Humphreys Co., TN. Heat
treated Dover chert.

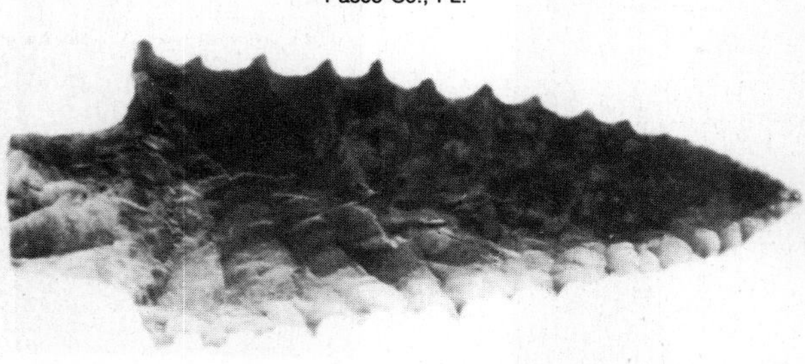
G10, $240-$400
Humphreys Co., TN. Heat
treated Dover chert.

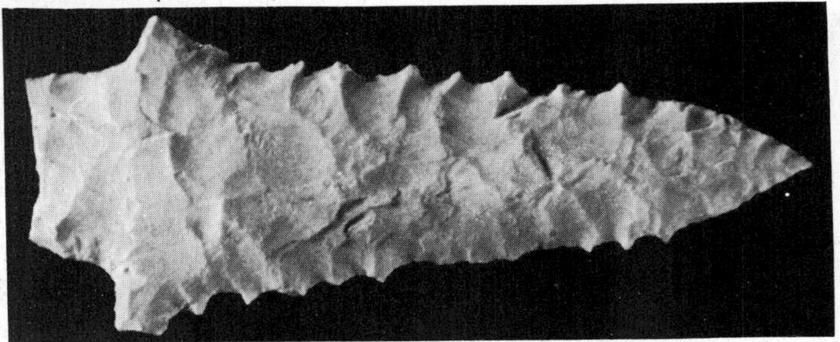

G9, $180-$300
Humphreys Co., TN.

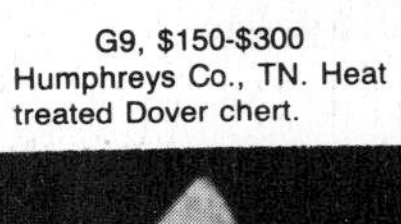

G9, $150-$300
Humphreys Co., TN. Heat
treated Dover chert.

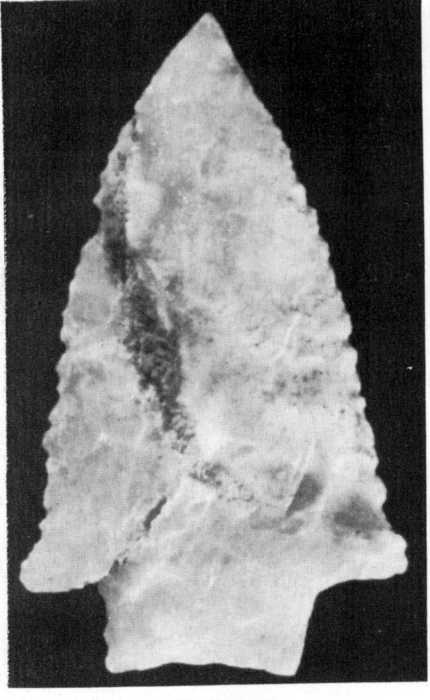

G8, $70-$130
Dodge Co., GA.

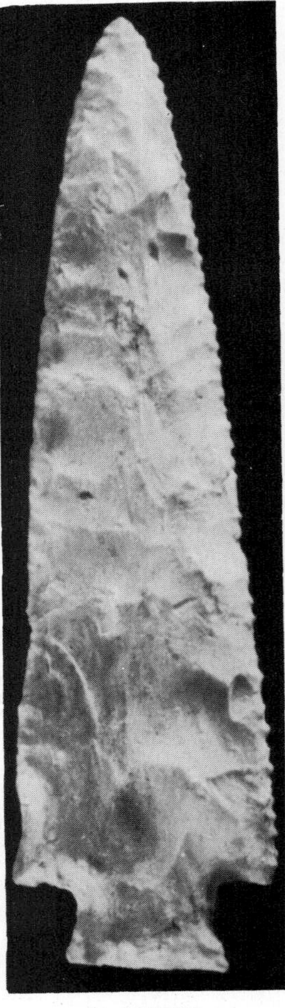

G7, $100-$150
Sante Fe River, FL.

KIRK SERRATED-BIFURCATED - Early Archaic, 9000 - 7000 B.P.

(Also see Cave Spring, Fox Valley, LeCroy, St. Albans, Southampton & Stanly)

G2, $4-$6
SE TN.

G2, $4-$6
Hiwassee Isle, Meigs Co.
TN. Hooked shoulder.

G2, $2-$3
SE TN.

G2. $3-$5
Sevier Co., TN. Tip nick.

G1, $2-$4-
SE TN.

G2, $3-$5
Bethany WV.

G2, $4-$6
Taylor Co., KY.

G3, $3-$5
McCreary Co., KY.

G3, $6-$10
McCreary Co., KY.

G6, $30-$50
Stewart Co., TN.

G6, $30-$50
White Co., TN.

LOCATION: Southeastern to Eastern states. **DESCRIPTION:** A medium to large size point with deep notches or fine serrations along the blade edges. The stem is parallel sided to expanded and is bifurcated. Believed to be an early form for the type which later developed into *Stanly* and other types. Some examples have a steep bevel on the right side of each blade edge.

KIRK SERRATED-BIFURCATED (continued)

G4, $15-$25
NE AR.

G3, $6-$10
Walker Co., AL.

G3, $6-$10
AR.

G2, $4-$6
Saluda Co., SC. Slate.

G4, $10-$20
Johnson Co., NC.

G4, $15-$25
Walker Co., GA.

G3, $8-$15
SE TN.

G4, $15-$25
Wilson Co., N.C.

G4, $15-$25
Cleveland, OH.

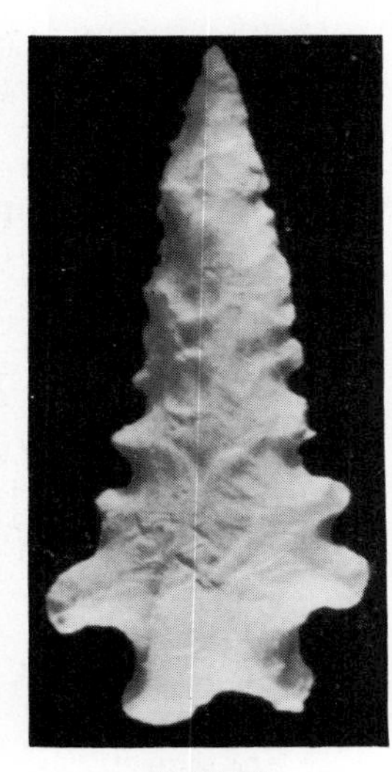

G6, $25-$45
Christian Co., KY.

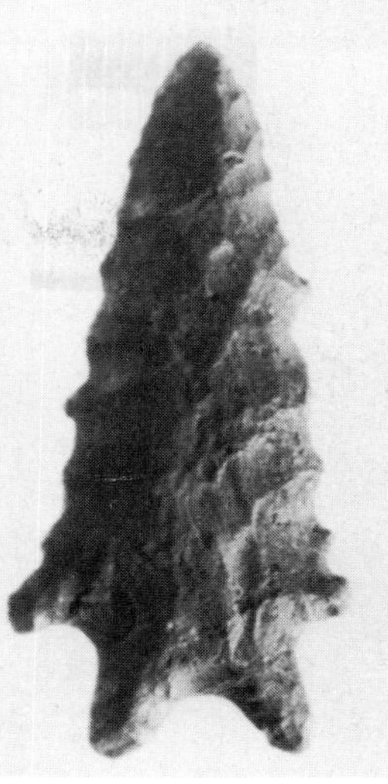

G5, $20-$30
White Co., TN.

G9, $180-$300
Barkley Lake, KY.

G6, $30-$50
Marshall Co., KY.

G7, $80-$120
Barkley Lake, KY.

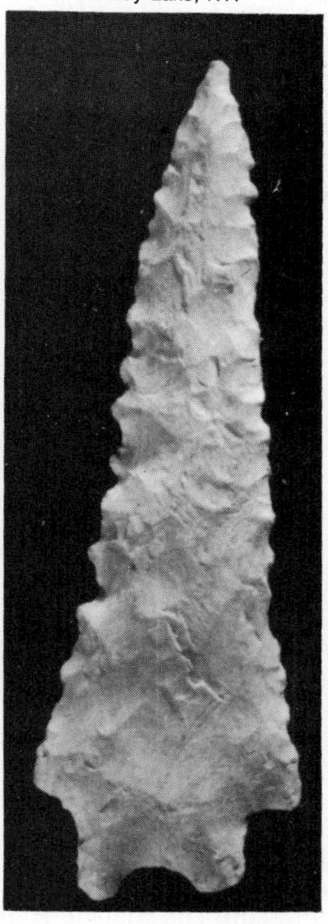

G5, $20-$35
Marshall Co., KY.

KIRK SNAPPED BASE - Early to mid-Archaic, 9000 - 6000 B.P.

G4, $6-$10
Humphreys Co., TN.

G3, $4-$6
Humphreys Co., TN.

G4, $6-$10
Humphreys Co., TN.

G5, $8-$12
Humphreys Co., TN.

G5, $8-$12
Humphreys Co., TN.

G6, $8-$15
Humphreys Co., TN.

LOCATION: Southeastern to Eastern states. **DESCRIPTION:** A medium to large size, usually serrated, blade with long tangs and a base that has been snapped or fractured off. The shoulders are also fractured on some examples. This proves that the fracturing was intentional as in *Decatur* and other types.

KIRK SNAPPED BASE (continued)

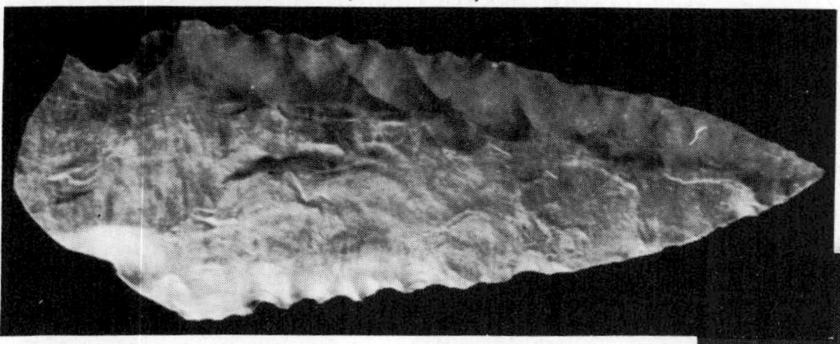

G9, $25-$40
Humphreys Co., TN.
Shoulders and base
are fractured. Classic.

G7, $10-$20
Coffee Lake, AL.

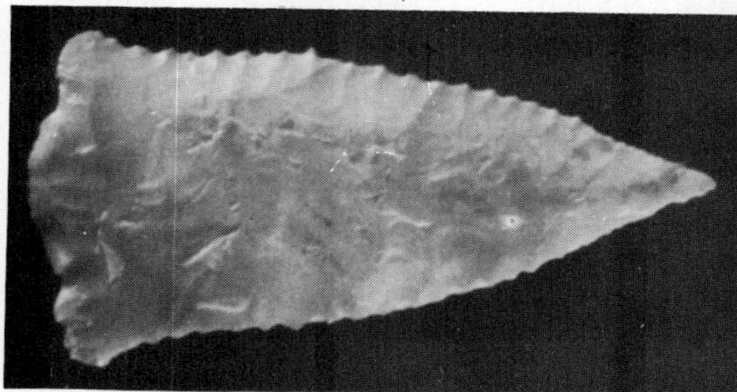

G8, $20-$35
Walker Co., AL.

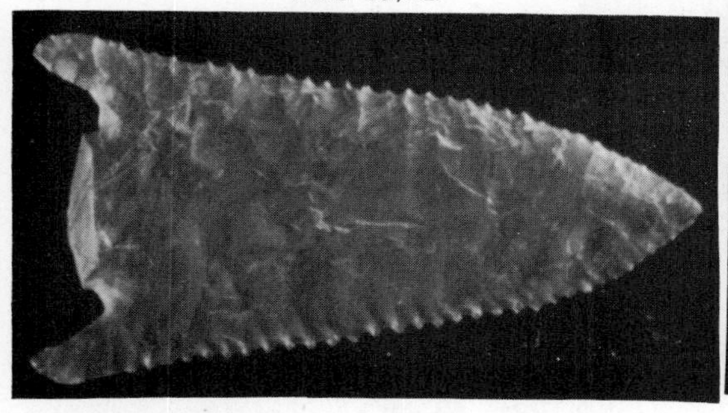

G10, $40-$60
Humphreys Co., TN. Dover chert.

G10, $150-$250
IL.

KLICKATAT DAGGER - Mississippian, 1200 - 400 B.P.

(Also see Hayes)

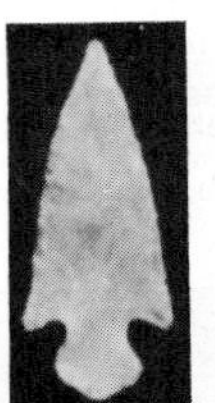
G6, $45-$70
The Dalles, OR.

G5, $25-$50
The Dalles, OR.

G3, $15-$30
The Dalles, OR.

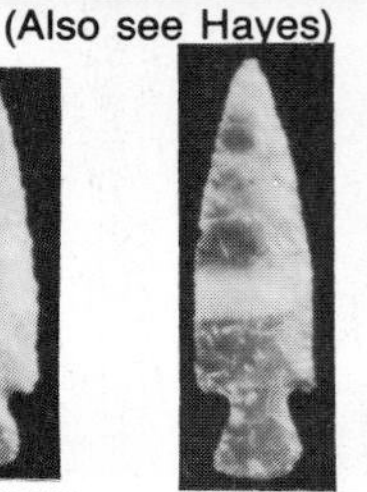
G4, $20-$35
The Dalles, OR.

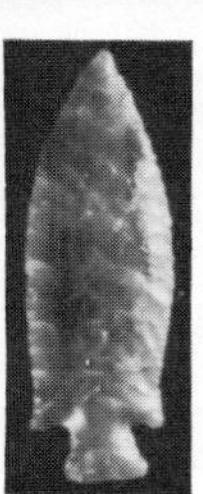
G6, $50-$80
Portland, OR.

G7, $60-$100
Wasco Co., OR.

G7, $60-$100
Wasco Co., OR.

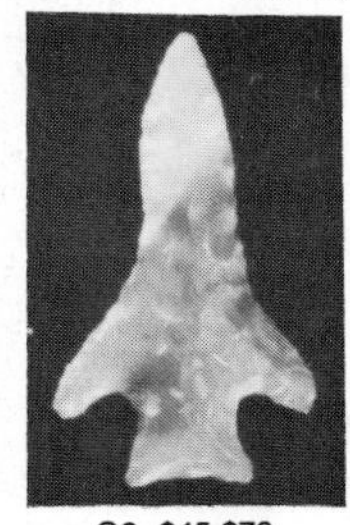
G6, $45-$70
WA/OR.

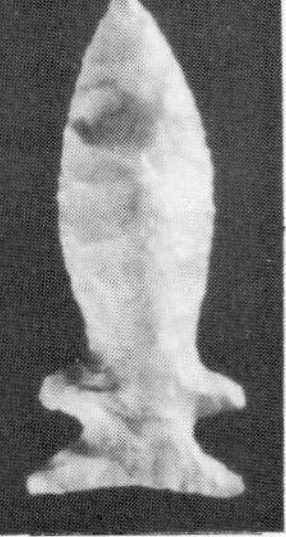
G8, $100-$180
WA/OR.

G10, $250-$400
Wasco Co., OR. Red
& green agate.

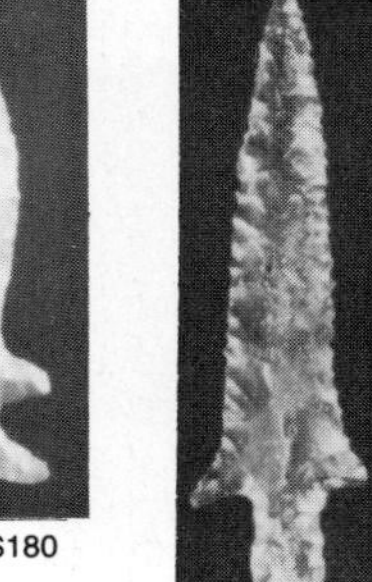
G8, $90-$150
Wasco Co., OR.

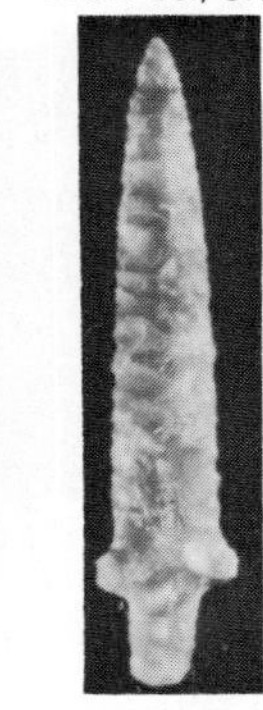
G8, $90-$150
Wasco Co., OR.

LOCATION: Northwestern states. **DESCRIPTION:** A small to medium size, narrow, thin, barbed point. Bases can be diamond shaped to square. Flaking is very high quality. **I.D. KEY:** Blade form.

KLUNK SIDE-NOTCHED - Woodland, 1500 - 1000 B.P.

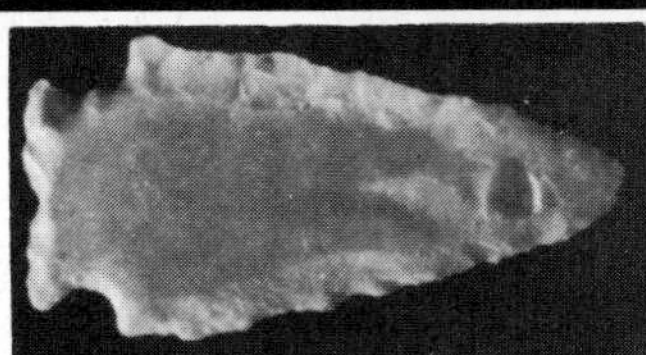
G3, $2-$3
Comanche Co., TX.

LOCATION: Midwest to Southeastern states. **DESCRIPTION:** A medium size double uniface side notched point made from a flake.

KNIGHT ISLAND - Late Woodland, 1500 - 1000 B.P.

(Also see Cache River, Jacks Reef and Reed)

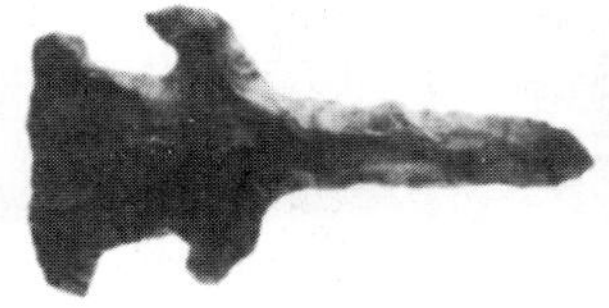
G6, $15-$25
Humphreys Co., TN.
Drill form.

G6, $15-$25
W. TN.

KNIGHT ISLAND (continued)

G3, $2-$3
Humphreys Co., TN.

G5, $8-$15
Humphreys Co., TN.

G9, $100-$180
Savannah, TN.

G9, $90-$160
Morgan Co., AL.

G8, $40-$75
Humphreys Co., TN. Dover chert.

G6, $15-$25
W. TN.

G5, $15-$25
MO.

G9, $80-$150
Humphreys Co., TN.
Dover chert.

G10, $180-$300
W. TN. Very thin.

G7, $20-$35
Humphreys Co., TN. Tip nick.

G9, $90-$160
Humphreys Co., TN.

LOCATION: Southeastern states. **DESCRIPTION:** A small to medium size, very thin, narrow, side-notched point with a straight base. Longer examples can have a pentagonal appearance. Called *Racoon Creek* in Ohio. A side-notched *Jacks Reef*. **I.D. KEY:** Thinness, basal form. Made by the bird point people.

LA JITA - Mid-Archaic, 7000 - 4000 B.P.

G6, $8-$12
Comanche Co., TX.

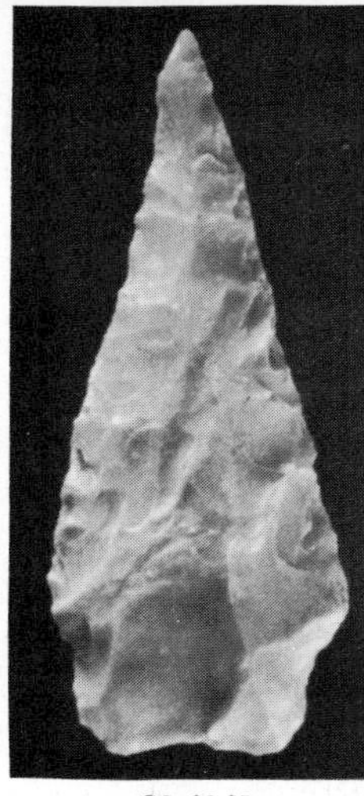

G3, $3-$5
Comanche Co., TX.

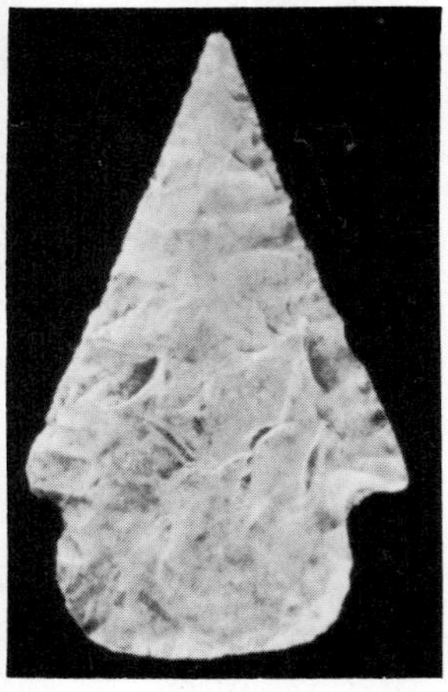

G7, $10-$20
Austin, TX.

G4, $5-$8
Comanche Co., TX.

LOCATION: Midwestern states. **DESCRIPTION:** A medium to large size, broad point with weak shoulders and a broad base that expands and has rounded base corners.

LACKAWAXEN - Woodland, 3000 - 1500 B.P.

G6, $15-$25
NJ.

LOCATION: Northeastern states. **DESCRIPTION:** A medium to large size point with weak squared to rounded shoulders and a roughly squared base. Many are made from slate.

G8, $25-$40
NJ.

LAFAYETTE - Late Archaic, 5000 - 3500 B.P.

(Also see Bolen, Clay, Culbreath, Kirk Corner, Leon and Ocala)

G5, $40-$60
Marion Co., FL.

G6, $90-$150
Sante Fe Rv., FL.

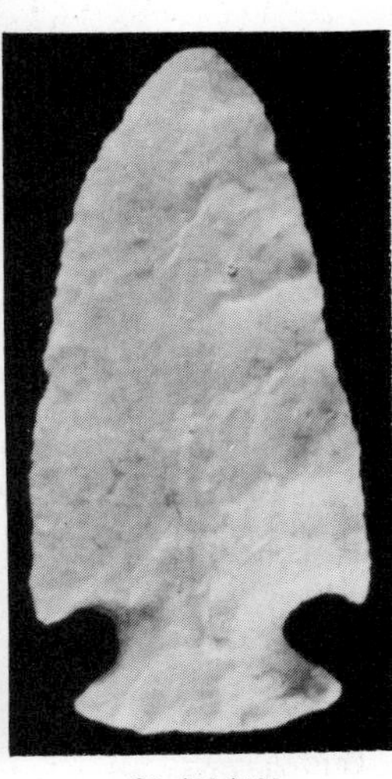

G6, $60-$100
Sante Fe Rv., FL.

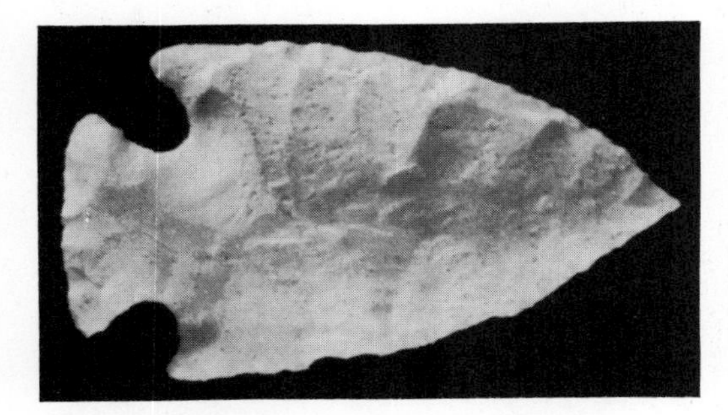

G7, $100-$170
Pinellas Co., FL.

LOCATION: Southern Southeastern states. **DESCRIPTION:** A medium size, broad, corner-notched point with a straight to concave base. Tangs and basal corners are more rounded than pointed. Related to *Clay* points.

LAFAYETTE (continued)

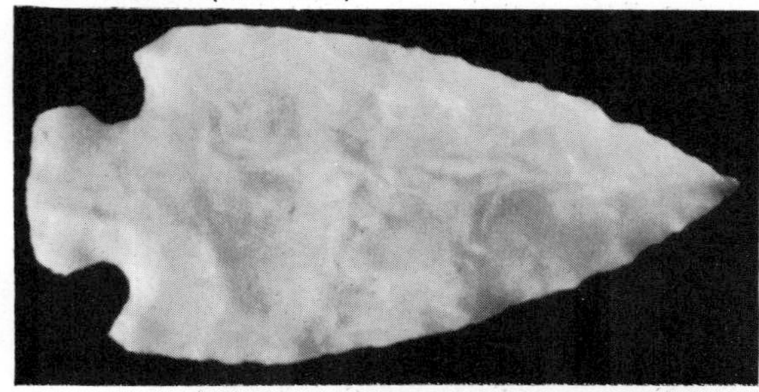

G7, $100-$170
Hillsborough Co., FL.

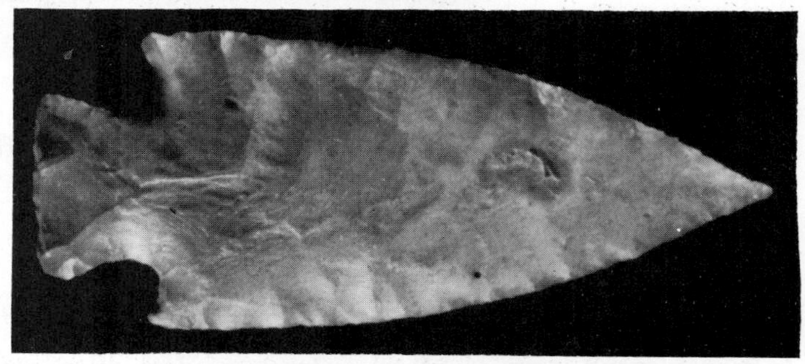

G10, $650-$900
Sante Fe River, FL.

LAKE ERIE - Early to mid-Archaic, 9000 - 5000 B.P.

(Also see Fox Valley, Jude, Kirk-Bifurcated, LeCroy, MacCorkle, Montell, St. Albans, Southampton and Stanly)

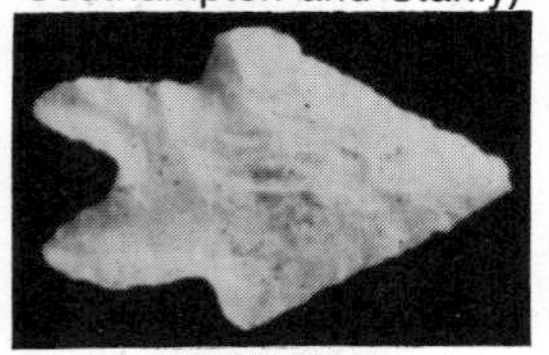

G4, $10-$20, IL.

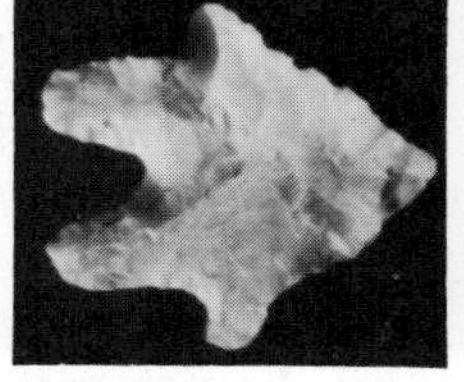

G6, $30-$45, Cleveland, OH.

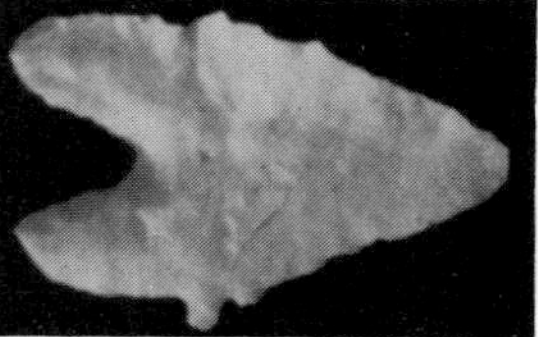

G4, $10-$20, IL.

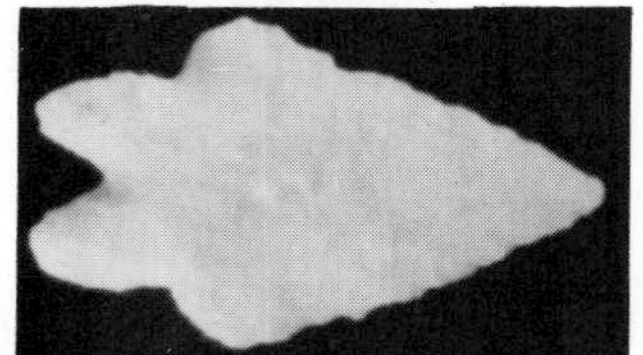

G5, $25-$45, IL.

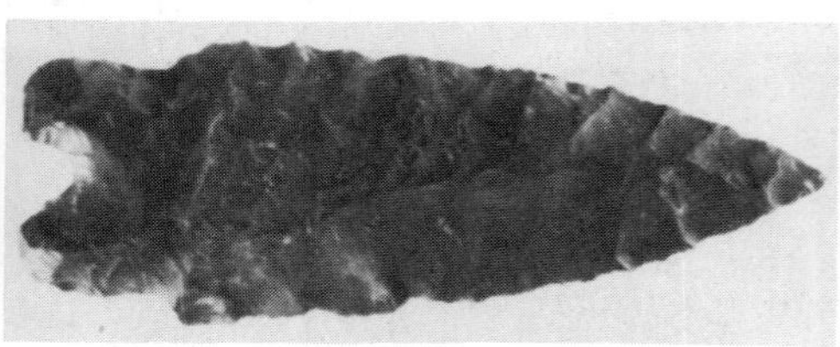

G7, $45-$70, Cleveland, OH. Coshocton chert.

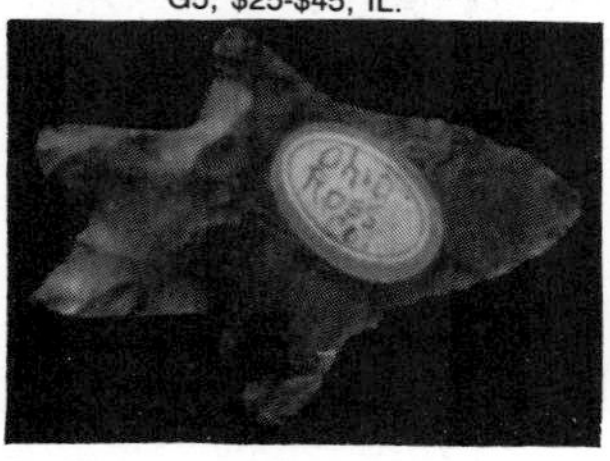

G6, $30-$45, OH. Fractured base sides.

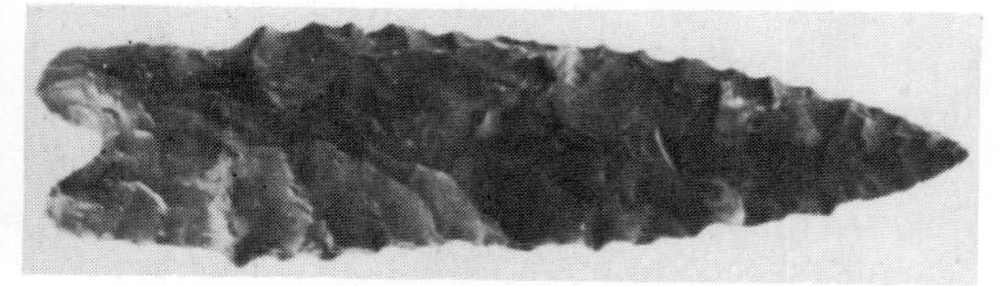

G8, $60-$100, Cleveland, OH. Coshocton chert.

LAKE ERIE (continued)

LOCATION: Northeastern states. **DESCRIPTION:** A small to medium size, thin, deeply notched or serrated, bifurcated stemmed point. The basal lobes are parallel with a tendency to turn inward and are pointed. The outward sides of the basal lobes are usually fractured from the base towards the tip and can be ground.

LAKE MOHAVE - Early Archaic, 8500 - 7000 B.P.

(Also see Hell Gap, Pelican and Rio Grande)

G4, $6-$10 G3, $4-$6 G2, $3-$5 G1, $1-$2
(All Wilkes Co., NC.)

G4, $6-$10 Person Co., NC.
G7, $10-$20 Wilkes Co., NC.
G5, $8-$12 Wilkes Co., NC.
G8, $25-$40 Stokes Co., NC.

LOCATION: California, although examples have been found in North Carolina. **DESCRIPTION:** A small to medium size lanceolate point with a long contracting stem. The widest part of the blade is close to the tip.

LAMOKA - Late Archaic, 5000 - 2500 B.P.

(Also see Flint Creek, Macpherson, Mountain Fork, Mud Creek, Swan Lake & Trinity)

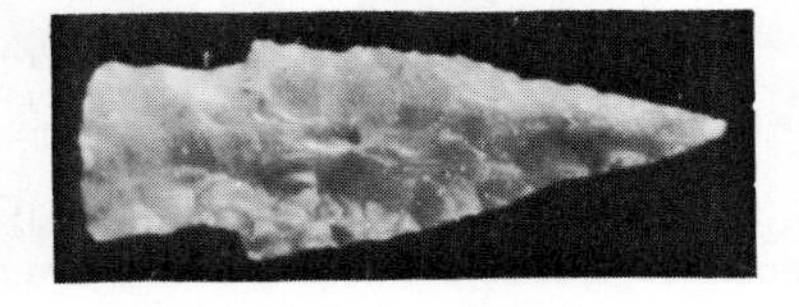

G6, $6-$10
Chattanooga, TN.

LAMOKA (continued)

G2, $1-$2
NJ.

G3, $2-$3
NJ.

LOCATION: Northeastern to Eastern states. **DESCRIPTION:** A small to medium size, thick, parallel stemmed point with tapered shoulders. Stems expand slightly and bases are straight to convex.

LAMPASOS - Early Archaic, 9000 - 6000 B.P.

(Also see Brazos, Darl, Hoxie and Uvalde)

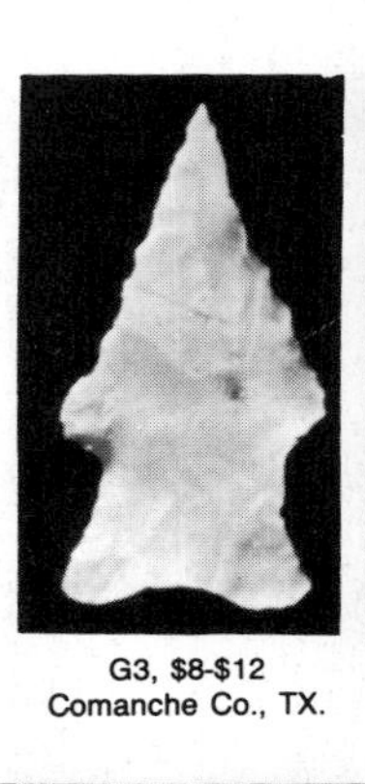

G3, $8-$12
Comanche Co., TX.

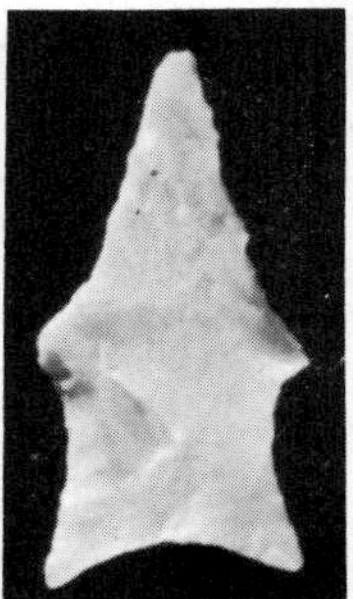

G2, $4-$6
Comanche Co., TX.

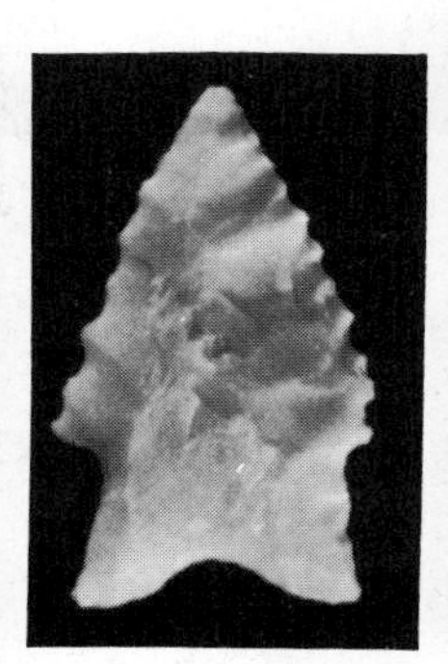

G4, $10-$20
Comanche Co., TX.

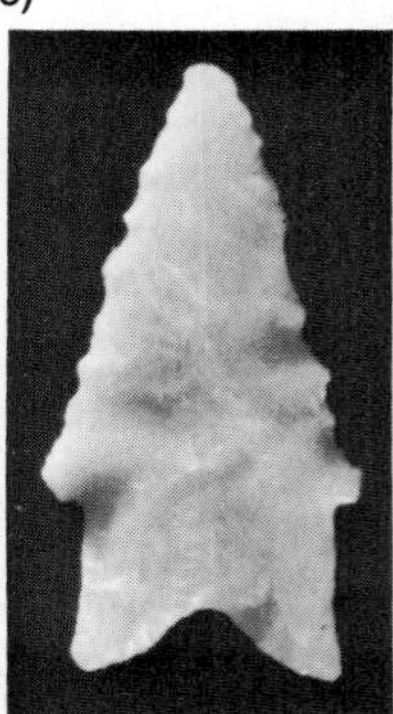

G3, $8-$12
Comanche Co., TX.

G8, $90-$150
Comanche Co., TX.

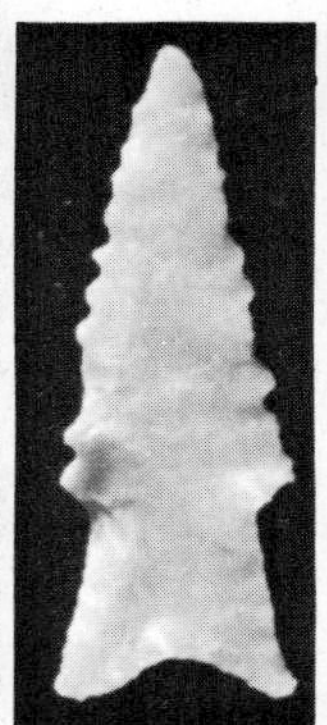

G3, $6-$10
Comanche Co., TX.

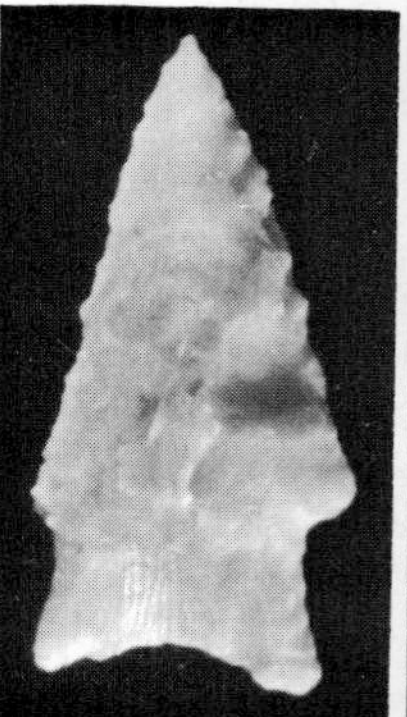

G3, $8-$12
Comanche Co., TX.

G5, $15-$25
Comanche Co., TX.

LOCATION: Midwestern states. **DESCRIPTION:** A medium to large size, serrated point with square to tapered shoulders. Blades are usually beveled on one side of each face and bases are always concave. Flaking is high quality.

G6, $30-$50
Comanche Co., TX. Note Donnaha tip.

G6, $30-$50
Comanche Co., TX.

G6, $30-$50
Comanche Co., TX.

G3, $8-$15
Comanche Co., TX.

G7, $60-$90
Comanche Co., TX.

G8, $90-$150
Austin, TX. Tang nick.

G5, $25-$40
Comanche Co., TX.

G7, $80-$120
Comanche Co., TX.

G8, $90-$150
Austin, TX.

G9, $250-$450
Comanche Co., TX.

LANCET - Paleo to Archaic, 15000 - 5000 B.P.

(Also see Scraper)

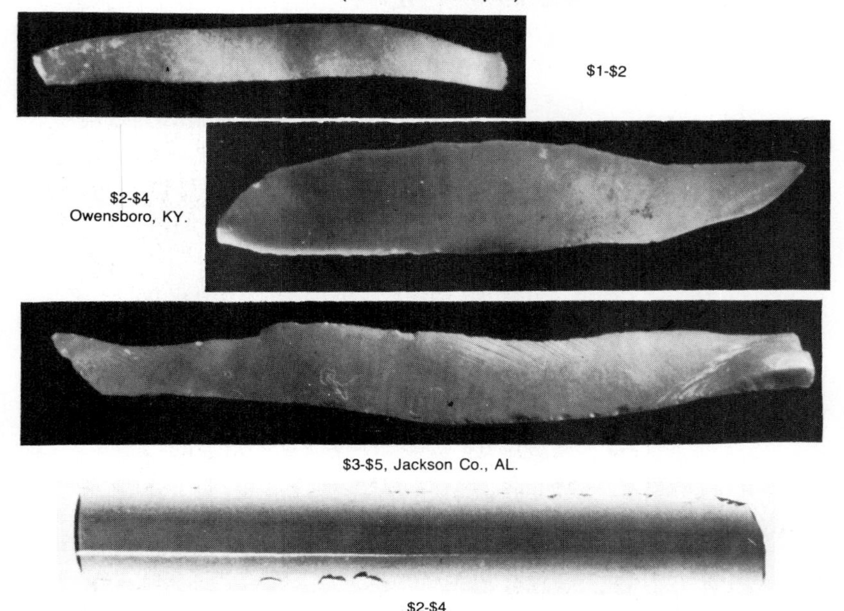

$1-$2

$2-$4
Owensboro, KY.

$3-$5, Jackson Co., AL.

$2-$4
Mexico. Obsidian.

LOCATION: Found on all early man sites. **DESCRIPTION:** A medium to large size sliver used as a knife for cutting. Recent experiments proved that these knives were sharper than a surgeon's scalpel. Similar to *burins* which are fractured at one end to produce a sharp point.

LANGE - Mid-Archaic to Woodland, 6000 - 1000 B.P.

(Also see Bulverde, Castroville, McIntire, Nolan, Table Rock & Travis)

G2, $2-$3
Comanche Co., TX.

G2, $2-$4
Comanche Co., TX.

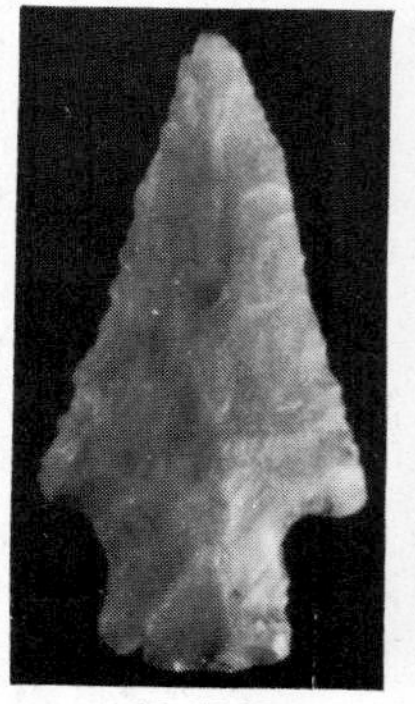

G3, $3-$5
Waco, TX.

G3, $3-$5
Comanche Co., TX.

LOCATION: Midwestern states. **DESCRIPTION:** A medium to large size expanded stem point with tapered shoulders and a straight to convex base.

LANGE (continued)

G3, $2-$4
Comanche Co., TX.

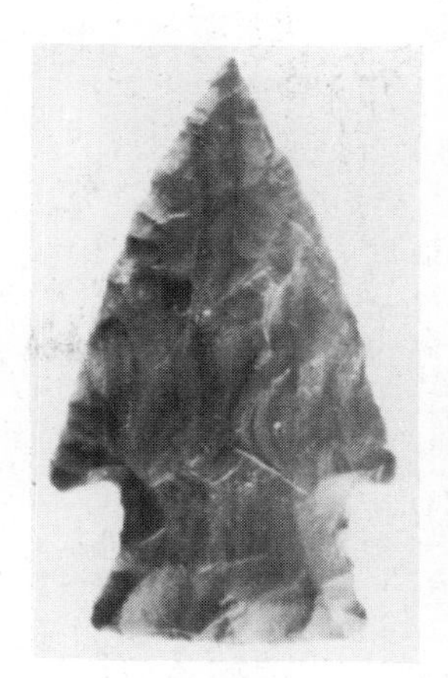

G7, $20-$30
Austin, TX.

G4, $5-$8
TN.

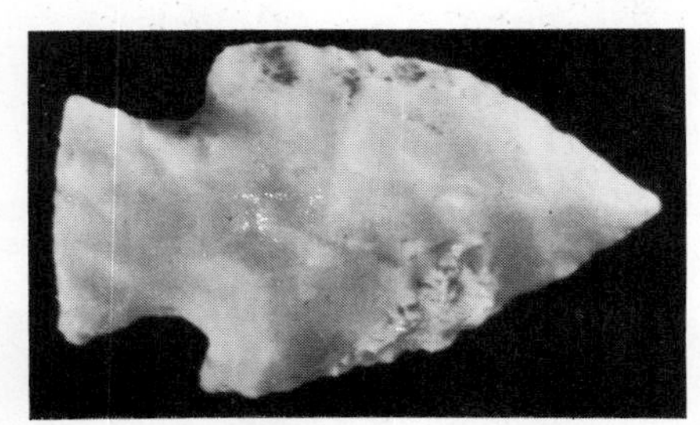

G3, $3-$5
Comanche Co., TX.

G7, $30-$50
Comanche Co., TX.

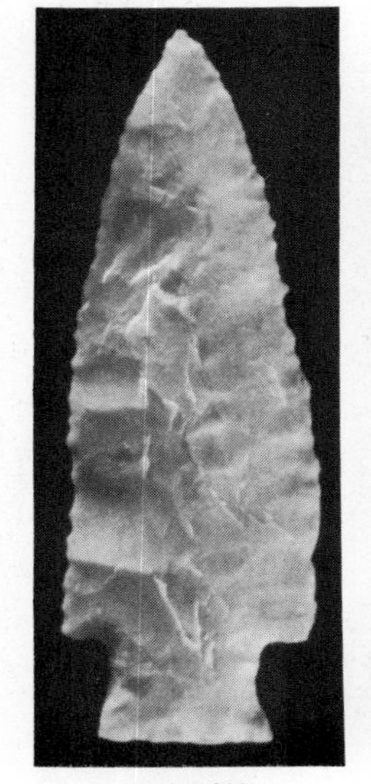

G6, $15-$25
Comanche Co., TX.

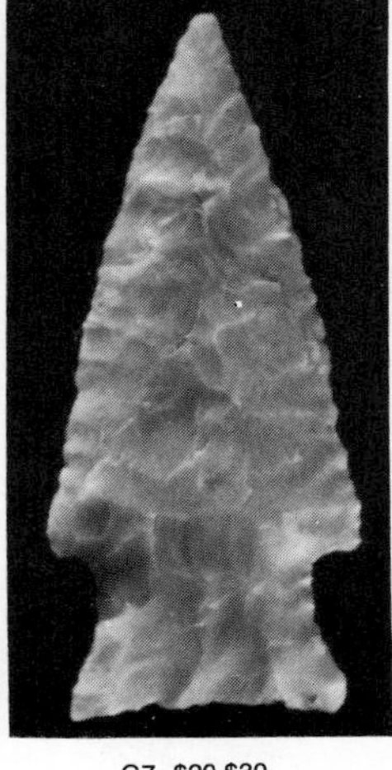

G7, $20-$30
Comanche Co., TX.

G3, $3-$5
Comanche Co., TX.

G7, $20-$30
Raleigh, NC.

G9, $70-$120
Comanche Co., TX.

G7, $20-$30
Comanche Co., TX.

G8, $35-$65
Comanche Co., TX.

G10, $250-$400
Austin, TX. Excellent quality.

G8, $40-$75
Comanche Co., TX.

G9, $60-$100
Austin, TX.

LANGTRY - Mid-Archaic to Woodland, 5000 - 2000 B.P.

(Also see Gary, Buggs Island, Hidden Valley, Morrow Mountain and Val Verde)

G4, $4-$6
Madison Co., AL.

G3, $2-$4
Meigs Co., TN.

G4, $6-$10
Austin, TX.

G5, $8-$12
Comanche Co., TX.

G7, $25-$40
Austin, TX.

G7, $25-$40
Comanche Co., TX.

G6, $15-$25
Cent. TX.

LOCATION: Midwestern states. **DESCRIPTION:** A medium size triangular point with a contracting stem. Shoulders can be square, tapered or barbed. Bases are concave to straight. **I.D. KEY:** Expanded barbs.

G8, $50-$80
Austin, TX.

G6, $15-$25
Waco, TX.

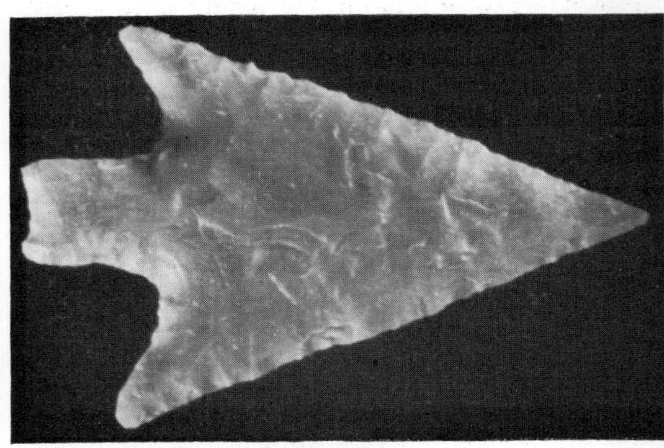

G9, $150-$280
Austin, TX.

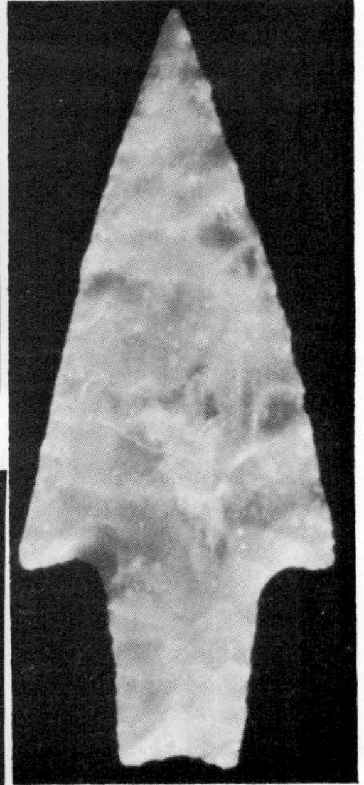

G8, $50-$90
Austin, TX.

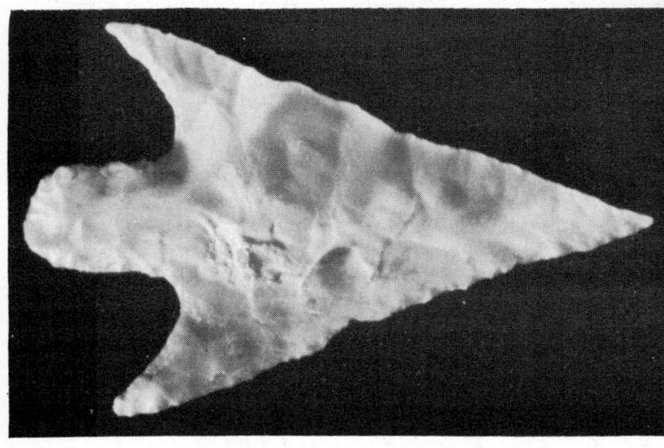

G9, $80-$125, Austin, TX. Very thin and colorful.

LECROY - Early to mid-Archaic, 9000 - 5000 B.P.

(Also see Decatur, Fox Valley, Jude, Kanawha, Kirk-Bifurcated, Lake Erie, MacCorkle, Montell, Pine Tree, Rice Lobbed, St. Albans, Southampton and Stanly)

G2, $2-$3
SE TN.

G2, $2-$3
SE TN.

G2, $2-$3
ILL.

G2, $2-$3
SE TN.

G2, $2-$3
Pikeville, TN.

G2, $2-$3
IL.

G2, $2-$3
Surry Co., NC. Milky quartz.

G2, $1-$2
Wilkes Co., NC.
Tip nick.

G2, $2-$3
Fentress Co., TN.

G3, $3-$5
Emporia Co., VA.
Milky quartz.

G3, $4-$6
Johnson Co., NC.

G3, $3-$5
Citico, TN.

G4, $5-$8
Stokes Co., NC.

G4, $5-$8
Washington Co., VA.

G2, $2-$4
Polk Co., GA.
Milky quartz.

G4, $5-8
IL.

G4, $5-$8
Dayton, TN.

G3, $3-$5
Alleghany Co., NC.
Milky quartz.

LOCATION: Southeastern states. **DESCRIPTION:** A small to medium size, thin, usually broad point with deeply notched or serrated blade edges and a deeply bifurcated base. Basal ears can either droop down or expand out. The stem is usually large in comparison to the blade size. Some stem sides are fractured in Northern examples (*Lake Erie*). Bases are usually ground. **I.D. KEY:** Basal form.

G4, $4-$6
Meigs Co., TN.

G2, $2-$3
Newberry Co., SC.
Milky quartz.

G4, $4-$6
Moccasin Bend,
Chattanooga, TN.

G4, $5-$8
Hamilton Co., TN.

G2, $2-$3
NJ. Shale.

G3, $3-$5
Sussex Co., VA.
Milky quartz.

G5, $8-$12
IL.

G5, $8-$12
Jackson Co., AL.

G5, $8-$12
Emporia Co., VA.
Milky quartz.

G5, $6-$10
Meigs Co., TN.

G4, $5-$8
Limestone Co., AL. Note
notched ears.

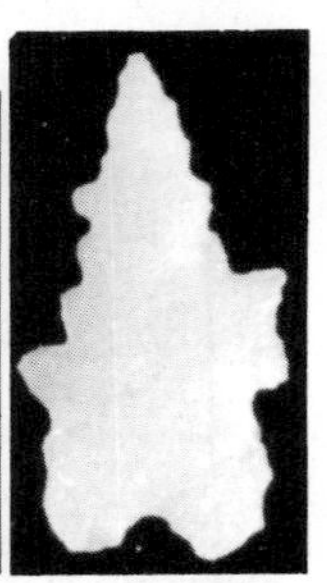

G4, $5-$8
Emporia Co., VA.
Milky quartz.

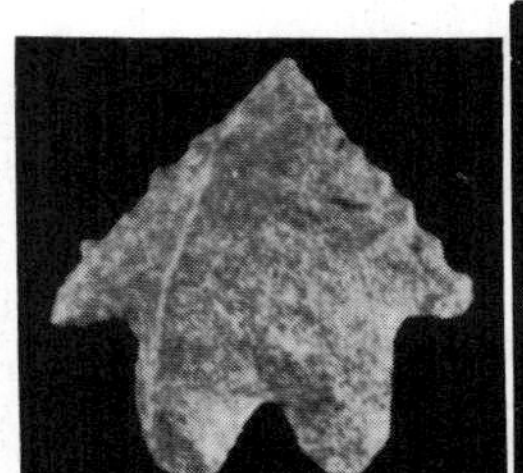

G5, $8-$12
Guilford Co., NC.

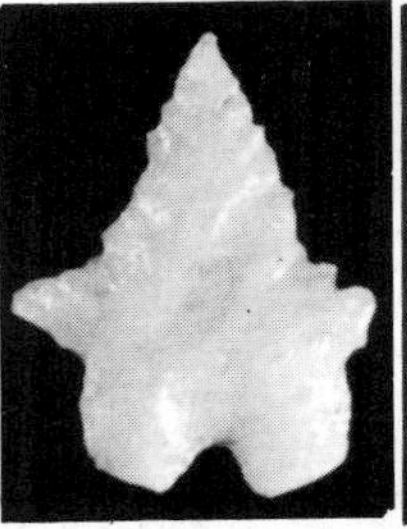

G4, $5-$8
Emporia Co., VA.
Milky quartz.

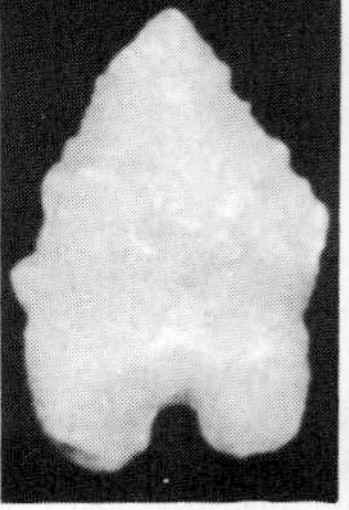

G3, $3-$5
Newberry Co., SC.
Milky quartz.

G5, $8-$12
Hamilton Co., TN.
LeCroy site.

G3, $4-$6
Fentress Co., TN.

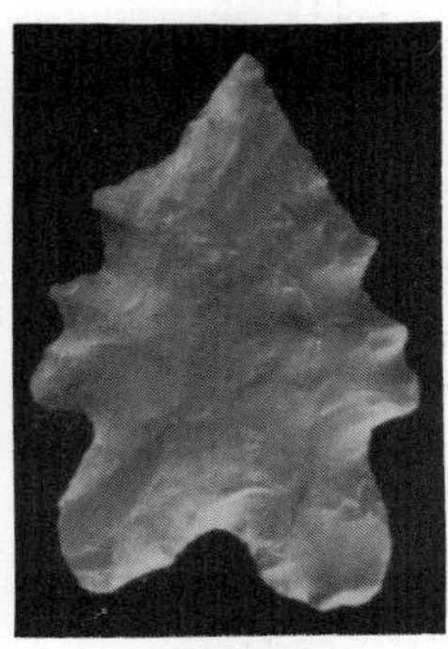

G6, $15-$25
Meigs Co., TN.

G5, $8-$15
Hamilton Co. TN. Very thin.

G5, $8-$15
N. AL.

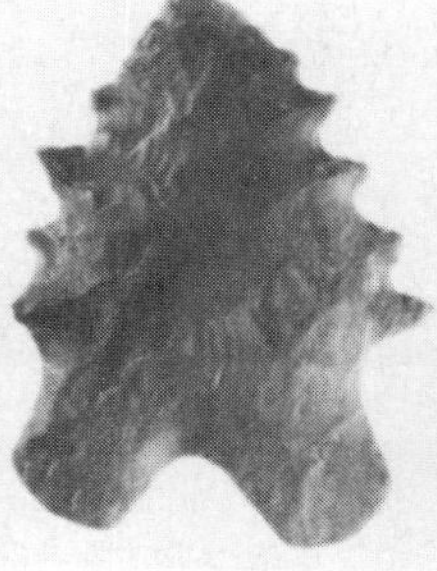

G7, $20-$35
Lauderdale Co., AL.

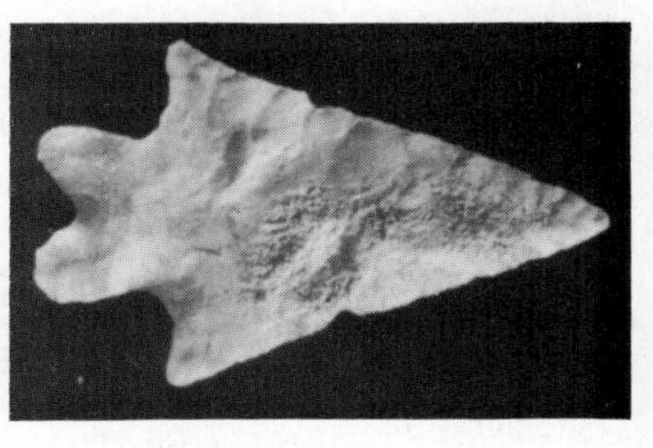

G7, $20-$35
Meigs Co., TN.

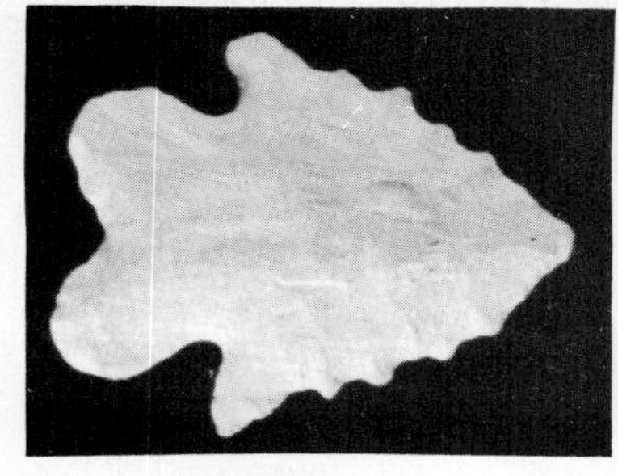

G5, $8-$15
Cent. NC.

G8, $30-$50
Montgomery Co., NC.

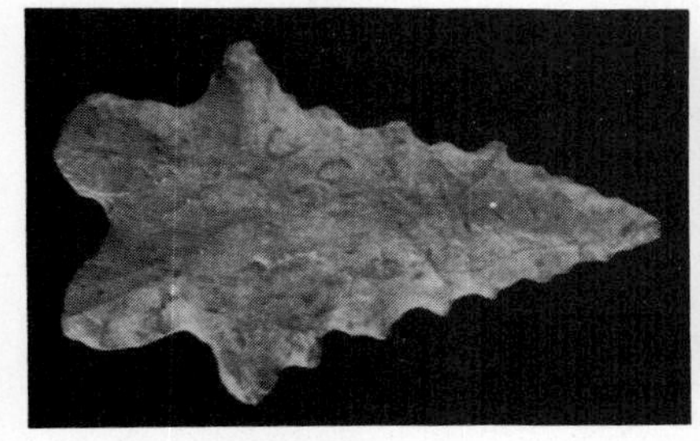

G8, $30-$50
Rowan Co., NC.

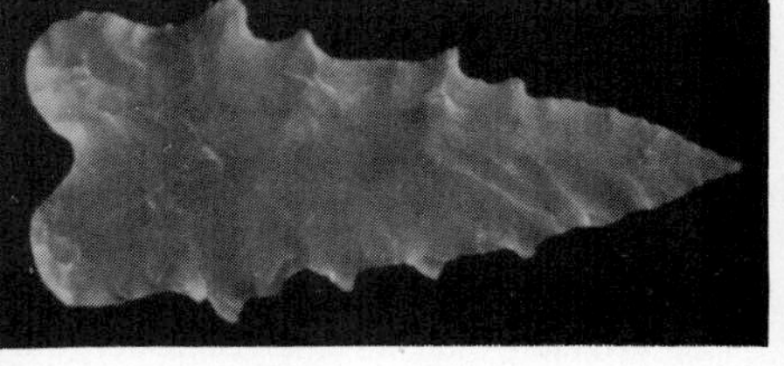

G8, $30-$50
Meigs Co., TN.

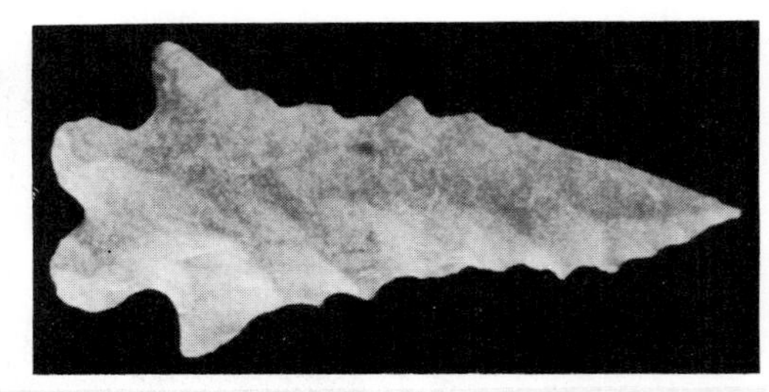

G9, $80-$120
Robeson, NC.

G7, $25-$40
Richmond Co., NC. Note unusual shoulder.

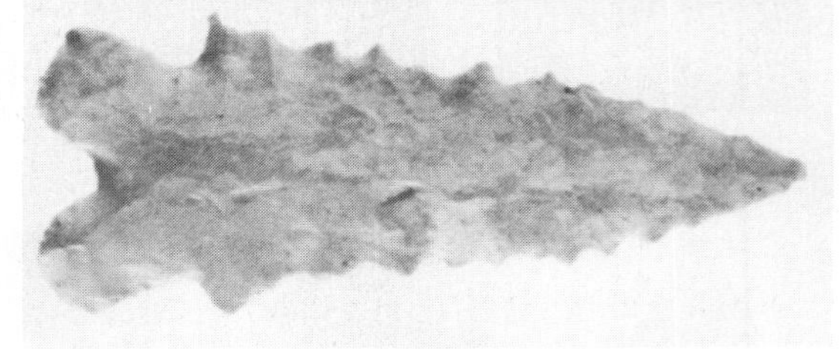

G9, $90-$150
Colbert Co., AL.

LEDBETTER - Mid to late Archaic, 6000 - 3500 B.P.

(Also see Pickwick)

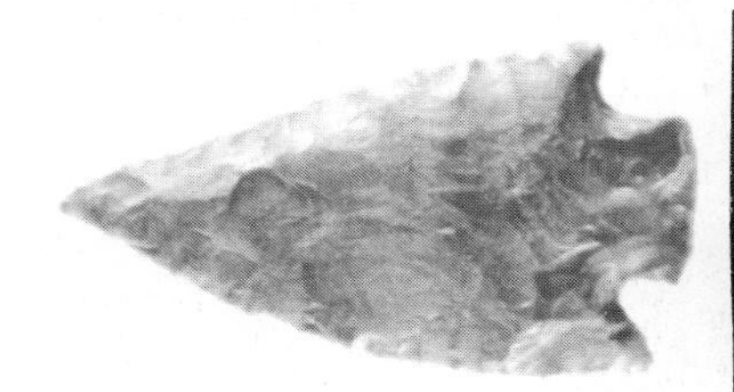

G3, $2-$4
E. TN.

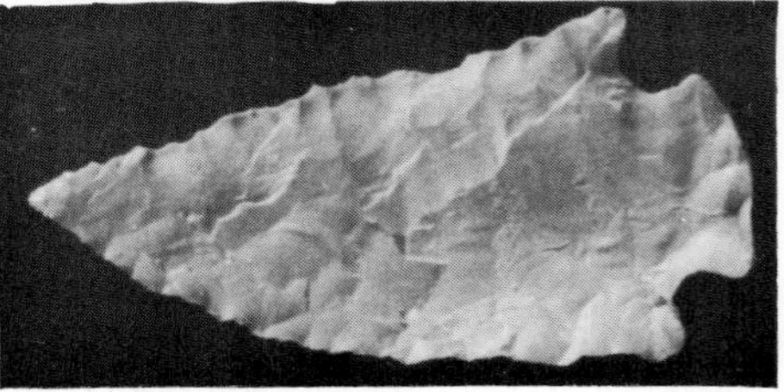

G3, $3-$5
Dunlap, TN.

G4, $5-$8
Florence, AL.

LOCATION: Southeastern states. **DESCRIPTION:** A medium to large size asymmetrical point with a short, usually fractured or snapped base. One blade edge is curved more than the other. Shoulders are tapered, squared or slightly barbed. Some examples show fine pressure flaking along the blade edges. Believed to be *Pickwick* knives. **I.D. KEY:** Blade form.

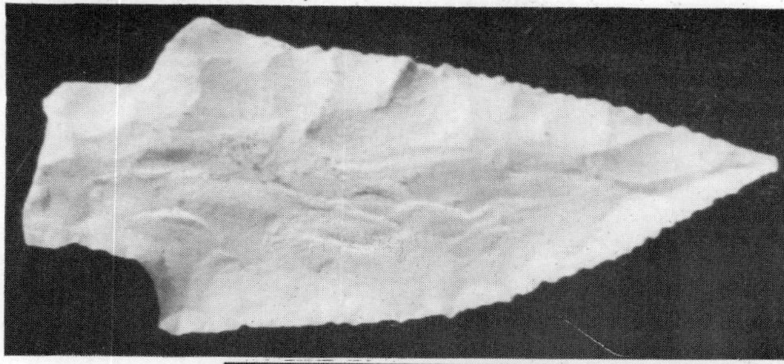

G5, $10-$20
E. TN.

G5, $20-$30
Yadkin Co., NC.

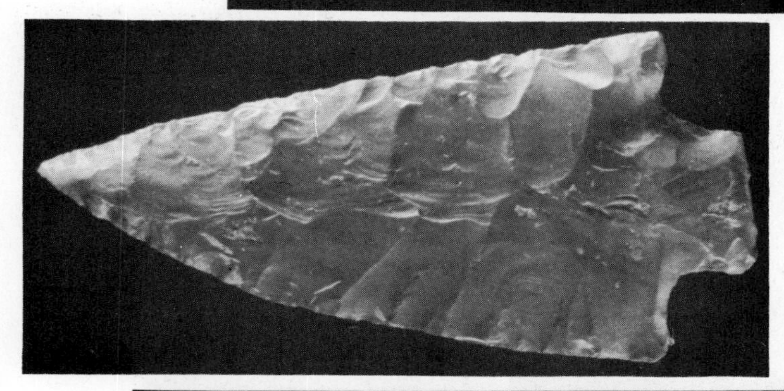

G6, $25-$40
E. TN.

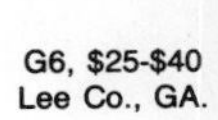

G6, $25-$40
Lee Co., GA.

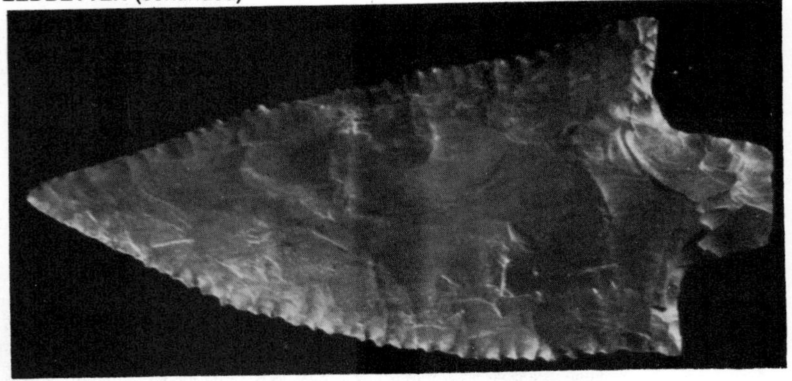

G10, $250-$400
Lauderdale Co., AL. Classic.

G7, $50-$90
Flint River, GA.

G8, $100-$150
Hardin Co., TN. Dover chert.

G8, $80-$130
Coffee Lake, AL.

G8, $90-$150
Humphreys Co., TN.

G9, $250-$400
Sante Fe Rv., FL.

LEIGHTON - Early Archaic, 8000 - 5000 B.P.

(Also see Benton, Big Sandy, Evans, Huffaker and Ohio Double-Notched)

G4, $20-$30
Dayton, TN. Tip nick.

G6, $30-$50
Florence, AL.

G4, $20-$30
Limestone Co., AL.

G5, $25-$45
W. TN.

G7, $50-$80
Humphreys Co., TN. Note basal thinning.

G5, $25-$45
Decatur, AL.

G8, $90-$150
Lauderdale Co., AL.

G5, $25-$40
Humphreys Co., TN.

G5, $25-$40
Humphreys Co., TN.

LOCATION: Southeastern states. **DESCRIPTION:** A medium to large size, double side-notched point that is usually serrated and has a concave base that is ground. **I.D. KEY:** Basal notching, archaic flaking.

LEIGHTON (continued)

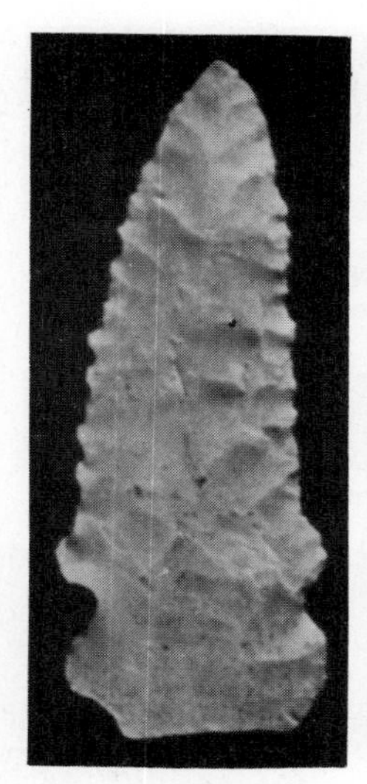

G4, $20-$30
Alexander City, AL.

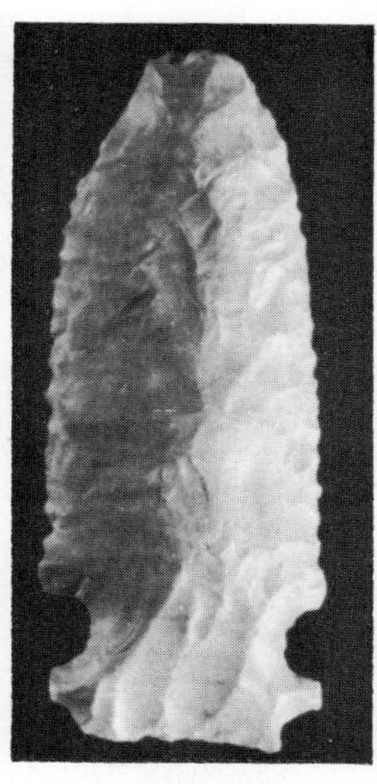

G3, $8-$12
Humphreys Co., TN. Tip damage.

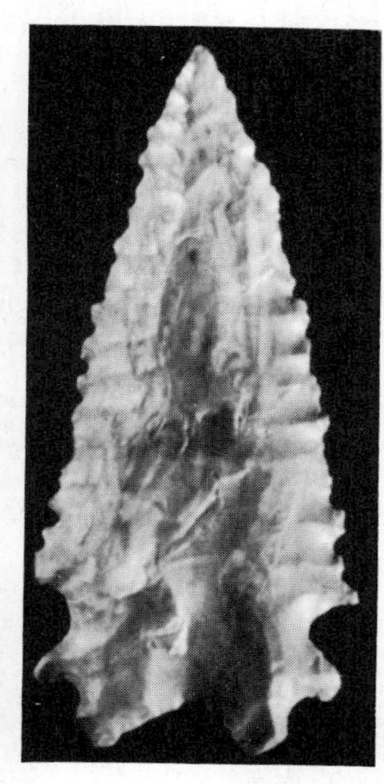

G9, $250-$400
Colbert Co., AL. Keller's bluff.

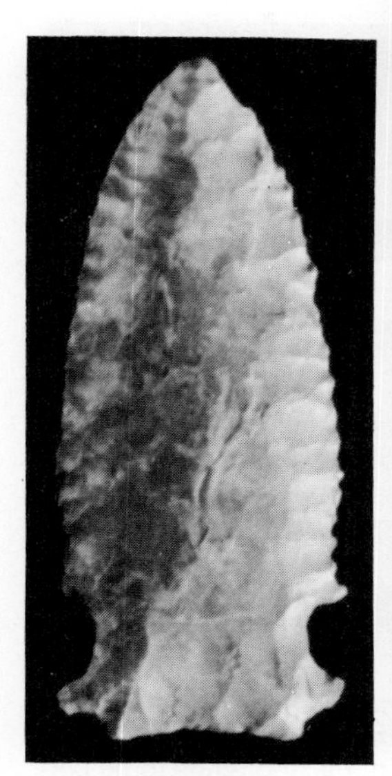

G6, $30-$50
Humphreys Co., TN.
Note basal thinning.

G5, $25-$40
Humphreys Co., TN.

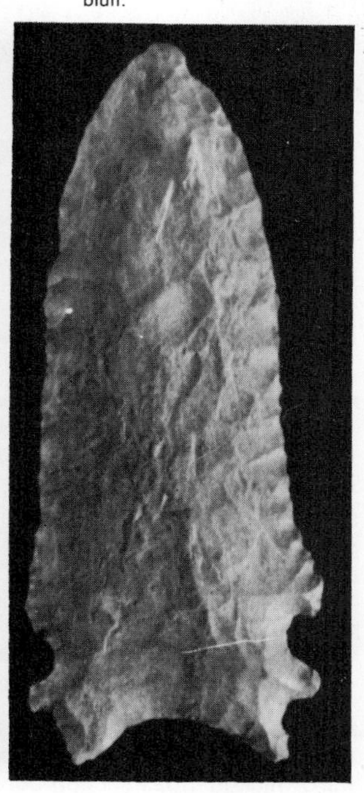

G7, $50-$80
Humphreys Co., TN. Tip nick.

LEON - Late Woodland, 2000 - 1000 B.P.

(Also see Duval, Keota, Merom and Scallorn)

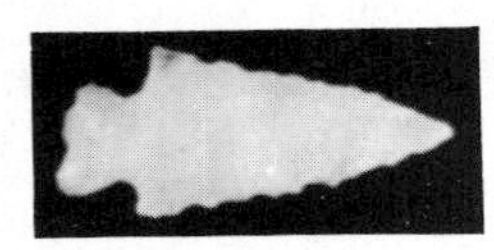

G4, $15-$25
Hillsborough Co., FL. Coral.

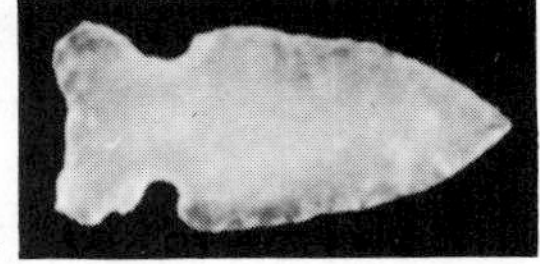

G5, $20-$35
Dyersburg, TN. Agate.

LOCATION: Southern Southeastern states. **DESCRIPTION:** A small, narrow, side to corner-notched point. Shoulders can be barbed to rounded. Base can be straight to convex.

LERMA POINTED BASE - Transitional Paleo to early Archaic, 10000 - 8000 B.P.

(Also see Agate Basin, Cobbs Triangular, Guilford and Sedalia)

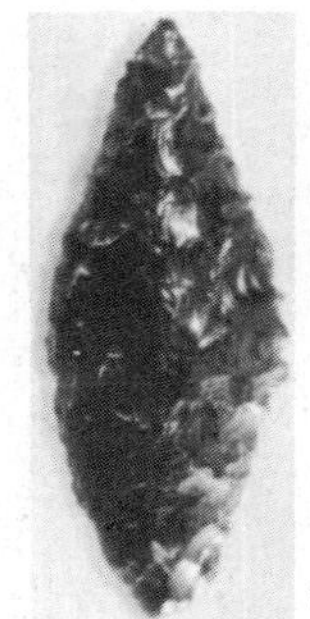

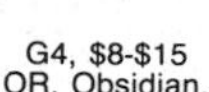

G4, $8-$15
OR. Obsidian.

G6, $35-$70
Austin, TX.

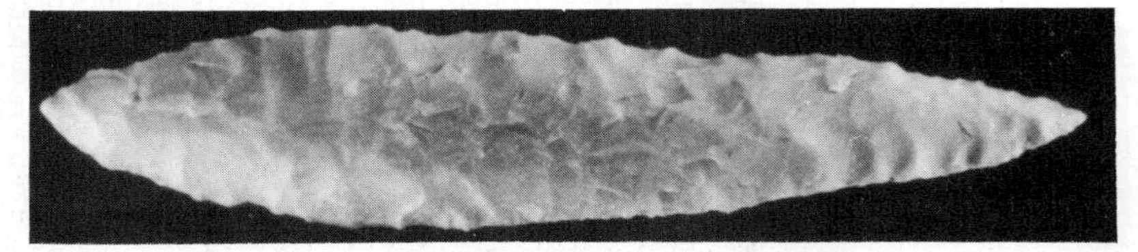

G7, $50-$80, Austin, TX.

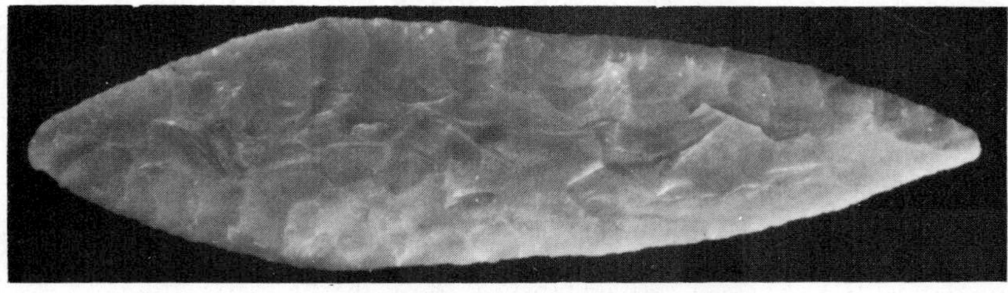

G8, $60-$90. Comanche Co., TX.

LOCATION: Siberia to Alaska, Canada, Mexico, South America and across the U.S. **DESCRIPTION:** A large size, narrow, lanceolate blade with a pointed base. Most are fairly thick in cross section but finer examples can be thin. Flaking tends to be collateral. Basal areas can be ground. Western forms are beveled on one side of each face. Similar forms have been found in Europe and Africa dating back to 20,000 - 40,000 B.P., but didn't enter the U.S. until after the advent of *Clovis*.

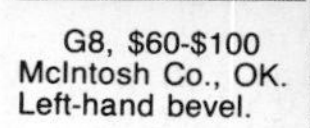

G8, $60-$100
McIntosh Co., OK.
Left-hand bevel.

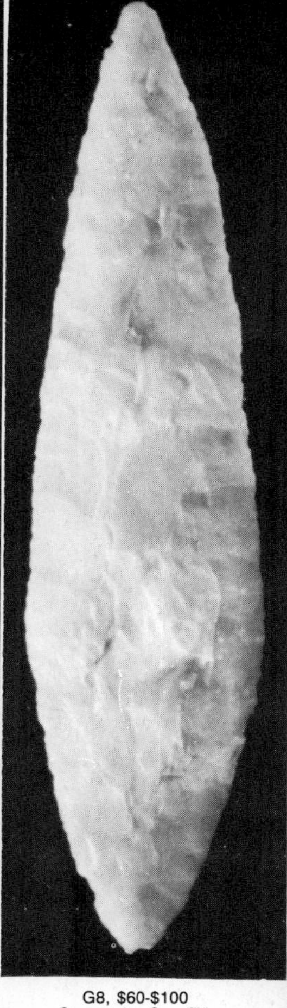

G8, $60-$100
Comanche Co., TX.

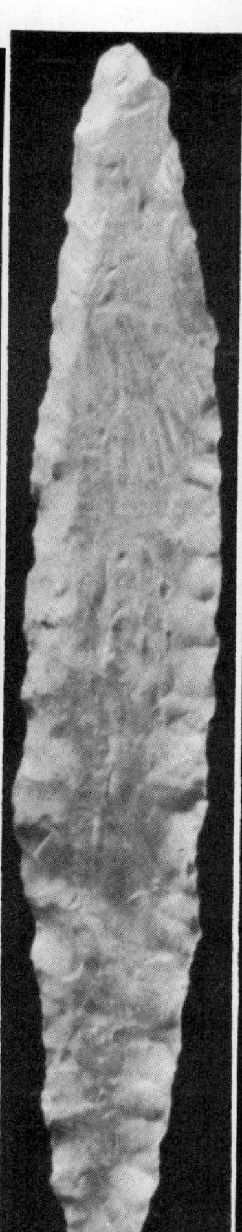

G8, $60-$100
McIntosh Co., OK.

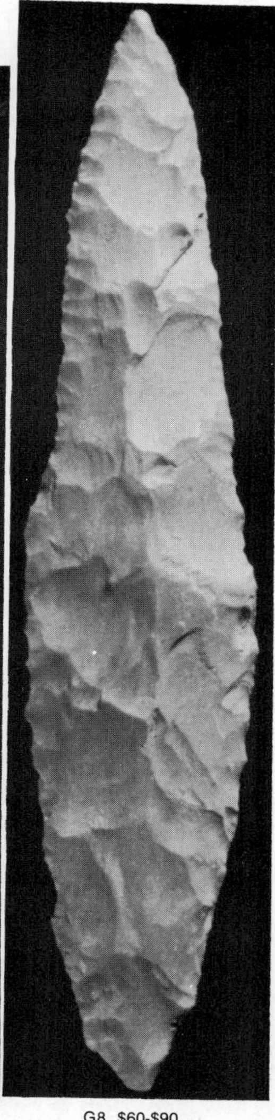

G8, $60-$90
Florence, AL. 7 Mile Isle.
Note resharpening of blade
& long hafting area.

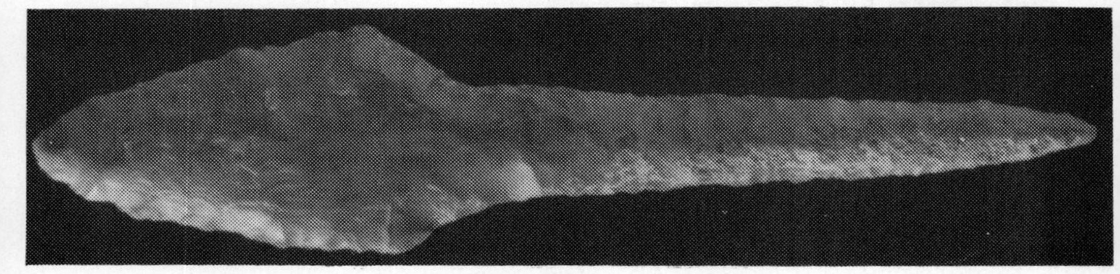

G9, $200-$300. Picnorsen Cave, KY. Drill form.

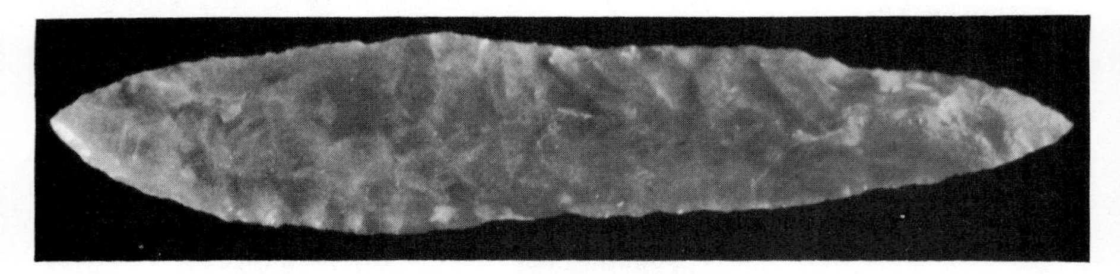

G8, $60-$100
Austin, TX. Torque blade. Nice parallel flaking.

LERMA ROUNDED BASE - Transitional Paleo to mid-Archaic, 10000 - 5000 B.P.

G3, $4-$8
WA/OR.

G4, $8-$15
Alachua Co., FL. Agate.

G4, $5-$7
Comanche Co., TX.

G8, $60-$100
Comanche Co., TX.

G6, $25-$45
Austin, TX.

LOCATION: Same as pointed base Lerma. **DESCRIPTION:** A large size, narrow, thick, lanceolate blade with a rounded base. Some Western examples are beveled on one side of each face. Flaking tends to be collateral and finer examples are thin in cross section.

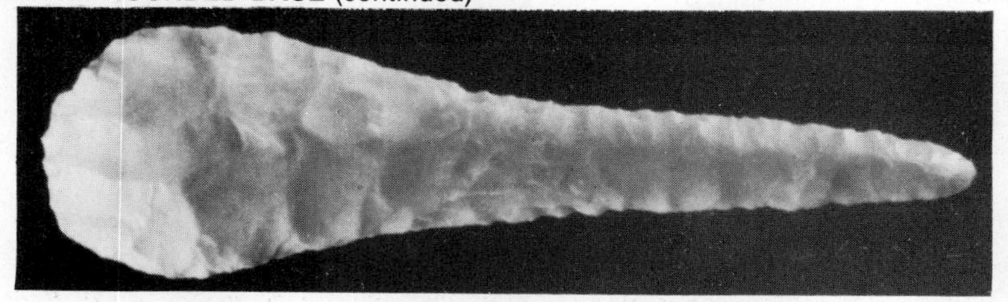

G7, $35-$60, Austin, TX. Drill form.

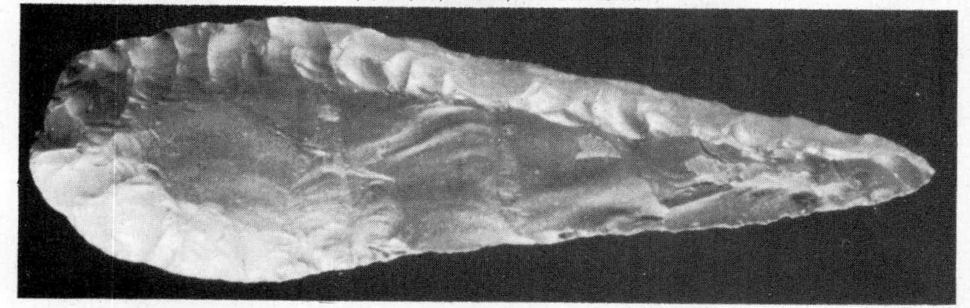

G7, $30-$50. AL/TN. Left-hand bevel.

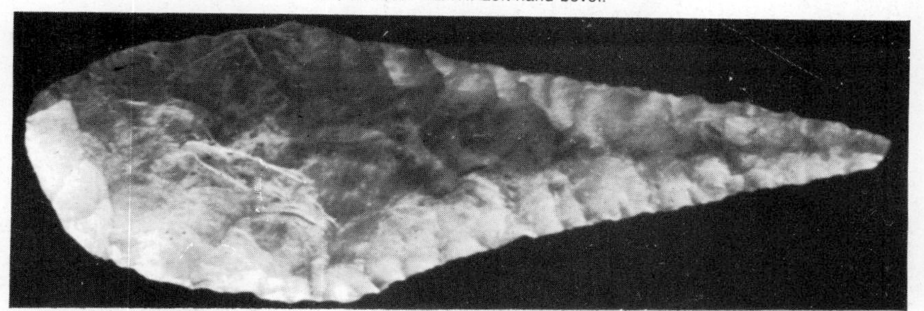

G6, $25-$40, Humphreys Co., TN. Dover chert.

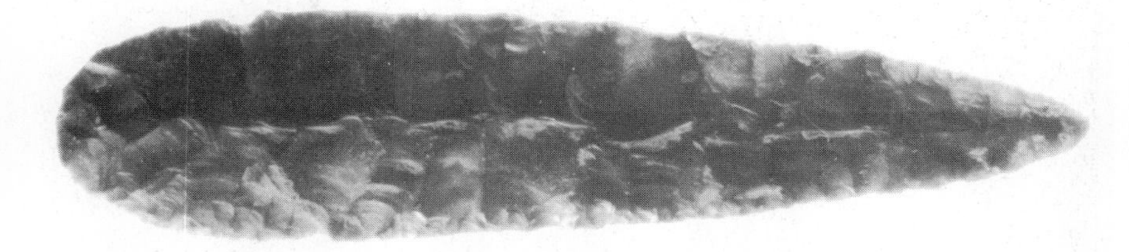

G8, $60-$100. KY. Black flint. Note parallel flaking. Very thin and excellent.

G7, $35-$60, Florence, AL.

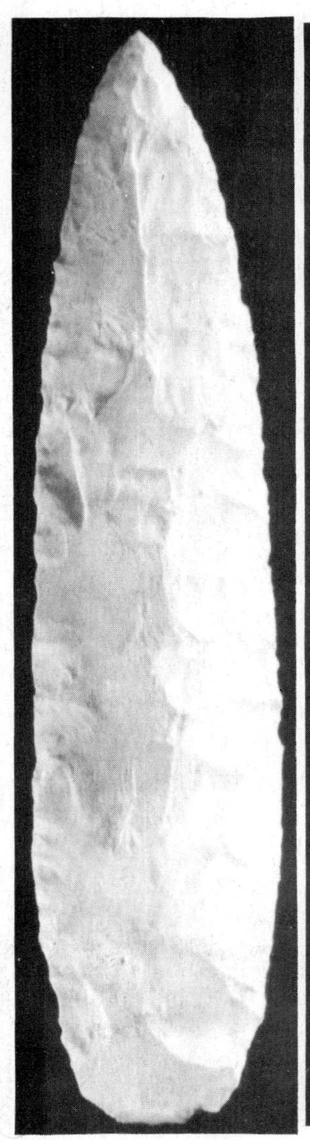

G9, $125-$225
Benton Co., TN.

G9, $150-$250
Humphreys Co., TN. Very thin.

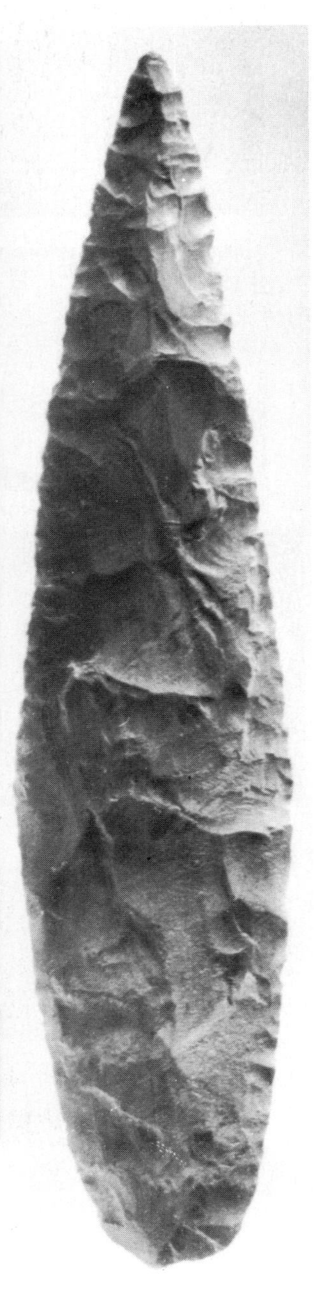

G10, $250-$400
Parsons, TN.

LEVANNA - Late Woodland to Mississippian, 1300 - 600 B.P.

(Also see Caraway, Clarksville, Madison and Yadkin)

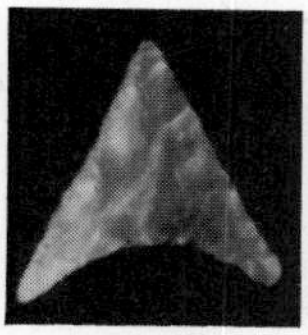

G4, $2-$4
SE TN.

G1, .50-$1
Wilkes Co., NC.

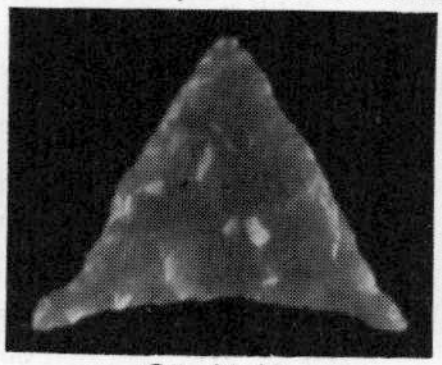

G5, $3-$5
Stokes Co., NC.

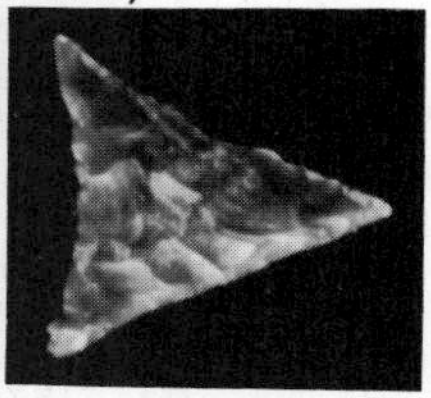

G6, $4-$6
Pulaski Co., KY.

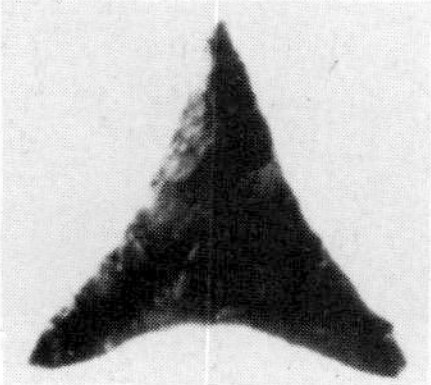

G8, $8-$15
Bristol, TN.

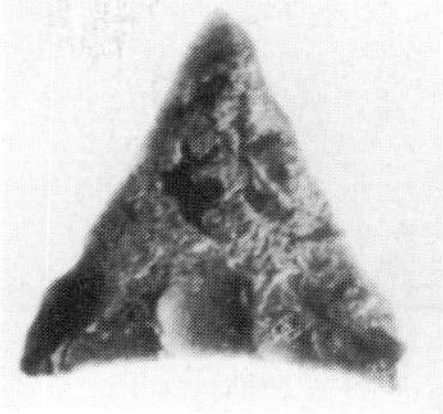

G5, $3-$5
Bristol, TN.

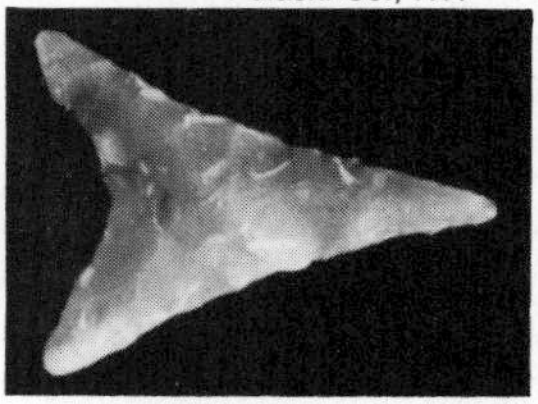

G8, $8-$15
Bristol, TN.

G9, $15-$25
Oswego Co., NY. Note base is fractured from both corners. Very rare.

G9, $15-$25
Bethany, WV. Base fractured from both corners. Rare.

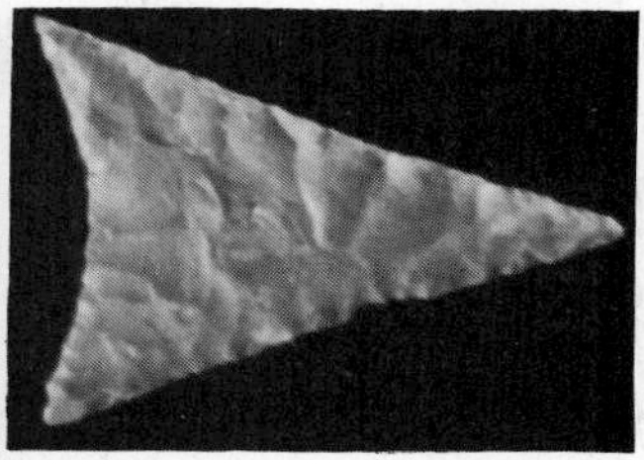

G9, $15-$25
Oswego Co., NY.

G10, $20-$35
Oswego Co., NY.

G9, $15-$25
Oswego Co., NY.

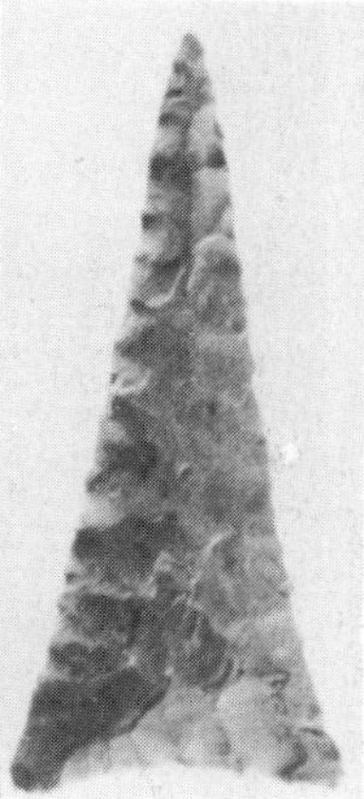

G9, $15-$25
Oswego Co., NY.

LOCATION: Southeastern to Northeastern states. **DESCRIPTION:** A small to medium size, thin, wide, triangular point with a concave to straight base. Believed to be replaced by *Madison* points in later times. Called *Yadkin* in North Carolina. **I.D. KEY:** Medium thick cross section.

LEVY - Late Archaic, 5000 - 3000 B.P.

(Also see Abbey, Adena-Dickson, Alachua, Elora, Hardee Beveled, Marion, Newnan, Oauchita, Putnam, Savannah River & Sumter)

G1, $10-$20
Alachua Co., FL.

G1, $10-$15
Hillsborough Co., FL.

G2, $20-$35
Dale Co., AL.

G3, $40-$70
Hillsborough Co., FL.

G3, $35-$65
Hillsborough Co., FL.

G4, $50-$80
Hillsborough Co., FL. Purple coral.

G3, $40-$70
Dale Co., AL.

LOCATION: Southern Southeastern states. **DESCRIPTION:** A medium size, broad, contracted stemmed point with wide, tapered to slightly barbed shoulders. May have evolved from the earlier *Newnan* form. **I.D. KEY:** Edgework and one ear is stronger.

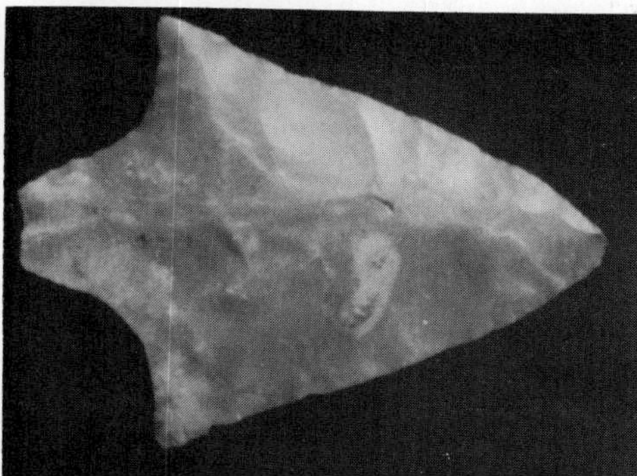

G4, $80-$120
NW Cent. FL.

G5, $150-$250
Burke Co., GA.

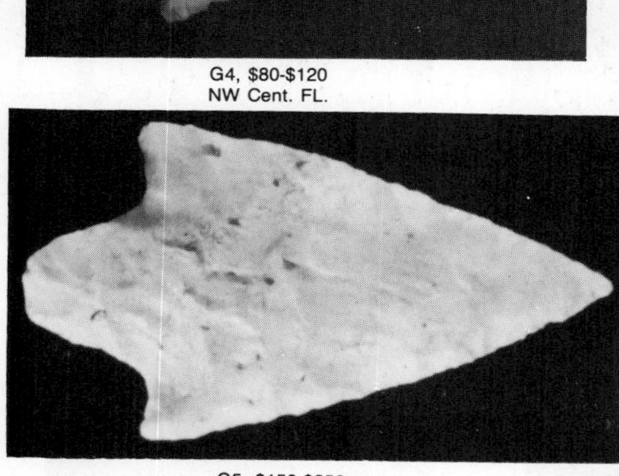

G5, $150-$250
Pasco Co., FL.

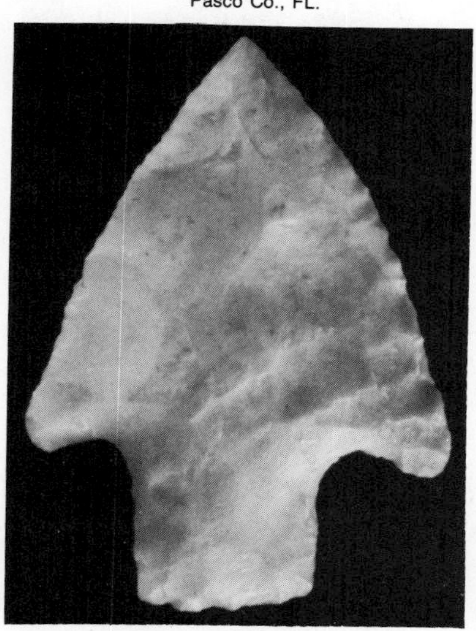

G6, $180-$300
Hillsborough Co., FL.

G7, $250-$400
N. Cent. FL.

G8, $350-$600
Jefferson Co., FL.

G3, $40-$70
Hillsborough Co., FL.

G8, $450-$750
NW FL.

G9, $500-$900
NW Cent. FL.

LIMESTONE - Late Archaic to early Woodland, 5000 - 2000 B.P.

(Also see Bulverde and McIntire)

G3, $5-$8
Walker Co., AL.

G8, $25-$40
Limestone Co., AL.

G3, $2-$4
Madison Co., AL.

G6, $8-$12
Limestone Co., AL.

G6, $8-$12
Madison Co., AL.

G7, $15-$25
Limestone Co., AL.

G10, $60-$100
Morgan Co., AL.

G8, $25-$40
Marion Co., AL.

LOCATION: Southeastern states. **DESCRIPTION:** A small to medium size, triangular stemmed point with an expanded, concave base and barbed to tapered shoulders. Blade edges are concave, convex or straight. **I.D. KEY:** Concave base, one barb is higher.

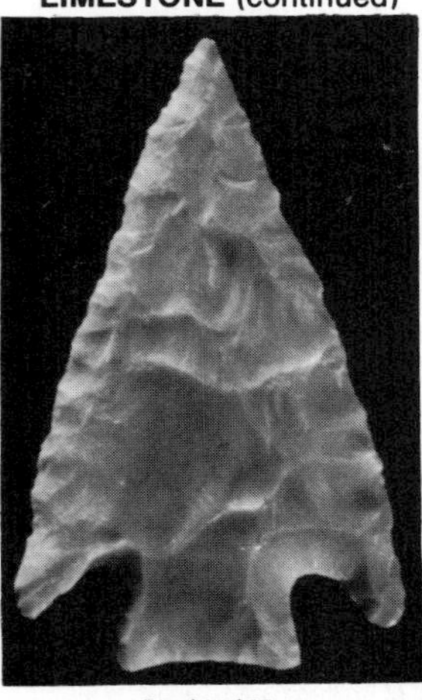

G7, $15-$25
Limestone Co., AL.

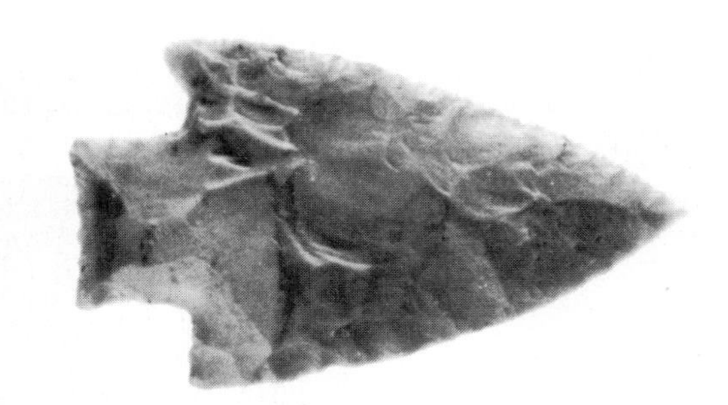

G6, $8-$12
Limestone Co., AL.

G9, $40-$75
Morgan Co., AL.

G9, $30-$50
Itawamba Co., MS.

G7, $15-$25
Meigs Co., TN.

LIMESTONE (continued)

G8, $20-$30
Parsons, TN.

LIMETON BIFURCATE - Early Archaic, 9000 - 6000 B.P.

(Also see Carrizo)

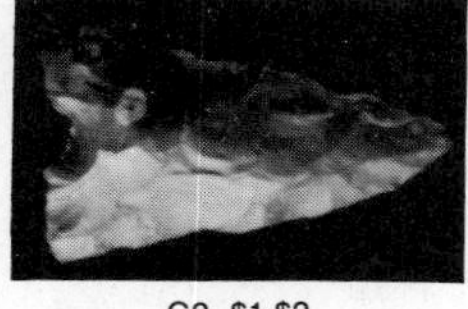

G2, $1-$2
SE TN.

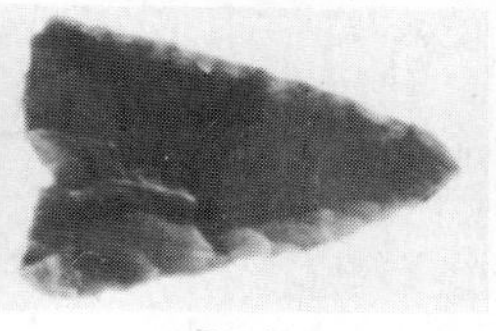

G4, $3-$5
SE TN.

G3, $2-$3
Meigs Co., TN. Hiwassee Isle.

LOCATION: Eastern states. **DESCRIPTION:** A medium size, crudely made, broad, lanceolate blade with a central notch in the base.

LITTLE BEAR CREEK - Late Archaic to late Woodland, 4000 - 1500 B.P.

(Also see Adena, Bare Island, Crump Lake Stemmed, Kays, Mulberry Creek, Pickwick & Ponchartrain)

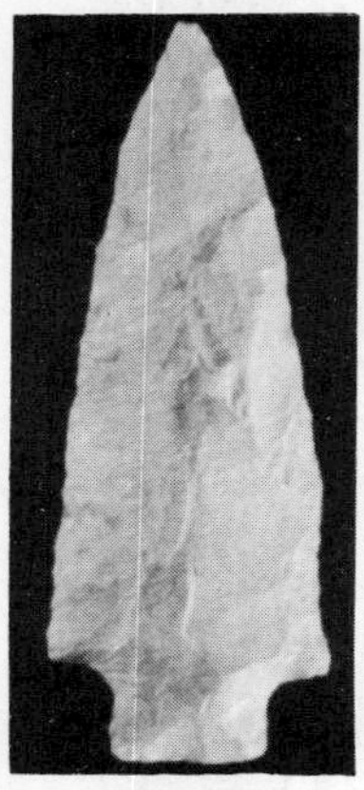

G3, $4-$6
Rockingham Co., NC.

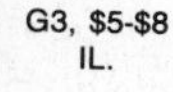

G3, $5-$8
IL.

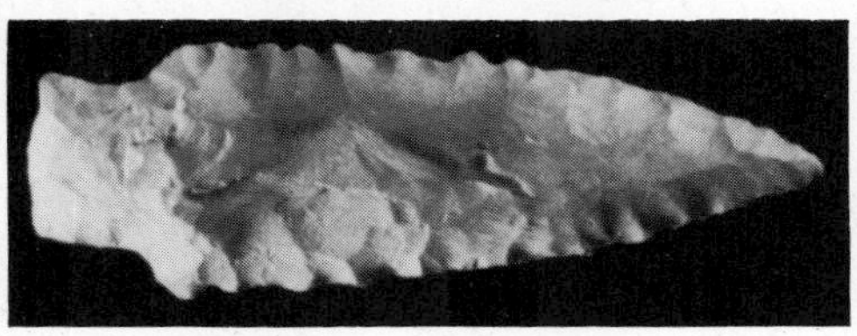

G3, $5-$8
Decatur, AL.

LOCATION: Southeastern states. **DESCRIPTION:** A medium to large size, narrow point with a long parallel stem that may contract or expand slightly. Blade edges are slightly convex. Shoulders are usually squared, tapered or slightly barbed. The base can be fractured or snapped off. Blade edges can be beveled on one side of each face and finely serrated. Called *Sarasota* in Florida. **I.D. KEY:** Straight base, woodland flaking.

LITTLE BEAR CREEK (continued)

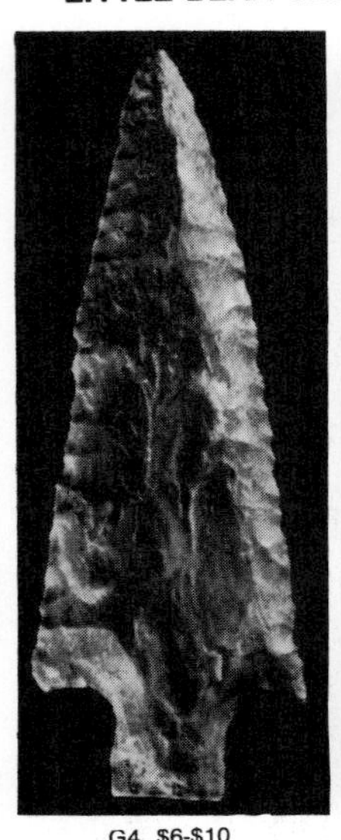

G4, $6-$10
Madison Co., AL. Classic form.

G4, $6-$10
Madison Co., AL.

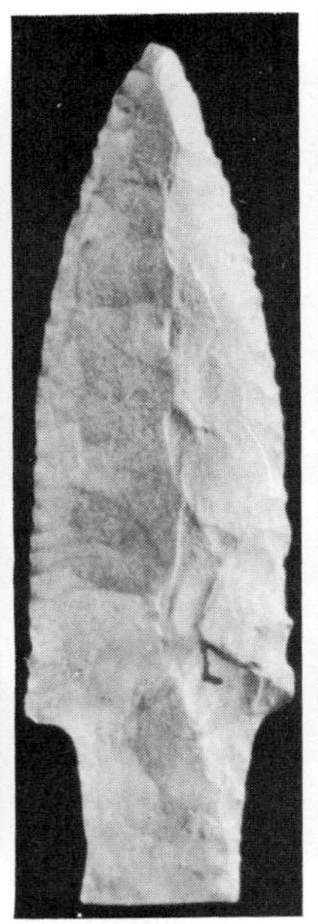

G6, $15-$25
Florence, AL.

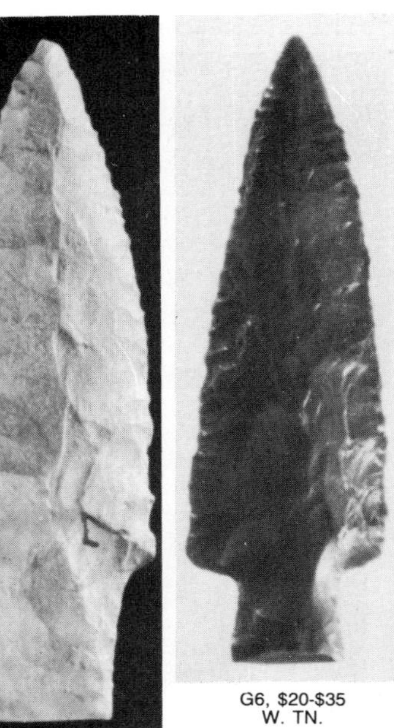

G6, $20-$35
W. TN.

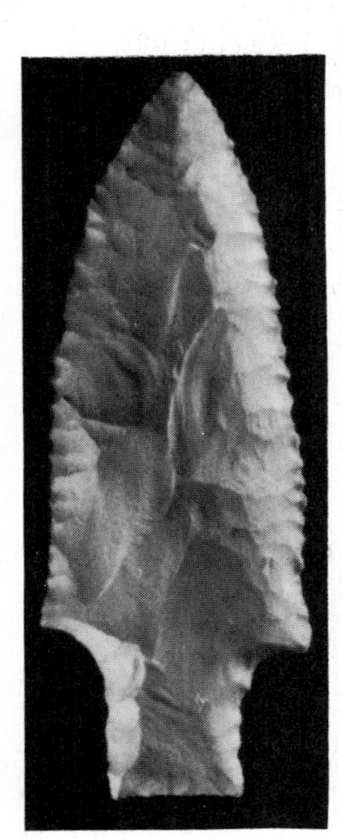

G6, $20-$35
Coffee Lake, AL.

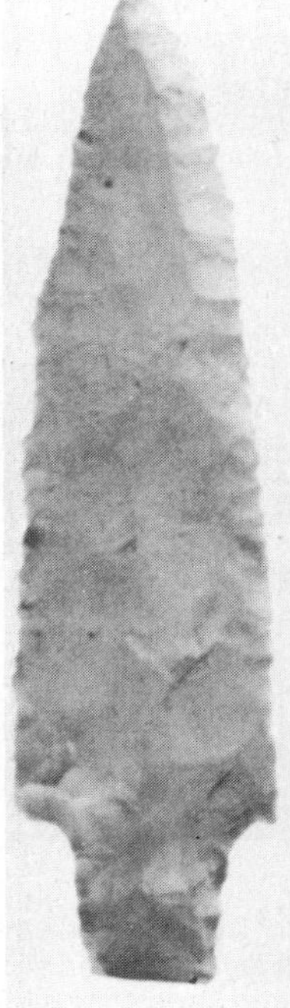

G5, $8-$15
Florence, AL.

G6, $20-$35
Humphreys Co., TN.
Classic form.

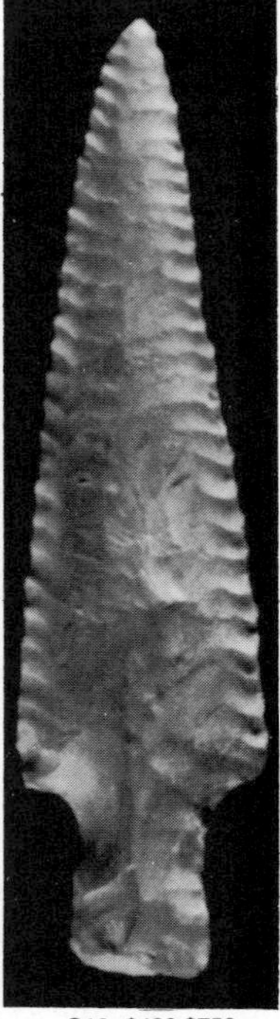

G10, $400-$750
Hardin Co., TN. Note excellent saw-tooth ripple serrations that line up diagonally. Very rare.

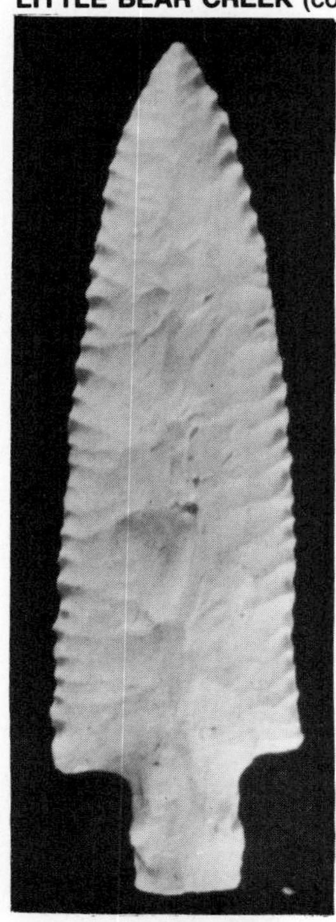

G10, $500-$800
Hardin Co., TN. Outstanding quality. Classic form. Very rare.

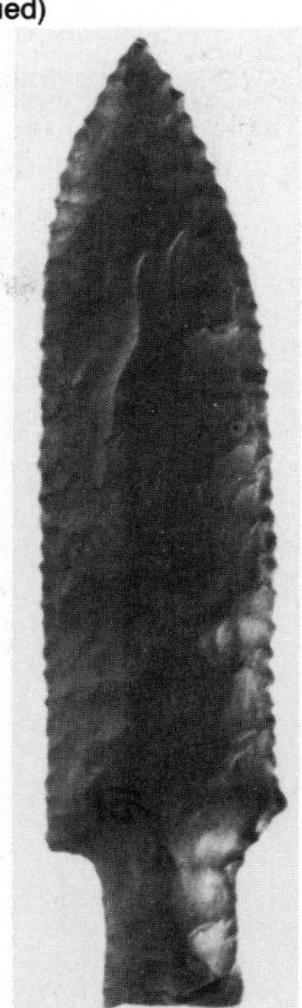

G9, $300-$450
Florence, AL. Excellent quality. Classic form.

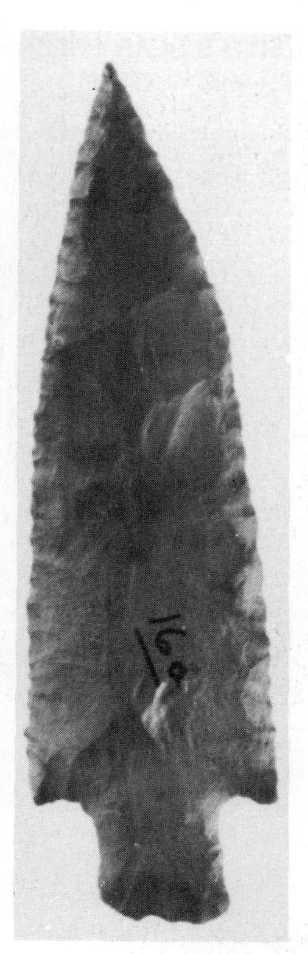

G8, $80-$120
Florence, AL.

G9, $150-$250, Cent. IL.

G8, $100-$150. 7 Mile Isle, Florence, AL. Classic form.

G8, $120-$200
Florence, AL., 7 Mile Isle.

G9, $120-$200
Florence, AL., 7 Mile Isle. Has unusual right-hand bevel on alternate sides. Classic form.

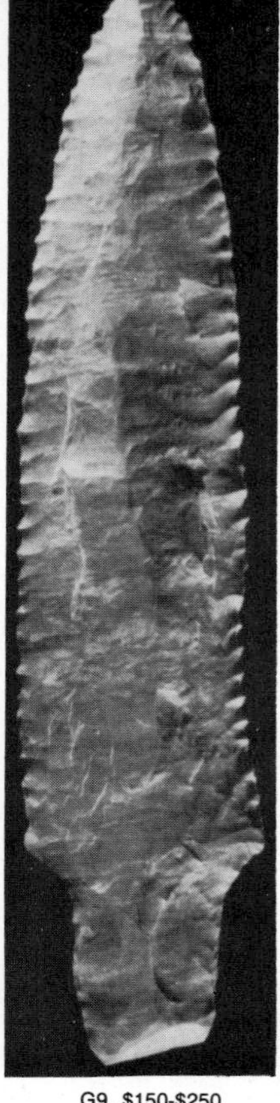

G9, $150-$250
Humphreys Co., TN. Dover chert. Note saw-tooth edges.

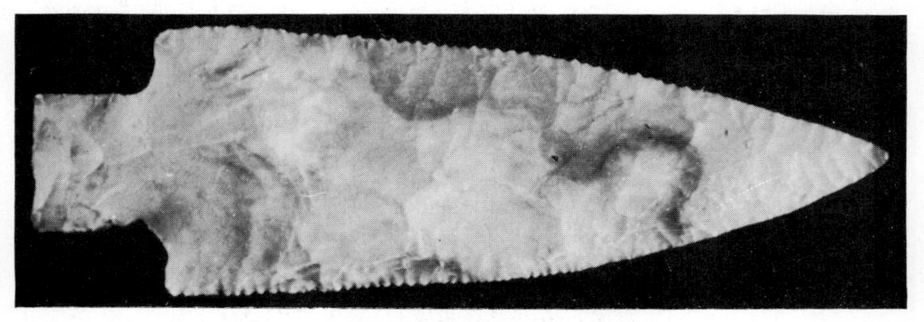

G10, $500-$900
Lauderdale Co., AL. 7 Mile Isle. Very thin with outstanding color and flaking. Note the fine secondary edgework. Classic form. Outstanding.

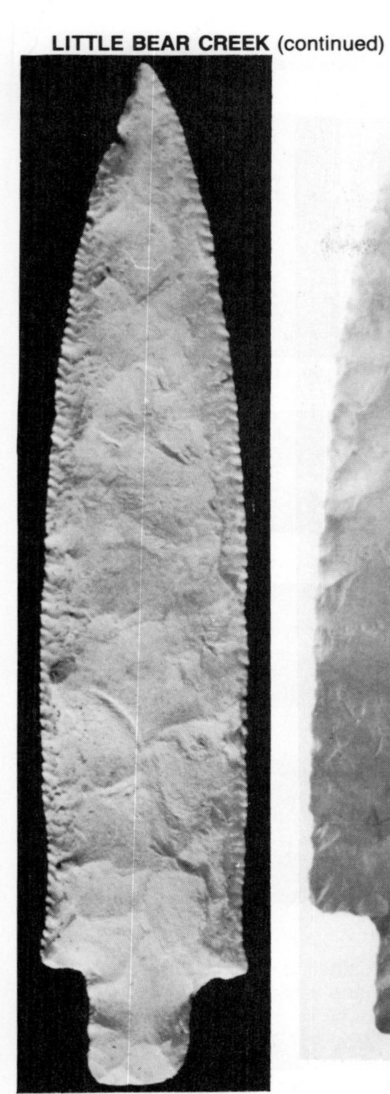

G9, $350-$600
Humphreys Co., TN. Minor nick at tip. Note fine edgework.

G8, $80-$120
Florence, AL.

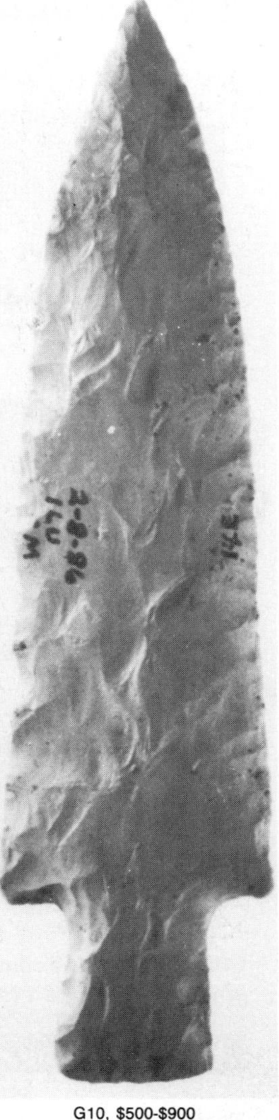

G10, $500-$900
Lauderdale Co., AL. Outstanding example.

G8, $80-$120. Florence, AL.

LIVERMORE - Mississippian, 1200 - 600 B.P.

(Also see Drill and Sequoyah)

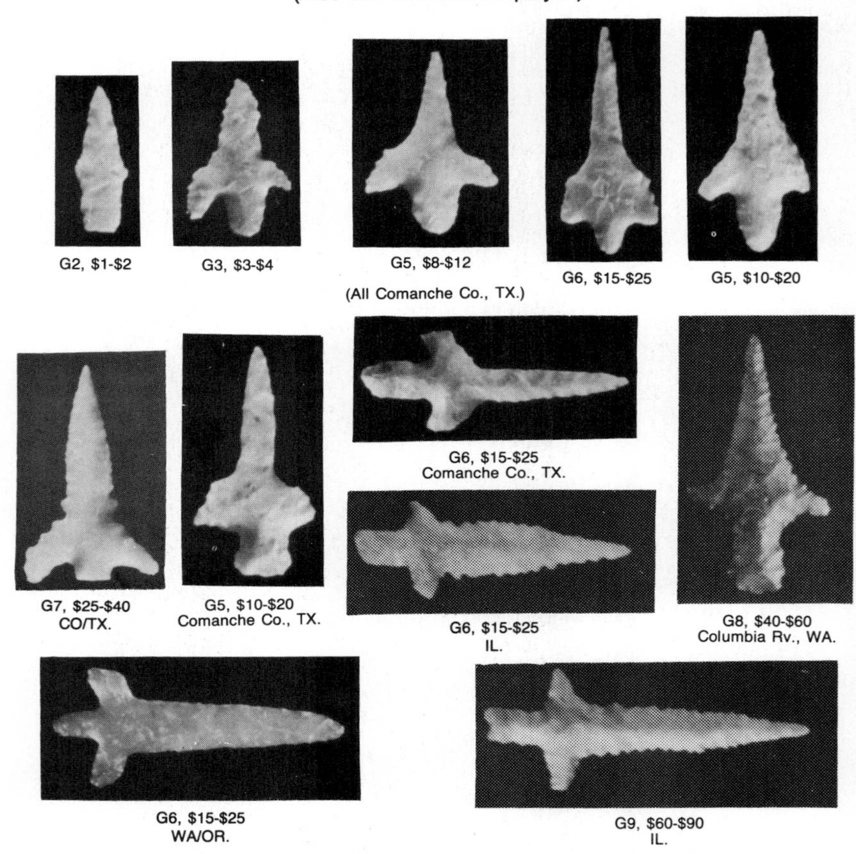

G2, $1-$2

G3, $3-$4

G5, $8-$12

G6, $15-$25

G5, $10-$20

(All Comanche Co., TX.)

G7, $25-$40 CO/TX.

G5, $10-$20 Comanche Co., TX.

G6, $15-$25 Comanche Co., TX.

G6, $15-$25 IL.

G8, $40-$60 Columbia Rv., WA.

G6, $15-$25 WA/OR.

G9, $60-$90 IL.

LOCATION: Midwestern states. **DESCRIPTION:** A small to medium size, very narrow, serrated, spike point with wide flaring barbs and a narrow stem.

LLANO - Late Paleo, 10000 - 7000 B.P.

(Also see Angostura, Clovis and Tortugas)

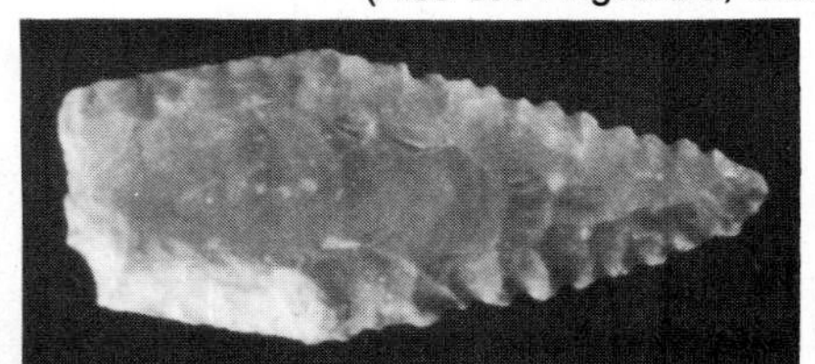

G7, $60-$100 Comanche Co., TX. Fluted.

LOCATION: Midwestern states. **DESCRIPTION:** A medium to large size triangle that is usually serrated. The base is either fluted or has long thinning strikes. Quality is excellent with early parallel flaking. Called *Paleo Triangle* in Texas. **I.D. KEY:** Basal thinning and edgework.

LLANO (continued)

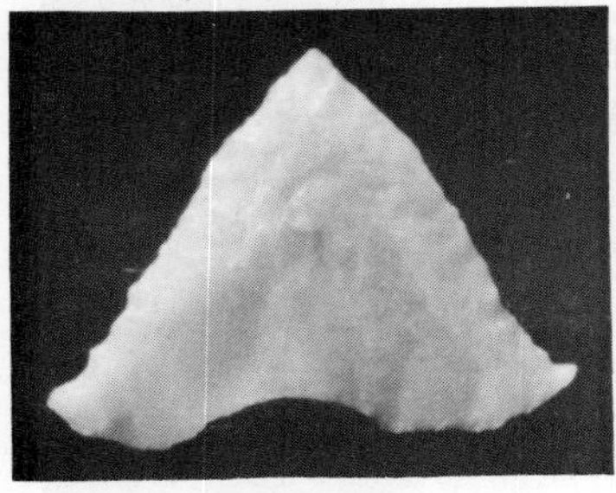

G8, $80-$150
Comanche Co., TX. Note basal thinning and outstanding form.

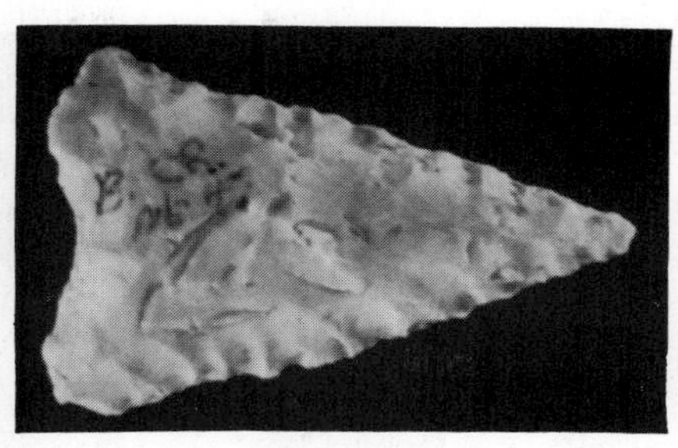

G6, $35-$60
Bell Co., TX.

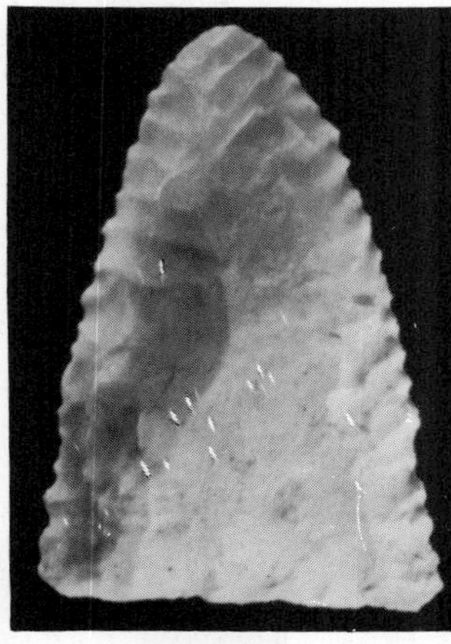

G6, $50-$80
Bell Co., TX.

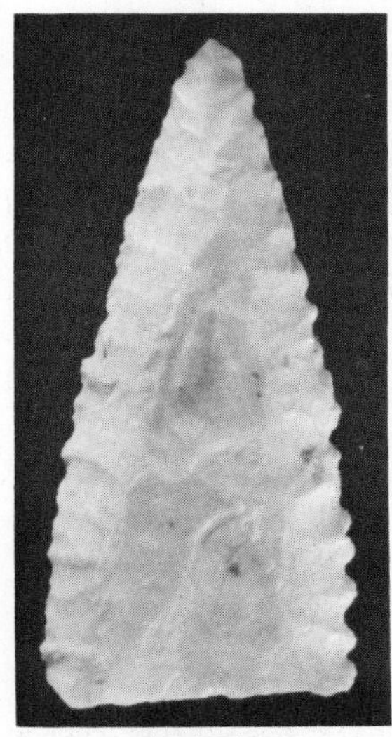

G8, $80-$120
Comanche Co., TX. Note basal thinning strikes.

G6, $35-$60
Austin, TX.

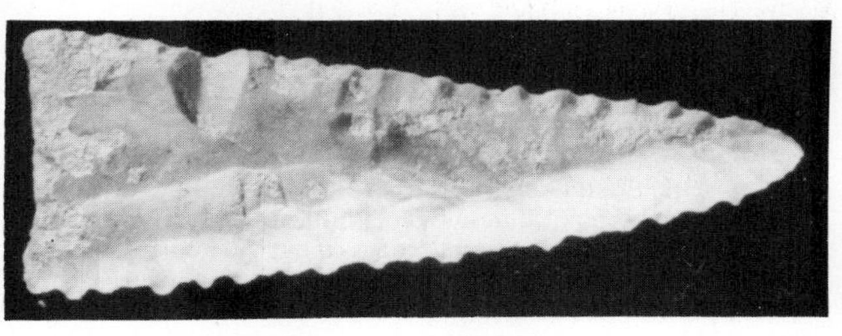

G5, $25-$45
Austin, TX. Blade nick.

LOST LAKE - Early Archaic, 9000 - 6000 B.P.

(Also see Bolen, Cobbs, Cypress Creek, Dovetail, Hardin, Kirk Corner Notched and Thebes)

G2, $10-$20
Decatur, AL.

G3, $15-$25
Spartanburg Co., SC.

G3, $20-$30
Henry Co., AL.

G3, $20-$30
Henry Co., AL.

G4, $25-$40
Henry Co., AL.

G5, $30-$50
Jackson Co., AL.

G7, $120-$200
NW Cent. FL.

G8, $250-$400
Marion Co., FL.

G7, $150-$250
NW Cent. FL.

LOCATION: Southeastern states. **DESCRIPTION:** A medium to large size, broad, corner notched point that is beveled on one side of each face. The beveling continues when resharpened and creates a flat rhomboid cross section. Most examples are finely serrated and exhibit high quality flaking and symmetry. Also known as *Deep Notch*, and typed as *Bolen Bevel Corner Notched* in Florida. **I.D. KEY:** Notching, secondary edgework is always opposite creating at least slight beveling.

G7, $120-$200
NW Cent. FL.

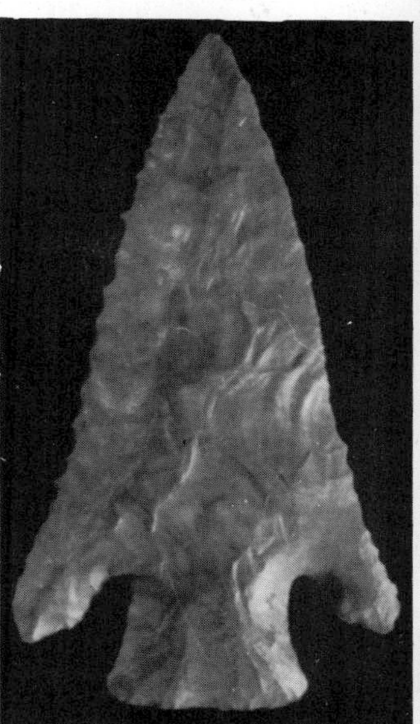

G7, $150-$250
KY.

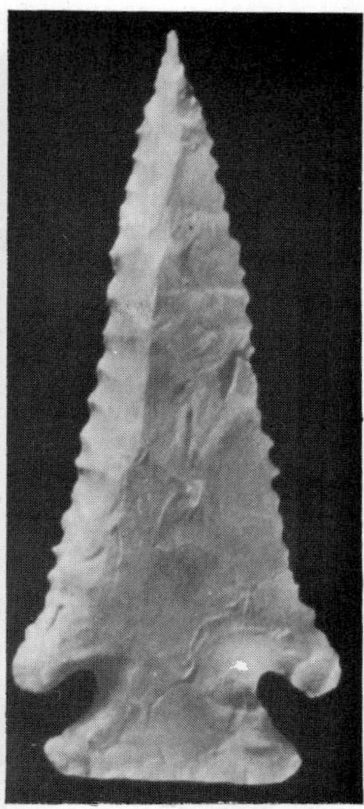

G8, $250-$450
Lauderdale Co., AL.

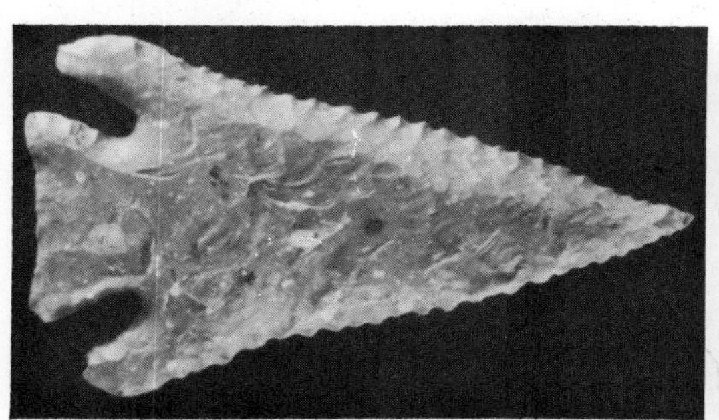

G7, $150-$250
Stewart Co., TN.

G7, $150-$250
Meade Co., KY.

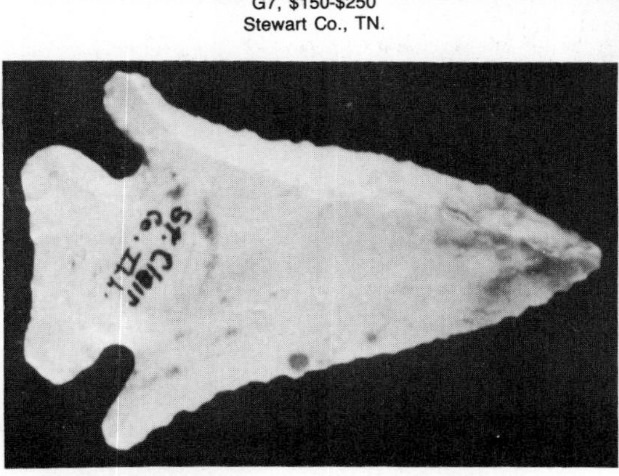

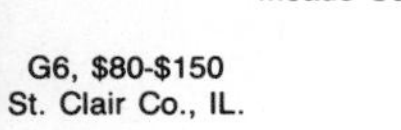

G6, $80-$150
St. Clair Co., IL.

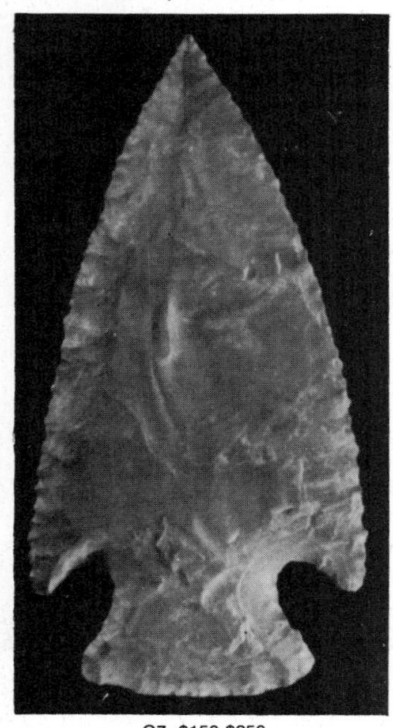

G7, $150-$250
7 Mile Isle, Florence, AL. This point was found by the *Lost Lake* people and rechipped around the edges—proof that indians found and rechipped older points.

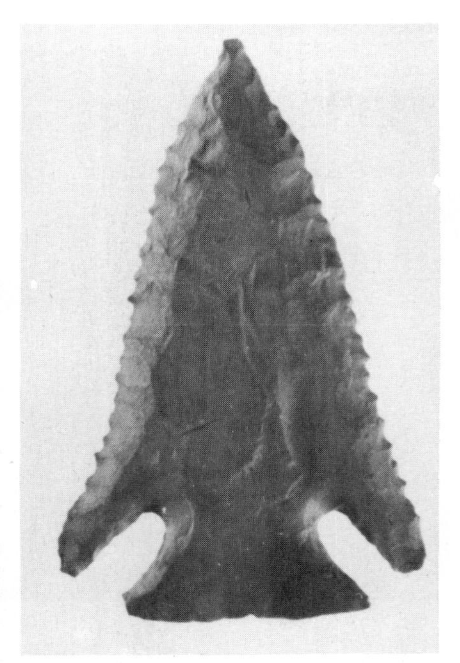

G8, $180-$300
Florence, AL.

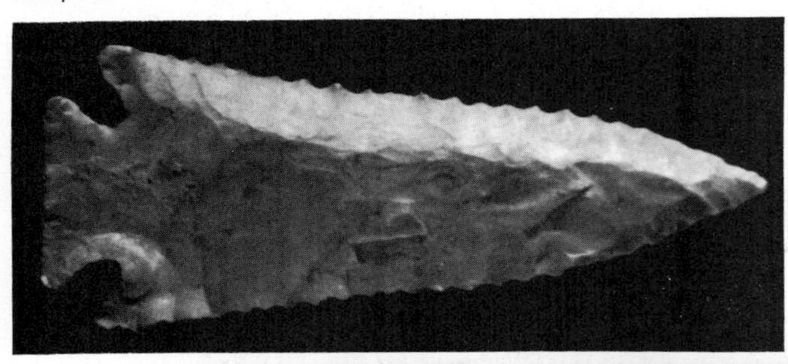

G7, $150-$250
Coffee Lake, AL.

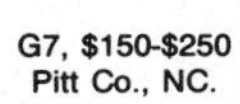

G7, $150-$250
Pitt Co., NC.

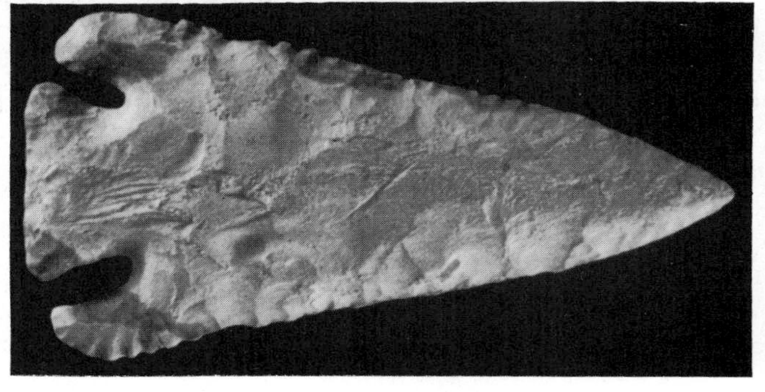

G8, $250-$400
TN.

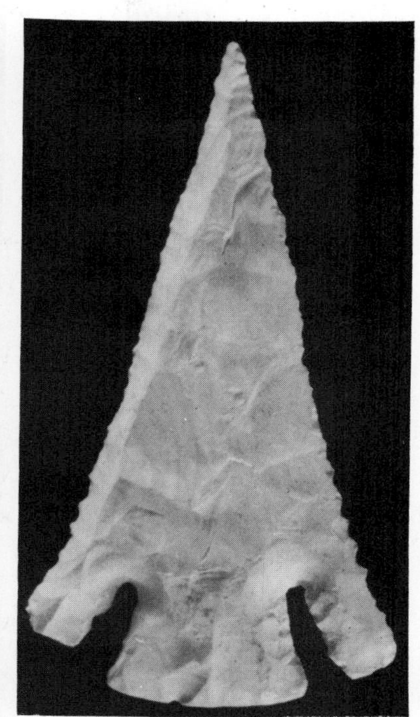

G6, $90-$180
Meigs Co., TN.

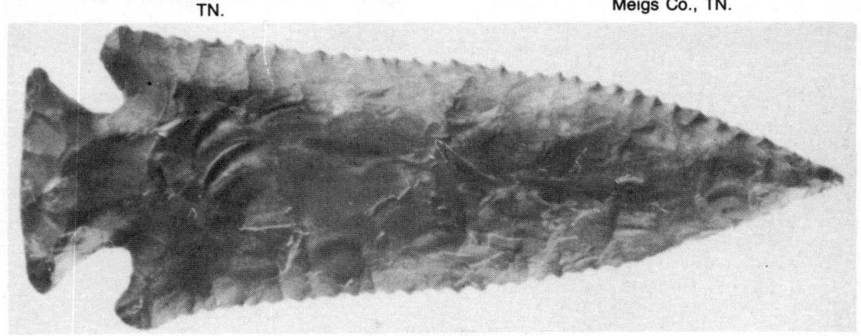

G9, $800-$1500
Saltillo, TN. Dover chert.

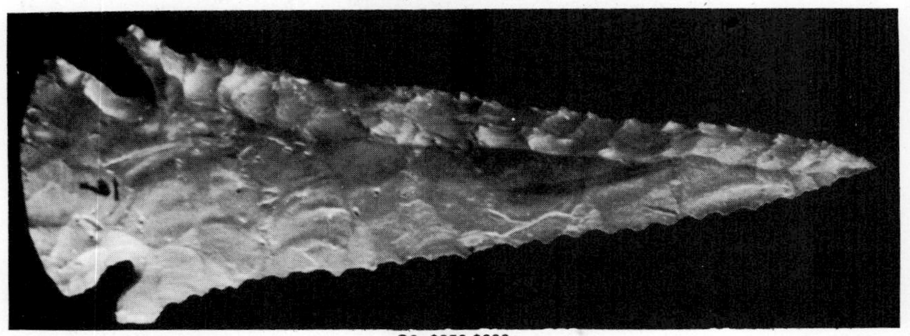

G8, $350-$600
Humphreys Co., TN.

G8, $250-$400
Humphreys Co., TN.

G10, $2000-$3500
Giles Co., TN. The classic form.
Outstanding quality.

G10, $2500-$4500
Humphreys Co., TN. Dover chert.
Points of this size and quality are
very rare.

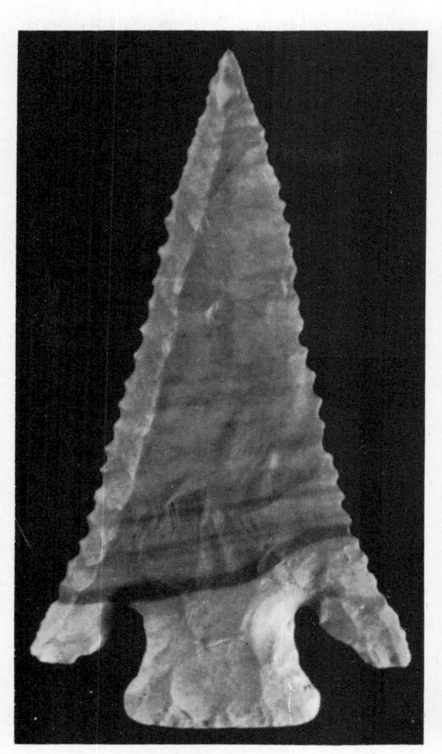

G9, $1000-$1700
Hardin Co., TN. Classic form.
High quality & good color.

G9, $800-$1500
Crossville, TN.

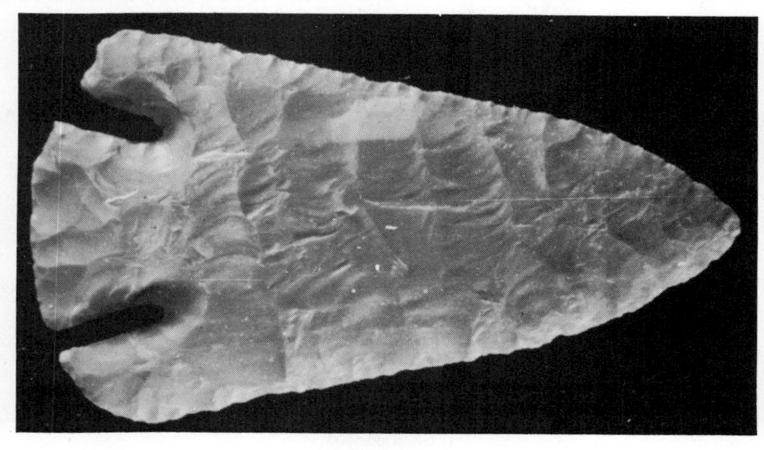

G7, $150-$280
Effingham Co., IL.

G9, $500-$800
Lawrence Co., TN.

G10, $2500-$4500
Humphreys Co., TN. Dover chert.
Outstanding high quality example.

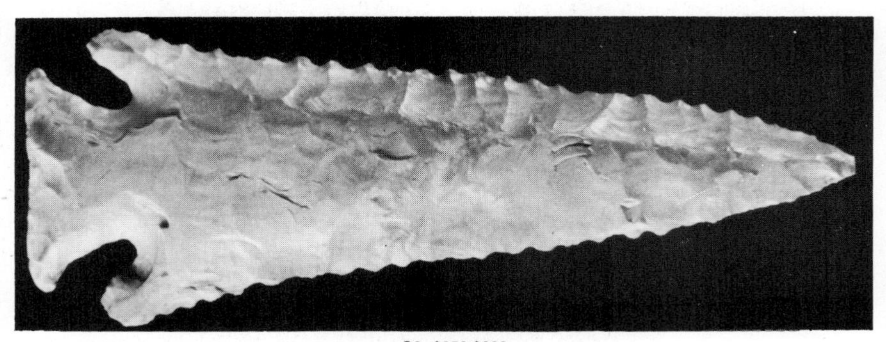

G8, $350-$600
Pemiscot Co., MO.

LOTT - Mississippian, 600 - 400 B.P.

(Also see Garza, Jetta & Pinto Basin)

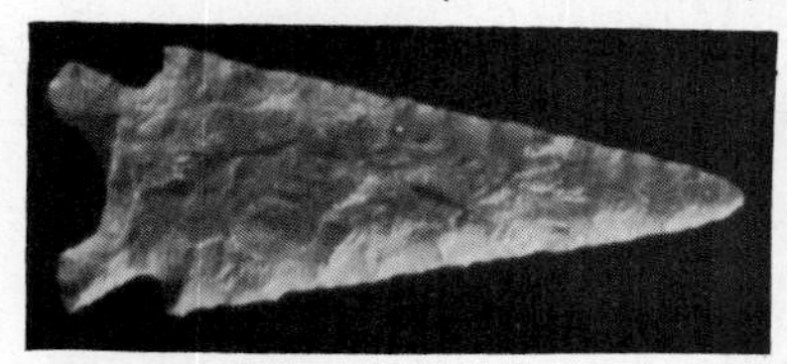

G8, $25-$35
WA/OR.

LOCATION: Northwestern states. **DESCRIPTION:** A medium size point with short, squared auricles and horizontal shoulders. The base is deeply concave.

Lozenge - Mississippian, 1000 - 400 B.P.

(Also see Nodena)

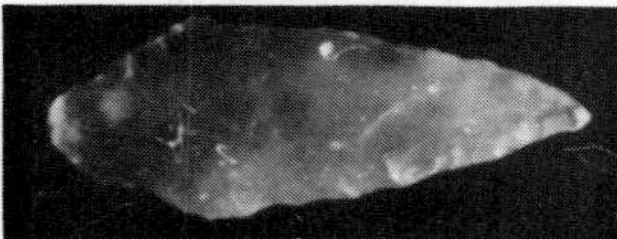

G3, $2-$4
Pendalis, OR.

G5, $6-$10
Pendalis, OR.

G9, $40-$60
KY.

LOCATION: Midwestern states. **DESCRIPTION:** A small size, narrow, thin, double pointed arrow point.

MACCORKLE - Early Archaic, 8000 - 6000 B.P.

(Also see Kirk-Bifurcated, LeCroy, Montell, Rice Lobbed, St. Albans, Southampton and Uvalde)

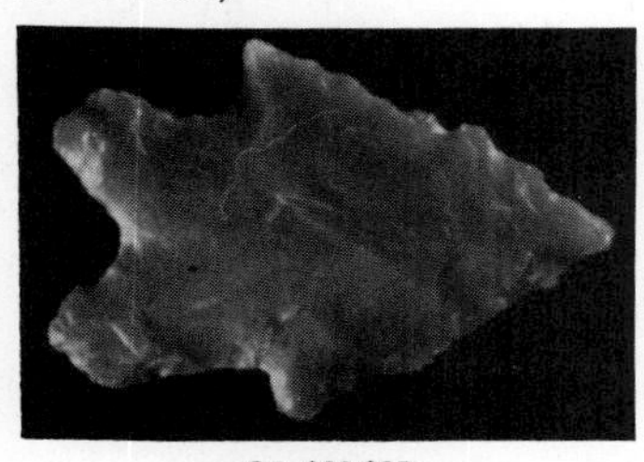

G5, $20-$35
Meigs Co., TN.

G7, $30-$50
Lauderdale Co., AL.

LOCATION: Midwest to Southeastern states. **DESCRIPTION:** A medium to large size, thin, usually serrated, widely corner notched point with large round ears and a deep notch in the center of the base. Bases are usually ground. The smaller examples can be easily confused with the *LeCroy* point. Shoulders and blade expand more towards the base than *LeCroy*, but only in some cases. Called *Nottoway River Bifurcate* in Virginia. **I.D. KEY:** Basal notching, early Archaic flaking.

G4, $15-$25
Wayne Co., OH.

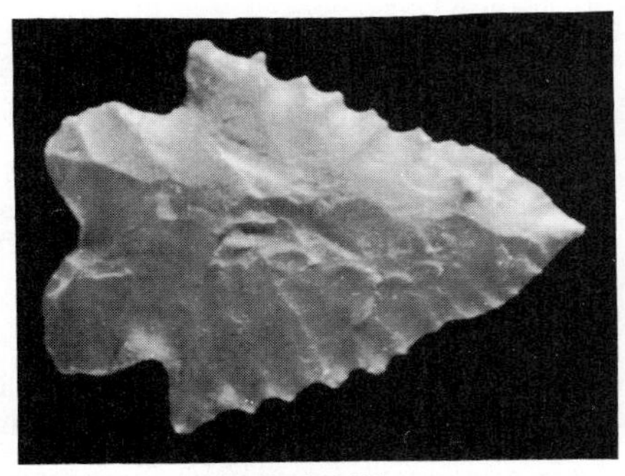

G8, $40-$60
Benton Co., KY.

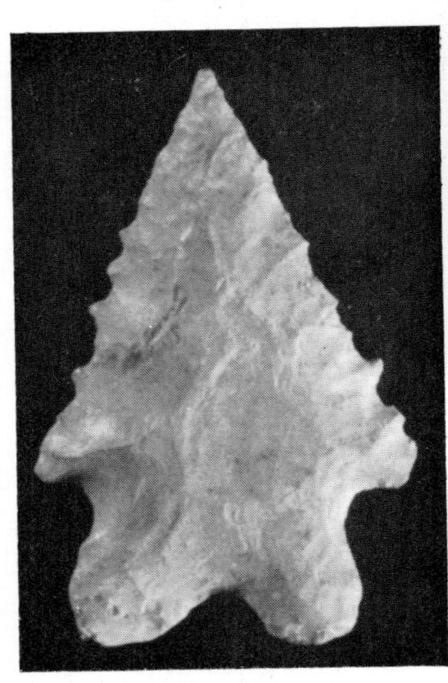

G7, $30-$50
KY.

G7, $30-$50
Lauderdale Co., AL.

G4, $15-$25
Cleveland, OH. Coshocton chert.

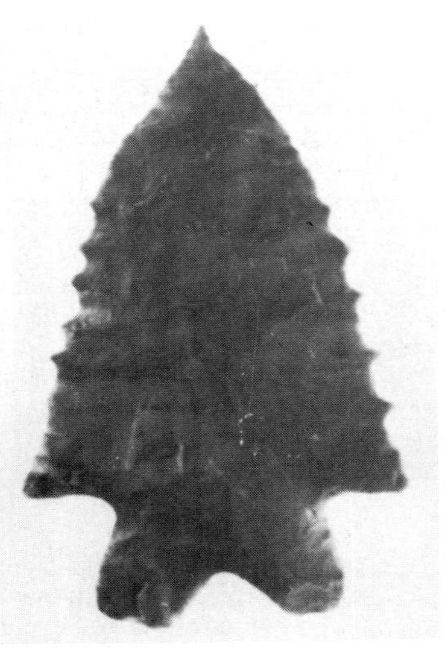

G10, $250-$400
Florence, AL.

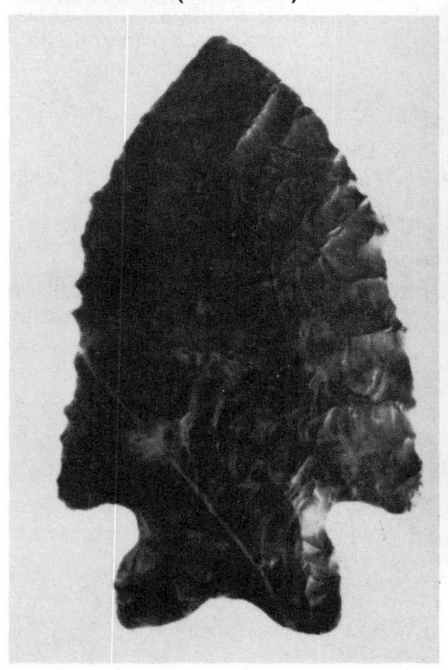

G8, $120-$200
OH. Coshocton chert.

G7, $70-$125
Adams Co., IL.

G8, $180-$250
Humphreys Co., TN.

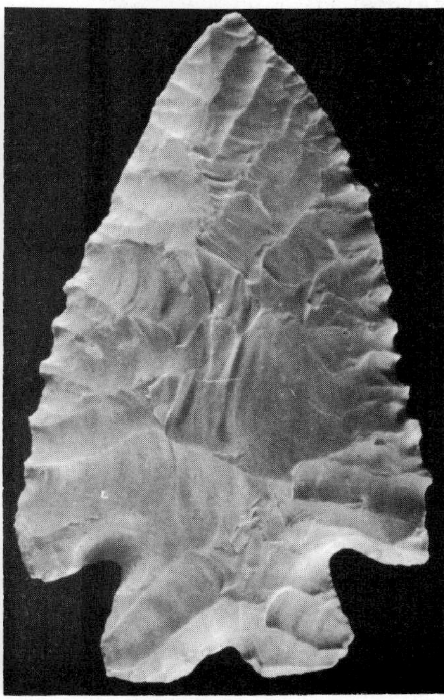

G9, $250-$450
Hardin Co., KY.

MACPHERSON - Woodland, 3500 - 1000 B.P.

(Also see Beacon Island, Durst, Duval, Godley, Lamoka, Palmillas and Swan Lake)

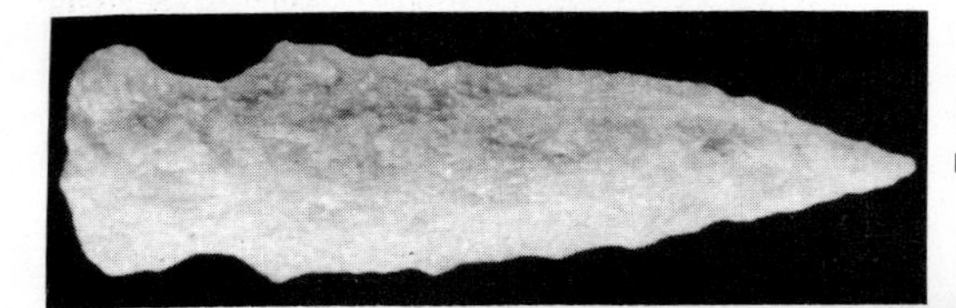

G5, $5-$8
Dinwiddie Co., VA.

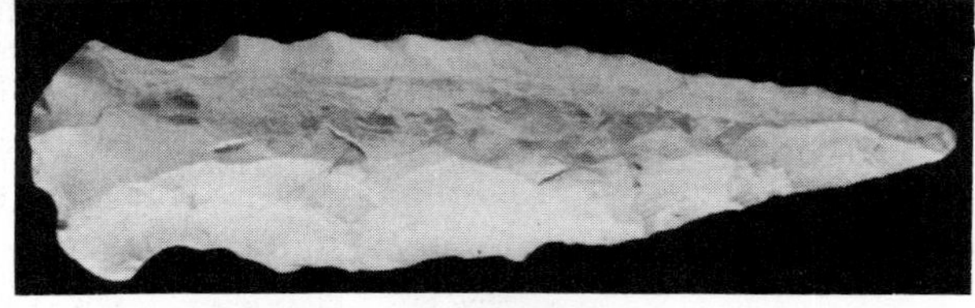

G4, $4-$6
Sussex Co., VA.

LOCATION: Far Eastern states. **DESCRIPTION:** A small to medium size narrow, thick, shallowly side-notched point. Shoulders taper and the stem expands. Bases are generally rounded.

MAD RIVER - Early Archaic, 8000 - 5000 B.P.

(Also see Desert and Kirk Corner Notched)

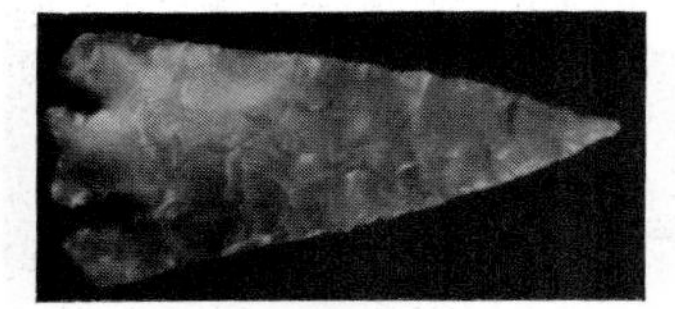

G6, $90-$150
Sherman Co., OR. Agate.

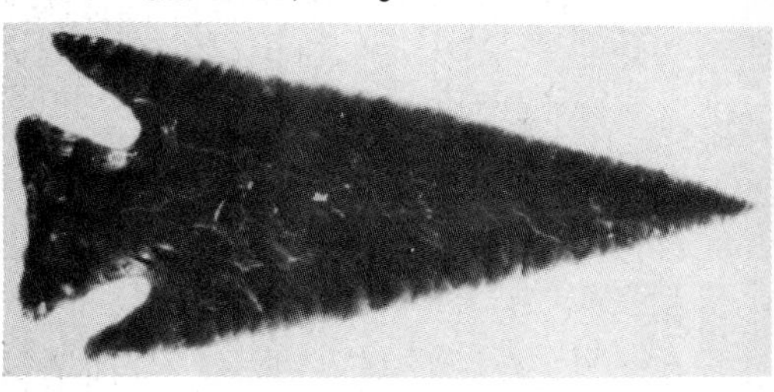

G9, $250-$400
Lake Co., OR. Crump Lake. Thin and excellent. Obsidian

G9, $250-$400
Chiloquin Or., Klamath Co. Note unusual notched tangs.

LOCATION: Northwestern states. **DESCRIPTION:** A medium size point with deep corner notches. Rare examples have notches in both shoulders. Barbs can be pointed to squared. Early parallel flaking is evident.

MADISON - Mississippian, 1100 - 200 B.P.

(Also see Camp Creek, Caraway, Clarksville, Fresno, Guntersville, Hamilton, Levanna, Maud, Pinellas & Valina)

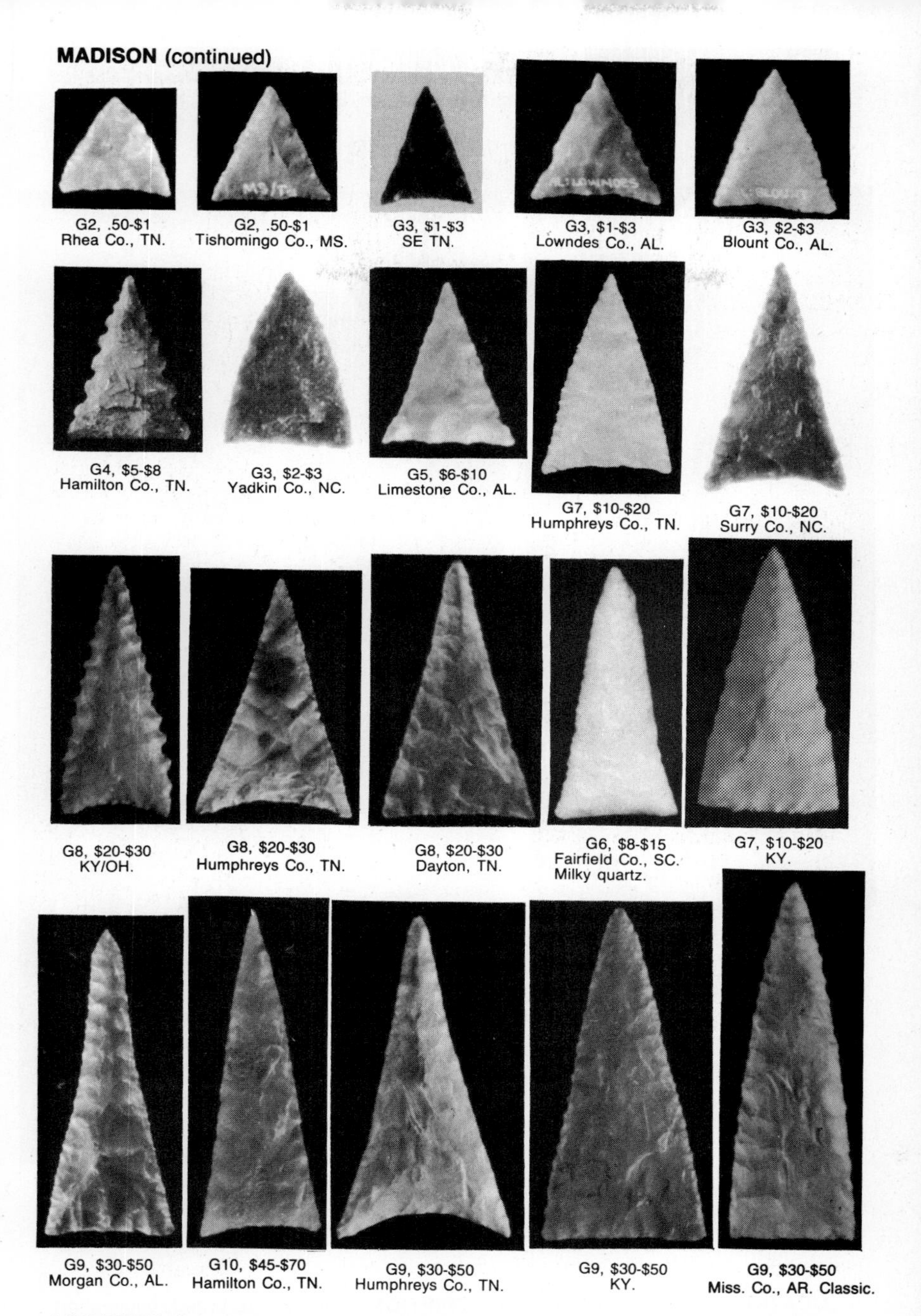

G2, .50-$1 Rhea Co., TN.
G2, .50-$1 Tishomingo Co., MS.
G3, $1-$3 SE TN.
G3, $1-$3 Lowndes Co., AL.
G3, $2-$3 Blount Co., AL.

G4, $5-$8 Hamilton Co., TN.
G3, $2-$3 Yadkin Co., NC.
G5, $6-$10 Limestone Co., AL.
G7, $10-$20 Humphreys Co., TN.
G7, $10-$20 Surry Co., NC.

G8, $20-$30 KY/OH.
G8, $20-$30 Humphreys Co., TN.
G8, $20-$30 Dayton, TN.
G6, $8-$15 Fairfield Co., SC. Milky quartz.
G7, $10-$20 KY.

G9, $30-$50 Morgan Co., AL.
G10, $45-$70 Hamilton Co., TN.
G9, $30-$50 Humphreys Co., TN.
G9, $30-$50 KY.
G9, $30-$50 Miss. Co., AR. Classic.

LOCATION: Coincides with the Mississippian culture in the Eastern states. **DESCRIPTION:** A small to medium size, thin, triangular point with usually straight sides and base. Some examples are notched on two to three sides. Many are of high quality and some are finely serrated.

MAPLES - Mid-Archaic, 4500 - 3500 B.P.

(Also see Abbey, Bascom, Elora, Morrow Mountain, Savannah River, Morrow Mountain and South Prong Creek)

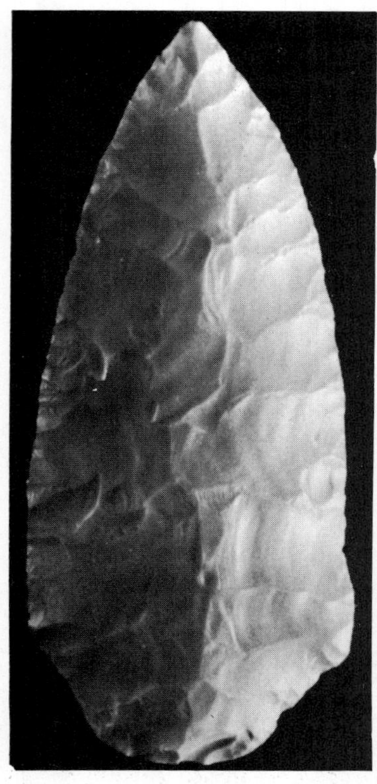

G8, $30-$50
Hardin Co., KY. Classic.

G6, $25-$40
Florence, AL. Cache point.

LOCATION: Southeastern states. **DESCRIPTION:** A very large, broad, thick, short stemmed blade. Shoulders are tapered and the stem is contracting with a concave to straight base. Usually thick and crudely made, but fine quality examples have been found. Flaking is random and this type should not be confused with *Morrow Mountain* which has Archaic parallel flaking. **I.D. KEY:** Thickness, notching, flaking.

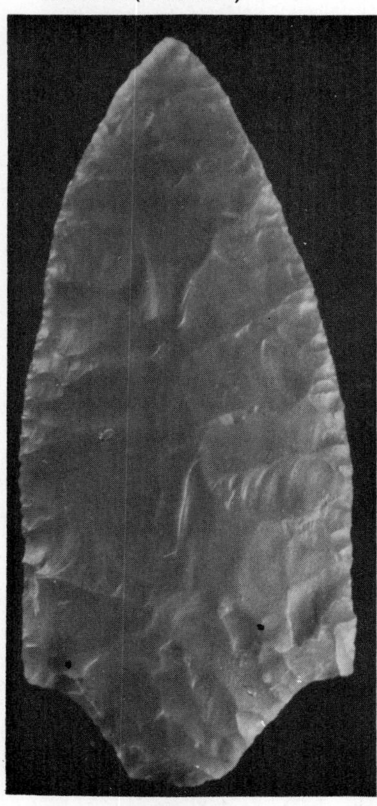

G9, $60-$80
Hamilton Co., TN.

G7, $40-$65
NE GA. Banded green quartzite.

G5, $20-$35
Florence, AL. Cache point.

MARCOS - Late Archaic to Woodland, 3500 - 1200 B.P.

(Also see Castroville, Ensor and Marshall)

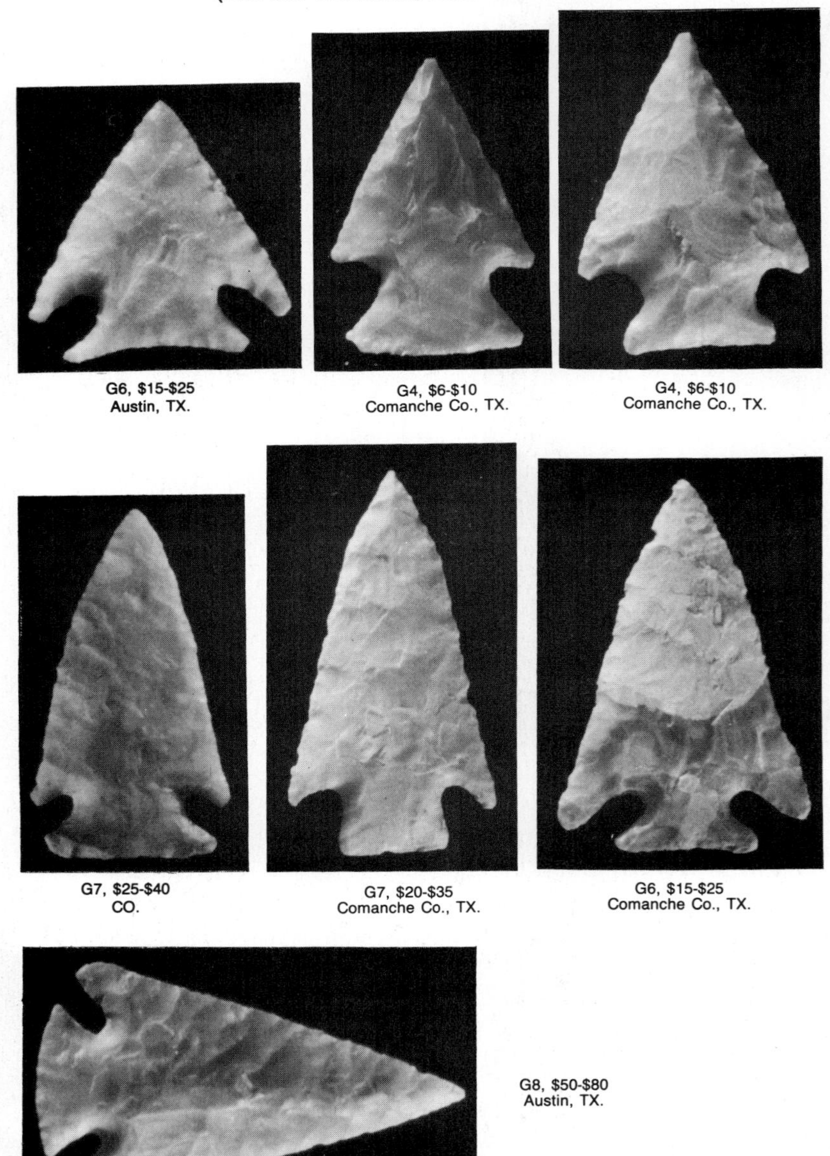

G6, $15-$25
Austin, TX.

G4, $6-$10
Comanche Co., TX.

G4, $6-$10
Comanche Co., TX.

G7, $25-$40
CO.

G7, $20-$35
Comanche Co., TX.

G6, $15-$25
Comanche Co., TX.

G8, $50-$80
Austin, TX.

LOCATION: Midwestern states. **DESCRIPTION:** A medium size, broad, corner notched point with an expanded stem. The blade edges are straight to recurved. Many examples have long barbs and a sharp pointed tip.

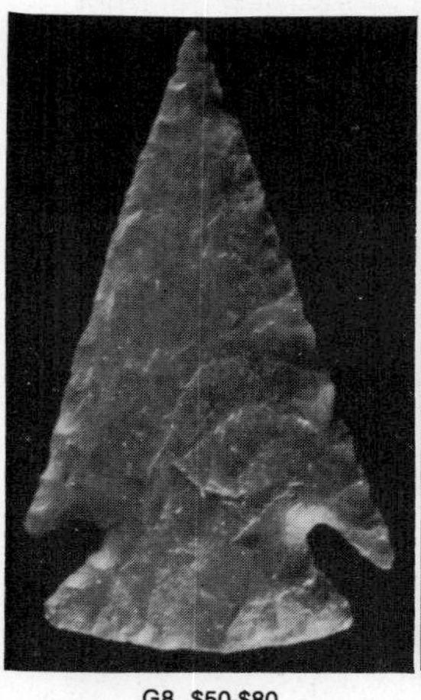

G8, $50-$80
Austin, TX.

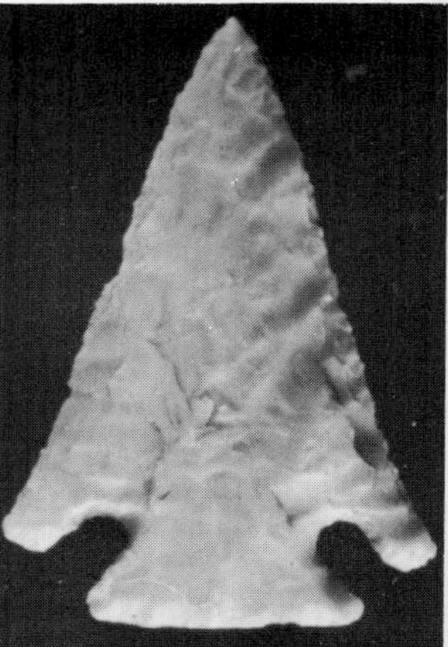

G7, $30-$50
Austin, TX.

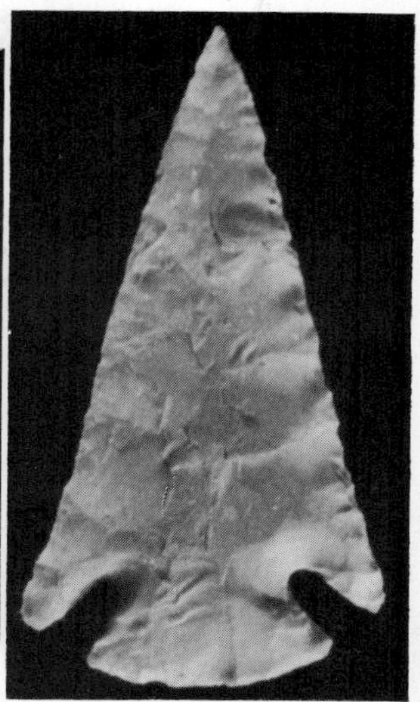

G9, $90-$150
Austin, TX.

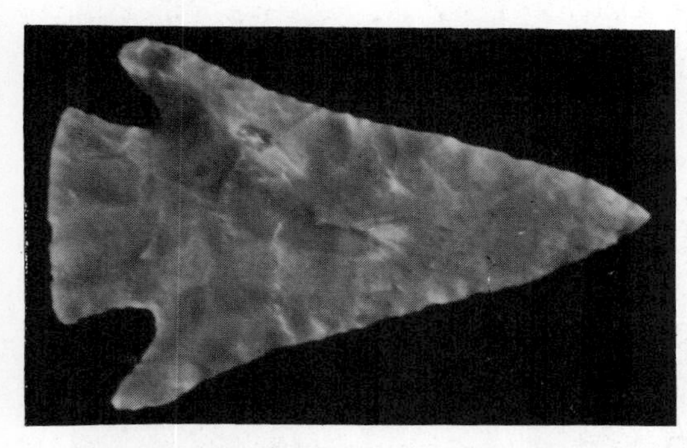

G9, $80-$120
Cent. TX.

MARIANNA - Transitional Paleo, 10,000 - 8500 B.P.

(Also see Angostura, Browns Valley and Conerly)

G8, $50-$80
Dayton, TN. Note diagonal flaking.

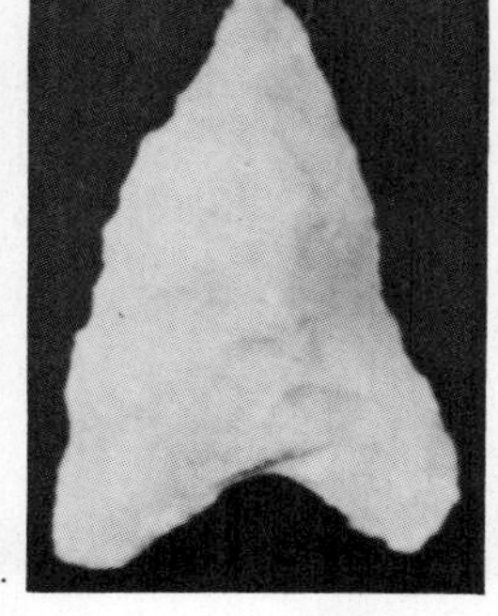

G3, $15-$25
Marion Co., FL.

LOCATION: Southern Southeastern states. **DESCRIPTION:** A medium size lanceolate point with a constricted, concave base. Look for parallel to oblique flaking.

MARION - Mid-Archaic, 7000 - 3000 B.P.

(Also see Adena-Dickson, Alachua, Cypress Creek, Gary, Hardee Beveled, Levy, Morrow Mountain, Newnan, Pickwick and Putnam)

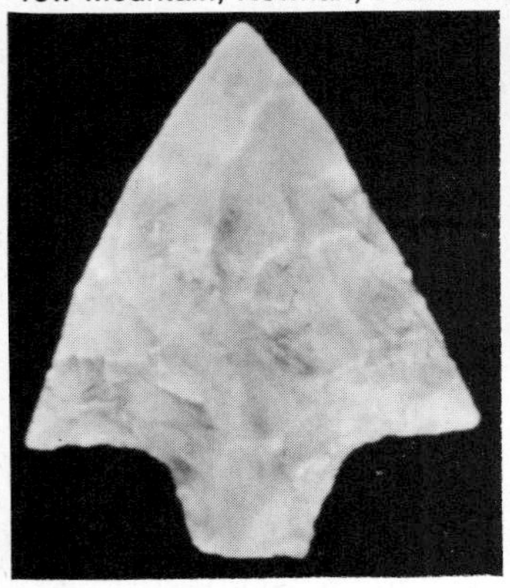

G5, $70-$120
Hillsborough Co., FL.

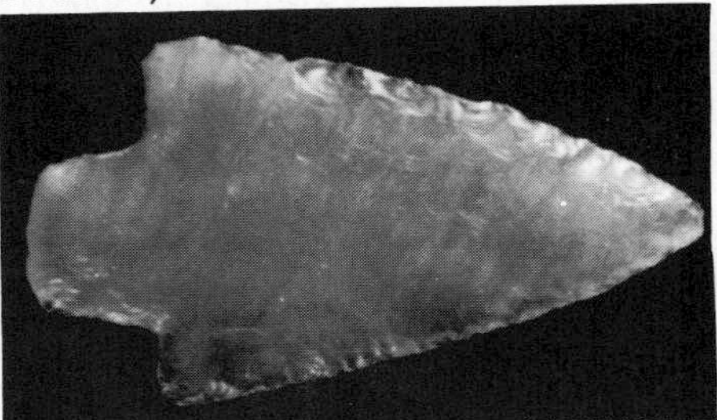

G4, $30-$50
Hillsborough Co., FL. Coral.
Tip nick.

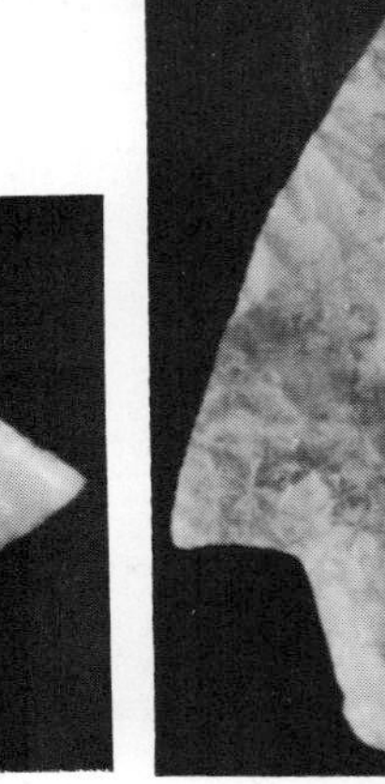

G5, $70-$120, Hillsborough Co., FL.

G5, $70-$120
Hillsborough Co., FL.

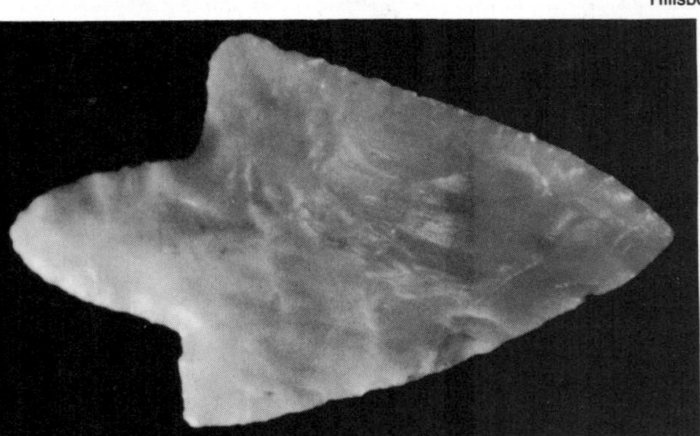

G6, $80-$125
Hillsborough Co., FL.

LOCATION: Southern Southeastern states. **DESCRIPTION:** A medium to large size, broad, contracted stemmed point with square to tapered shoulders and rounded basal corners. *Marions* with *Newnan* type squarish bases represent a *Marion/Newnan* cross type.

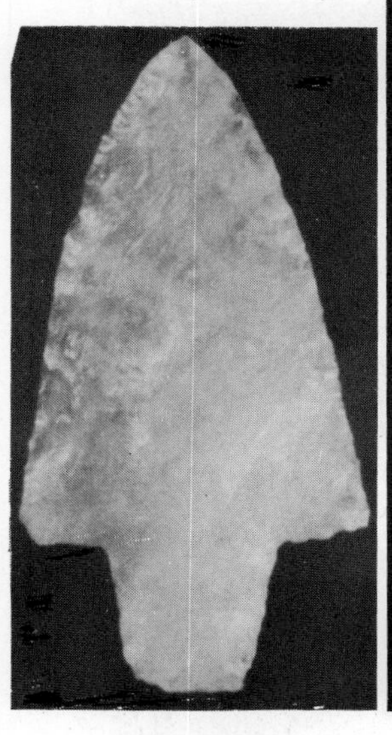

G6. $80-$125
NW Cent. Fl. Tang nick.
Agatized coral.

G5, $70-$120
Sante Fe Rv., FL.

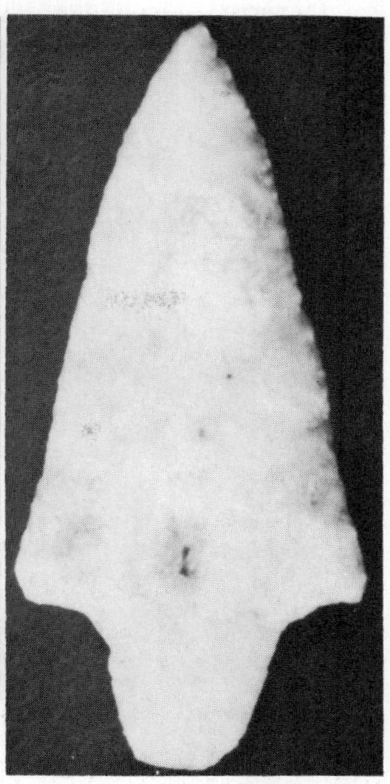

G6, $90-$160
Marion Co., FL.

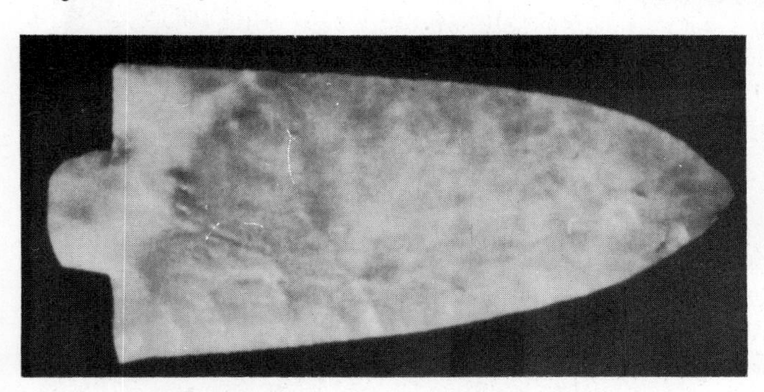

G8, $350-$500
NW Cent. FL.

G6, $90-$160
Suwannee Rv., FL.

G8, $100-$200
St. Johns Rv., FL. Slight blade nick and glued tip. Classic.

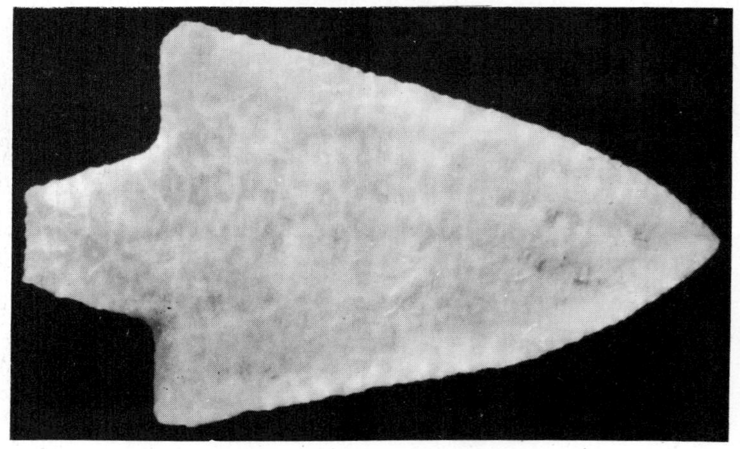

G9, $600-$800
Taylor Co., FL. Colorful coral. Shoulder nick.

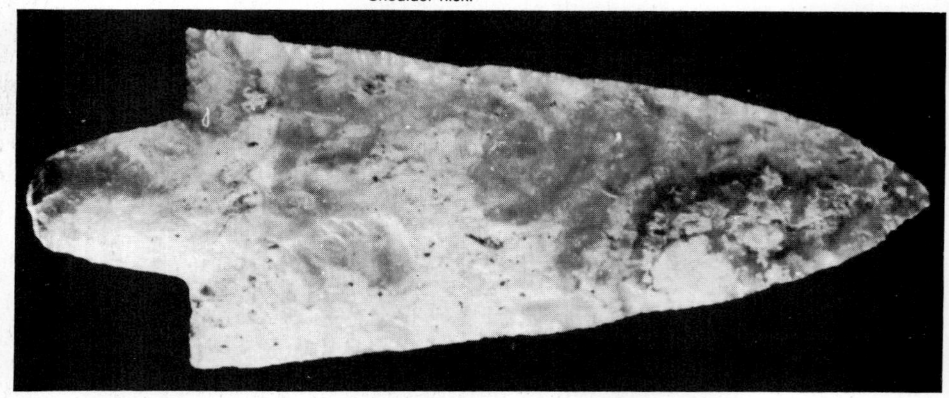

G10, $1200-$2000
Hillsborough Co., FL. Coral.

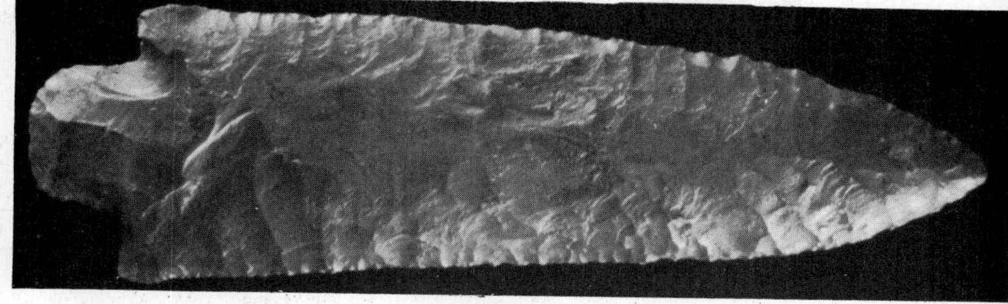

G7, $250-$400
NW Cent. FL.

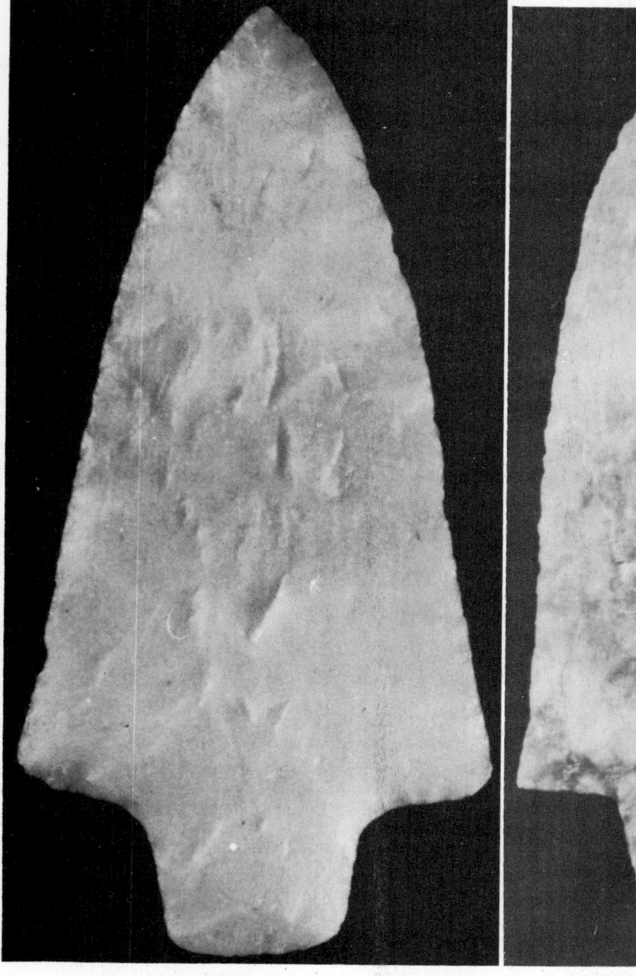

G8, $350-$500
NW Cent. FL.

G10, $1500-$2500
NW Cent. FL.

MARSHALL - Mid-Archaic to Woodland, 6000 - 2000 B.P.

(Also see Castroville, Ensor and Marcos)

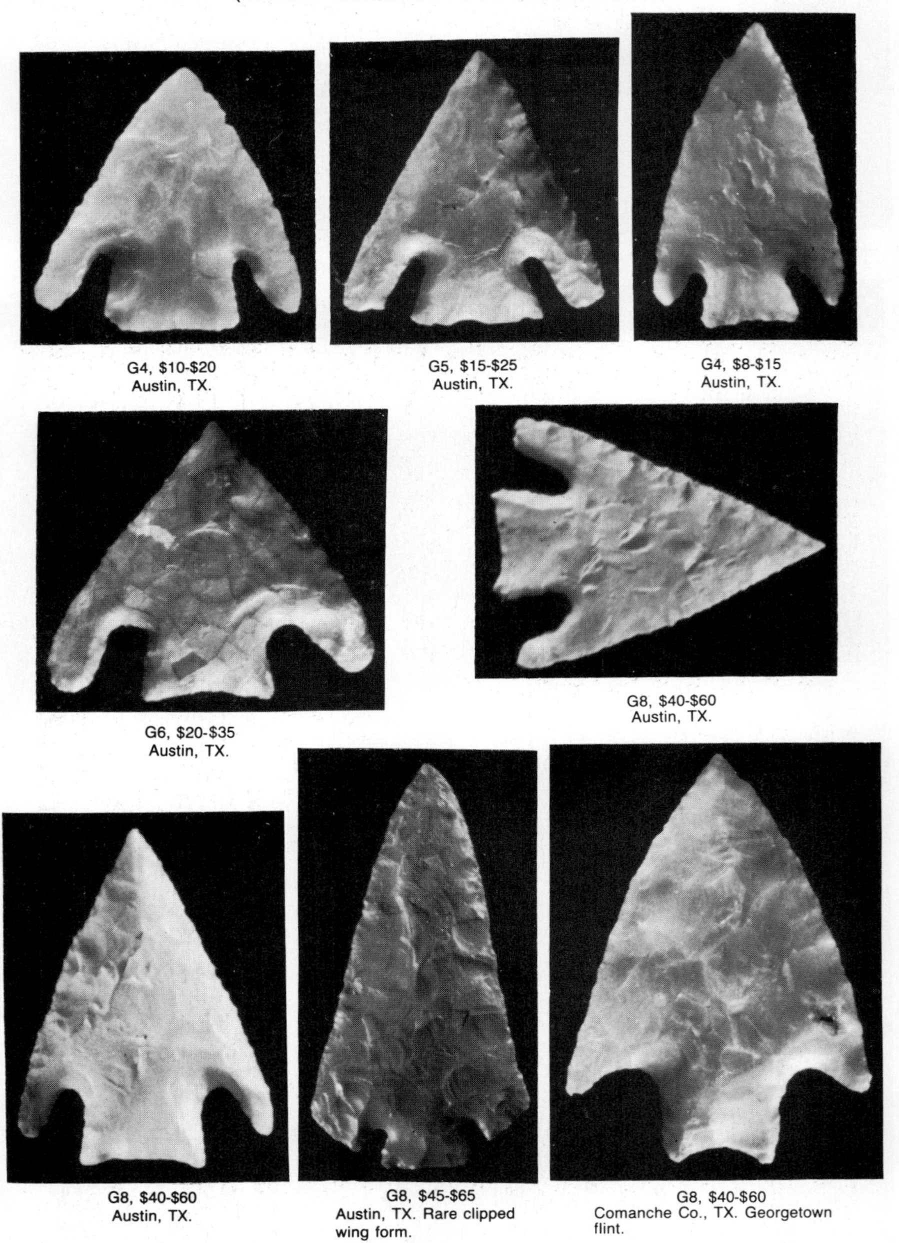

G4, $10-$20
Austin, TX.

G5, $15-$25
Austin, TX.

G4, $8-$15
Austin, TX.

G6, $20-$35
Austin, TX.

G8, $40-$60
Austin, TX.

G8, $40-$60
Austin, TX.

G8, $45-$65
Austin, TX. Rare clipped wing form.

G8, $40-$60
Comanche Co., TX. Georgetown flint.

LOCATION: Midwestern states. **DESCRIPTION:** A large size, broad, crude to high quality, corner to basal notched point with long barbs.

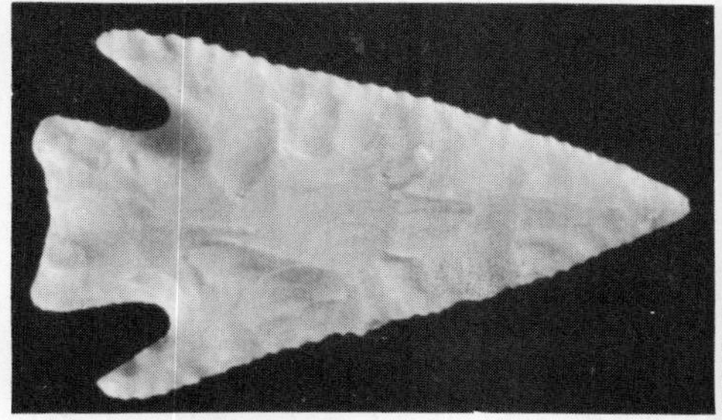

G8, $50-$80
Comanche Co., TX.

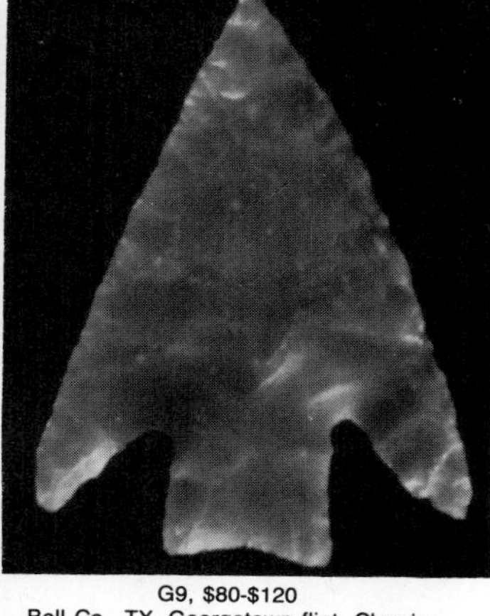

G9, $80-$120
Bell Co., TX. Georgetown flint. Classic

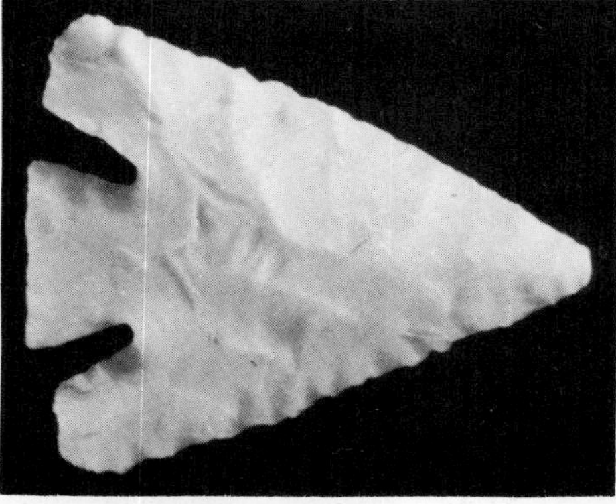

G7, $30-$50
Comanche Co., TX. Square shoulder.

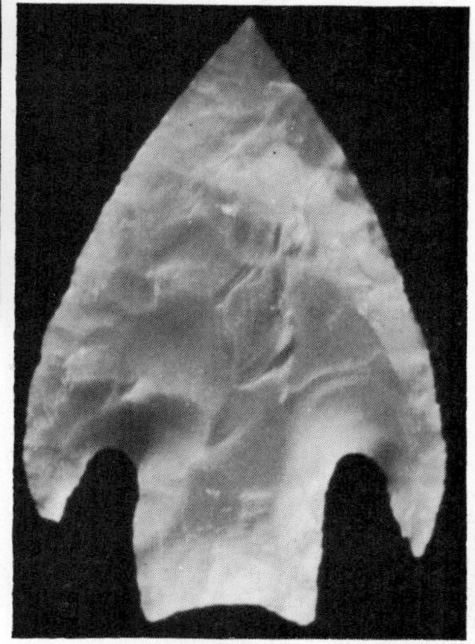

G9, $90-$150
Austin, TX.

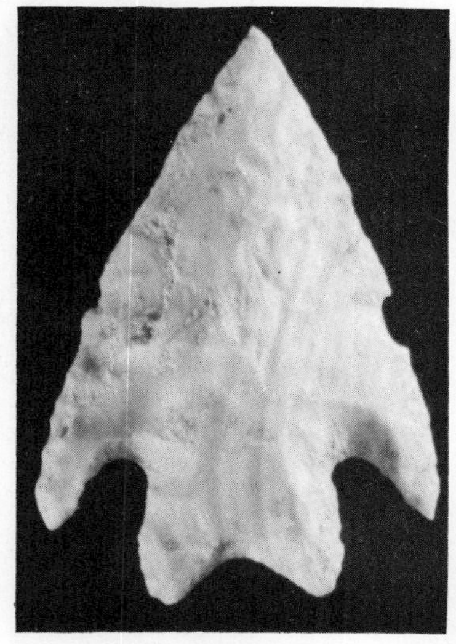

G8, $50-$80
Austin, TX. Note unusual side notches for hafting.

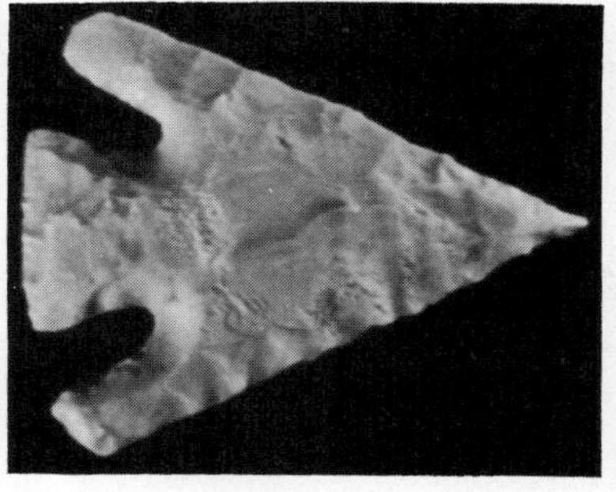

G8, $40-$60. Austin, TX.

G9, $125-$200
Austin, TX.

G9, $150-$250
Austin, TX.

G9, $120-$200
Comanche Co., TX. Very thin & excellent quality.

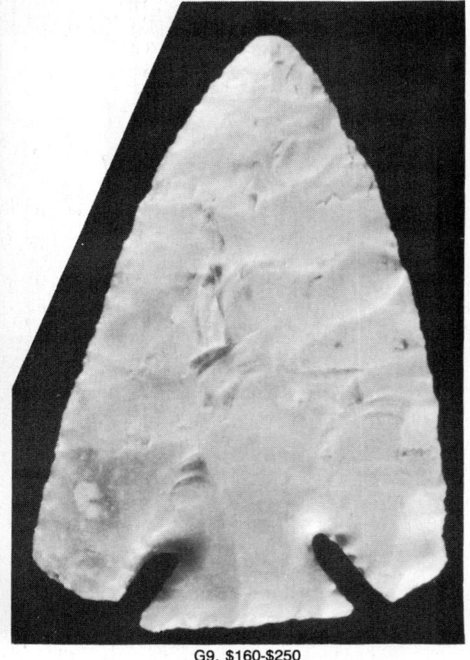

G9, $160-$250
Comanche Co., TX. Square shoulder.

MARTINDALE - Early Archaic, 8000 - 5000 B.P.

(Also see Marcos and Marshall)

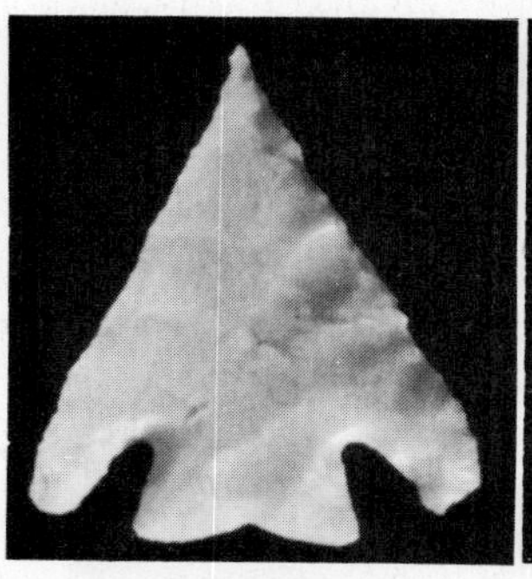

G7, $30-$45
Comanche Co., TX. Classic.

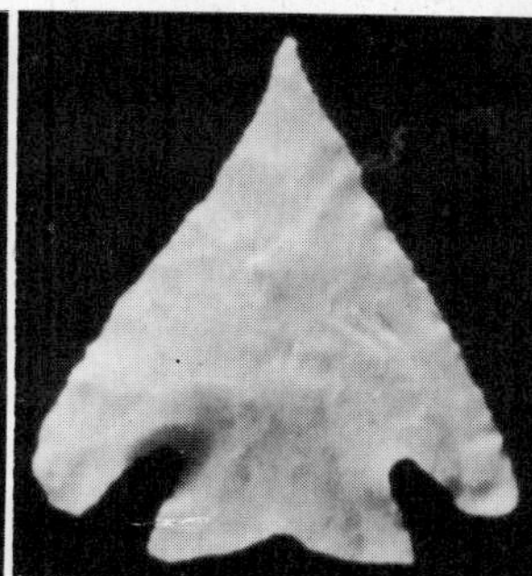

G7, $30-$45
Austin, TX. Classic.

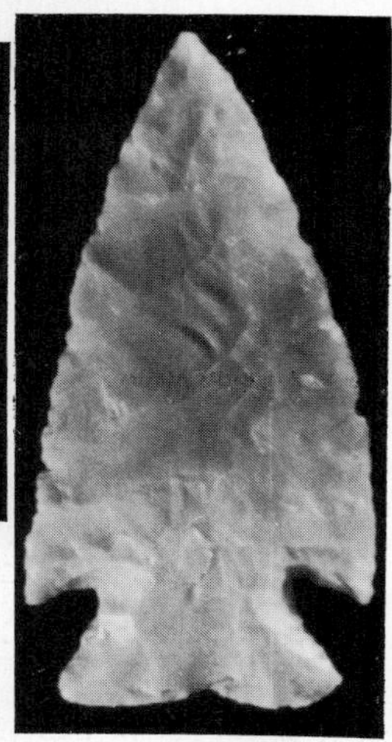

G6, $25-$35
Austin, TX.

G8, $40-$70
Austin, TX.

G6, $30-$45
Austin, TX. Georgetown flint.

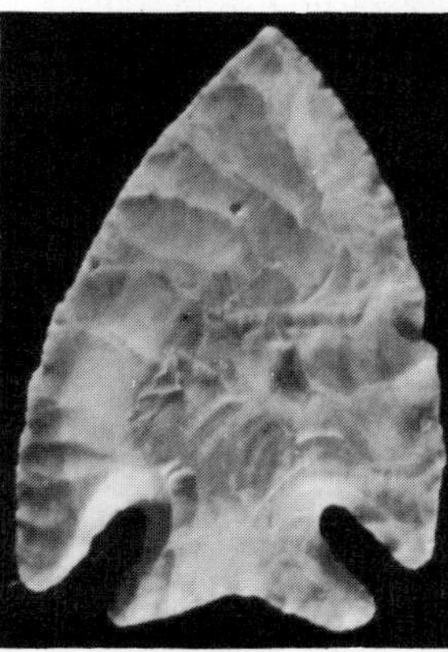

G7, $30-$50
Austin, TX.

G10, $250-$400
Austin, TX.

LOCATION: Midwestern states. **DESCRIPTION:** A medium size corner notched to expanded stem point. The base is unique in that it is formed by two curves meeting at the center. Called *Bandy* in southern Texas. **I.D. KEY:** Basal form, early flaking.

MARTIS - Woodland, 3000 - 1500 B.P.

(Also see Mount Albion)

G4, $6-$10
Yavapai Co., AZ.

G3, $3-$5
Yavapai Co., AZ.

LOCATION: Southwestern states. **DESCRIPTION:** A medium size side to corner notched point with a straight to convex base.

MATAMOROS - Late Archaic to Mississippian, 4000 - 300 B.P.

(Also see Abasolo, Catan, Madison, Montgomery, O'Leno and Tortugas)

G5, $3-$5
SE TN.

G4, $2-$3
SE TN.

G3, $1-$2
SE TN.

G3, $1-$2
SE TN.

G5, $3-$5
SE TN.

LOCATION: Midwestern states. **DESCRIPTION:** A small to medium size, broad, triangular point with a concave, straight or convex base. On some examples, beveling occurs on one side of each face as in *Tortugas* points. Larger points would fall under the *Tortugas* type.

MATANZAS - Late Archaic to Woodland, 4500 - 2500 B.P.

(Also see Fishspear, Mount Albion and Tablerock)

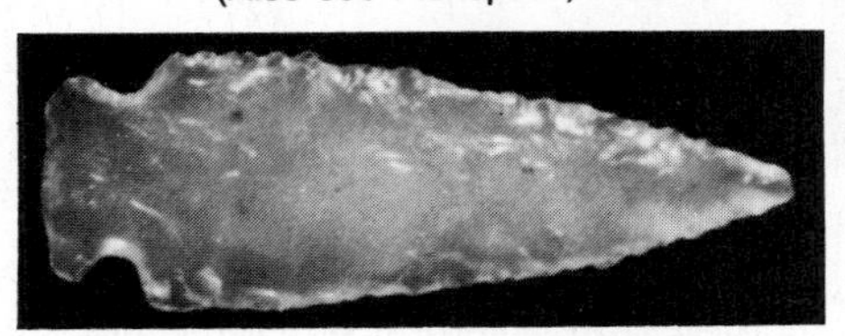

G7, $30-$50
AR. Agate.

LOCATION: Midwestern states. **DESCRIPTION:** A small to medium size, narrow, side notched point with a concave, convex or straight base.

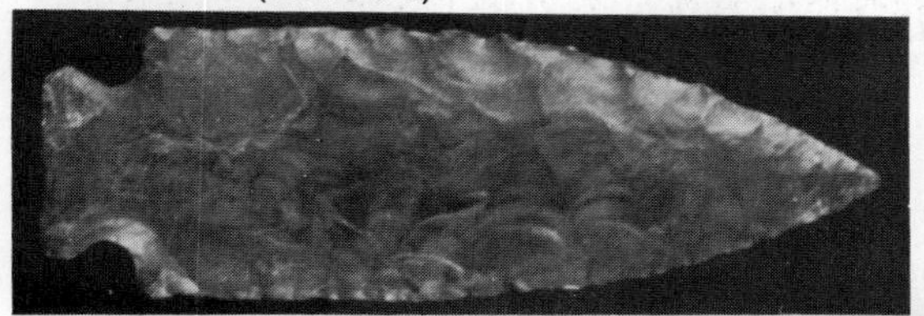

G8, $35-$55
AR.

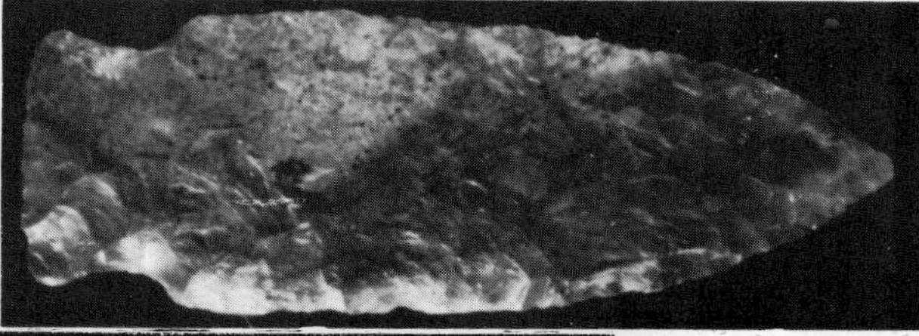

G6, $10-$20
Cass Co., IL.

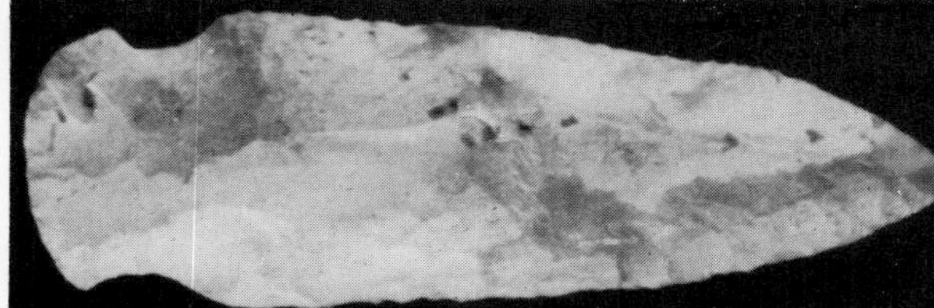

G7, $25-$40
SE TN.

MAUD - Mississippian, 800 - 500 B.P.

(Also see Cottonwood Triangle, Fresno, Greeneville, Hamilton, Madison, McGloin, Rogue River U-Back & San Jose)

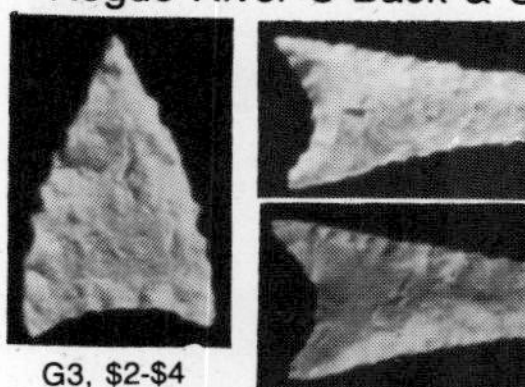

G3, $2-$4
Waco, TX.

G5, $6-$10 ea.
Red Rv., Co., TX.

G6, $10-$20
Red Rv., Co., TX.

G6, $10-$20, Smith Co., TX.

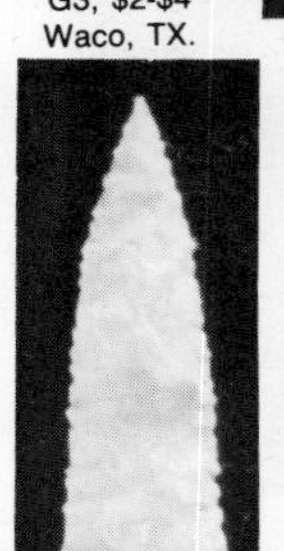

G9, $60-$100
Smith Co., TX.

G9, $80-$150
Red Rv., Co., TX.

G9, $60-$100
Red Rv. Co., TX.

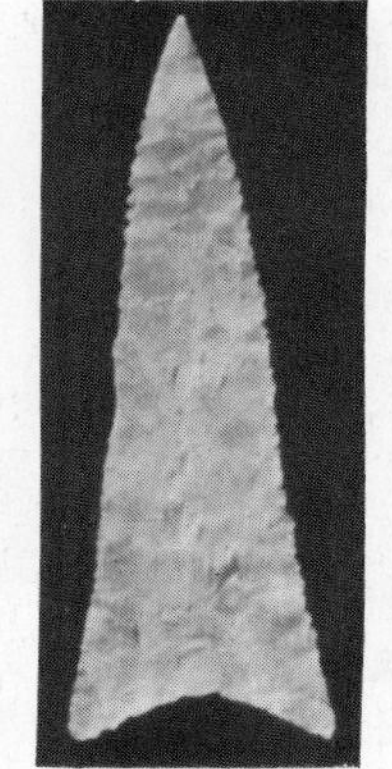

G10, $160-$300
CO/TX.

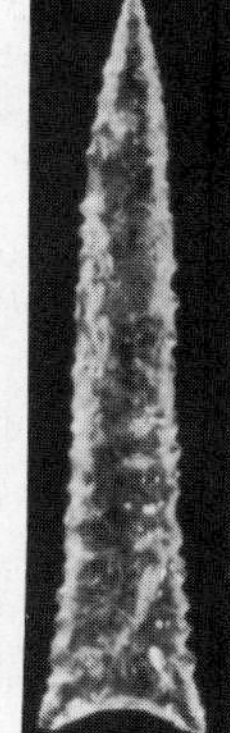

G10, $150-$250
Little Rv. Co., TX.

LOCATION: Midwestern states. **DESCRIPTION:** A small size, thin, triangular point with straight sides and a concave base. Associated with the Caddo culture in the Midwest. Blades are usually very finely serrated.

MCGLOIN - Mississippian, 1200 - 250 B.P.

(Also see Clarksville, Fresno. Madison, Maud & Starr)

G4, $2-$4
Comanche Co., TX.

LOCATION: Midwestern states. **DESCRIPTION:** A small size triangle with a concave base.

MCINTIRE - Mid to late Archaic, 6000 - 4000 B.P.

(Also see Kays, Lange, Limestone, Mud Creek & Smithsonia)

G3, $3-$5
Meigs Co., TN.

G6, $6-$10
E. TN.

G6, $6-$10
Limestone Co., AL.

G8, $30-$50
Limestone Co., AL.

G7, $8-$15
Limestone Co., AL.

LOCATION: Southeastern states. **DESCRIPTION:** A medium to large point with straight to convex blade edges and a broad parallel to expanding stem. Shoulders are square to slightly barbed and the base is usually straight.

MCINTIRE (continued)

G6, $6-$10
Limestone Co., AL.

G4, $4-$6
Morgan Co., AL.

G3, $3-$5
Morgan Co., AL.

G9, $40-$60
Humphreys Co., TN.

G8, $25-$40
Crossville, TN.

G9, $30-$50
Decatur, AL. Classic.

G7, $10-$20
Meigs Co., TN.

MCKEAN - Transitional Paleo to mid-Archaic, 9000 - 4000 B.P.

(Also see Wheeler)

G3, $4-$6
E. TN.

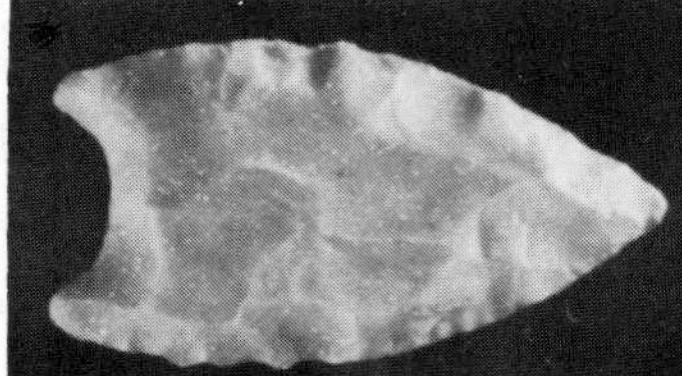

G7, $25-$40
Comanche Co., TX.

G5, $10-$20
OR. Obsidian.

G5, $15-$25
Limestone Co., AL.

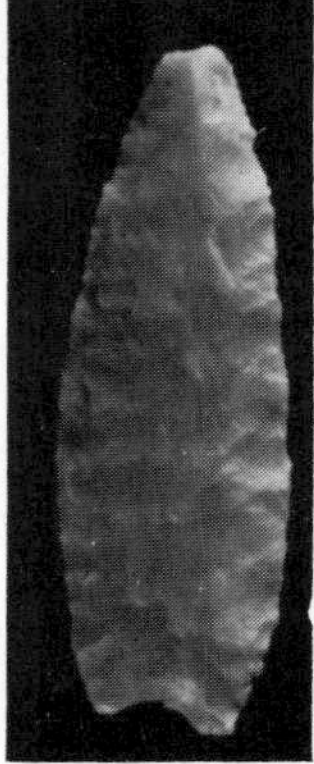

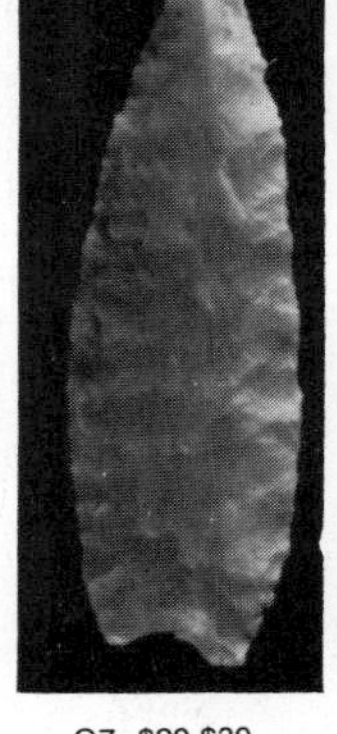

G7, $20-$30
Decatur, AL. Tip & ear nick.

G10, $250-$400
W. TX. Classic.

LOCATION: Midwest to Southeastern states. **DESCRIPTION:** A small to medium size, narrow, basal notched point. No basal grinding is evident. Believed to be derived from the *Wheeler* point. Flaking is more random than on its ancestor, although early forms do have parallel flaking.

MEHLVILLE - Mid-Archaic, 7000 - 4000 B.P.

(Also see Citrus, Culbreath, Eva, Smith and Wade)

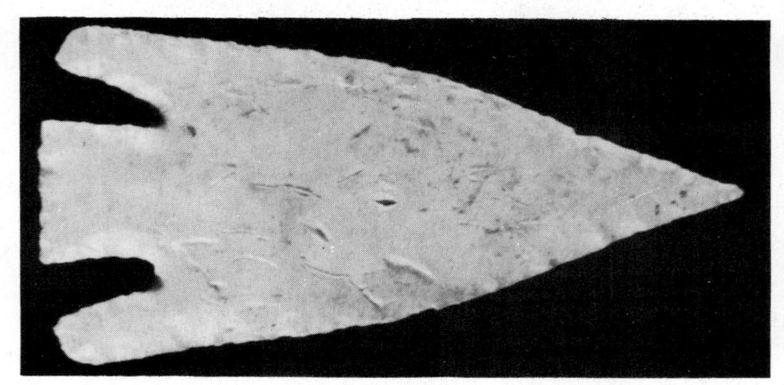

G10, $400-$750
St. Charles Co., MO.

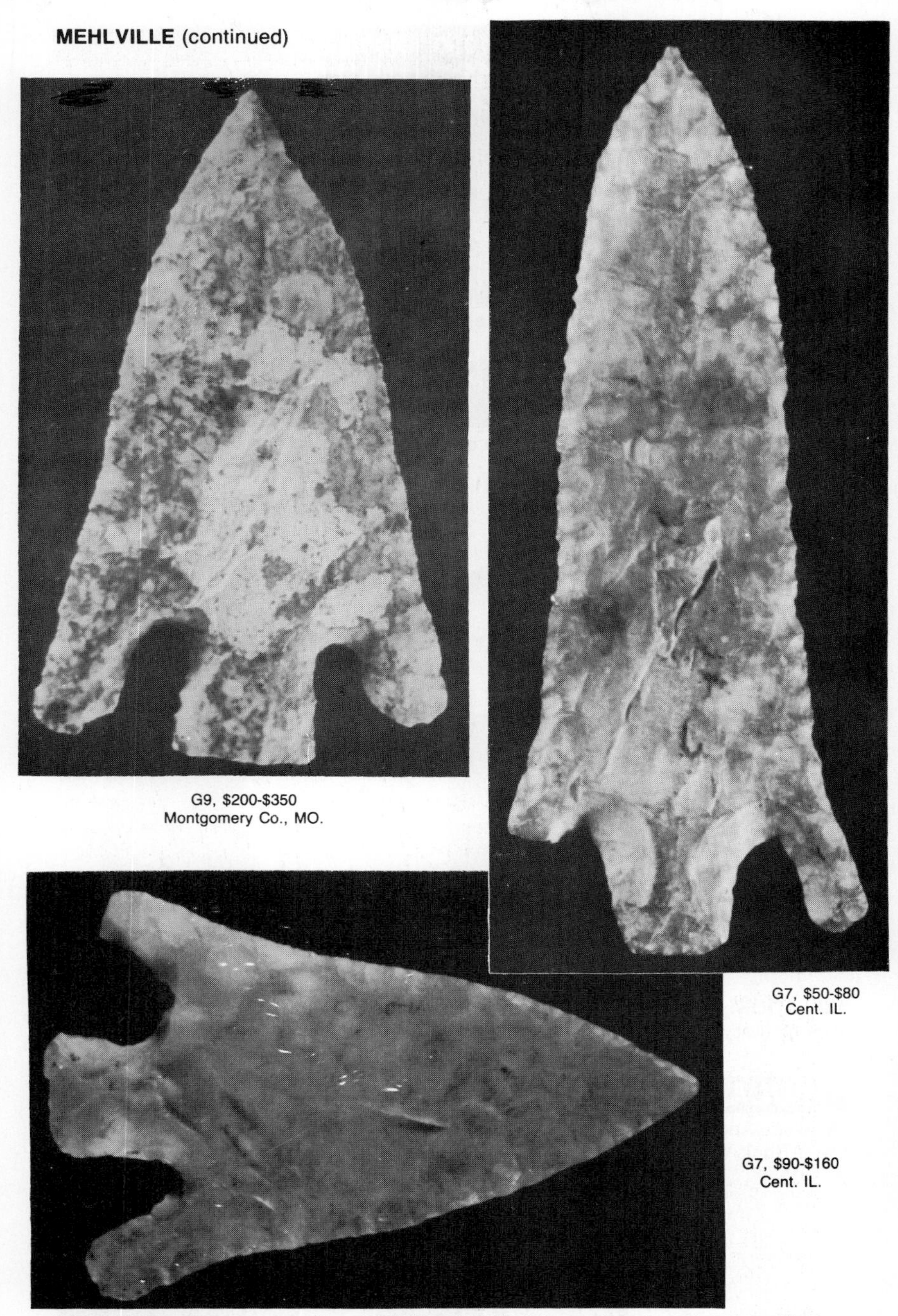

G9, $200-$350
Montgomery Co., MO.

G7, $50-$80
Cent. IL.

G7, $90-$160
Cent. IL.

LOCATION: Midwestern states. **DESCRIPTION:** A large size, broad, point with expanding shoulders and a squared base. The long barbs give the appearance of basal notching. **I.D. KEY:** Expanding barbs.

MEROM - Late Archaic, 4000 - 3000 B.P.

(Also see Keota and Leon)

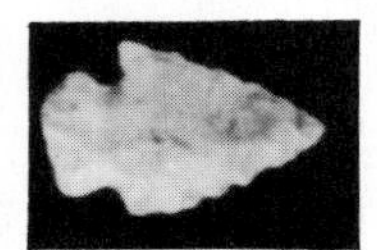

G2, $1-$3
TN.

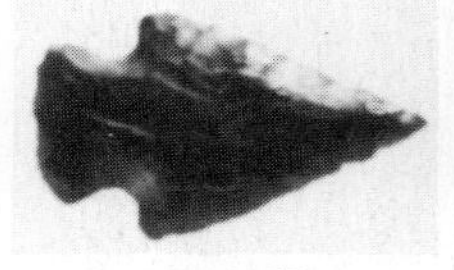

G5, $5-$8
TN.

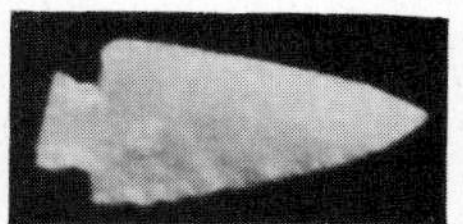

G3, $3-$5
Friendship Co., AR.

LOCATION: Midwestern to Southeastern states. **DESCRIPTION:** A small size, triangular, point with wide side notches and a convex base.

MESERVE - Transitional Paleo to mid-Archaic, 9000 - 4000 B.P.

(Also see Dalton)

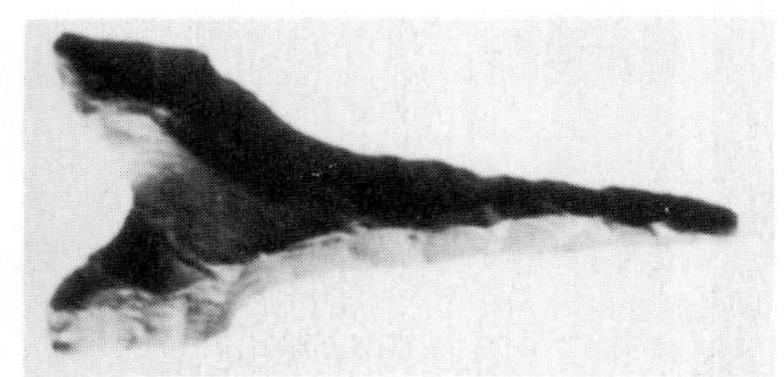

G7, $40-$60
TN/KY.

G8, $50-$90
OH.

G7, $40-$60
Bossier Parrish, LA.

LOCATION: Midwestern states. **DESCRIPTION:** A medium size, auriculate form with a blade that is beveled on one side of each face. This type is related to *Dalton* points.

MIDLAND - Paleo, 11000 - 9000 B.P.

(Also see Angostura, Browns Valley, Clovis, Cowhouse Slough, Folsom, Milnesand, Paint Rock Valley and Plainview)

G5, $150-$250
Comanche Co., TX.

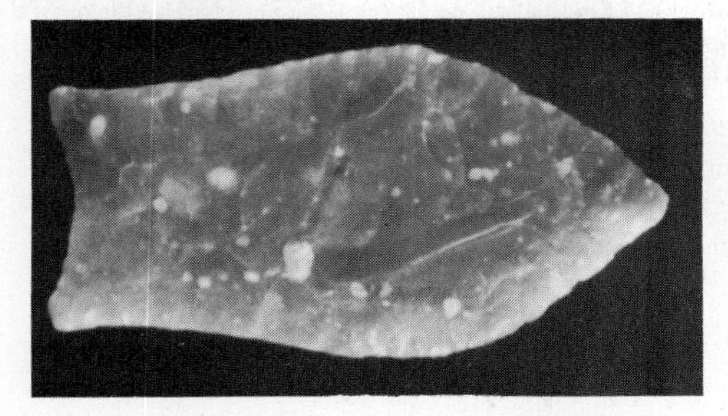

G10, $600-$1000
Comanche Co., TX. Sides are ground two-thirds the way up from the base. Very thin. Classic eared form. Typical *Midlands* do not have the ears.

LOCATION: Midwestern to Northwestern states and Canada. **DESCRIPTION:** A small to medium size, thin, lanceolate point with the widest part near the tip. Bases have a shallow concavity. Basal thinning is weak and the blades exhibit fine edgework.

MILNESAND - Transitional Paleo, 11000 - 8000 B.P.

(Also see Agate Basin, Hell Gap and Rio Grande)

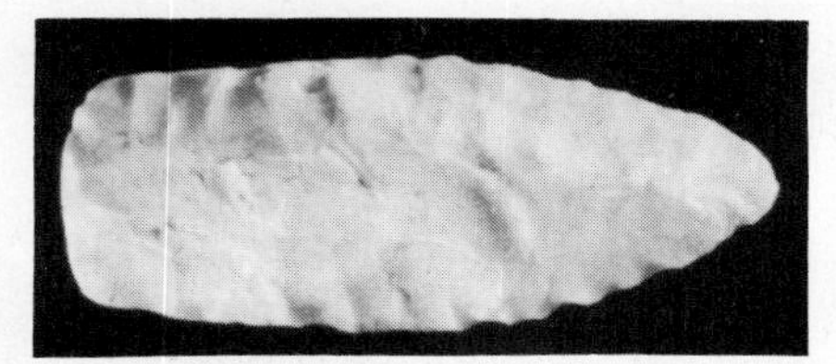

G5, $60-$100
Comanche Co., TX. Ground basal area and thicker toward the tip.

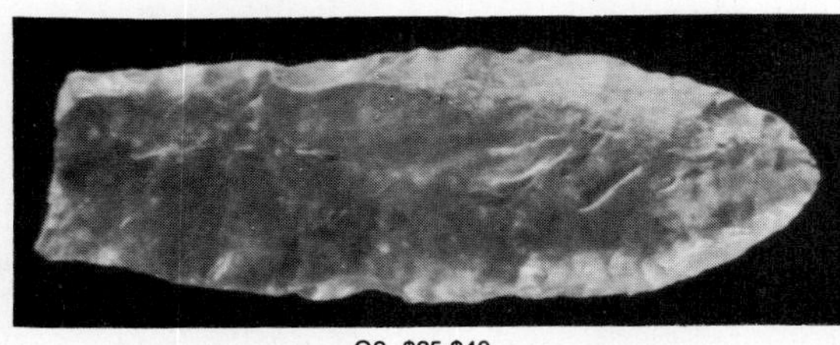

G2, $25-$40
Austin, TX.

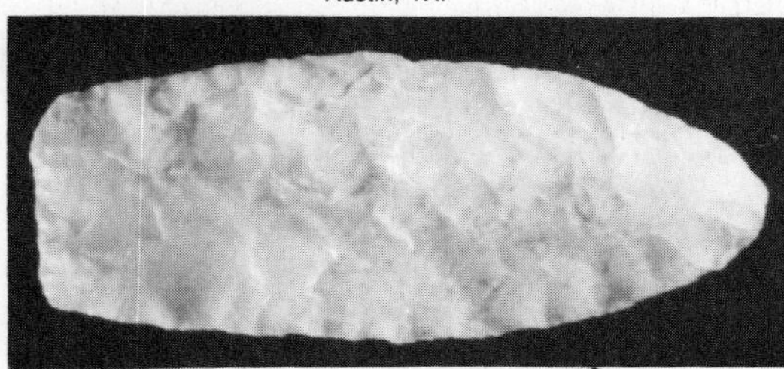

G7, $90-$150
Comanche Co., TX. Thick cross section. Classic.

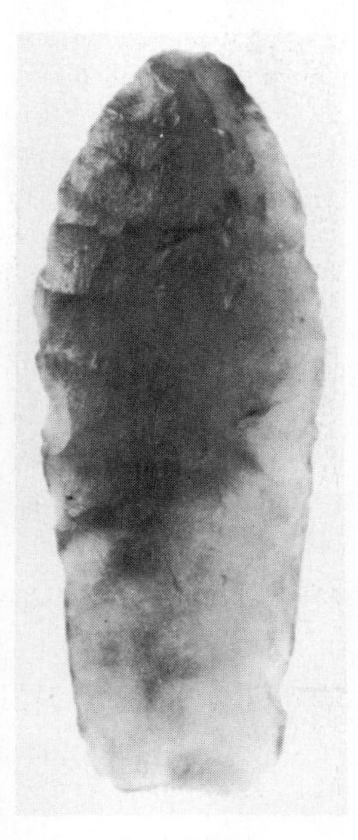

G4, $50-$80
NW AR. Quartz.

LOCATION: Midwestern states. **DESCRIPTION:** A medium size lanceolate point that becomes thicker and wider towards the tip. The base is basically square and ground. Thicker than *Midland*. **I.D. KEY:** Thickness and Paleo flaking.

MONTELL - Mid-Archaic to late Woodland, 5000 - 1000 B.P.

(Also see Arredondo, Buzzard Roost Creek, Kanawha, LeCroy, MacCorkle & Uvalde)

G5, $8-$15
Waco, TX.

G4, $5-$8
Waco, TX.

G5, $8-$15
Comanche Co., TX.

G8, $75-$125
Austin, TX. Drill form.

G2, $1-$2
Waco, TX.

G9, $90-$150
Austin, TX. Drill form.

G7, $40-$60
Austin, TX.

LOCATION: Midwestern to Southeastern states. **DESCRIPTION:** A small to medium size, bifurcated point with barbed shoulders. The ears are usually squared and some examples are beveled on one side of each face and are serrated. **I.D. KEY:** Square basal lobes.

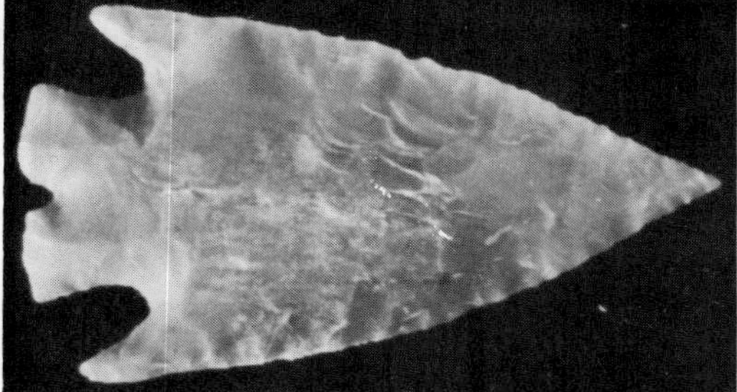

G8, $60-$90
Austin, TX.

G8, $50-$80
Austin, TX. Georgetown flint.
Tang nick. Classic.

G8, $60-$90
Austin, TX.

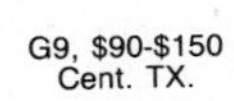

G9, $90-$150
Cent. TX.

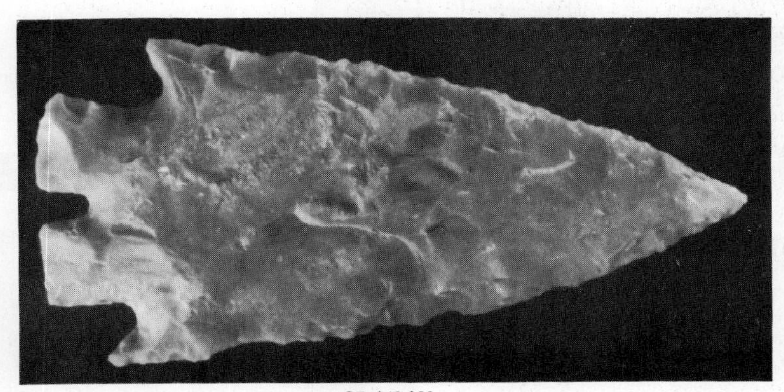

G7, $40-$60
Bell Co., TX.

MONTGOMERY - Woodland, 2500 - 1000 B.P.

(Also see Abasolo, Benjamin, Catan, Desmuke, Ebenezer, Morrow Mountain and Young)

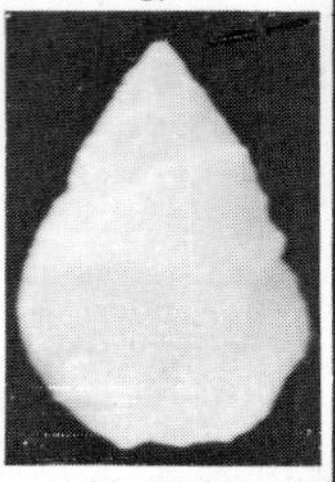

G2, .50-$1
Mont. Co., AL.

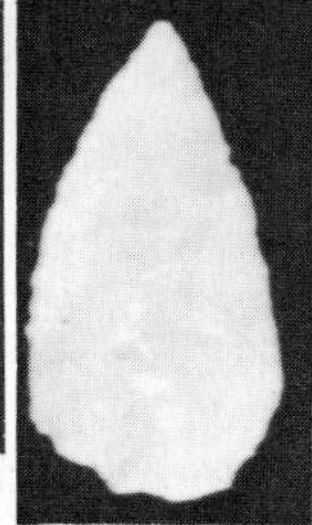

G3, $1-$2
Autauga Co., AL. Milky quartz.

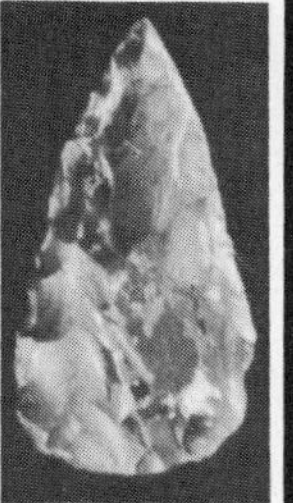

G2, .50-$1
Autauga Co., AL.

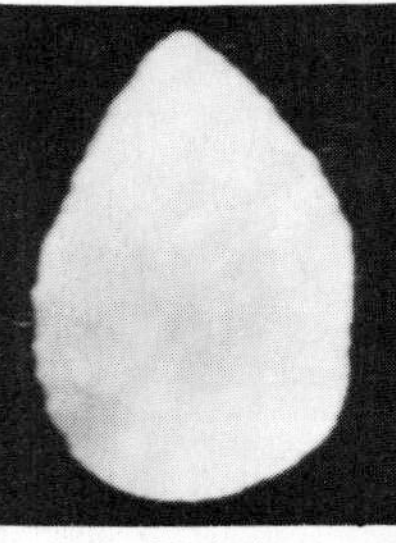

G4, $1-$3
Montgomery Co., AL.
Milky quartz.

G4, $2-$3
Mont. Co., AL.

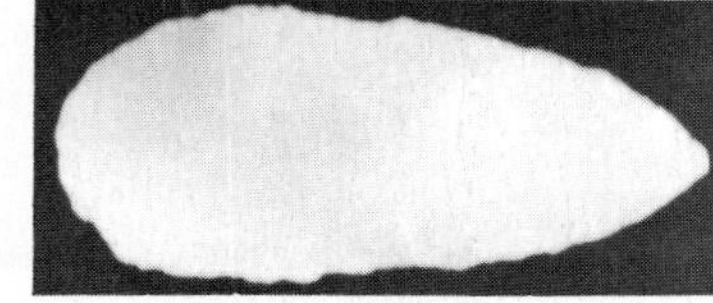

G6, $2-$4
Autauga Co., AL.
Milky quartz.

LOCATION: Southeastern states. **DESCRIPTION:** A small, broad, tear-drop shaped point with a rounded base. Flaking is random. This type is similar to *Catan* found in Texas.

MORHISS - Late Archaic to Woodland, 4000 - 1000 B.P.

(Also see Adena)

G6, $8-$12
Comanche Co., TX.

LOCATION: Midwestern states. **DESCRIPTION:** A medium to large size, thick, stemmed point with weak shoulders and a convex base.

MORRILL - Woodland, 3000 - 1000 B.P.

(Also see Lamoka)

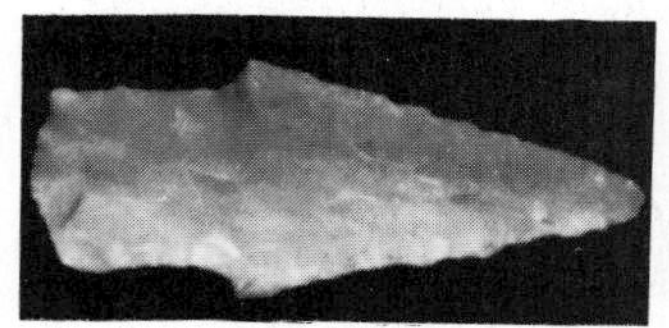

G4, $3-$5
Waco, TX.

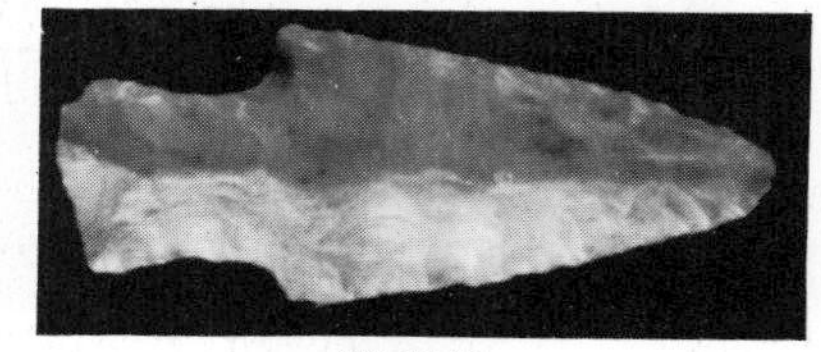

G5, $4-$6
Waco, TX.

MORRILL (continued)

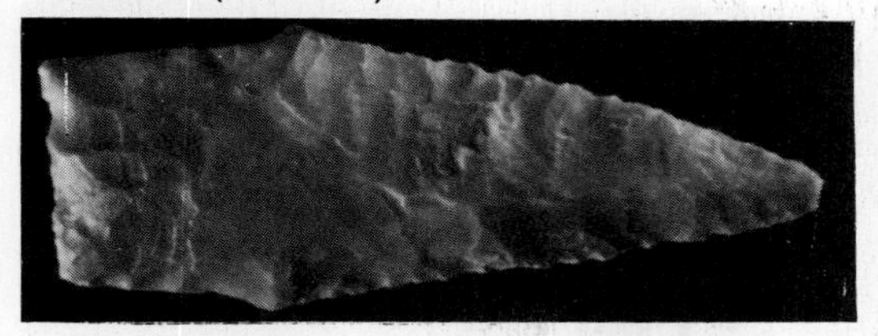

G7, $8-$15
Comanche Co., TX.

LOCATION: Midwestern states. **DESCRIPTION:** A medium size, thick, narrow, triangular point with weak, squared shoulders and a long rectangular stem.

MORRIS - Mississippian, 1200 - 400 B.P.

(Also see Cuney and Sallisaw)

G6, $20-$35
OR. Obsidian.

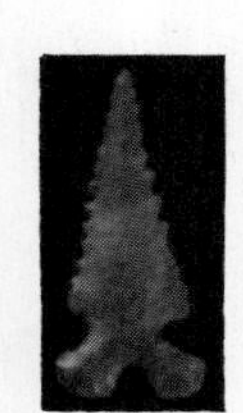

G6, $20-$35
Spiro Mound, OK.

G5, $15-$25
Spiro Mound, OK.

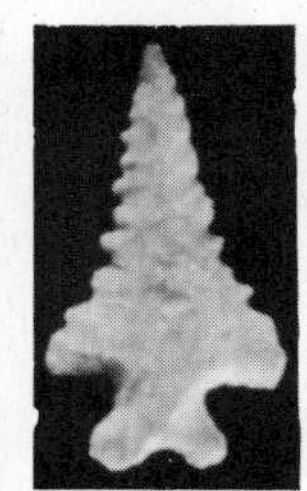

G7, $25-$45
Comanche Co., TX.

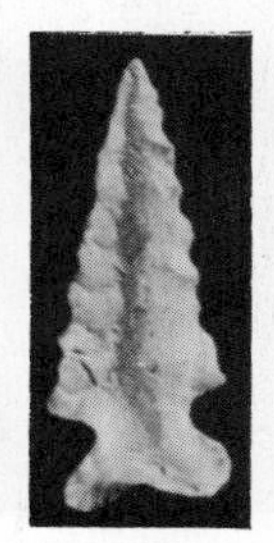

G5, $10-$20
McCurtain Co., OK.

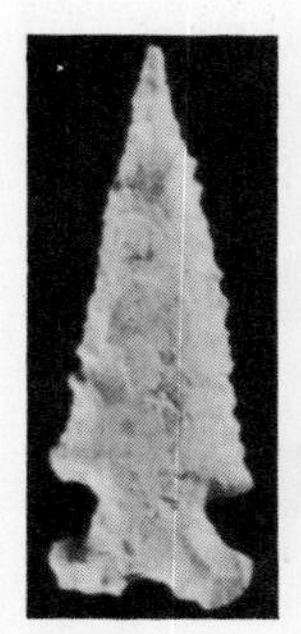

G6, $25-$35
McCurtain Co., OK.

G8, $40-$70
OR.

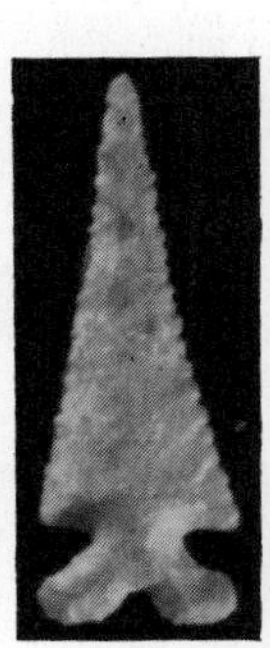

G9, $60-$100
Spiro Mound, OK.
Classic.

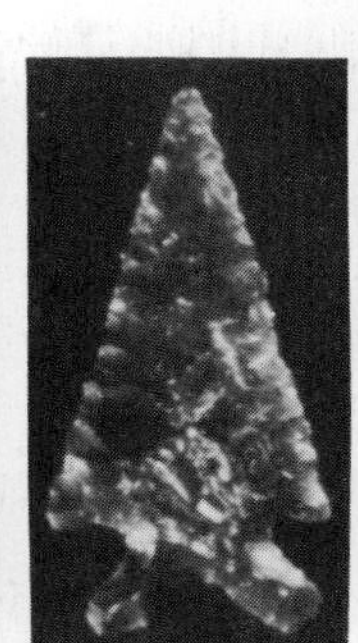

G7, $25-$45
OR/WA.

G8, $40-$70
OR/WA.

LOCATION: Midwestern to Western states. **DESCRIPTION:** A small size, thin, barbed point with a bifurcated base with rounded ears. **I.D. KEY:** Rounded basal ears.

MORROW MOUNTAIN - Mid-Archaic, 7000 - 5000 B.P.

(Also see Augustin, Bascom, Buggs Island, Chesapeake Diamond, Cypress Creek, Ebenezer, Eva, Gary, Gypsum Cave, Jerome, Langtry, Maples, Marion, Putnam, Santa Cruz and Thonotosassa)

G2, $1-$2
Kershaw Co., SC. Slate.

G7, $20-$30
Moore Co., NC.

G7, $20-$30
Bristol, VA. Note parallel flaking to center.

G5, $5-$8
Sussex Co., VA.

G1, .50-$1
Fairfield Co., SC. Quartz.

G5, $6-$10
Stokes Co., NC.

G2, $1-$2
Kershaw Co., SC. Slate.

G3, $2-$3
Fairfield Co., SC. Milky quartz.

G6, $10-$20
Caswell Co., NC.

G5, $6-$10
Stokes Co., NC.

G7, $15-$25
Newberry Co., SC. Milky quartz.

G5, $6-$10
Autauga Co., AL. Vein quartz.

LOCATION: Midwestern to Southeastern states. **DESCRIPTION:** A medium to large size, triangular point with a very short contracting to rounded stem. Shoulders are usually weak but can be barbed. The blade edges on some examples are serrated with needle points. Look for Archaic parallel flaking.

G7, $15-$25
Rockingham Co., NC.

G6, $8-$15
Coffee Lake, AL.

G8, $25-$40
Iredell Co., NC.

G6, $10-$20
Southampton
Co., VA.

G5, $7-$12
Dinwidie
Co., VA.

G6, $8-$15
Johnson Co., NC.

G8, $25-$40
Randolph Co., NC.

G9, $50-$80
Lauderdale Co., AL. Classic.

G6, $8-$15
Barboar Co., AL.

G3, $2-$4
Newberry Co., SC. Banded slate.

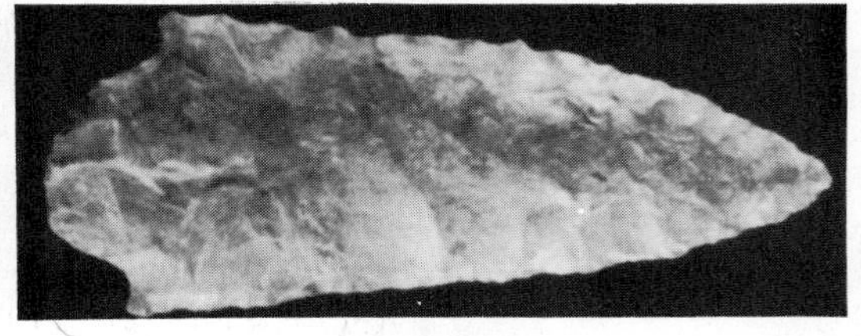

G4, $4-$8
Humphreys Co., TN.

G7, $20-$30
Stokes Co., NC. Rare knife form.
Note typical base on both ends.

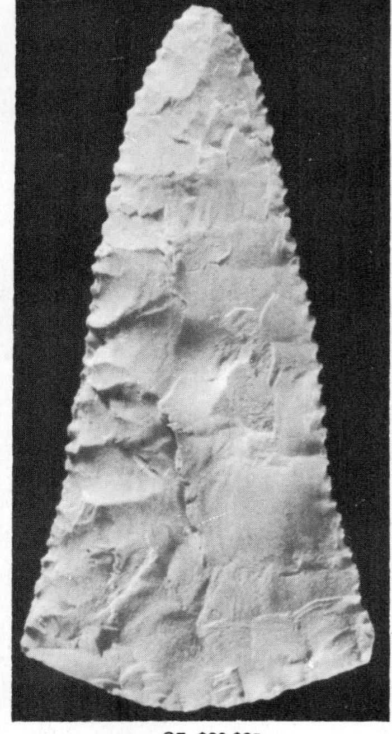

G7, $20-$30
Morgan Co., AL.

G7, $20-$30
W. TN.

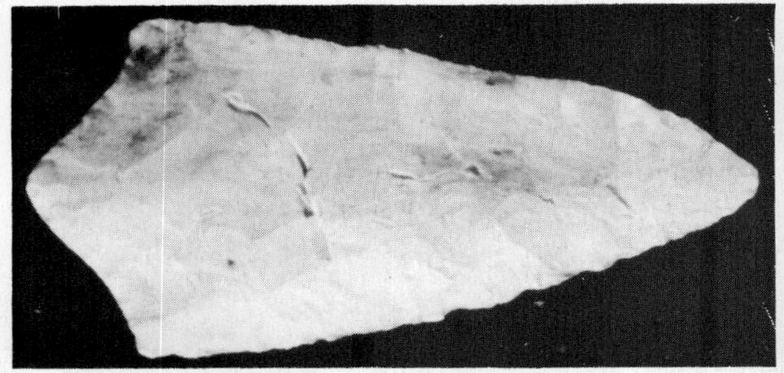

G7, $20-$30
Humphreys Co., TN. Note thinning strikes from base.

G8, $25-$40
Humphreys Co., TN.

MORROW MOUNTAIN ROUNDED BASE, Mid-Archaic, 7000 - 5000 B.P.

(Also see Abasolo, Catan, Desmuke, Ebenezer, Montgomery and Young)

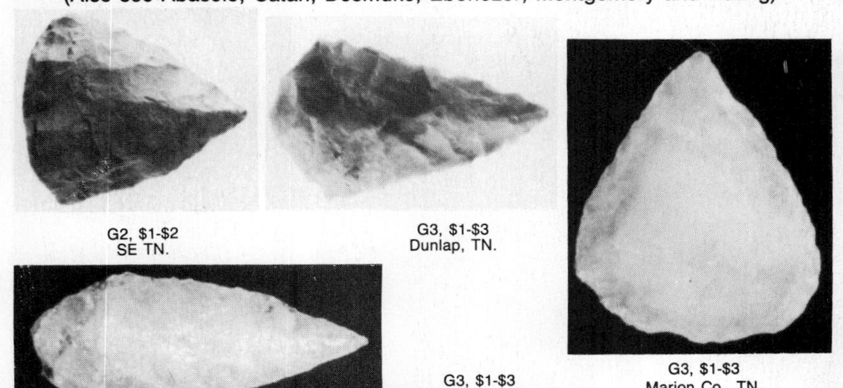

G2, $1-$2
SE TN.

G3, $1-$3
Dunlap, TN.

G3, $1-$3
Union Co., SC. Quartz.

G3, $1-$3
Marion Co., TN.

LOCATION: Midwestern to Southeastern states. **DESCRIPTION:** A small to medium size tear-drop shaped point with a pronounced, short, rounded base and no shoulders. Some examples have a straight to slightly convex base. This type has similarities to *Gypsum Cave* points found in the Western states.

G4, $2-$4
Limestone Co., AL.

G8, $12-$20
Limestone Co., AL.

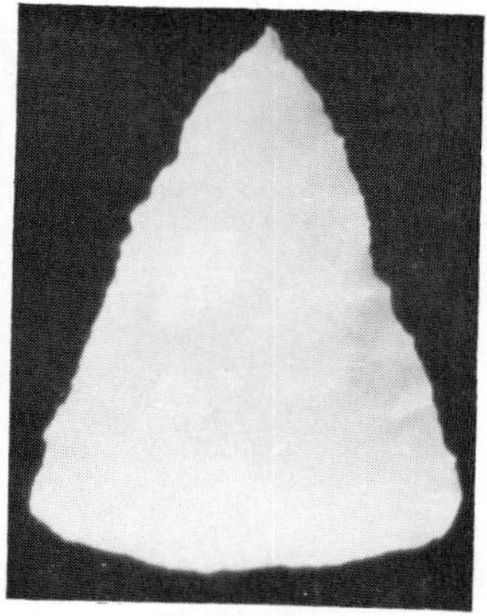

G8, $12-$20
Nickajack Lake, TN.
Milky quartz.

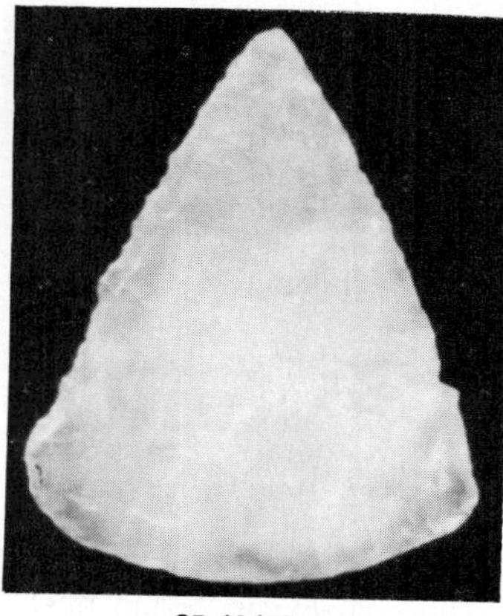

G7, $6-$10
Marion Co., TN. Agate.

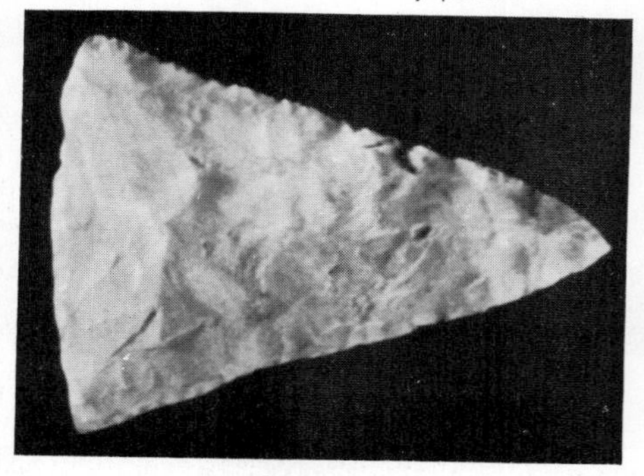

G8, $15-$25
Colbert Co., AL. Classic.

G6, $4-$6
Newberry Co., SC. Vein quartz.

G8, $15-$25
Marion Co., TN.

G9, $20-$35
Morgan Co., AL.

MORROW MOUNTAIN STRAIGHT BASE - Mid-Archaic, 7000 - 5000 B.P.

(Also see Alachua and Mud Creek)

G5, $4-$6
E. TN.

G5, $4-$6
N. AL.

G4, $3-$4
Dunlap, TN.

G5, $3-$5
Marion Co., TN. Agate.

G3, $2-$4
Decatur, AL.

G4, $3-$4
Marion Co., TN. Quartz.

G6, $6-$10
Autauga Co., AL. Vein quartz.

G8, $10-$20
Johnson Co., NC. Vein quartz. Classic.

G8, $10-$20
Decatur, AL. Classic.

LOCATION: Southeastern states. **DESCRIPTION:** A medium size, thin, strongly barbed, point with a contracting stem and a straight base. Some examples are serrated and have a needle tip. Look for Archaic parallel flaking.

MORSE KNIFE - Woodland, 3000 - 1500 B.P.

(Also see Cotaco Creek & Ramey Knife)

G6, $80-$120. Calhoun Co., IL. Side nick.

LOCATION: Midwestern states. **DESCRIPTION:** A large lanceolate blade with a long contracting stem and a rounded base. The widest part of the blade is towards the tip.

G8, $500-$800
Calhoun Co., IL.

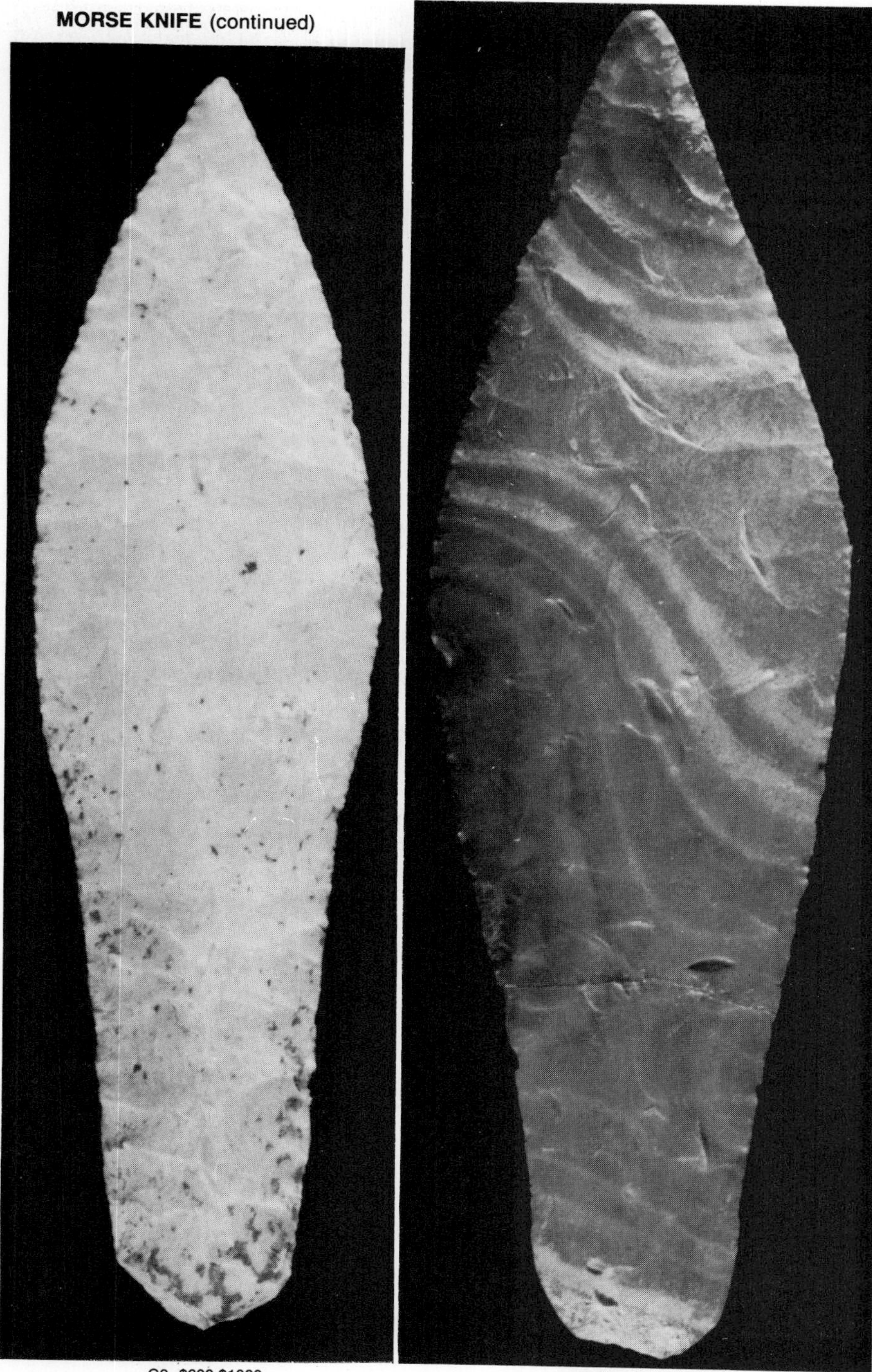

G9, $600-$1000
Lasalle Co., IL.

G7, $100-$200
IN. Broken & glued.

G10, $1500-$2500
IL. Heat treated Burlington chert.

MOTLEY - Late Archaic to Woodland, 4500 - 2500 B.P.

(Also see Buck Creek, Cupp, Epps, Hamilton, Smithsonia, Snyders and Wade)

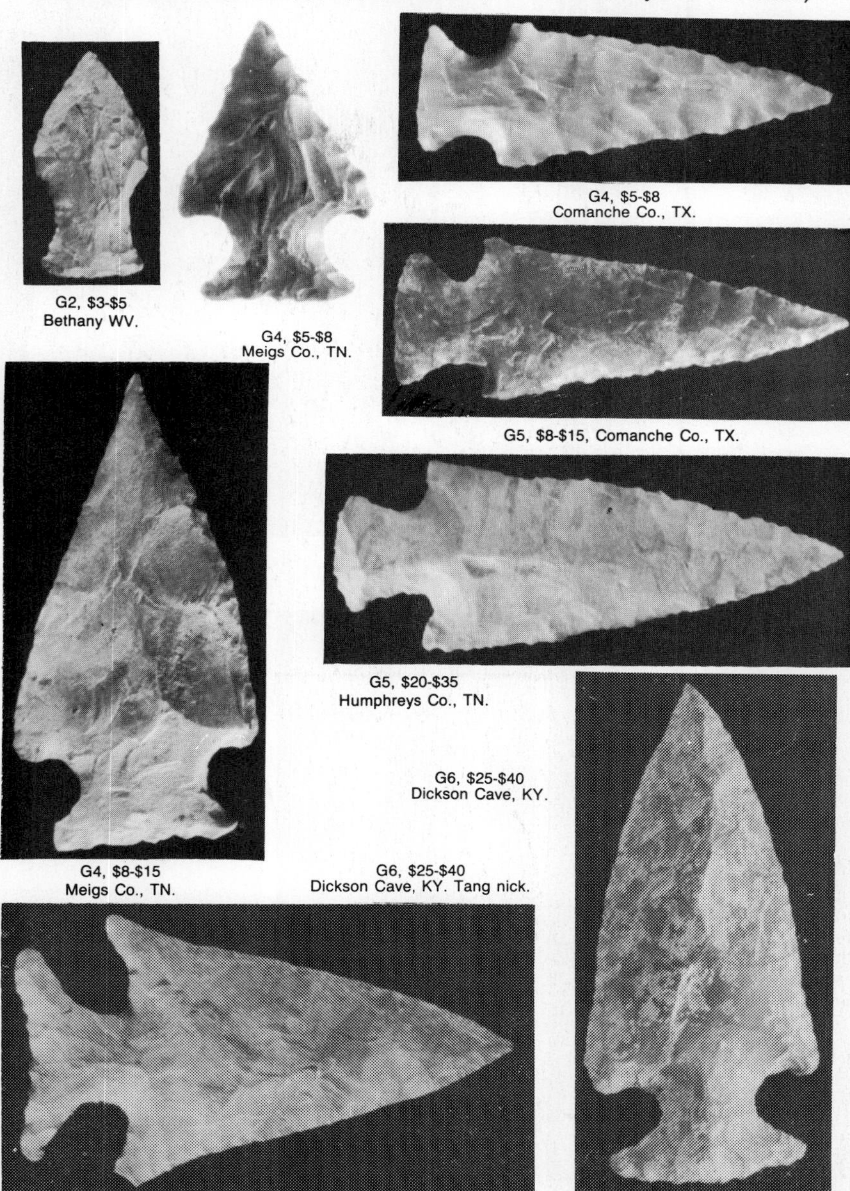

G2, $3-$5
Bethany WV.

G4, $5-$8
Meigs Co., TN.

G4, $5-$8
Comanche Co., TX.

G5, $8-$15, Comanche Co., TX.

G4, $8-$15
Meigs Co., TN.

G5, $20-$35
Humphreys Co., TN.

G6, $25-$40
Dickson Cave, KY.

G6, $25-$40
Dickson Cave, KY. Tang nick.

LOCATION: Southeastern states. **DESCRIPTION:** A medium to large size, expanded stemmed to widely corner notched point with strong barbs. The blade edges and the base are convex to straight. Has been found associated with *Wade* points in caches. Called *Epps* in Louisiana.

G6, $25-$40
Dickson Cave, KY.

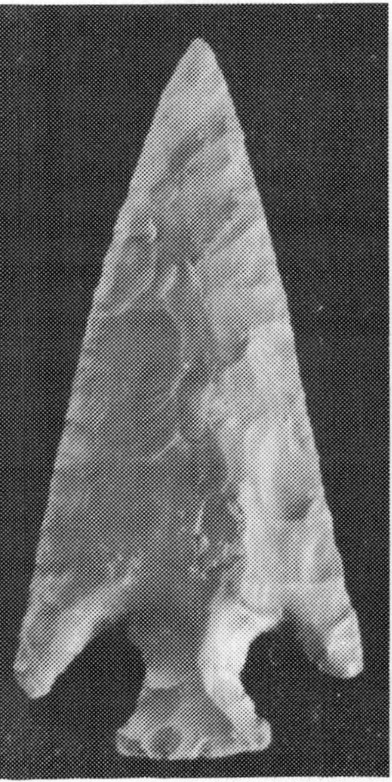

G7, $60-$100
Dickson Cave, KY.

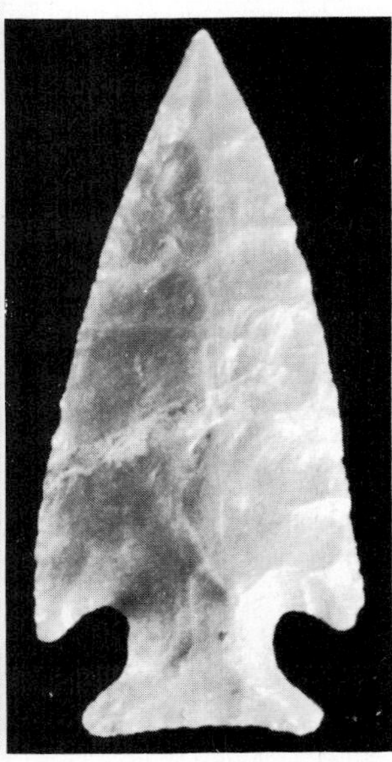

G8, $80-$120
Meigs Co., TN.

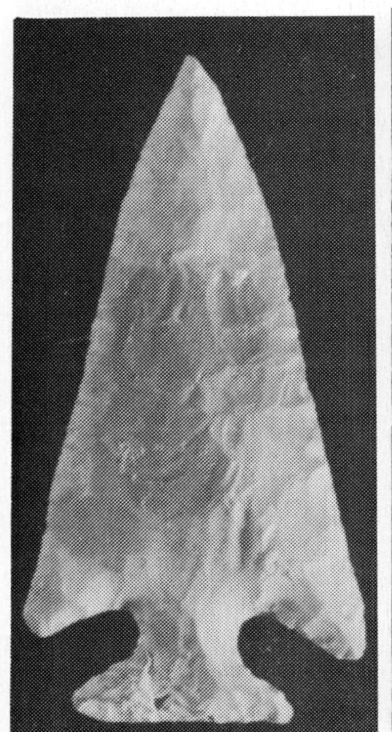

G9, $200-$300
Dickson Cave, KY.

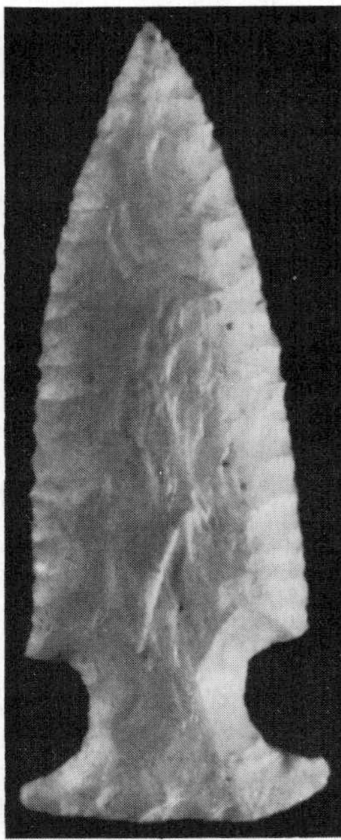

G9, $150-$250
Lauderdale Co., AL. White chert.
Oldest form.

G6, $25-$40
Dickson Cave, KY.

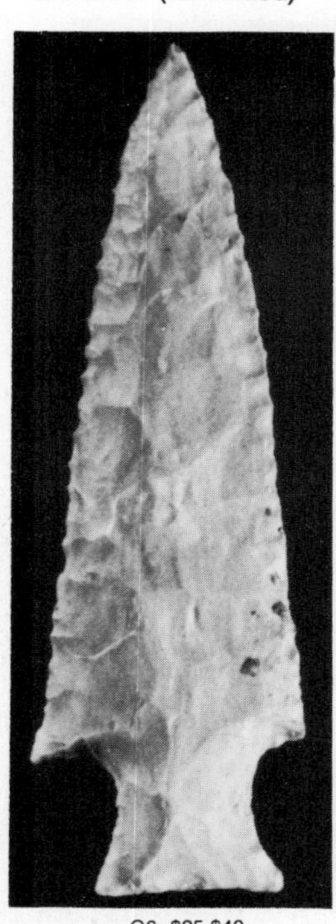

G6, $25-$40
Mid. TN.

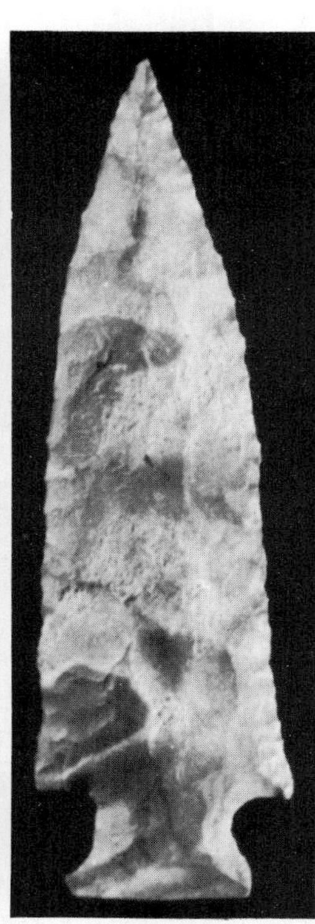

G7, $40-$60
Humphreys Co., TN.

G9, $300-$450
Humphreys Co., TN. Dover.

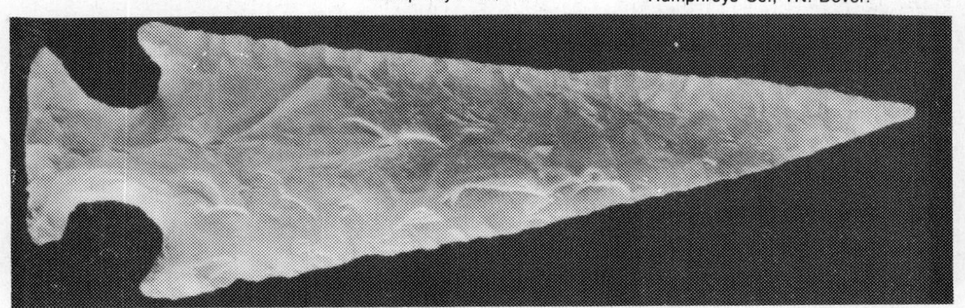

G10, $800-$1500
Dickson Cave, KY.

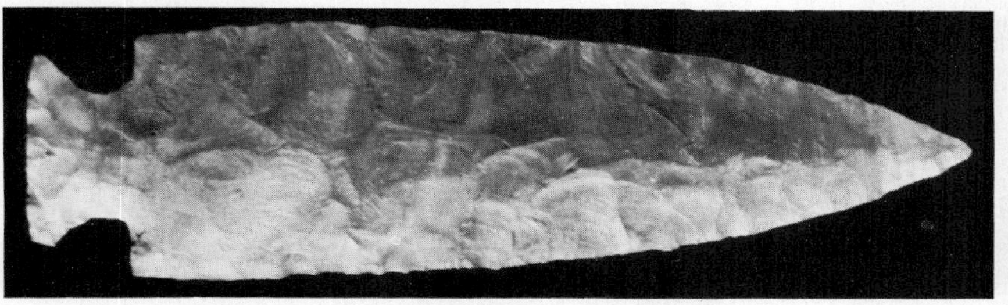

G7, $60-$100, Humphreys Co., TN. Minor tip nick.

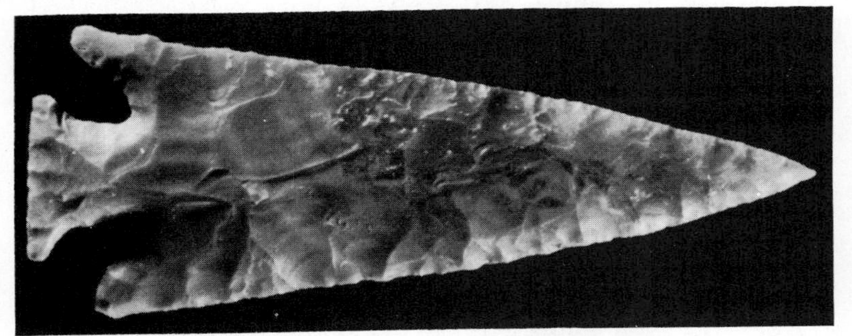

G10, $800-$1200, Humphreys Co., TN. High grade Kentucky flint. Classic.

G10, $1200-$2000. Dickson Co., TN. Dover chert. Cache point.

G10, $1500-$2000, Dickson Co., TN. Dover chert. Cache point.

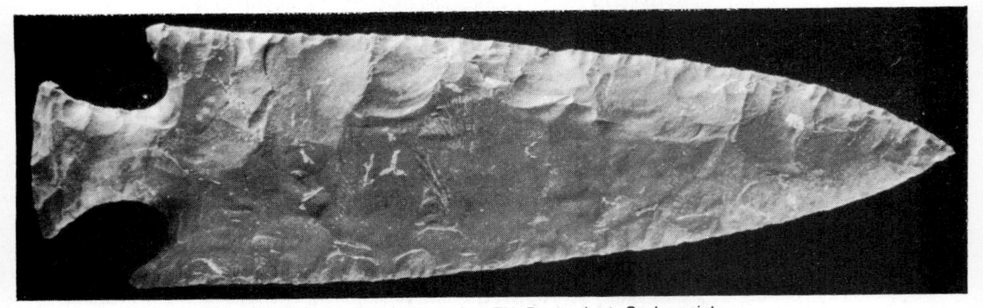

G10, $2000-$3000, Dickson Co., TN. Dover chert. Cache point.

MOUNT ALBION - Mid-Archaic, 6000 - 4000 B.P.

(Also see Martis and Matanzas)

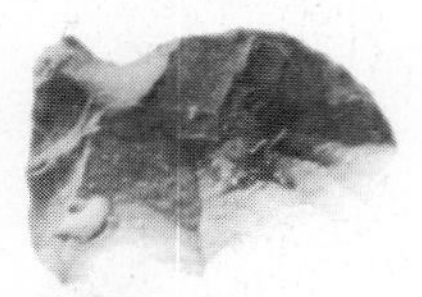

G1, $1-$2
Yavapai Co., AZ.

G2, $2-$4
Yavapai Co., AZ.

LOCATION: Southwestern states. **DESCRIPTION:** A medium size, narrow, side to corner notched point with a convex base.

MOUNTAIN FORK - Mid-Archaic to Woodland, 6000 - 2000 B.P.

(Also see Bradley, Flint River and Schild Spike, Duval, Lamoka, New Market and Randolph)

G4, $2-$4
Dunlap, TN.

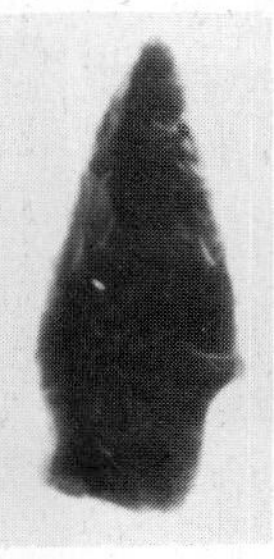

G4, $2-$4
Dunlap, TN.

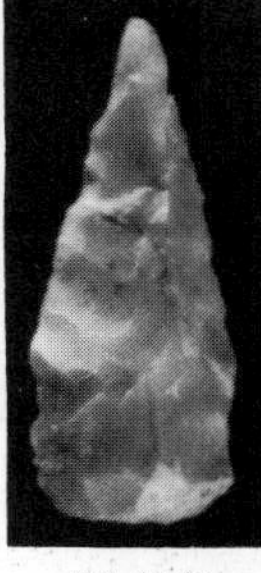

G4, $2-$4
Decatur, AL.

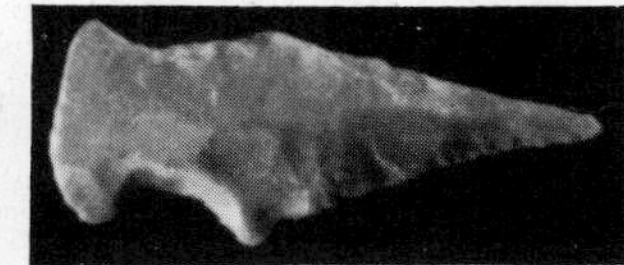

G4, $2-$4
Decatur, AL.

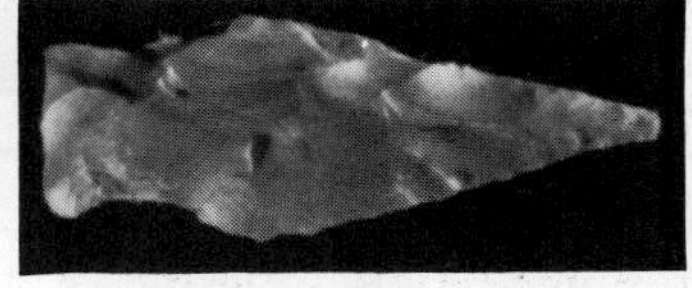

G5, $3-$5
Decatur, AL.

LOCATION: Southeastern states. **DESCRIPTION:** A small to medium size, narrow, thick, stemmed spike point with tapered shoulders.

MOUSE CREEK - Woodland, 1500 - 1000 B.P.

(Also see Jacks Reef Pentagonal)

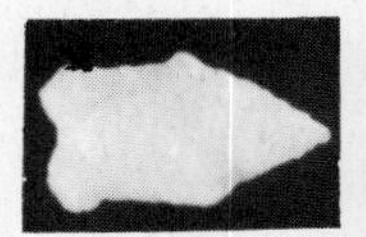

G2, $5-$10
Dallas Co., AL.
Milky quartz.

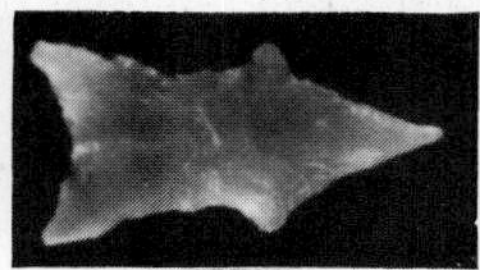

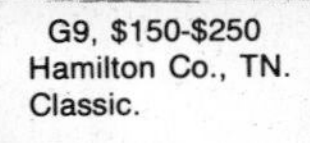

G9, $150-$250
Hamilton Co., TN.
Classic.

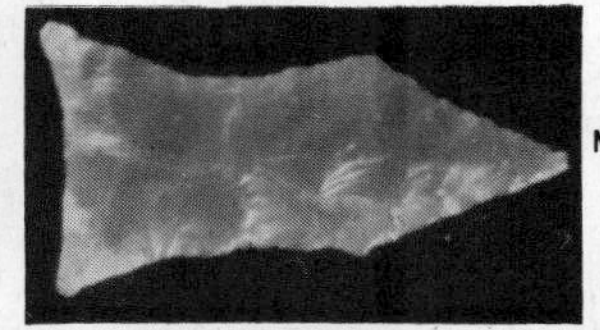

G8, $80-$150
Morgan Co., TN.

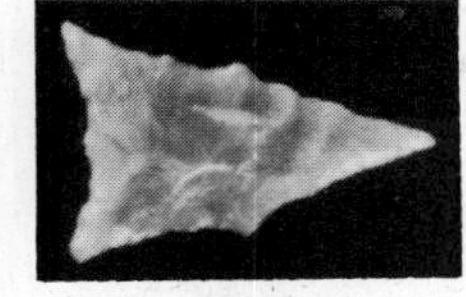

G6, $50-$80
Madison Co., AL.

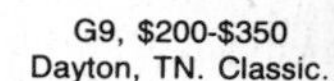

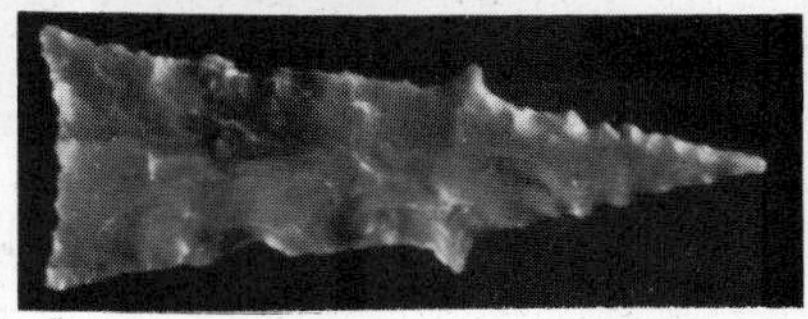

G9, $200-$350
Dayton, TN. Classic.

LOCATION: Southeastern states. **DESCRIPTION:** A small to medium size, thin, pentagonal point with prominent shoulders, a short pointed blade and a long, expanding stem. The base is concave with pointed ears. The hafting area is over half the length of the point. This type is very rare and could be related to *Jacks Reef*.

MUD CREEK - Late Archaic to Woodland, 4000 - 2000 B.P.

(Also see Bakers Creek, Beacon Island, Flint Creek, Lamoka, Little Bear Creek, McIntire, Mulberry Creek & Palmillas)

G2, $2-$3
E. TN.

G2, $1-$3
E. TN.

G4, $2-$4
E. TN.

G4, $3-$5
Dunlap, TN.

G2, $2-$3
E. TN.

G6, $5-$8
Walker Co., AL. Classic.

G4, $2-$4
Meigs Co., TN.

G7, $8-$15
Meigs Co., TN.

G7, $8-$15
Dayton, TN.

G5, $4-$6
SE TN.

G7, $8-$15
Decatur, AL.

LOCATION: Southeastern states. **DESCRIPTION:** A medium size point with slightly recurved blade edges, a narrow, needle like tip, square to tapered shoulders and an expanded stem. Called *Patuxent* in Virginia. **I.D. KEY:** Thickness, point form, high barb.

G6, $6-$10
SE TN.

G8, $10-$20
Walker Co., AL.

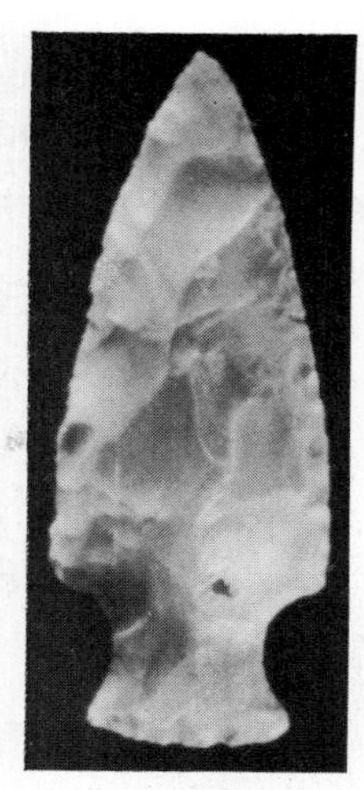

G5, $4-$6
Meigs Co., TN.

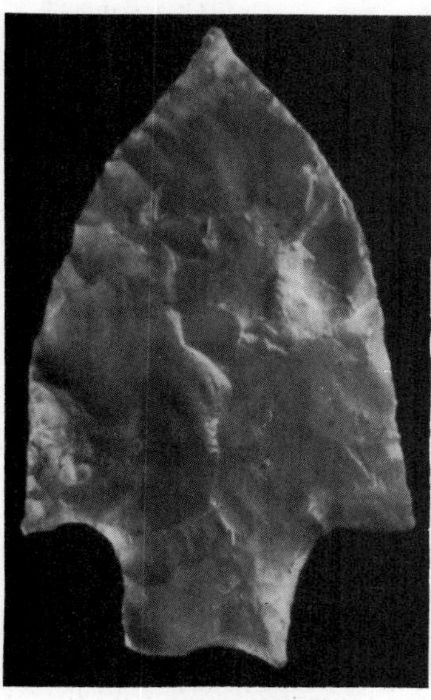

G8, $10-$20
Greene Co., AR.

G9, $35-$60
Humphreys Co., TN.

G10, $500-$800
Parsons, TN. Made of rare Horse Creek chert (red, yellow & blue). The vertical center streak is bright yellow. One side is deep red, the other deep blue. The colors are very striking.

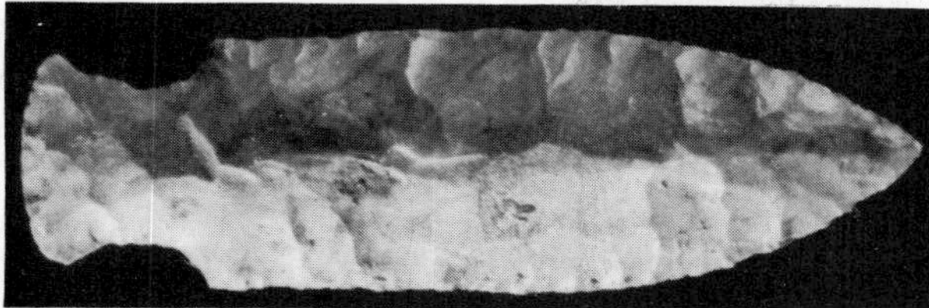

G9, $25-$40
Florence, AL. 7 Mile Isle.

MULDBERRY CREEK - Late Archaic to Woodland, 5000 - 3000 B.P.

(Also see Little Bear Creek and Pickwick)

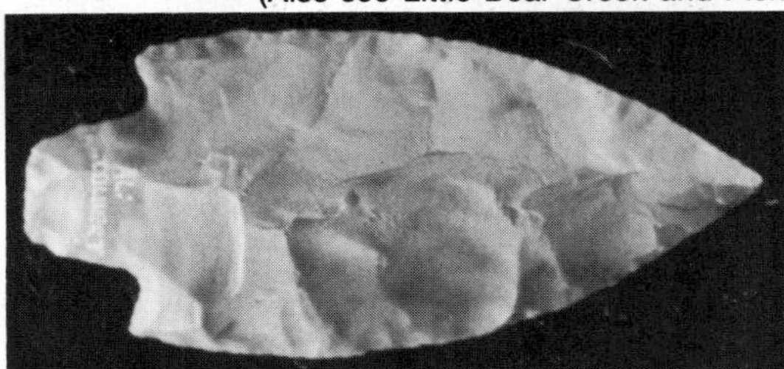

G6, $25-$40
Colbert Co., AL.

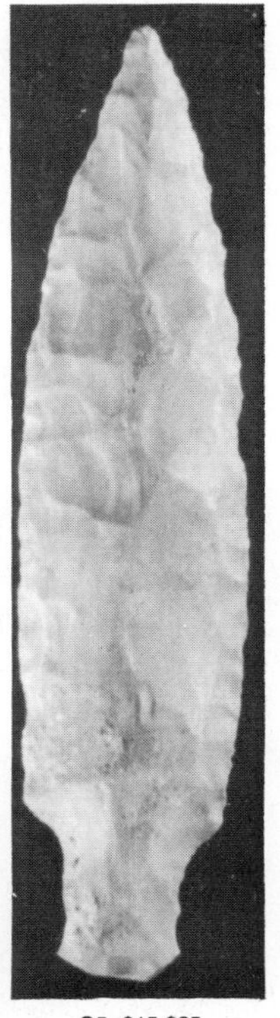

G5, $15-$25
Florence, AL., 7 Mile Isle.

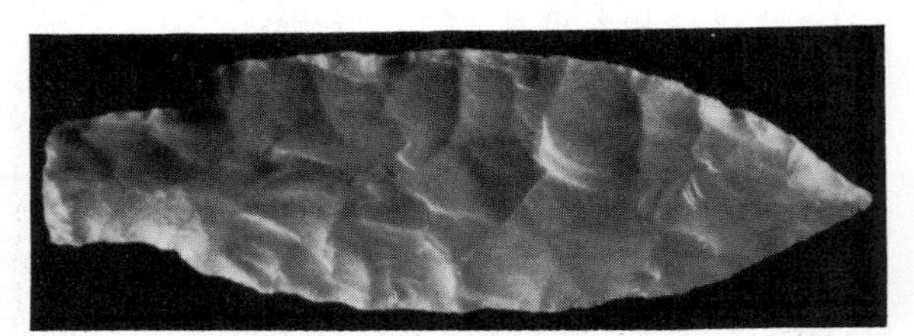

G3, $5-$8
Decatur, AL.

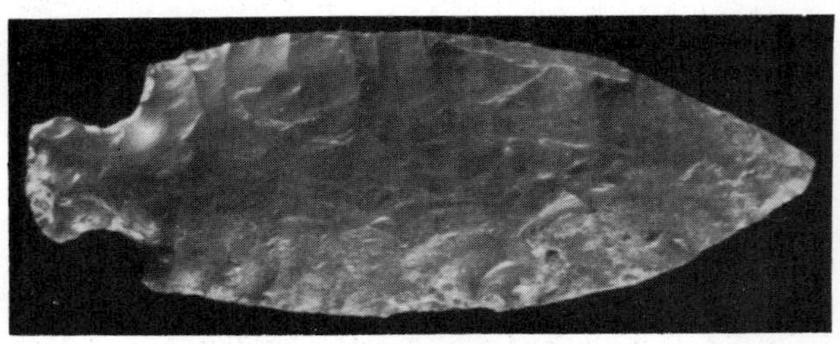

G5, $15-$25
Florence, AL., 7 Mile Isle.

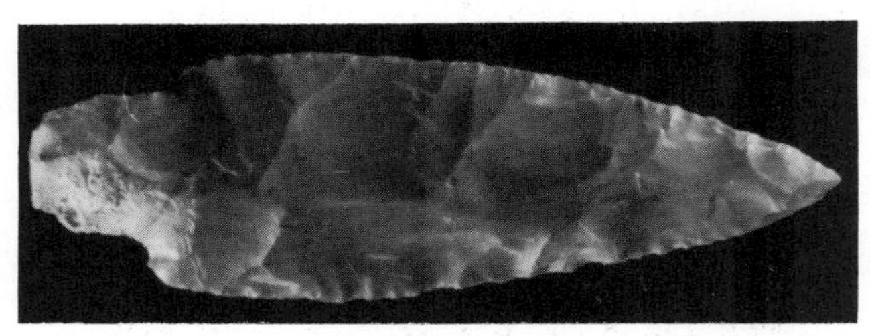

G5, $15-$30
Decatur, AL.

LOCATION: Southeastern states. **DESCRIPTION:** A medium to large size, thick, stemmed point with recurved blade edges. Shoulders are usually tapered, but can be barbed. The blade is widest near the center of the point. Stems can be expanding, parallel or contracting.

G5, $15-$25
Humphreys Co., TN.

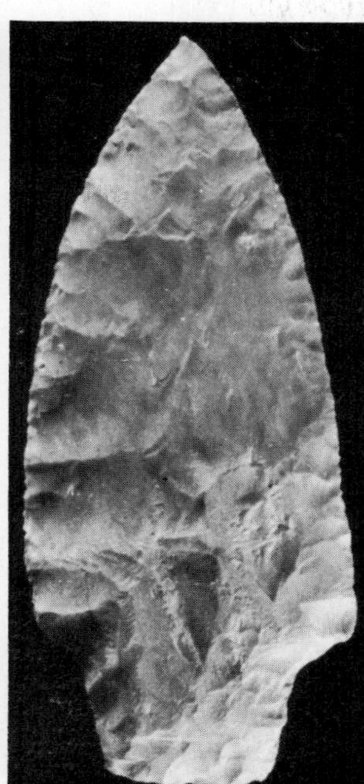

G7, $30-$50
Benton Co., TN.

G6, $20-$35
N. AL. Classic.

G8, $80-$120
Florence, AL. Needle tip.

G5, $15-$25
N. AL.

G8, $90-$150
Florence, AL.

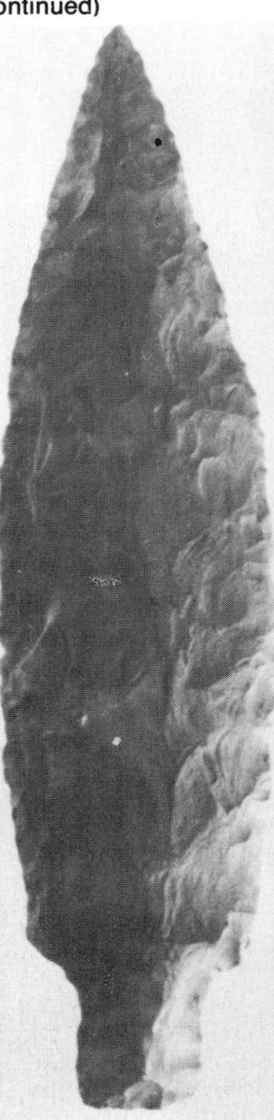

G8, $90-$150
Coffee Lake, Florence, AL.

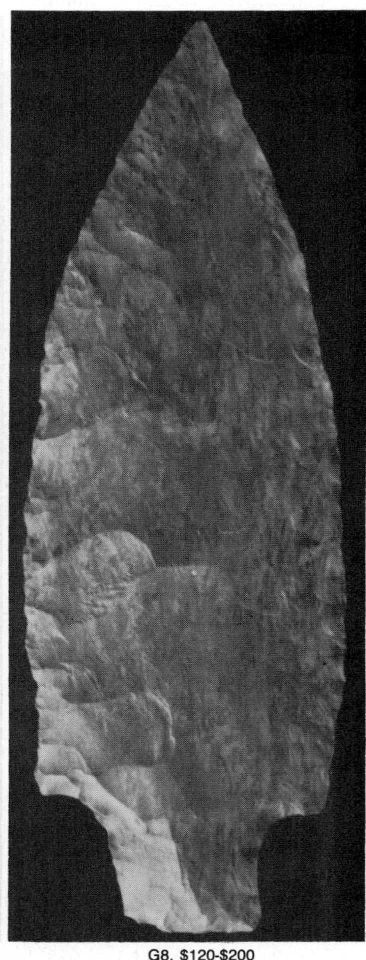

G8, $120-$200
Humphreys Co., TN.

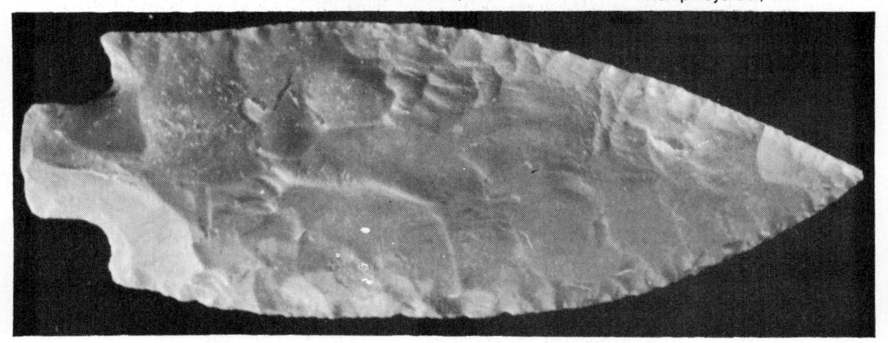

G8, $80-$120
Morgan Co., AL.

G8, $120-$200
Lauderdale Co., AL.

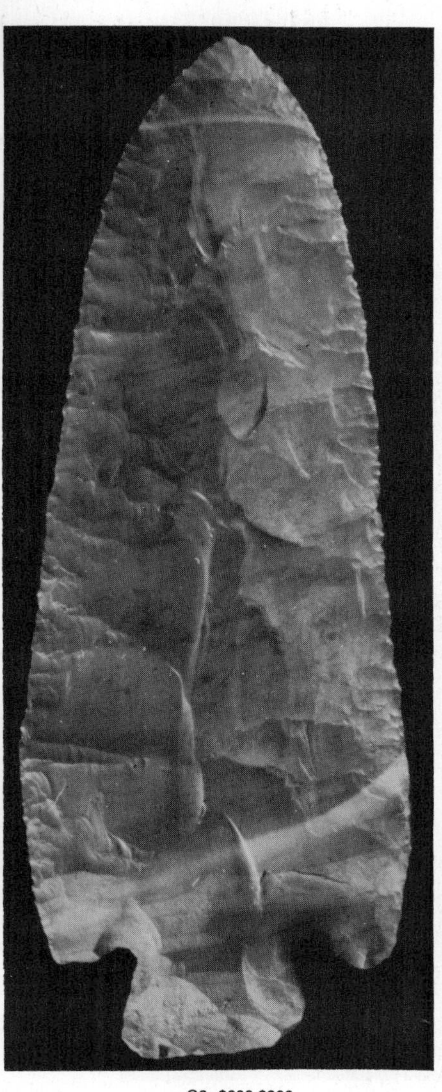

G9, $600-$900
Hardin Co., TN. Rare red, yellow & blue Horse Creek chert. One of the largest points known out of this material.

G7, $60-$100
Coffee Lake, AL.

MULE EAR - Early Archaic, 9000 - 6000 B.P.

(Also see Fort Ancient Knife)

G6, $40-$60
Wasco Co., OR. The Dalles, Note basal thinning

G8, $80-$125
Wasco Co., OR., The Dalles. Note basal thinning.

G8, $90-$150
Wasco Co., Or., The Dalles.

G9, $150-$250
Wasco Co., OR., The Dalles. Classic. Note basal thinning.

LOCATION: Northwestern states. **DESCRIPTION:** A medium size auriculate point with a thinned concave base land expanding shoulders. Shoulders are more prominent on resharpened forms. **I.D. KEY:** Broad base, early flaking.

NEBO HILL - Early Archaic, 7500 - 6000 B.P.

(Also see Agate Basin, Lerma, Rio Grande and Sedalia)

G5, $80-$120
Mexico. Obsidian. Note diagonal flaking.

G6, $150-$250
Mexico. Note oblique flaking.

G9, $450-$600
St. Louis Co., MO.

LOCATION: Western and Midwestern states and Mexico. **DESCRIPTION:** A large size, narrow, lanceolate blade with convex sides and a convex, straight or concave base. Some examples have collateral flaking.

NEW MARKET - Woodland, 3000 - 1000 B.P.

(Also see Bradley, Duval, Flint River and Schild Spike, and Randolph)

G2, $1-$2 Ft. Payne, AL.

G5, $3-$5 Limestone Co., AL.

G3, $2-$3 Ft. Payne, AL.

G4, $2-$4 Hamilton Co., TN.

G4, $2-$4 Madison Co., AL.

G5, $3-$5 Humphreys Co., TN.

G7, $6-$10 Limestone Co., AL.

G8, $15-$25 Morgan Co., AL.

G10, $150-$200 New Market, AL. Outstanding form & quality. Needle tip.

G8, $15-$25 Walker Co., AL.

G7, $6-$12 Decatur, AL.

G3, $2-$3 Meigs Co., TN.

LOCATION: Southeastern states. **DESCRIPTION:** A small to medium size point with tapered shoulders and an extended, rounded base. Shoulders are usually asymmetrical with one higher than the other.

NEWNAN - Mid-Archaic, 7000 - 3000 B.P.

(Also see Adena-Dickson, Alachua, Cypress Creek, Hardee Beveled, Hillsborough, Levy, Marion, Morrow Mountain, Oauchita and Putnam)

G3, $40-$60
Alachua Co., FL.

G3, $35-$60
Lake Mattie, FL.

G3, $35-$50
Marion Co., FL.

G4, $50-$80
Hillsborough Co., FL.

G5, $60-$90
Hillsborough Co., FL. Coral.

G4, $50-$80
Hillsborough Co., FL.

LOCATION: Southern Southeastern states. **DESCRIPTION:** A medium to large size, broad, stemmed point with a short to long contracting base. Shoulders are barbed. Stems have contracted, straight sides and a straight base. *Newnans* with *Marion*-type rounded bases represent a *Newnan/Marion* cross type.

G5, $80-$125
Marion Co., FL. Coral.

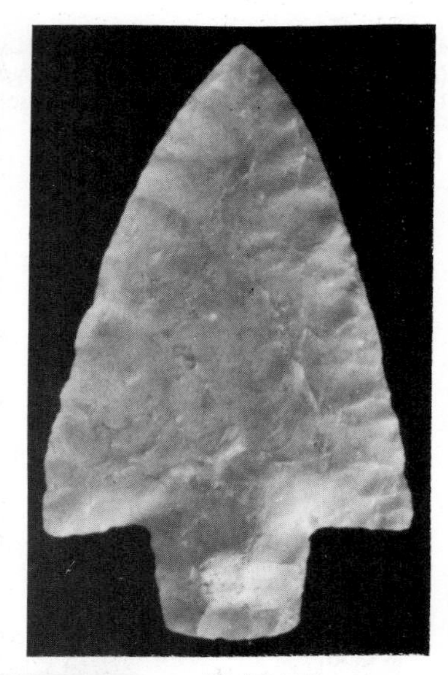

G5, $80-$125
Hillsborough Co., FL.

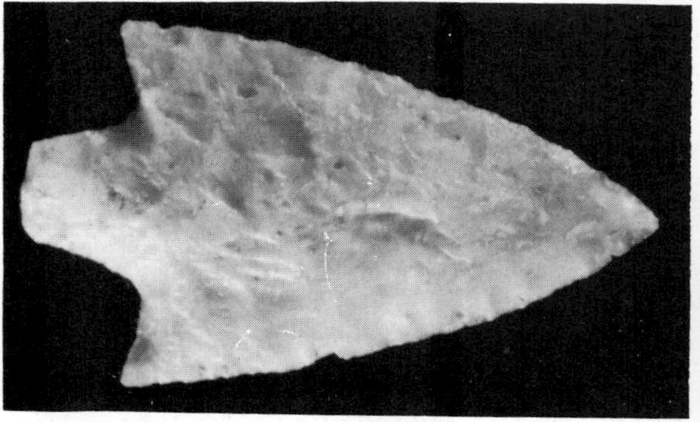

G4, $60-$90
N. Cent. FL.

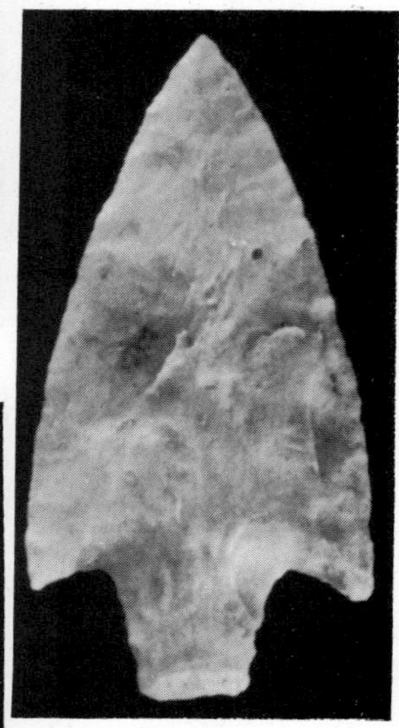

G5, $80-$140
Newnan Lake, Alachua Co., FL.

G4, $60-$90
Hillsborough Co., FL.

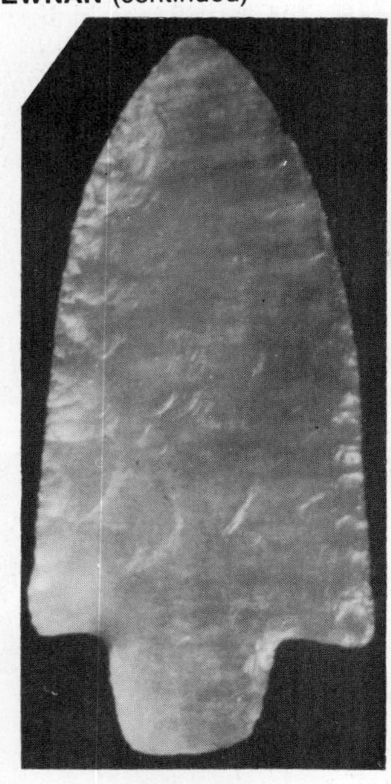

G7, $200-$350
NW Cent. FL. Coral.

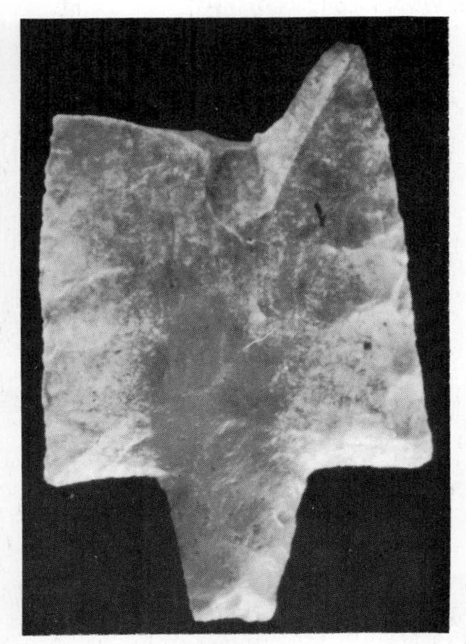

G1, $10-$25
St. Johns Rv., FL. Broken.

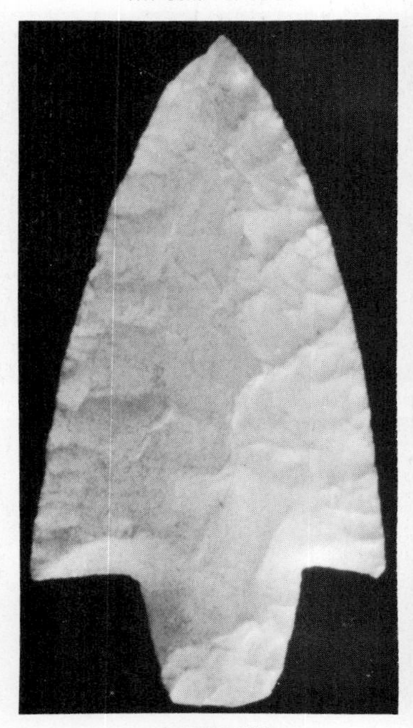

G6, $160-$250
Hillsborough Co., FL.

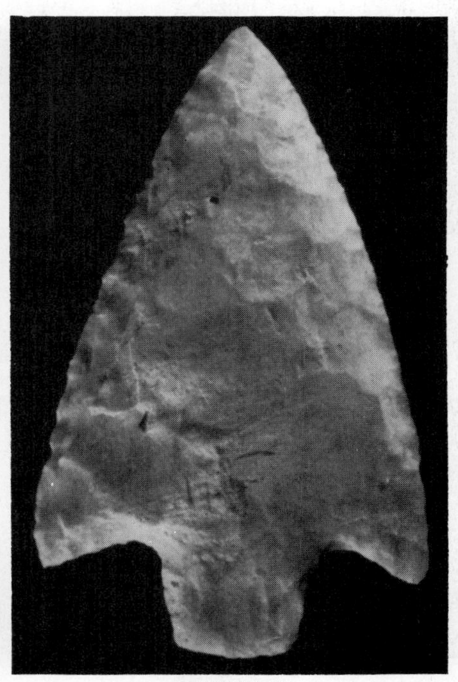

G7, $180-$300
Pasco Co., FL.

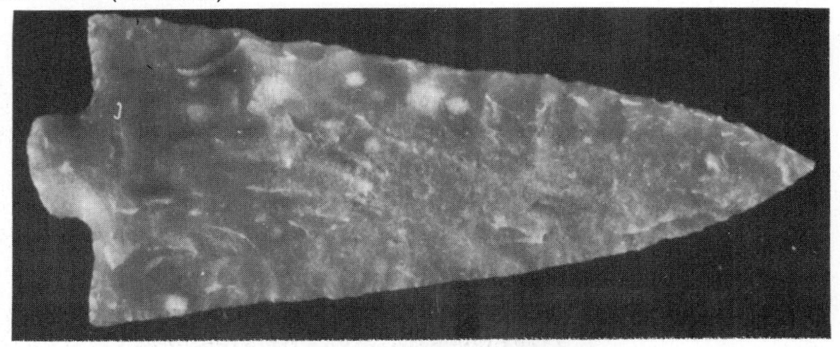

G7, $200-$350, Jasper Co., SC.

G6, $160-$250, Pasco Co., FL. Repair on right side of blade near base.

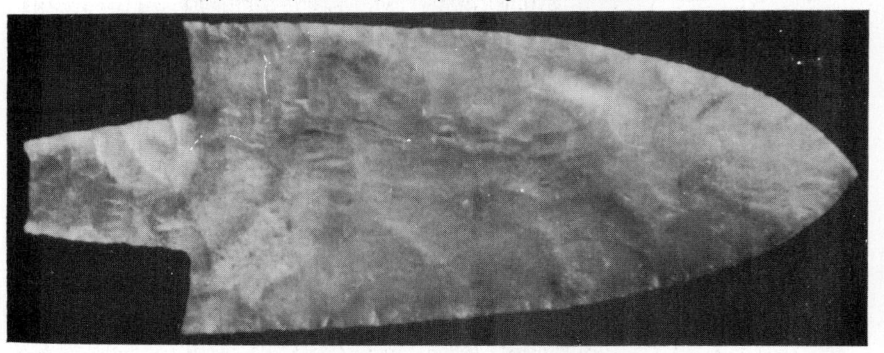

G10, $2000-$3500, NW Cent. FL. Outstanding example. Classic.

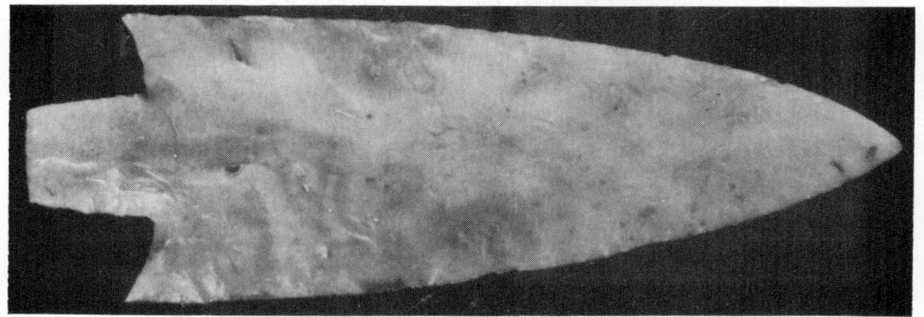

G10, $2500-$4000, NW Cent. FL. Excellent. Classic.

G10, $1000-$1700
NW Cent. FL.

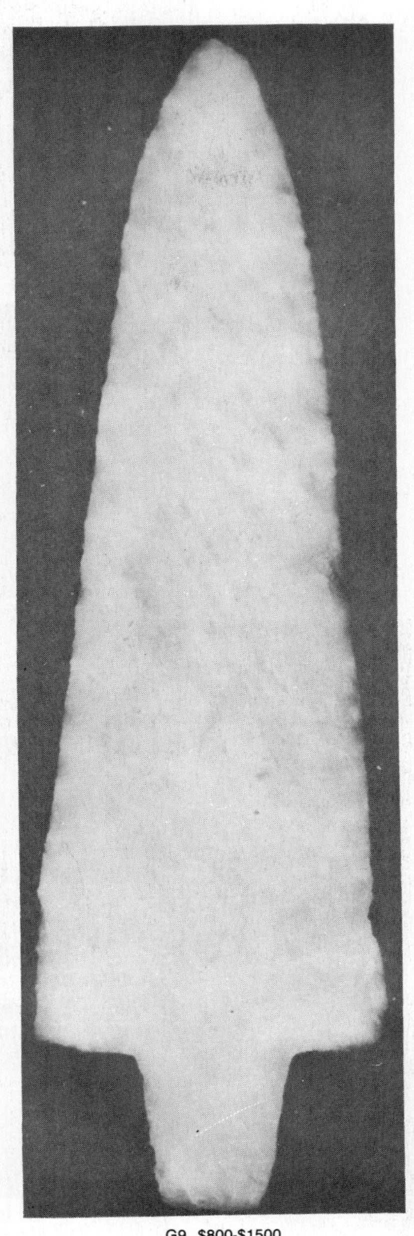

G9, $800-$1500
Marion Co., FL. Agatized coral.

NODENA - Mississippian to Historic, 600 - 400 B.P.

(Also see Dardanelle, Guntersville & Lozenge)

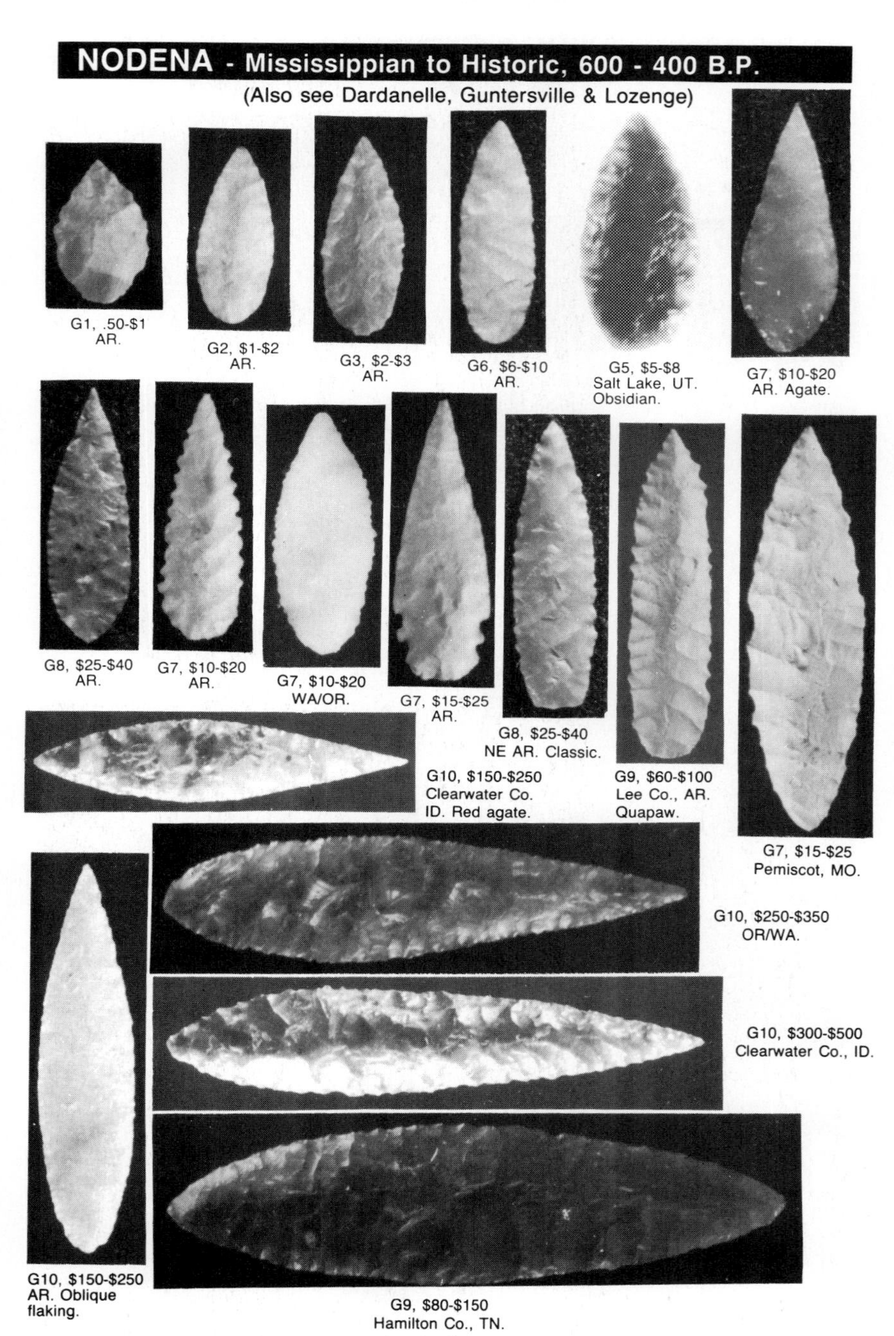

G1, .50-$1
AR.

G2, $1-$2
AR.

G3, $2-$3
AR.

G6, $6-$10
AR.

G5, $5-$8
Salt Lake, UT.
Obsidian.

G7, $10-$20
AR. Agate.

G8, $25-$40
AR.

G7, $10-$20
AR.

G7, $10-$20
WA/OR.

G7, $15-$25
AR.

G8, $25-$40
NE AR. Classic.

G10, $150-$250
Clearwater Co.
ID. Red agate.

G9, $60-$100
Lee Co., AR.
Quapaw.

G7, $15-$25
Pemiscot, MO.

G10, $250-$350
OR/WA.

G10, $300-$500
Clearwater Co., ID.

G10, $150-$250
AR. Oblique
flaking.

G9, $80-$150
Hamilton Co., TN.

LOCATION: Midwestern states. **DESCRIPTION:** A small to medium size, narrow, thin, elliptical shaped point with a pointed to rounded base. Some examples have oblique, parallel flaking. Called *Tampa* in Florida. Used by the Quapaw Indians.

NOLAN - Mid-Archaic to Woodland, 6000 - 1500 B.P.

(Also see Bulverde, Kent, Lange, Travis and Zorra)

G6, $15-$25
Austin, TX.

G7, $25-$40
Comanche Co., TX.

G5, $10-$15
Travis Co., TX.

G7, $25-$40
Bell Co., TX.

G7, $25-$40
Austin, TX.

G6, $15-$25
Comanche Co., TX.

LOCATION: Midwestern states. **DESCRIPTION:** A medium to large size, stemmed point with a needle like point. Shoulders are tapered to rounded. The stem is unique in that it is steeply beveled on one side of each face. **I.D. KEY:** Beveled stem.

NOLAN (continued)

G9, $150-$250
Bell Co., TX.

G9, $90-$150
Austin, TX.

G9, $90-$150
Comanche Co., TX.

G8, $40-$75
Austin, TX.

G7, $20-$35
Comanche Co., TX.

G7, $20-$35
Bell Co., TX.

NOLAN (continued)

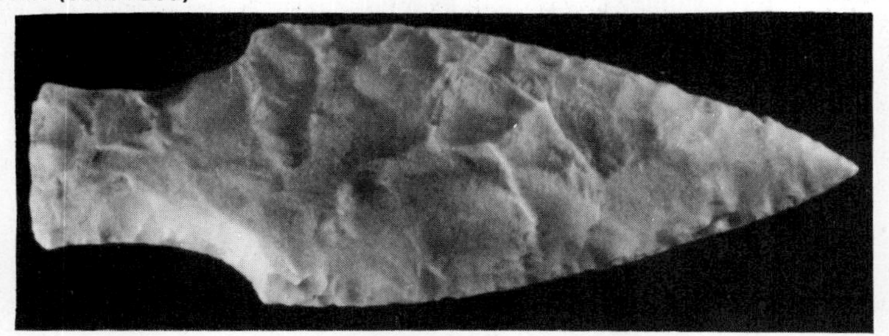

G9, $90-$150
Austin, TX.

G9, $120-$200
Austin, TX.

G10, $250-$400
Comanche Co., TX.

NOLICHUCKY - Woodland, 3000 - 1500 B.P.

(Also see Camp Creek, Candy Creek, Copena Auriculate, Greeneville and Yadkin)

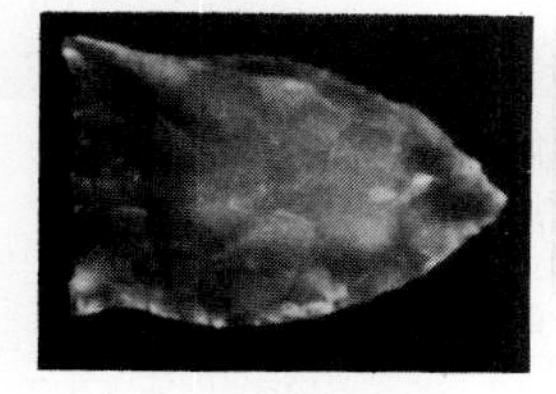

G5, $5-$8
Bristol, VA.

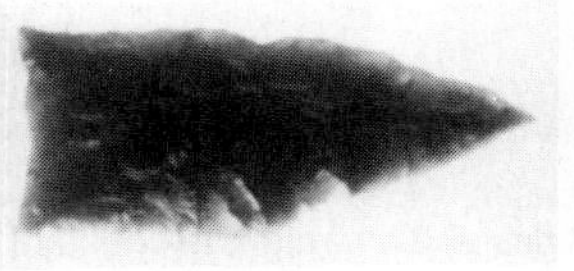

G6, $6-$10
Bristol, VA.

G5, $5-$8
Newport, TN.

NOLICHUCKY (continued)

G6, $6-$10
Bristol, VA.

G6, $6-$10
Meigs Co., TN.

G10, $40-$60
Bristol, VA.

G10, $40-$60
Cent. NC.

G7, $8-$12
Meigs Co., TN.

G8, $8-$15
Clarksville, TN.
Classic form.

G9, $10-$20
Dayton, TN.

G9, $15-$25
W. TN.

G7, $8-$12
W. TN.

G9, $10-$20
Whitwell, TN.

G7, $8-$12
Pulaski Co., KY.

LOCATION: Southeastern states. **DESCRIPTION:** A small to medium size, triangular point with recurved blade edges and a straight to concave base. Most examples have small pointed ears at the basal corners. Bases could be ground. Believed to have evolved from *Candy Creek* points and later developed into *Camp Creek, Greeneville* and *Guntersville* points. Found with *Adena, Ebenezer, Camp Creek, Candy Creek* and *Greeneville* in caches (Rankin site, Cocke Co. TN). **I.D. KEY:** Thickness and hafting area.

NORTH - Woodland, 2200 - 1600 B.P.

(Also see Hopewell, Ross and Snyders)

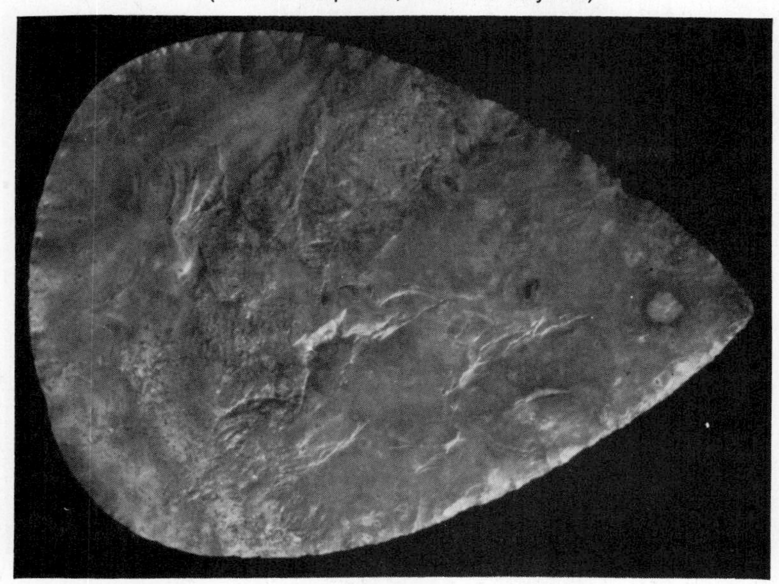

G9, $500-$800
MO.

G8, $250-$400
Pike Co., IL.

LOCATION: Midwestern to Eastern states. **DESCRIPTION:** A large, thin, elliptical, broad, well made blade with a concave base. This type is usually found in caches and is related to the *Snyders* point of the Hopewell culture.

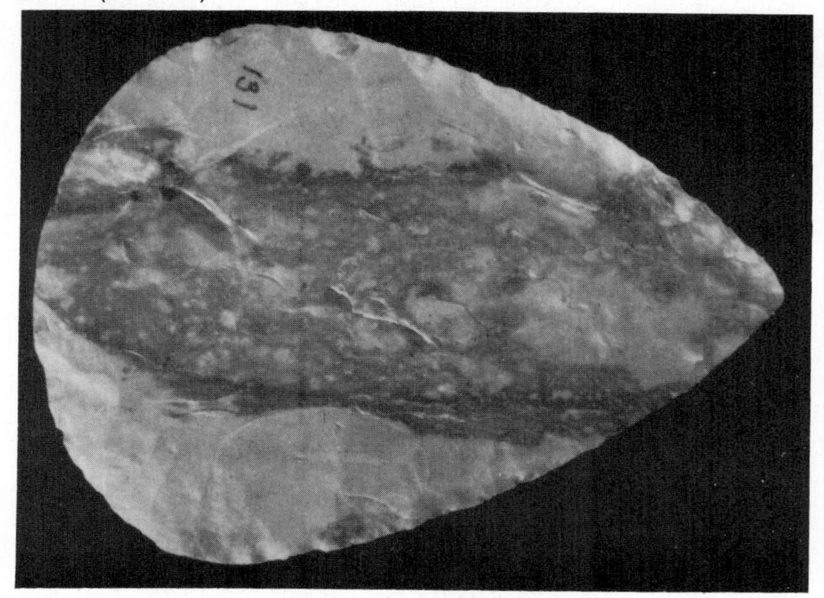

G7, $200-$350
Osage Co., MO.

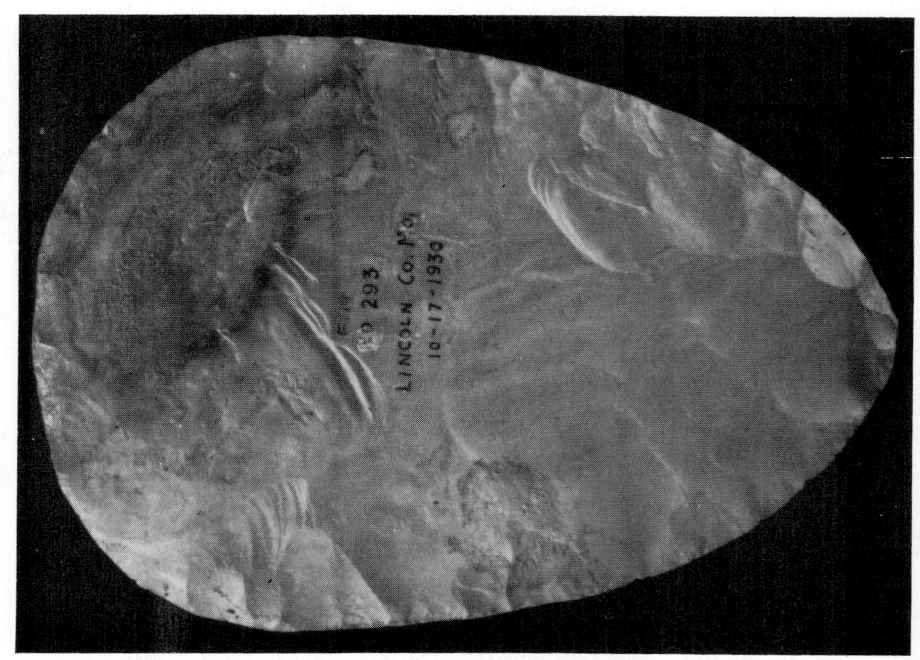

G7, $200-$350
Lincoln Co., MO.

NORTHERN SIDE NOTCHED - Early to Late Archaic 9000 - 4000 B.P.

(Also see Big Sandy, Desert Side-Notched & Fox Ear)

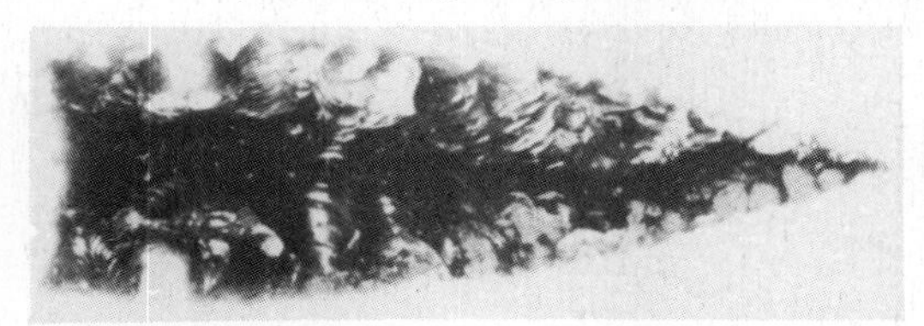

G9, $250-$400
Lake Co., OR., Crump Lake.
Obsidian.

LOCATION: Northwestern states. **DESCRIPTION:** A medium to large size, narrow side-notched point with early forms showing basal grinding and parallel flaking.

NOTTOWAY RIVER (See MacCorkle)

NOVA - Woodland to Mississippian, 1600 - 1000 B.P.

(Also see Durant's Bend and Washington)

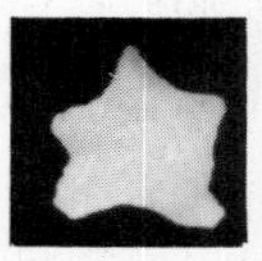

G7, $3-$5
Dallas Co., AL.

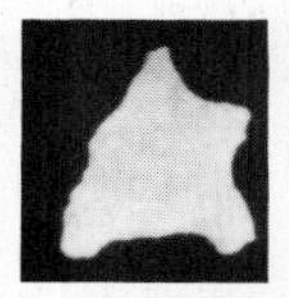

G2, .25-.50
Dallas Co., AL.

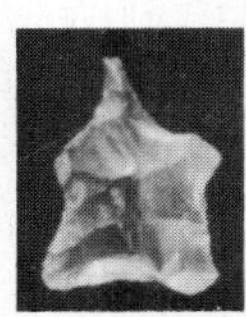

G3, .50-$1
Dallas Co., AL.

G4, $1-$2
Dallas Co., AL.

LOCATION: Southeastern states. **DESCRIPTION:** A small point shaped like a five pointed star.

NUCKOLLS (See Dalton-Nuckolls)

OAUCHITA - Woodland, 3000 - 1500 B.P.

(Also see Levy and Newnan)

G4, $15-$25
Henry Co., AL.

OAUCHITA (continued)

LOCATION: Southern Southeastern states. **DESCRIPTION:** A medium to large size, broad, point with a short contracted stem and drooping shoulders.

G10, $2500-$4000
Red River Co., TX. Quartzite.
Outstanding example.

OCALA - Woodland, 2500 - 1500 B.P.

(Also see Gibson, Hopewell, Lafayette & Snyders)

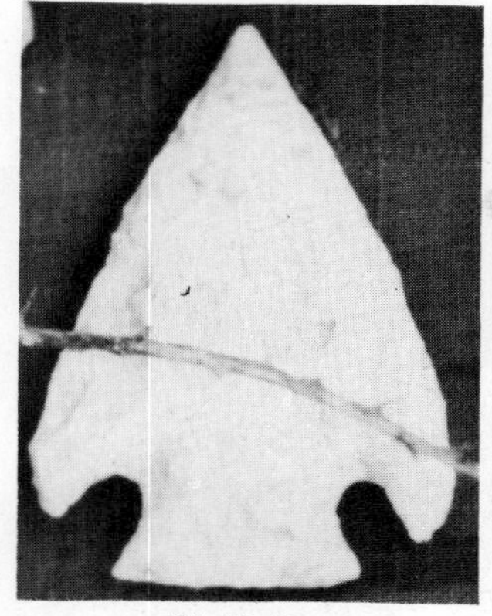

G5, $50-$80
Marion Co., FL.

G3, $12-$20
Marion Co., FL.

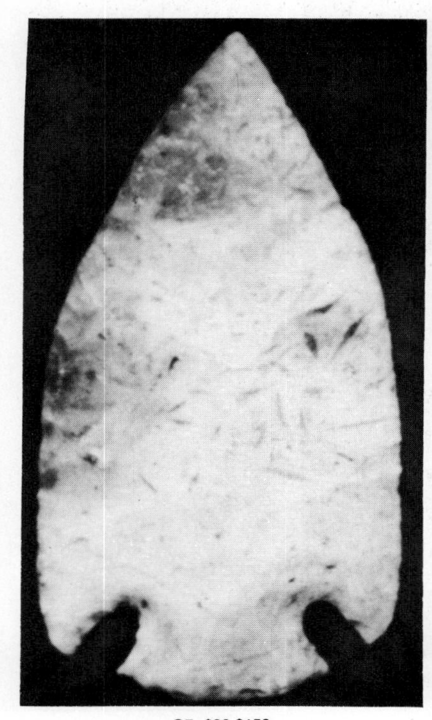

G7, $90-$150
Marion Co., FL.

G8, $150-$250
Marion Co., FL.

LOCATION: Southern Southeastern states. **DESCRIPTION:** A medium to large size corner notched blade. Basal stem usually occurs with sharp corners.

OHIO DOUBLE NOTCHED - Woodland, 3000 - 2000 B.P.

(Also see Benton, Evans and Leighton)

G5, $20-$35
OH.

G7, $50-$80
OH.

G7, $40-$60
Adair Co., KY.

G9, $250-$400
OH.

LOCATION: Ohio and surrounding states. **DESCRIPTION:** A medium to large size, narrow, rather crude, point with side notches on both sides and a short base that is usually notched.

O'LENO - Woodland, 2000 - 800 B.P.

(Also see Matamoros, Tortugas, Valina and Yadkin)

G3, $2-$3
Henry Co., AL.

G6, $10-$20
Henry Co., AL.

G5, $8-$12
Henry Co., AL.

G5, $8-$12
Silver Rv., FL.

G4, $5-$8
NW FL.

G8, $35-$50
Sante Fe Rv., FL.

LOCATION: Southern Southeastern states. **DESCRIPTION:** A medium size, broad, triangle point with a straight to slightly concave base.

ORIENT - Late Archaic to Woodland, 4000 - 2500 B.P.

(Also see Big Sandy Auricuiate, Oxbow and Rowan)

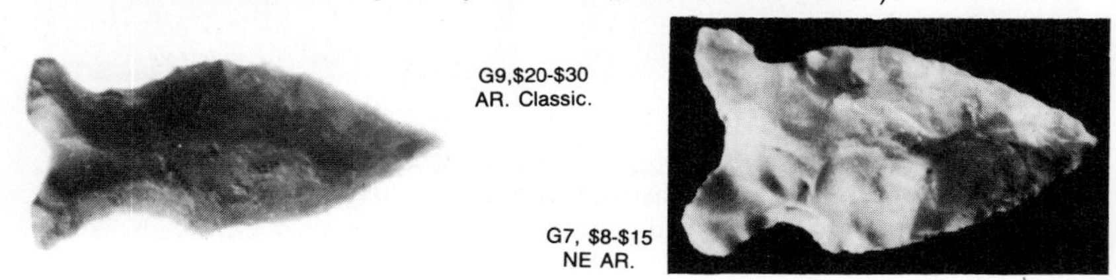

G9,$20-$30
AR. Classic.

G7, $8-$15
NE AR.

ORIENT (continued)

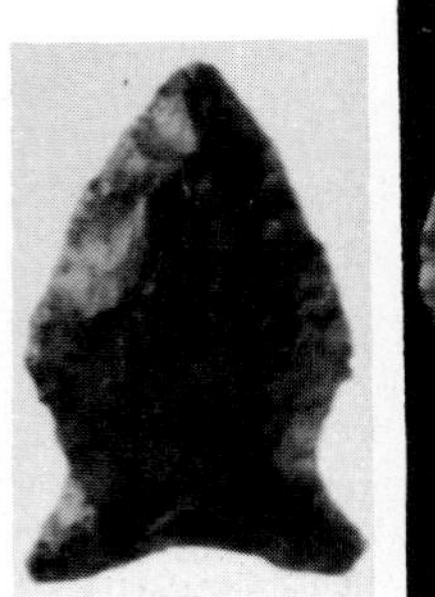
G6, $8-$12
Perry Co., TN.

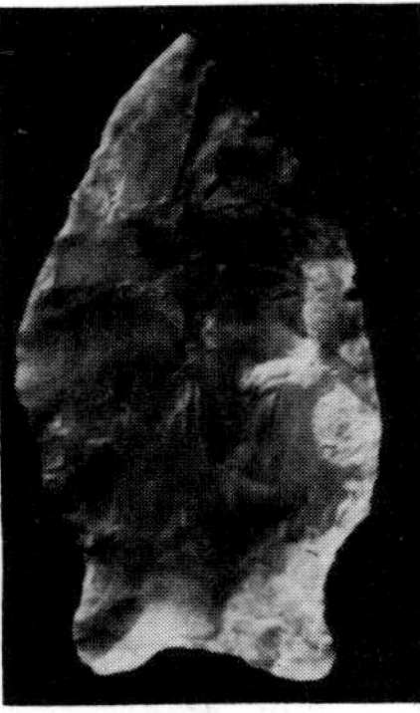
G6, $8-$12
NE AR.

G9, $20-$30
Madison Co., AL.

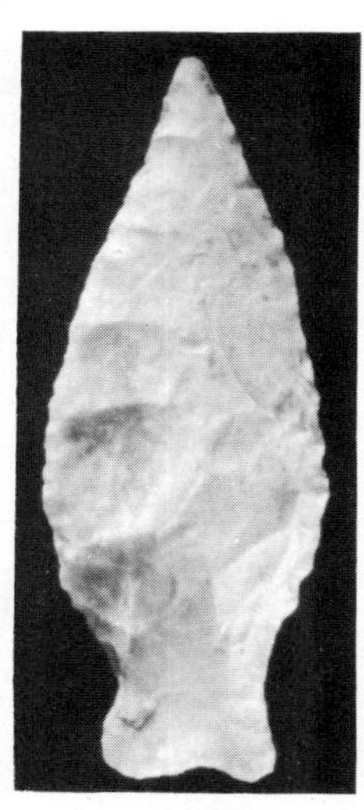
G7, $10-$20
Comanche Co., TX.

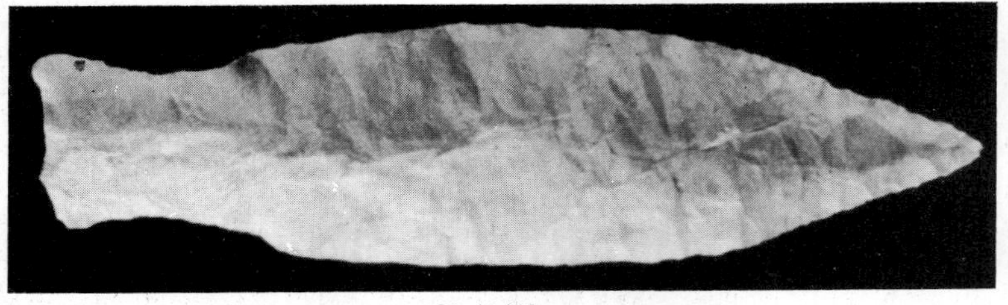
G6, $8-$12
Humphreys Co., TN. Dover chert.

LOCATION: Midwestern to Eastern states. **DESCRIPTION:** A small to medium size point with wide, shallow side notches and an auriculate fishtail base.

OSCEOLA - Early to mid-Archaic, 7000 - 5000 B.P.

(Also see Big Sandy, Cache River, Godar, Hemphill, Raddatz and Savage Cave)

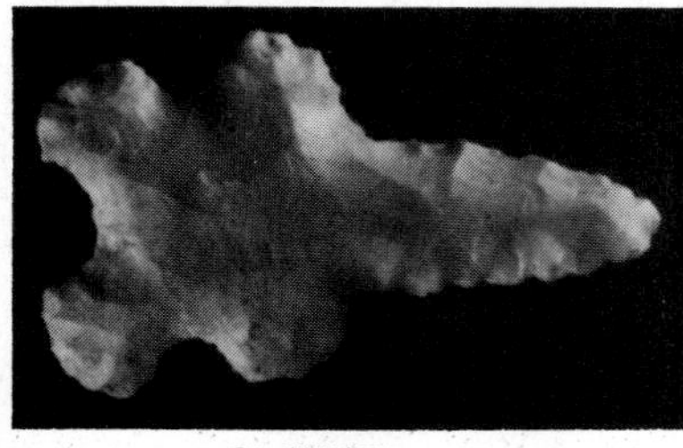
G2, $15-$25
MO. Drill.

G3, $20-$35
MO.

LOCATION: Midwestern to Southeastern states. **DESCRIPTION:** A large size, narrow, side notched point with parallel sides on longer examples and a straight to concave to notched base which could be ground. **I.D. KEY:** Always have early flaking to the middle of the blade.

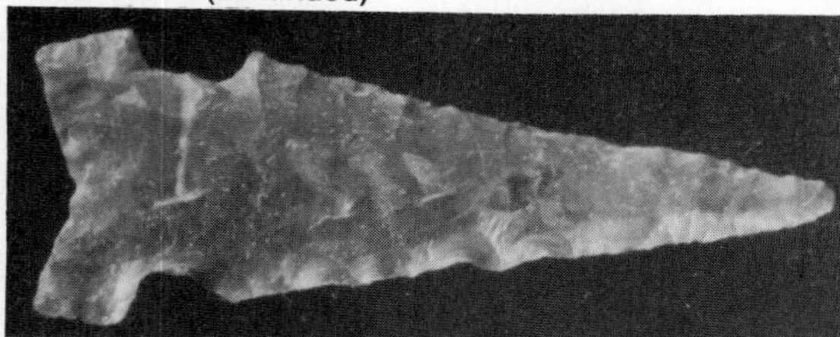

G4, $35-$60
TX/AR.

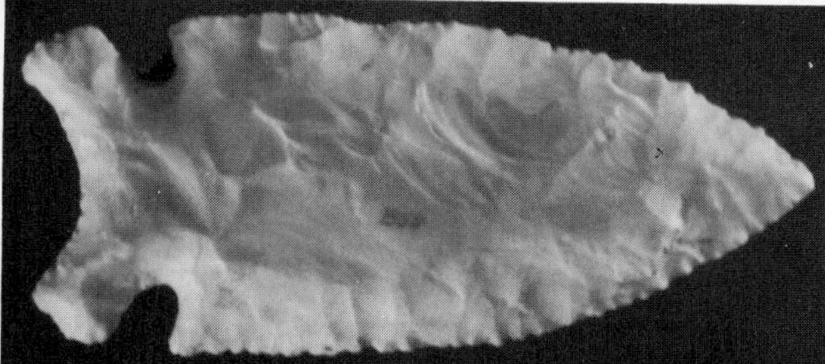

G6, $90-$150
MO.

G3, $15-$25, Morgan Co., AL.
Restored tip. IN AL type book.

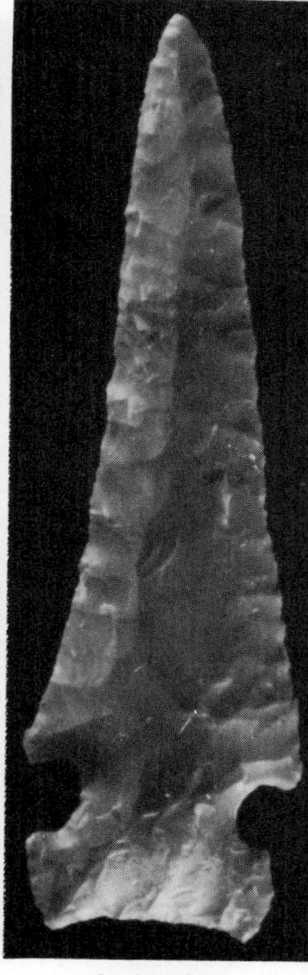

G8, $200-$350
Sumner Co., TN.

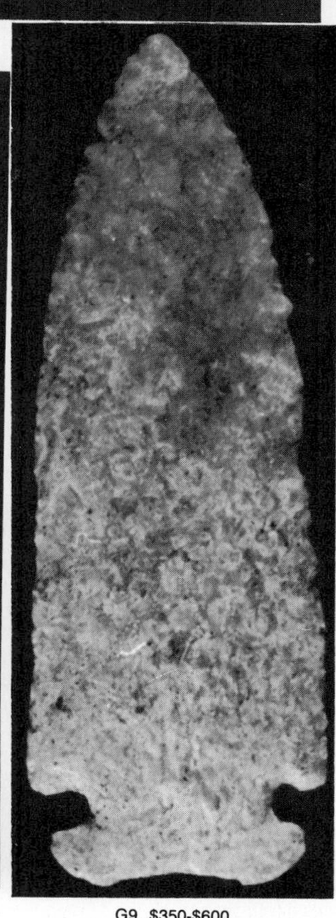

G9, $350-$600
Keokuk Co., IA.

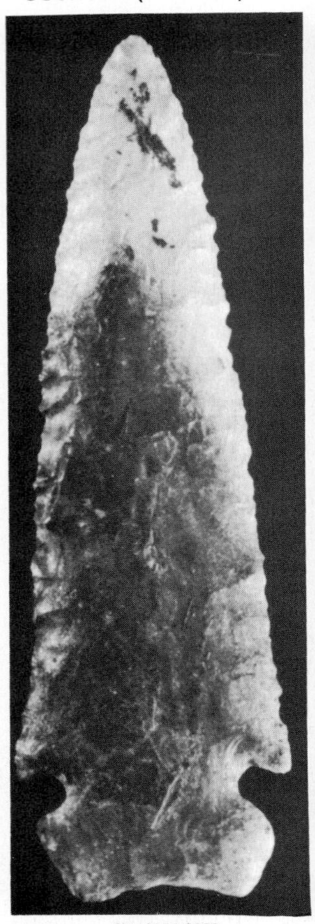

G9, $350-$600
Schuyler Co., IL.

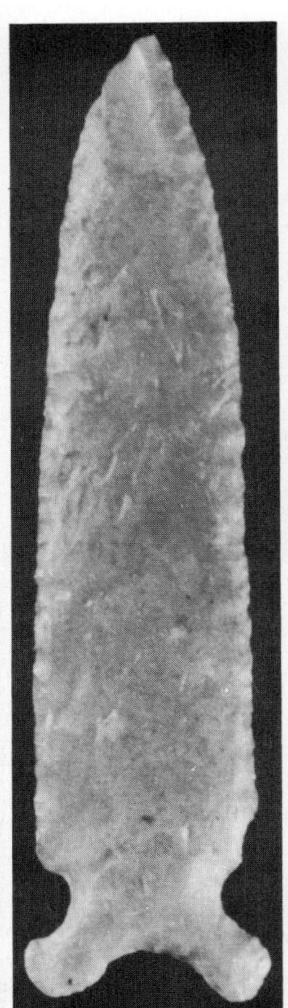

G7, $120-$200
MO.

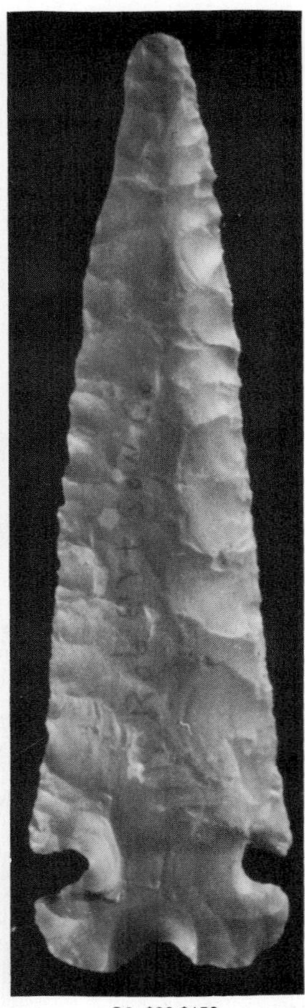

G6, $90-$150
Robertson Co., TN.

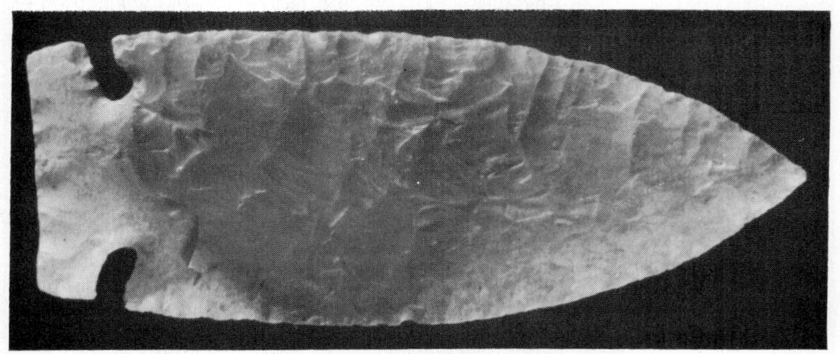

G9, $600-$1000
Scott Co., KY.

G5, $70-$100
Cass Co., IL. Torque blade.

G7, $150-$250
Cent. IL.

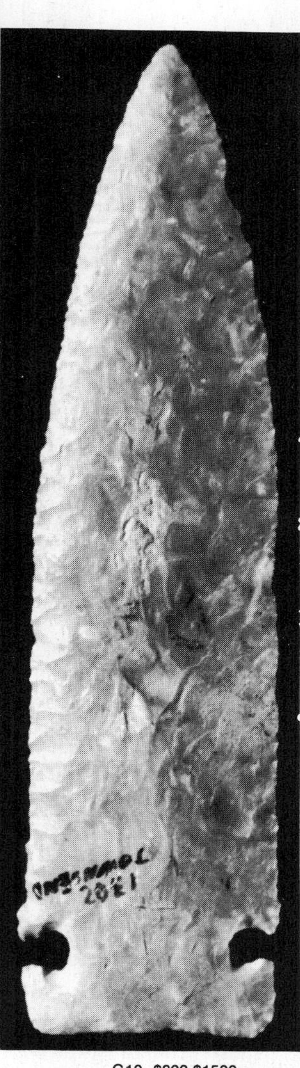

G10, $800-$1500
Clarksville, TN. Outstanding example. Classic.

OSCEOLA-GREENBRIER - Transitional Paleo, 9500 - 6000 B.P.

(Also see Bolen, Greenbrier and Osceola)

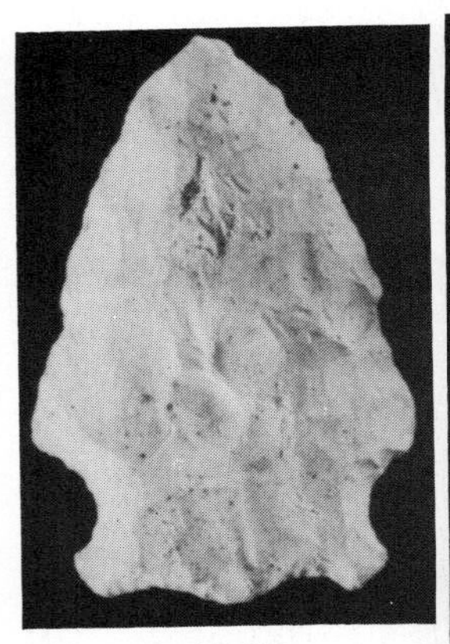

G4, $20-$40
Type I. N. Cent. FL.

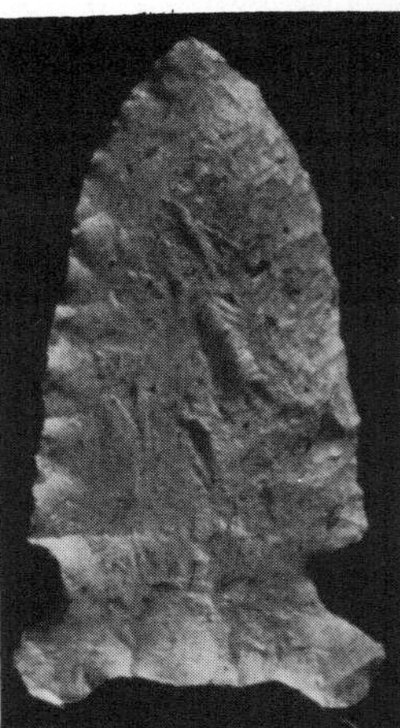

G7, $120-$200
Type I. Sante Fe Rv., FL.

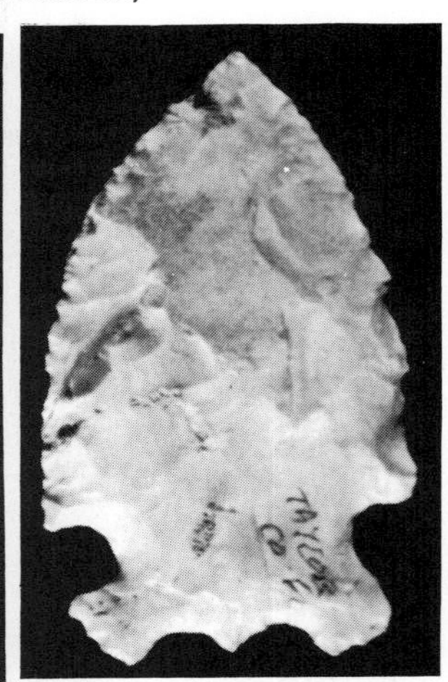

G5, $50-$90
Type I. Taylor Co., FL.

G7, $120-$200
Type I. NW Cent. FL.

G9, $350-$600
Type I. NW Cent. FL.

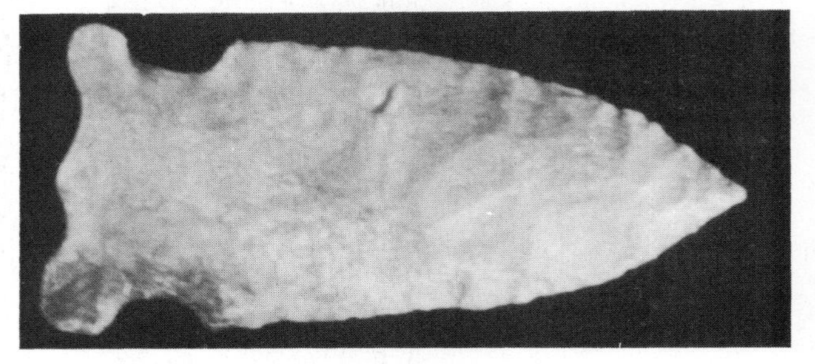

LOCATION: Southern Southeastern states. **DESCRIPTION:** A medium to large size, broad, side-notched point with two base variations. The base is either concave or has two shallow notches creating a high point in the center. Bases and notches are usually ground. This type is found in the same layer with *Bolen* points in Florida.

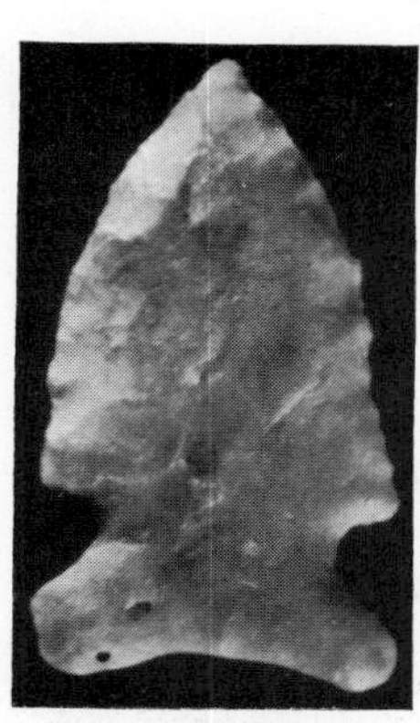

G4, $20-$40
Type II, Santa Fe
River, FL.

G5, $50-$90
Type II. Sante Fe Rv., FL.

G7, $120-$200
Type II. Sante Fe Rv., FL.

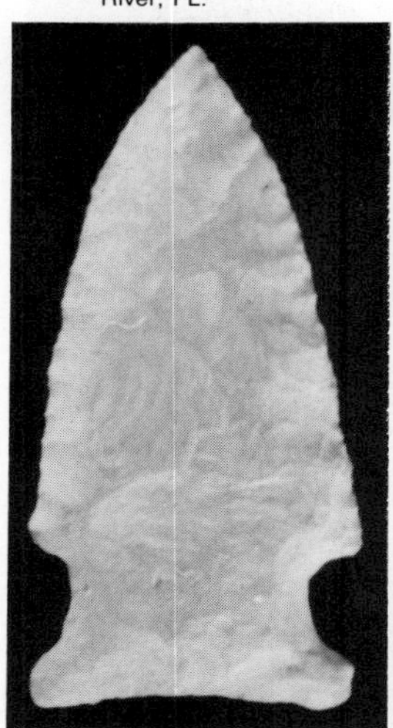

G8, $150-$250
Type II. Pasco Co., FL.

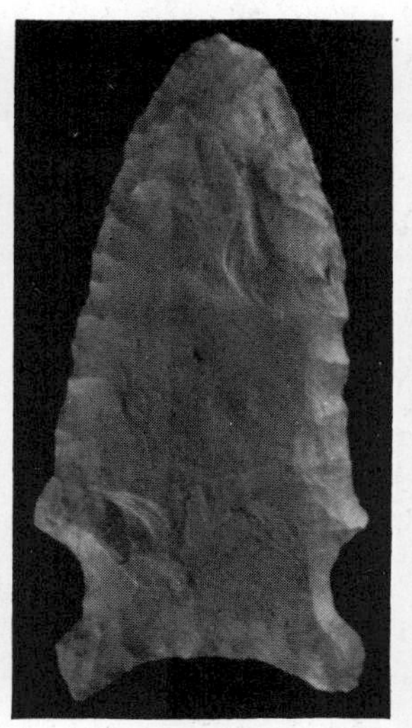

G7, $120-$200
Type II. Sante Fe Rv., FL.

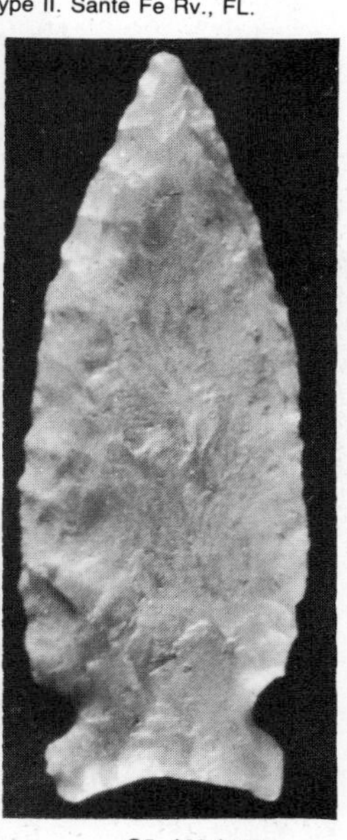

G5, $60-$100
Type II. N. FL.

G7, $120-$200
Type II. Sante Fe Rv., FL.

G8, $200-$300
Type II. NW Cent. FL.

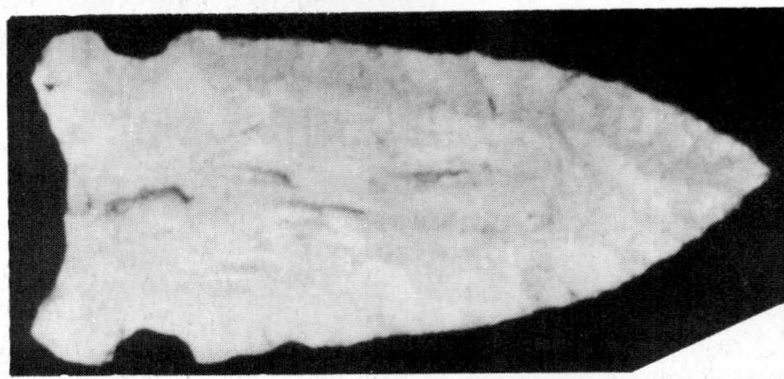

G7, $120-$250
Type II. NW Cent. FL.

G5, $50-$90
Type II. Marion Co., FL.

G8, $250-$350
Type II. Citrus Co., FL.

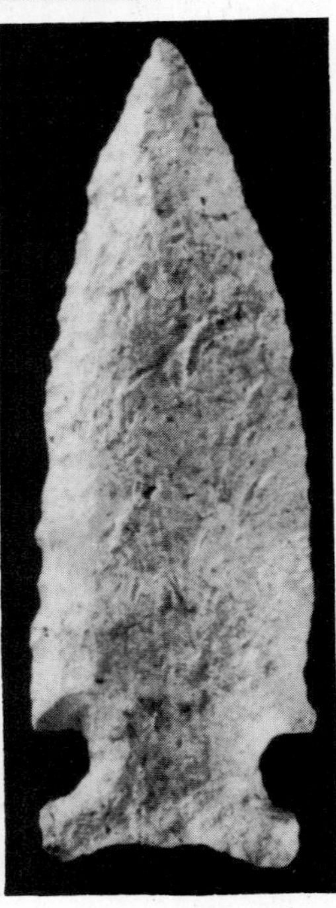

G8, $200-$300
Sante Fe Rv., FL.

OTTER CREEK - Mid to Late Archaic, 6000 - 3500 B.P.

(Also see Big Sandy, Godar & Raddatz)

G6, $30-$50
Bethany WV.

LOCATION: Northeastern states. **DESCRIPTION:** A medium to large size, narrow side-notched point.

OXBOW - Late Archaic, 5000 - 3000 B.P.

(Also see Big Sandy Auriculate, Frio, Graham Cave, Orient, Rodgers Side-Hollowed, Rowan & Southampton)

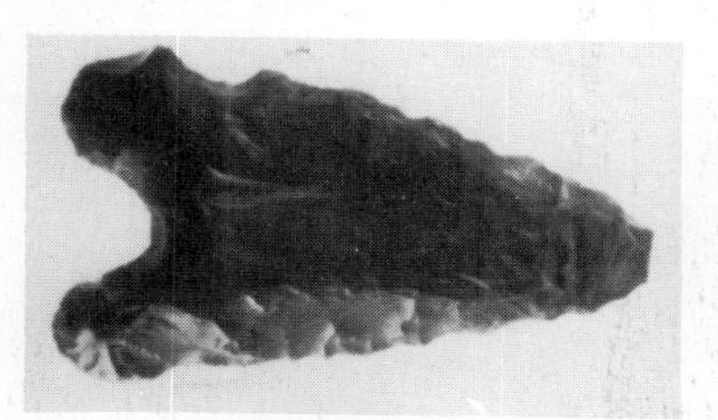

G4, $6-$10
SE TN.

G5, $8-$15
AR.

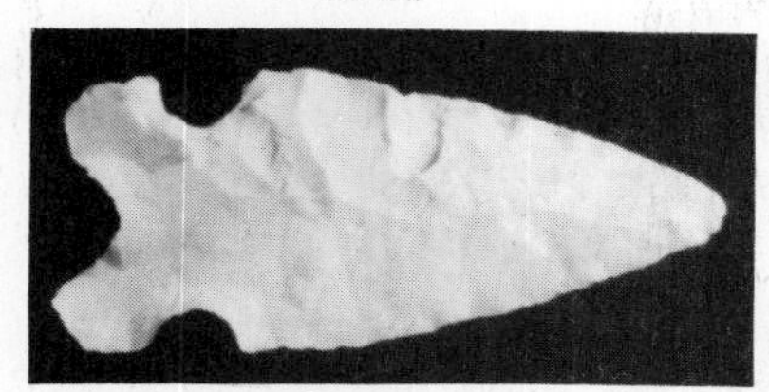

G5, $8-$15
Comanche Co., TX.

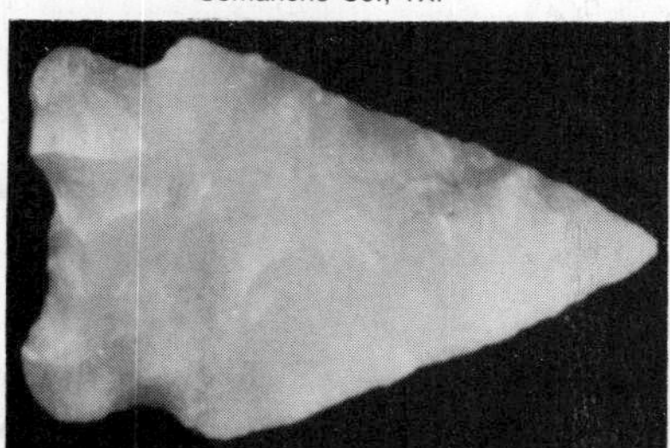

G5, $10-$20
AR. Novaculite.

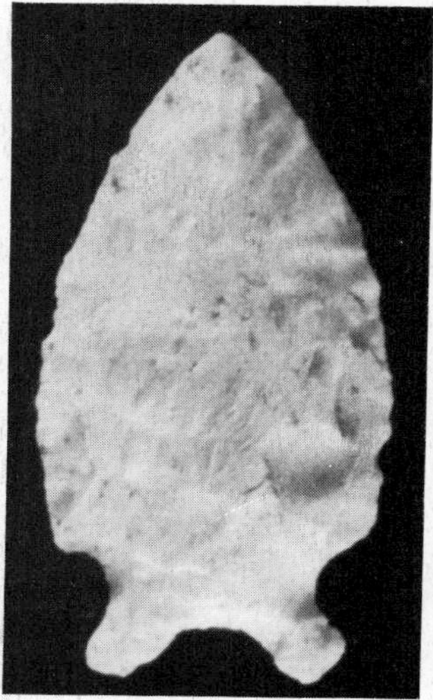

G7, $25-$40
Craighead, AR.

LOCATION: Midwestern states and Canada. **DESCRIPTION:** A small to medium size, side notched, auriculate point with a concave to bifurcated base.

PAINT ROCK VALLEY - Transitional Paleo, 10000 - 6000 B.P.

(Also see Angostura, Cowhouse Slough, Frazier, Hardaway Blade, Jeff, Kinney and, Tortugas)

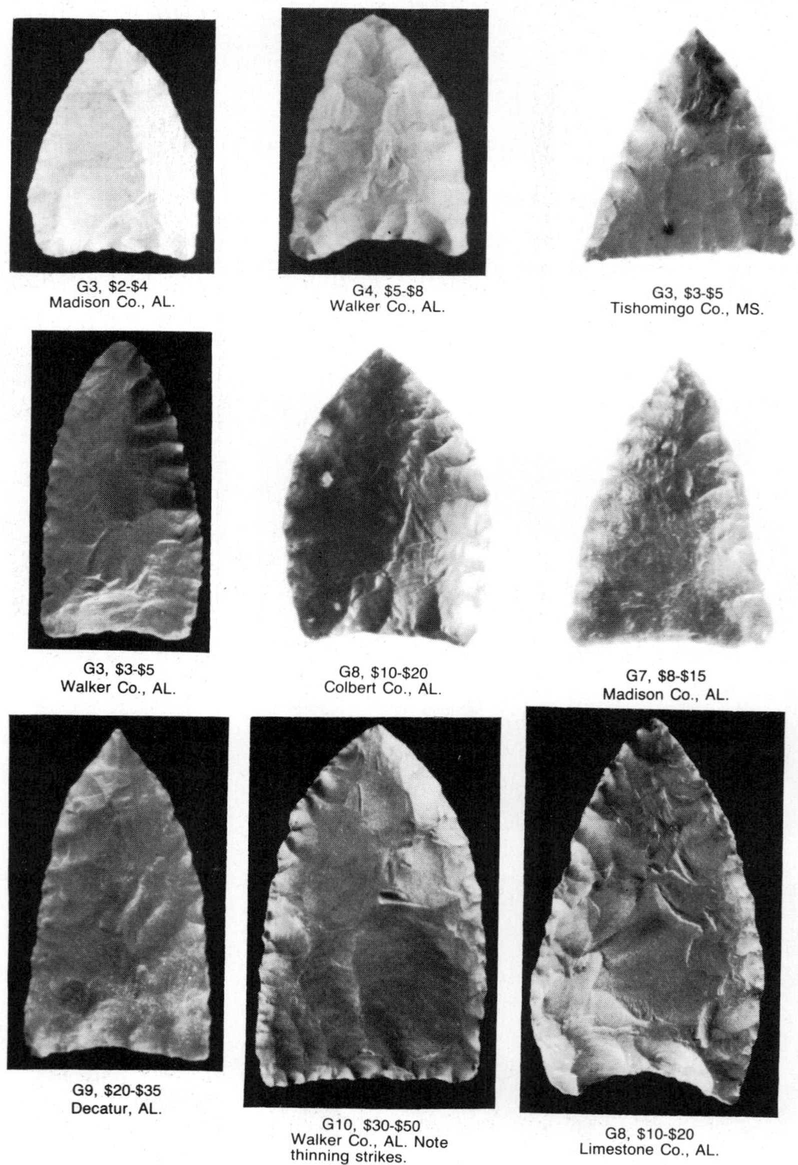

G3, $2-$4
Madison Co., AL.

G4, $5-$8
Walker Co., AL.

G3, $3-$5
Tishomingo Co., MS.

G3, $3-$5
Walker Co., AL.

G8, $10-$20
Colbert Co., AL.

G7, $8-$15
Madison Co., AL.

G9, $20-$35
Decatur, AL.

G10, $30-$50
Walker Co., AL. Note thinning strikes.

G8, $10-$20
Limestone Co., AL.

LOCATION: Southeastern states. **DESCRIPTION:** A medium size, wide, lanceolate point with a concave base. Flaking is usually parallel with fine secondary work on the blade edges. The bases may be multiple fluted, thinned or beveled.

PAISANO - Woodland, 2500 - 1500 B.P.

(Also see Big Sandy and Candy Creek)

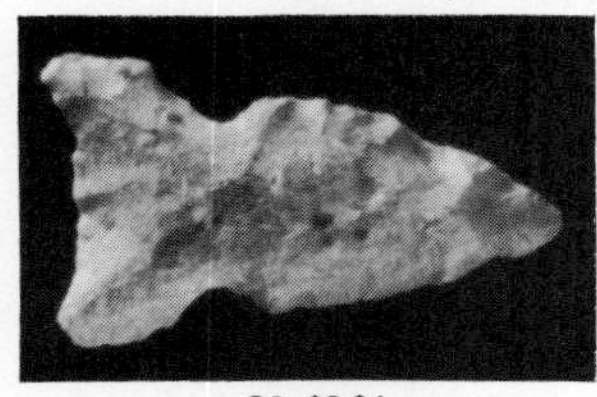

G2, $2-$4
Comanche Co., TX.

G8, $25-$40
Comanche Co., TX. Classic.

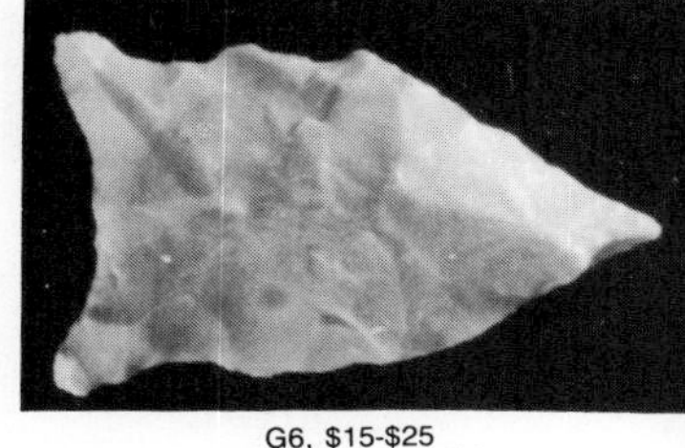

G6, $15-$25
Comanche Co., TX.

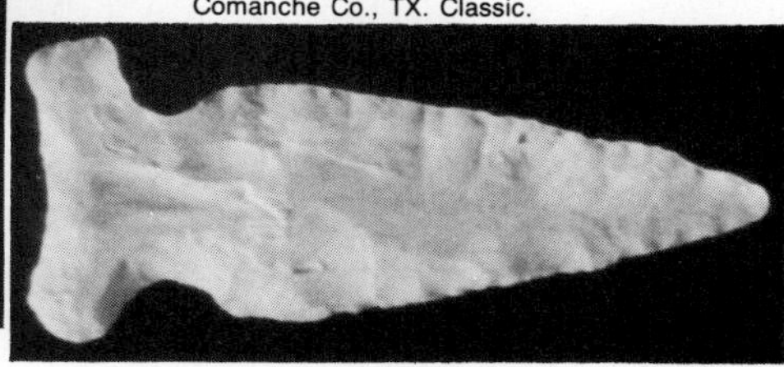

G9, $50-$80
McIntosh Co., OK. Classic.

LOCATION: Midwestern states: **DESCRIPTION:** A medium size side notched to auriculate point with a concave base.

PALEO KNIFE - Transitional Paleo, 10000 - 8000 B.P.

(Also see Kansas Knife, Scraper and Square Knife)

$8-$12
Side 1. Florence, AL.

Side 2

PALEO KNIFE (continued)

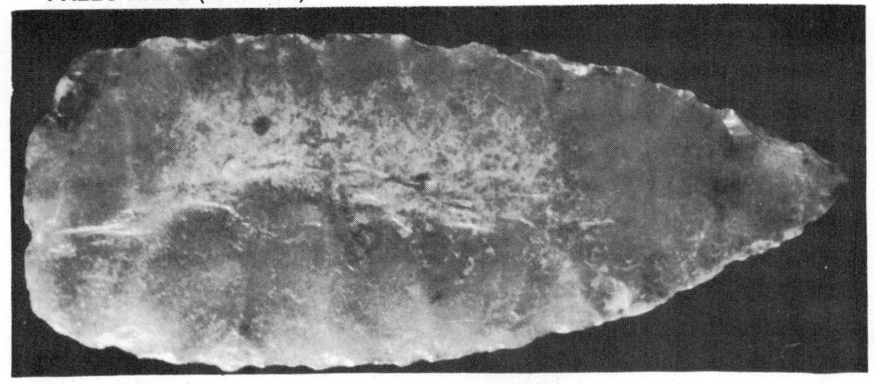

$60-$100, Cortes, CA. Agate. Very thin. Note early parallel transverse flaking.

LOCATION: All of North America. **DESCRIPTION:** A large size lanceolate blade finished with broad parallel flakes. Some examples are uniface, being made from large flakes. These are found on Paleo sites in Northern Alabama and Western Tennessee and were probably used as knives.

PALMER - Early Archaic, 9000 - 6000 B.P.

(Also see Autauga, Ecusta, Hardaway-Palmer, Kirk Corner Notched, Pine Tree, San Patrice and Taylor)

G3, $10-$20
Union Co., SC.
Crystal.

G2, $8-$12
Union Co., SC.
Crystal.

G4, $12-$25
Alexander City, AL.
Crystal.

G3, $10-$18
Newberry Co., SC.
Crystal.

G3, $10-$20
Anderson Co., SC.
Crystal.

G5, $18-$30
Wilson Co., NC.

G3, $10-$20
Surry Co., NC.

G4, $12-$20
Wayne Co., NC.

G4, $12-$20
Wayne Co., NC.

LOCATION: Southeastern states. **DESCRIPTION:** A small size, corner notched, triangular point with a ground concave, convex or straight base. Many are serrated and large examples would fall under the *Pine Tree* or *Kirk* type. This type developed from *Hardaway* in North Carolina where cross types are found.

PALMER (continued)

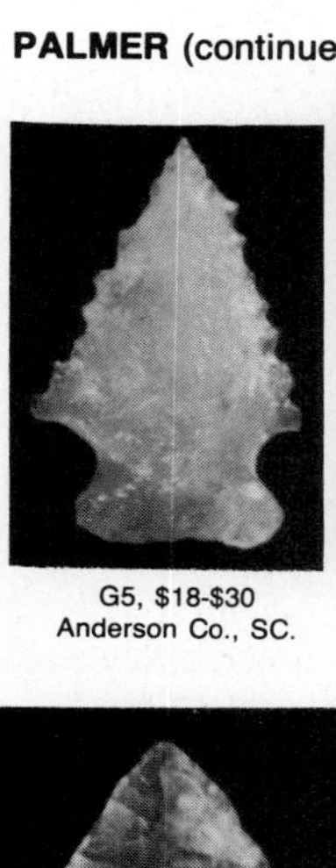

G5, $18-$30
Anderson Co., SC.

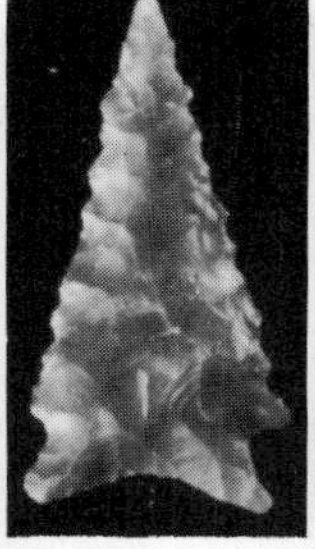

G4, $12-$20
Newport, TN.

G4, $12-$20
Newberry Co., SC. Slate.

G5, $15-$25
Rockingham Co., NC.

G5, $18-$30
Limestone Co., AL.

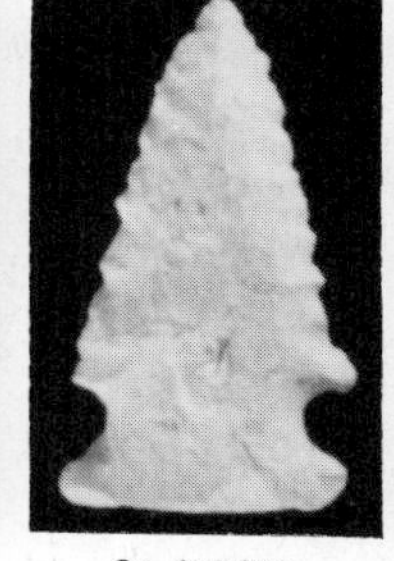

G4, $12-$20
Greene Co., NC.

G4, $12-$20
Montgomery Co., NC.

G5, $18-$30
Meigs Co., TN.

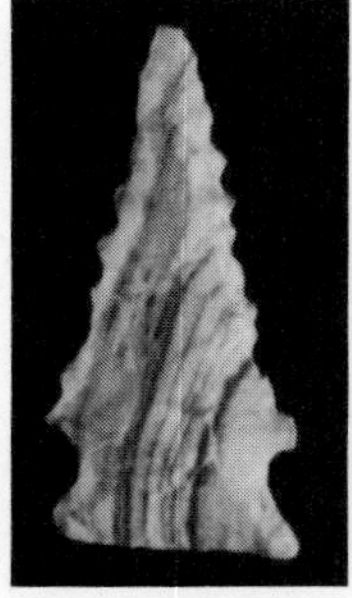

G3, $8-$12
Durham Co., NC

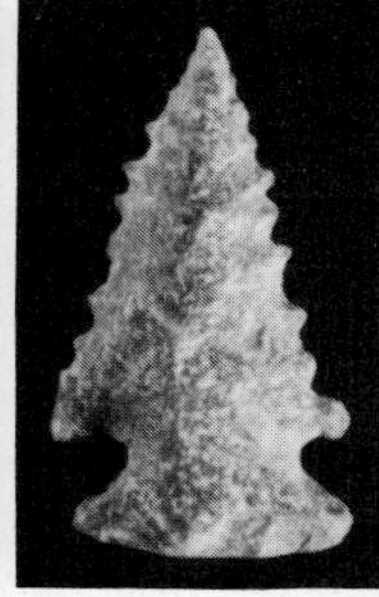

G8, $45-$80
Randolph Co., NC.

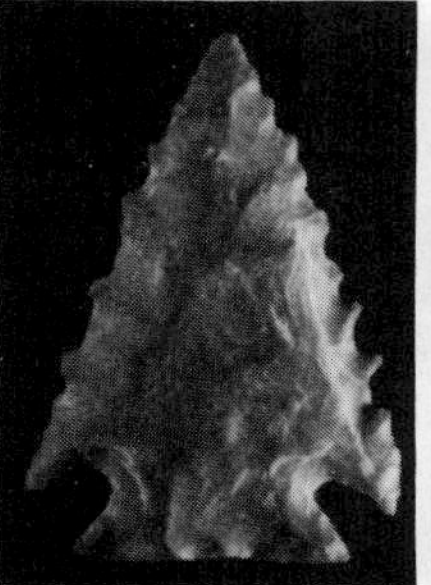

G7, $35-$60
Davidson Co., NC.

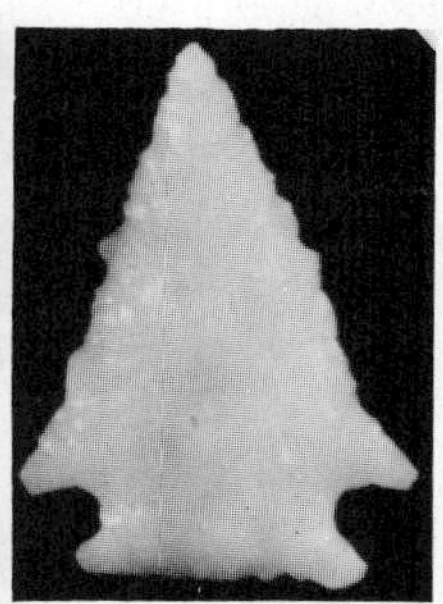

G8, $50-$90
Surry Co., NC.
Milky quartz.

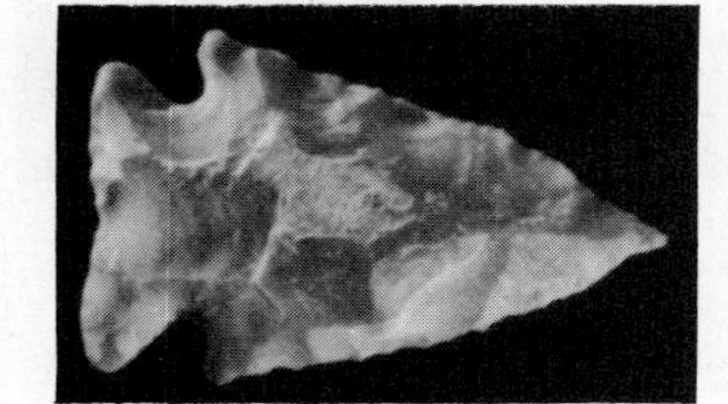

G5, $18-$30
Greene Co., NC.

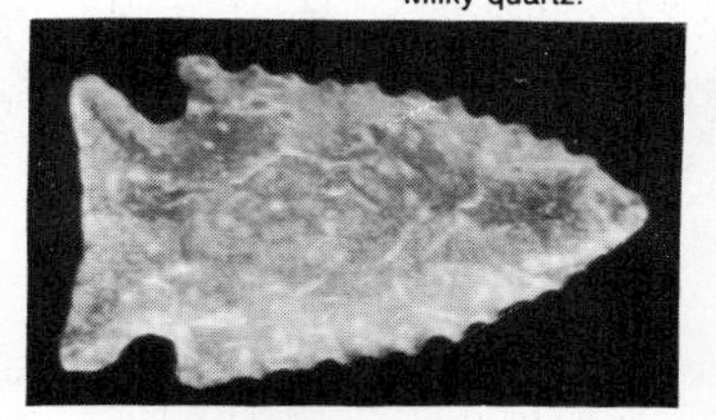

G6, $18-$30
Rockingham Co., NC.

PALMER (continued)

G6, $25-$45
Union Co., SC. Vein quartz. Note clear spot at tip.

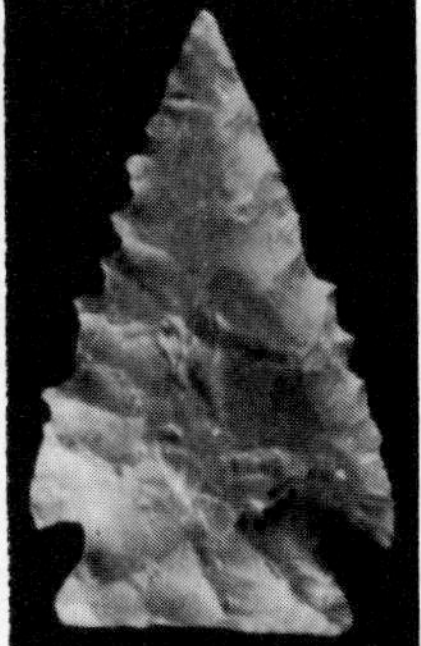
G9, $90-$200
Surry Co., NC.

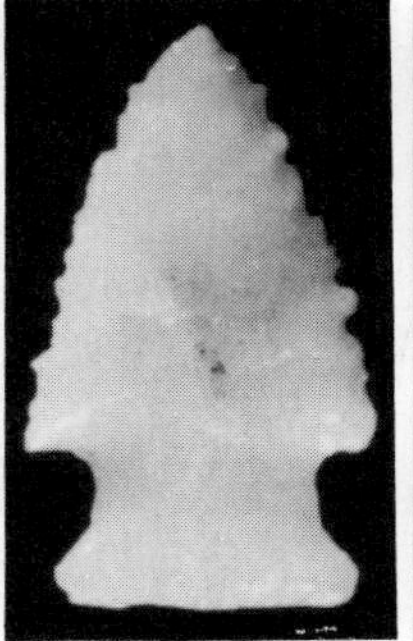
G5, $15-$25
Elmore Co., AL.

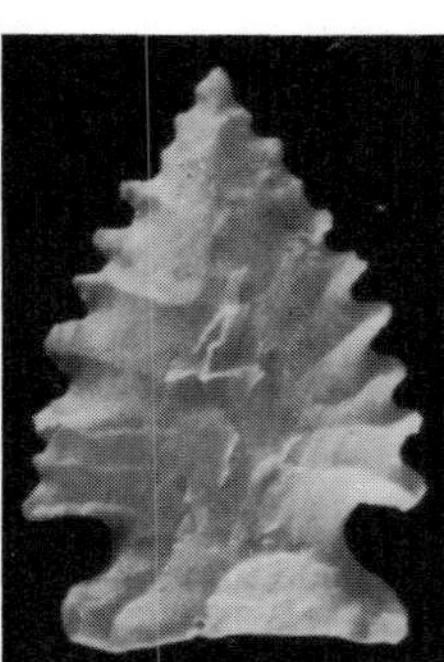
G10, $150-$250
Meigs Co., TN.

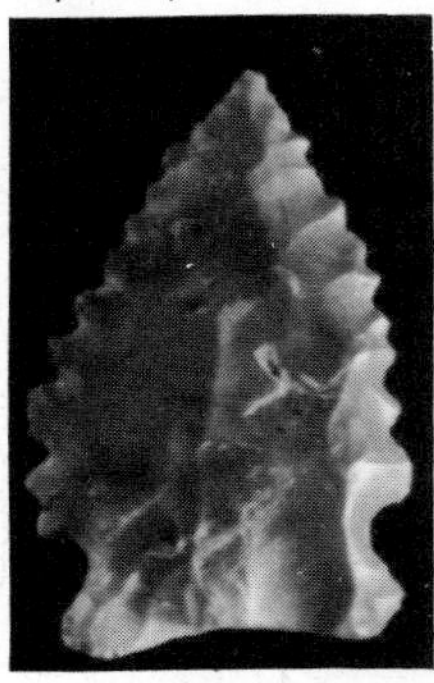
G4, $12-$20
NE AL.

G10, $150-$250
Stanly Co., NC.

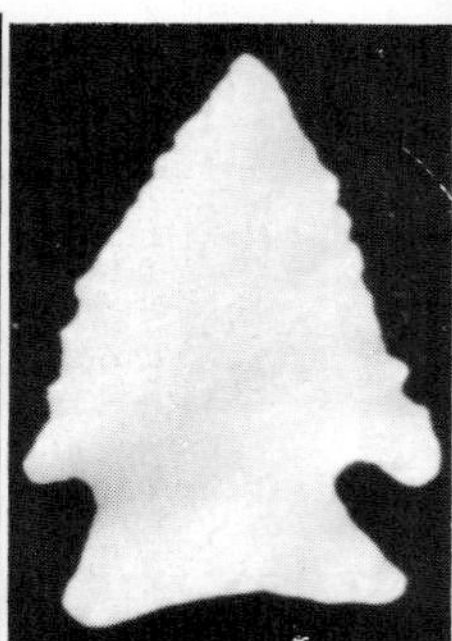
G6, $25-$40
Autauga Co., AL.
Milky quartz.

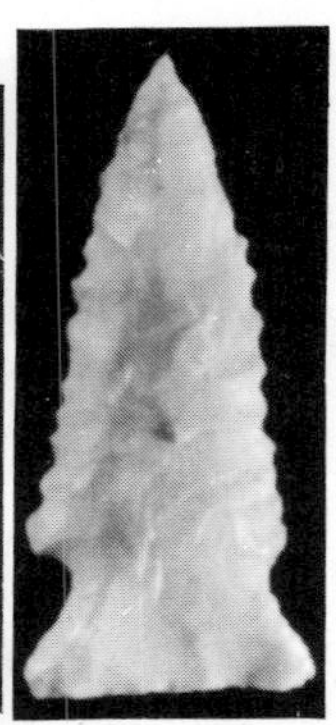
G6, $25-$40
SE TN.

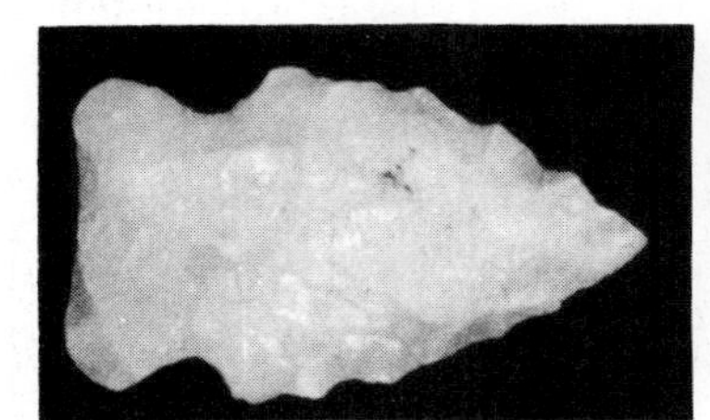
G4, $12-$20
Newberry Co., SC
Milky quartz.

G6, $25-$40
Marion Co., TN.

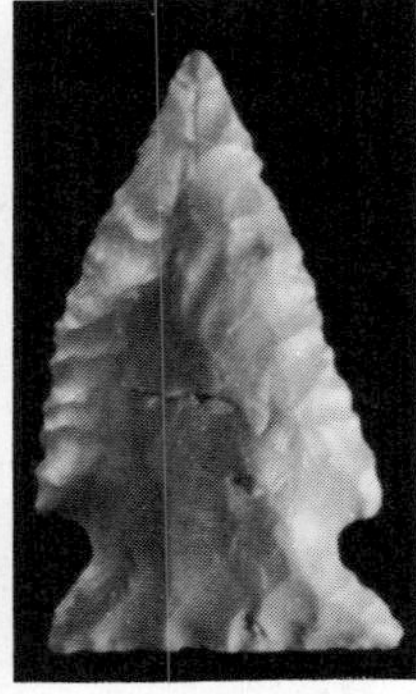
G6, $25-$45
Walker Co., AL.

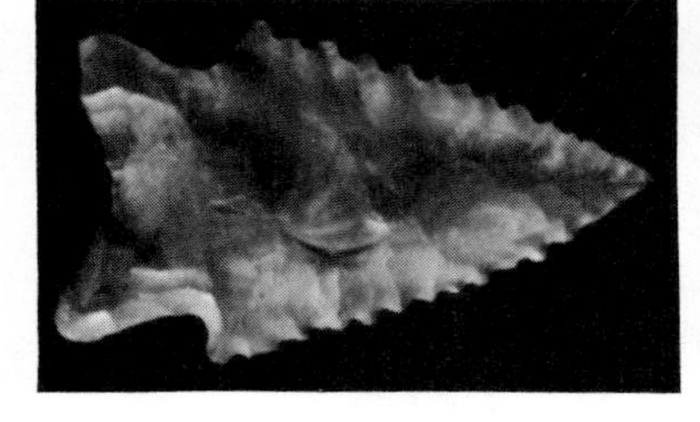
G8, $45-$80
Walker Co., AL.

G4, $12-$20
Walker Co., AL.

G7, $35-$60
Walker Co., AL.
Classic.

G5, $18-$30
Walker Co., AL.

G8, $50-$80
Newport, TN.

G4, $12-$20
Surry Co., NC.

G4, $12-$20
Randolph Co., NC.

G6, $25-$40
Portland Lake, TN.

G6, $25-$45
Surry Co., NC.

G7, $35-$60
Surry Co., NC.

G10, $150-$200
Surry Co., NC.

G6, $25-$40
Catawba Co., NC.

G8, $40-$75
W. TN.

PALMILLAS - Mid to Late Archaic, 6000 - 3000 B.P.

(Also see Beacon Island, Flint Creek & Williams)

G3, $3-$5
OR.

G3, $3-$5
Comanche Co., TX.

G2, $1-$2
Comanche Co., TX.

G3, $2-$4
Comanche Co., TX.

G2, $2-$3
Comanche Co., TX.

G6, $15-$25
AR.

G5, $10-$20
Comanche Co., TX.

G4, $5-$8
Comanche Co., TX.

G1, .50-$1
Comanche Co., TX.

G4, $5-$8
Comanche Co., TX.

G1, .50-$1
Comanche Co., TX.

LOCATION: Midwestern states. **DESCRIPTION:** A small to medium size triangular point with a bulbous stem. Shoulders are prominent and can be horizontal to barbed. This type is indistinguishable from its Southern cousin, *Beacon Island*.

PALMILLAS (continued)

G5, $10-$20
Comanche Co., TX.

G4, $8-$15
Comanche Co., TX.

G5, $10-$20
Comanche Co., TX.

G5, $10-$20
Cent. TX.

G7, $20-$30
Comanche Co., TX.

G4, $5-$8
Comanche Co., TX.

G9, $90-$150
Waco, TX.

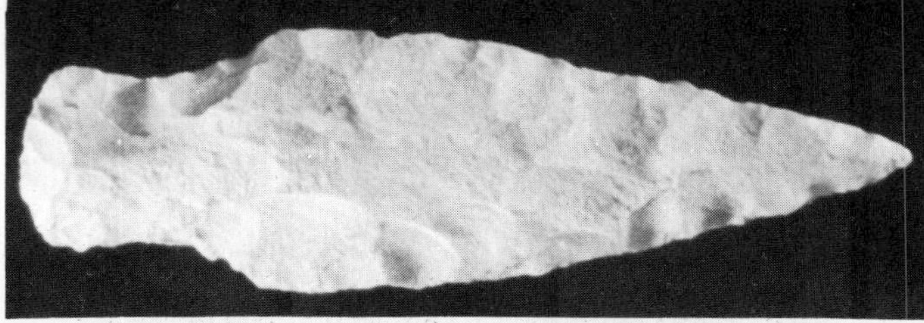

G6, $15-$25
Bell Co., TX.

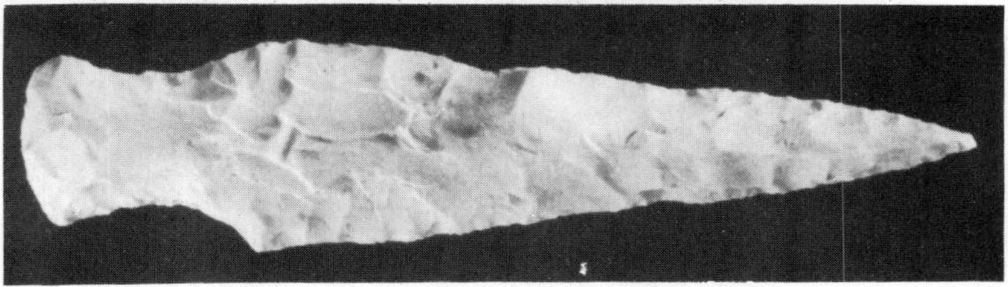

G6, $15-$25
Bell Co., TX.

G8, $50-$90
Bell Co., TX. Classic.

PANDALE - Mid-Archaic, 6000 - 3000 B.P.

(Also see Darl and Travis)

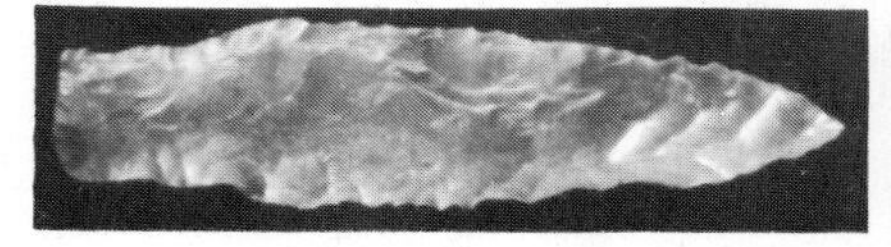

G3, $3-$5
Rhea Co., TN.

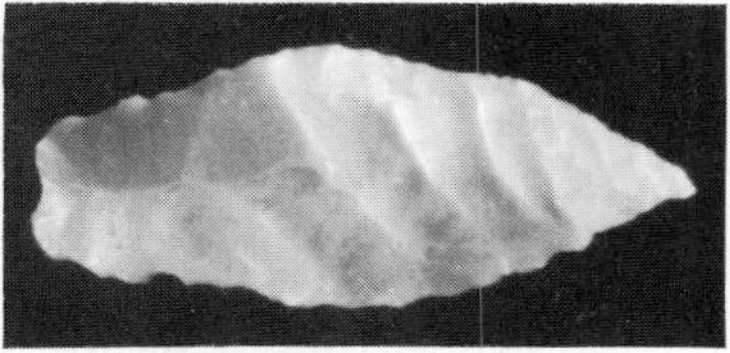

G6, $15-$25
Comanche Co., TX. Note oblique flaking.

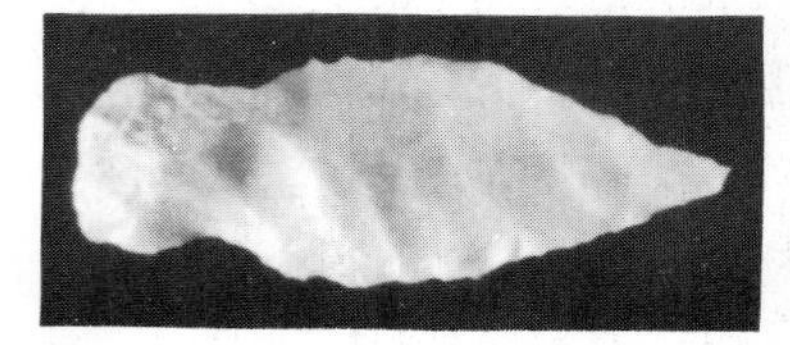

G6, $15-$25
Comanche Co., TX. Note oblique flaking.

LOCATION: Midwestern states. **DESCRIPTION:** A medium size, narrow, stemmed point or spike with a steeply beveled or torque blade. Some examples show oblique parallel flaking.

PANDALE (continued)

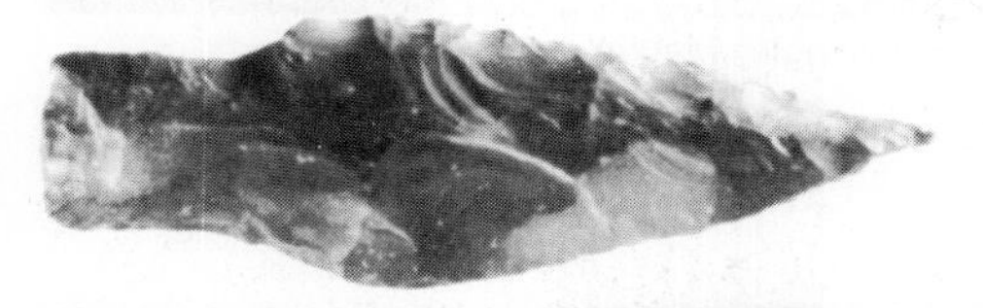

G7, $25-$40
Comanche Co., TX. Blade is steeply beveled on alternated edges. Leon River chert.

PANDORA - Late Archaic to Woodland, 4000 - 1000 B.P.

(Also see Adena Blade, Benjamin, Frazier, Kinney and Refugio)

G3, $5-$8
Comanche Co., TX.

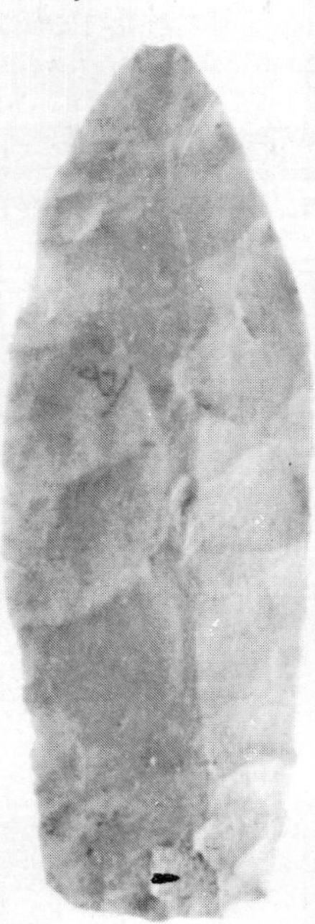

G5, $8-$12
Colbert Co., AL.

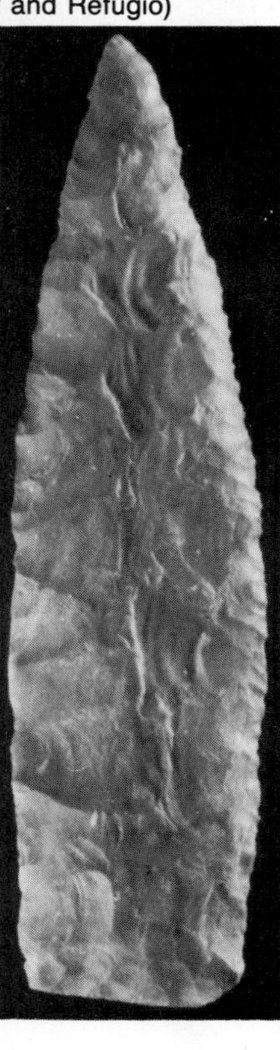

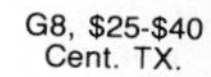

G8, $25-$40
Cent. TX.

G6, $15-$25
Florence, AL.

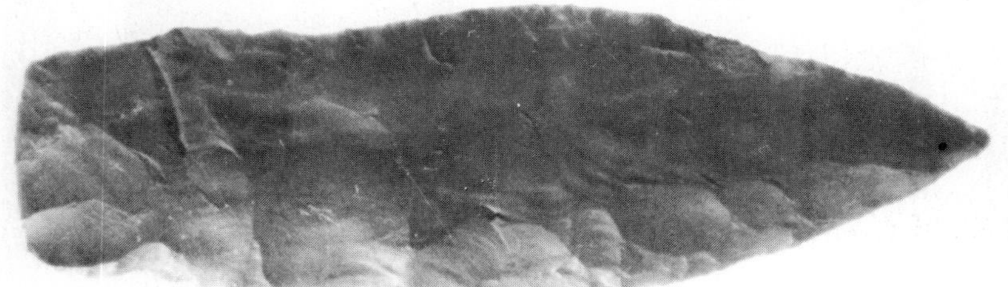

LOCATION: Midwestern states. **DESCRIPTION:** A medium to large size, lanceolate blade with a straight base. Blade edges can be parallel to convex.

PAPAGO - Mississippian, 800 - 400 B.P.

(Also see Cottonwood Triangle, Maude and San Jose)

G6, $1-$3
Yavapai Co., AZ.

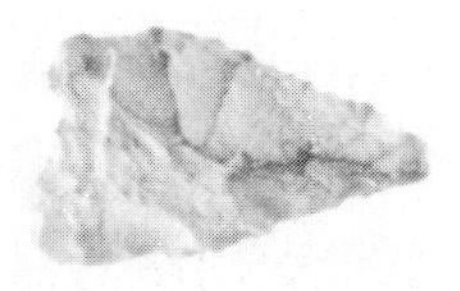

G3, .50-$1
Yavapai Co., AZ.

LOCATION: Southwestern states. **DESCRIPTION:** A small size triangle with rounded basal corners and a concave base.

PAROWAN - Woodland to Mississippian, 1200 - 700 B.P.

(Also see Citrus, Eva, Hernando, Rockwall and Shumla)

G5, $5-$8
AR.

G8, $30-$60
OR. Obsidian.

G7, $10-$20
AR.

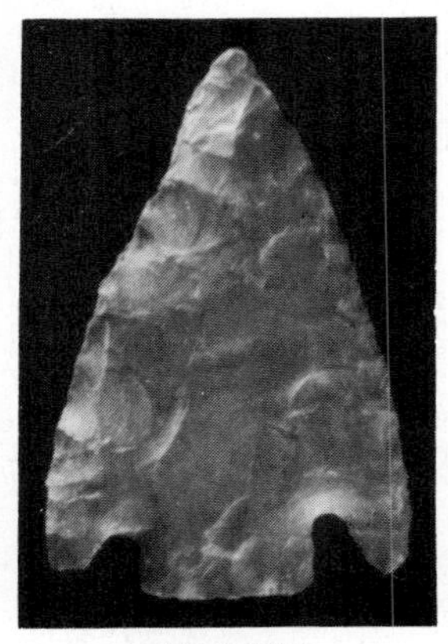

G7, $10-$20
Comanche Co., TX.

LOCATION: Midwestern to Western states. **DESCRIPTION:** A medium size, triangular point that has basal notches producing tangs that line up with the base. Some examples are serrated.

PATRICK - Late Archaic, 5000 - 3000 B.P.

(Also see Cave Spring, Hanna, Pinto Basin, SW Hanna & Wheeler)

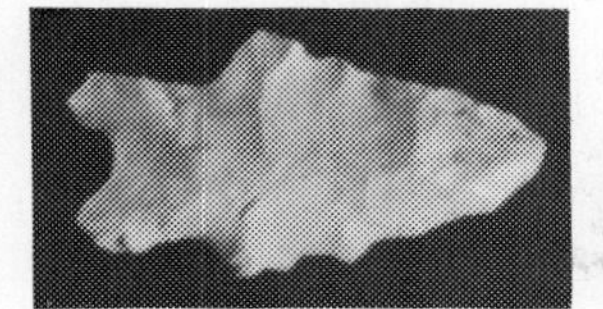

G5, $5-$8
SE TN.

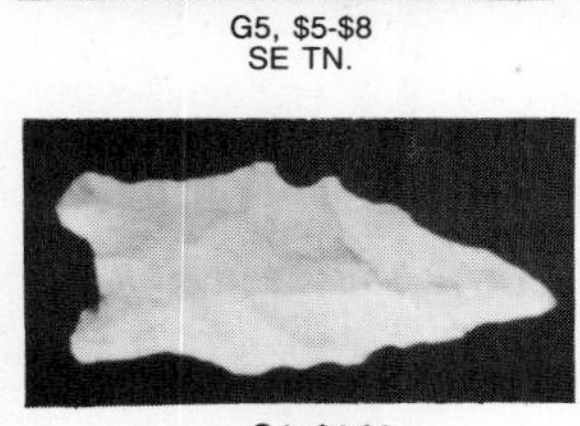

G4, $4-$6
Johnson Co., NC.

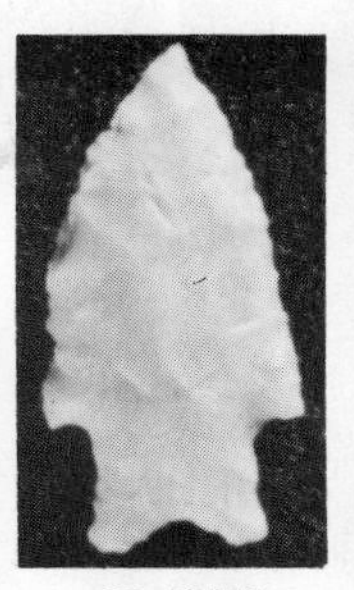

G6, $6-$10
Whitwell, TN.

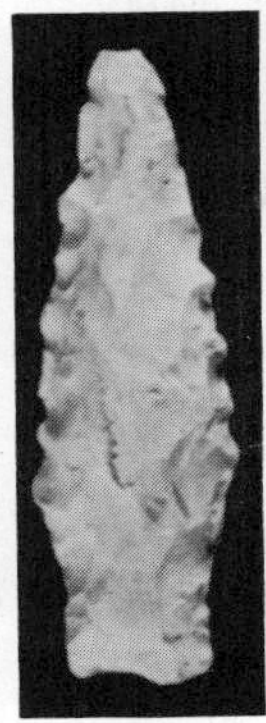

G1, .25-.50
Dinwiddie Co., VA.

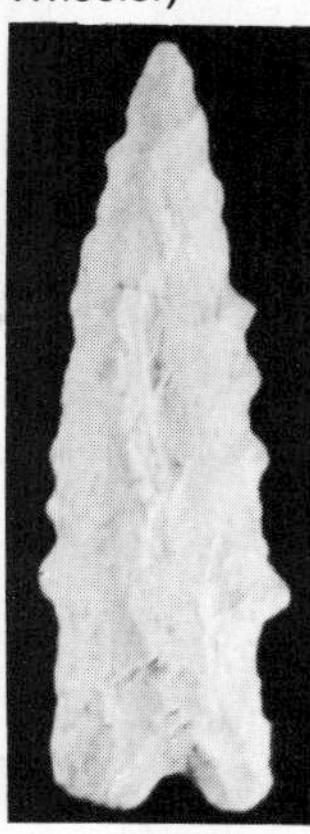

G8, $25-$45
Dinwiddie Co., VA.

LOCATION: Eastern states. **DESCRIPTION:** A small to medium size, narrow point with very weak shoulders and a long, parallel sided, bifurcated base.

PATUXENT (See Mud Creek)

PEDERNALIS - Mid-Archaic to Woodland, 6000 - 2000 B.P.

(Also see Hoxie, Jetta, Kirk Serrated, Montell, Uvalde & Val Verde)

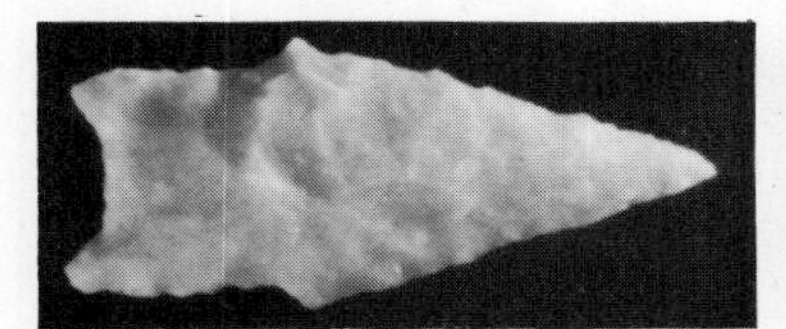

G2, $3-$5
Comanche Co., TX.

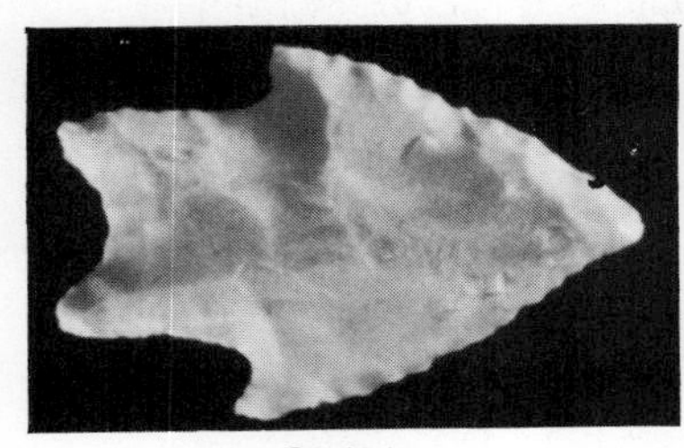

G2, $3-$5
Comanche Co., TX.

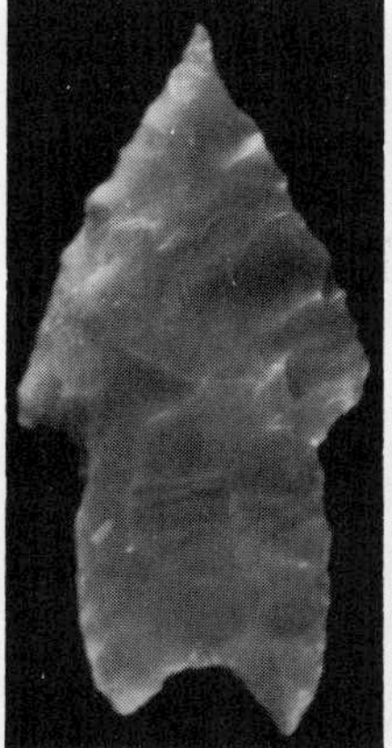

G3, $8-$15
Bell Co., TX.

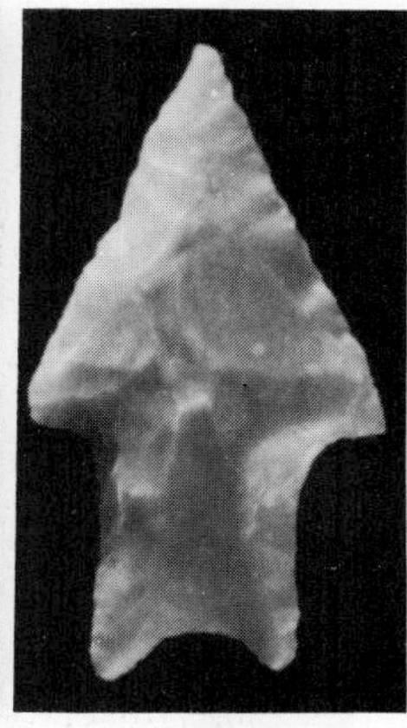

G3, $10-$20
Comanche Co., TX.

LOCATION: Midwestern states. **DESCRIPTION:** A medium to large size, usually barbed, point with a broad, long, bifurcated stem. Blade edges are convex, concave to recurved. These points are thin with high quality flaking.

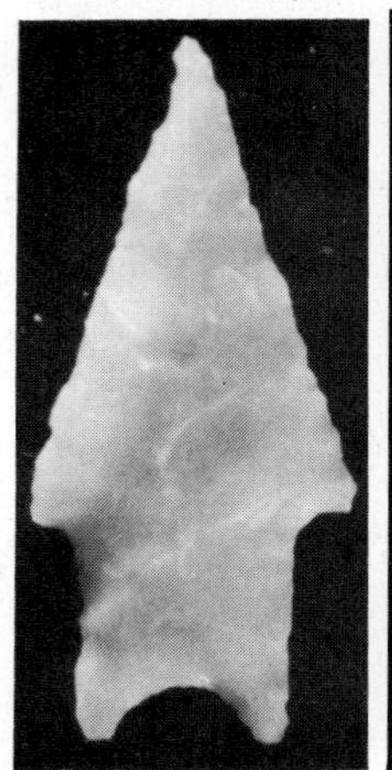

G3, $8-$15
Comanche Co., TX.

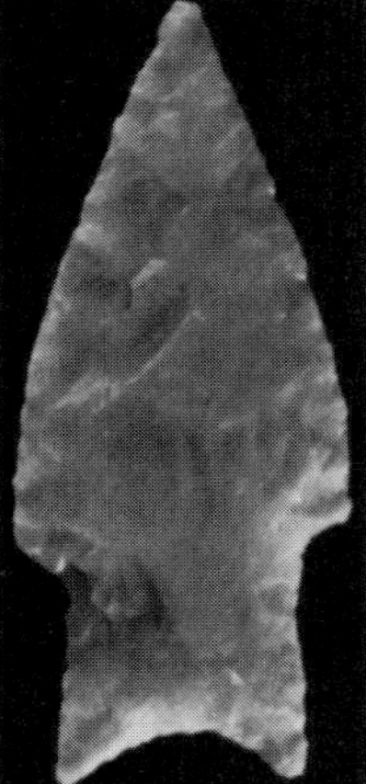

G3, $10-$20
Bell Co., TX.

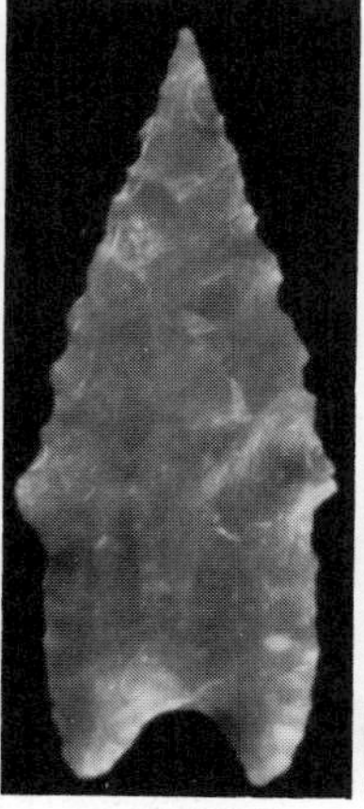

G4, $15-$20
Bell Co., TX.

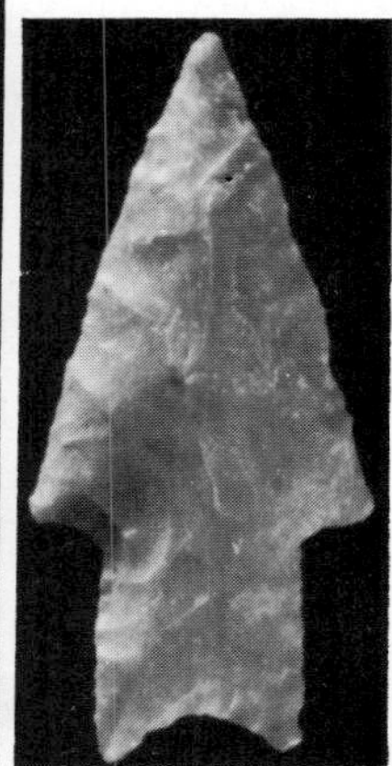

G5, $20-$30
Comanche Co., TX.

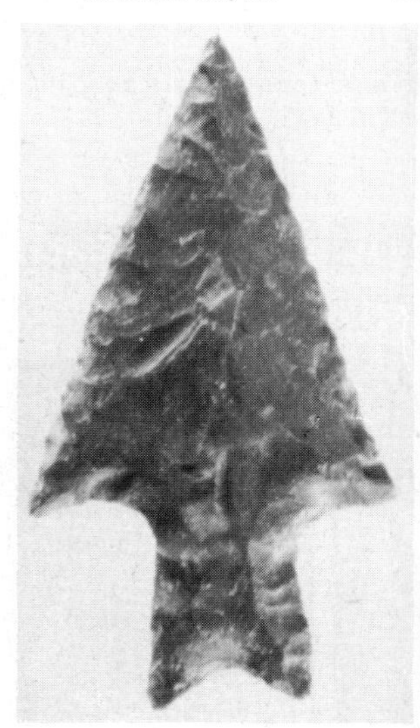

G7, $50-$90
Austin, TX. Leon River chert.

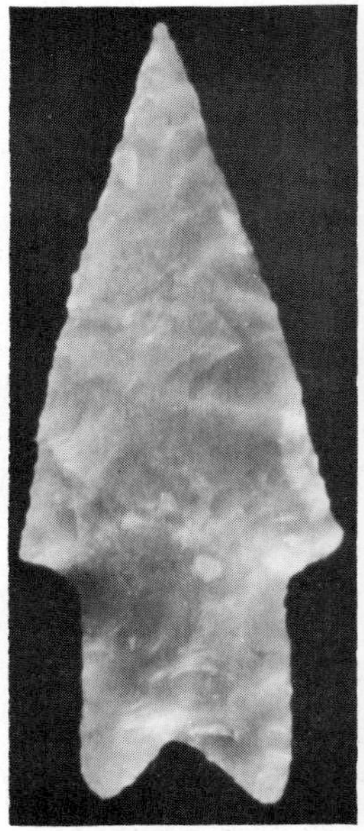

G8, $70-$120
Cent. TX.

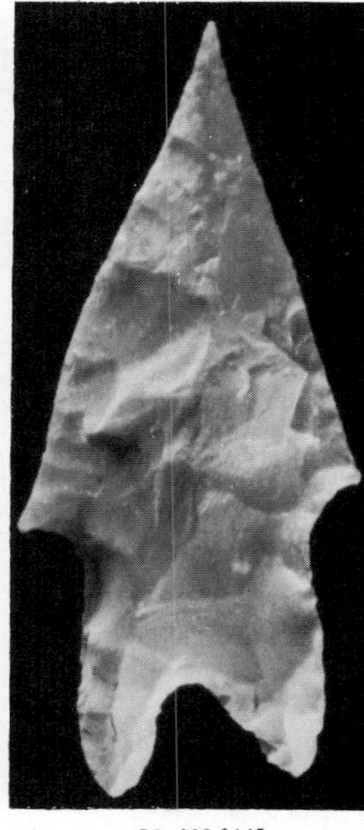

G8, $80-$140
Austin, TX.

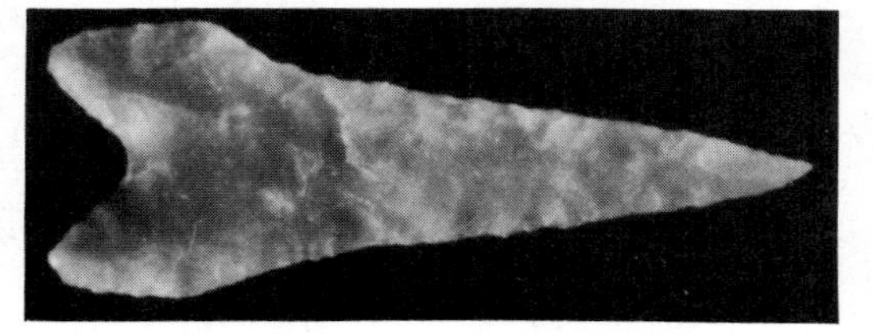

G6, $30-$50
Austin, TX.

PEDERNALIS (continued)

G10, $250-$400
Cent. TX.

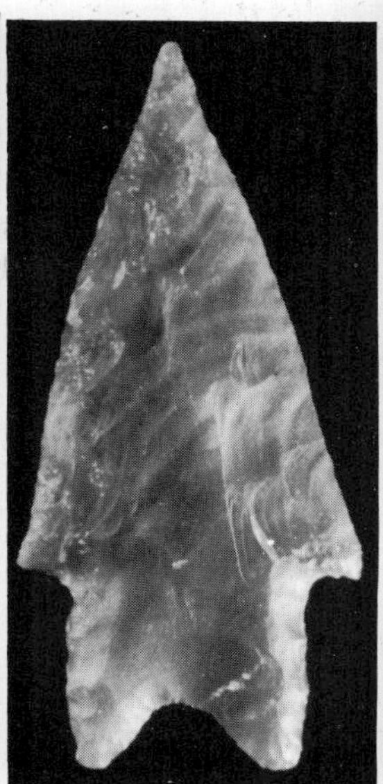

G8, $80-$140
Cent. TX. Georgetown flint.

G7, $60-$100
Austin, TX.

G8, $80-$140
Cent. TX. Georgetown flint.

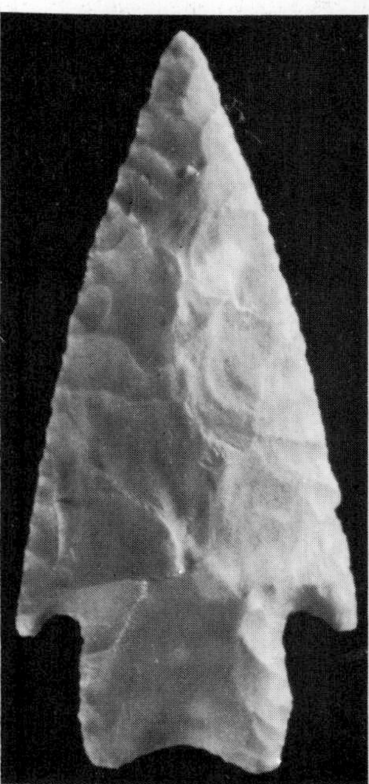

G7, $50-$90
Austin, TX.

G7, $60-$100
Austin, TX. Classic.

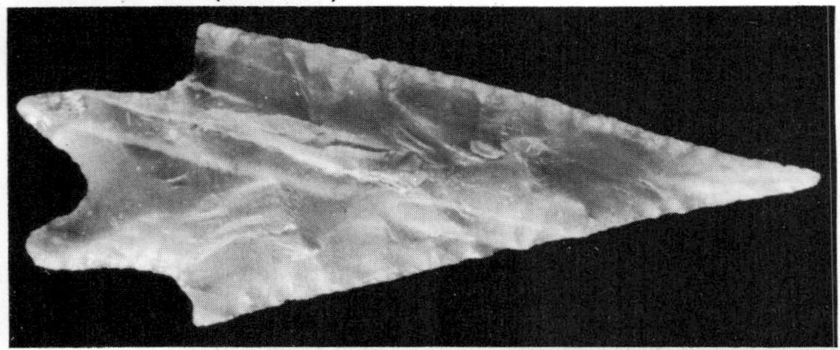

G9, $150-$250
Cent. TX. Georgetown flint.

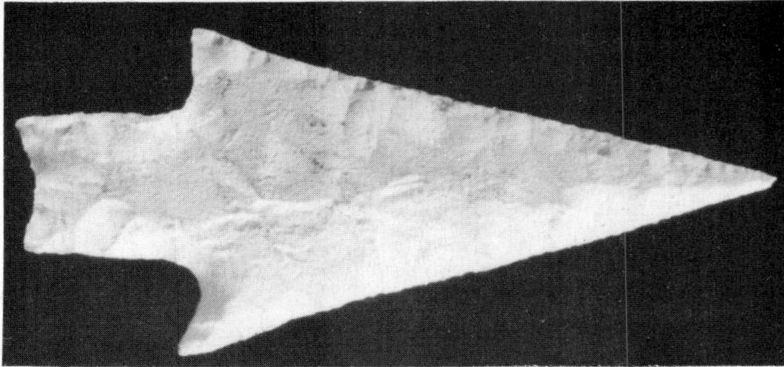

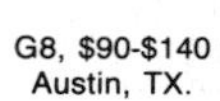

G8, $90-$140
Austin, TX.

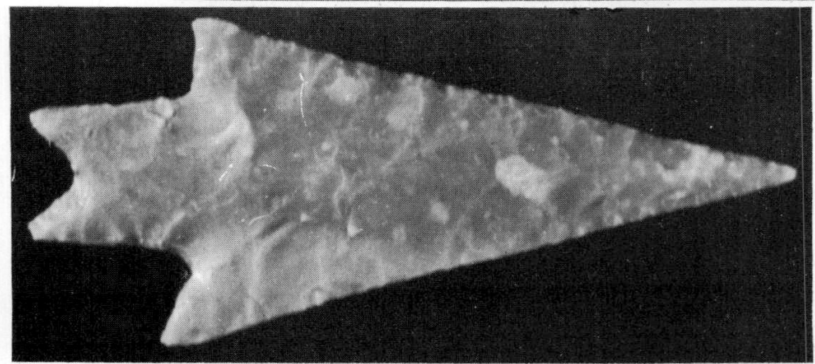

G9, $150-$250
Cent. TX.

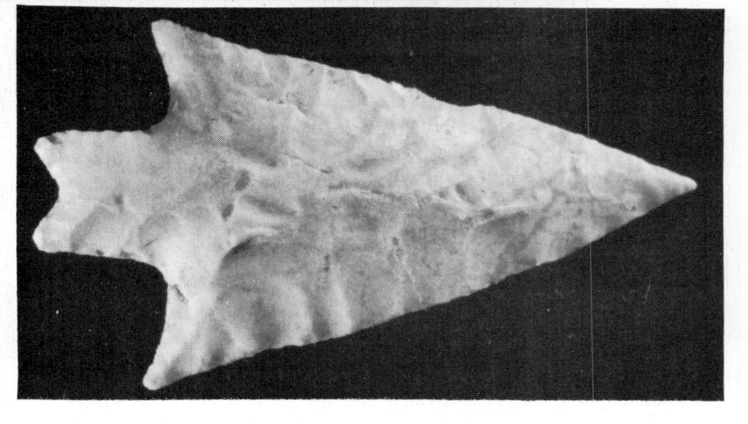

G8, $70-$120
Austin, TX.

G9, $150-$250, Austin, TX.

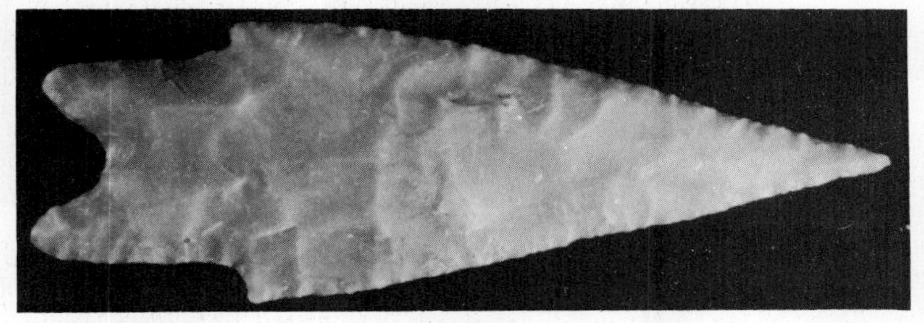

G10, $250-$400, Cent. TX.

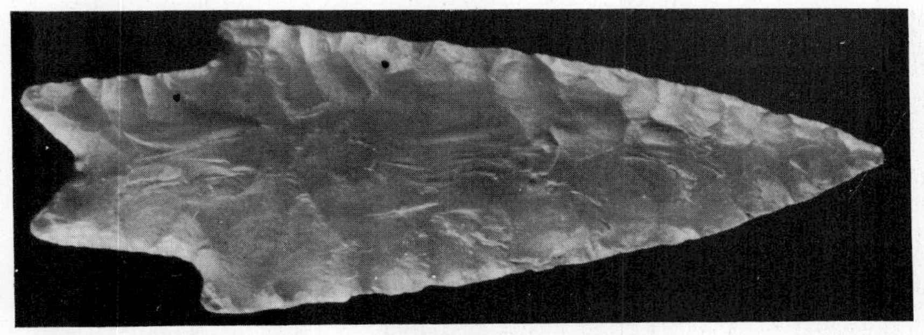

G9, $100-$200, Cent. TX.

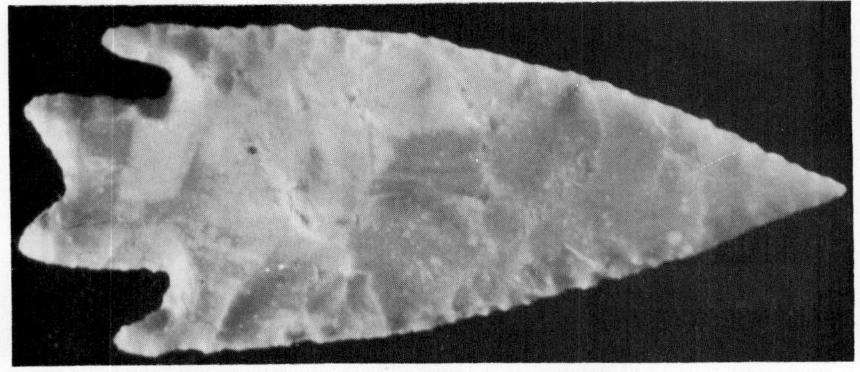

G10, $350-$600, Austin, TX. Georgetown flint. Very thin and excellent.

PEE DEE (See Jacks Reef Pentagonal)

PELICAN - Transitional Paleo, 10000 - 6000 B.P.

(Also see Hell Gap, Lake Mohave, Midland, Rio Grande, Quad and San Patrice)

G2, $8-$15
Comanche Co., TX.

G5, $50-$80
Dyersburg, TN.

G7, $80-$120
Hardin Co., TN.

G7, $90-$150
NW TN. Fluted.

G6, $60-$90
LA. Fluted.

G8, $200-$350
AR.

G4, $40-$60
AR. Basal thinning.

LOCATION: Midwestern states. **DESCRIPTION:** A short, broad, usually auriculate point with basal grinding. Shoulders taper into a long contracting stem. Some examples are thinned or fluted.

PELONA - Mid-Archaic, 6000 - 4000 B.P.

(Also see Guilford and Lerma)

G7, $8-$12
Yavapai Co., AZ.

G6, $6-$10
Yavapai Co., AZ.

G4, $2-$4
Yavapai Co., AZ.

LOCATION: Southwestern states. **DESCRIPTION:** A small to medium size, narrow, lanceolate point with a rounded to pointed base. Blade edges are usually serrated to barbed.

PERDIZ - Mississippian, 1000 - 500 B.P.

(Also see Alba, Bassett, Bonham, Cuney, Double Tip, Hayes, Homan & Keota)

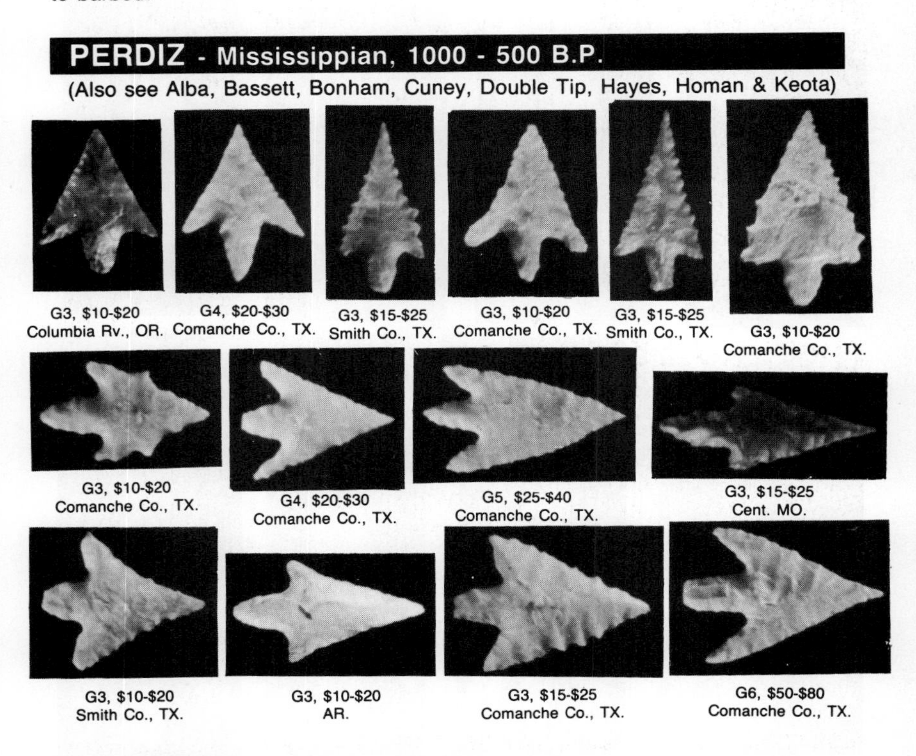

G3, $10-$20
Columbia Rv., OR.

G4, $20-$30
Comanche Co., TX.

G3, $15-$25
Smith Co., TX.

G3, $10-$20
Comanche Co., TX.

G3, $15-$25
Smith Co., TX.

G3, $10-$20
Comanche Co., TX.

G3, $10-$20
Comanche Co., TX.

G4, $20-$30
Comanche Co., TX.

G5, $25-$40
Comanche Co., TX.

G3, $15-$25
Cent. MO.

G3, $10-$20
Smith Co., TX.

G3, $10-$20
AR.

G3, $15-$25
Comanche Co., TX.

G6, $50-$80
Comanche Co., TX.

LOCATION: Midwest to Western states. **DESCRIPTION:** A small to medium size, narrow, triangular point with pointed barbs and a pointed to near pointed stem.

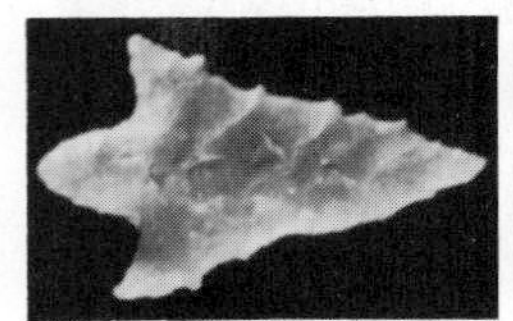
G3, $12-$20
Waco, TX.

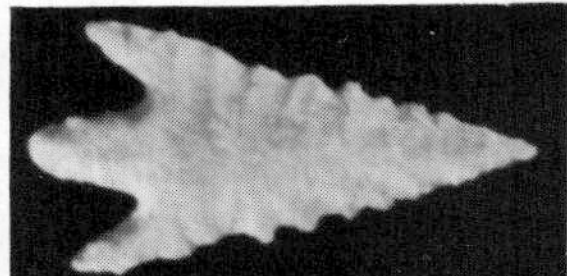
G7, $60-$100
Comanche Co., TX.

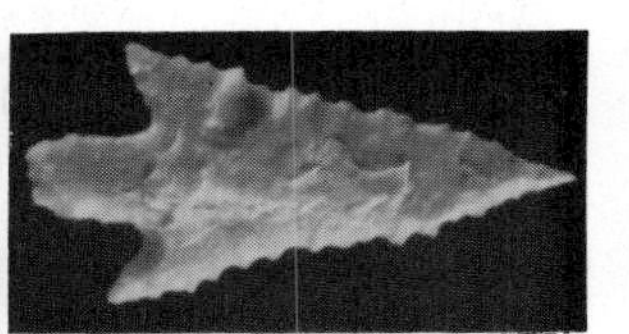
G8, $90-$150
Waco, TX.

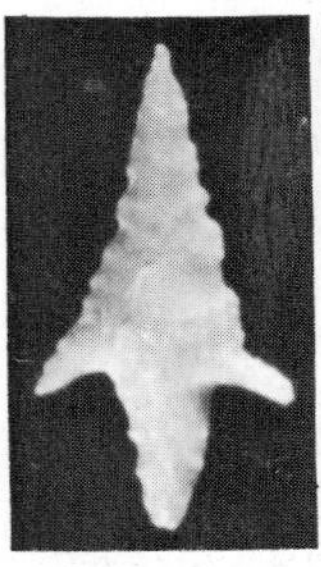
G4, $20-$30
Comanche Co., TX.

G9, $100-$200
CO/TX.

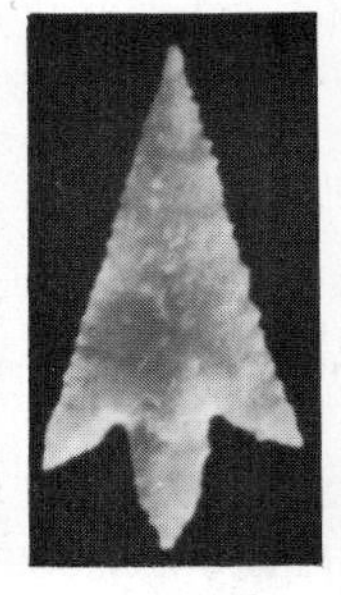
G7, $60-$100
Smith Co., TX.

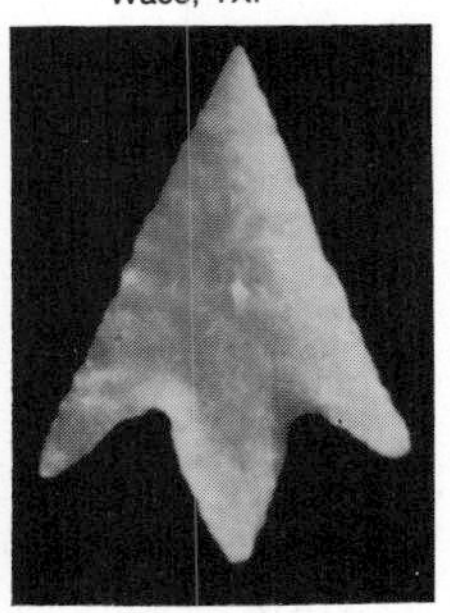
G8, $80-$120
Cent. TX.

G7, $60-$90
Waco, TX.

G8, $90-$150
CO/TX.

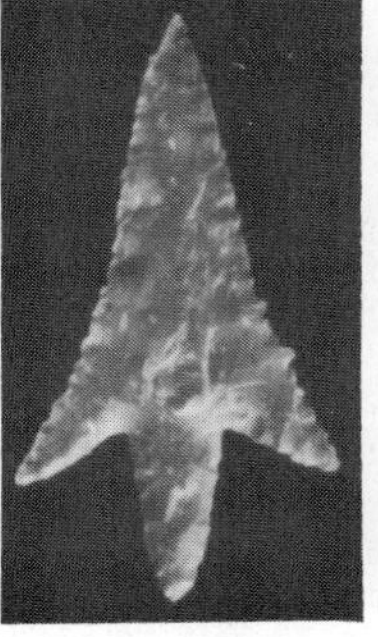
G8, $80-$120
CO/TX.

G9, $150-$250
CO/TX.

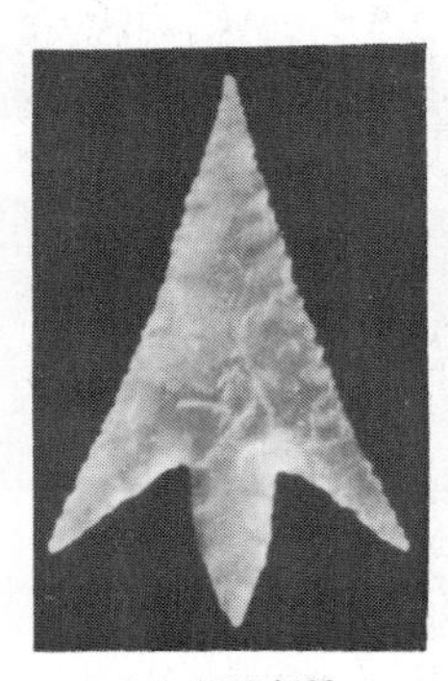
G10, $250-$400
CO/TX.

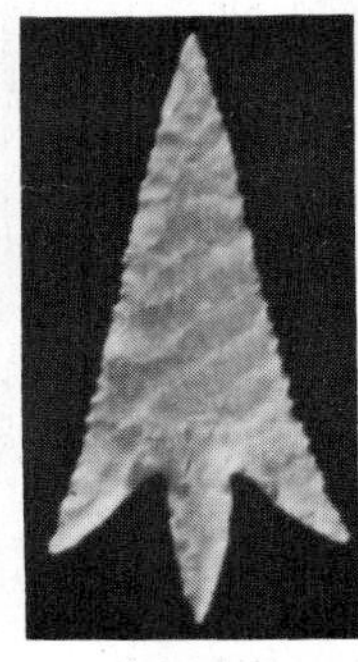
G10, $300-$500
Comanche Co., TX.

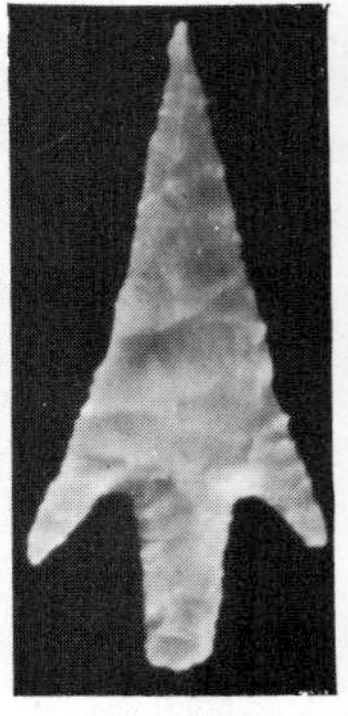
G9, $120-$200
Comanche Co., TX.

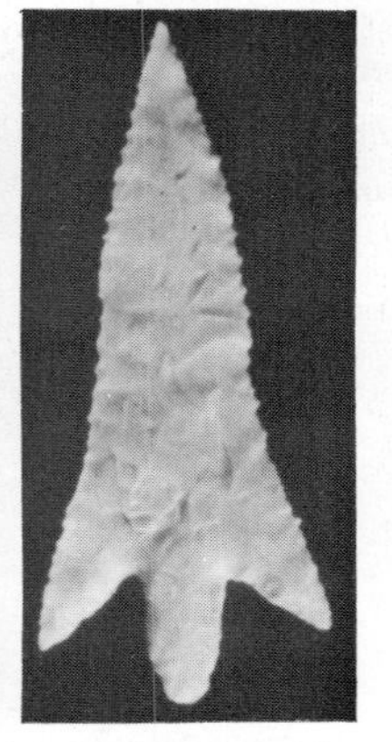
G10, $300-$500
CO/TX.

PERFORATOR - Archaic to Mississippian, 9000 - 400 B.P.

(Also see Drill and Graver)

G1, .50-$1
Meigs Co., TN.

G1, .50-$1
Hamilton Co., TN.

G2, $1-$2
Walker Co., GA.

G6, $4-$6
Barren Co., KY.

G2, $1-$2
Tifton, GA.

G1, .50-$1
Tifton, GA.

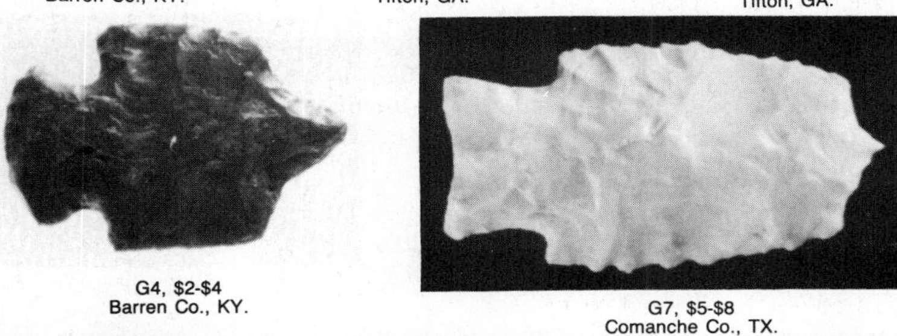

G4, $2-$4
Barren Co., KY.

G7, $5-$8
Comanche Co., TX.

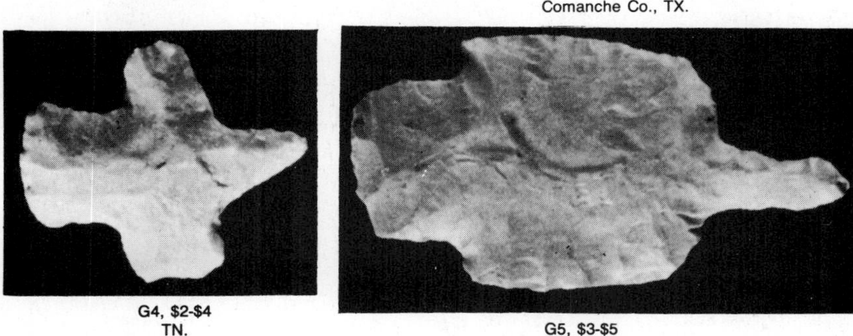

G4, $2-$4
TN.

G5, $3-$5
Hamilton Co., TN.

LOCATION: Archaic and Woodland sites everywhere. **DESCRIPTION:** A jabbing projection at the tip would qualify for the type. It is believed that *perforators* were used for tatooing, incising or to punch holes in leather or other materials or objects. Paleo peoples used *Gravers* for the same purpose. All Archaic and Woodland cultures converted their points into this type. Therefore, most point types could occur in this form.

PERFORATOR (continued)

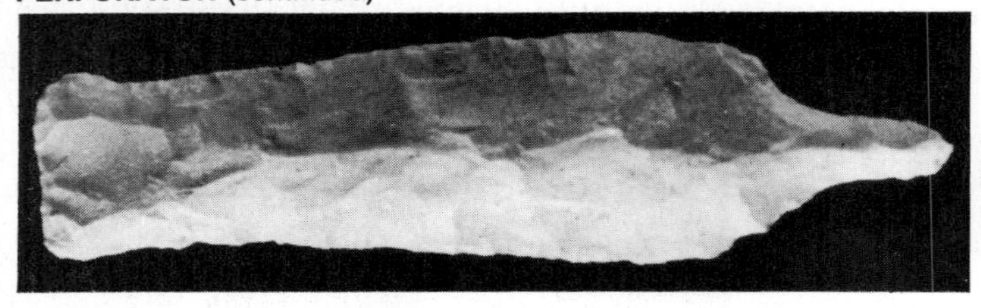

G6, $4-$6
Humphreys Co., TN.

PERKINSVILLE - Mississippian, 1000 - 600 B.P.

(Also see San Jose)

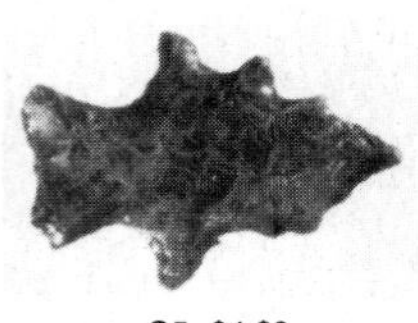

G5, $4-$6
Yavapai Co., AZ.

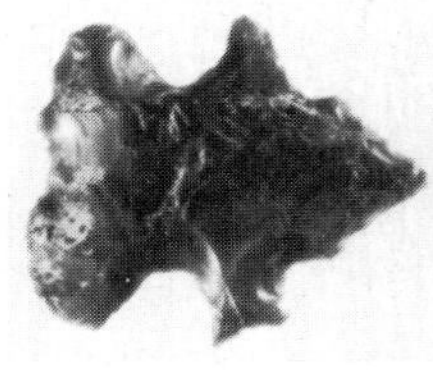

G6, $6-$10
Yavapai Co., AZ.

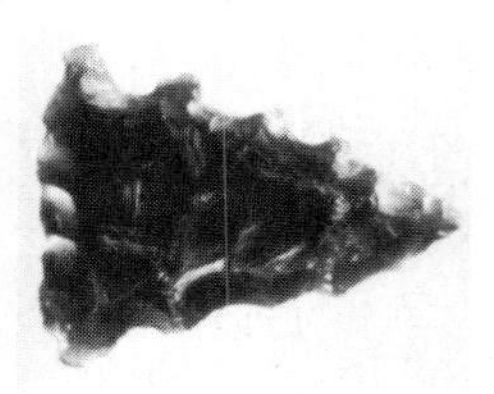

G4, $3-$5
Yavapai Co., AZ.

LOCATION: Southwestern states. **DESCRIPTION:** A small to medium size barbed point with an expanded base. Blade edges are usually serrated.

PICKWICK - Mid to late Archaic, 6000 - 3500 B.P.

(Also see Elora, Flint River, Ledbetter, Little Bear Creek & Mulberry Creek)

G3, $8-$12
Florence, AL.

G2, $3-$5
Florence, AL.

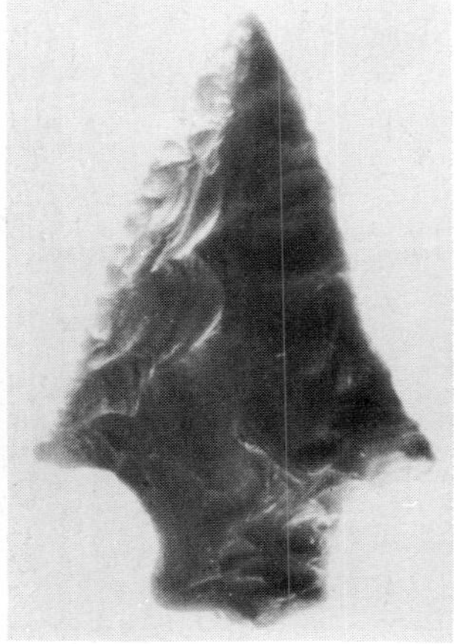

G2, $4-$8
Decatur, AL.

LOCATION: Southeastern states. **DESCRIPTION:** A medium to large size, expanded shouider, contracted to expanded stem point. Blade edges are recurved, and many examples show fine secondary flaking with serrations. Some are beveled on one side of each face. The bevel is steep and shallow. Shoulders are horizontal, tapered or barbed and form sharp angles. Some stems are snapped off or may show original rind.

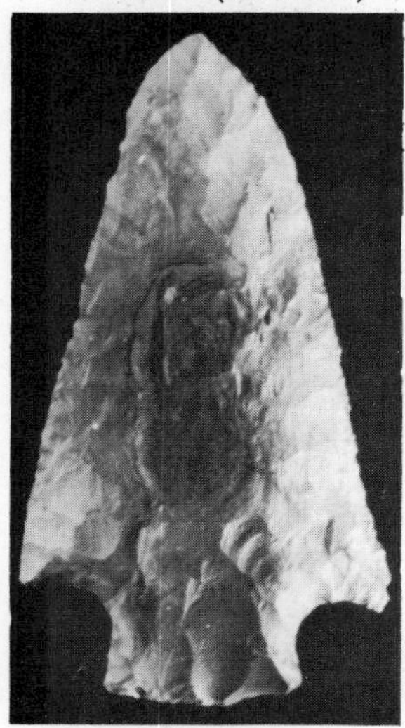

G3, $8-$12
Tishomingo Co., MS.

G4, $50-$100
Humphreys Co., TN.
Horse Creek chert.

G2, $3-$5
Meigs Co., TN. Blade nick.

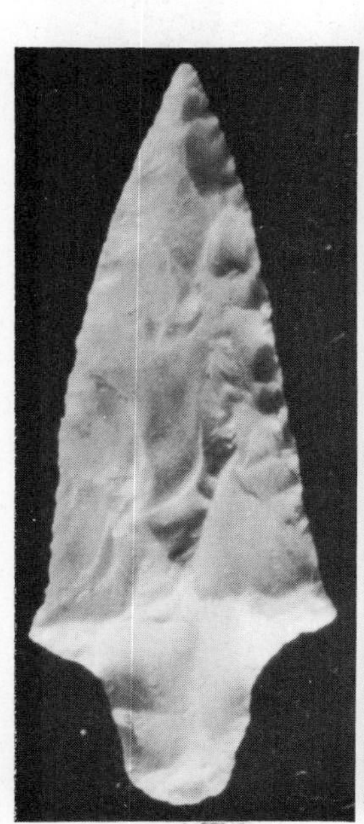

G3, $8-$15
Meigs Co., TN.

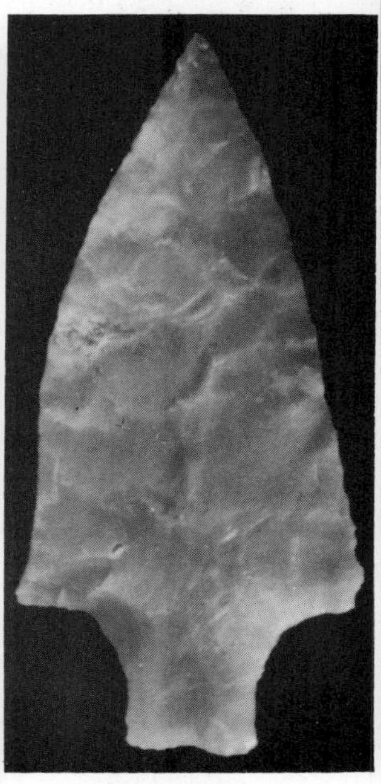

G4, $20-$35
Union Co., FL.

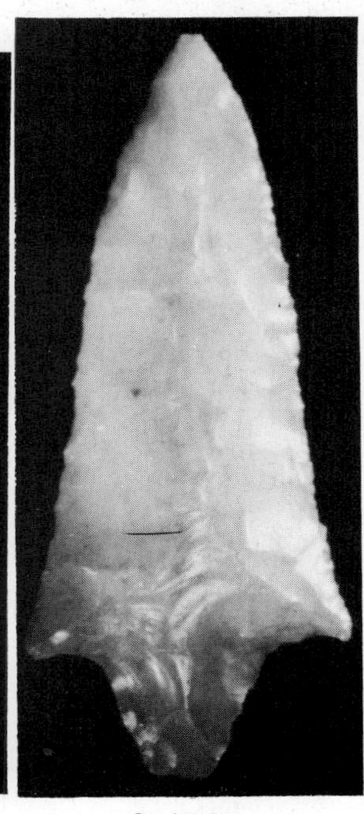

G4, $25-$40
Suwannee Co., FL.

PICKWICK (continued)

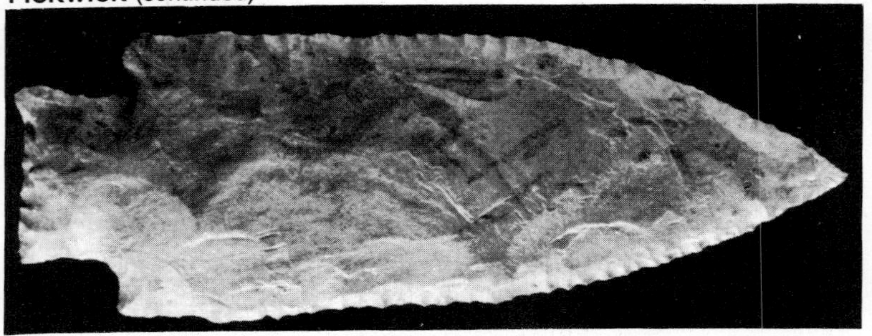

G6, $50-$80
Humphreys Co., TN. Dover chert.

G7, $150-$250
Humphreys Co., TN. Note fine edgework. Excellent quality.

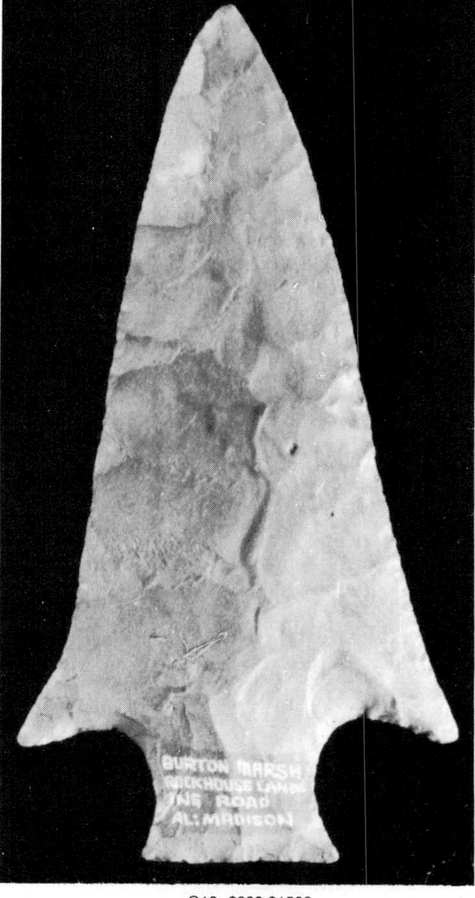

G10, $800-$1500
Madison Co., AL. Field find. Classic example.

G6, $50-$80
Florence, AL. Red jasper.

G8, $200-$350
Humphreys Co., TN.

G8, $250-$400
Marion Co., AL. Sugar quartz.

G8, $200-$350
Allendale Co., SC.

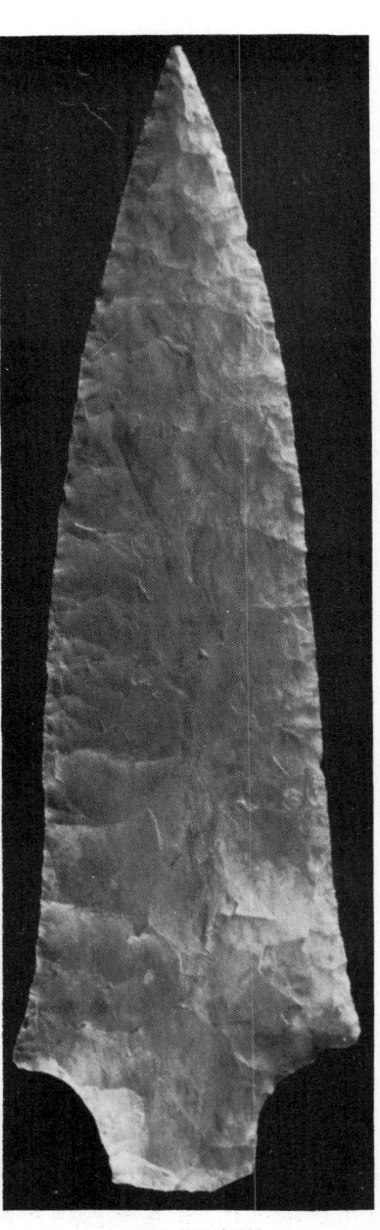

G10, $800-$1500
Humphreys Co., TN. Outstanding quality and form. Classic.

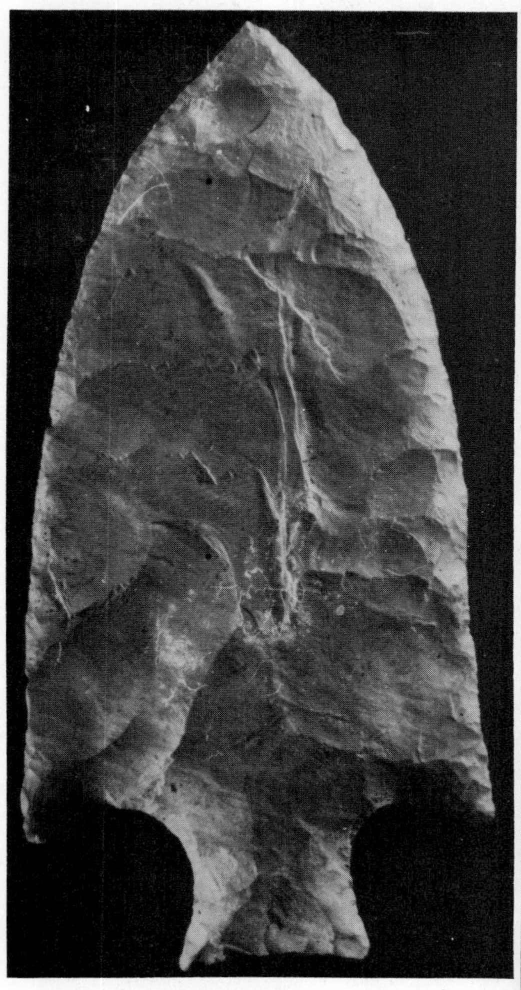

G10, $700-$1200
Benton Co., TN.

G9, $450-$700
Benton Co., TN.

PINE TREE - Early Archaic, 8000 - 5000 B.P.

(Also see Big Sandy, Greenbrier, Kirk and Palmer)

G4, $20-$40
Stanly Co., NC.

G3, $8-$15
Richmond Co., NC.

G3, $15-$25
Coffee Lake, AL.

G2, $5-$8
Humphreys Co., TN.

G4, $20-$35, Marion Co., TN

G4, $20-$35
Parsons, TN.

G7, $70-$100
Parsons, TN.

G5, $25-$40
Decatur, AL. Tang nick.

LOCATION: Southeastern states. **DESCRIPTION:** A medium to large size, side notched, usually serrated point with parallel flaking to the center of the blade forming a median ridge. The bases are gound and can be concave, convex, straight, or auriculate. This type developed from the earlier *Greenbrier* point. Small examples would fall into the *Palmer* type. **I.D. KEY:** Archaic flaking with long flakes to the center of each blade.

PINE TREE (continued)

G7, $120-$180
Clifton, TN. Patinated red jasper.

G5, $25-$40
Christian Co., KY.

G6, $45-$80
Person Co., NC. Rhyolite.

G7, $70-$100
Humphreys Co., TN.

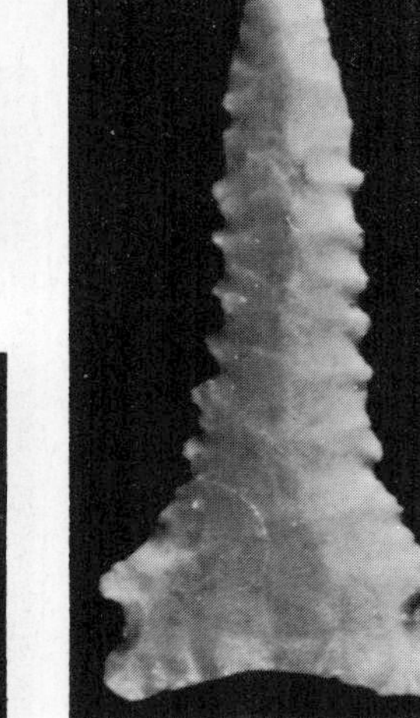

G5, $25-$40
Albany, KY.

G8, $100-$150
Coffee Lake, AL.

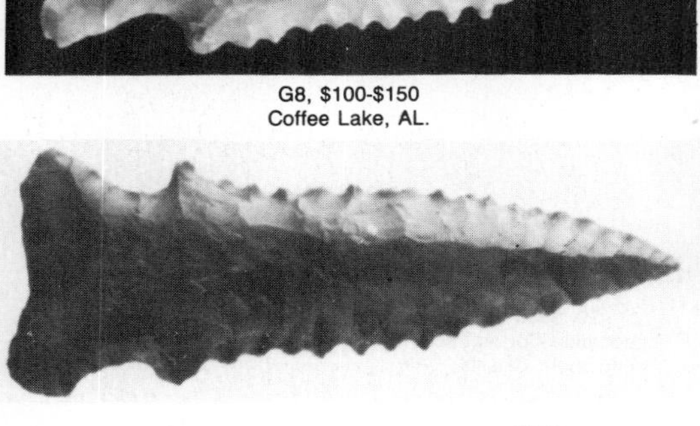

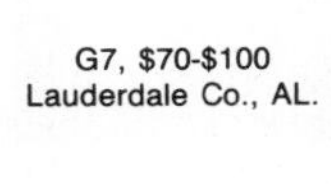

G7, $70-$100
Lauderdale Co., AL.

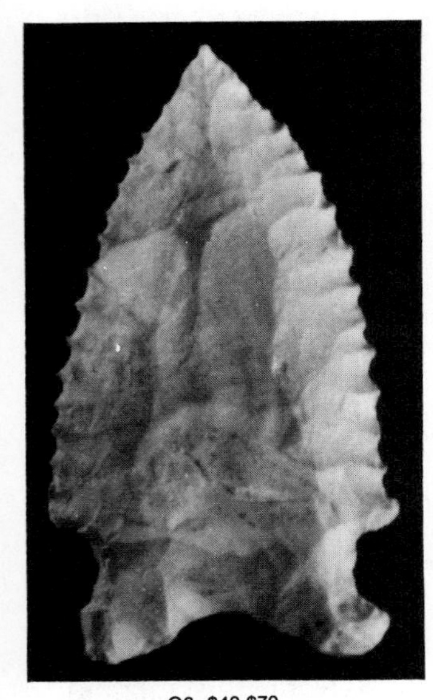
G6, $40-$70
Humphreys Co., TN. Buffalo River chert.

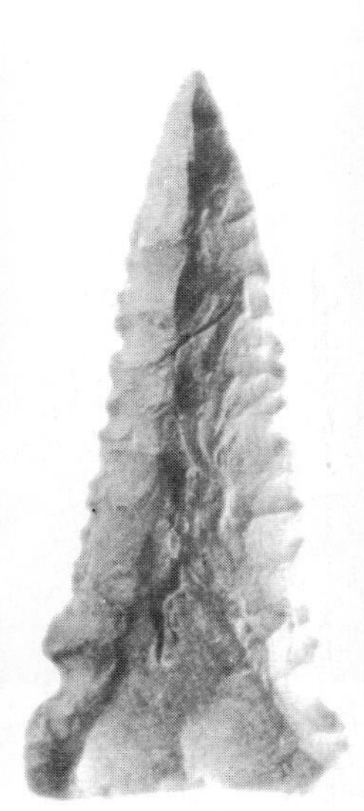
G5, $25-$40
Rockingham Co., NC.

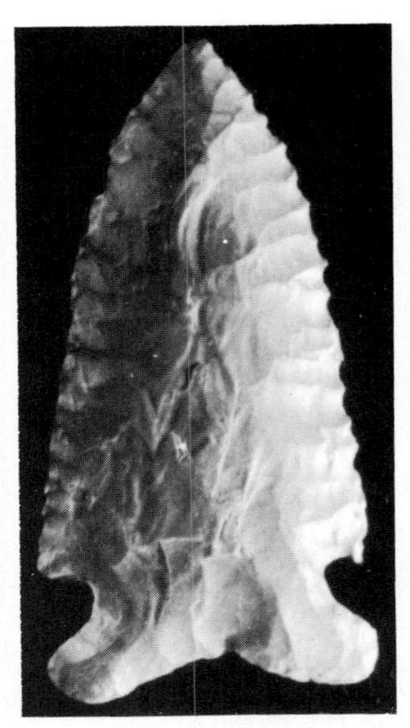
G5, $25-$40
Humphreys Co., TN.

G8, $250-$400
Humphreys Co., TN.

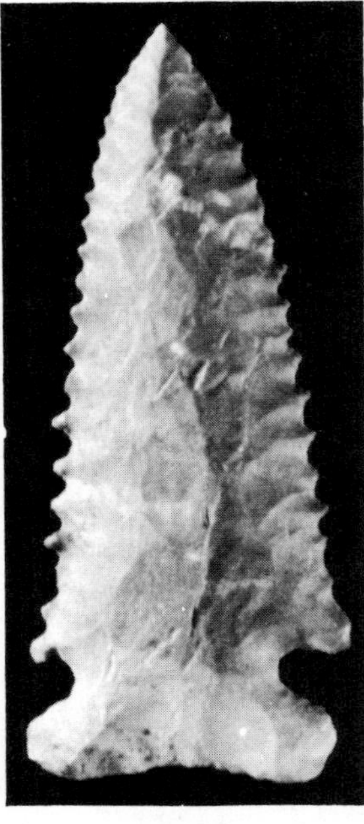
G9, $350-$500
Lauderdale Co., AL. Fort Payne chert. Classic.

G10, $400-$700
Giles Co., TN. Outstanding with needle tip. Field find.

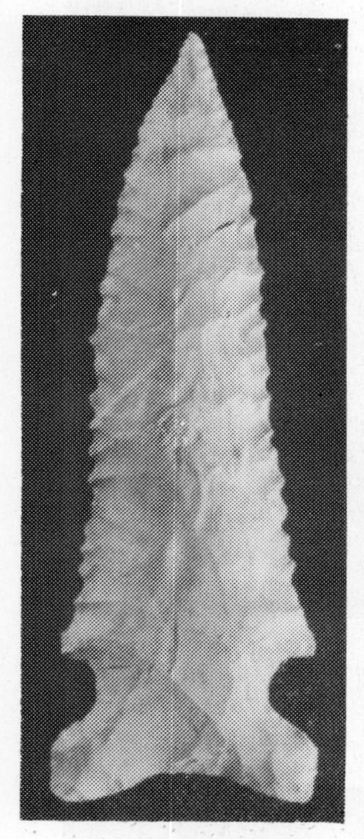

G9, $200-$300
KY.

G8, $250-$400
Humphreys Co., TN. Buffalo River chert. Excellent quality. Classic.

G6, $50-$90
Humphreys Co., TN. Base nick.

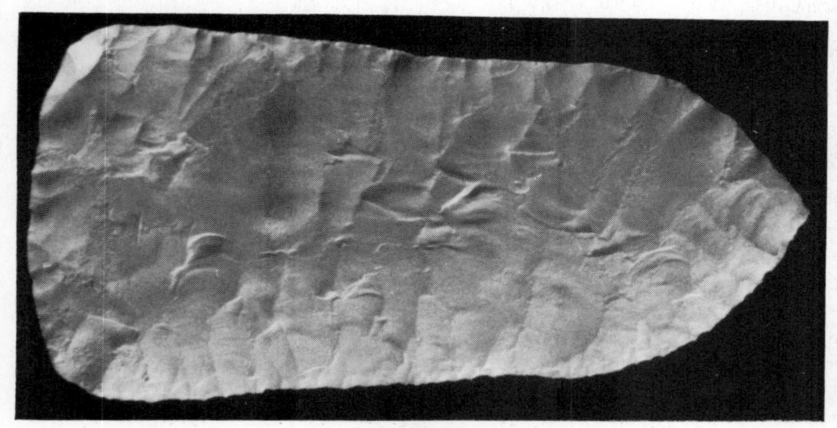

G9, $90-$150
Coffee Lake, AL. A Pine Tree unnotched preform. Very rare.

PINE TREE CORNER NOTCHED - Early Archaic, 8000 - 5000 B.P.

(Also see Kirk and Palmer)

G6, $50-$80
Harrison Co., IN.

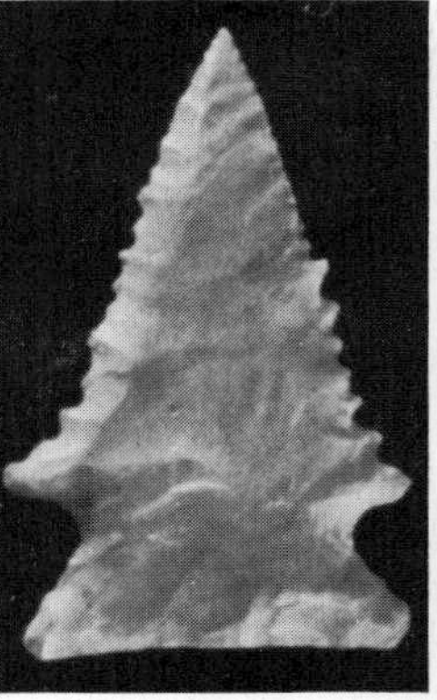

G6, $50-$80
Humphreys Co., TN.

G4, $20-$30
Humphreys Co., TN. Tang nick.

G5, $30-$50
Barkley Lake, KY.

G8, $100-$200
MO.

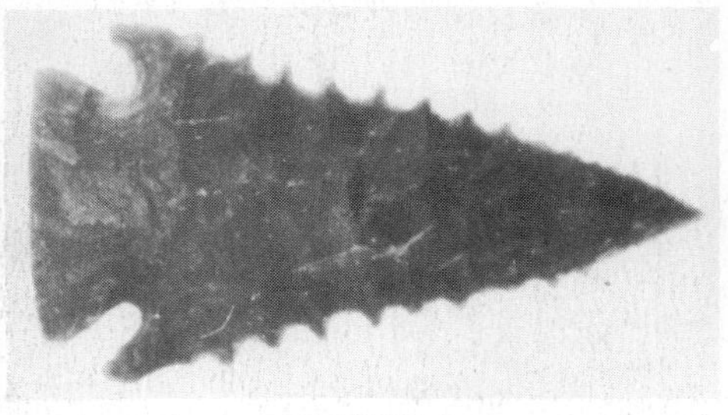

G9, $250-$400
Nashville, TN. Classic.

LOCATION: Southeastern States. **DESCRIPTION:** A small to medium size, thin, corner notched point with a concave, convex, straight, bifurcated or auriculate base. Blade edges are usually serrated and flaking is parallel to the center of the blade. The shoulders expand and are barbed. The base is ground. Small examples would fall under the *Palmer* type. **I.D. KEY:** Archaic flaking to the center of each blade.

G9, $200-$350
Davidson Co., TN.

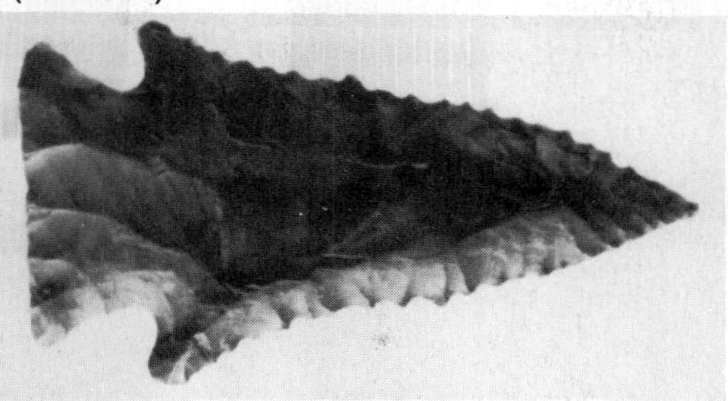

G8, $100-$200
Florence, AL.

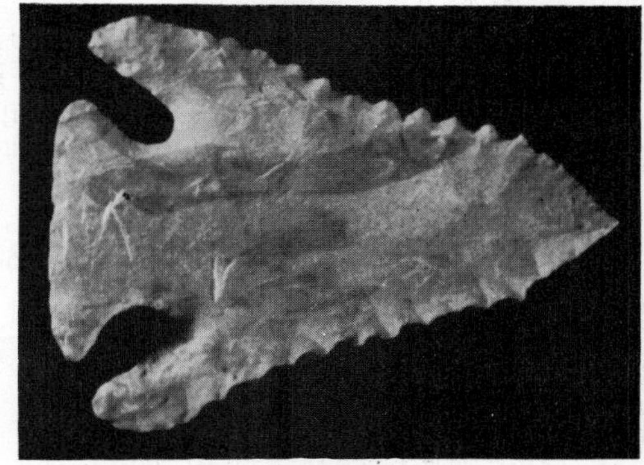

G9, $200-$350
7 Mile Isle, Florence, AL. Excellent quality.

G10, $450-$600
Humphreys Co., TN.

G9, $250-$450
KY.

PINELLAS - Mississippian, 800 - 400 B.P.

(Also see Fort Ancient & Madison)

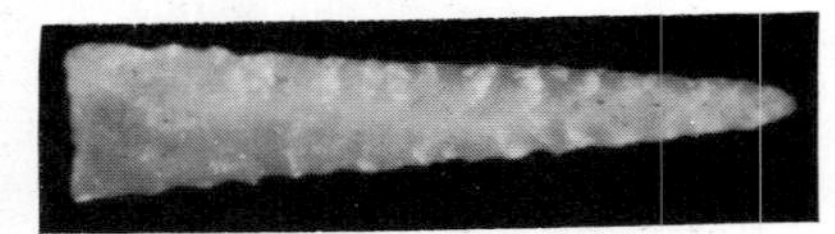

G8, $50-$80
Pasco Co. FL.

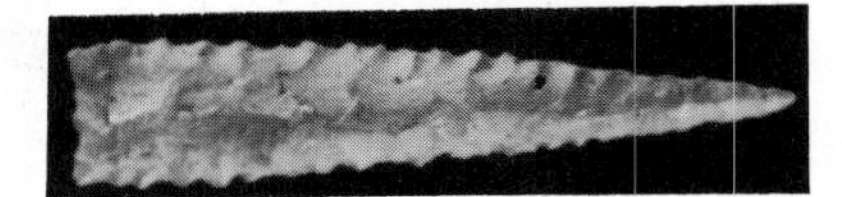

G9, $60-$90
Gilchrist Co., FL.

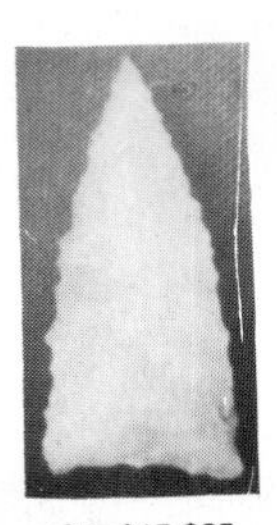

G5, $15-$25
Marion Co., FL.

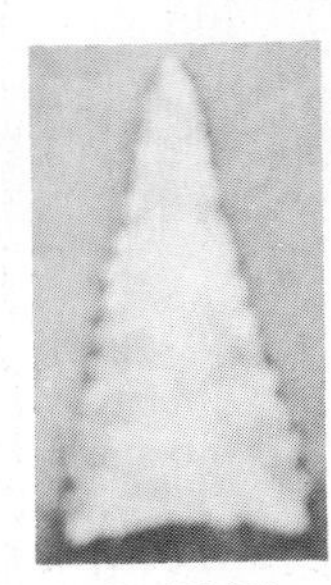

G6, $30-$45
Marion Co.. FL.

LOCATION: Southern Southeastern states. **DESCRIPTION:** A small, narrow, thick, serrated, triangular point with a straight to slightly concave base.

PINTO BASIN - Late Archaic to Woodland, 4000 - 2000 B.P.

(Also see Lott)

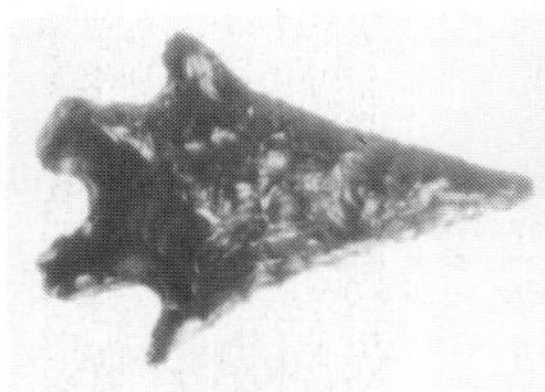

G8, $40-$70
WA/OR.

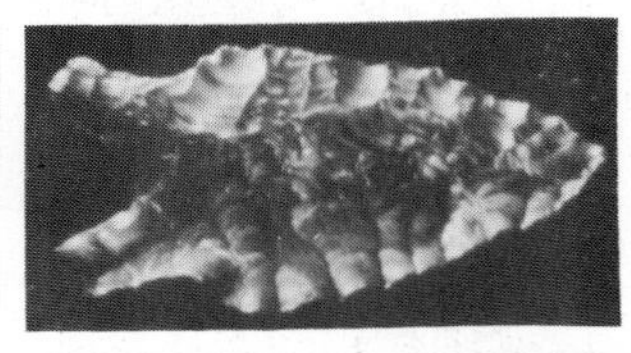

G6, $20-$35
WA/OR.

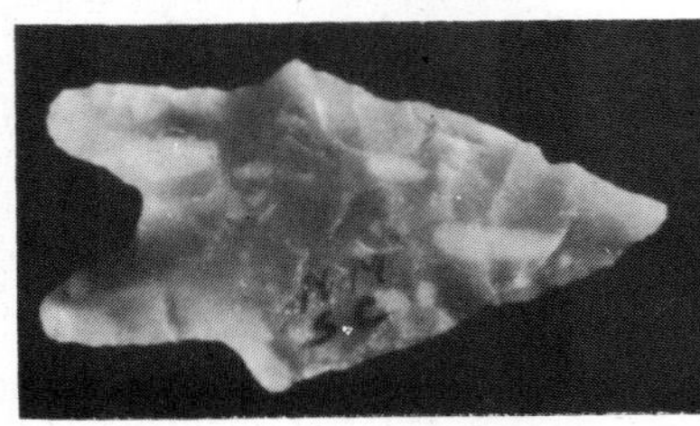

G5, $15-$25
CO.

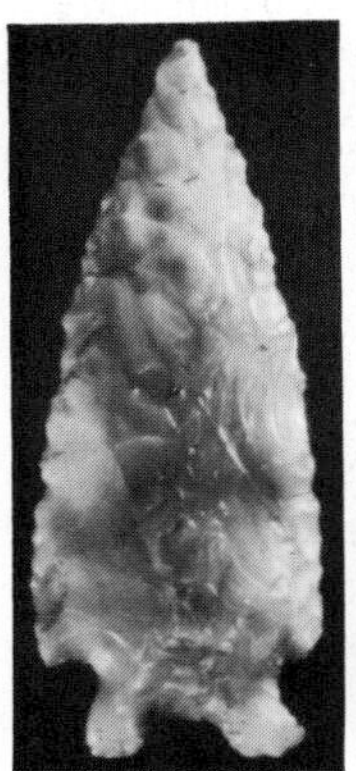

G7, $30-$45
Wasco Co., OR. The Dalles.

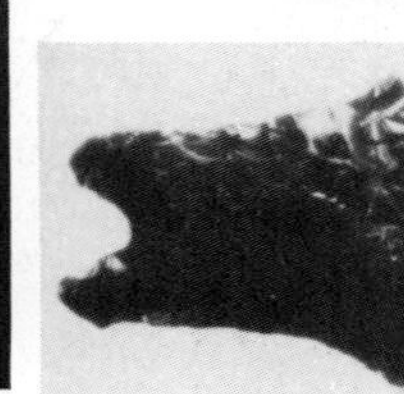

G10, $180-$300
Lake Co., OR., Crump Lake.

LOCATION: Northwestern states. **DESCRIPTION:** A medium sized, narrow, auriculate point. Shoulders can be tapered, horizontal or barbed. Bases are deeply bifurcated.

PLAINVIEW - Late Paleo, 10000 - 7000 B.P.

(Also see Angostura, Browns Valley, Clovis, Dalton, Guilford and Midland)

G1, $5-$10
CO/TX. Broken.

G1, $8-$12
CO/TX. Broken.

G3, $80-$120
Comanche Co., TX.

G1, $10-$20
CO/TX. Broken.

G1, $8-$12
CO/TX. Broken

G4, $120-$200
Comanche Co., TX., Fluted.

G8, $300-$450
MO.

G7, $200-$300
W. Memphis, TN.

G8, $350-$500
Cent. IA.

LOCATION: Midwestern to Western states and Canada. **DESCRIPTION:** A medium size, thin, lanceolate point with usually parallel sides and a concave base that is ground. Some examples are thinned or fluted and is believed to be related to the earlier *Clovis* and contemporary *Dalton* type. Flaking is of high quality and can be collateral to oblique transverse.

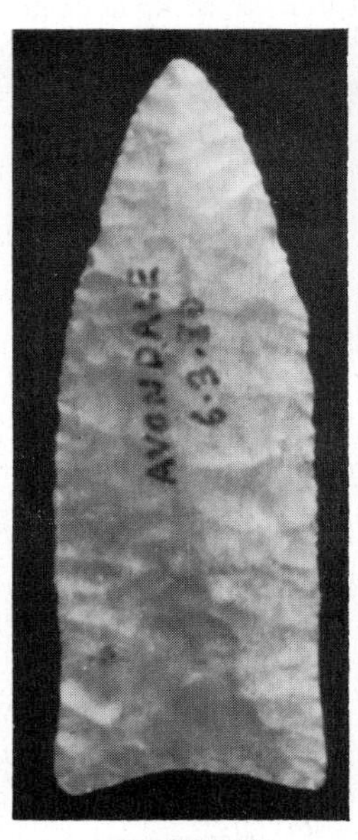

G7, $200-$300
Platt Co., MO.

G7, $200-$300
Cent. IA.

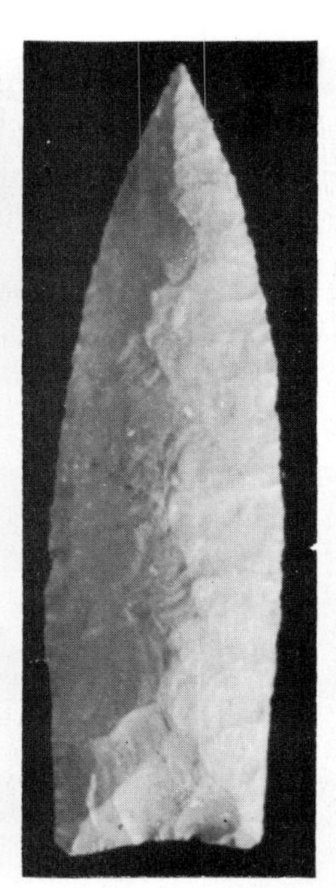

G8, $350-$500
Kansas City, MO.

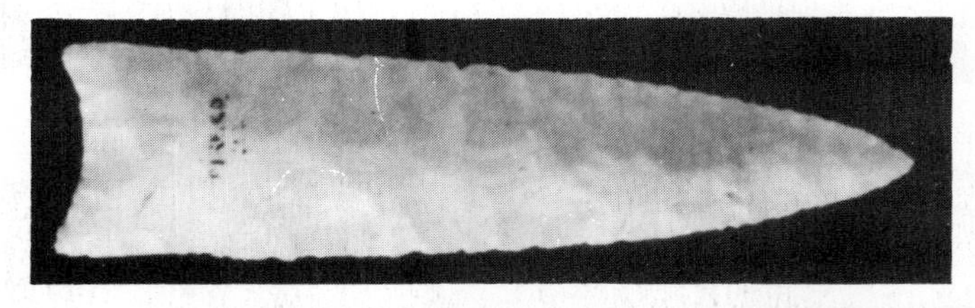

G8, $350-$500
Pike Co., IL.

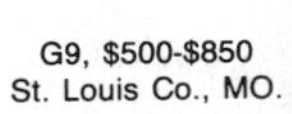

G9, $500-$850
St. Louis Co., MO.

G9, $500-$850
Adams Co., IL.
Collateral Flaking.
Classic.

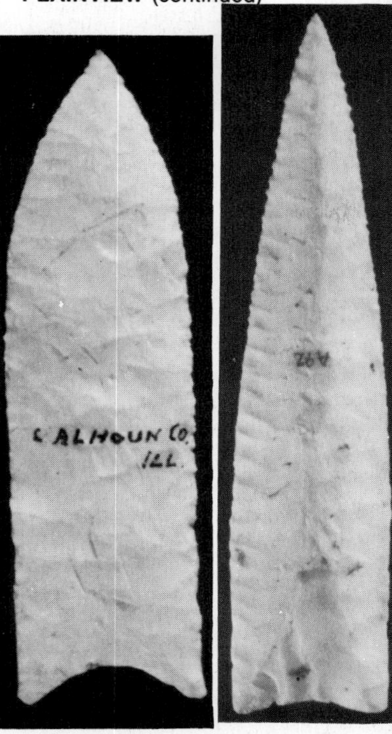

G9, $500-$850
Calhoun Co., IL.

G9, $500-$850
Warren Co., MO.

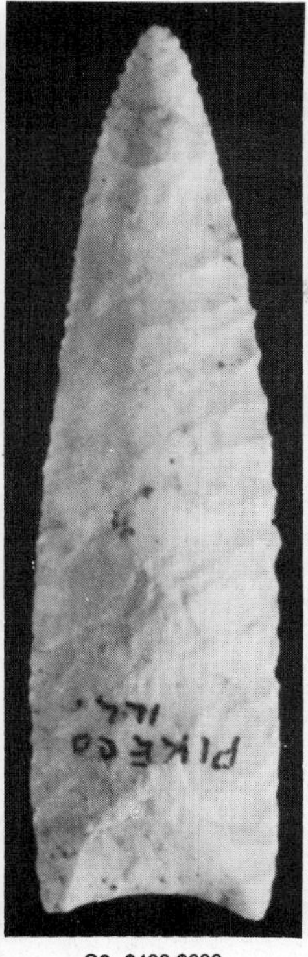

G9, $400-$600
Pike Co., IL. Note oblique flaking.

G10, $800-$1500
Adams Co., IL. Note transverse flaking.

G9, $550-$900, Cent. IA. Note oblique flaking.

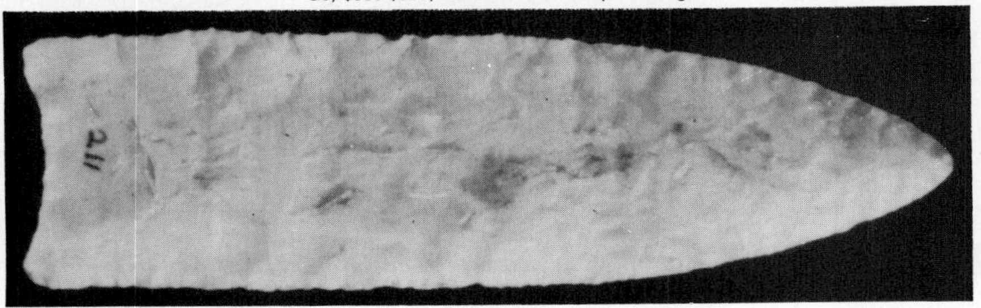

G9, $500-$850, IL.

G7, $200-$300, Schuyler Co., IL.

G10, $700-$1200, St. Louis Co., MO.

G8, $350-$500, IL.

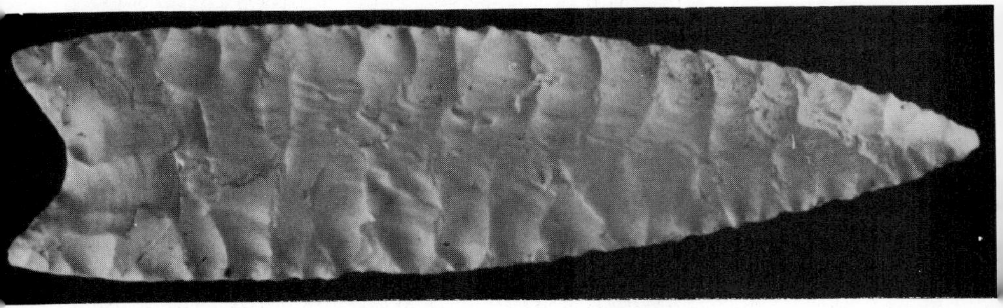

G10, $800-$1500, East Prairie, MO.

PLEVNA (See Dovetail)

PONTCHARTRAIN (Type I) - Late Archaic to Woodland, 4000 - 2000 B.P.

(Also see Little Bear Creek, Flint Creek and Mulberry Creek)

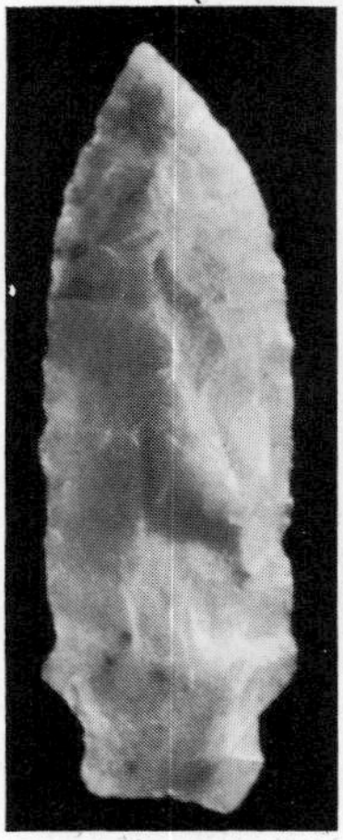

G2, $1-$2
Comanche Co., TX.

G4, $3-$5
SE TN.

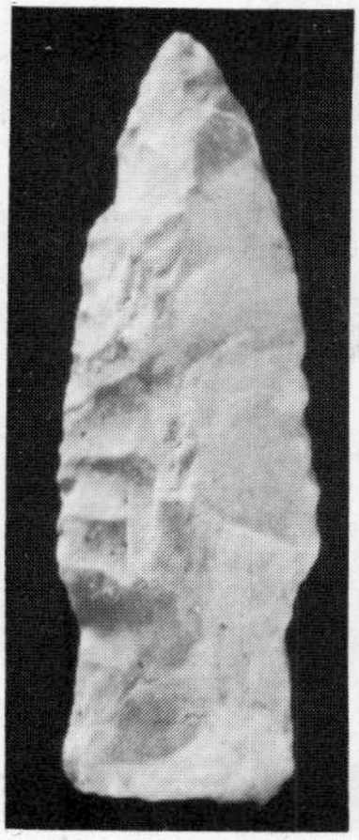

G3, $1-$3
Comanche Co., TX.

G3, $1-$3
Comanche Co., TX.

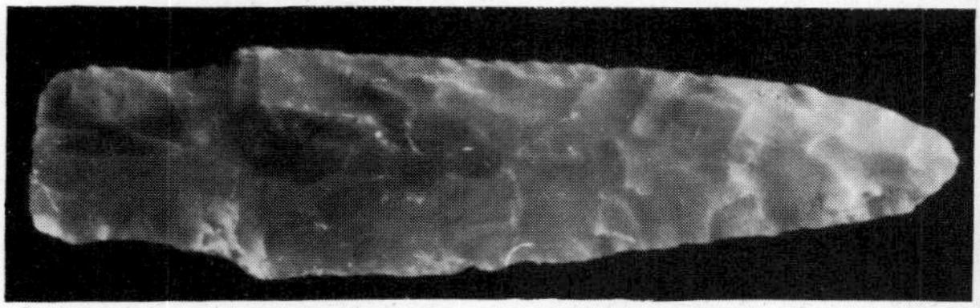

G4, $5-$8. Comanche Co., TX.

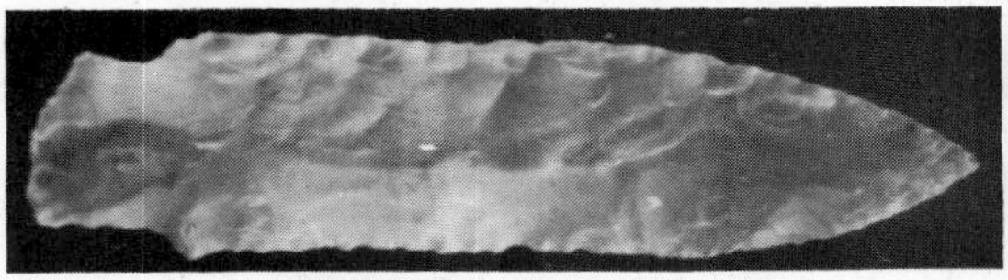

G3, $1-$3. W. TN.

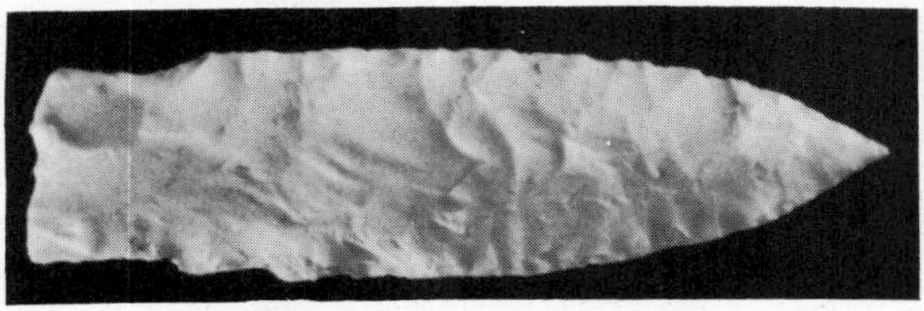

G3, $1-$3. Comanche Co., TX.

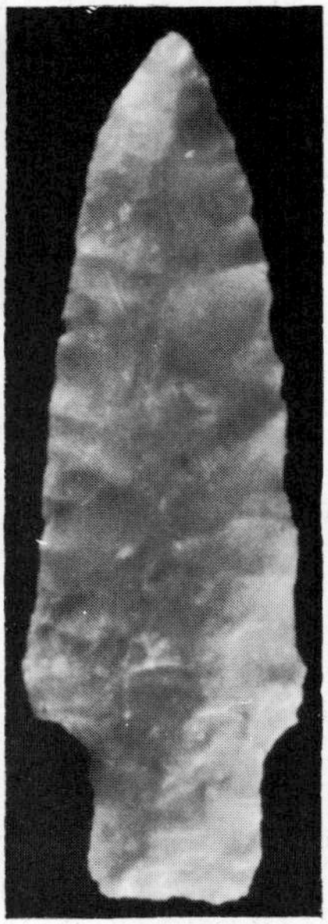

G5, $8-$12
Comanche Co., TX.

LOCATION: Mid-southeastern states. **DESCRIPTION:** A medium to large size, thick, narrow, stemmed point with weak, tapered or barbed shoulders. The stem is parallel sided with a concave base. Some examples are finely serrated and are related and similar to the *Flint Creek* type.

PONTCHARTRAIN (Type I) (continued)

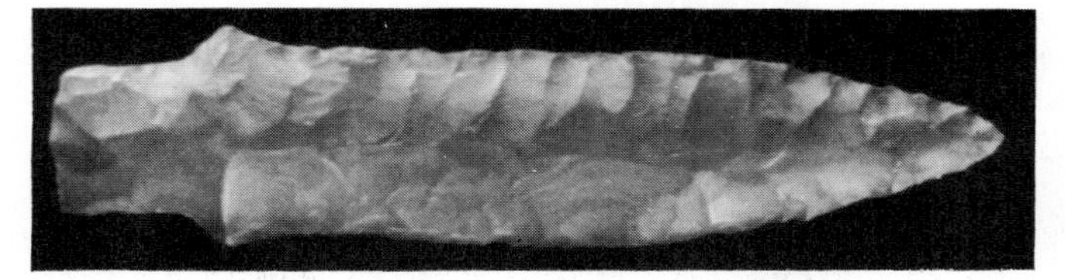

G5, $8-$12
W. TN.

G9, $60-$100
W. TN. Classic.

G10, $250-$400. Parsons, TN. Excellent symmetry and quality.

PONTCHARTRAIN (Type II) - Woodland, 3400 - 2000 B.P.

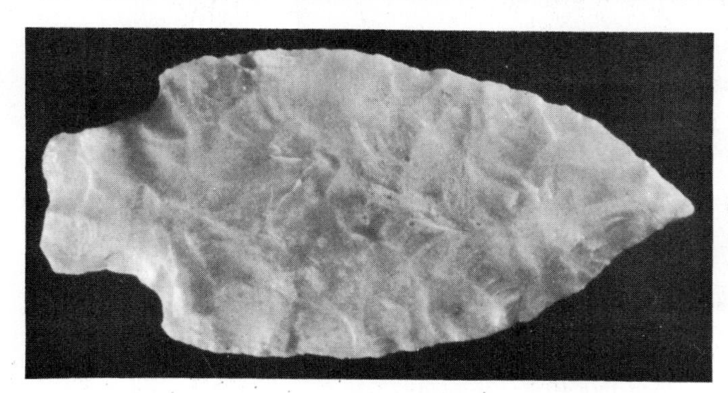

G6, $25-$40
Comanche Co., TX.

LOCATION: Mid-southeastern states. **DESCRIPTION:** A medium to large size, broad, stemmed point with barbed shoulders. The stem is parallel to slightly contracting and the base is straight to convex.

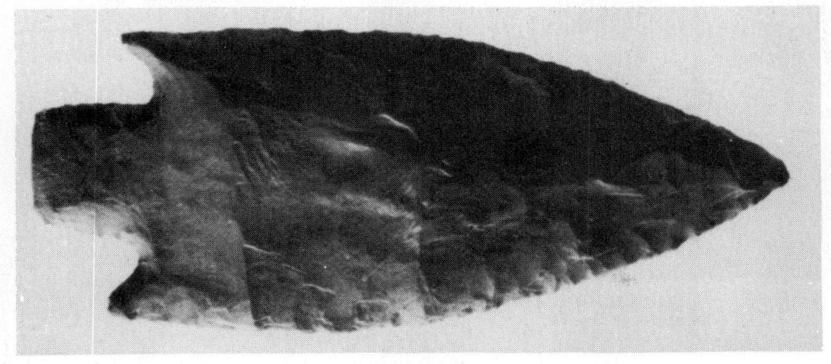

G9, $80-$120
W. TN.

POTTS - Woodland, 3000 - 1000 B.P.

(Also see Waratan and White Springs)

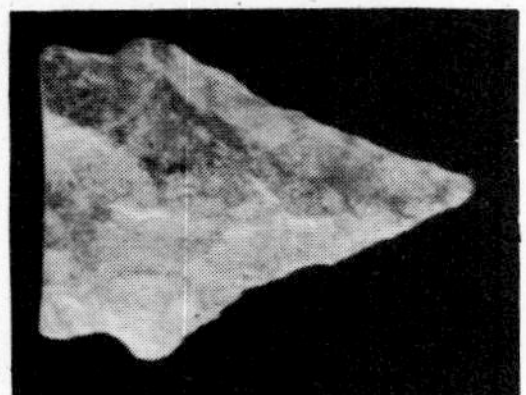

G4, $2-$3
Rockingham Co., NC.

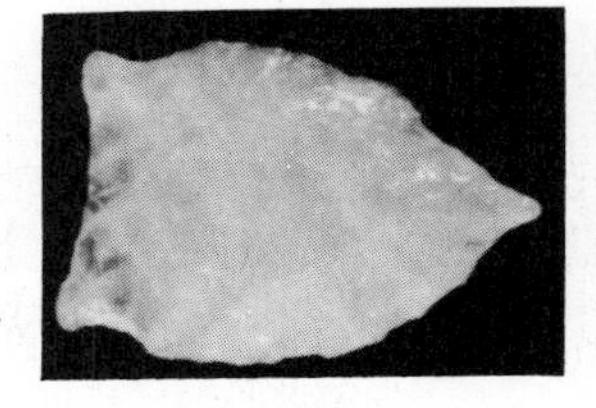

G5, $2-$4
Sussex Co., VA.
Vein quartz.

LOCATION: Far Eastern states. **DESCRIPTION:** A medium size triangular point with a short, straight base that has shallow corner notches.

PUTNAM - Late Archaic, 5000 - 3000 B.P.

(Also see alachua, Cypress Creek, Hardee Beveled, Levy, Marion, Morrow Mountain, Newnan & Sumter)

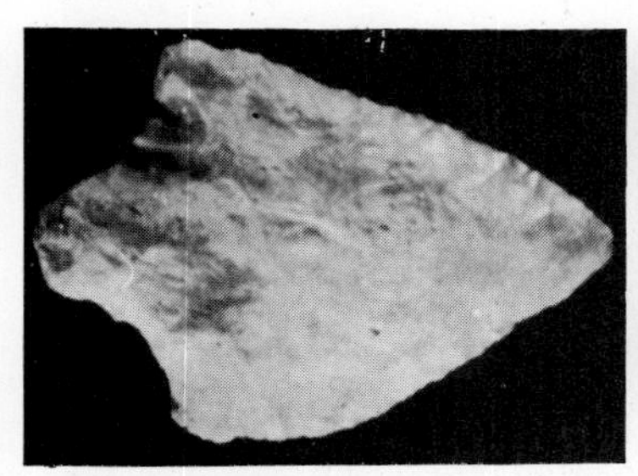

G2, $5-$10
Hillsborough Co., FL.

G3, $10-$20
Daw Island, SC.

LOCATION: Southern Southeastern states. **DESCRIPTION:** A medium to large size, broad, contracted stemmed point. The stem is fairly long with a convex base. The shoulders are tapered and can be rounded. May have evolved from the *Marion* type.

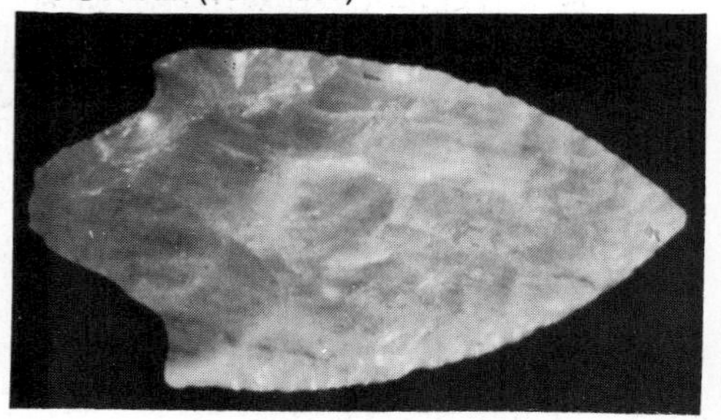

G4, $25-$40
Hillsborough Co., FL.

G3, $15-$25
Hillsborough Co., FL.

G4, $30-$45
Hillsborough Co., FL.

G5, $60-$100
Alachua Co., FL.

G6, $70-$120
Hillsborough Co., FL.

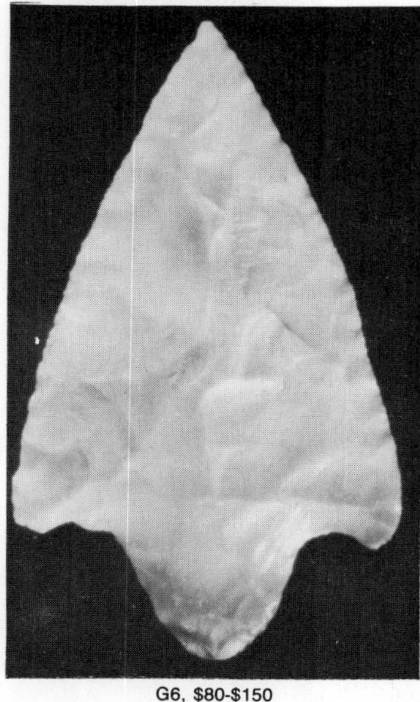

G6, $80-$150
Pasco Co., FL.

G7, $180-$300, Sante Fe Rv., FL.

QUAD - Late Paleo, 10000 - 6000 B.P.

(Also see Beaver Lake, Candy Creek, Cumberland, Golondrina and Pelican)

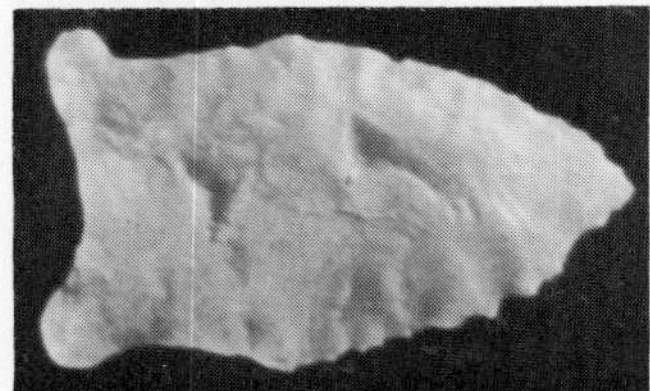

G2, $25-$40
Nickajack Lake, TN.

G2, $30-$45
Huntsville, AL.

G4, $70-$110
Humphreys Co., TN.
Buffalo Rv. chert.

G2, $20-$30
Myrtle Beach, SC.

LOCATION: Southeastern states. **DESCRIPTION:** A medium to large size lanceolate point with flaring "squared" auricles and a concave base which is ground. Most examples show basal thinning and some are fluted. Believed to be related to the earlier *Cumberland* point. **I.D. KEY:** Paleo flaking, squarish aruicles.

G5, $70-$125
Florence, AL. Keller's bluff.
Fort Payne chert.

G5, $70-$125
Humphreys Co., TN.

G4, $60-$100
Lauderdale Co., AL.

G6, $125-$225
Lauderdale Co., AL.

G6, $125-$225
Orangeburg Co., SC.

G5, $80-$140
Licking Co., OH.

G7, $250-$350
W. TN. Dover chert.
Classic form.

QUAD (continued)

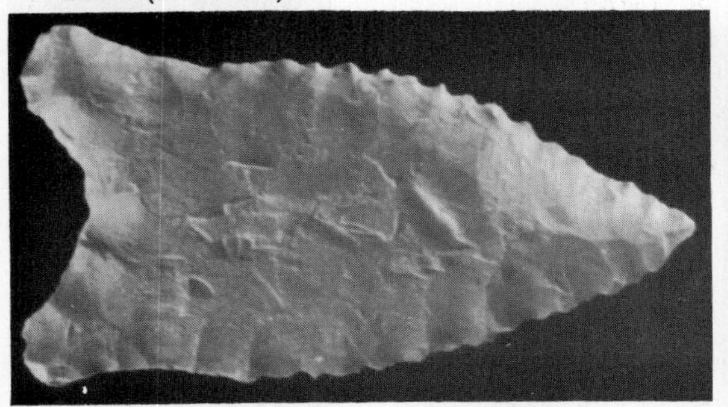

G7, $150-$250. Lauderdale Co., AL.

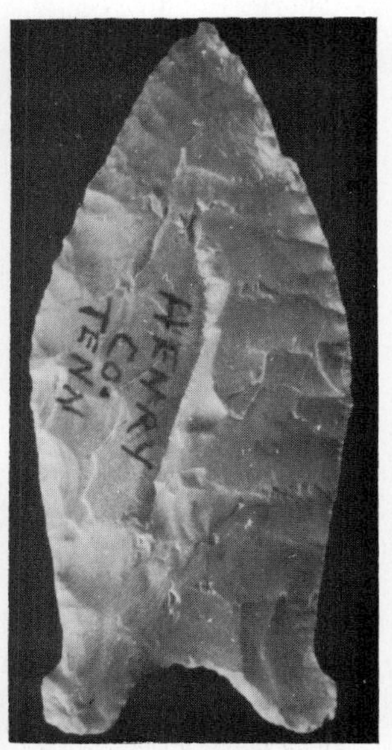

G7, $150-$250
Henry Co., TN. Minor tip & blade nick.

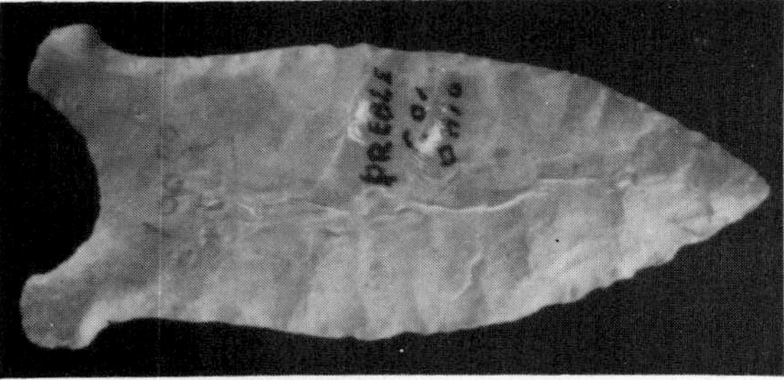

G8, $350-$650, Preble Co., OH.

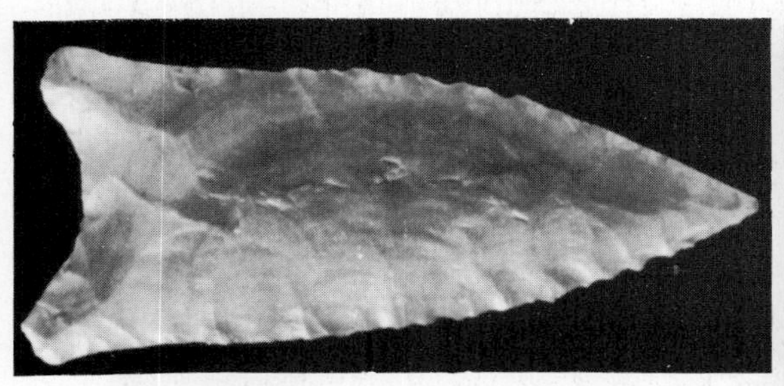

G8, $350-$650, Scott Co., KY. Colorful Carter Cave flint.

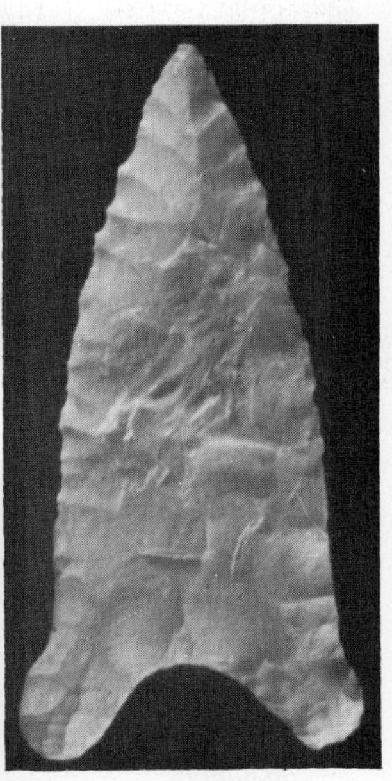

G8, $350-$600
Lauderdale Co., AL. Excellent quality & form.

G7, $150-$250. Cape Girardeau Co., MO.

G7, $200-$350
Butler Co., OH.

G9, $600-$1000
TN/AL. Classic example. Note basal thinning. Very thin.

G7, $150-$250
Coffee Lake, AL.

G8, $400-$700, Henry Co., TN.

G9, $800-$1500, Trimble Co., KY.

QUAD (continued)

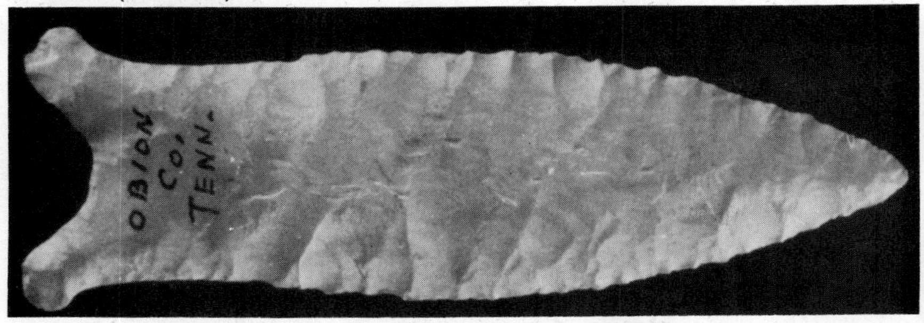

G10, $1800-$3000, Obion Co., TN. Note weak shoulders created by basal grinding.

RACOON CREEK (See Knight Island)

RADDATZ - Late Archaic to Woodland, 5000 - 2000 B.P.

(Also see Big Sandy, Bolen, Cache River, Hemphill, Osceola, Otter Creek, Rowan & Savage Cave)

G3, $3-$5
AR.

G5,$6-$8
Jonesboro, AR.

G2, $1-$3
Colbert Co., AL.

G3, $3-$5
Jonesboro, AR.

G6, $6-$10
Jonesboro, AR.

LOCATION: Midwestern states. **DESCRIPTION:** A medium size, side notched point with a concave to straight base. Similar in outline to *Big Sandy* points found in the Southeast.

RADDATZ (continued)

G6, $8-$12
MO.

G5, $5-$8
Jonesboro, AR.

G5, $5-$8
Jonesboro, AR.

G5, $5-$8
MO.

G8, $20-$30
Jonesboro, AR.

G6, $8-$12
Jonesboro, AR.

G6, $8-$12
Jonesboro, AR.

RAMEY KNIFE - Mid-Archaic, 5000 - 4000 B.P.

(Also see Cotaco Creek & Morse Knife)

LOCATION: Midwestern states. **DESCRIPTION** A large size, broad, lanceolate blade with a rounded base and high quality flaking.

G8, $400-$700
Calloway Co., MO.

G10, $1200-$2200
St. Clair Co., IL. Classic.

RANDOLPH - Woodland to Historic, 2000 - 200 B.P.

(Also see Bradley, Flint River and Schild Spike, Duval, Mountain Fork and New Market)

G2, $1-$2
Waco, TX.

G4, $2-$4
Surry Co., NC.

G3, $2-$3
Rockingham Co., NC.

G6, $4-$5
Guilford Co., NC.

G4, $2-$4
Randolph Co., NC.

G1, .25-.50
Kershaw Co., SC.
Slate.

G7, $5-$8
Randolph Co., NC.

G1, .25-.50
Kershaw Co., SC.
Broken half. Slate.

G1, .25.-.50
Kershaw Co., SC.
Slate.

G7, $5-$8
Guilford Co., NC.

G4, $2-$4
Guilford Co., NC.

G2, $1-$2
Randolph Co., NC.

G8, $8-$15
Randolph Co., NC.

G6, $4-$5
Guilford Co., NC.

G5, $3-$5
Randolph Co., NC.

LOCATION: Far Eastern states. Type site is Randolph Co., NC. **DESCRIPTION:** A medium size, narrow, thick, spike point with tapered shoulders and a short to medium contracted, rounded stem. Many examples from North Carolina have exaggerated spikes along the blade edges.

G7, $5-$8
Guilford Co., NC.

G2, $1-$2
Montgomery Co., NC.

G5, $3-$5
Person Co., NC.

G5, $3-$5
Rockingham Co., NC.

G4, $2-$4
Guilford Co., NC.

RED OCHRE - Woodland, 3000 - 1500 B.P.

(Also see Adena Blade, Copena Round Base, Tennessee River and Wadlow)

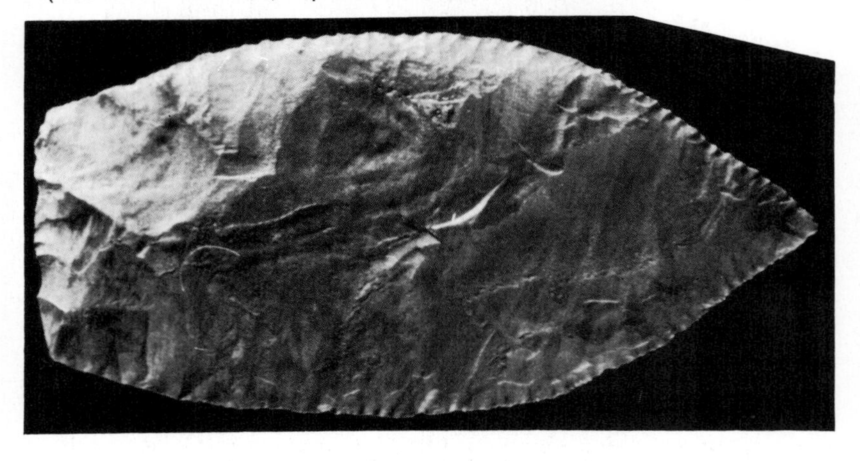

G9, $80-$120
Parsons, TN. Dover chert. Note fine edgework.

LOCATION: Midwestern to Southeastern states. **DESCRIPTION:** A large, thin, broad blade with a contracting basal area. The base is convex to straight. Very similar to *Wadlow* which has the parallel sides. Possibly related to the *Turkeytail* type.

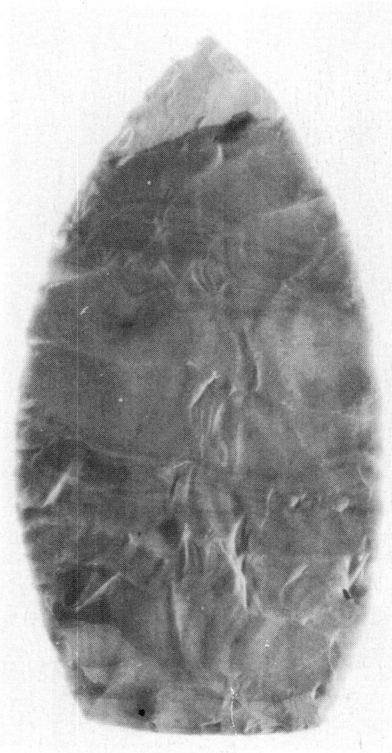

G8, $45-$70
Sikeston, MO. Classic.

G5, $10-$20
Parsons, TN.

REDSTONE - Paleo, 15000 - 9000 B.P.

(Also see Clovis)

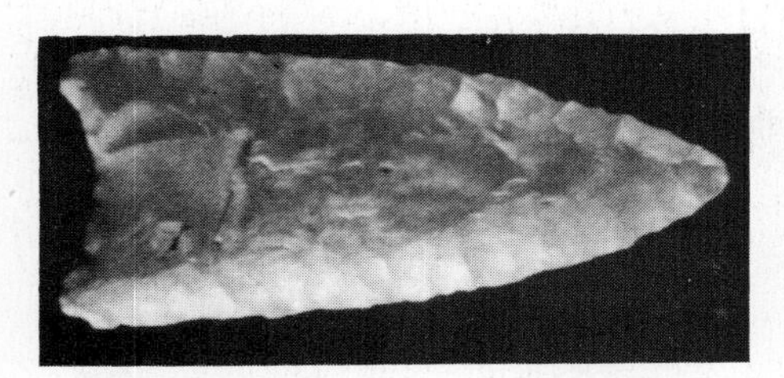

G2, $60-$100
Jackson Co., AL., weak fluting.

LOCATION: Southeastern states. **DESCRIPTION:** A medium to large size, thin, auriculate, fluted point with convex sides expanding to a wide, deeply concave base. The hafting area is ground. This point is widest at the base. Fluting can extend most of the way down each face. Multiple flutes are usual. (**Warning:** The more common resharpened *Clovis* point is often sold as this type. *Redstones* are extremely rare and are almost never offered for sale.) **I.D. KEY:** Batan fluted, edgework on the hafting area.

REDSTONE (continued)

G7, $700-$1200
Cooper Rv., SC.

G6, $550-$850
Edgefield Co., SC.

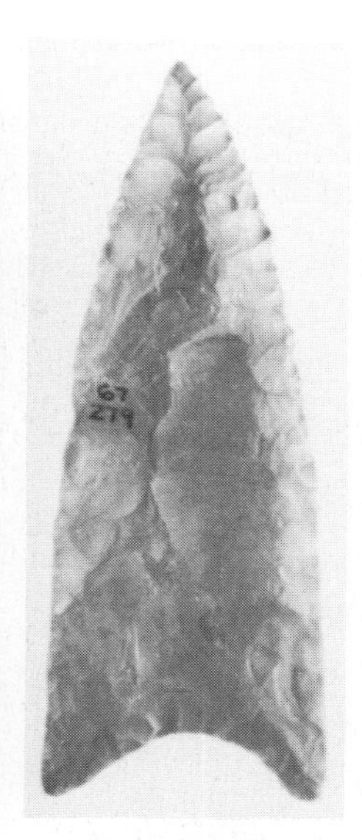

G9, $1000-$1800
Limestone Co., AL. Quad site.

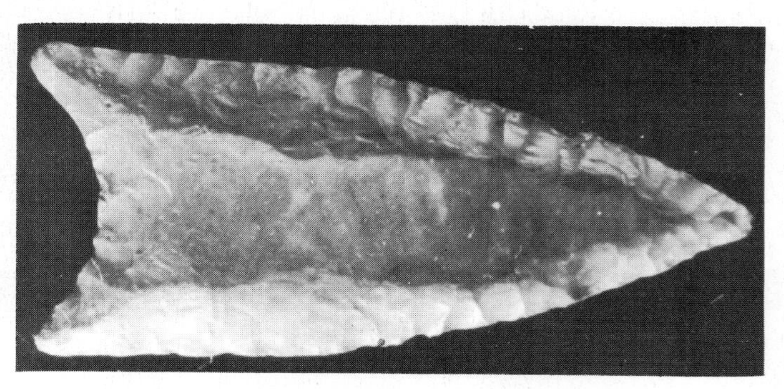

G10, $2500-$4000, Humphreys Co., TN., Nuckolls site. Classic form.
Fluted to the tip on both sides. Patenated Dover chert.

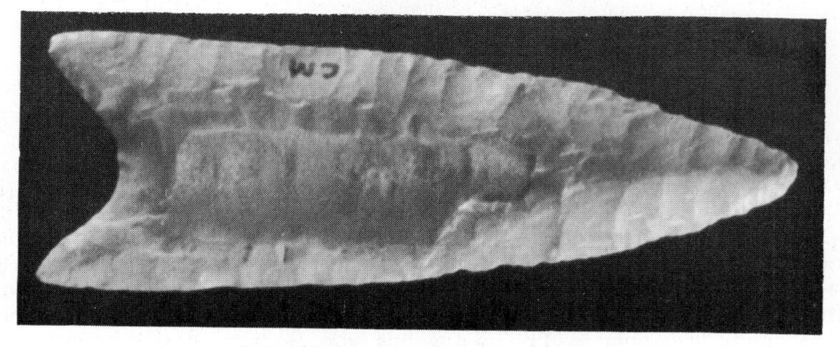

G10, $2500-$3500, Florence, AL. Classic form.

G10, $5000-$8000
Humphreys Co., TN. Dover chert. Found in cache of 3. Fluted to tip on both sides. Minor tip nick.

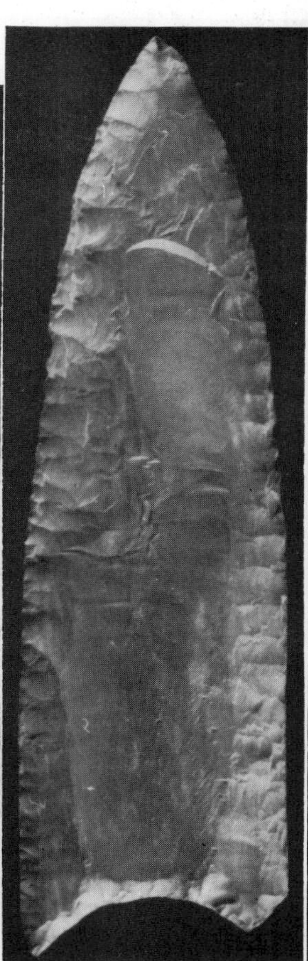

G10, $3500-$6500
Humphreys Co., TN. Dover chert. Found in cache of 3. Ear damage.

G10, $3500-$7000
Humphreys Co., TN. Found in cache of 3. Note multiple flutes.

REED - Woodland to Mississippian, 1500 - 500 B.P.

(Also see Cahokia and Knight Island)

G8, $40-$60
Clearwater Co., ID.

G5, $15-$25
WA/OR.

G7, $25-$40
Clearwater Co., ID.

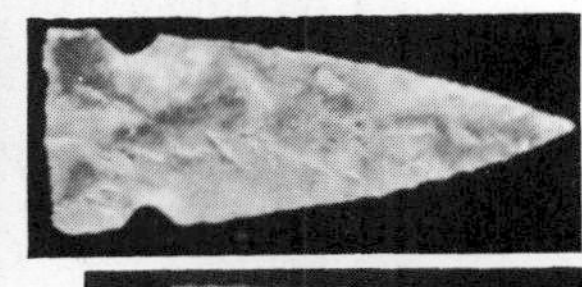

G8, $45-$70
AR.

G10, $180-$300
Spiro Mound, OK.

LOCATION: Midwestern states. **DESCRIPTION:** A small size, thin, triangular, side notched point with a straight base.

REFUGIO - Mid-Archaic, 5000 - 2000 B.P.

(Also see Benjamin, Gahagan, Pandora, Sabine and Texas Blade)

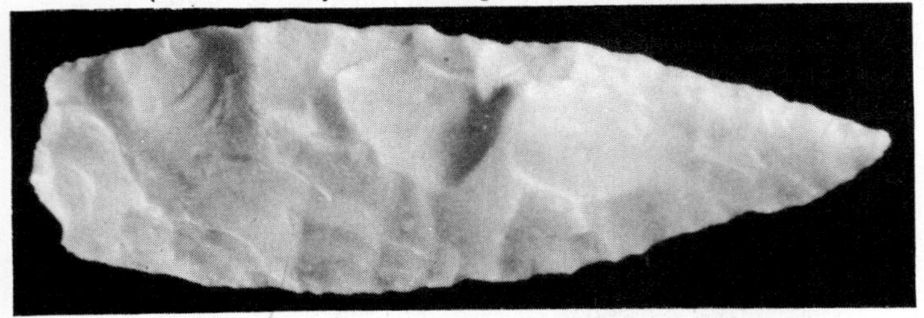

G5, $6-$10
Comanche Co., TX.

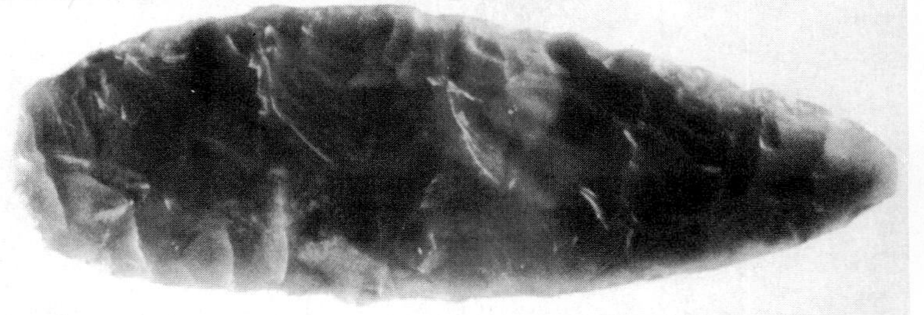

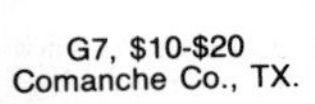

G7, $10-$20
Comanche Co., TX.

LOCATION: Midwestern states. **DESCRIPTION:** A medium to large size, narrow, lanceolate blade with a rounded base.

RHEEMS CREEK - Woodland, 4000 - 2000 B.P.

(Also see Dallas, Elam, Halifax and Jude)

G4, $1-$3
SE TN.

G5, $2-$3
N. AL.

G4, $1-$3
Huntsville, AL.

G5, $2-$3
N. AL.

G4, $1-$3
Meigs Co., TN.

G6, $3-$5
N. AL.

G7, $4-$6
Walker Co., AL.

LOCATION: Southeastern states. **DESCRIPTION:** A small size, stubby, parallel sided, stemmed point with straight shoulders. Similar to *Halifax* which expands at the base.

RICE CONTRACTED STEMMED (See Hidden Valley)

RICE LOBBED - Early Archaic, 9000 - 5000 B.P.

(Also see Fox Valley, LeCroy, MacCorkle, Pine Tree, Southampton & Uvalde)

G3, $2-$4
Hamilton Co., TN.

G4, $3-$5
Meigs Co., TN.

G6, $20-$30
E. TN.

G7, $25-$40
Salt Lick, KY.

G8, $50-$70
OH. Coshocton chert.

G9, $80-$120
Salt Lick, KY.

G8, $50-$80
Salt Lick, KY. Classic.

LOCATION: Midwestern to Northeastern states. **DESCRIPTION:** A medium to large size bifurcated to lobbed base point with serrated blade edges. The base has a shallow indentation compared to the other bifurcated types. Shoulders are sharp and prominent. Called *Culpepper Bifurcate* in Virginia.

RIO GRANDE - Early Archaic, 7500 - 6000 B.P.

(Also see Agate Basin, Hell Gap, Lake Mohave and Pelican)

G1, $3-$5
Comanche Co., TX.

G6, $20-$30
Comanche Co., TX.

G6, $20-$30
Comanche Co., TX.

G7, $30-$50
Mexico, Obsidian.

G7, $40-$70
McIntosh Co., OK.

G5, $15-$25
Comanche Co., TX.

G7, $35-$60
Sante FE, NM. Blade nick.

G7, $35-$60
Sante Fe, NM.

LOCATION: Southwestern states and Mexico. **DESCRIPTION:** A medium to large size, lanceolate point with tapered shoulders and a long parallel sided to contracting stem. The base can be straight, concave or convex.

ROBBINS (See Adena-Robbins)

ROCKWALL - Late Woodland, 1400 - 1000 B.P.

(Also see Alba, Deadman, Gunther, Parowan, Sabinal, Scallorn & Shumla)

G6, $30-$50 Hamilton Co., TN. | G5, $25-$40 Cent. TX. | G2, $3-$5 Comanche Co., TX. | G3, $15-$25 Smith Co., TX. | G3, $8-$15 Cent. TX. | G2, $4-$6 Comanche Co., TX.

G2, $4-$6 Columbia Rv., WA. | G4, $20-$30 Col. Rv., WA. | G4, $20-$30 Comanche Co., TX. | G8, $50-$80 CA. | G3, $10-$20 Comanche Co., TX. | G3, $8-$15 Comanche Co., TX.

G8, $50-$80 WA/OR. | G9, $60-$100 WA/OR. | G5, $25-$40 WA/OR. | G4, $20-$30 WA/OR.

G5, $25-$40 WA/OR. | G7, $40-$60 WA/OR. | G6, $30-$50 WA/OR. | G5, $25-$40 Clearwater Co., ID. | G5, $25-$40 Clearwater Co., ID.

G9, $60-$90 Comanche Co., TX. | G5, $25-$40 Comanche Co., TX. | G8, $50-$80 WA/OR. | G8, $50-$90 WA/OR. | G5, $25-$35 Comanche Co., TX.

LOCATION: Midwestern to Western states. **DESCRIPTION:** A small, thin, triangular point with corner notches. Shoulders are barbed and usually extend almost to the base.

G6, $30-$50
Comanche Co., TX.

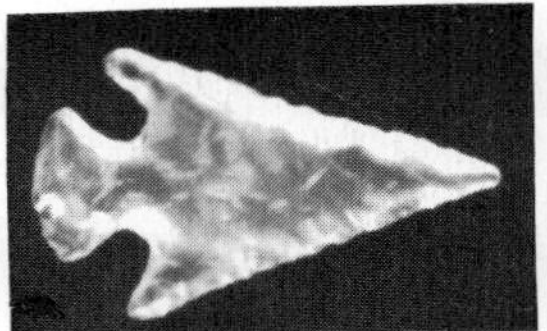
G7, $40-$60
Clearwater Co., ID.

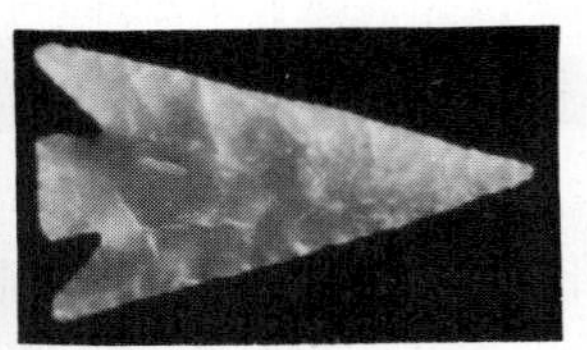
G9, $60-$100
WA/OR.

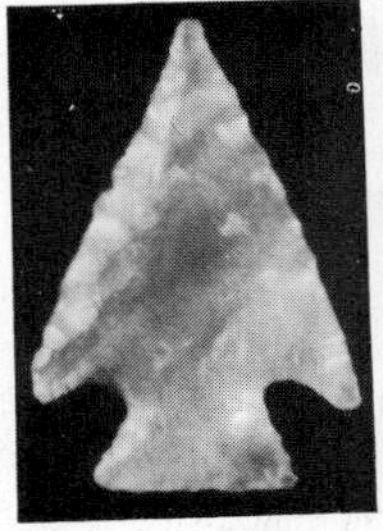
G7, $40-$60
Columbia Rv., WA.

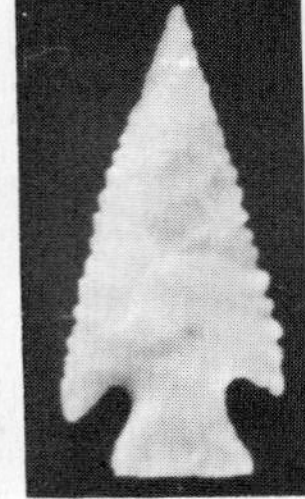
G7, $40-$60
Comanche Co., TX.

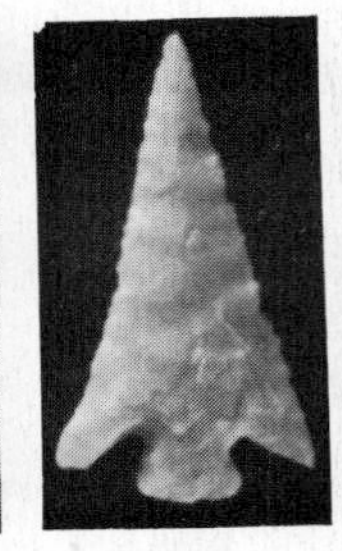
G7, $30-$50
Comanche Co., TX.

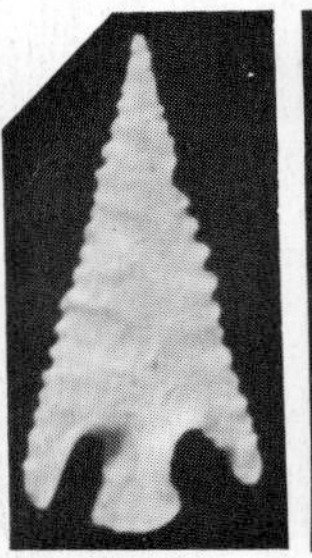
G8, $50-$80
Comanche Co., TX.

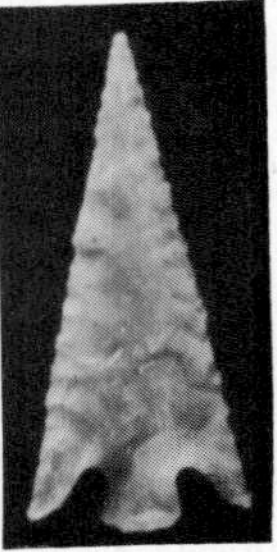
G8, $50-$80
WA/OR.

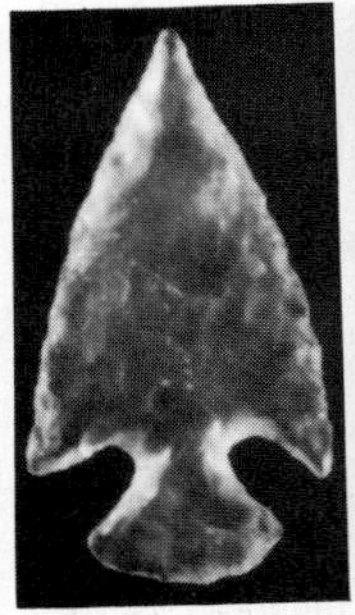
G9, $120-$200
Columbia Rv., WA.

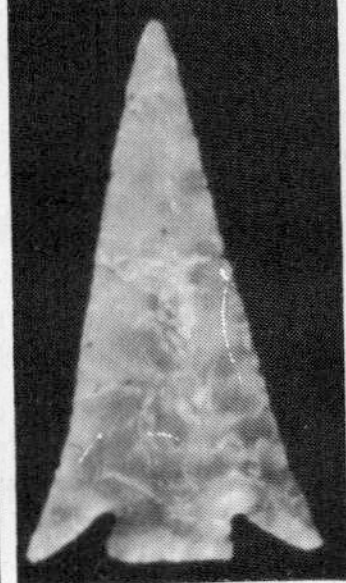
G9, $60-$100
WA/OR.

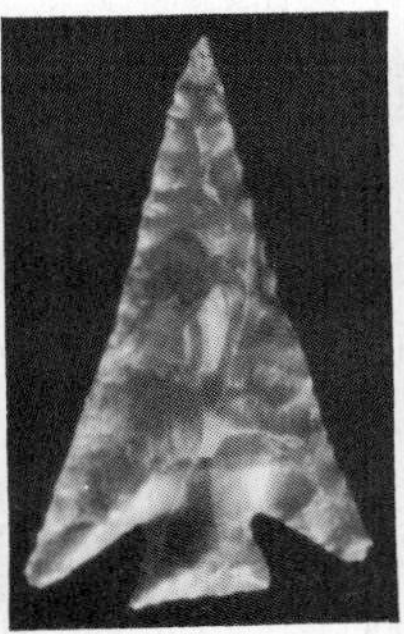
G8, $45-$70
WA/OR.

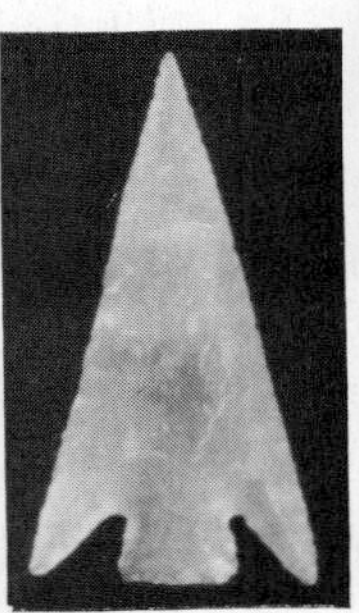
G10, $150-$250
WA/OR.

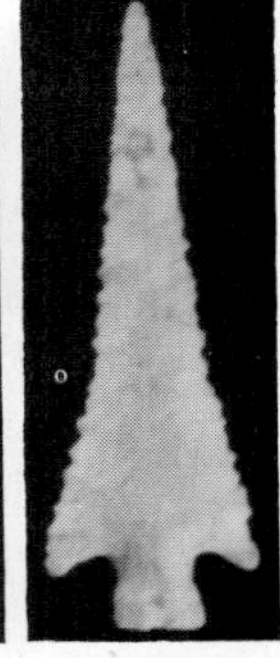
G9, $80-$120
Spiro Mound, OK.

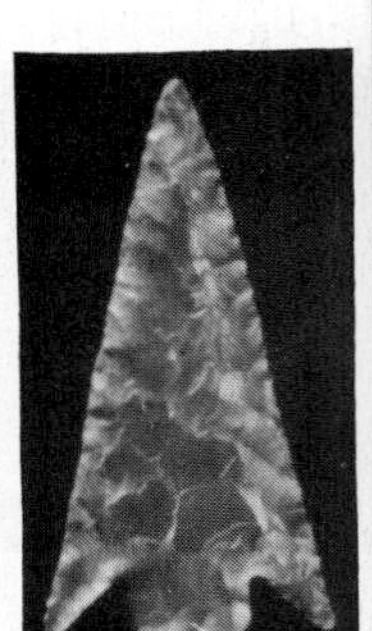
G9, $70-$110
WA/OR.

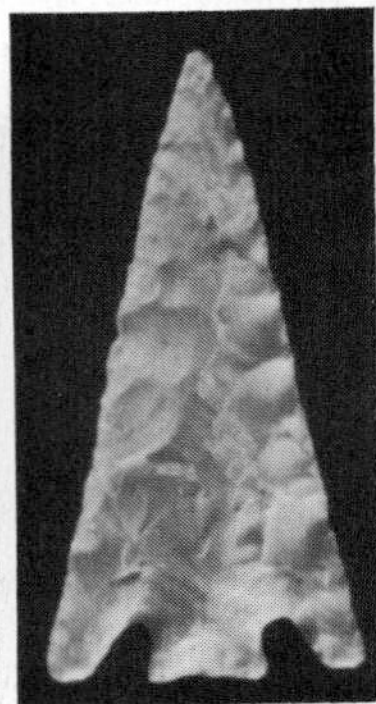
G9, $80-$120
WA/OR.

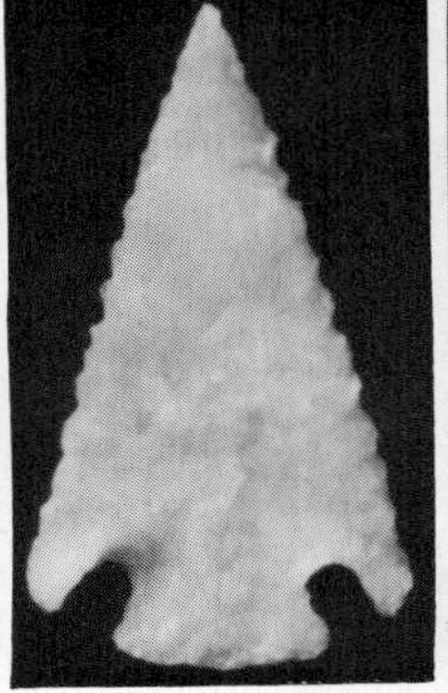
G9, $60-$100
WA/OR.

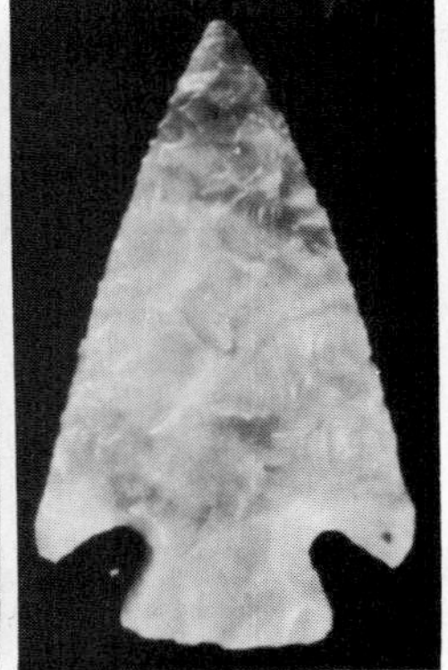
G9, $60-$100
WA/OR.

RODGERS SIDE-HOLLOWED - Late Paleo, 11,000 - 8,000 B.P.

(Also see Dalton, Hardaway, Oxbow, Pelican & San Patrice)

G5, $35-$60
Austin, TX., Ear nick.

LOCATION: Midwestern states. **DESCRIPTION:** A medium size, broad, auriculate point which is a variant form of the *San Patrice* type.

ROGERS CREEK - Woodland, 2000 - 1000 B.P.

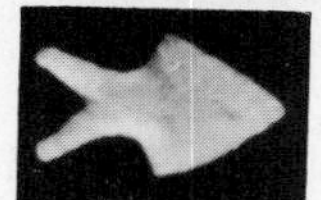

G8, $60-$100
Hamilton Co., TN.

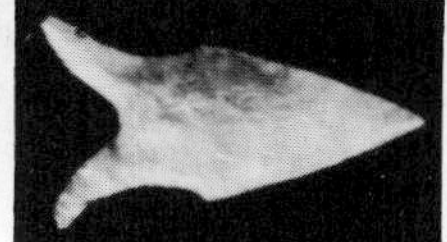

G10, $90-$150
Hamilton Co., TN. Classic.

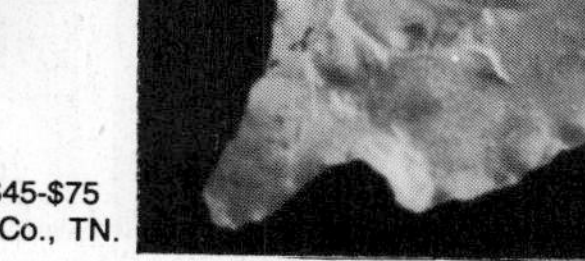

G6, $45-$75
Meigs Co., TN.

LOCATION: Southeastern states. **DESCRIPTION:** A small size, thin, triangular point with weak shoulders and flaring, pointed ears. The base is deeply concave. This point is rare, even in the area of occurrence.

ROGUE RIVER - Mississippian, 1000 - 600 B.P.

(Also see Calapooia, Catahoula Eiffel Tower & John Day River)

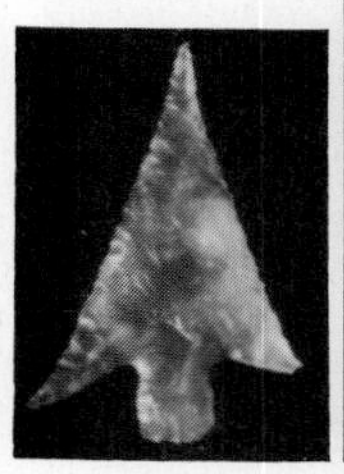

G7, $30-$50
The Dalles, OR.

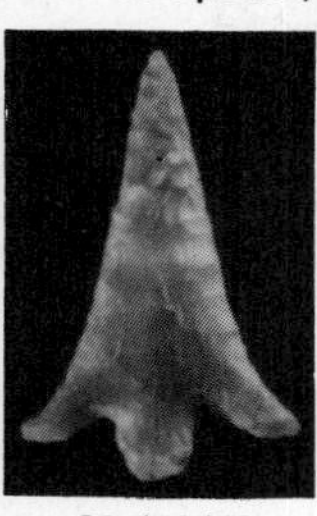

G8, $40-$60
Portland, OR.

G10, $150-$250
Wasco Co., OR.

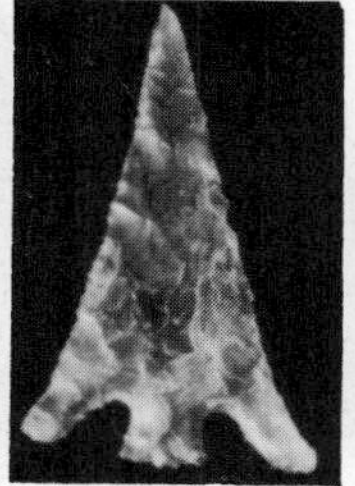

G9, $75-$100
The Dalles, OR.

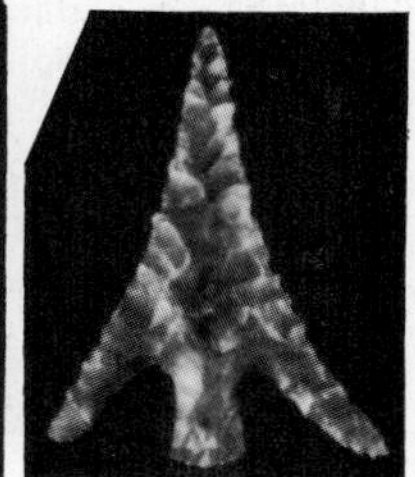

G10, $200-$300
Klamath Co., OR. Green & red agate. Classic.

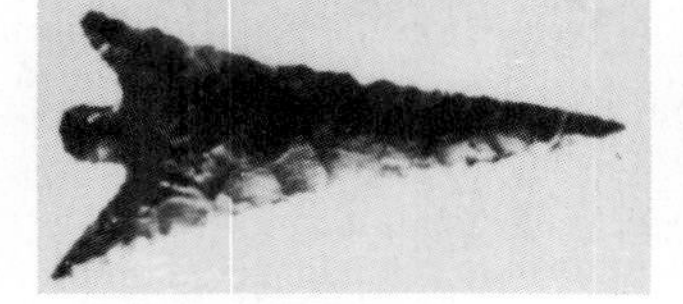

G8, $60-$100
Portland, OR.

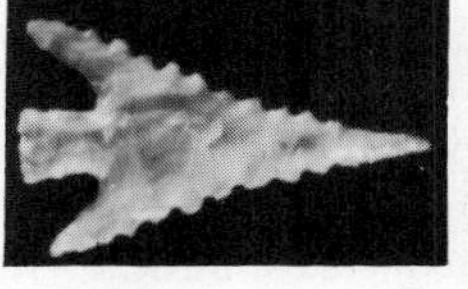

G8, $50-$80, Lane Co., OR.
Calapooia cross type.

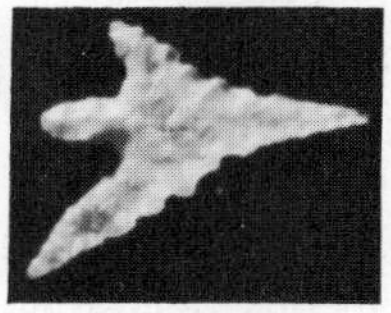

G6, $20-$45, Lane Co., OR.
Calapooia cross type.

LOCATION: Northwestern states. **DESCRIPTION:** A small size, expanded barb point with a short stem. Barbs are usually asymmetrical and one barb can extend down beyond the base. Serrated forms are a Calapooia type cross.

ROGUE RIVER U-BACK - Mississippian, 1000 - 600 B.P.

(Also see Calapooia & Maud)

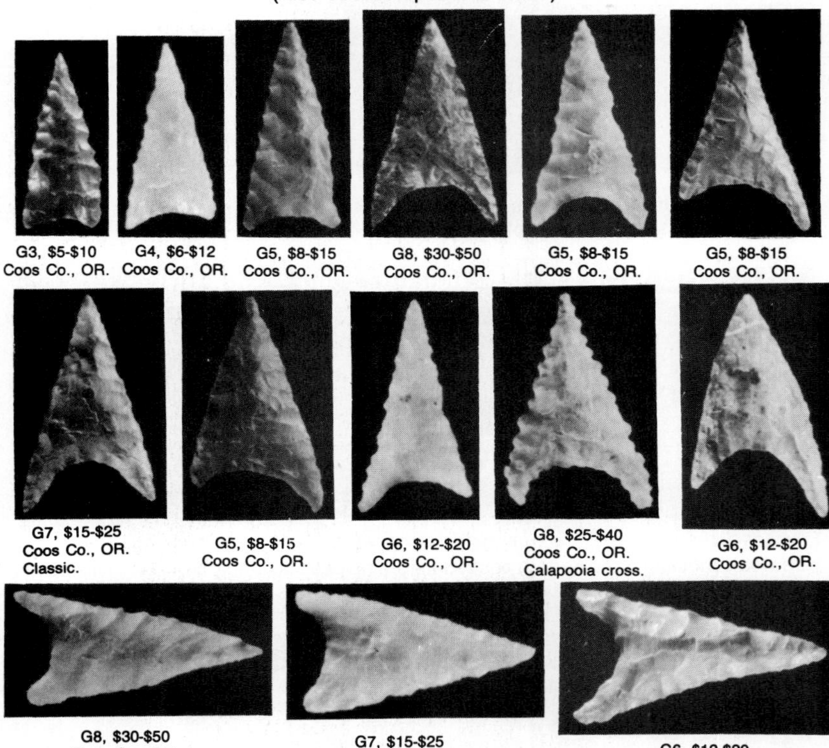

G3, $5-$10
Coos Co., OR.

G4, $6-$12
Coos Co., OR.

G5, $8-$15
Coos Co., OR.

G8, $30-$50
Coos Co., OR.

G5, $8-$15
Coos Co., OR.

G5, $8-$15
Coos Co., OR.

G7, $15-$25
Coos Co., OR.
Classic.

G5, $8-$15
Coos Co., OR.

G6, $12-$20
Coos Co., OR.

G8, $25-$40
Coos Co., OR.
Calapooia cross.

G6, $12-$20
Coos Co., OR.

G8, $30-$50
Coos Co., OR.

G7, $15-$25
Coos Co., OR.

G6, $12-$20
Coos Co., OR.

LOCATION: Northwestern states. **DESCRIPTION:** A small size triangular point with a concave base. Rare examples are serrated (Calapooian influence). The classic form is asymmetrical with one basal ear lower than the other.

ROSE SPRINGS - Woodland to Miss., 1600 - 600 B.P.

(Also see Colonial)

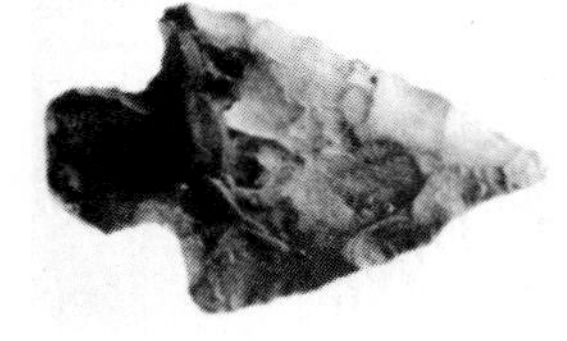

G6, $4-$6
Yavapai Co., AZ.

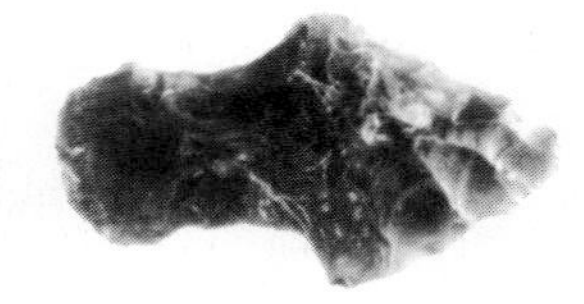

G3, $2-$3
Yavapai Co., AZ.

LOCATION: Southwestern states. **DESCRIPTION:** A small to medium size corner or side notched or stemmed point.

ROSS - Woodland, 2000 - 1800 B.P.

(Also see Hopewell, North and Snyders)

LOCATION: Midwestern to Eastern states. **DESCRIPTION:** A large size ceremonial blade with an expanded, rounded base. Some examples have a contracting "V" shaped base.

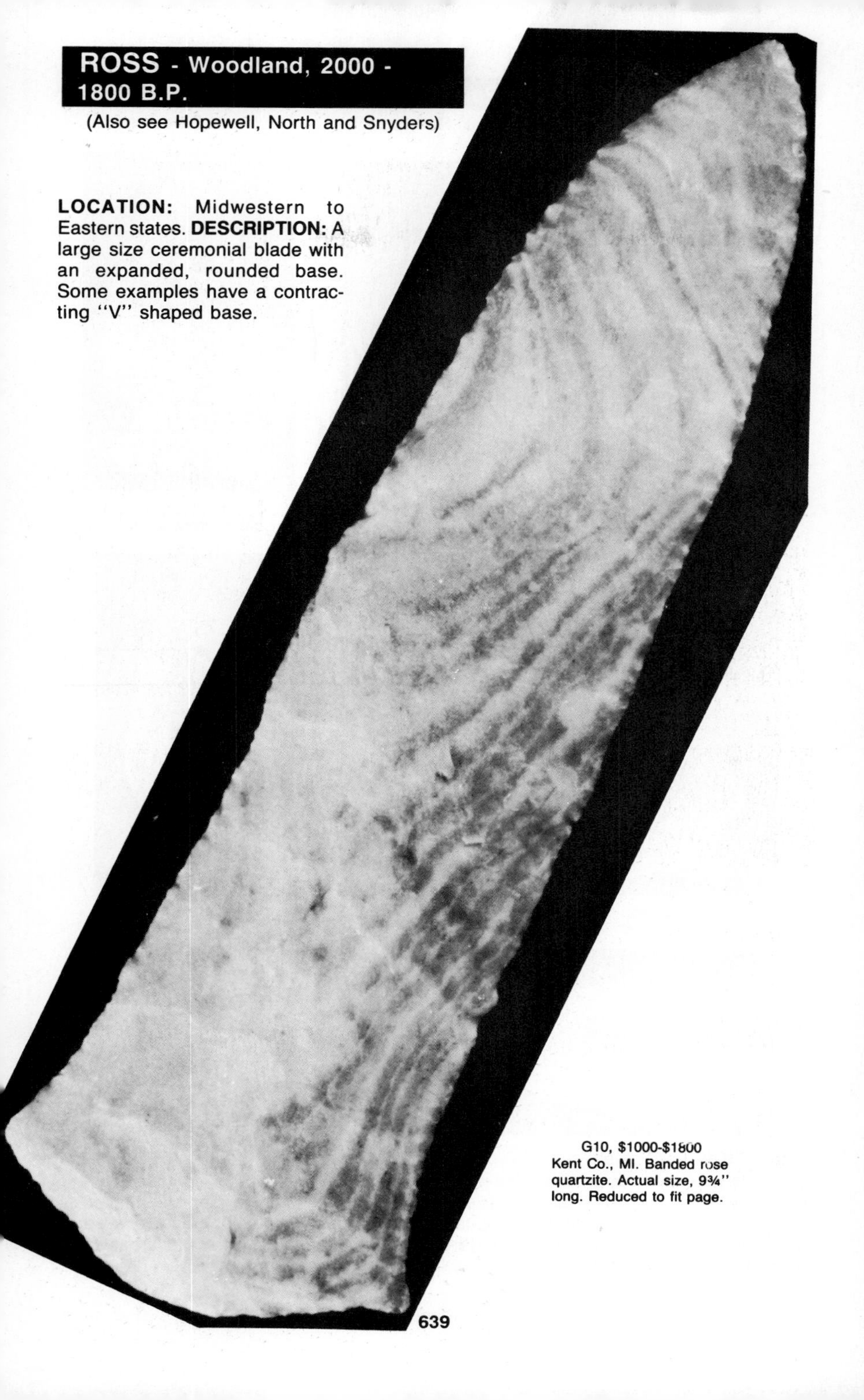

G10, $1000-$1800
Kent Co., MI. Banded rose quartzite. Actual size, 9¾" long. Reduced to fit page.

ROSS COUNTY (See Clovis)

ROWAN - Transitional Paleo, 9500 - 8000 B.P.

(Also see Big Sandy, Bolen, Godar, Raddatz, Savage Cave and Pine Tree)

G2, $8-$15
Caswell Co., NC.

G7, $35-$65
Johnson Co., NC.

G3, $12-$20
Montgomery Co., NC.

G6, $30-$50
Yadkin Co., NC.

G5, $25-$40
Southampton Co., VA.

G5, $25-$40
Southampton Co., VA.

G4, $20-$30
Durham Co., NC.

LOCATION: Far Eastern states. Type site is Rowan Co., North Carolina. **DESCRIPTION:** A medium to large size, side-notched point that can be easily confused with the *Big Sandy* type. The basal area is usually wider than the blade. Some examples have expanded ears and grinding usually occurs around the basal area. Believed to be an intermediate form developing from *Dalton, Quad, Greenbrier* or *Hardaway* and changing into *Big Sandy* and other later side notched forms.

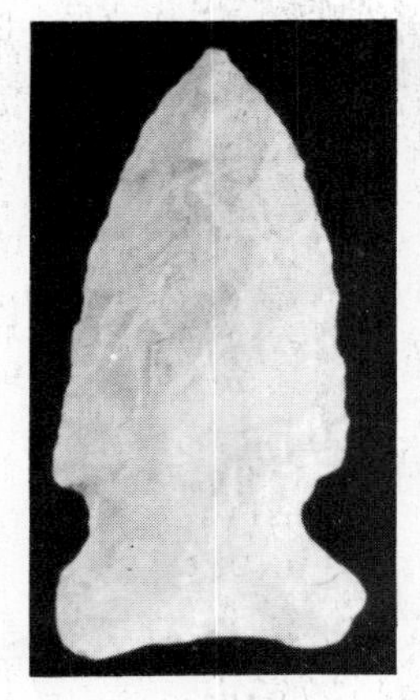

G5, $20-$40
Rockingham Co., NC.

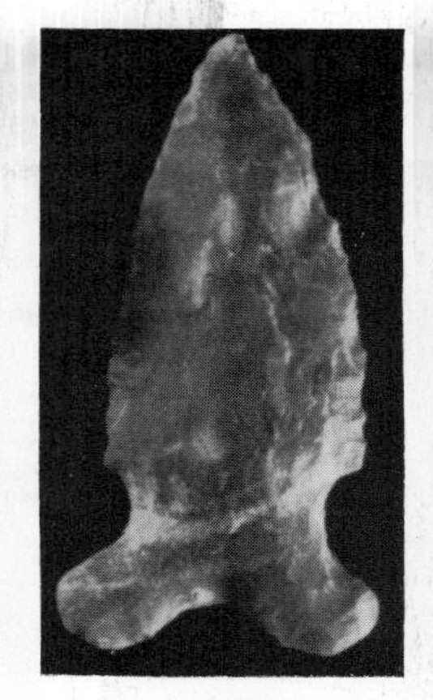

G6, $30-$50
Moore Co., NC.

G7, $35-$55
Montgomery Co., NC.

G4, $20-$30
Rockingham Co., NC.

G6, $25-$45
Danville Co., VA. Classic.

G6, $30-$50
Randolph Co., NC.

G9, $60-$100
Montgomery Co., NC.

G7, $35-$60
Randolph Co., NC.

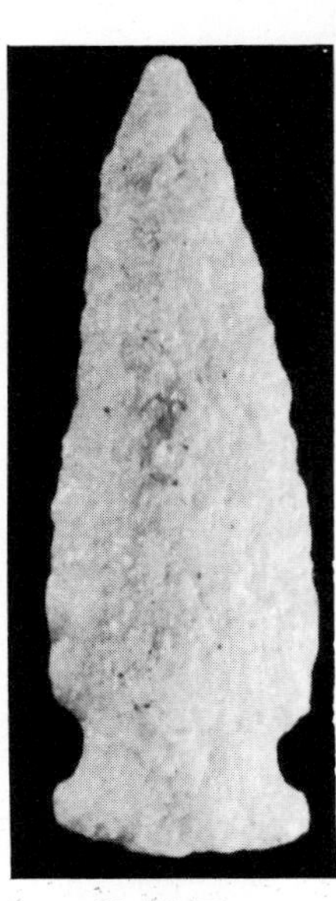

G6, $30-$50
Sussex Co., VA.

G6, $30-$50
Stokes Co., NC.

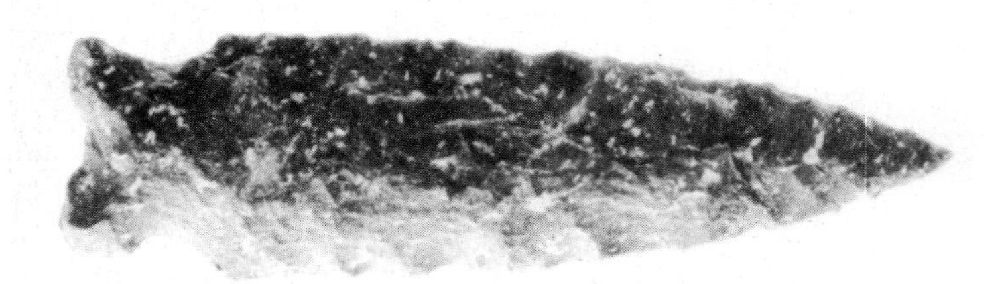

G8, $45-$80
Iredell Co., NC.

G9, $80-$120
Moore Co., NC.

RUSSELL CAVE - Transitional Paleo to early Archaic, 9000 - 7000 B.P.

(Also see Hardaway, Harpeth River, Pine Tree and Searcy)

G6, $10-$20
TN.

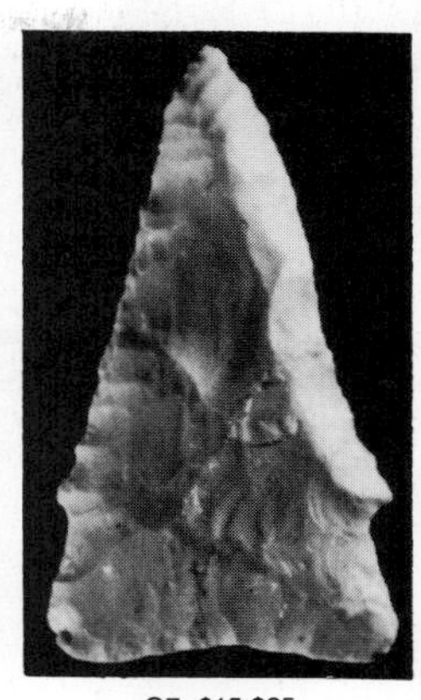

G7, $15-$25
Clarksville, TN.

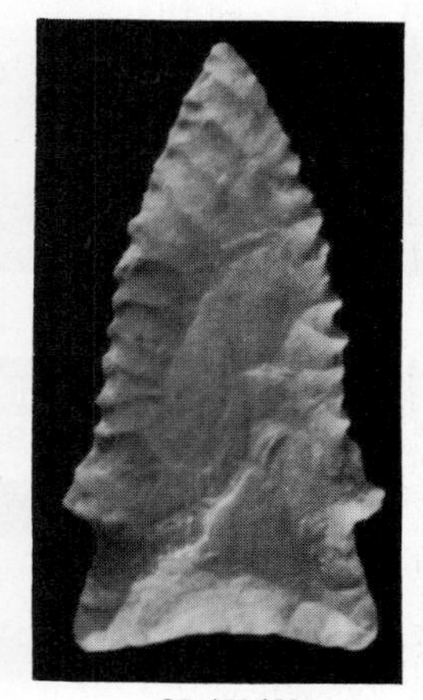

G9, $50-$80
Huntsville, AL.

G8, $25-$40
Limestone Co., AL.

G10, $90-$120
Humphreys Co., TN. Classic.

G5, $8-$15
Limestone Co., AL.

LOCATION: Southeastern states. **DESCRIPTION:** A medium size, triangular point with weak shoulders and an an expanding to auriculate base. The stem appears to be an extension of the blade edges, expanding to the base. Most examples are serrated and beveled on one side of each face, although some examples are beveled on all four sides. The base is straight, concave, bifurcated or auriculate. **I.D. KEY:** Notched base and edgework.

RUSSELL CAVE (continued)

G9, $50-$80
Humphreys Co., TN.

SABINAL - Mississippian, 1000 - 700 B.P.

(Also see Bonham, Deadman, Gunther & Rockwall)

G8, $25-$40
Comanche Co., TX.

LOCATION: Midwestern states. **DESCRIPTION:** A small size, thin, point with rounded shoulders that flare outward and a short expanding stem.

SABINE - Late Archaic to Woodland, 4000 - 2000 B.P.

(Also see Covington, Friday, Gahagan and Texas Blade)

G7, $15-$25
Comanche Co., TX.

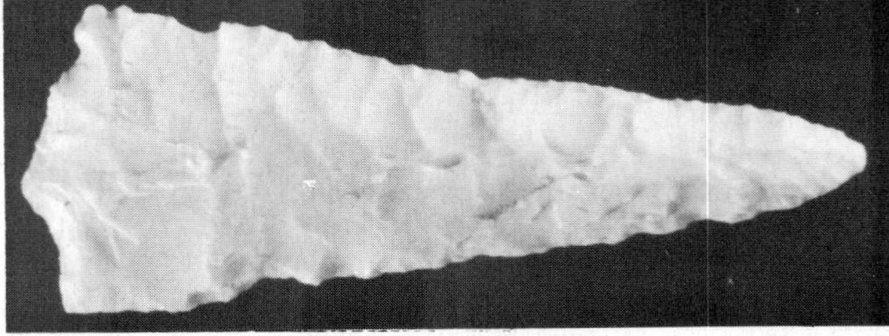

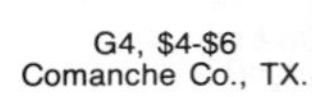

G4, $4-$6
Comanche Co., TX.

LOCATION: Midwestern states. **DESCRIPTION:** A medium to large size, thin, lanceolate blade with a contracting, rounded to "V" base. Blade edges can be serrated.

SABINE (continued)

G6, $10-$20
Comanche Co., TX.

SAFETY HARBOR - Mississippian, 800 - 600 B.P.

(Also see Camp Creek, Madison & Maude)

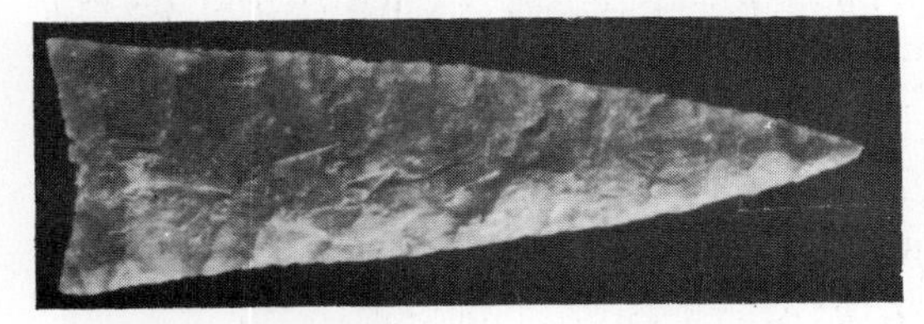

G10, $125-$225
Sumpter Co., FL. Silver Lake.

LOCATION: Southern Southeastern states. **DESCRIPTION:** A medium size, narrow, thin, triangular point with a concave base.

ST. ALBANS - Early to mid-Archaic, 9000 - 5000 B.P.

(Also see Decatur, Fox Valley, Jude, Kanawha, Kirk-Bifurcated, Lake Erie, LeCroy, MacCorkle, Montell, Pine Tree, Rice Lobbed, Southampton and Stanly)

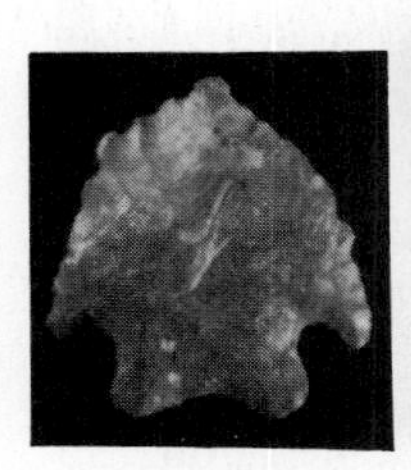

G3, $2-$3
Yadkin Co., NC.

G5, $4-$6
Autauga Co., AL.
Milky quartz.

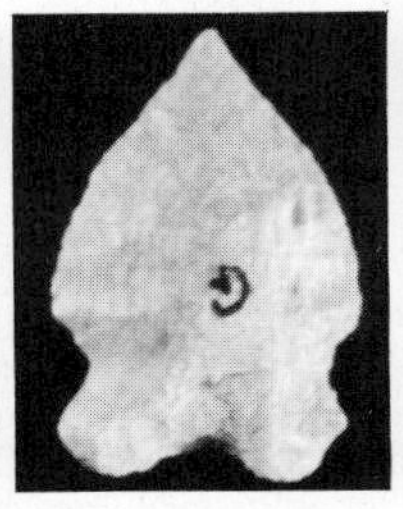

G6, $6-$10
Dinwiddie Co., VA.

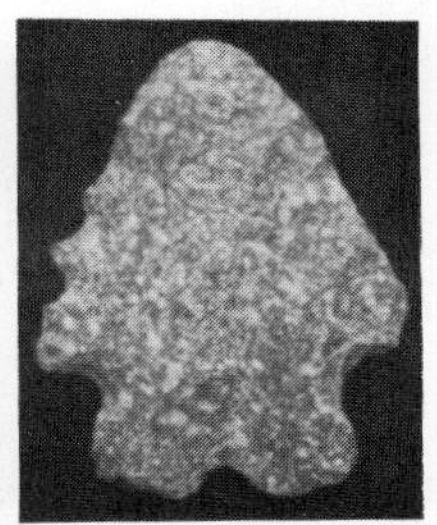

G4, $3-$5
Union Co., SC.
Slate.

ST. ALBANS (continued)

G4, $3-$5
Fairfield Co., SC.
Slate.

G6, $6-$10
Moore Co., NC.

G5, $4-$8
Fairfield Co., SC. Slate.

G7, $8-$15
Sussex Co., VA.

G8, $15-$25
Moore Co., NC.

G6, $6-$10
Rockingham Co., VA.

G9, $25-$40
Johnson Co., NC. Vein quartz.

G9, $20-$35
Hamilton Co., TN.

G6, $6-$10
Dinwiddie Co., VA.

G7, $10-$18
Dinwiddie Co., VA.

LOCATION: Eastern states. **DESCRIPTION:** A small to medium size, usually serrated, bifurcated point. Basal lobes usually flare outward and most examples are sharply barbed. The basal lobes are more shallow than in the *LeCroy* type, otherwise they are easily confused.

ST. CHARLES - Late Archaic, 4000 - 2000 B.P.

(Also see Bolen, Dovetail, Gibson and Kirk Corner Notched)

G1, $2-$3
TN/AL.

G4, $40-$70
CO.

G5, $60-$100
Williamson Co., TN.
Unusual base.

G8, $300-$650
Humphreys Co., TN. Cliopped wing form. Red chert.

G8, $250-$400
Florence, AL.

LOCATION: Midwestern to Eastern states. **DESCRIPTION:** A medium to large size, broad, thin, elliptical, corner notched point with a dovetail base. Believed to be descended from the *Dovetail* type with the blade beveling gone. The base is convex and most examples exhibit high quality flaking. There is a rare variant that has the barbs clipped (clipped wing) as in the *Decatur* type.

G9, $400-$750, Adams Co., IL.

G10, $1500-$2500
Florence, AL. Excellent and very thin. One of the best known.

G8, $250-$400
Columbia, MO. Unusual base form.

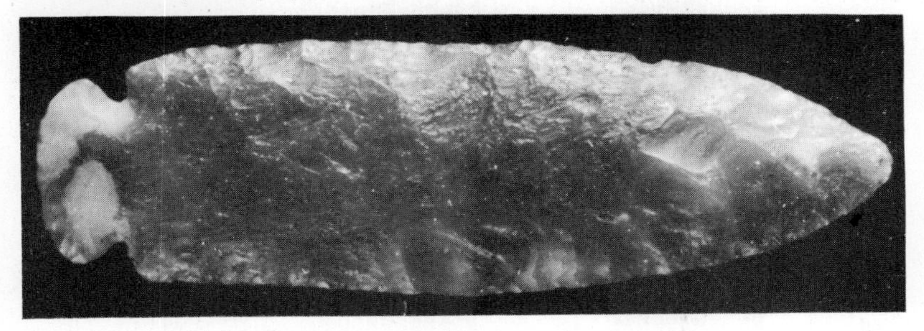

G5, $50-$80
Dickson Cave, KY. Flint.

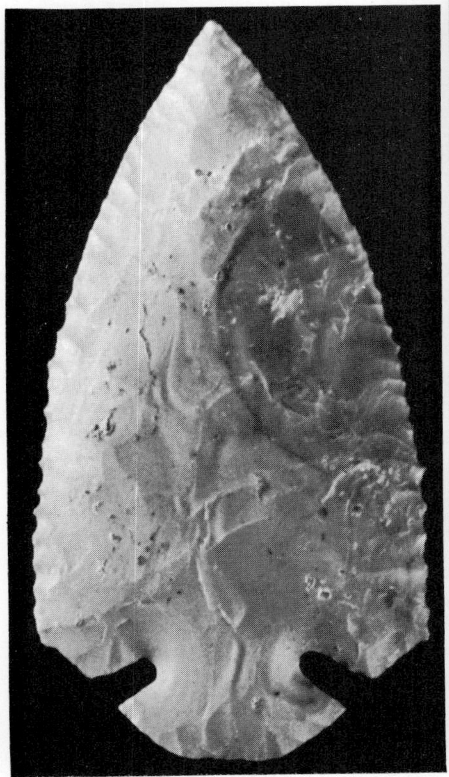

G10, $1200-$2000
Humphreys Co., TN. Rare clipped wing form. Outstanding quality. The base is ground.

G8, $250-$450
Marion Co., IL.

SALLISAW - Mississippian, 800 - 600 B.P.

(Also see Morris)

G10, $250-$400
Comanche Co., Tx. Very thin and excellent quality.

LOCATION: Midwestern states. **DESCRIPTION:** A small size, thin, serrated, barbed point with long drooping basal tangs and a deeply concave base.

SAN JOSE - Mid-Archaic, 6000 - 4500 B.P.

(Also see Cottonwood Triangle, Papago and Perkinsville)

G5, $6-$10
Yavapai Co., AZ.

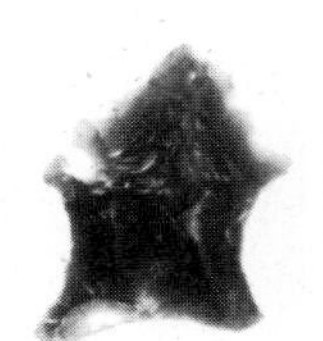

G4, $3-$5
Yavapai Co., AZ.

G3, $2-$4
Yavapai Co., AZ.

G4, $3-$5
Yavapai Co., AZ.

LOCATION: Southwestern states. **DESCRIPTION:** A small to medium size, expanded base point. Blade edges are usually serrated and the base can be straight to concave. Shoulders can be weak to barbed.

SAN PATRICE - Late Paleo, 10000 - 8000 B.P.

(Also see Chipola, Dalton, Hardaway, Palmer, Pelican & Rodgers Side-Hollowed)

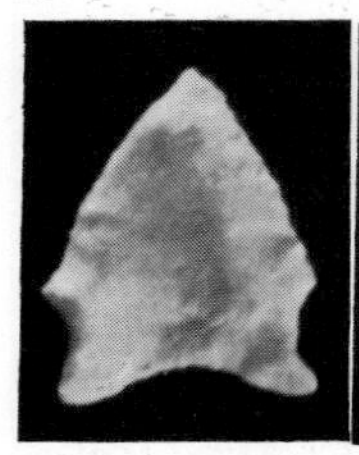

G4, $15-$25
Fluted.

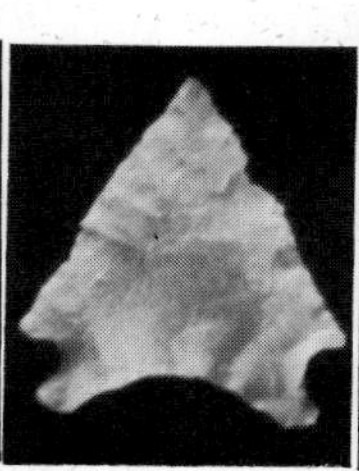

G4, $15-$25
Fluted, Classic.

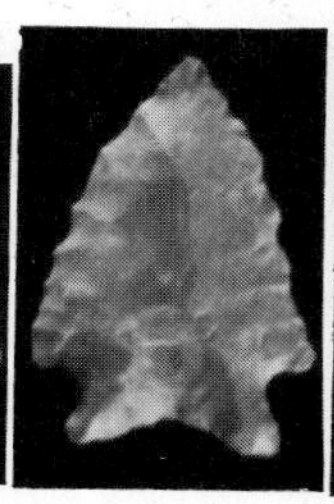

G5, $20-$40

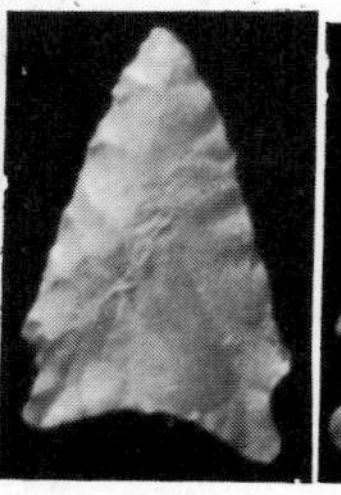

G5, $25-$40

G6, $30-$50

(All Williamson Co., TX.)

LOCATION: Midwestern states. **DESCRIPTION:** A small size, thin, auriculate to side notched point with a concave base. Some examples are fluted, others are thinned from the base. Basal area is usually ground.

SAN PATRICE (continued)

G6, $30-$50

G5, $25-$40

G8, $60-$100
Fluted. Classic.

G7, $50-$80
Classic.

(All Williamson Co., TX.)

G8, $60-$100
Fluted, Classic.

G4, $15-$25

G4, $15-$25

(All Williamson Co., TX.)

G6, $30-$50
Catahoula Parrish, LA.

G6, $30-$50
Comanche Co., TX.

G5, $25-$40
Lincoln Parrish, LA.

G5, $20-$35
Walker Co., AL.

G7, $45-$80
Marksville, LA.

SAN PEDRO - Late Archaic, 4000 - 2500 B.P.

(Also see Durst, Godley and Yavapai Stemmed)

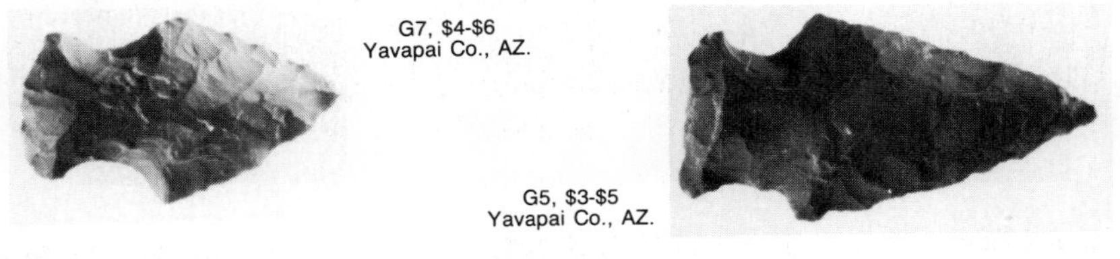

G7, $4-$6
Yavapai Co., AZ.

G5, $3-$5
Yavapai Co., AZ.

LOCATION: Southwestern states. **DESCRIPTION:** A small to medium size point with broad side to corner notches and a straight to convex base.

SAN PEDRO (continued)

G4, $2-$4
Yavapai Co., AZ.

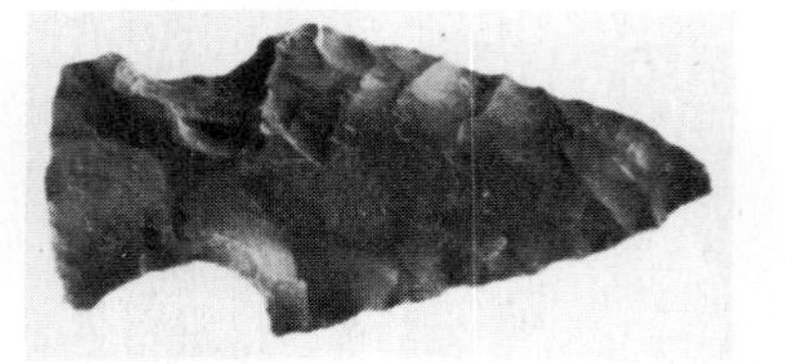

G4, $2-$4
Yavapai Co., AZ.

SAN SABA - Woodland, 3000 - 2000 B.P.

(Also see Base Tang, Citrus, Corner Tang, Culbreath, Eva and Hernando)

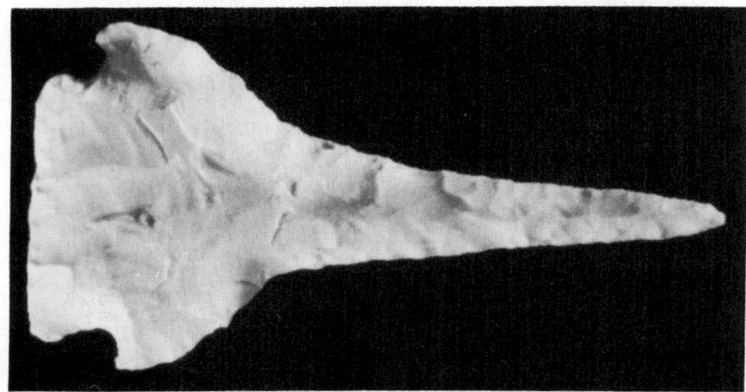

G6, $50-$90
Austin, TX.

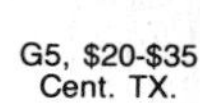

G5, $20-$35
Cent. TX.

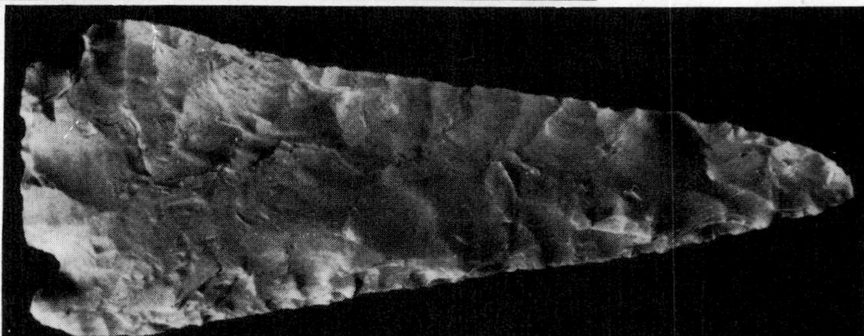

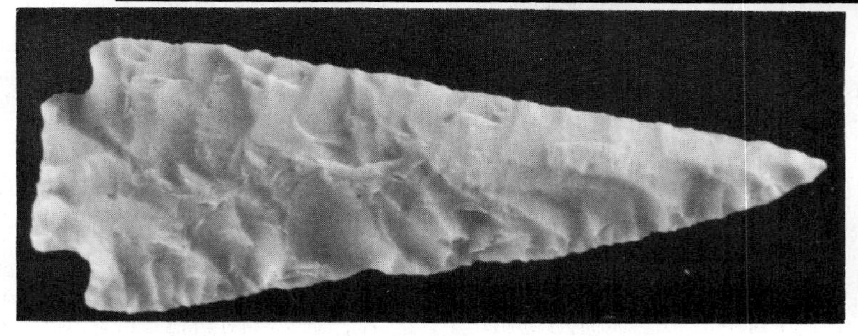

G6, $40-$60
Comanche Co., TX.

LOCATION: Midwestern states. **DESCRIPTION:** A large size, triangular blade with shallow, narrow, basal notches. Bases usually are straight.

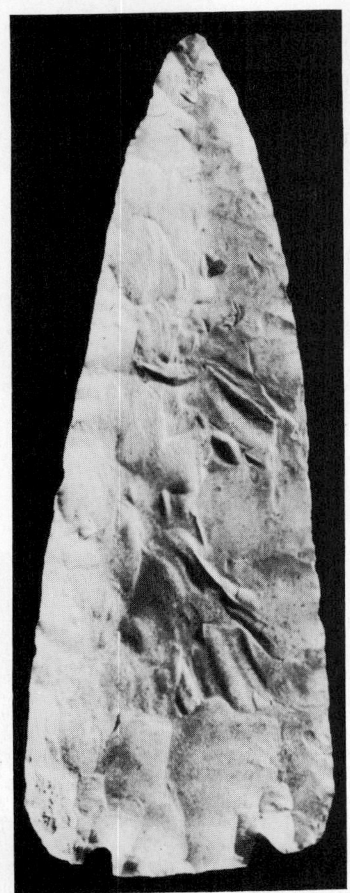

G8, $90-$160
Cent. TX.

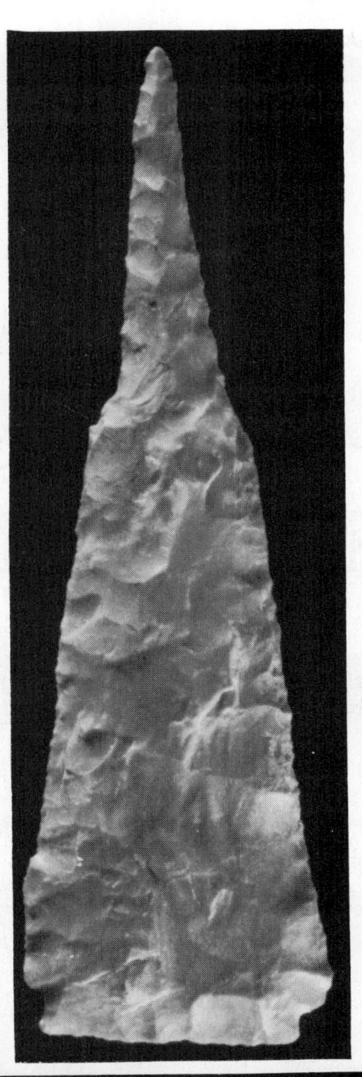

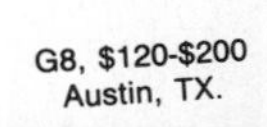

G8, $120-$200
Austin, TX.

G7, $80-$120
Cent. TX.

SAN SABA (continued)

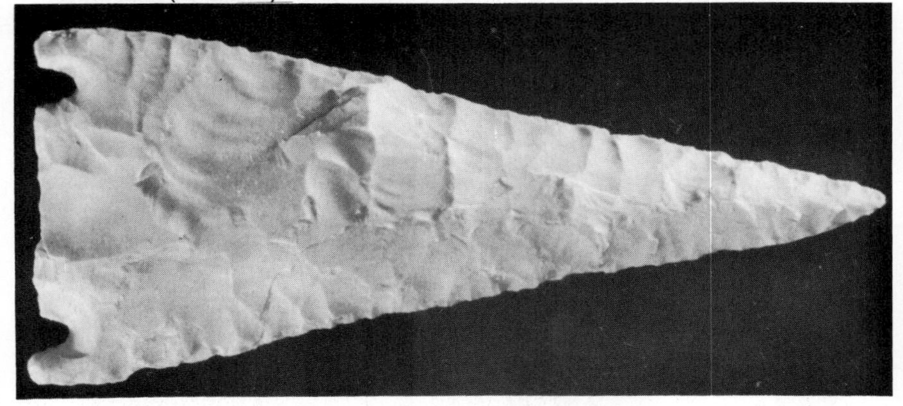

G9, $150-$250
Comanche Co., TX.

SAND MOUNTAIN - Late Woodland to Mississippian, 1500 - 400 B.P.

(Also see Durant's Bend, Fort Ancient and Madison)

G3, $1-$2 Morgan Co., AL. — G3, $1-$2 SE TN. — G5, $3-$5 Mid TN. — G4, $2-$3 SE TN. — G8, $15-$25 Limestone Co., AL. — G6, $4-$6 Limestone Co., AL.

G6, $4-$6 Huntsville, AL. — G9, $25-$30 Decatur, AL. — G6, $4-$6 Limestone Co., AL. — G9, $30-$50 Limestone Co., AL. — G7, $12-$20 Limestone Co., AL. — G8, $15-$25 Florence, AL.

G4, $2-$3 Morgan Co., AL. — G8, $15-$25 Morgan Co., AL. — G8, $15-$25 Limestone Co., AL.

LOCATION: Southeastern states. **DESCRIPTION:** A small size, triangular point with serrated blade edges and a concave base. A straight base would place it in the *Fort Ancient* type. **I.D. KEY:** Serrations are not symmetrical.

SANDIA Transitional Paleo, 10000 - 8000 B.P.

(also see Clovis, Dalton, Pedernalis & Spedis)

G8, $600-$1000
Western U.S. Heavy patina.

G9, $1500-$2500
W. TN. Dover chert. Note basal thinning. Fluted on reverse side.

G6, $250-$400
Wasco Co., OR.
The Dalles.

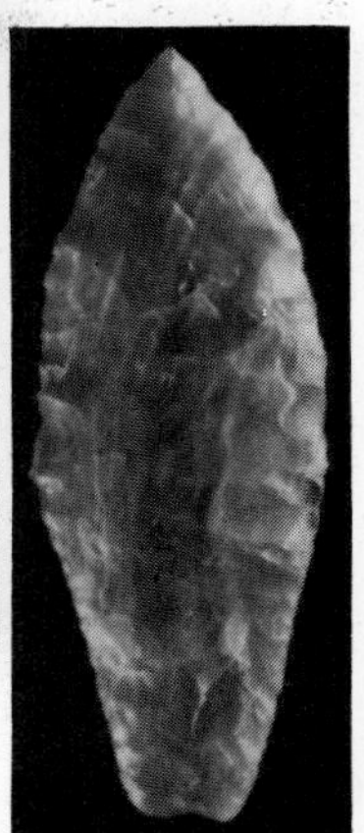

G7, $350-$600
Wasco Co., OR.
The Dalles.

LOCATION: Western to Southeastern states. **DESCRIPTION:** This point occurs in three forms: The first form is a narrow, elliptical shape with only one shoulder and a rounded base. The second form has a slightly concave base, otherwise it is the same as the first form. The third form has a deeply concave base with drooping auricles. This, as well as the second form have been found fluted on one or both faces. This type is extremely rare everywhere and is now believed to be later than *Clovis*.

SANTA CRUZ - Woodland to Miss., 1500 - 1000 B.P.

(Also see Augustin, Gypsum Cave, Jerome and Morrow Mountain)

G3, $2-$4
Yavapai, AZ.

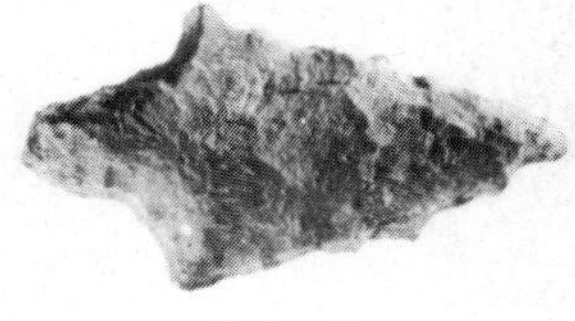

G8, $10-$20
Yavapai, AZ.

G6, $5-$8
Yavapai, AZ.

LOCATION: Southwestern states. **DESCRIPTION:** A small size lanceolate point with tapered shoulders and a contracting stem.

SANTA FE (See Dalton-Santa Fe)

SARASOTA - Woodland, 3000 - 1500 B.P.

(Also see Little Bear Creek and Pickwick)

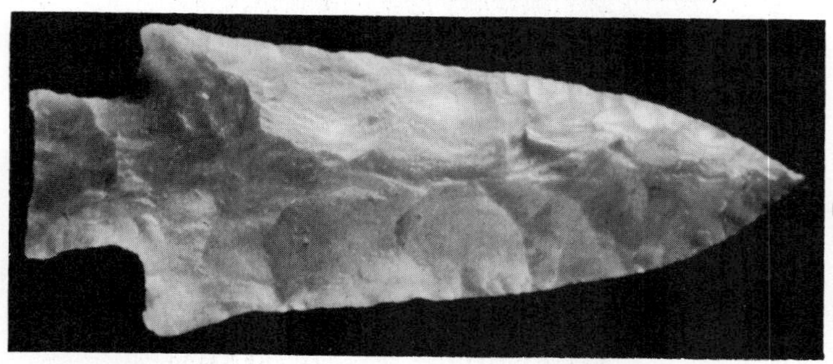

G8, $80-$120
Buddy Lake, FL.

LOCATION: Southern Southeastern states. **DESCRIPTION:** A medium to large size stemmed point with horizontal shoulders. The base can be parallel sided to slightly expanding or contracting. Blade edges are slightly convex to recurved. Similar to the northern *Pickwick* type.

SAVAGE CAVE - Early to mid-Archaic, 7000 - 4000 B.P.

(Also see Big Sandy, Bolen, Osceola, Raddatz and Rowan)

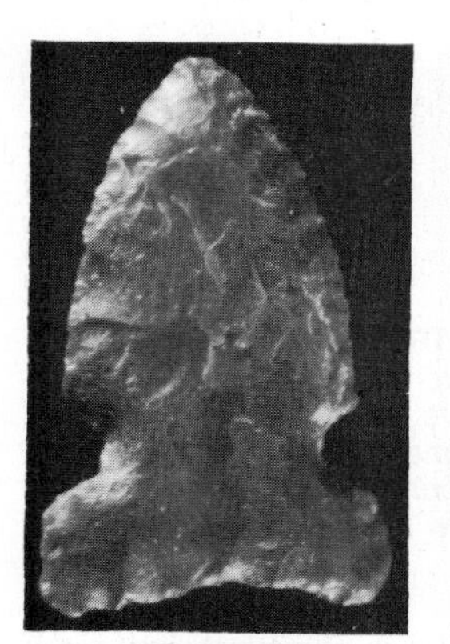

G5, $8-$15
Dayton, TN.

G4, $6-$10
Meigs Co., TN.

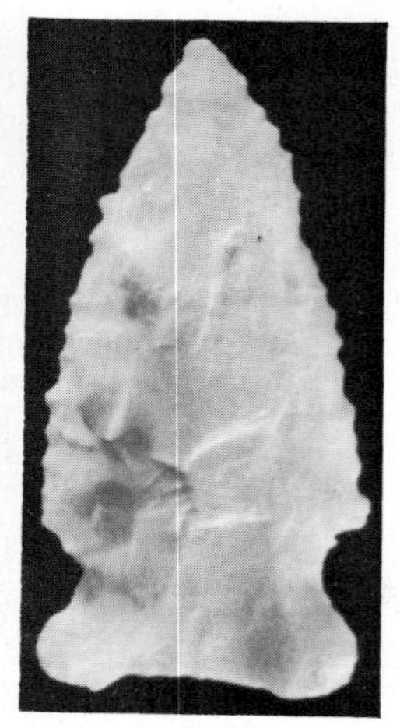

G6, $15-$25
Henry Co., AL.

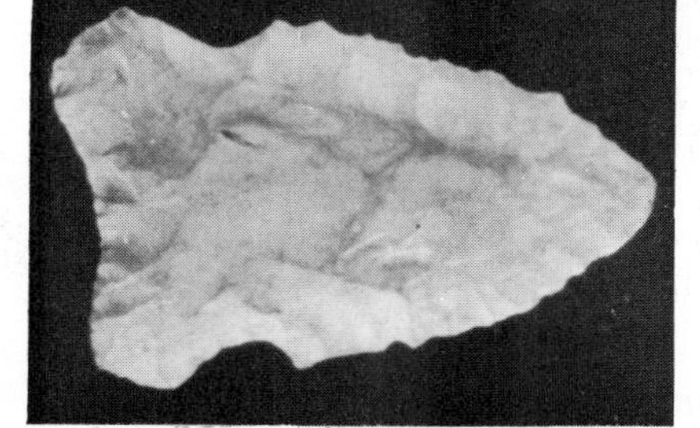

G5, $8-$15
Humphreys Co., TN.

LOCATION: Kentucky and surrounding states. **DESCRIPTION:** A medium to large size, broad, side notched point that is usually serrated. Bases are generally straight but can be slightly concave or convex.

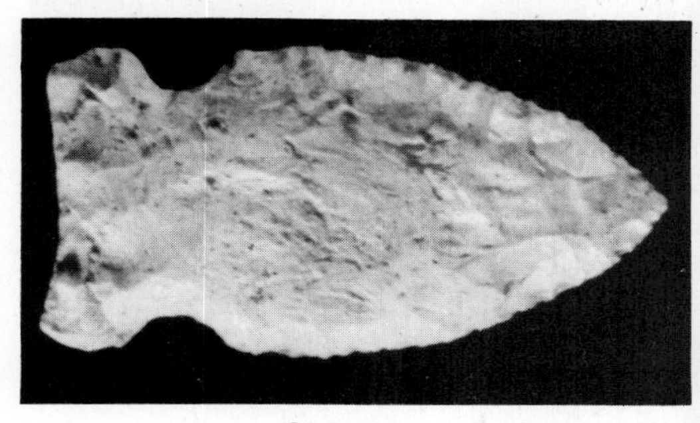
G9, $40-$60
Jonesboro, AR.

G7, $25-$40
NE AR.

SAVANNAH RIVER - Mid-Archaic to Woodland, 5000 - 2000 B.P.

(Also see Abbey, Appalachian, Arredondo, Bascom, Elora, Hamilton, Holmes, Johnson, Kirk, Levy, Maples, Seminole, Stanly and Thonotosassa)

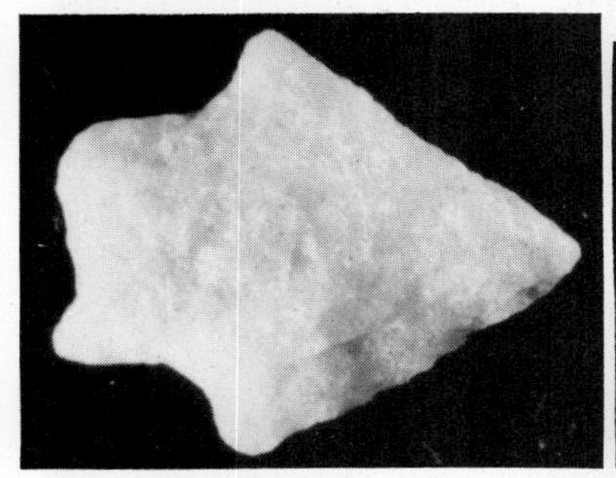
G2, $8-$15
Meigs Co., TN. Quartzite.

G4, $35-$55
Henry Co., AL.

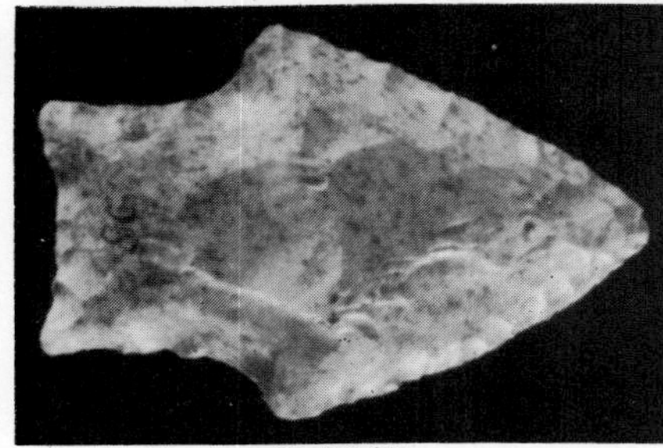
G3, $25-$35
Seminole Co., GA.

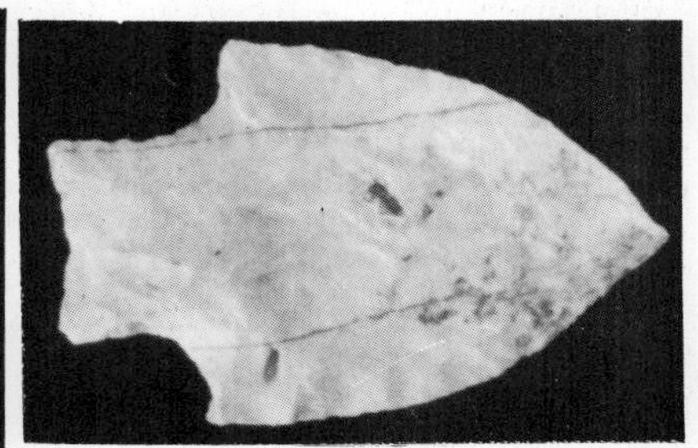
G3, $25-$35
Lee Co., GA.

LOCATION: Southeastern to Eastern states. **DESCRIPTION:** A medium to large size, straight to contracting stemmed point with a concave to bifurcated base. The shoulders are tapered to square. The stems are narrow to broad. Believed to be related to the earlier *Stanly* point.

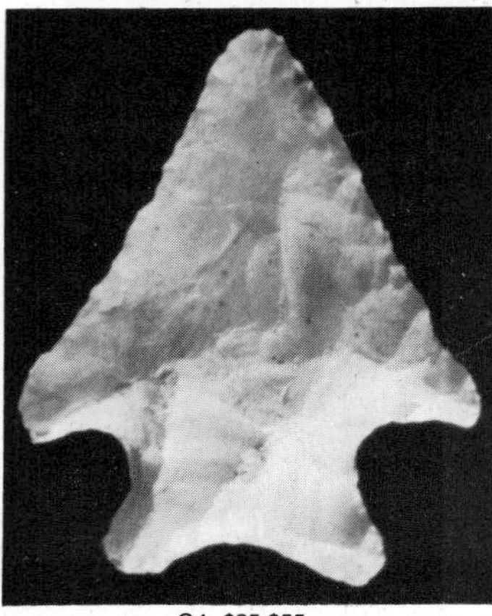
G4, $35-$55
Early Co., GA.

G5, $40-$60
Silver Rv., FL.

G6, $70-$110, Lee Co., GA.

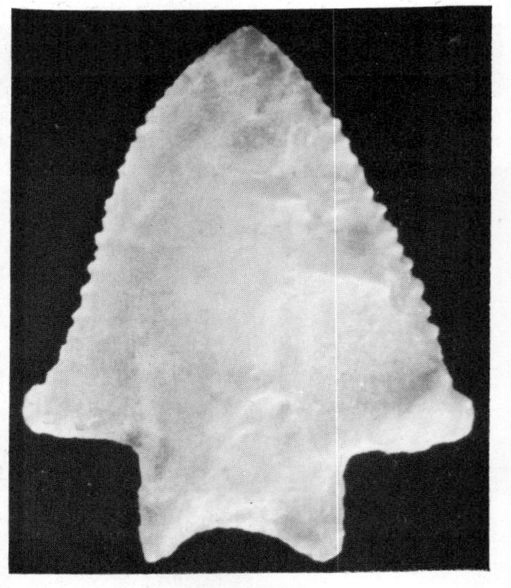
G8, $250-$400
Worth Co., GA.

G7, $150-$225
Dougherty Co., GA.

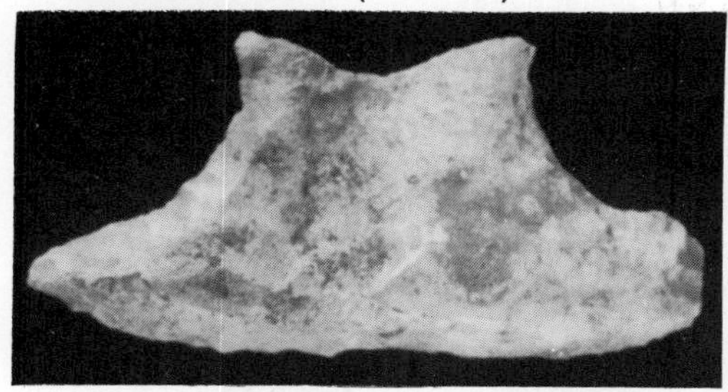

G2, $4-$10
Dougherty Co., GA. Blunt form.

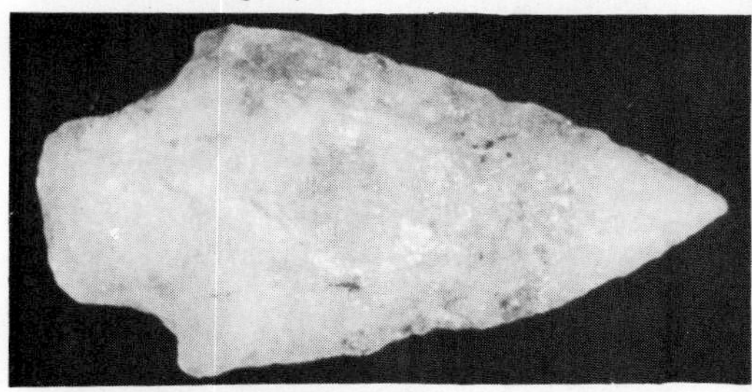

G2, $10-$20
Newberry Co., SC. Milky quartz.

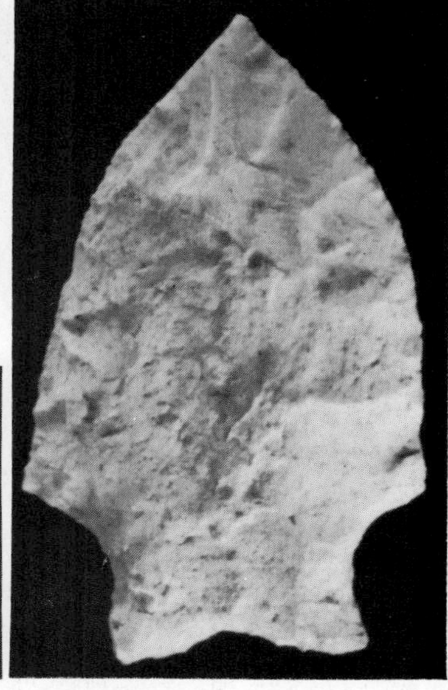

G6, $70-$110
Clay Co., GA.

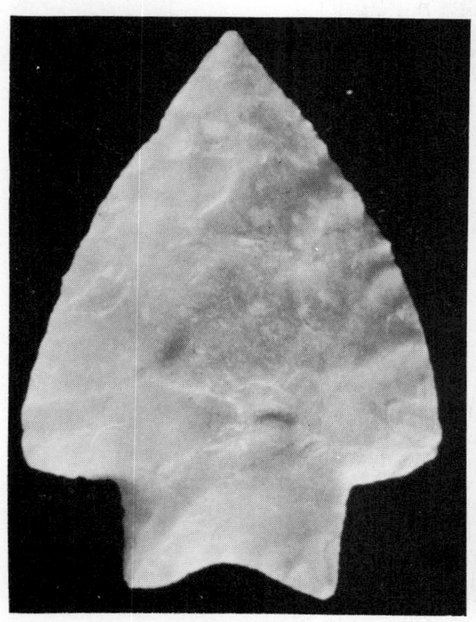

G8, $200-$300
Lee Co., GA.

G8, $200-$300
Sante Fe Rv., FL.

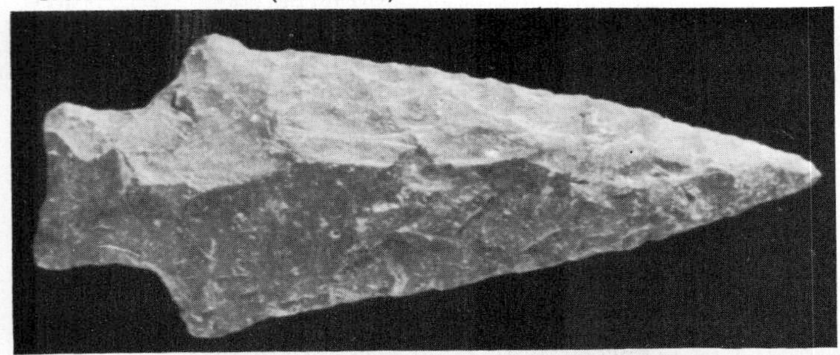

G5, $50-$80
Iredell Co., NC.

G8, $200-$300
Davidson Co., NC.

G7, $150-$250
Taylor Co., FL.

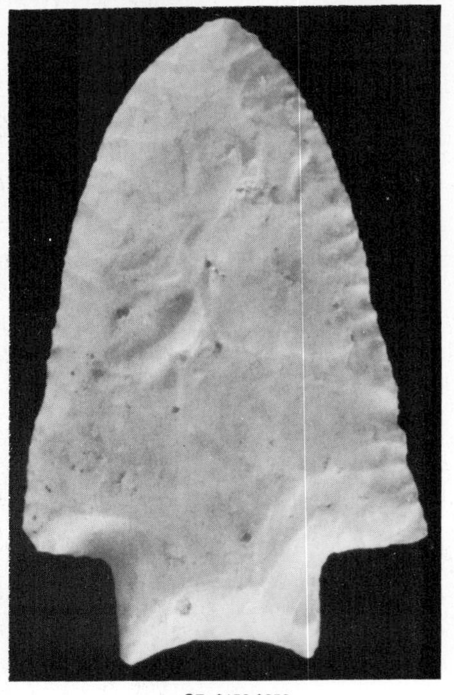

G7, $150-$250
Crisp Co., GA. Tang nick.

G8, $200-$300
Cent. NC. Rhyolite.

G7, $150-$250
Sante Fe Rv., FL.

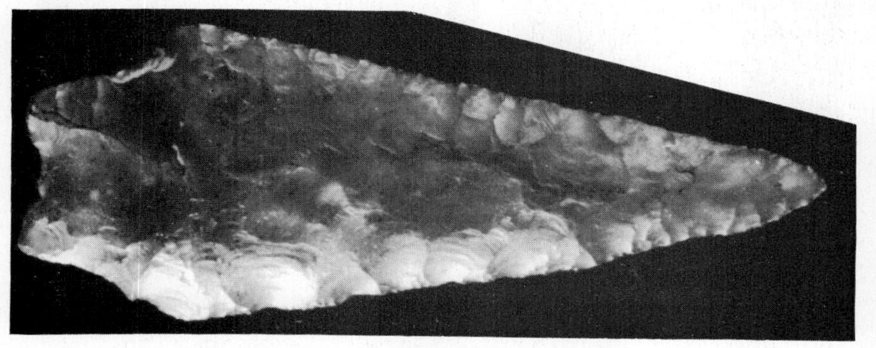

G5, $60-$100
Hillsborough Co., FL. Agatized coral.

G9, $400-$750
Cent. NC. Classic.

G9, $500-$900
Randolph Co., NC.

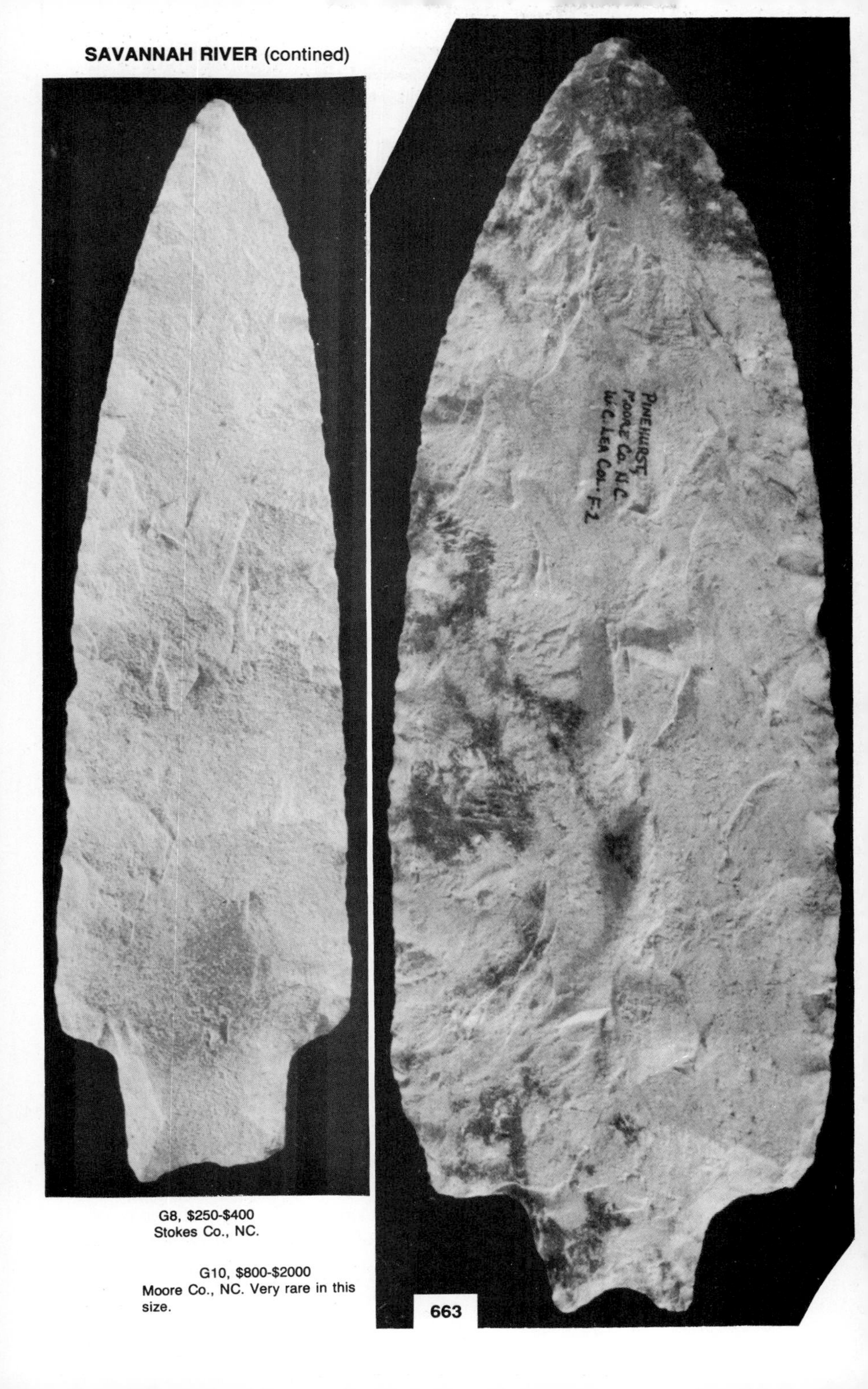

G8, $250-$400
Stokes Co., NC.

G10, $800-$2000
Moore Co., NC. Very rare in this size.

SCALLORN - Woodland to Mississippian, 1300 - 500 B.P.

(Also see Alba, Catahoula, Colbert, Cuney, Ellis, Homan, Keota, Leon, Rockwall, Sequoyah & Steiner)

G5, $10-$20 G6, $20-$30 G2, $3-$5 G6, $15-$25 G7, $30-$50 G6, $15-$25

(All Comanche Co., TX)

G6, $15-$25
WA/OR.

G3, $4-$6

G7, $30-$50 G3, $4-$6 G8, $60-$80

G6, $25-$40
Spiro Mound,
OK.

G6, $15-$25

G7, $40-$70
MO.

G7, $40-$65
CO/TX.

G8, $60-$80
WA/OR. Agate

G8, $60-$100
Comanche Co., TX.

G8, $50-$80
Columbia Rv., WA.

G10, $125-$250
WA/OR.

G9, $80-$120
WA/OR.

LOCATION: Midwestern states. **DESCRIPTION:** A small size, corner notched point with a flaring stem. Bases and blade edges are straight, concave or convex and many examples are serrated.

SCHILD SPIKE - Woodland, 1500 - 1000 B.P.

(Also see Bradley and Flint River Spike, Duval, New Market and Randolph)

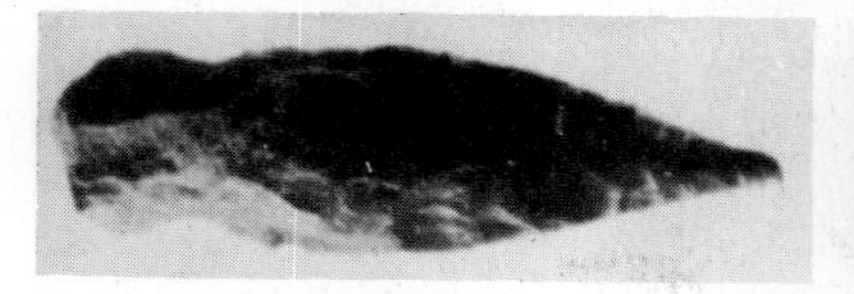

G9, $20-$30
Dunlap, TN.

G5, $3-$5
Ft. Payne, AL.

LOCATION: Northeastern states. **DESCRIPTION:** A small to medium size, narrow, thick, spike point with shallow side notches.

SCHUGTOWN - Mississippian, 1000 B.P.

(Also see Big Sandy, Cahokia and Reed)

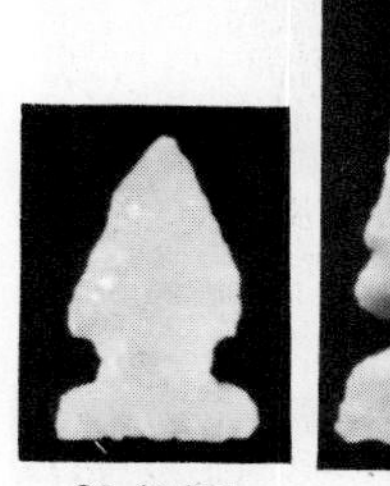

G2, $8-$15
Columbia Rv., WA.

G5, $25-$40
Comanche Co., TX.

G9, $150-$250
WA/OR.

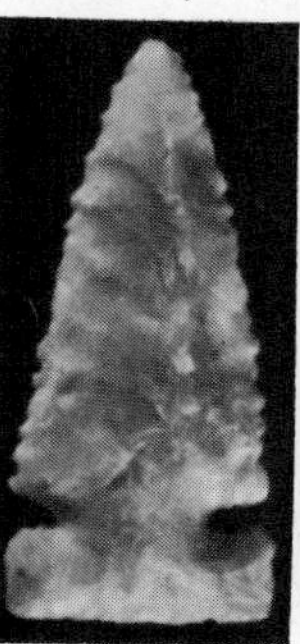

G7, $60-$100
WA/OR.

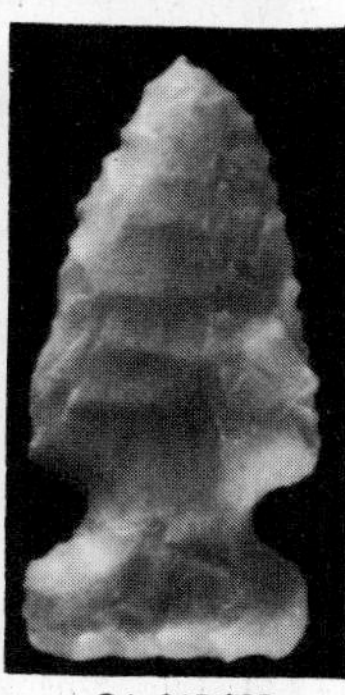

G4, $15-$25
Comanche Co., TX.

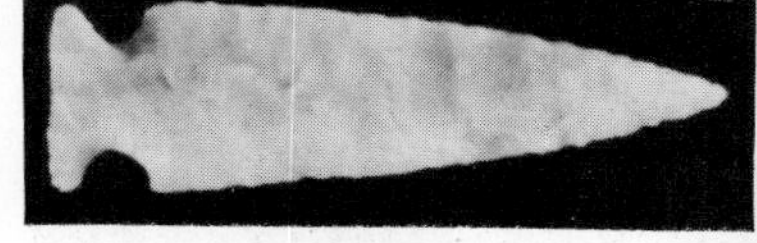

G8, $90-$150
WA/OR.

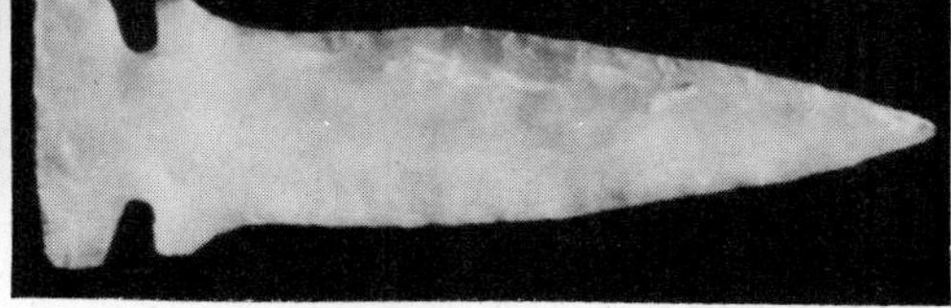

G10, $250-$400
WA/OR.

LOCATION: Midwestern states. **DESCRIPTION:** A small to medium size side notched point with a straight base. Some examples are serrated.

SCOTTSBLUFF I - Transitional Paleo, 9500 - 7000 B.P.

(Also see Hardin, Holland and Steubenville)

LOCATION: Midwestern states. **DESCRIPTION:** A medium to large size, lanceolate point with convex to parallel sides, weak shoulders, and a broad parallel to expanding stem. The hafting area is ground. Most examples have horizontal to oblique parallel flaking and are of high quality and thinness.

G4, $45-$70
MO.

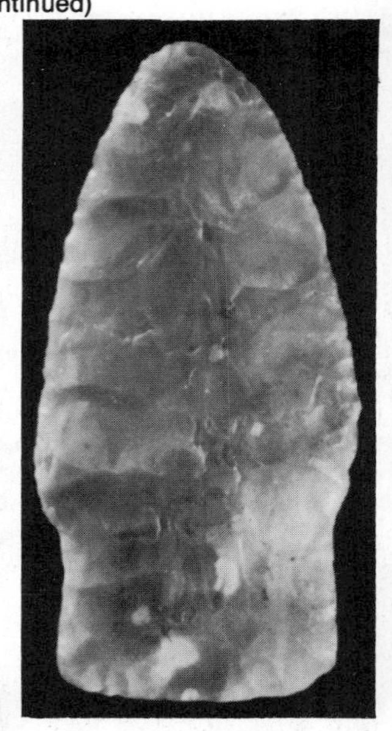

G4, $45-$70
Monroe, LA.

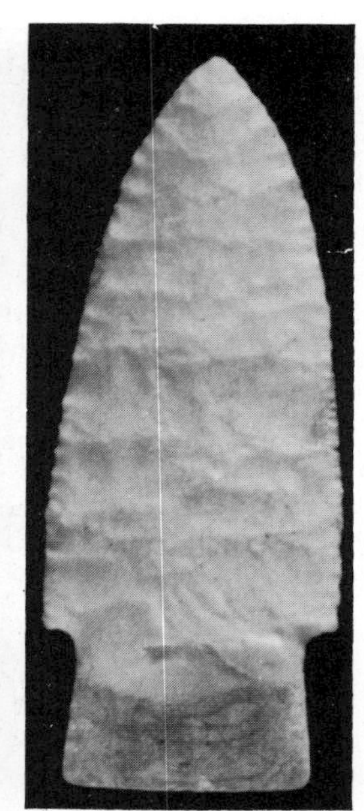

G8, $350-$500
Kansas City, MO. Note horizontal transverse flaking.

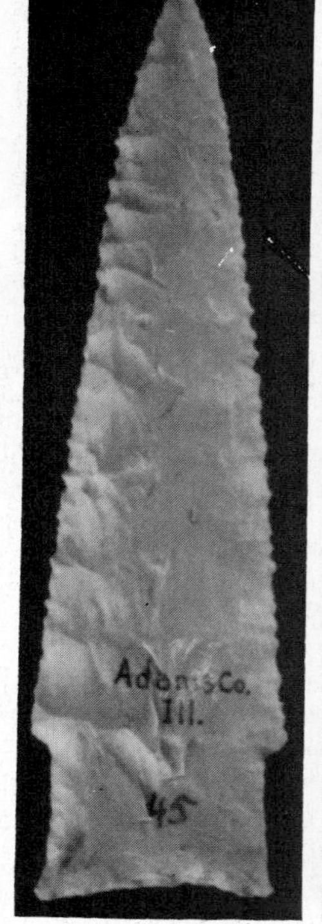

G9, $400-$700
Adams Co., IL.

G8, $350-$500
Brown Co., IL. Oblique transverse flaking.

G6, $150-$250
Pike Co., IL. Note oblique flaking.

SCOTTSBLUFF I (continued)

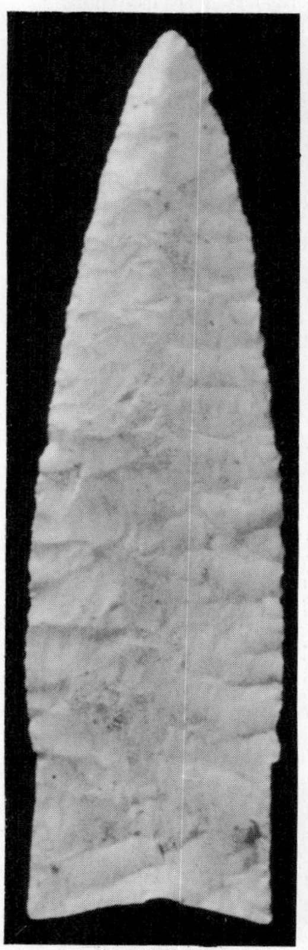

G8, $300-$450
MO.

G8, $350-$500
Booneville, MO. Note transverse flaking.

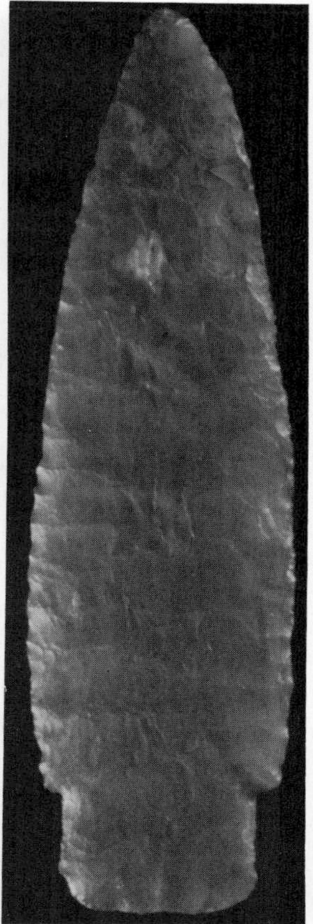

G7, $200-$300
AR.

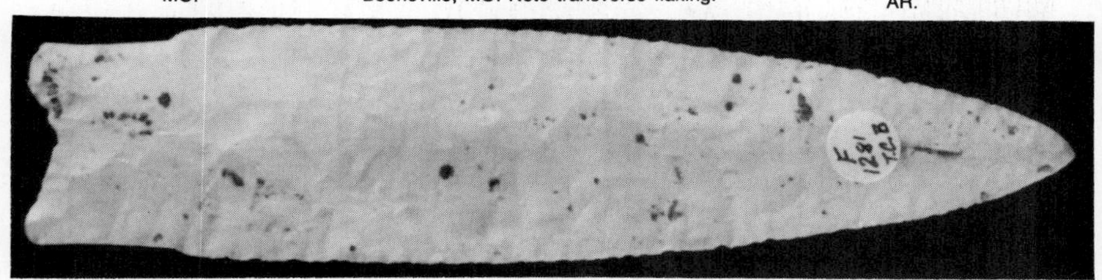

G9, $450-$800, MO.

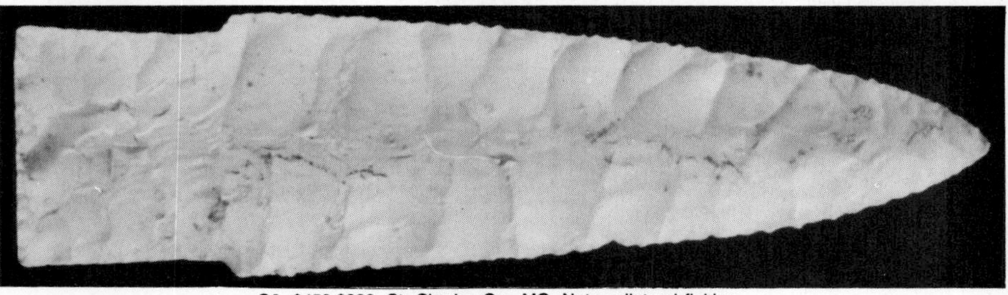

G9, $450-$800, St. Charles Co., MO. Note collateral flaking.

SCOTTSBLUFF II - Late Paleo, 9500 - 7000 B.P.

(Also see Hardin)

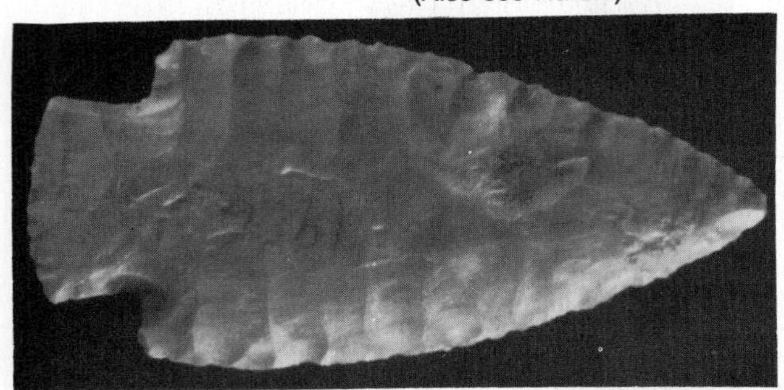

G5, $45-$70
AR.

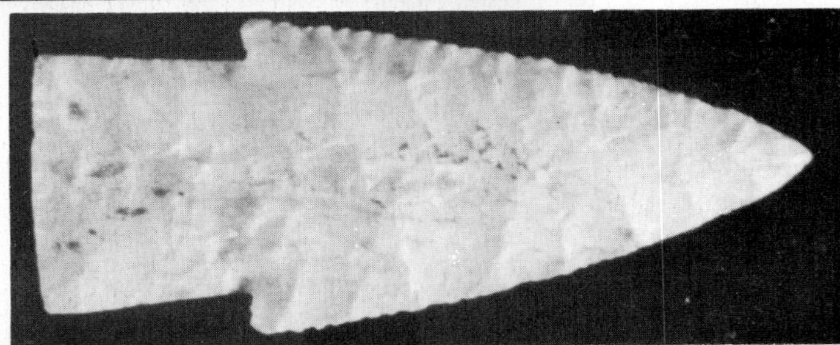

G8, $350-$600
N. Cent. AR.

G7, $250-$350
Jackson Co., MO.

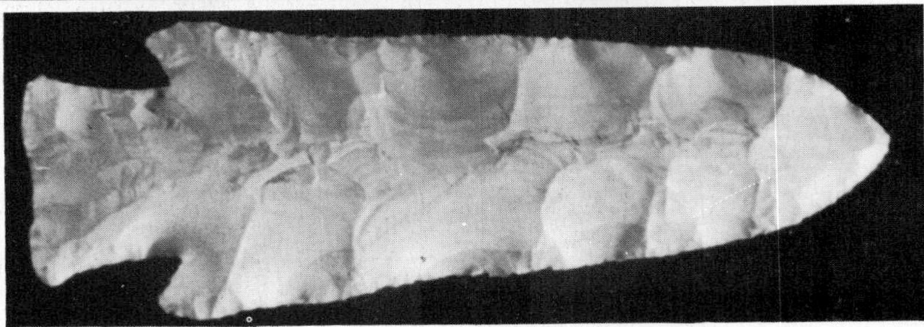

G6, $150-$250
Greene Co., MO. A rare example showing unusual flaking on the blade faces. Each flake removed is deep and broad and extends to the center of the blade. The deep flaking scars form a wavy edge when the point is viewed from its side.

LOCATION: Midwestern states. **DESCRIPTION:** A medium to large size triangular point with shoulders a little stronger than on Type I and a broad parallel sided stem.

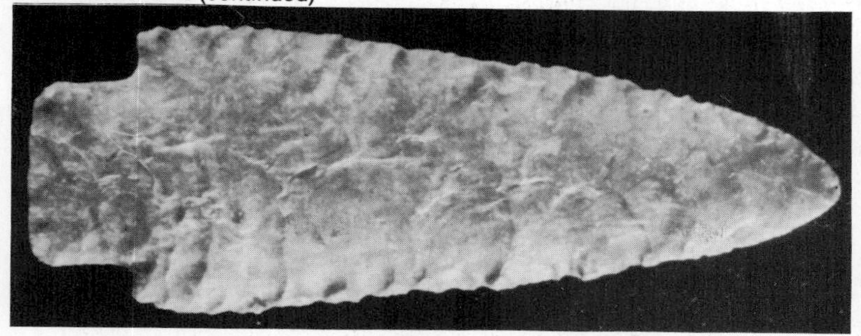

G6, $100-$200, AR/MO.

G7, $250-$400
Taos, NM

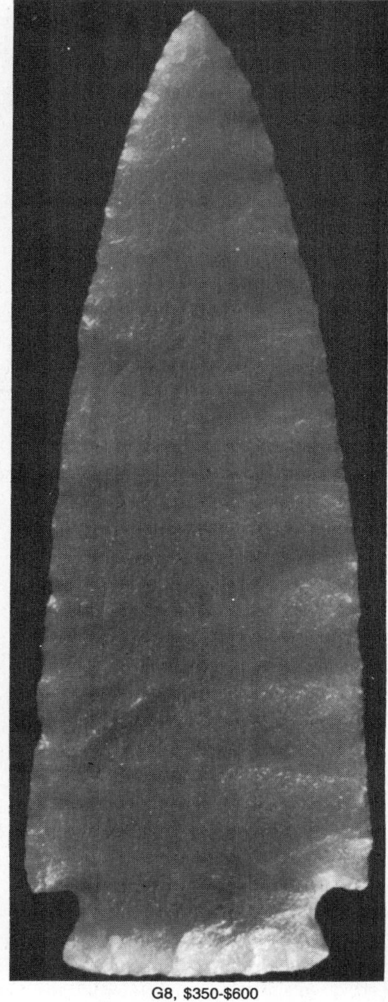

G8, $350-$600
Upper midwest. Sugar quartz.

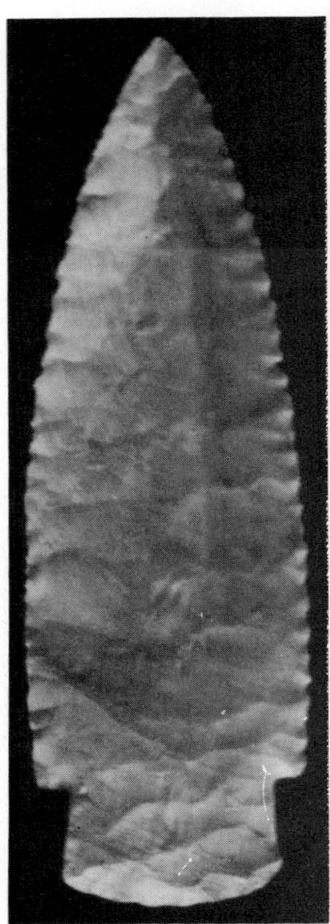

G9, $450-$850
Cooper Co., MO. Classic.

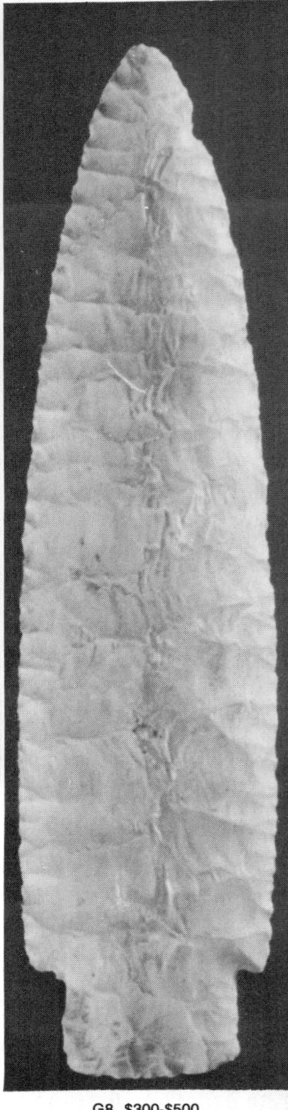

G8, $300-$500
Moniteau Co., MO.

G8, $350-$500
Deerfield, ND.

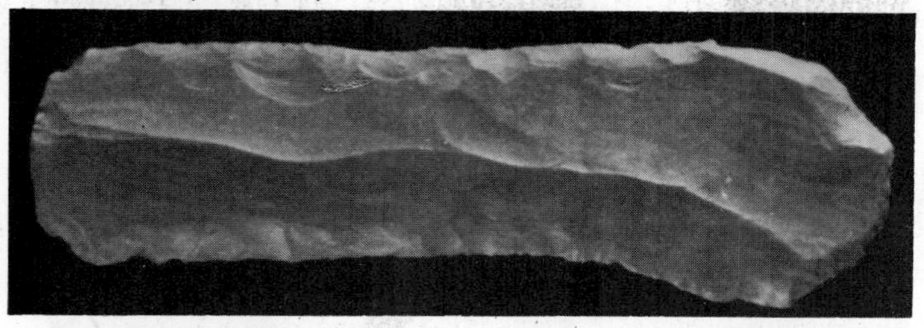

G7, $15-$30
Humphreys Co., TN.

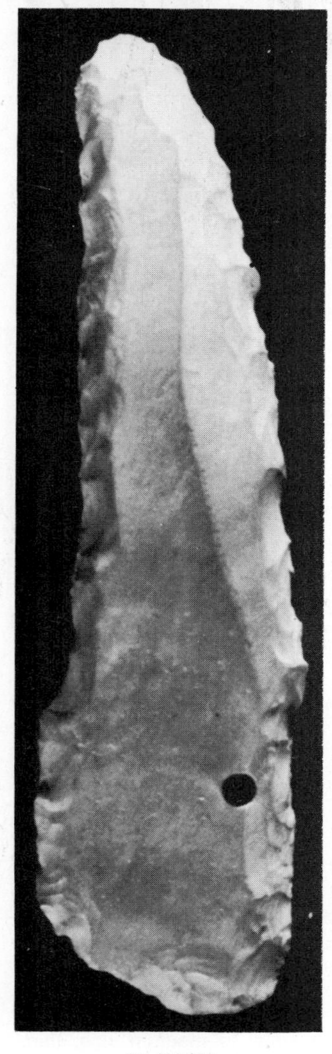

G7, $20-$30
OH.

G8, $35-$60
OH.

SEARCY - Early to mid-Archaic, 7000 - 5000 B.P.

(Also see Dalton-Colbert, Harpeth River and Russell Cave)

G4, $15-$25
Walker Co., AL.

G4, $10-$20
Meigs Co., TN.

G5, $20-$35
Meigs Co., TN.

G3, $8-$15
SE.

G4, $15-$25
Vernon Parrish, LA.

G6, $30-$50
Jonesboro, AR.

G7, $40-$70
New Market, AL. Tip nick.

G6, $30-$50
AR.

LOCATION: Midwestern states. **DESCRIPTION:** A small to medium size, thin, lanceolate point with a squared hafting area that (usually) has concave sides and base which is ground. Many examples are serrated.

SEDALIA - Early Archaic, 8000 - 5000 B.P.

(Also see Agate Basin, Eden, Guilford, Lerma and Nebo Hill)

G6, $90-$150
Cooper Co., MO.

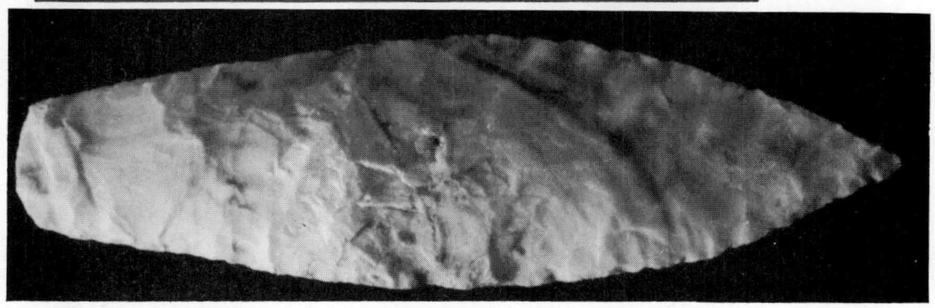

G9, $250-$400. MO.

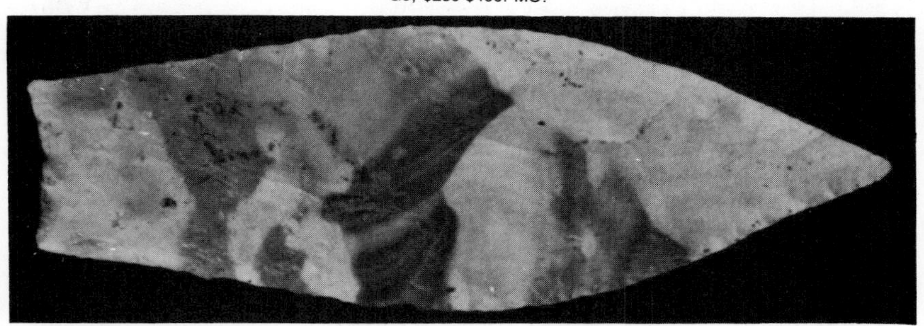

G9, $250-$400, Cent. MO. Classic.

G7, $120-$225, Cent. IL.

LOCATION: Midwestern states. **DESCRIPTION:** A medium to large size, narrow, lanceolate blade with straight to concave sides and base. Flaking is usually cruder than in *Agate Basin*.

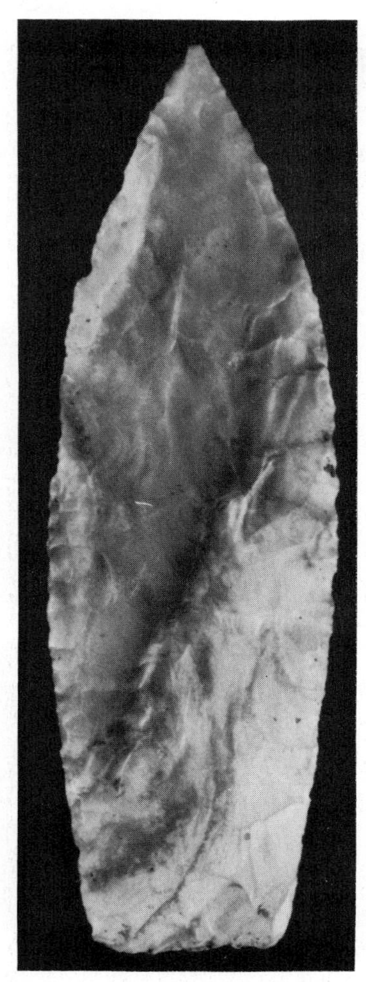

G7, $150-$250
Cooper Co., MO.

G7, $150-$250
Cooper Co., MO.

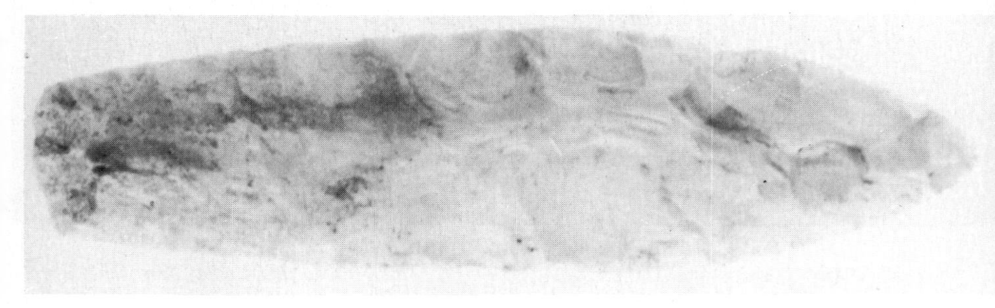

G7, $150-$250. Marion Co., AL.

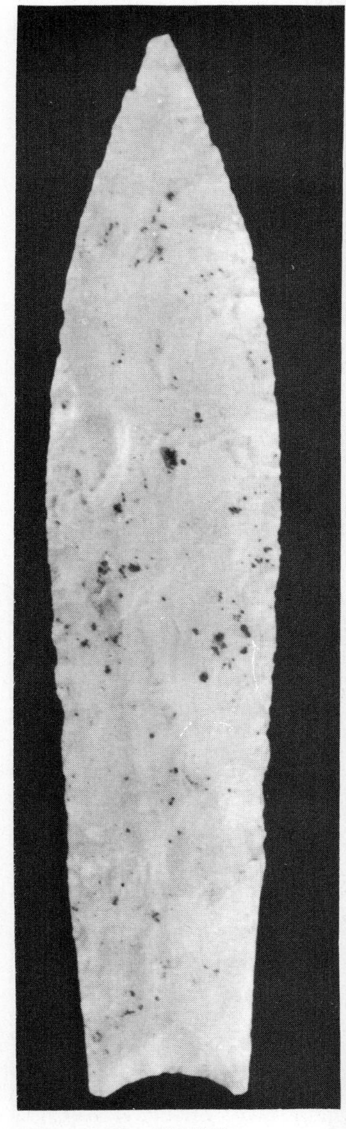

G8, $250-$400
MO.

G8, $200-$300
Menard Co., IL.

SEMINOLE - Late Archaic, 5000 - 3500 B.P.

(Also see Abbey, Elora, Hamilton, Levy, Savannah River)

G3, $20-$35
Marion Co., FL.

G8, $300-$500
Burke Co., GA.

G5, $40-$70
Gadsden Co., FL. Classic.

G9, $350-$650
Seminole Co., GA.

LOCATION: Southern Southeastern states. **DESCRIPTION:** A medium to large size, broad point with barbed shoulders and a concave base.

SEQUOYAH - Mississippian, 1000 - 600 B.P.

(Also see Alba, Blevins, Hayes, Homan, Livermore, Scallorn and Steiner)

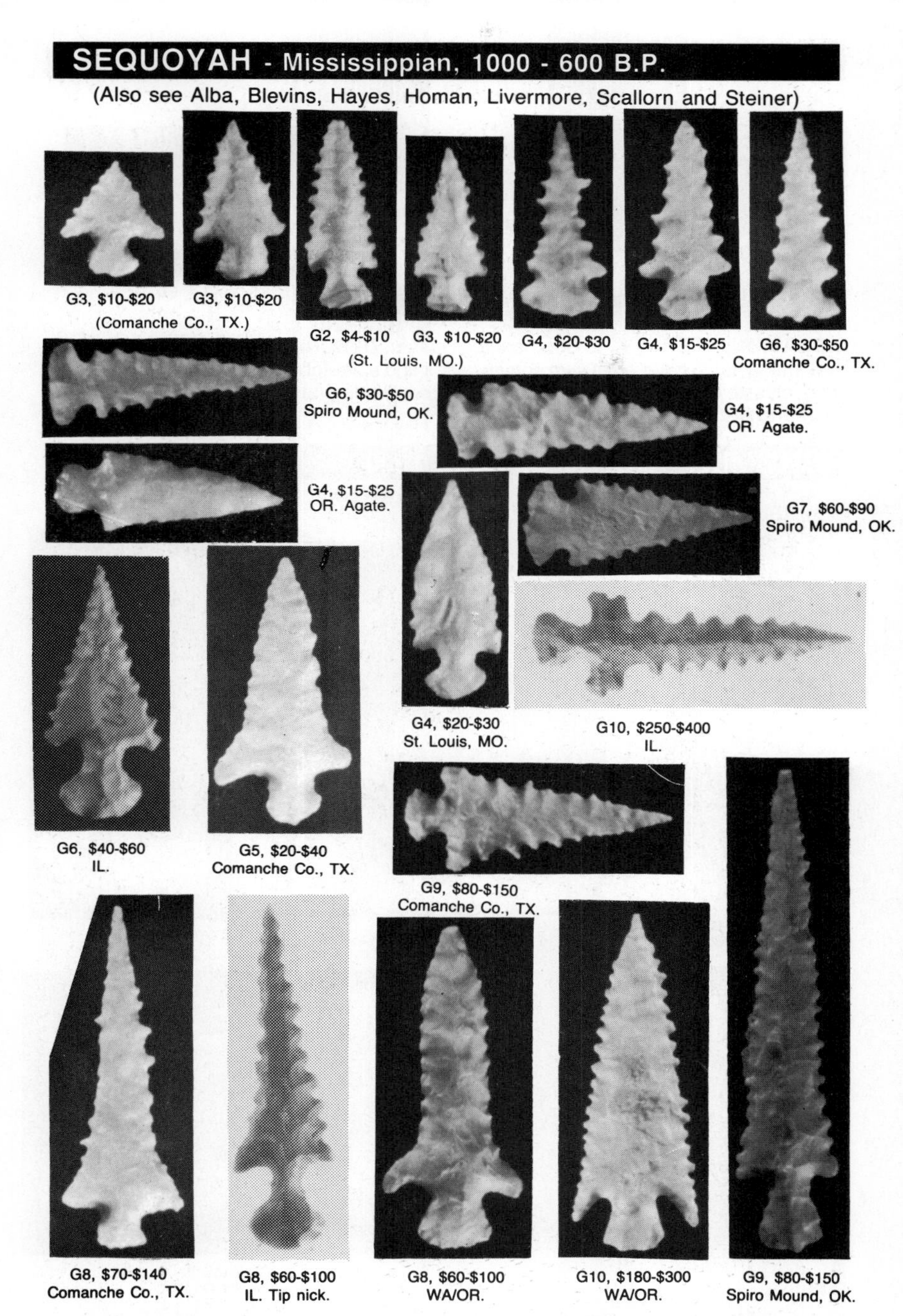

G3, $10-$20 G3, $10-$20
(Comanche Co., TX.)

G2, $4-$10 G3, $10-$20
(St. Louis, MO.)

G4, $20-$30

G4, $15-$25

G6, $30-$50
Comanche Co., TX.

G6, $30-$50
Spiro Mound, OK.

G4, $15-$25
OR. Agate.

G4, $15-$25
OR. Agate.

G7, $60-$90
Spiro Mound, OK.

G4, $20-$30
St. Louis, MO.

G10, $250-$400
IL.

G6, $40-$60
IL.

G5, $20-$40
Comanche Co., TX.

G9, $80-$150
Comanche Co., TX.

G8, $70-$140
Comanche Co., TX.

G8, $60-$100
IL. Tip nick.

G8, $60-$100
WA/OR.

G10, $180-$300
WA/OR.

G9, $80-$150
Spiro Mound, OK.

LOCATION: Midwestern to Northwestern states. **DESCRIPTION:** A small size, thin, narrow, serrated point with an expanded, bulbous stem. Believed to have been made by Caddo and other people.

SHETLEY - Mississippian to Historic, 700 - 350 B.P.

(Also see Greeneville and Guntersville)

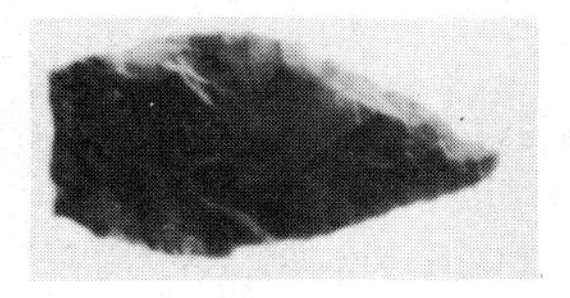

G3, $2-$3
Dunlap, TN.

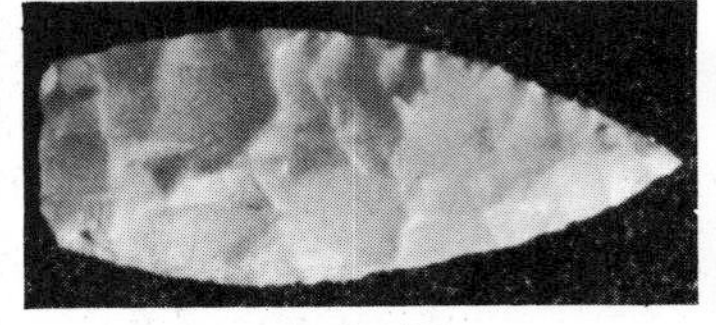

G7, $10-$20
E. TN.

LOCATION: Midwestern to Southeastern states. **DESCRIPTION:** A small size, thin, well made, lanceolate point with convex sides and a straight, convex or concave base. The classic form has a definite contracted hafting area where *Greeneville* or *Guntersville* do not.

SHUMLA - Woodland, 3000 - 1000 B.P.

(Also see Citrus, Eva, Hernando, Parowan & Rockwall)

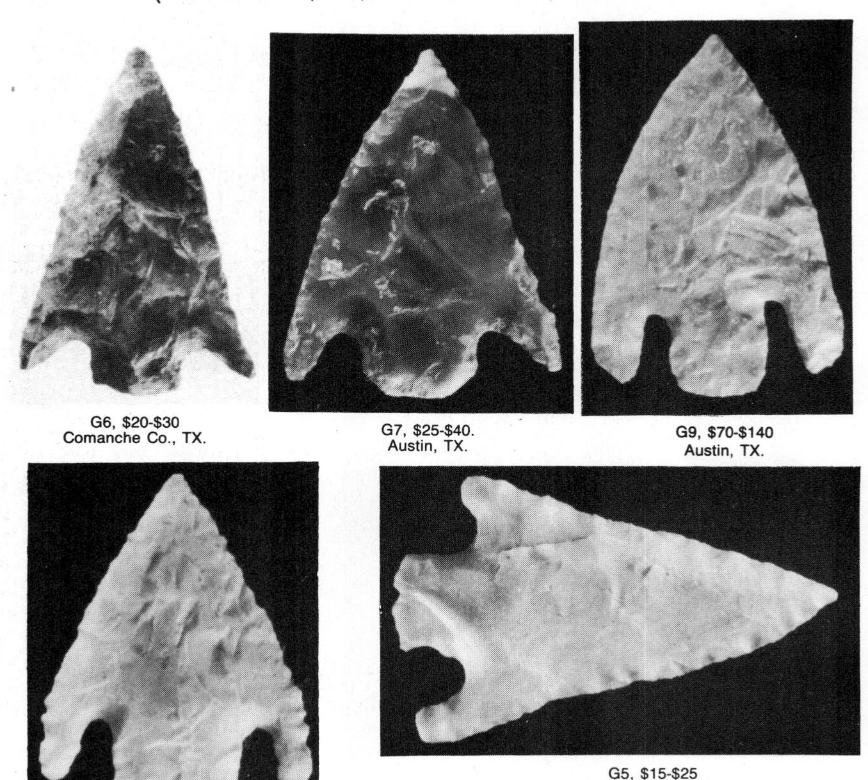

G6, $20-$30
Comanche Co., TX.

G7, $25-$40.
Austin, TX.

G9, $70-$140
Austin, TX.

G7, $25-$40
Austin, TX.

G5, $15-$25
Comanche Co., TX.

LOCATION: Midwestern states. **DESCRIPTION:** A small size, basal notched point with convex, straight or recurved sides. Barbs usually extend to the base.

SIMPSON - Late Paleo, 12000 - 8000 B.P.

(Also see Beaver Lake, Clovis-unfluted, Conerly, Golondrina, Quad and Suwannee)

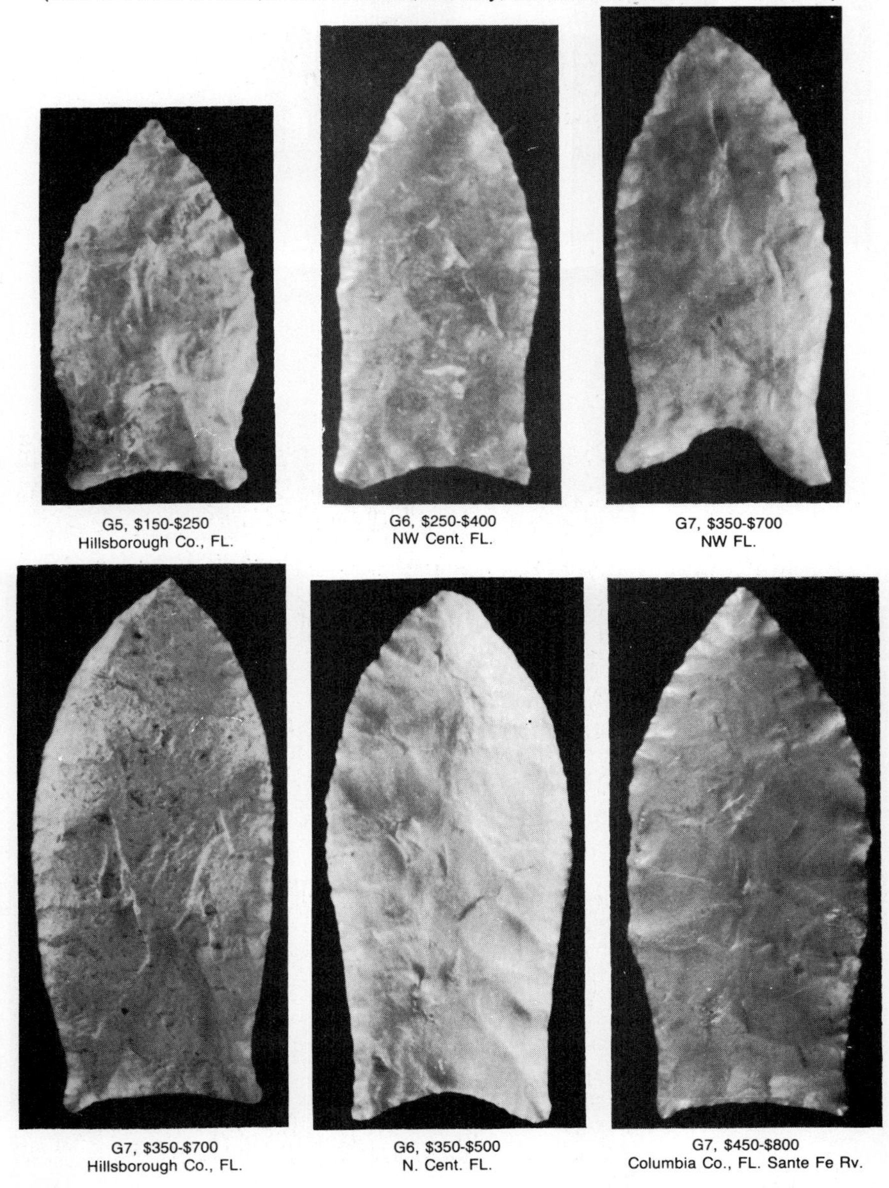

G5, $150-$250
Hillsborough Co., FL.

G6, $250-$400
NW Cent. FL.

G7, $350-$700
NW FL.

G7, $350-$700
Hillsborough Co., FL.

G6, $350-$500
N. Cent. FL.

G7, $450-$800
Columbia Co., FL. Sante Fe Rv.

LOCATION: Southern Southeastern states. **DESCRIPTION:** A medium to large size lanceolate, auriculate blade with recurved sides, outward flaring ears and a concave base. The hafting area constriction is more narrow than in the *Suwannee* type. Fluting is absent.

SIMPSON (continued)

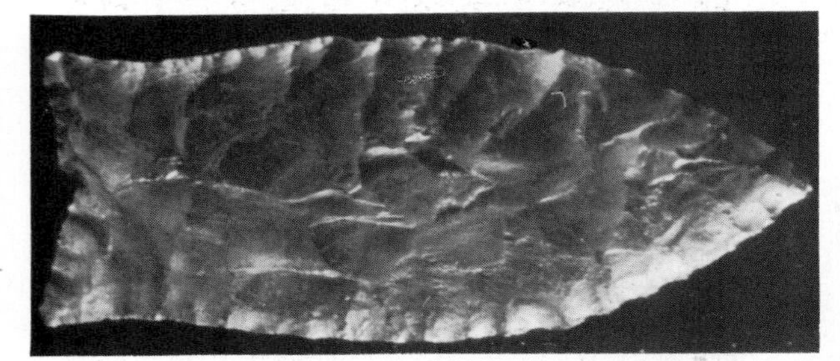

G8, $600-$1000
Stienhatchee Rv., FL.

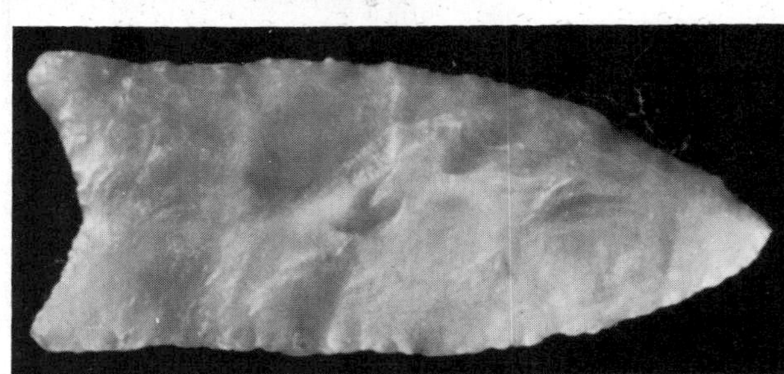

G6, $350-$500
Suwannee Co., FL. Banded translucent coral.

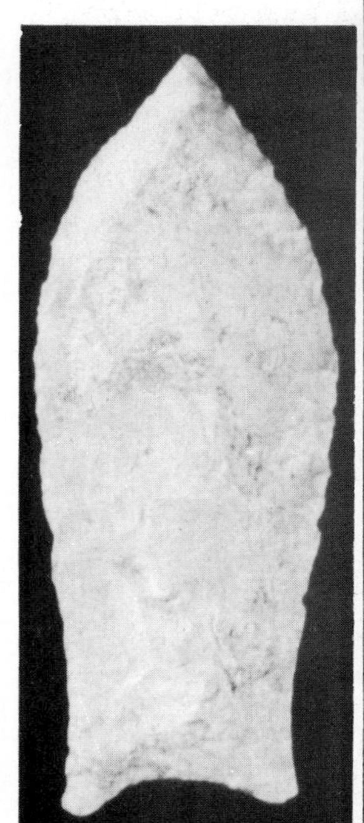

G7, $500-$900
NW Cent. FL.

G9, $800-$1200
NW Cent. FL.

G9, $900-$1400
Sante Fe Rv., FL. Classic Bull Tongue Simpson.

G9, $800-$1500
NW Cent. FL.

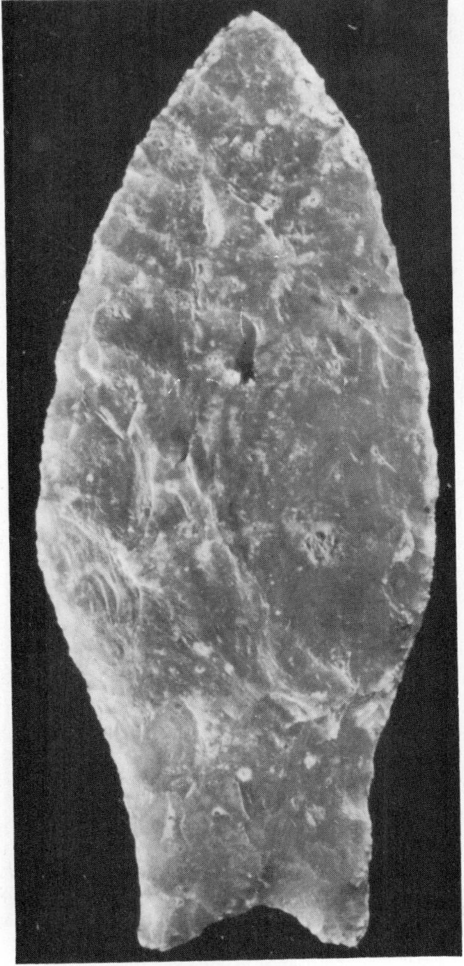

G10, $3000-$5500
Hamilton Co., FL.

G9, $800-$1500
Citrus Co., FL.

G10, $3000-$5000
Lake Marion, SC. Rhyolite.

G8, $500-$900
Tallahassee, FL. Broken & glued.

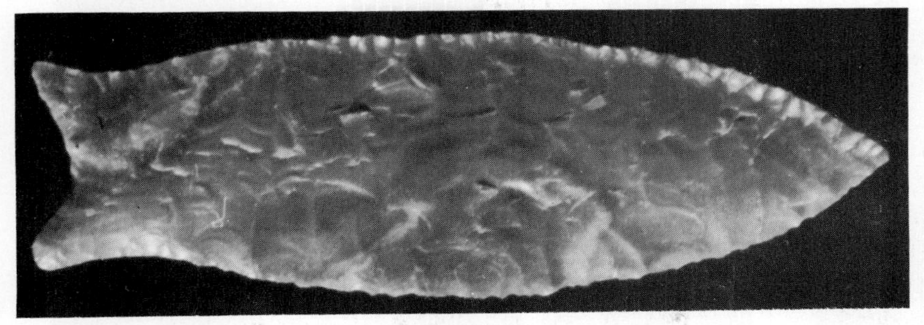

G10, $3000-$5000
McIntosh Co., OK.

SINNER - Woodland, 3000 - 2000 B.P.

(Also see Evans)

G2, $1-$2
Lincoln Parrish, LA.

G3, $2-$3
Waco, TX.

G5, $3-$5
Lincoln Parrish, LA.

G7, $8-$12
Lincoln Parrish, LA.

G7, $6-$10
Lincoln Parrish, LA.

G8, $10-$20
Lincoln Parrish, LA. Classic.

G6, $4-$6
Lincoln Parrish, LA.

LOCATION: Southern Midwestern states. **DESCRIPTION:** A medium size, expanded stemmed point with several barbs occurring above the shoulders.

SIX MILE CREEK - Mid-Archaic, 7500 - 5000 B.P.

(Also see Kirk and South Prong Creek)

G5, $50-$80
Seminole Co., GA.

G6, $60-$90
Burke Co., GA.

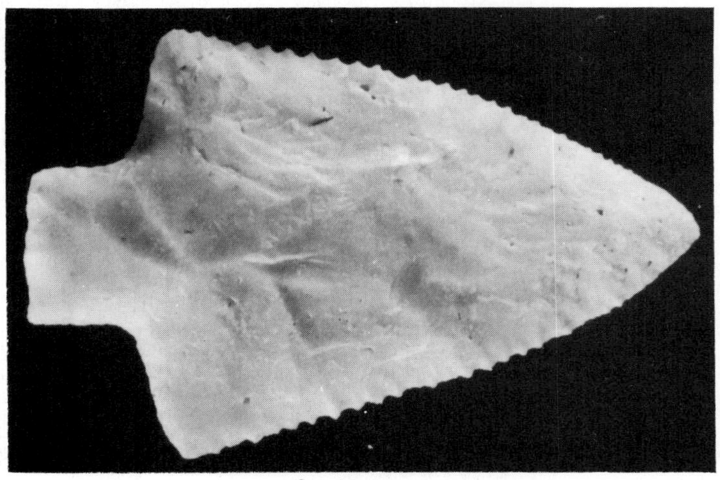

G10, $500-$800
Taylor Co., FL. Classic.

LOCATION: Southern Southeastern states. **DESCRIPTION:** A medium to large size, broad, stemmed, serrated point. The serrations are uniquely formed by careful pressure flaking applied from the side of only one face. Normal *Kirk* serrations are pressure flaked alternately from both faces. Believed to be a later *Kirk* variant.

SMITH - Mid-Archaic, 7000 - 4000 B.P.

(Also see Calf Creek, Citrus, Culbreath, Eva, Hernando, Mehlville and Wade)

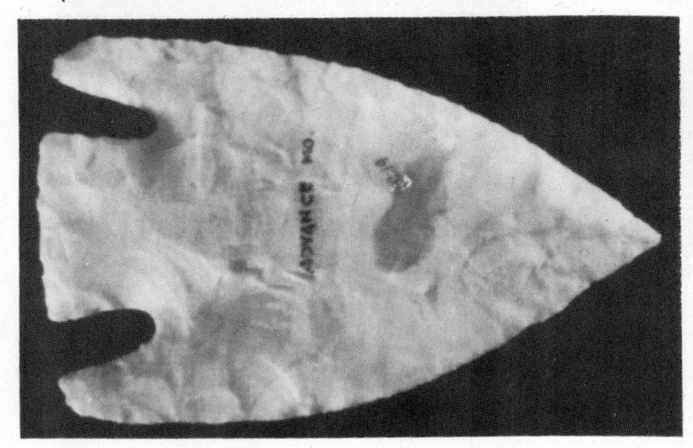

G9, $350-$750
Advance, MO. Classic.

G8, $250-$400
Cent. IL.

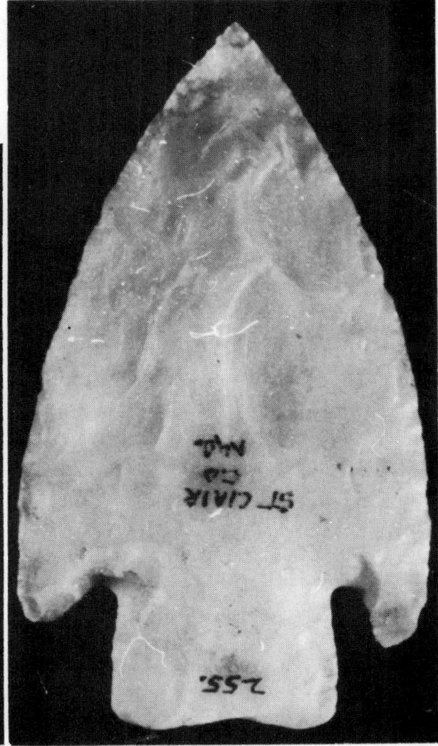

G8, $250-$400
St. Clair Co., MO.

LOCATION: Midwestern states. **DESCRIPTION:** A large size, broad, point with long parallel shoulders and a squared base. Some examples may appear to be basal notched due to the long barbs.

G5, $25-$40
MO.

G7, $120-$200
Howard Co., MO.

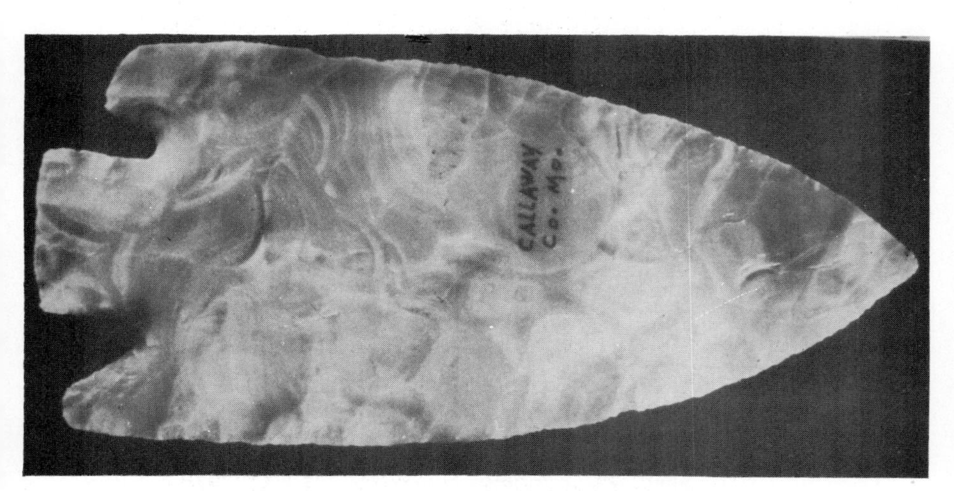

G9, $450-$800
Callaway Co., MO.

G9, $600-$1000
IN.

SMITHSONIA - Late Archaic - Woodland, 4000 - 1500 B.P.

(Also see Buck Creek, Hamilton, Motley, Table Rock and Wade)

G6, $30-$50
Meigs Co., TN.

G4, $8-$12
Colbert Co., AL.

G3, $5-$8
Putnam Co., TN.

G6, $30-$50
Hardin Co., TN.

G8, $90-$150
Hardin Co., TN. Colorful red, yellow & blue Horse Creek chert.

G5, $10-$15
Humphreys Co., TN.

LOCATION: Southeastern states. **DESCRIPTION:** A medium size, triangular point with tapered to barbed shoulders and a parallel sided stem with a straight base. Many examples have finely serrated blade edges which are usually straight. **I.D. KEY:** High barb on one side & fine edgework.

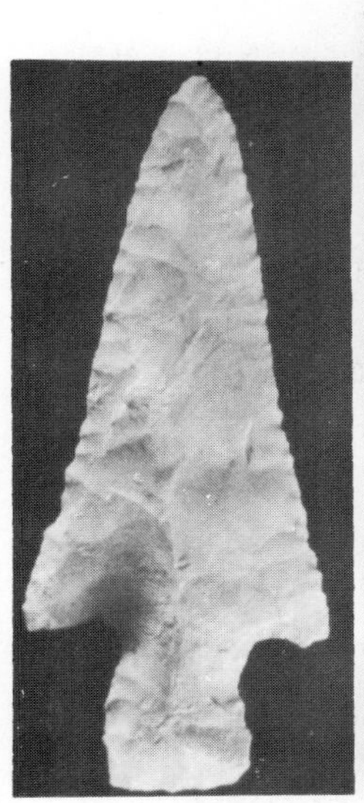

G4, $8-$12
Humphreys Co., TN.

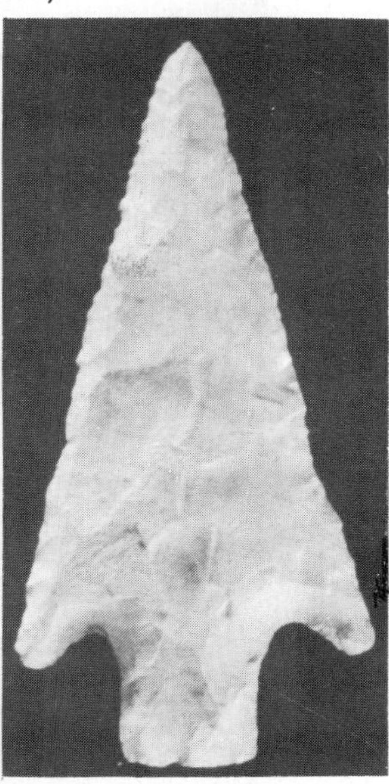

G6, $35-$60
Colbert Co., AL.

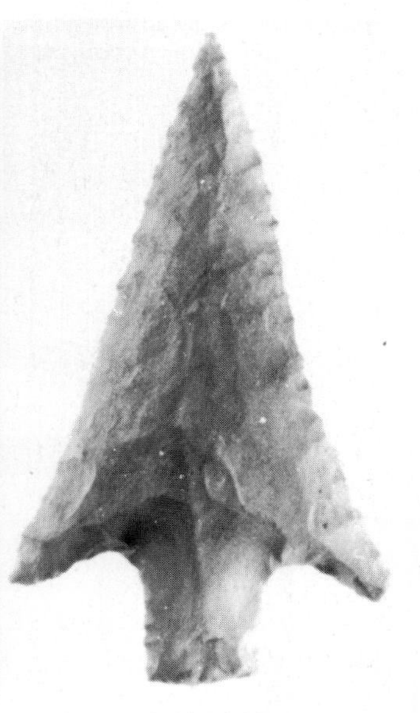

G8, $60-$100
Humphreys Co., TN.

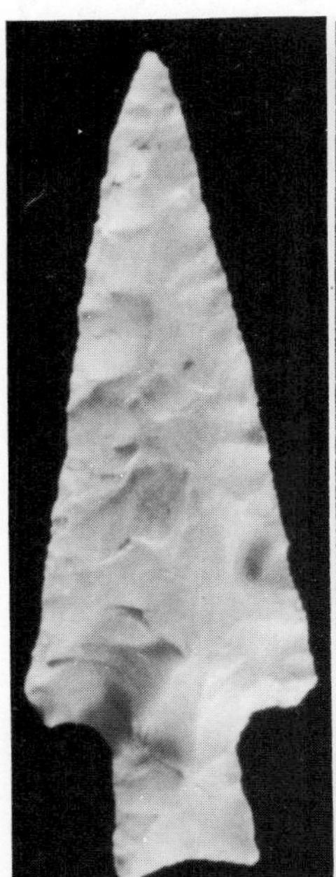

G5, $15-$25
Meigs Co., TN. Note unusual clipped shoulders.

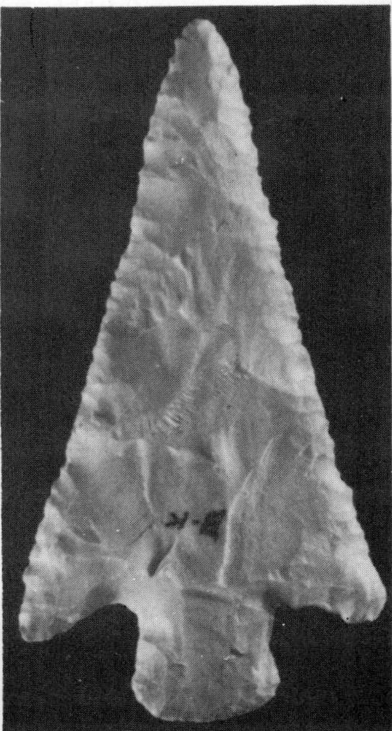

G8, $60-$90
Humphreys Co., TN.

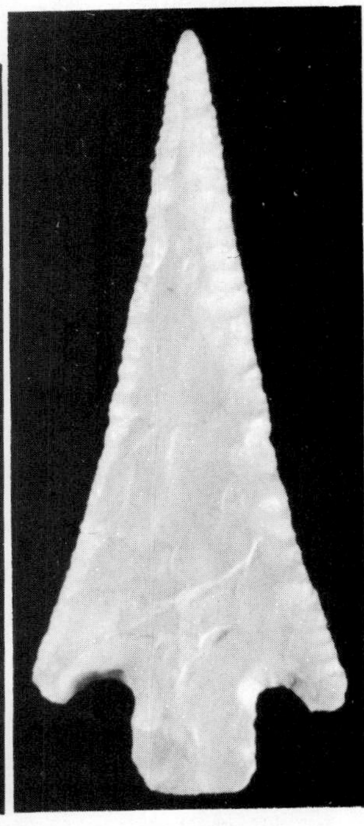

G9, $250-$350
Hardin Co., TN.

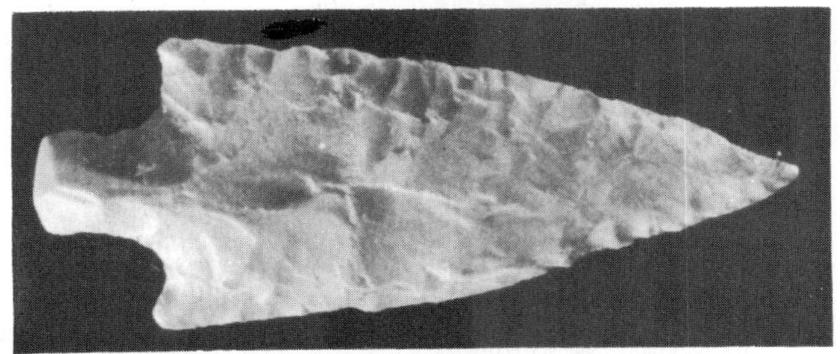

G6, $35-$60
Colbert Co., AL.

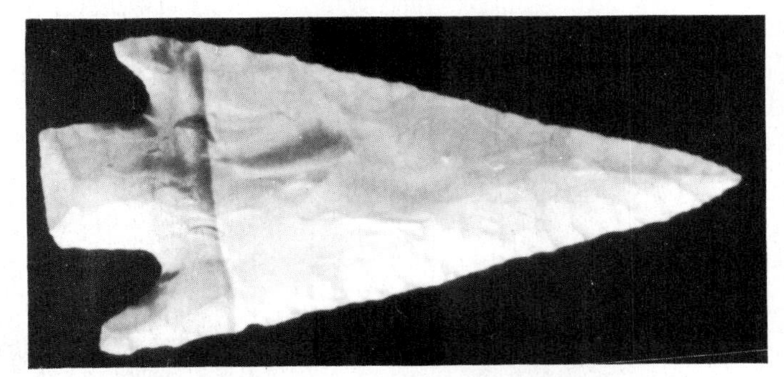

G9, $250-$400, Hardin Co., TN. Classic form. Brown & beige color.

G8, $80-$140, Humphreys Co., TN.

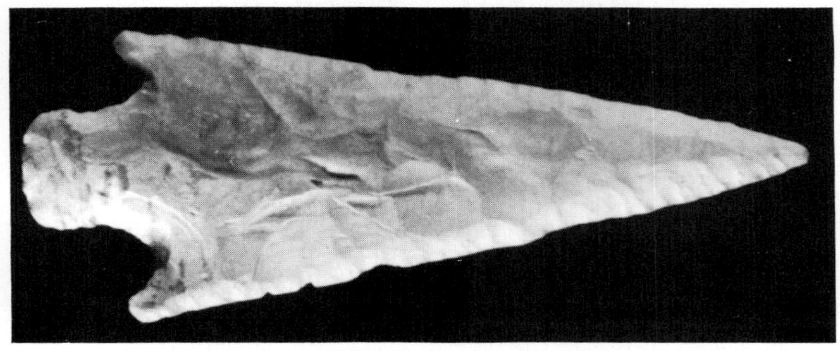

G7, $45-$70, Hardin Co., TN.

SNAKE CREEK - Late Archaic, 4000 - 3000 B.P.

(Also see Morse Knife)

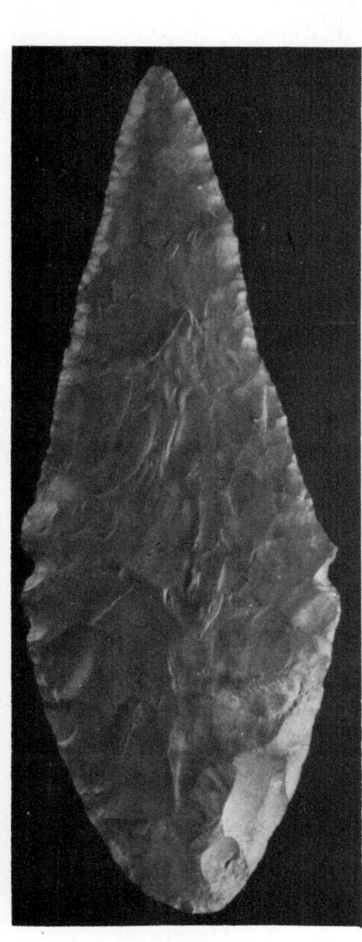

G6, $50-$80
Hardin Co., TN. Note double side notch on left side.

G7, $60-$90
Hardin Co., TN. Arch blade. Note double side notches.

LOCATION: Southeastern states. **DESCRIPTION:** A large size, broad, ovoid blade with shallow side notches about half way between the base and tip. Double side notches are common. The stem contracts to a rounded base.

SNYDERS (Hopewell) - Woodland, 2500 - 1500 B.P.

(Also see Buck Creek, Hopewell, Motley, North and Ross)

G5, $150-$250
Cent. IL.

G6, $180-$300
Cent. IL. Red chert.

G7, $200-$350
Greene Co., IN.

G6, $180-$300
Lincoln Co., MO.

LOCATION: Midwestern to Eastern states. **DESCRIPTION:** A medium to large size, broad, thin, wide corner notched point of high quality. Blade edges and base are convex. Many examples have intentional fractured bases. This point has been reproduced in recent years.

SNYDERS (continued)

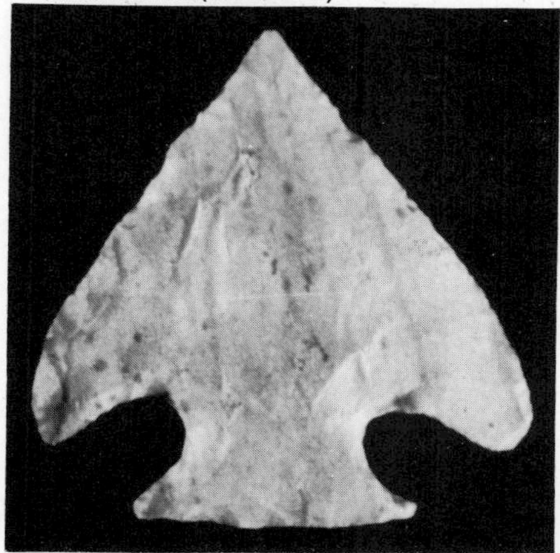

G6, $180-$300
Lincoln Co., MO.

G5, $150-$250
St. Louis Co., MO.

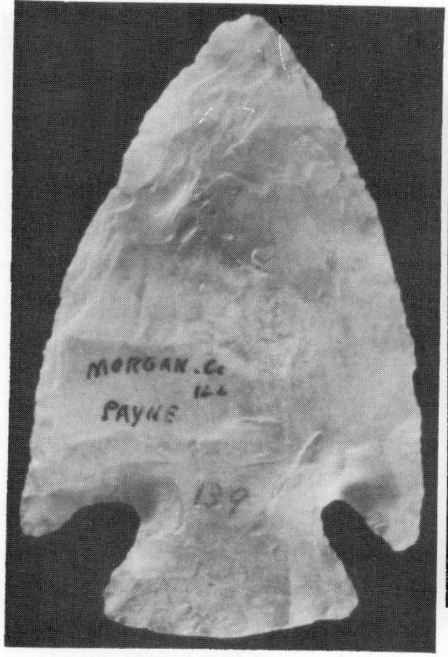

G4, $125-$200
Morgan Co., IL.

G5, $150-$250
Humphreys Co., TN.

G6, $200-$320
MO.

G6, $180-$300
IL.

G6, $200-$320
IL.

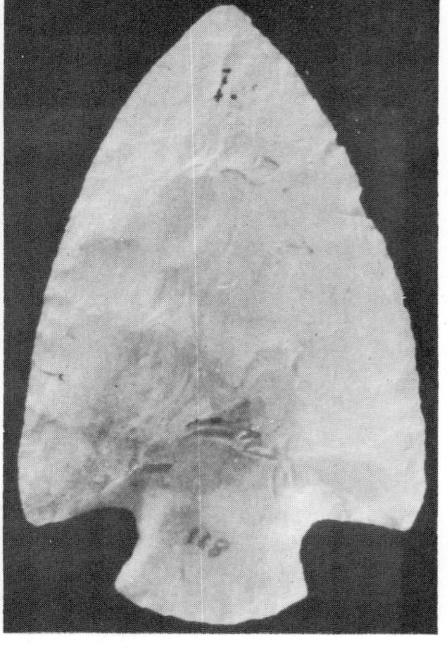

G6, $200-$325
IL.

G7, $250-$450
Greene Co., IL.

G8, $300-$500
IL.

SOUTH PRONG CREEK - Late Archaic, 5000 - 3000 B.P.

(Also see Abbey, Elora, Maples, Savannah River & Six Mile Creek)

G3, $2-$4
Hamilton Co., TN.

G3, $3-$5
Warner Robbins, GA.

G5, $8-$15
Andersonville, GA. Flint River.

G6, $10-$20
Walker Co., AL.

G8, $60-$90
Henry Co., AL.

LOCATION: Southern Southeastern states. **DESCRIPTION:** A large size, broad shouldered point with a small rectangular stem. Blade edges are usually bifacially serrated beginning at each shoulder and terminating about ⅓ the way from the tip.

G7, $25-$40
Tallahassee, FL.

SOUTHAMPTON - Early Archaic, 8000 - 6000 B.P.

(Also see Buzzard Roost Creek, Holmes, Kanawha, Oxbow, Rice Lobbed, St. Albans & Stanly)

G4, $2-$3
Sussex Co., VA.

G4, $2-$3
Southampton Co., VA.

G3, $1-$2
Cent. NC.

G2, .50-$1
Sussex Co., VA.

G4, $2-$3
Sussex Co., VA. Vein quartz.

G5, $3-$5
Sussex Co., VA.

G5, $3-$5
Dinwiddie Co., VA.

G3, $1-$2
Sussex Co., VA.

LOCATION: Far Eastern states. **DESCRIPTION:** A medium to large size, narrow, thick, bifurcated stemmed point. The basal lobes can expand and the center notch is shallow. Bases are usually ground.

SOUTHAMPTON (continued)

G9, $25-$45
Sussex Co., VA.

G8, $10-$20
Johnson Co., NC.

G7, $6-$10
Southampton
Co., VA.

G7, $6-$10
Sussex Co., VA.

G7, $8-$12
Dinwiddie Co., VA.

SPEDIS - Early Archaic, 10000 - 8000 B.P.

(Also see Cascade Leaf and Sandia)

G10, $35-$60
Wasco Co., OR.
Classic.

G8, $25-$45
Lake Co., OR.

G7, $20-$40
Wasco Co., OR. Classic.

G6, $15-$25
Wasco Co., OR.

G9, $30-$50
Wasco Co., OR.

G6, $15-$25
Wasco Co., OR.

LOCATION: Northwestern states. **DESCRIPTION:** A small to medium size, thin, narrow, lanceolate point with a contracting basal area. Base can be concave or convex. Oblique parallel flaking occurs on some examples.

SQUARE KNIFE - Late Paleo to Early Archaic, 10000 - 8000 B.P.

(Also see Angostura, Fort Ancient Knife, Frazier, Pandora & Victoria)

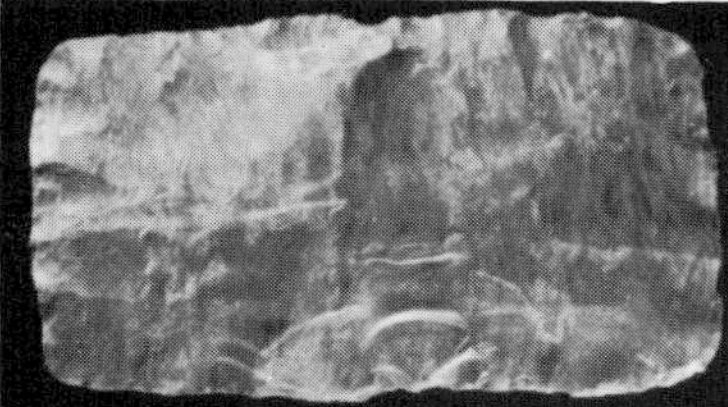

G3, $4-$6
Humphreys
Co., TN.

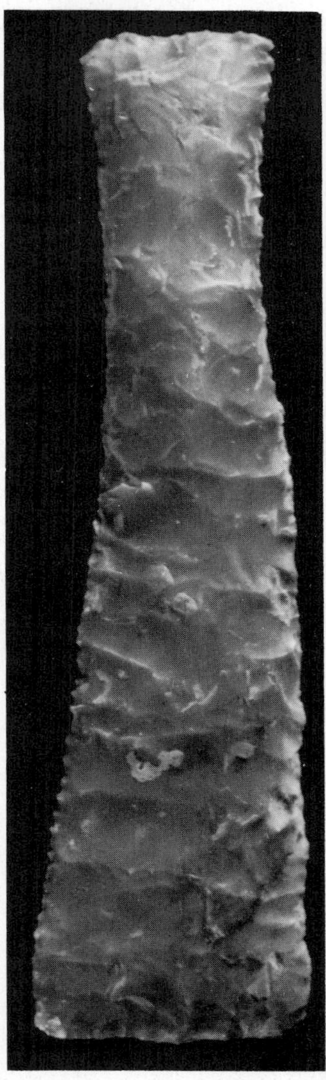

G10, $250-$450
Dickson Cave, KY. Very rare.

LOCATION: Midwestern states. **DESCRIPTION:** A medium to large size squared blade that is sometimes fluted from either or both ends.

G10, $350-$650
Douglas Co., KS. Classic.

STANFIELD - Transitional Paleo, 10000 - 8000 B.P.

(Also see Angostura, Fort Ancient Knife, Frazier, Pandora & Victoria)

G5, $10-$20
Lawrence Co., AL.

G8, $25-$40
Humphreys Co., TN. Basal area is ground.

G4, $6-$10
Colbert Co., AL.

G7, $20-$35
Lauderdale Co., AL.

G9, $150-$250
Hardin Co., TN.

G6, $15-$25
Colbert Co., AL.

G7, $20-$35
Colbert Co., AL.

G5, $10-$20
Humphreys Co., TN.
Base is ground.

LOCATION: Southeastern states. **DESCRIPTION:** A medium to large size, narrow, lanceolate point with parallel sides and a straight base. Some rare examples are fluted.

STANFIELD (continued)

G8, $45-$80
Humphreys Co., TN.
Classic.

STANLY- Early Archaic, 8000 - 5000 B.P.

(Also see Fox Valley, Garth Slough, Kirk-Bifurcated, Pedernalis, Savannah River & Southampton)

G3, $15-$25
IL.

G3, $15-$25
IL.

G4, $20-$30
Marion Co., TN.

G5, $30-$55
IL.

G2, $8-$15
Bakewell, TN.

G4, $20-$35
Meigs Co., TN.

G2, $6-$10
IL. Tip damage.

G3, $15-$30
IL.

G4, $20-$40
Cumberland Co., KY.

LOCATION: Southeastern to Eastern states. Type site is Stanly Co., NC. **DESCRIPTION:** A small to medium size, broad shoulder point with a small bifurcated stem. Some examples are serrated and show high quality flaking. The shoulders are very prominent and can be tapered, horizontal or barbed.

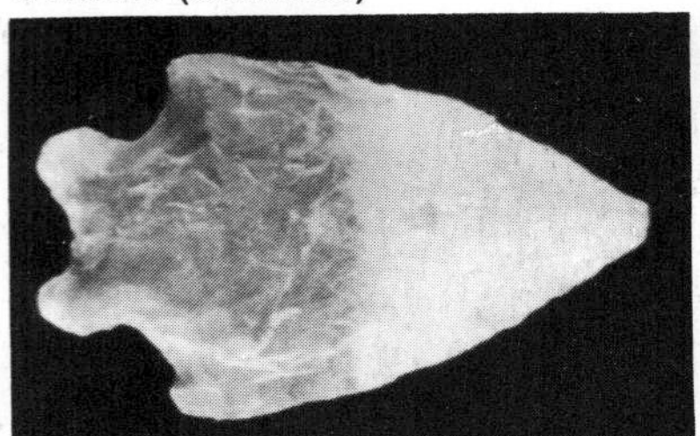

G3, $10-$20
Davidson Co., NC. Tip nick.

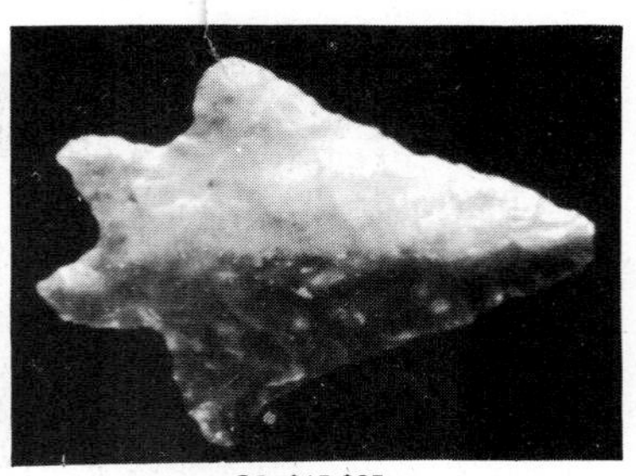

G3, $15-$25
Jackson Co., AL. Tip nick.

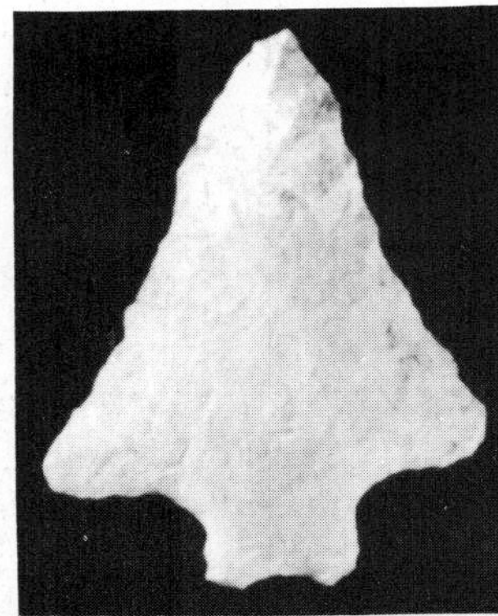

G5, $25-$45
Moore Co., NC.

G7, $60-$100
Stanly Co., NC.

G8, $40-$60
Central NC.

G6, $45-$70, Cent. NC.

G4, $20-$40
Pearson Co., NC.

G4, $20-$40, Cent. NC.

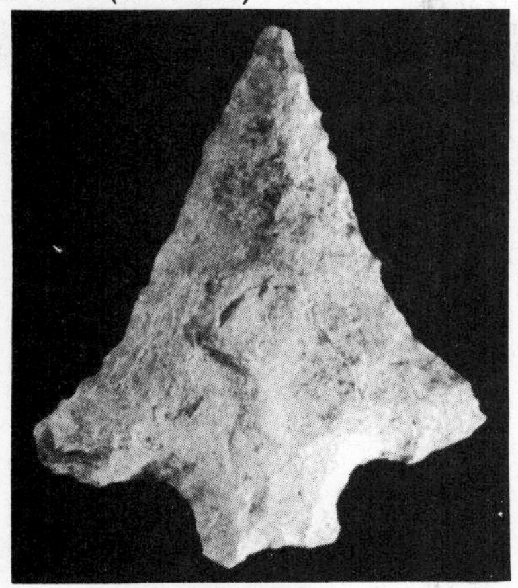

G5, $30-$50
Cent. NC.

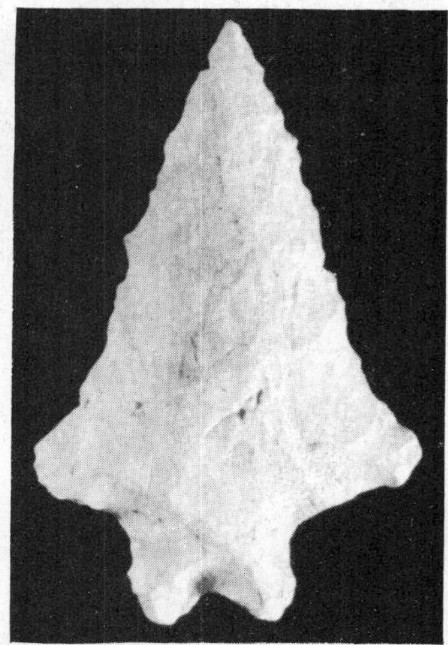

G7, $60-$100
Rockingham Co., NC. Classic.

G9, $100-$160
Randolph Co., NC.

G4, $20-$40
Stanly Co., NC.

G5, $30-$50
Mecklinburg Co., NC.

STANLY NARROW BLADE - Early Archaic, 8000 - 5000 B.P.

(Also see Kirk Serrated-Bifurcated, Pedernalis and Savannah River)

G4, $20-$35
Alleghany Co., NC.

G4, $20-$40
Stokes Co., NC.

G4, $20-$40
Randolph Co., NC.

G4, $20-$40
Stokes Co., NC.

G6, $45-$70
Randolph Co., NC.

G5, $30-$50
Randolph Co., NC.

G6, $45-$70
Moore Co., NC.

G6, $45-$70
Chatham Co., NC.

G5, $30-$50
Randolph Co., NC.

LOCATION: Far Eastern states. **DESCRIPTION:** A medium size, narrow shoulder point with a parallel sided stem and a concave base. Believed to have evolved from *Kirk* points and later evolved into *Savannah River* points.

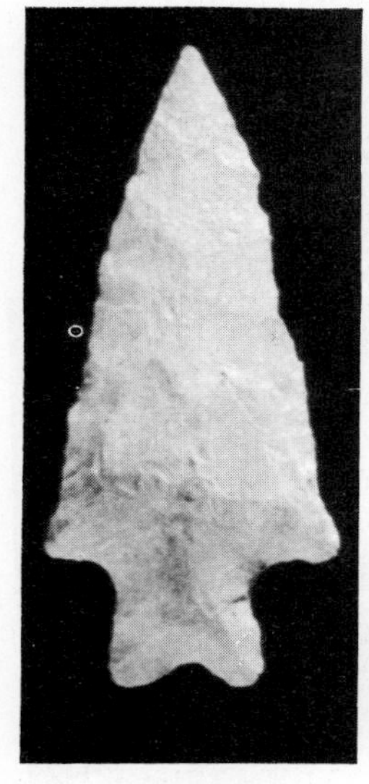

G7, $80-$120
Catawba Co., NC. Classic.

G5, $25-$45
Stokes Co., NC.

G6, $50-$80
Guilford Co., NC.

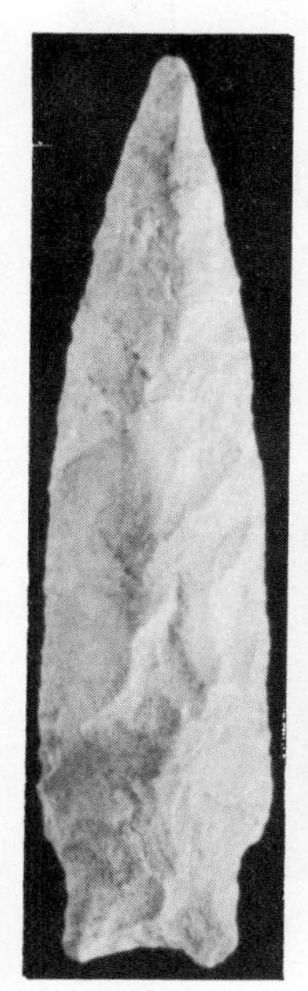

G6, $50-$80
Moore Co., NC.

G9, $150-$250
Montgomery Co., NC.
Excellent example.

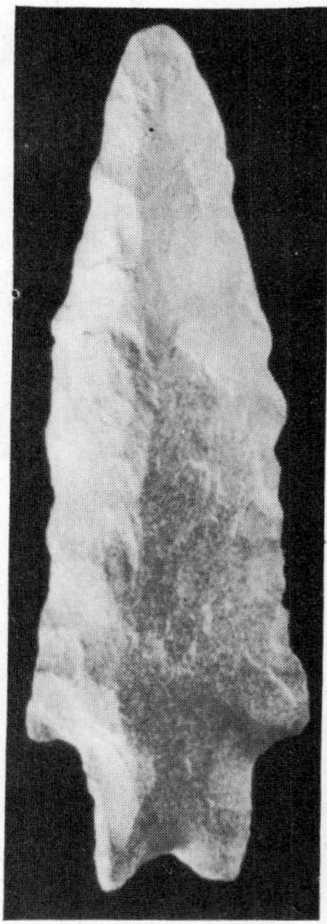

G5, $30-$50
Randolph Co., NC.

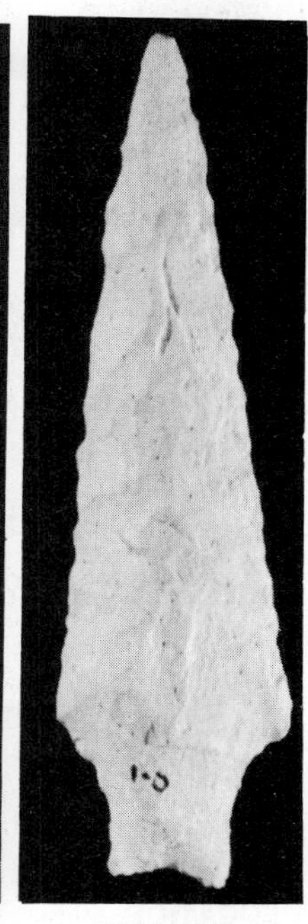

G5, $30-$45
Chatham Co., NC.

STANLY NARROW BLADE (continued)

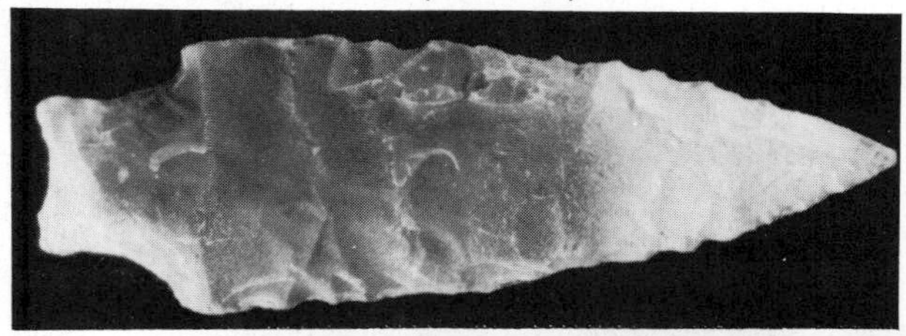

G8, $100-$180
Randolph Co., NC.

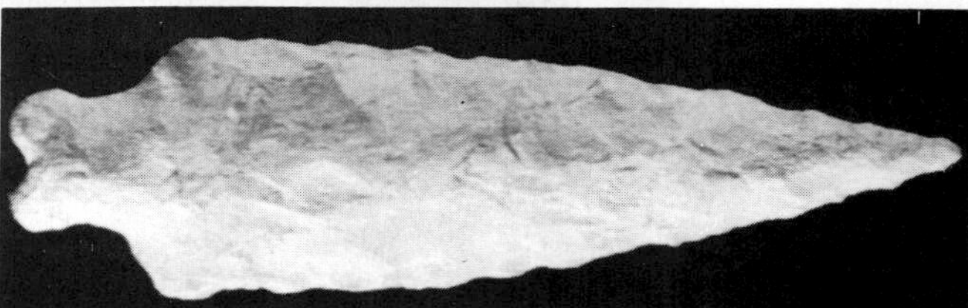

G9, $150-$250
Davidson Co., NC.

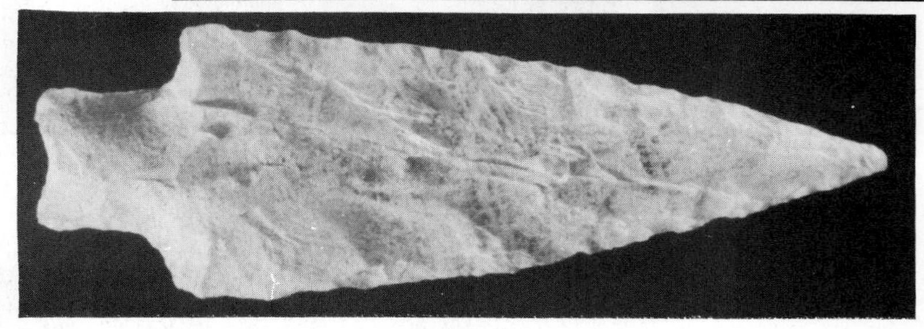

G8, $90-$150
Moore Co., NC.

STARR - Mississippian to Historic, 1000 - 250 B.P.

(Also see Hamilton, Maud and McGloin)

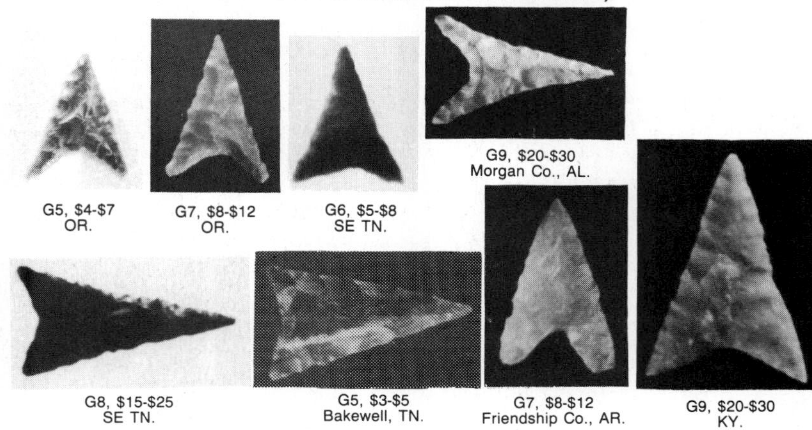

G5, $4-$7
OR.

G7, $8-$12
OR.

G6, $5-$8
SE TN.

G9, $20-$30
Morgan Co., AL.

G8, $15-$25
SE TN.

G5, $3-$5
Bakewell, TN.

G7, $8-$12
Friendship Co., AR.

G9, $20-$30
KY.

LOCATION: Midwestern states. **DESCRIPTION:** A small size, thin, triangular point with a "V" base concavity. Blade edges can be concave to straight.

STEINER - Mississippian, 1000 - 400 B.P.

(Also see Friley, Scallorn and Sequoyah)

G4, $3-$5 Comanche Co., TX.
G5, $5-$8 Comanche Co., TX.
G7, $15-$25 Waco, TX.
G8, $25-$40 Waco, TX.
G7, $20-$30 Comanche Co., TX.
G6, $8-$12 Waco, TX.
G7, $20-$30 Waco, TX.
G7, $20-$30 Comanche Co., TX.
G7, $15-$25 Comanche Co., TX.
G8, $25-$40 Limestone Co., TX.
G9, $50-$80 Red Rv. Co., TX.
G7, $20-$30 Waco, TX.
G9, $45-$80 Comanche Co., TX.
G9, $50-$80 Comanche Co., TX. Classic.
G8, $25-$40 Comanche Co., TX.

LOCATION: Midwestern states. **DESCRIPTION:** A small size, thin, barbed arrow point with strong shoulders. The stem is short and may be horizontal or expanded.

STEUBEN - Woodland, 2000 - 1000 B.P.

(Also see Bakers Creek, Mud Creek, Palmillas and Table Rock)

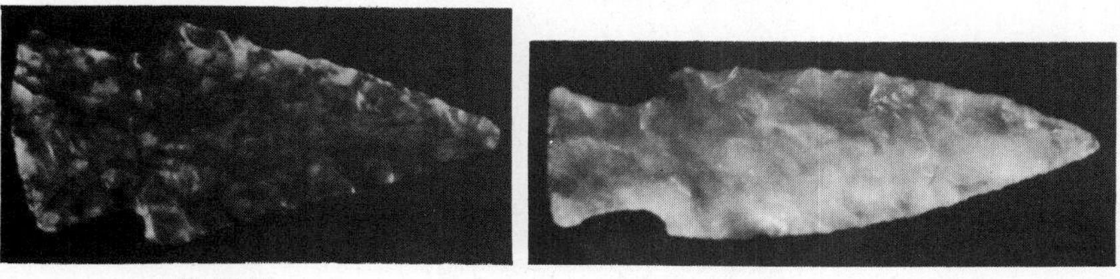

G5, $5-$8
CO.

G7, $6-$10
AR. Note basal thinning.

LOCATION: Midwestern states. **DESCRIPTION:** A medium to large size, narrow, expanded stem point. Shoulders can be tapered to straight. The base is straight to convex. This type is very similar to *Bakers Creek* in the Southeast.

STEUBENVILLE - Early Archaic, 9000 - 6000 B.P.

(Also see Holland and Scottsbluff)

G6, $10-$20
W. TN.

G7, $15-$25
W. TN.

LOCATION: Midwest to Western states. **DESCRIPTION:** A medium to large size, broad, triangular point with weak tapered shoulders, a wide parallel sided stem and a concave base. The basal area is ground. Believed to be developed from the *Scottsbluff* type.

STILWELL - Early Archaic, 9000 - 7000 B.P.

(Also see Kirk Corner Notched and Pine Tree)

G10, $800-$1500
Benton Co., TN. Thin and excellent. Dover chert.

LOCATION: Midwestern to Eastern states. **DESCRIPTION:** A medium to large size, corner notched point with usually serrated blade edges. The shoulders are usually barbed. The base is concave and ground. The blade edges are convex, parallel or recurved. This type may be related to *Kirk*.

G9, $450-$700, IL.

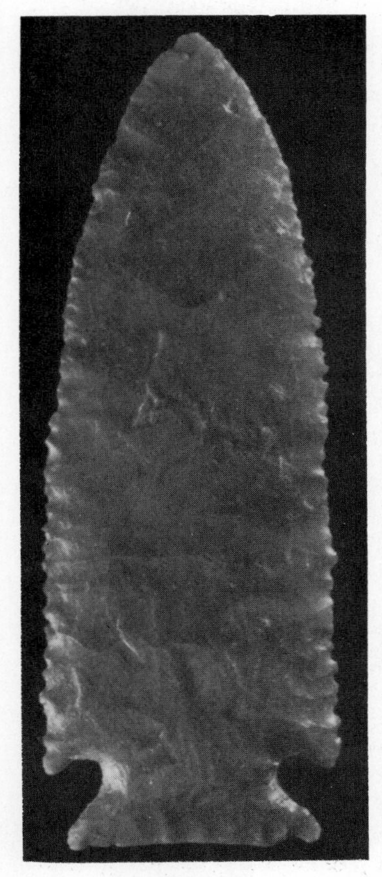

G9, $450-$800
KY.

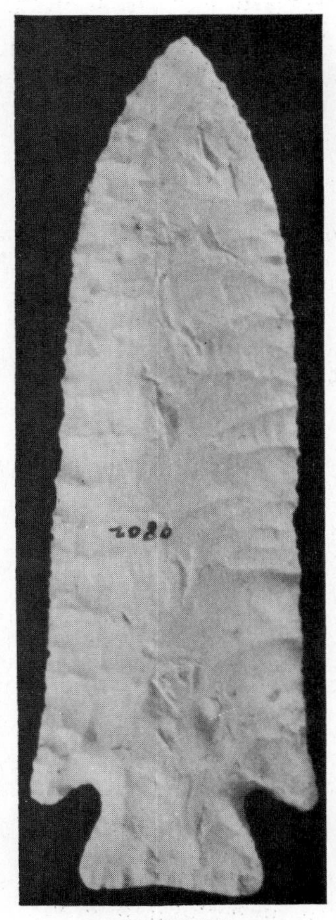

G9, $400-$750
Adams Co., IL.

G5, $60-$100
Greene Co., AR.

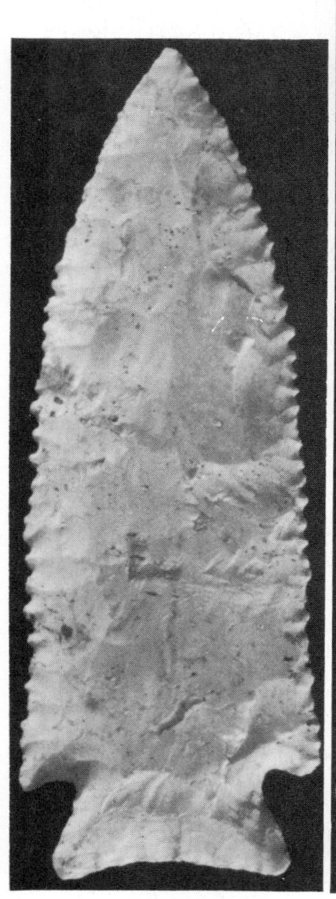

G9, $500-$900
Pike Co., IL.

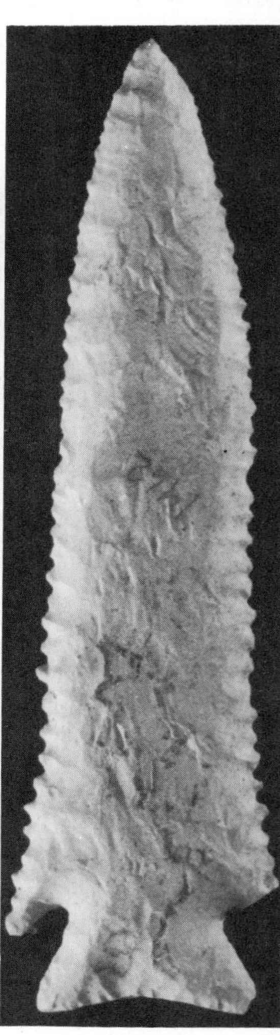

G7, $80-$140
MO. Tang damage.

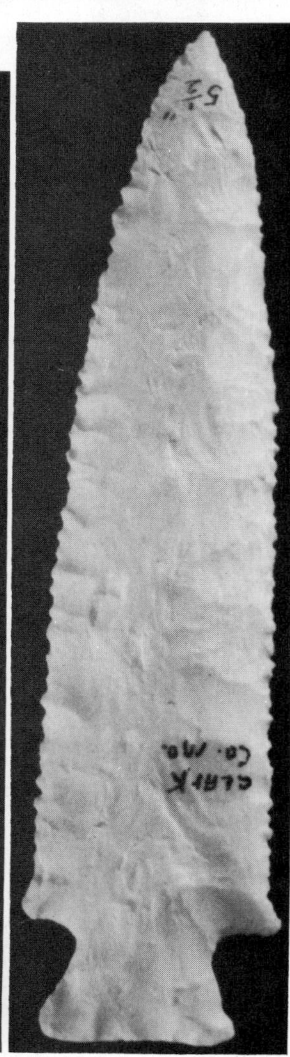

G8, $350-$600
Clark Co., MO.

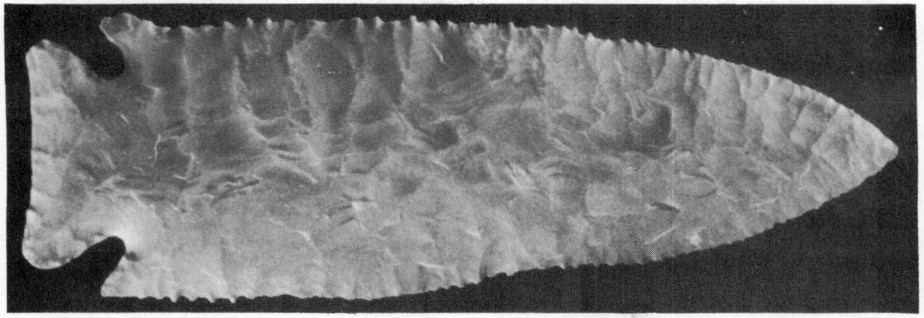

G10, $800-$1500. Limestone Co., AL. Outstanding example.

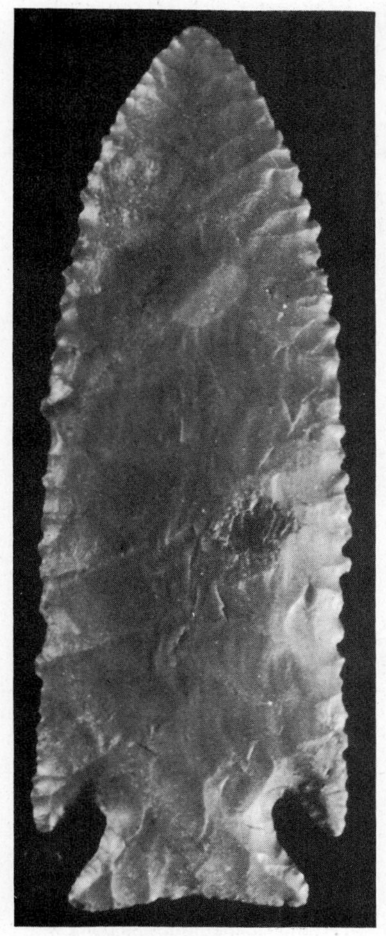

G7, $90-$150
KY. Right shoulder is restored. If complete, would be G10, $1200-$2000.

G7, $90-$150
Schuyler Co., IL. Restored right base & tang. Colorful chert.

STOCTON - Early Archaic, 9000 - 5000 B.P.

(Also see Kirk Serrated)

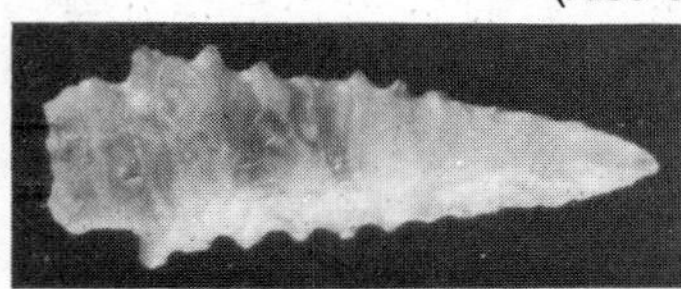

G6, $20-$40
Wasco Co., OR., The Dalles.

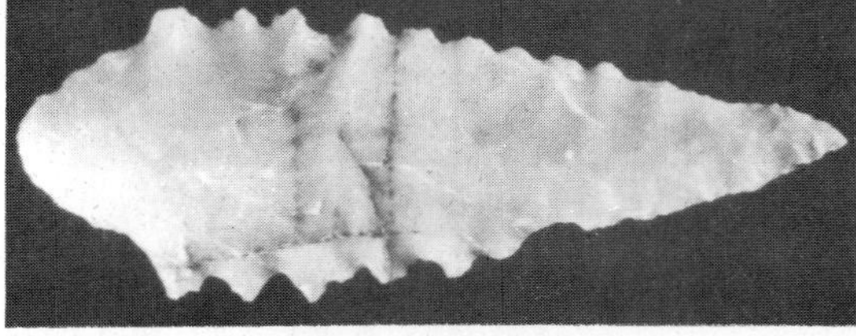

G8, $50-$80
Josephine Co., Pistol Rv., Or.

LOCATION: Northwestern states. **DESCRIPTION:** A medium to large size, narrow, serrated point with a short stem. The base can be rounded to parallel sided. Flaking is identical to the *Kirk* type.

STONE SQUARE STEM - Mid-Archaic, 6000 - 4000 B.P.

(Also see Etley, Heavy Duty and Kays)

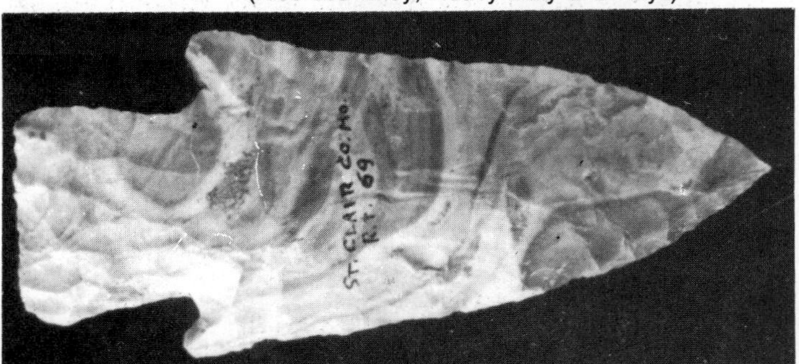

G8, $45-$70
St. Clair Co., MO.

LOCATION: Midwestern states. Type site is in Stone Co., MO. **DESCRIPTION:** A medium to large size, broad stemmed point. Blade edges are convex to recurved. The shoulders are horizontal to barbed and the base is square to slightly expanding with a prominent stem.

SUBLET FERRY - Woodland, 4000 - 2000 B.P.

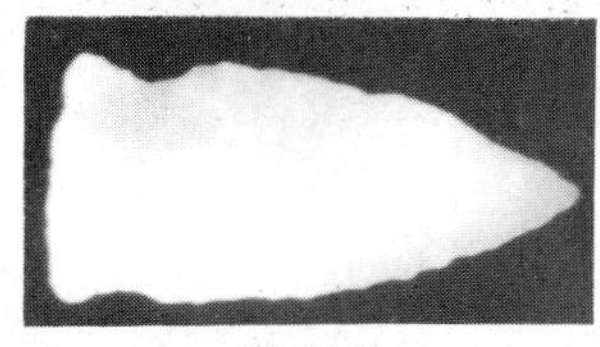

G3, $2-$3
Jackson Co., AL.
Milky quartz.

G4, $2-$4
Jackson Co., AL.

LOCATION: Southeastern states. **DESCRIPTION:** A small to medium size point with side notches that are very close to the base. The base is straight to slightly convex. Blade edges are straight to convex and may be serrated.

G4, $2-$4
Autauga Co., AL.
Milky quartz.

G6, $6-$10
Walker Co., AL.

G5, $3-$5
Dallas Isle, Hamilton Co., TN.

G5, $3-$5
Jackson Co., AL.

G7, $8-$15
Putnam Co., TN.

G8, $15-$25.
Humphreys Co., TN.

G8, $15-$25. Dayton, TN.

G8, $25-$40
Humphreys Co., TN.

G10, $60-$100
Humphreys Co., TN. Classic.

SUMTER - Mid-Archaic, 7000 - 5000 B.P.

(Also see Adena, Kirk, Levy, Putnam & Thonotosassa)

LOCATION: Southern Southeastern states. **DESCRIPTION:** A medium to large size, broad, thick point with weak, tapered shoulders and a contracting stem. These may be small versions of the *Thonotosassa* type and are believed to be related.

G3, $2-$3
Hillsborough Co., FL.

G4, $2-$4
Hillsborough Co., FL.

G4, $3-$5
Hillsborough Co., FL.

G6, $10-$20
Hillsborough Co., FL.

G8, $35-$60
Hillsborough Co., FL.

G6, $10-$20
Pasco Co., FL.

G4, $3-$5
Hillsborough Co., FL.

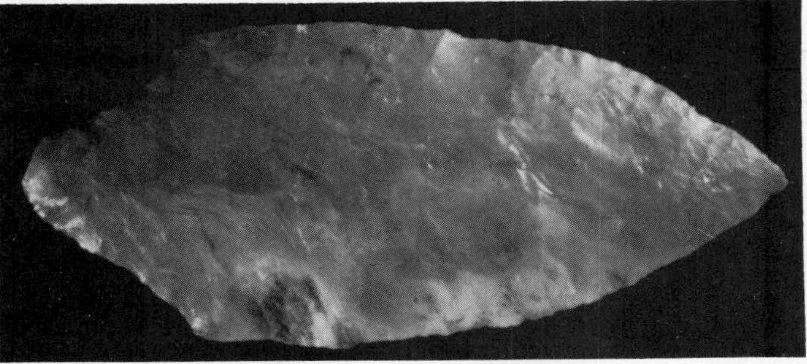

G8, $30-$50
Polk Co., FL.

G7, $15-$25
Hillsborough Co., FL.

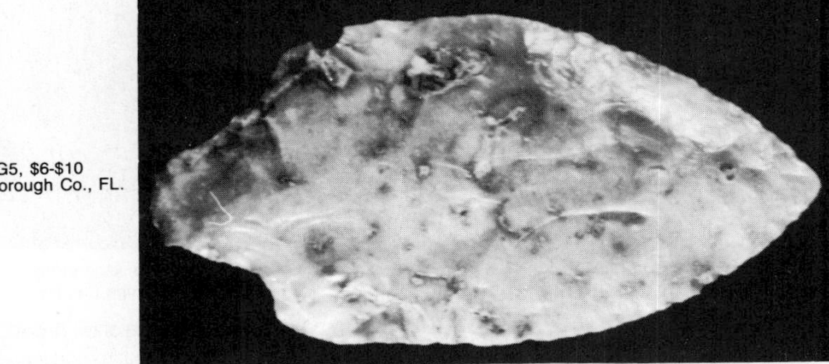

G5, $6-$10
Hillsborough Co., FL.

G7, $15-$25. Hillsborough Co., FL.

SUSQUEHANNA BROAD - Early Woodland, 3000 - 2000 B.P.

(Also see Ashtabula and Waratan)

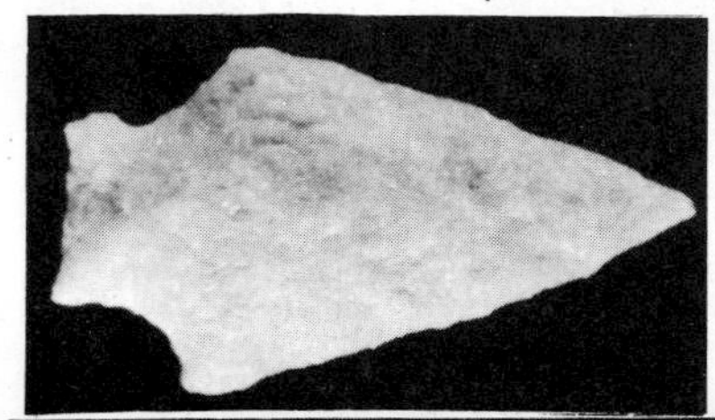

G5, $10-$20
Sussex Co., VA.

G9, $250-$400
W. PA. Classic.

G10, $600-$1000
Cayuga Co., NY.

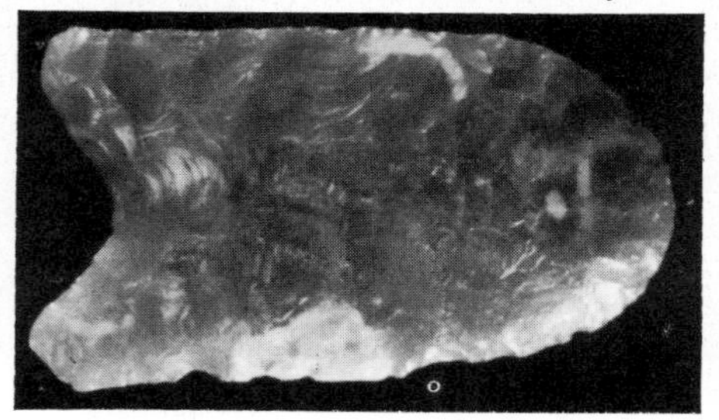

G7, $50-$80
NY. Note heavy patina.

LOCATION: Northeastern states. **DESCRIPTION:** A medium to large size, broad, expanded stem point with clipped wing shoulders.

SUWANNEE - Late Paleo, 12000 - 9000 B.P.

(Also see Beaver Lake, Clovis, Conerly, Golondrina, Quad and Simpson)

G3, $25-$40
Hillsborough Co., FL. Coral. Made into a blunt.

G5, $150-$250
Allendale Co., SC.

G7, $400-$750
Baker Co., GA. Coastal Plain chert.

G7, $450-$700
Mouth of Sante Fe Rv., FL.

G8, $600-$1000
NW Cent. FL. Agatized coral.

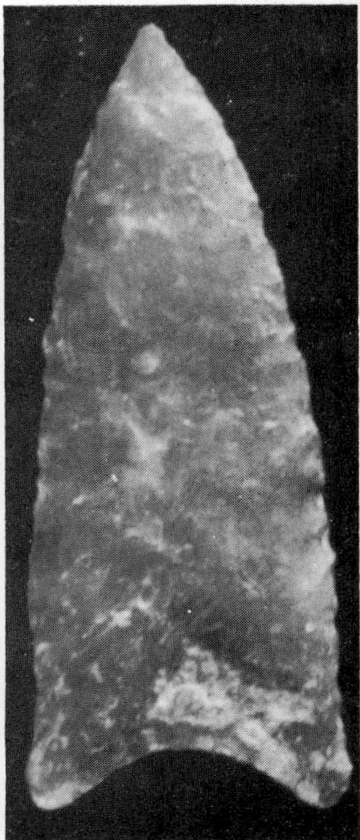

G9, $1500-$2500
NW Cent. FL. Agatized coral. Classic.

G7, $500-$800
NW Cent. FL.

G9, $1500-$2500
Wakulla Co., FL., St. Marks Rv.

G8, $600-$1000
NW Cent. FL. Thick cross section.

G10, $3000-$5500
Sante Fe Rv., FL. Black chert.

LOCATION: Southern Southeastern states. **DESCRIPTION:** A medium to large size, fairly thick, broad, auriculate point. The basal constriction is not as narrow as in *Simpson* points. Most examples have ground bases and are usually unfluted.

SUWANNEE (continued)

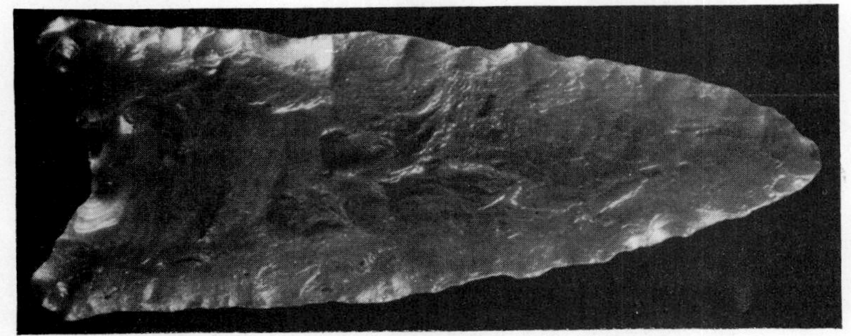

G6, $200-$350, Suwannee River, N. FL. River Patina.

SW HANNA - Mid-Archaic, 6000 - 4000 B.P.

(Also see Chiricahua, Duncan, Hanna & Pinto Basin)

G6, $5-$8
Yavapai Co., AZ.

G7, $10-$20
Yavapai Co., AZ.

G5, $4-$6
Yavapai Co., AZ.

LOCATION: Southwestern states. **DESCRIPTION:** A small to medium size point with tapered to barbed shoulders, an expanding stem and a concave base.

SWAN LAKE - Late Archaic to Woodland, 3500 - 2000 B.P.

(Also see Bakers Creek, Durst, Ellis, Godley, Halifax, Lamoka, Macpherson and Trinity)

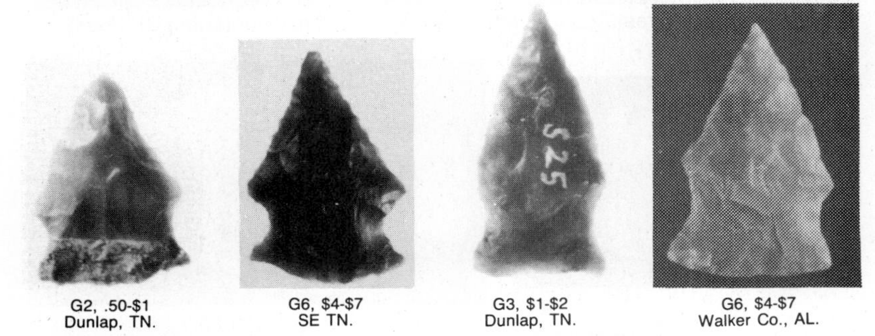

G2, .50-$1
Dunlap, TN.

G6, $4-$7
SE TN.

G3, $1-$2
Dunlap, TN.

G6, $4-$7
Walker Co., AL.

LOCATION: Southeastern to Eastern states. **DESCRIPTION:** A small size, thick, triangular point with wide, shallow side notches. Some examples have an unfinished rind or base. Similar to the side-notched *Lamoka* in New York. Called *Jackson* in Florida.

SWAN LAKE (continued)

G7, $6-$10. Dayton, TN.

G4, $2-$3. Dunlap, TN.

G8, $8-$12
Walker Co., AL.

G7, $6-$10
SW KY.

G4, $2-$3
Meigs Co., TN.

G9, $15-$25
Walker Co., AL.

G5, $3-$6
Meigs Co., TN.

G9, $15-$25
TN/AL.

G7, $6-$10
SE TN.

TABLE ROCK - Late Archaic, 4000 - 3000 B.P.

(Also see Buck Creek, Lange, Matanzas, Motley, Smithsonia and Steuben)

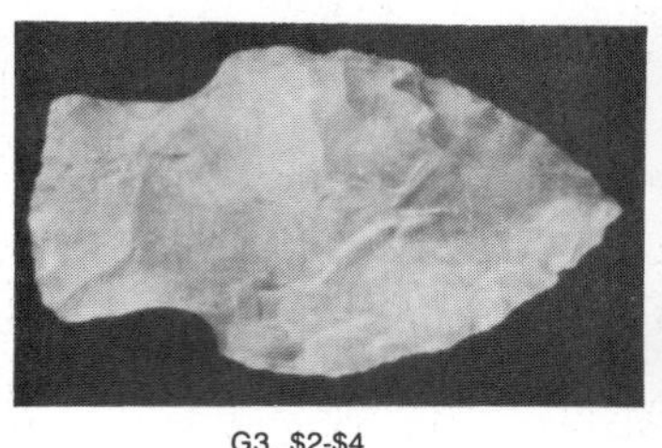
G3, $2-$4
IL.

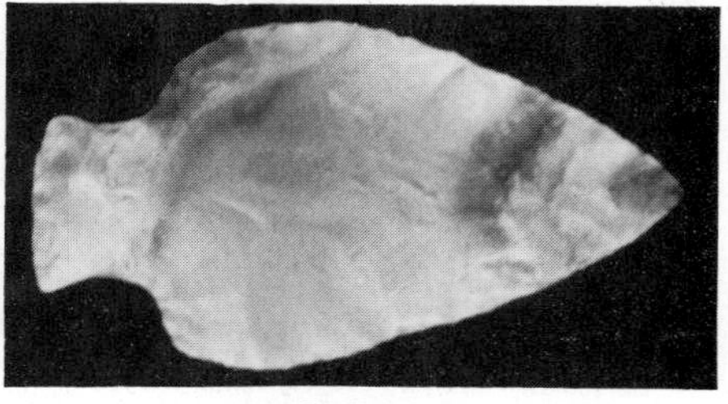
G5, $8-$15
MO.

LOCATION: Midwestern to Northeastern states. **DESCRIPTION:** A medium to large size, expanded stem point with straight to tapered, shoulders. Shoulders can be sharp or rounded. This type is also known as "Bottleneck" points.

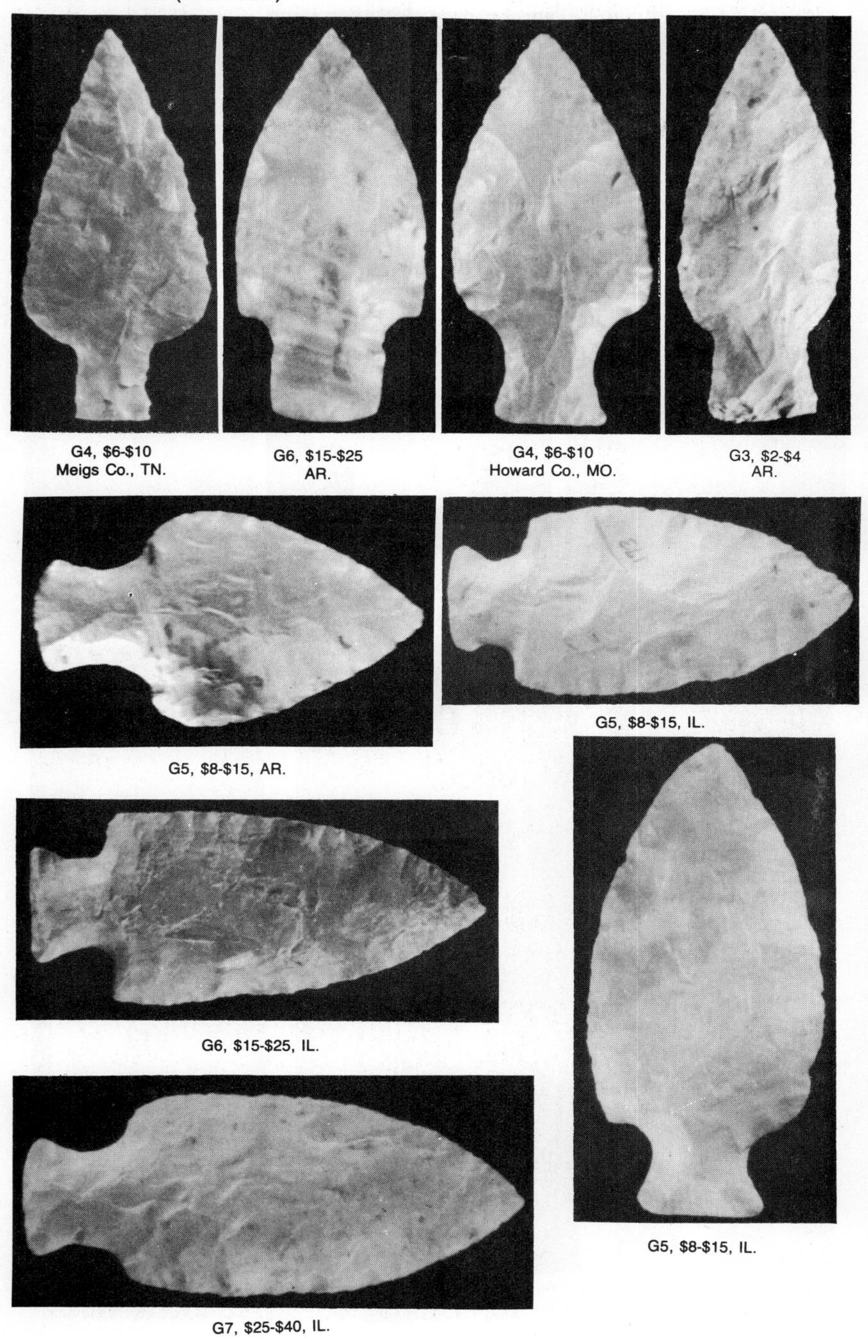

G4, $6-$10
Meigs Co., TN.

G6, $15-$25
AR.

G4, $6-$10
Howard Co., MO.

G3, $2-$4
AR.

G5, $8-$15, AR.

G5, $8-$15, IL.

G6, $15-$25, IL.

G5, $8-$15, IL.

G7, $25-$40, IL.

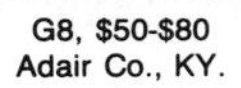

G8, $50-$80
Adair Co., KY.

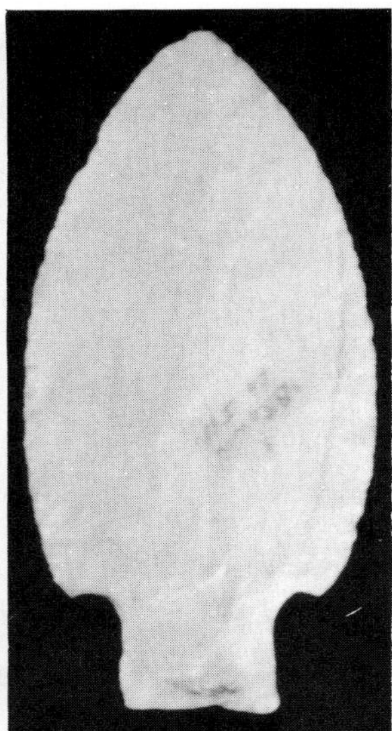

G7, $25-$40
Brown Co., IL.

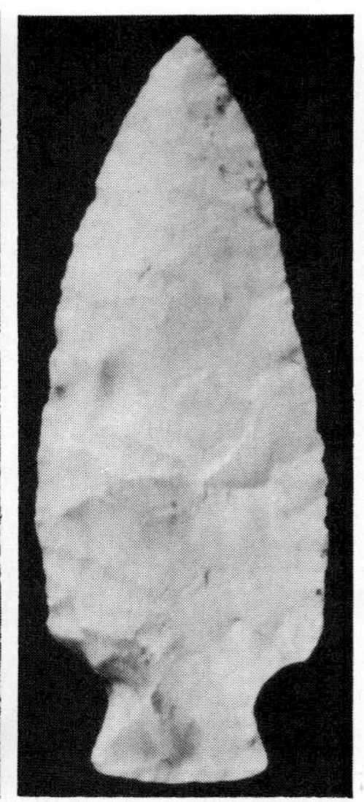

G5, $8-$15
Bureau Co., IL.

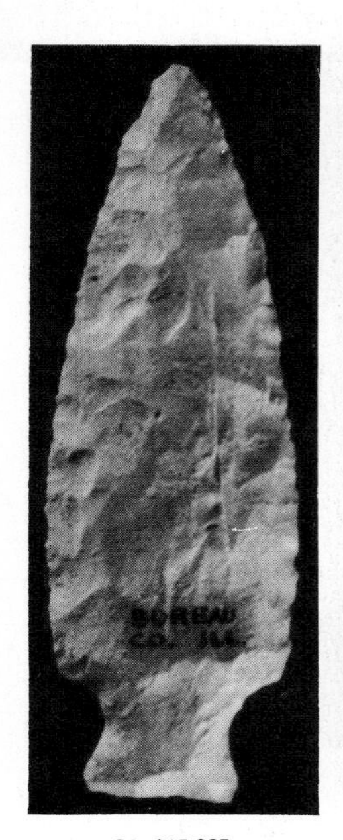

G6, $15-$25
Bureau Co., IL.

G8, $50-$70
Knox Co., IL. Classic.

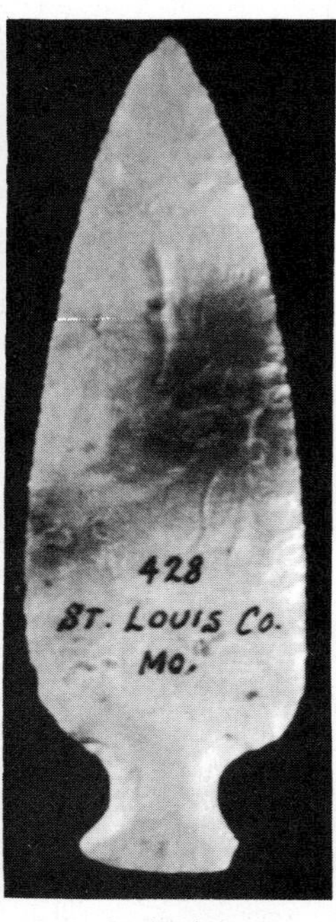

G7, $25-$40
St. Louis Co., MO. Base nick.

TABLE ROCK (continued)

G9, $60-$100
AR. Colorful chert.

G4, $6-$10
Cent. IL. Tip nick.

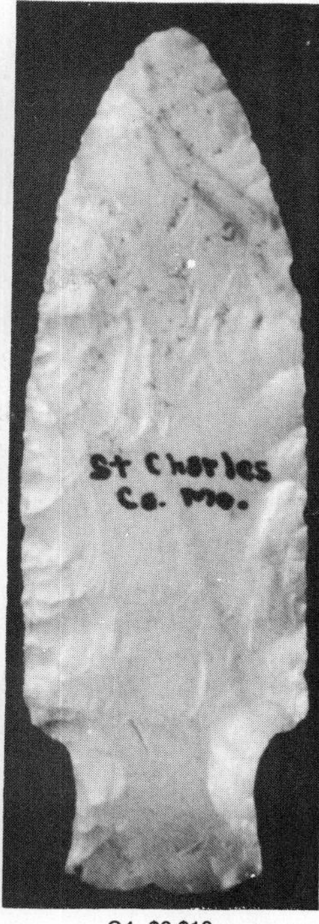

G4, $6-$10
St. Charles Co., MO. Tip nick.

TALCO - Mississippian to Historic, 800 - 500 B.P.

(Also see Hamilton and Maud)

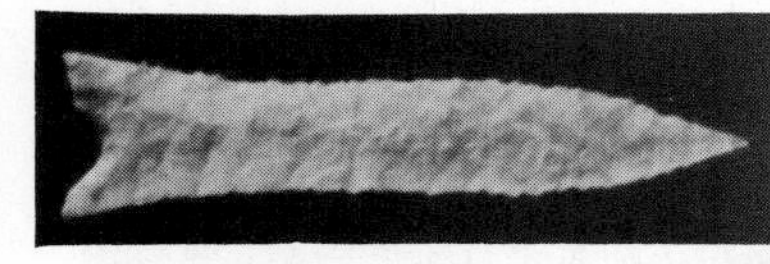
G10, $250-$400
Smith Co., TX. Very thin with extremely fine serrations.

G7, $25-$40
Red Rv. Co., TX.

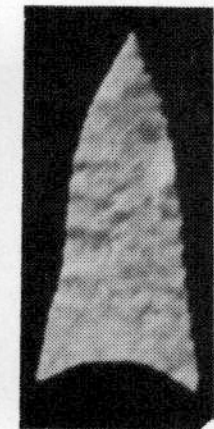
G8, $25-$40
Smith Co., TX.

G9, $40-$70
Smith Co., TX.

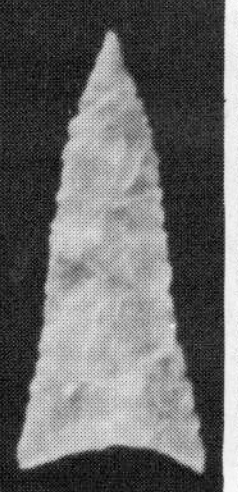
G8, $30-$50
Smith Co., TX.

G9, $80-$120
Red Rv. Co., TX.

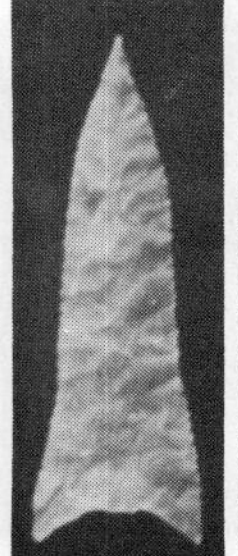
G10, $120-$200
Smith Co., TX.

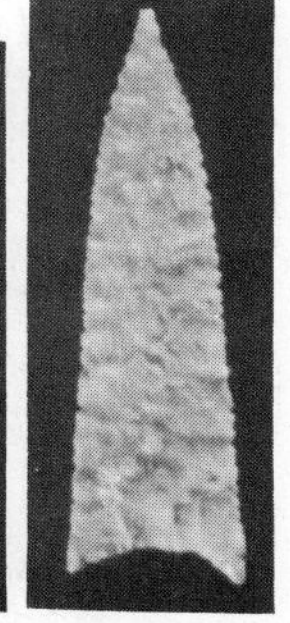
G9, $90-$150
Comanche Co., TX.

LOCATION: Midwestern states. **DESCRIPTION:** A small to medium size, thin, narrow, triangular point with recurved sides and a concave base. Blade edges are very finely serrated. This type is found on Caddo and related sites.

TALCO (continued)

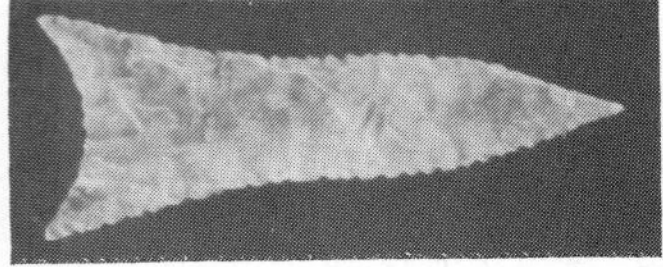

G10, $250-$400
CO/TX.

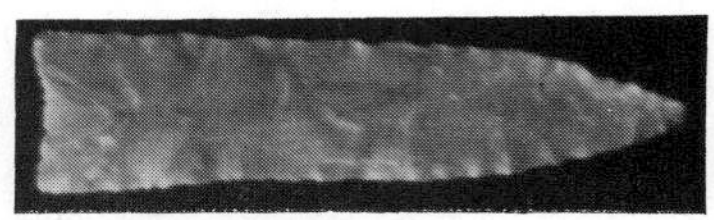

G7, $25-$40
KY.

TALLAHASSEE (See Dalton-Tallahassee)

TAMPA - Mississippian, 800 - 400 B.P.

(Also see Nodena and Young)

G2, .25-.50
Hillsborough Co., FL.

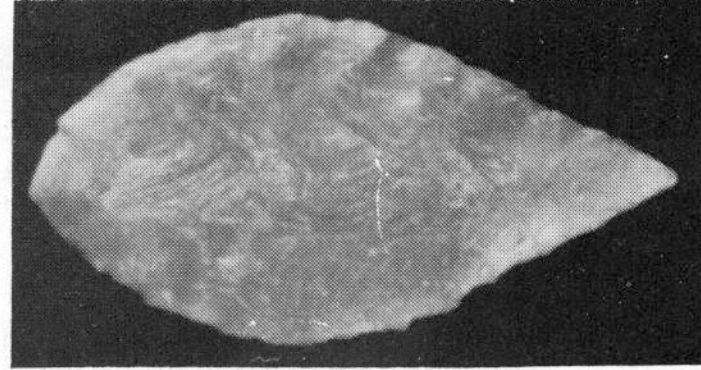

G6, $10-$20
Hillsborough Co., FL.

G8, $25-$40
Pasco Co., FL.

LOCATION: Southern Southeastern states. **DESCRIPTION:** A small size, narrow to broad, tear drop shaped point with a rounded base. Similar to the *Nodena* type found further North.

TAYLOR - Early Archaic, 9000 - 6000 B.P.

(Also see Autauga, Ecusta, Hardaway, Kirk and Palmer)

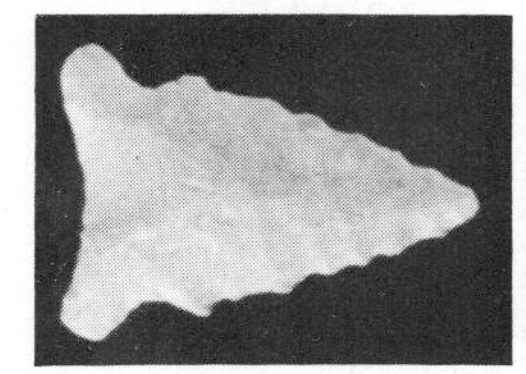

G6, $15-$25
Wilkes Co., NC.

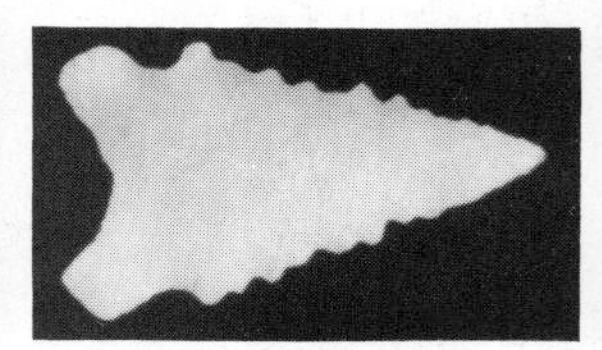

G8, $35-$65
Moore Co., NC.

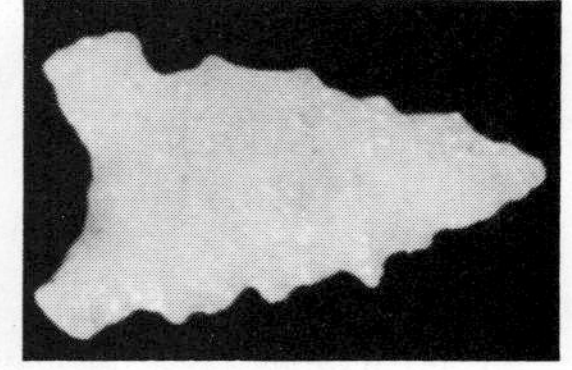

G5, $6-$10
Randolph Co., NC.

LOCATION: Far Eastern states. **DESCRIPTION:** A medium to large size, side notched to auriculate point with a concave base. Basal areas are ground. Blade edges can be serrated. A cross between *Hardaway* and *Palmer*. Called *Van Lott* in South Carolina.

TAYLOR (continued)

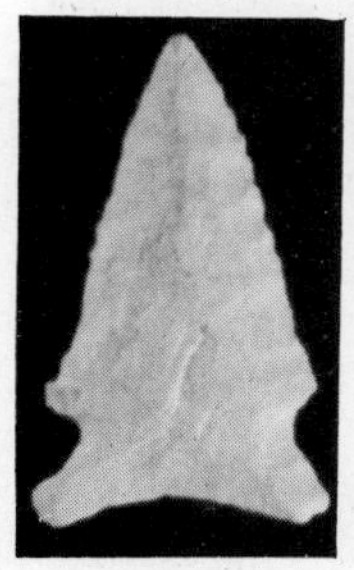

G6, $10-$20
Durham Co., NC.

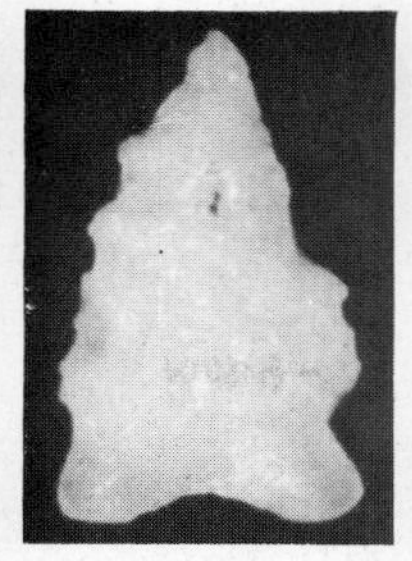

G4, $4-$7
Union Co., SC.
Milky quartz.

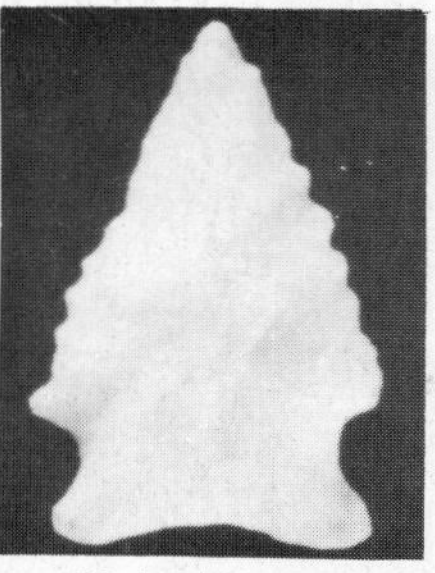

G6, $15-$25
Autauga Co., AL. Milky quartz.

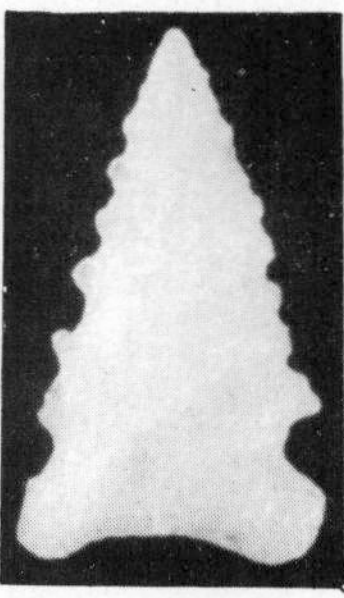

G7, $20-$35
Pearson Co., NC. Milky quartz.

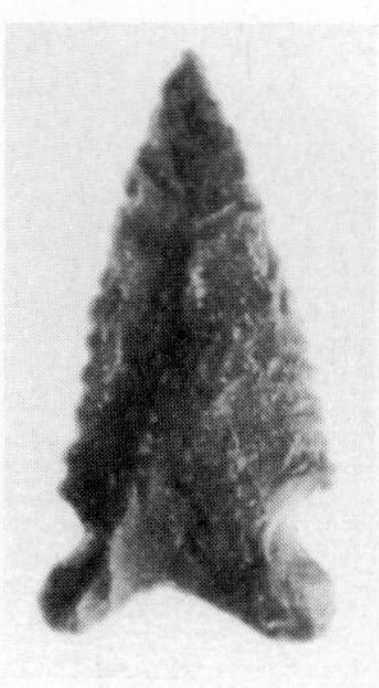

G6, $10-$20
Randolph Co., NC.

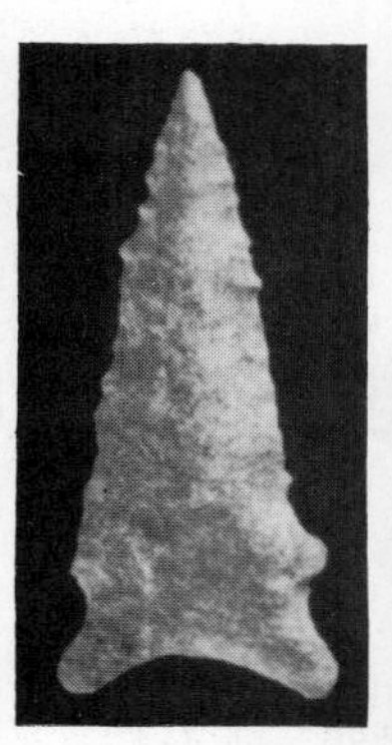

G7, $20-$35
Moore Co., NC.

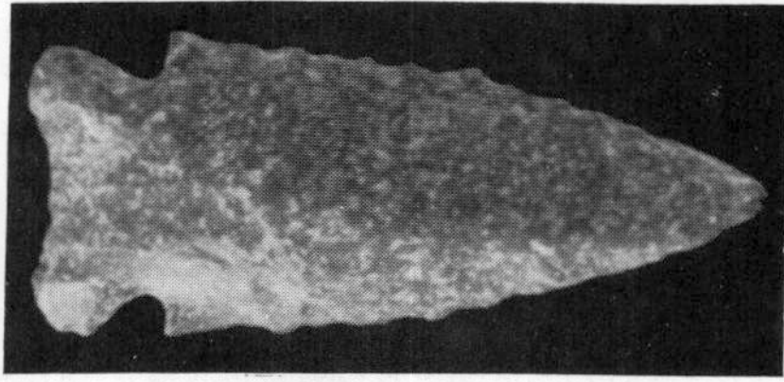

G9, $50-$80
Caswell Co., NC.

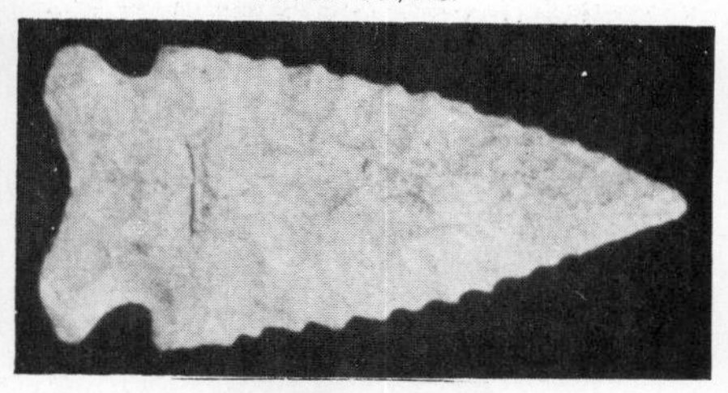

G10, $90-$150
Kershaw Co., SC. Classic.

TAYLOR - Woodland, 2500 - 1600 B.P.

(Also see Bakers Creek and Gilchrist)

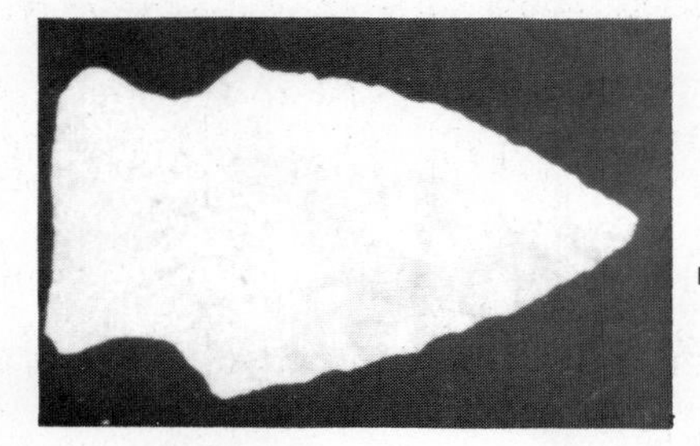

G6, $4-$7
Hillsborough Co., FL.

LOCATION: Southern Southeastern states. **DESCRIPTION:** A medium size point with tapered shoulders and an expanded base which is straight. Basal corners are usually rounded.

TEAR DROP - Woodland, 2000 - 1000 B.P.

(Also see Adena Blade)

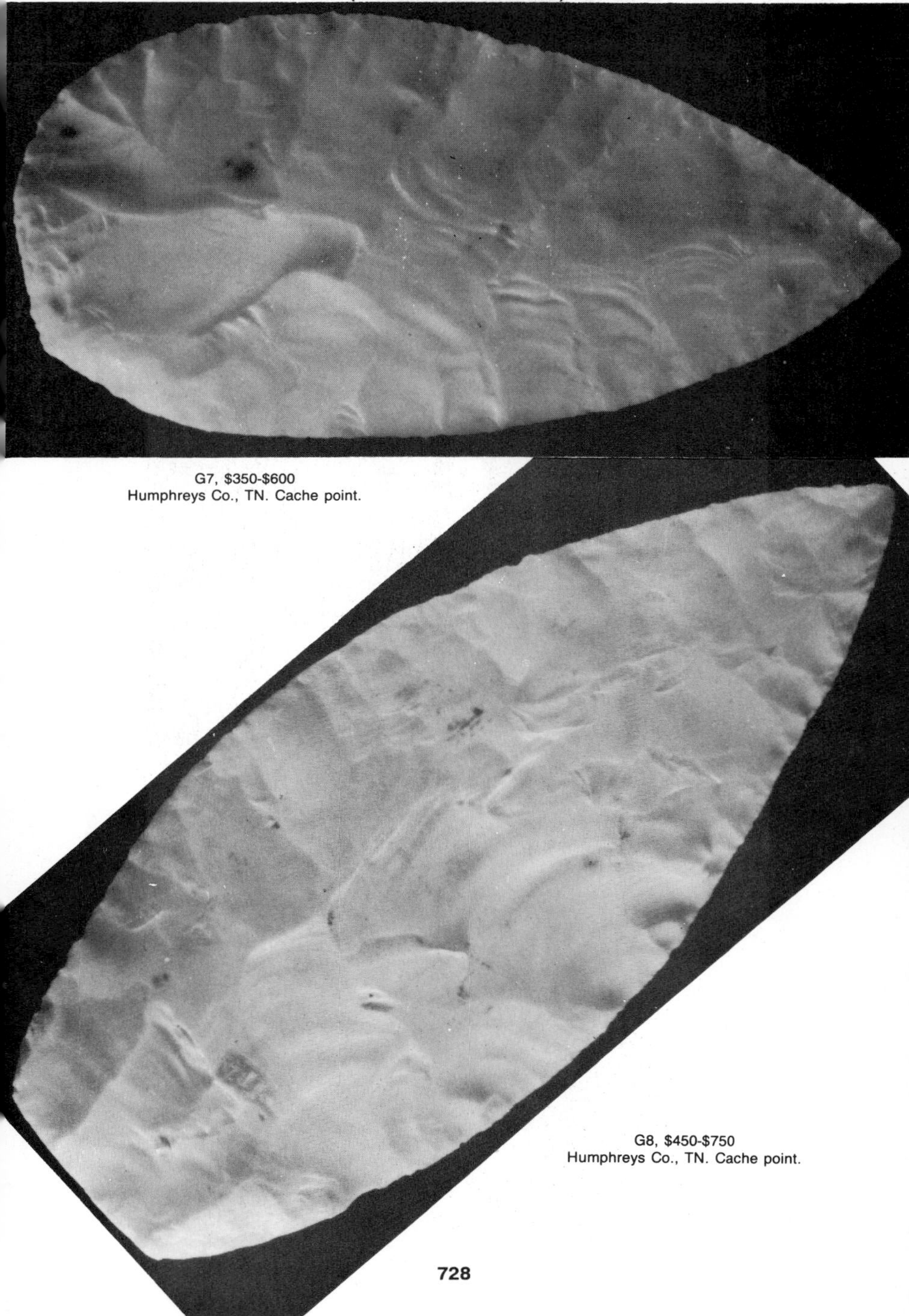

G7, $350-$600
Humphreys Co., TN. Cache point.

G8, $450-$750
Humphreys Co., TN. Cache point.

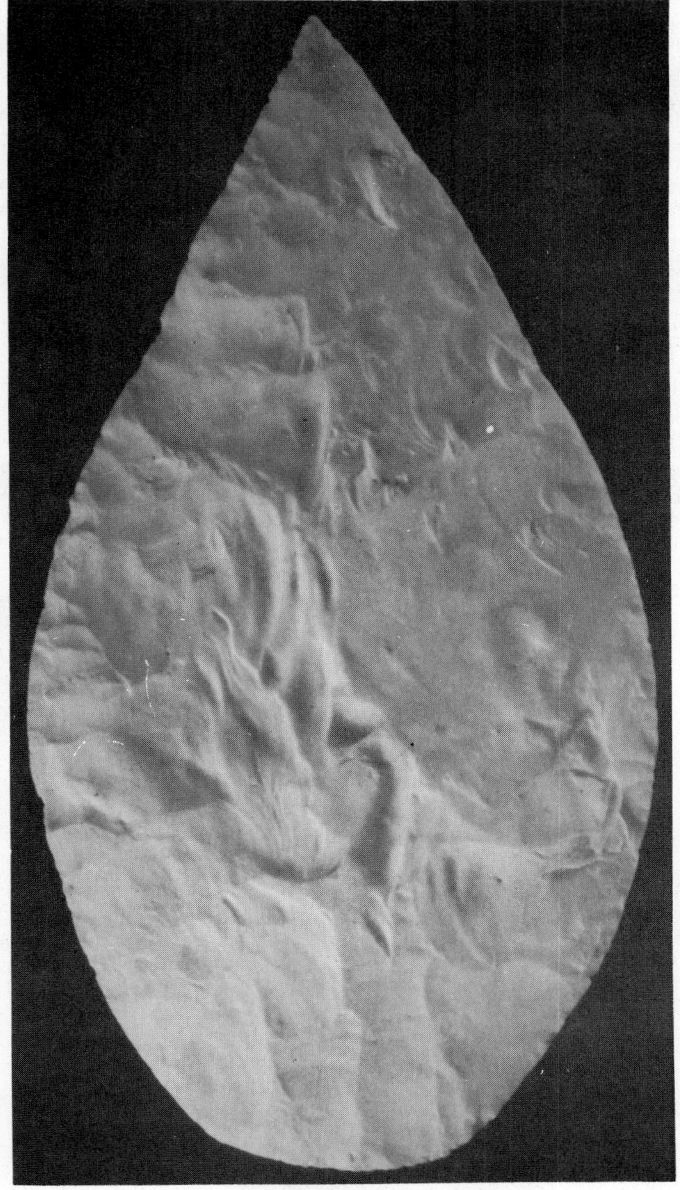

G9, $600-$1000
Humphreys Co., TN. Cache point.
Classic example.

LOCATION: Southeastern states. **DESCRIPTION:** A large size, broad, thin, ellipitcal blade with a rounded to straight base. Usually found in caches and are believed to be a little later than the *Adena* blades.

TEMPORAL - Mississippian, 1000 - 400 B.P.

(Also see Sinner)

(All Otero Co., NM.)

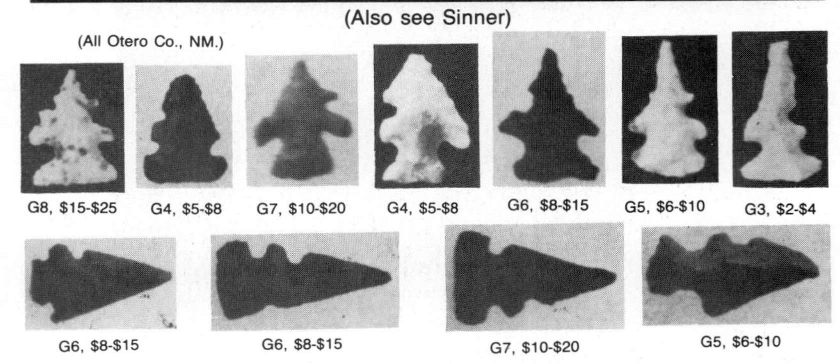

G8, $15-$25 G4, $5-$8 G7, $10-$20 G4, $5-$8 G6, $8-$15 G5, $6-$10 G3, $2-$4

G6, $8-$15 G6, $8-$15 G7, $10-$20 G5, $6-$10

LOCATION: Western New Mexico to eastern central Arizona to Guadalupe Peak, Texas. **DESCRIPTION:** A small size point with two notches on one side and a single notch on the other.

TENNESSEE RIVER - Early Archaic, 9000 - 6000 B.P.

(Also see Adena blade, Cobbs Triangular, Kirk, Red Ochre and Wadlow)

G5, $20-$35
Coffee Lake, AL.

G4, $10-$20
Whitwell, TN.

G8, $60-$100, Parsons, TN. Kirk preform.

LOCATION: Southeastern states. **DESCRIPTION:** These are unnotched preforms for early Archaic types such as *Kirk, Eva*, etc. and would have the same description as that type without the notches. Bases can be straight, concave or convex.

G6, $30-$55, Humphreys Co., TN.

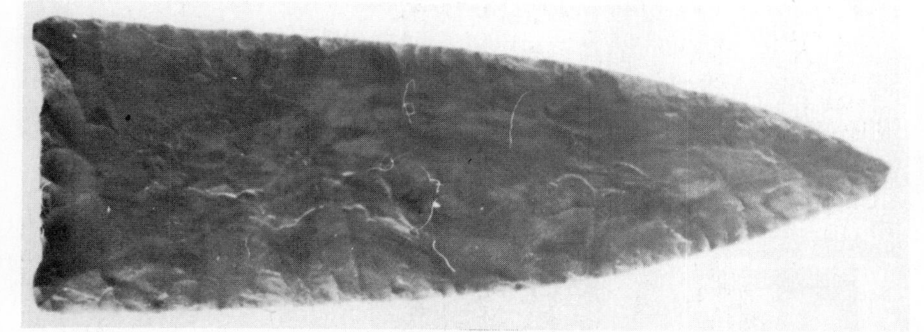

G8, $60-$100. Parsons, TN. Eva preform.

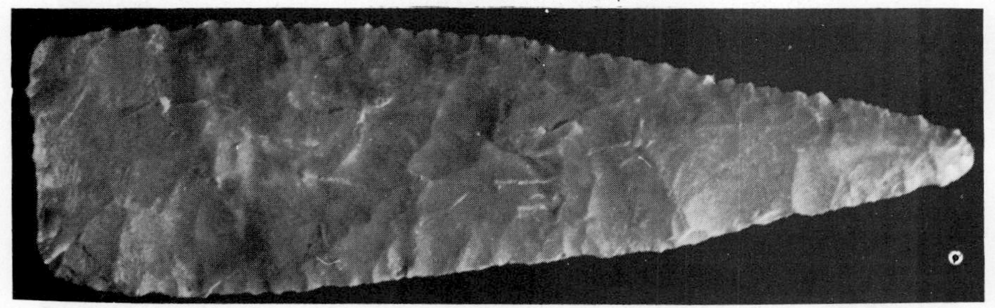

G7, $40-$70. Humphreys Co., TN. Kirk preform.

G7, $40-$70. Humphreys Co., TN.

TEXAS BLADE - Late Archaic to Woodland, 4000 - 1000 B.P.

(Also see Covington, Friday, Gahagan and Sabine)

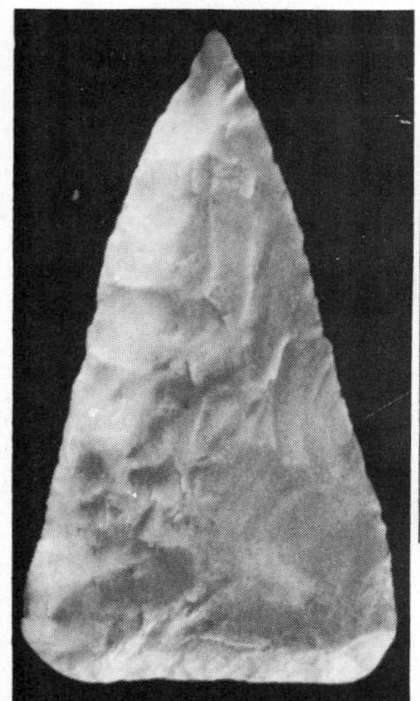

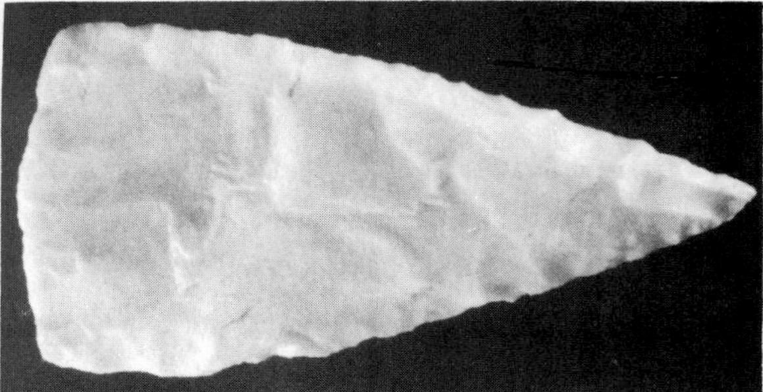

G6, $20-$35. Comanche Co., TX.

G7, $25-$40. Comanche Co., TX.

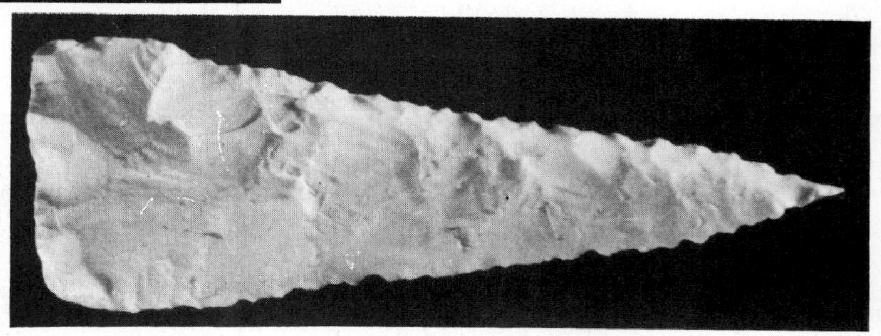

F8, $45-$80. Comanche Co., TX.

G9, $60-$100. Comanche Co., TX.

LOCATION: Texas. **DESCRIPTION:** Medium to large size, broad, lanceolate blades with straight to rounded bases. Some examples are beveled on one side of each face and may prove to be early Archaic in age.

G8, $45-$80. Comanche Co., TX.

THEBES - Early Archaic, 10000 - 8000 B.P.

(Also see Big Sandy, Bolen, Dovetail and Lost Lake)

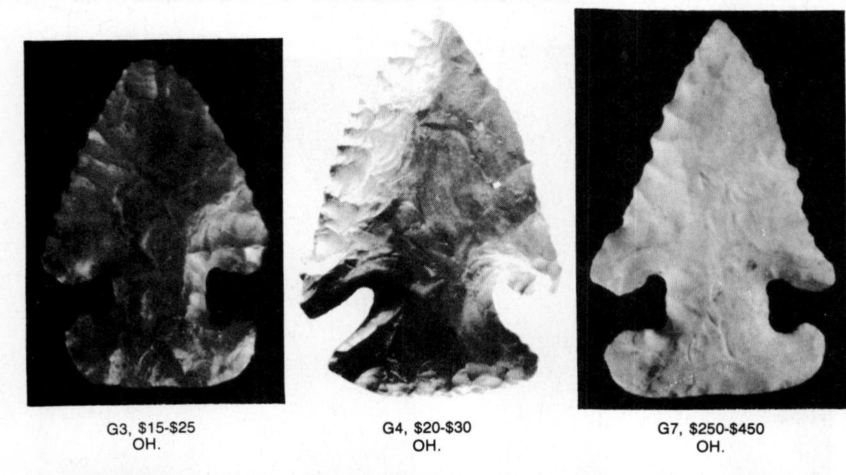

G3, $15-$25
OH.

G4, $20-$30
OH.

G7, $250-$450
OH.

LOCATION: Midwestern states. **DESCRIPTION:** A medium to large size, wide, blade with deep, angled side notches that are parallel sided and squared. Resharpened examples have beveling on one side of each face. The bases of this type have broad proportions and are concave, straight or convex and are ground. Some examples have unusual side notches called Key notch. This type of notch is angled into the blade to produce a high point in the center, forming the letter E. See *Big Sandy E-Notched.*

G7, $250-$450
Knox Co., OH. Classic.

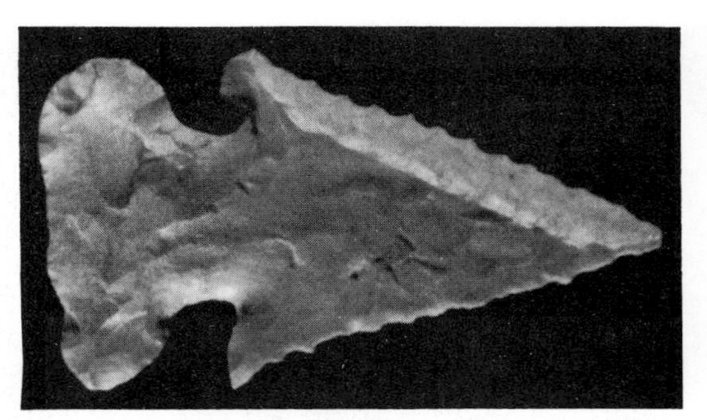

G6, $140-$225
Monroe Co., IN.

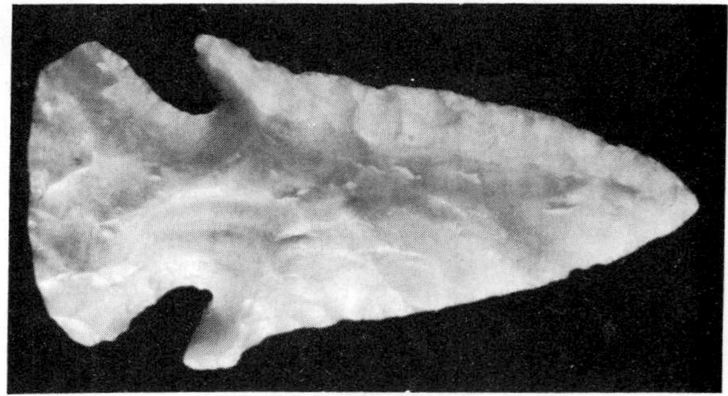

G5, $70-$120
Fairfield Co., OH. Flint Ridge flint.

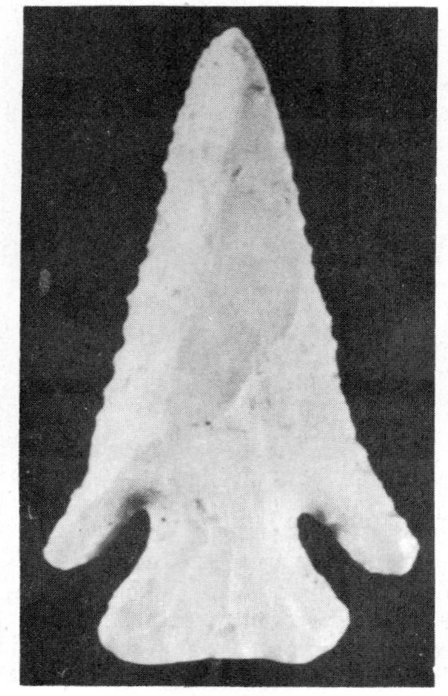

G6, $120-$200
White Co., IL.

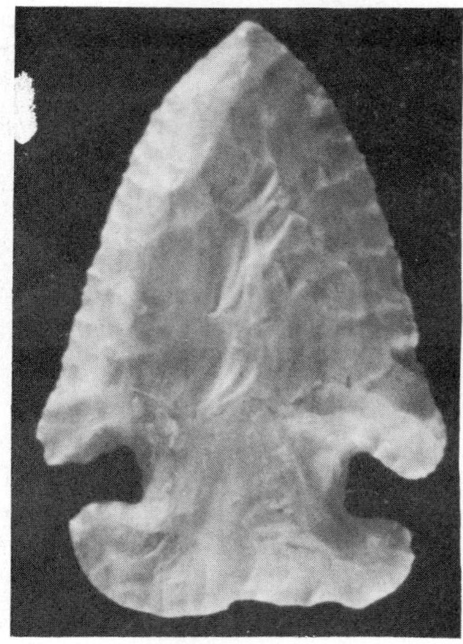

G5, $60-$130
OH. E-notched form.

G5, $60-$100
Harrison Co., IN. E-notched form.

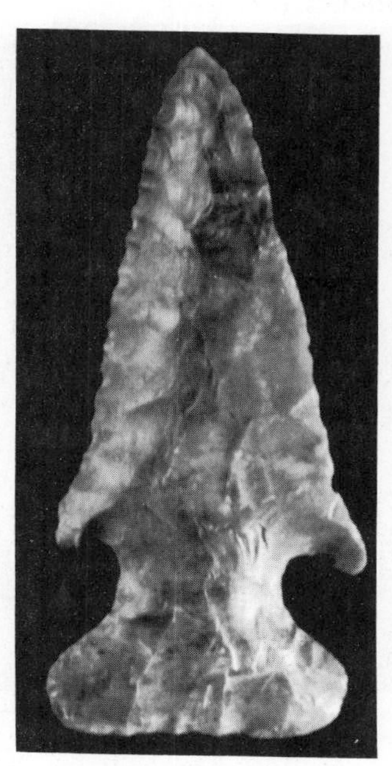

G5, $80-$130
Coshocton Co., OH. Flint Ridge flint.

G5, $70-$130
KY.

G8, $400-$850
Randolph Co., IL.

G6, $120-$170
Larue Co., KY.

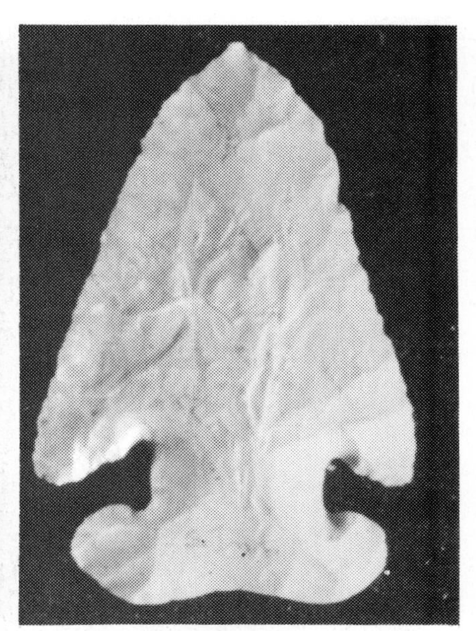

G6, $120-$180
Sou. IN.

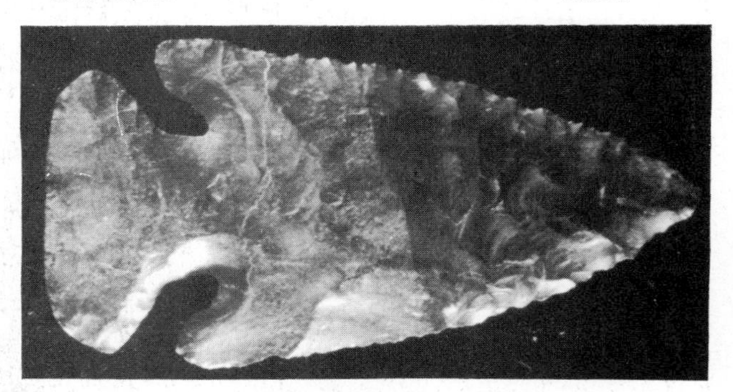

G7, $150-$250, OH. Coshocton chert.

G7, $150-$250, Cent. IL.

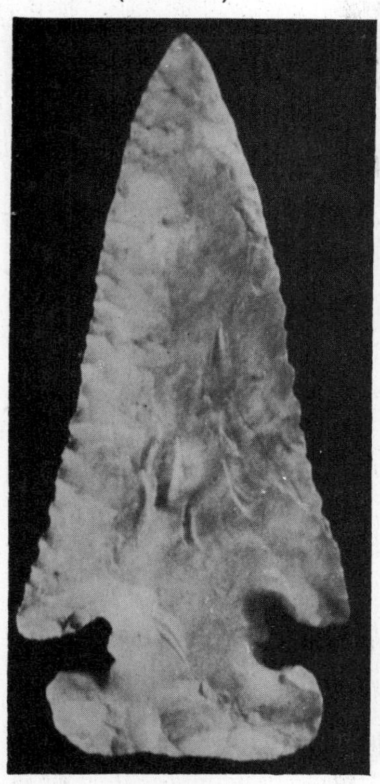

G8, $450-$850
Champlain Co., OH. Classic.

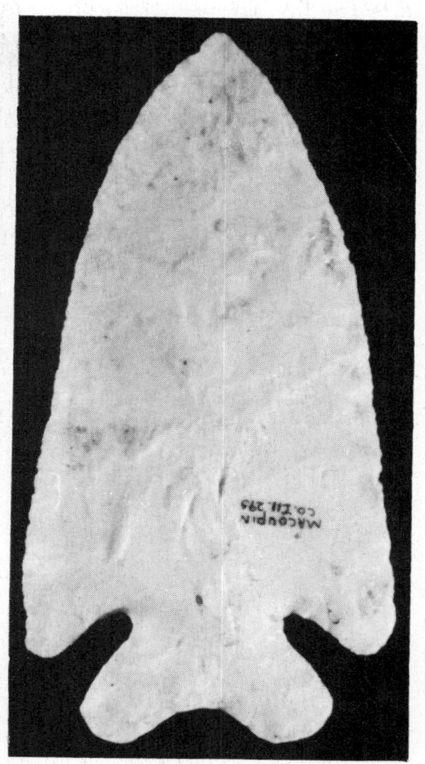

G8, $450-$850
Macoupin Co., IL.

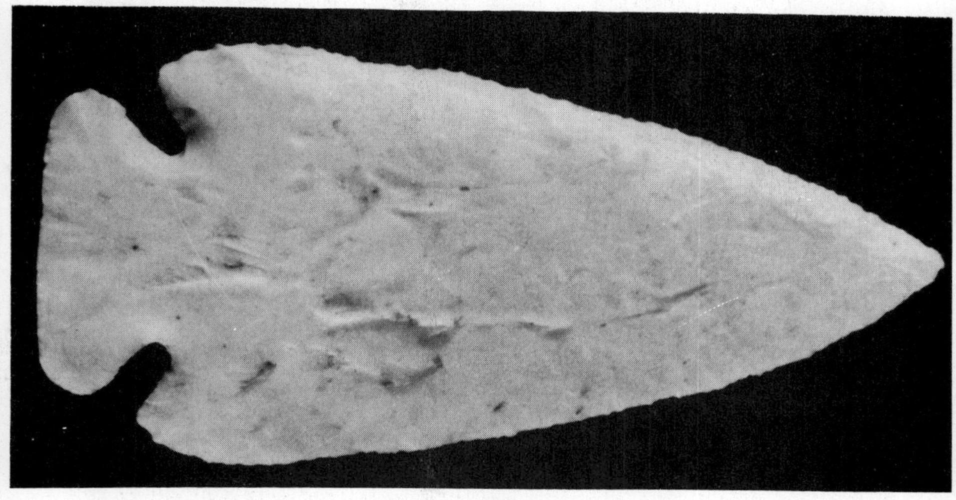

G8, $500-$900
Richland Co., IL.

G8, $600-$1000
OH.

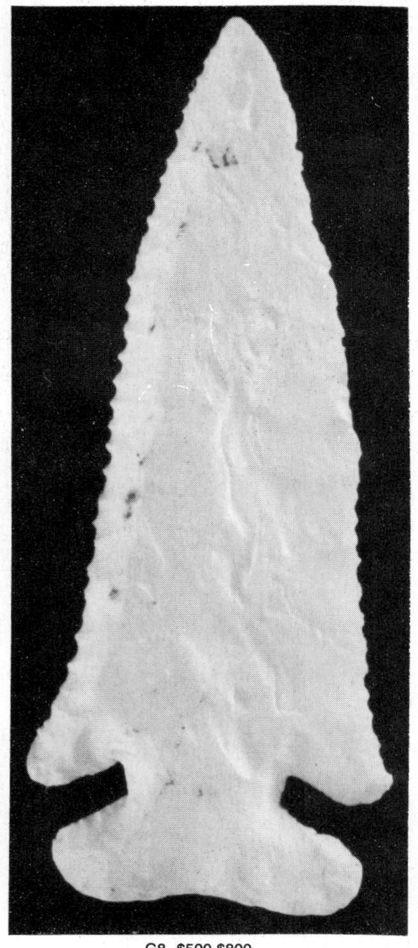

G8, $500-$800
IL.

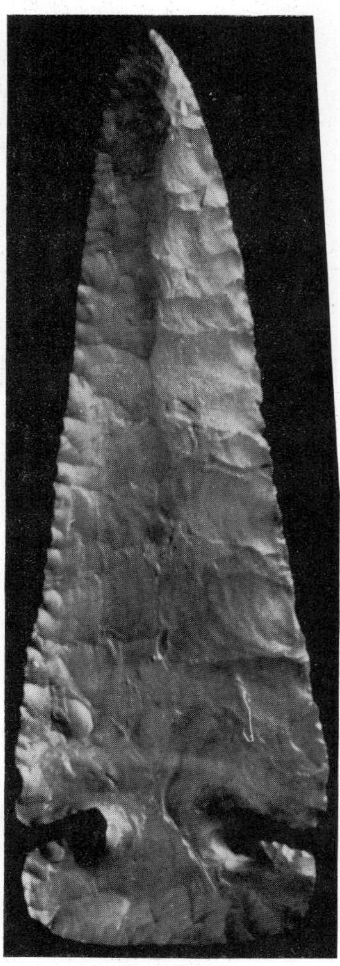

G9, $800-$1500
Richland Co., IL.

G8, $450-$850
Taswell Co., IL. Broken & glued. Sugar quartz. If not borken, G10, $1500-$2500.

G10, $1500-$2500
St. Louis Co., MO.

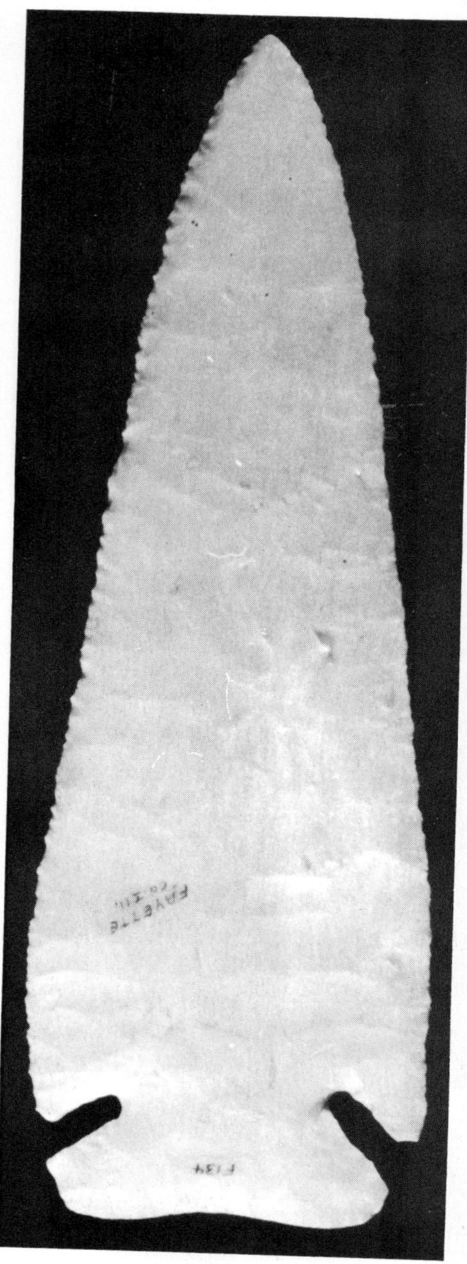

G10, $2000-$4000
Fayette Co., IN.

G8, $400-$750
Pike Co., IL. Tip damage.

THONOTOSASSA - Mid-Archaic, 7000 - 5000 B.P.

(Also see Hamilton, Morrow Mountain, Savannah River & Sumter)

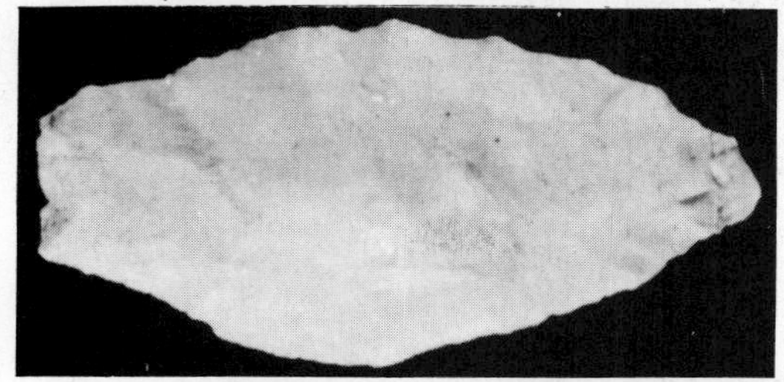

G2, $6-$10
Hillsborough Co., FL.

G8, $125-$250
Hillsborough
Co., FL. Color.

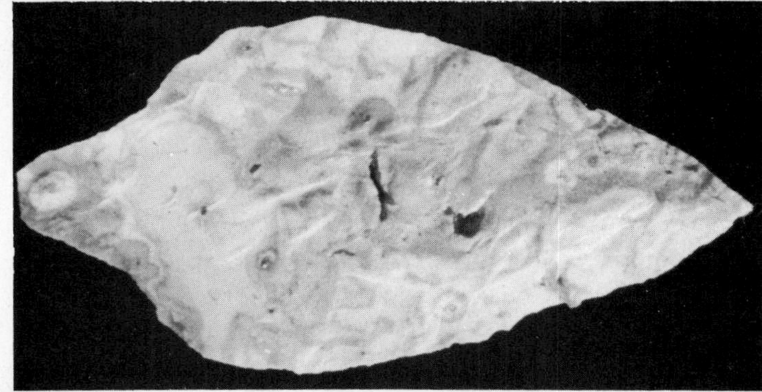

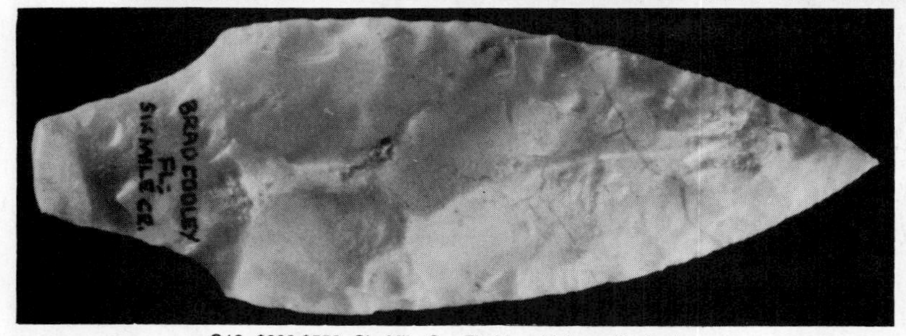

G10, $300-$550, Six Mile Cr., FL. Very high quality for type.

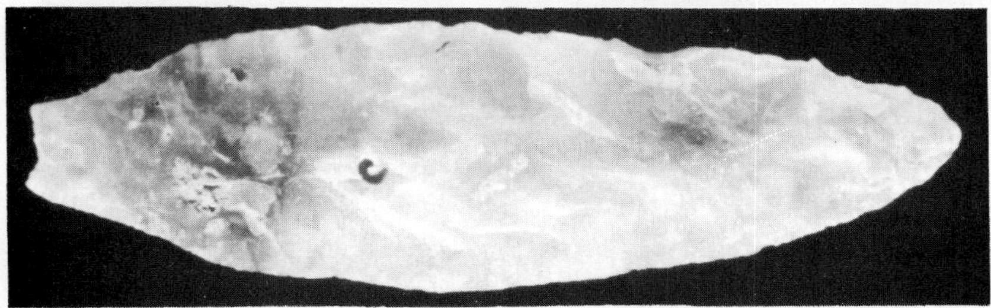

G4, $35-$50, Hillsborough Co., FL.

LOCATION: Southern Southeastern states. **DESCRIPTION:** A large size, narrow, usually heavy, crudely made blade with weak shoulders and a stem that can be parallel sided to contracting. The base can be straight to rounded. Believed to be related to the smaller *Sumter* type.

G5, $60-$100
Hillsborough Co., FL.

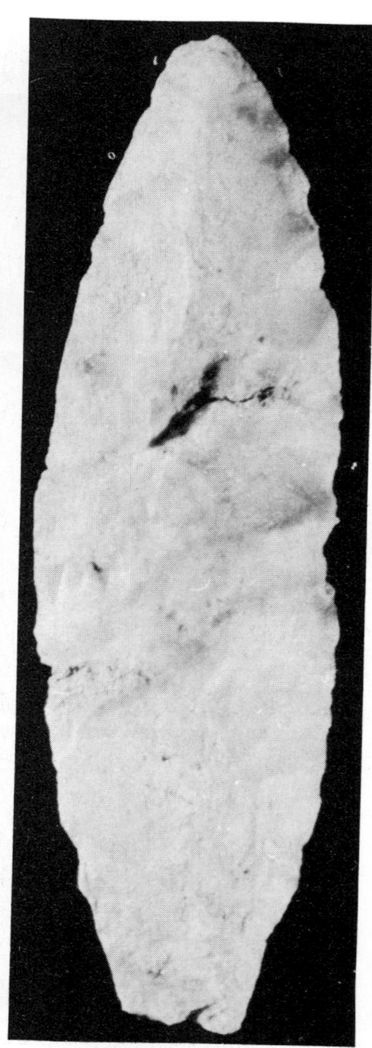

G3, $15-$25
Hillsborough Co., FL.

TORTUGAS - Mid-Archaic to Woodland, 6000 - 1000 B.P.

(Also see Llano, Madison, Matamoros and O'Leno)

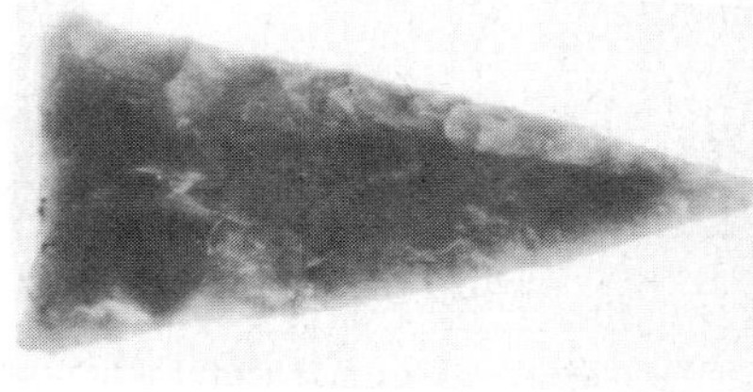

G6, $6-$10
E. TN. Flint.

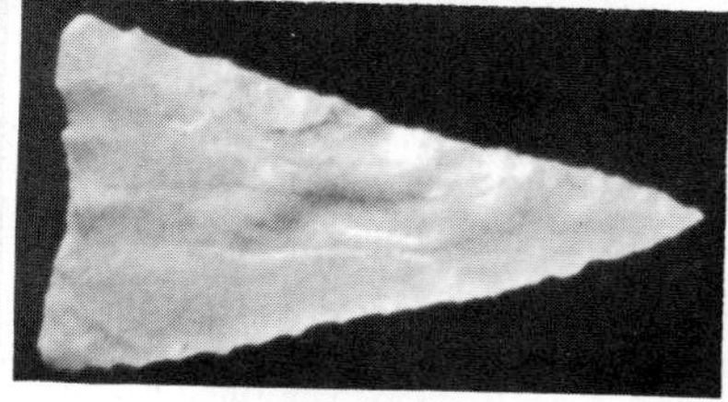

G7, $10-$15
Cent. TX.

TORTUGAS (continued)

G7, $10-$15
Florence, AL.

G8, $15-$25
Comanche Co., TX. Note long thinning strikes from base.

G5, $3-$5
Bell Co., TX.

G7, $10-$15
Comanche Co., TX.

G7, $10-$15
Comanche Co., TX.

G8, $15-$25
Parsons, TN.

G6, $5-$10
Comanche Co., TX.

G5, $3-$5
Bell Co., TX.

LOCATION: Midwestern to Southeastern states. **DESCRIPTION:** A medium size, fairly thick, triangular point with straight to convex sides and base. Some examples are beveled on one side of each face. Bases are usually thinned. This type is much thicker than *Madison* points. Smaller examples would fall in the *Matamoros* type.

TORTUGAS (continued)

G7, $10-$15
Tremont, MS.

G6, $10-$15
Humphreys Co., TN.

G8, $15-$25
Hardin Co., TN.

G6, $25-$40
Bell Co., TX.

TOYAH - Mississippian to Historic, 600 - 400 B.P.

(Also see Harrell)

G7, $15-$25
Cent. TX.

G5, $6-$10
Cent. TX.

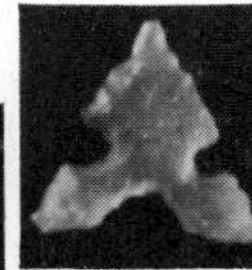

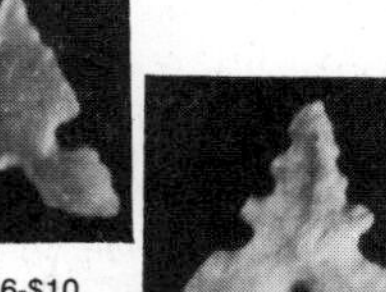

G5, $6-$10
Cent. TX.

G6, $8-$15
Cent. TX.

G4, $4-$6
Comanche Co., TX.

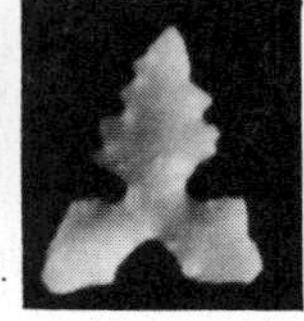

G8, $25-$40
Cent. TX.

LOCATION: Midwestern states. **DESCRIPTION:** A small size, thin, triangular point with one or more notches on each side and a basal notch.

TOYAH (continued)

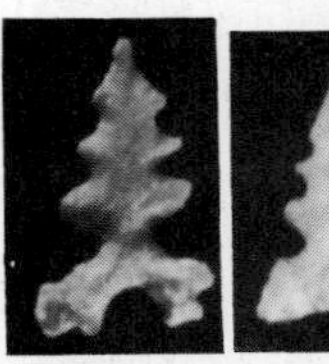
G9, $60-$90
Comanche Co., TX.

G5, $6-$10
Cent. TX.

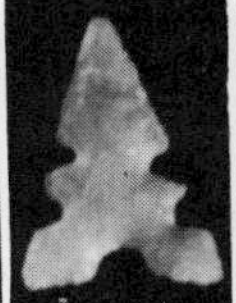
G6, $8-$15
Cent. TX.

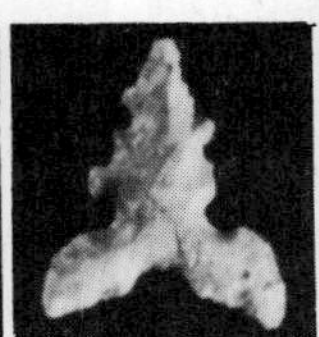
G6, $8-$15
Cent. TX.

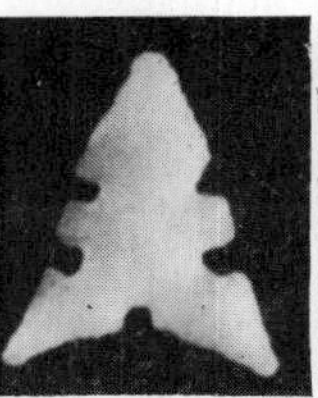
G7, $15-$25
Cent. TX.

G8, $25-$40
Cent. TX.

TRADE POINTS - Historic, 450 - 170 B.P.

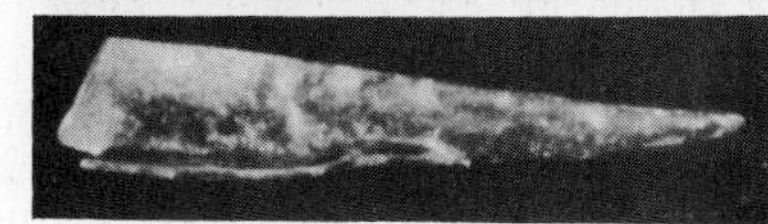
$10-$20
Elmore Co., AL. French conical. Ca. 1700-1763.

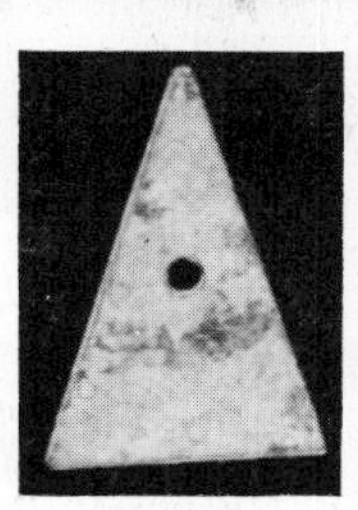
$15-$25
NC. Copper.
Ca. 1800.

$6-$10
NC. French conical trade point. Ca. 1700-1763.

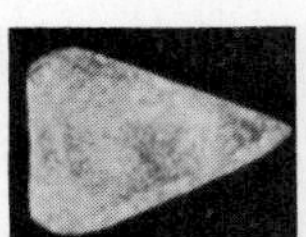
$6-$10
Tellico Plains, TN.

$6-$10
NC. Copper.

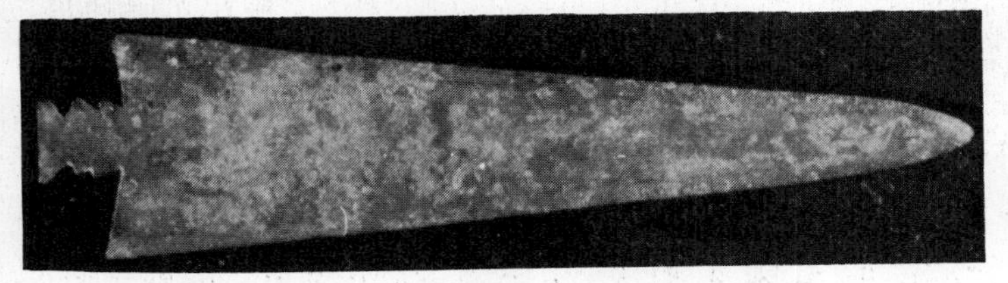
$90-$150. Iron. Cheyenne. Little Big Horn area, Mont. Ca. 1850.

These points were made of copper, iron and steel and were traded to the indians by the French, British and others. Examples have been found all over the United States.

TRAVIS - Mid-Archaic to Woodland, 5500 - 1000 B.P.

(Also see Bare Island, Darl, Kent, Lange, Nolan and Pandale)

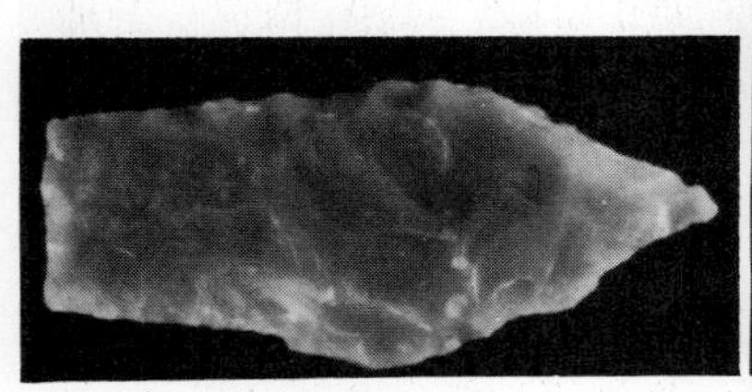
G2, $1-$2
Comanche Co., TX.

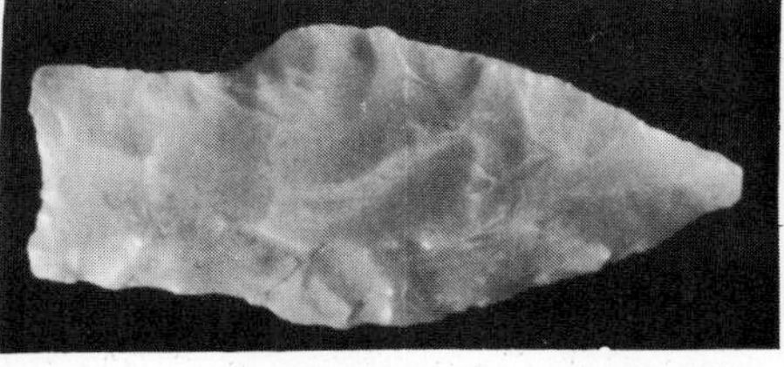
G2, $2-$3
Comanche Co., TX.

TRAVIS (continued)

G6, $6-$10
Comanche Co., TX.

G7, $10-$20
Comanche Co., TX.

G7, $10-$20
Austin, TX.

G6, $6-$10
Austin, TX.

G5, $5-$8
Comanche Co., TX.

G4, $2-$5
Comanche Co., TX.

G6, $6-$10
Austin, TX.

G5, $5-$8
Travis Co., TX.

G6, $6-$10
Austin, TX.

G7, $10-$20
Austin, TX.

LOCATION: Midwestern states. **DESCRIPTION:** A small to medium size point with weak, tapered shoulders and a parallel to expanded stem. The base is straight to convex. Some examples have sharp needle like tips.

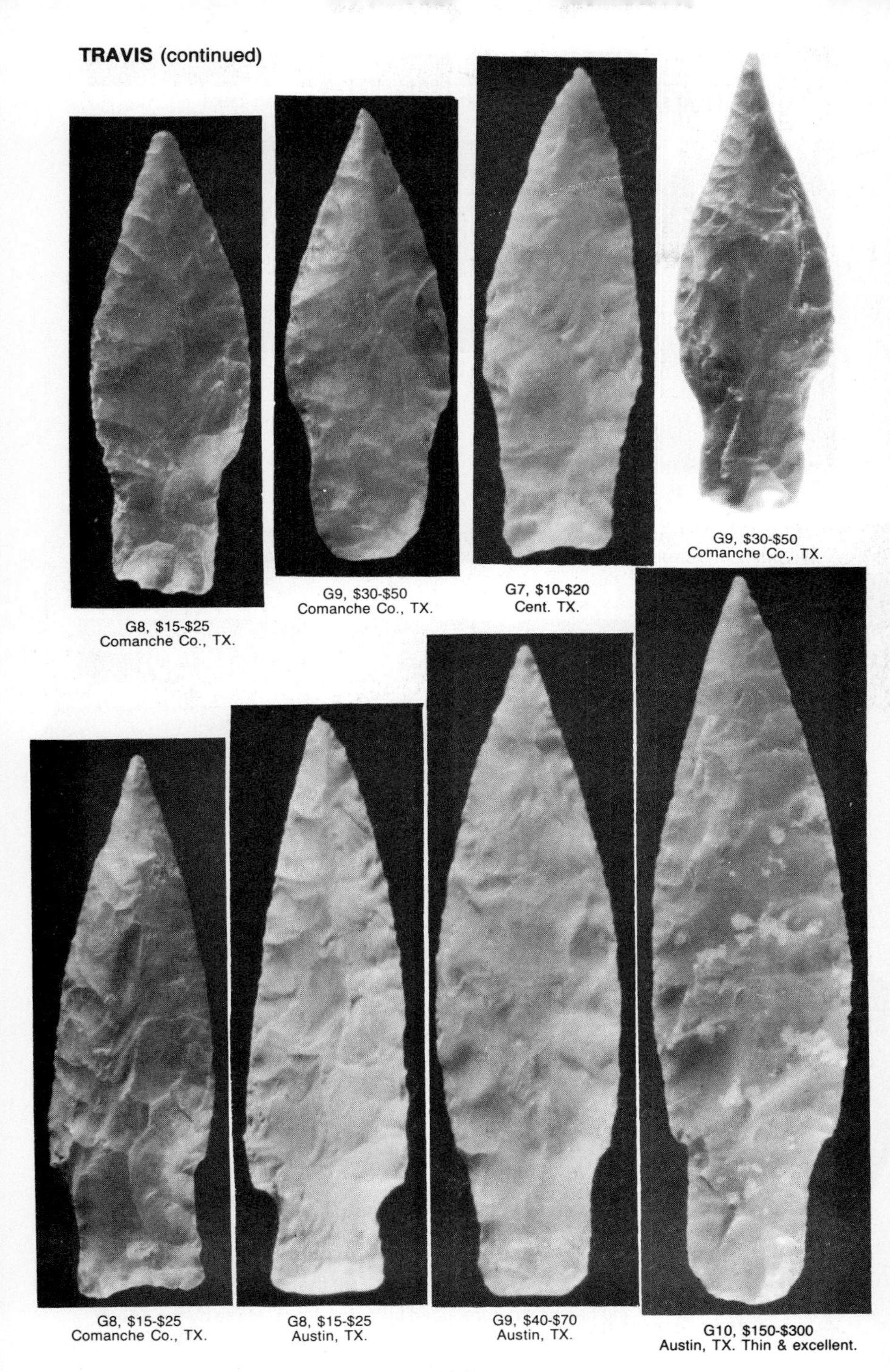

G8, $15-$25
Comanche Co., TX.

G9, $30-$50
Comanche Co., TX.

G7, $10-$20
Cent. TX.

G9, $30-$50
Comanche Co., TX.

G8, $15-$25
Comanche Co., TX.

G8, $15-$25
Austin, TX.

G9, $40-$70
Austin, TX.

G10, $150-$300
Austin, TX. Thin & excellent.

TRINITY - Late Archaic, 4000 - 2000 B.P.

(Also see Ellis, Godley, Halifax, Lamoka and Swan Lake

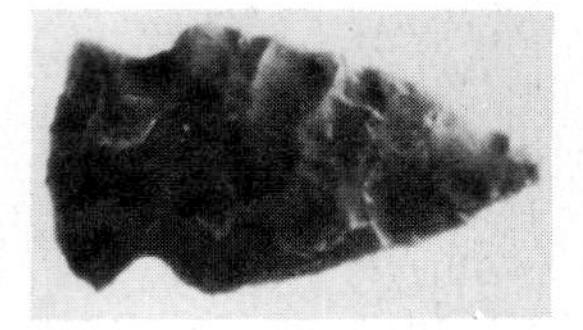

G5, $5-$8
Comanche Co., TX.

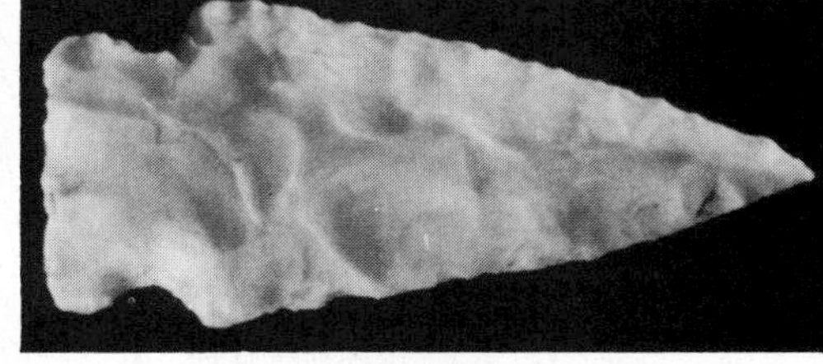

G7, $15-$25
Comanche Co., TX.

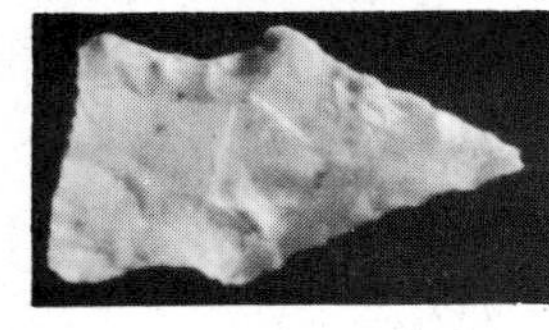

G3, $2-$4
Comanche Co., TX.

LOCATION: Midwestern to Southeastern states. **DESCRIPTION:** A small to medium size point with broad side notches, weak shoulders and a broad convex base which is usually ground.

TURKEYTAIL (Fulton) - Late Archaic to Woodland, 4000 - 2500 B.P.

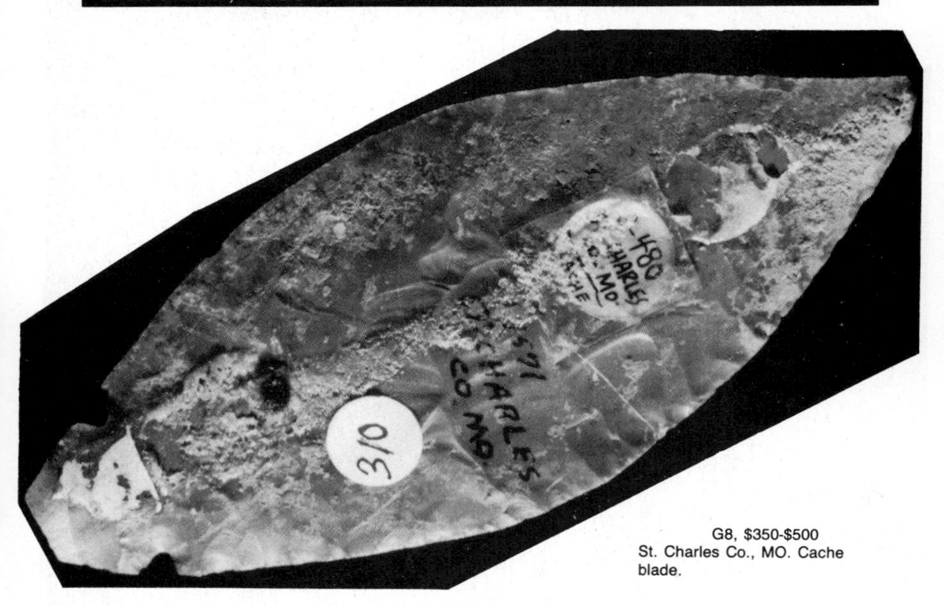

G8, $350-$500
St. Charles Co., MO. Cache blade.

LOCATION: Midwestern to Eastern states. **DESCRIPTION:** A medium to large size, wide, thin, elliptical blade with shallow notches very close to the base. This type is usually found in caches and has been reproduced in recent years. Made by the Adena culture. Found in late *Benton* caches in Mississippi dated to about 4000 B.P.

G8, $200-$350
St. Charles Co., MO. Cache blade.

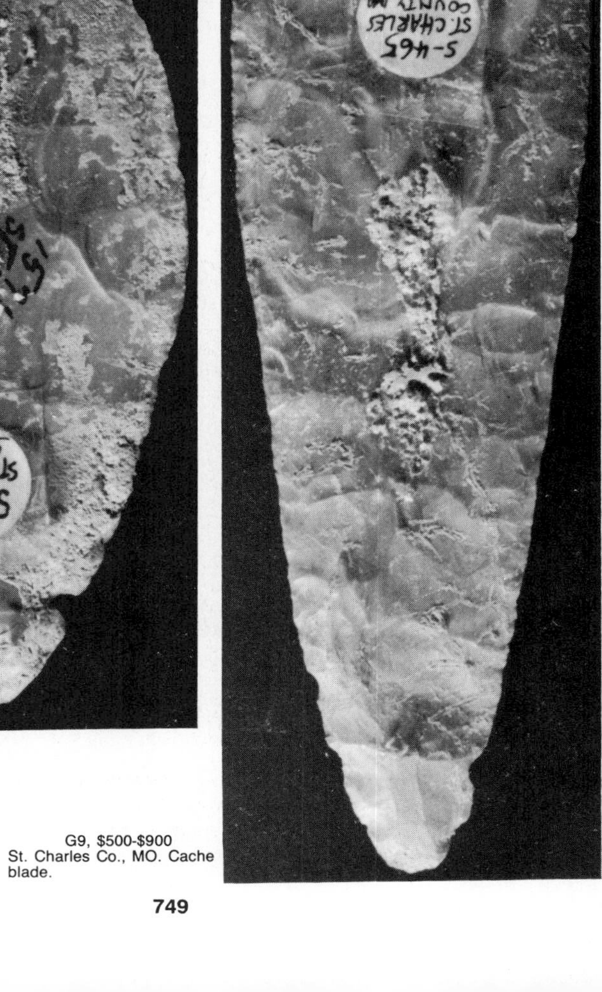

G9, $500-$900
St. Charles Co., MO. Cache blade.

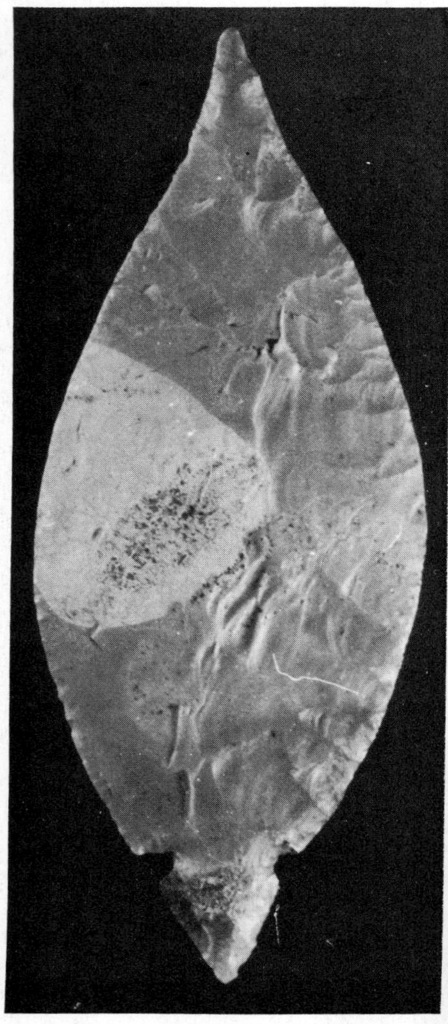

G8, $800-$1200
KY. Repaired tip. If whole, G10, $1500-$2500.

G9, $1000-$1800
Morgan Co., IL.

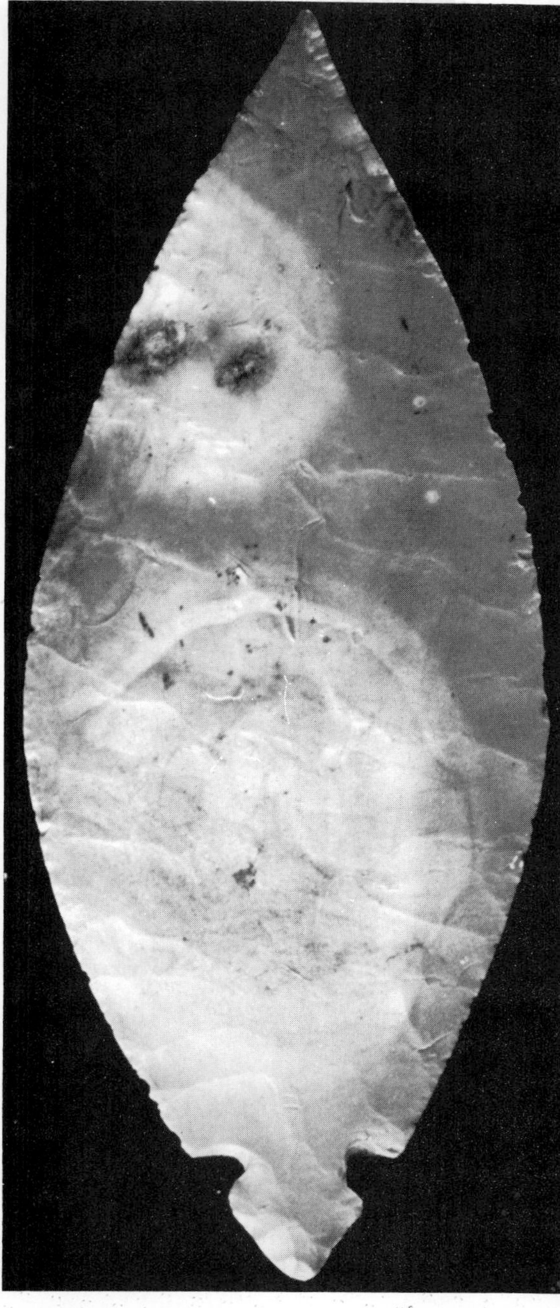

G10, $3500-$6000
KY. Classic. Later form.

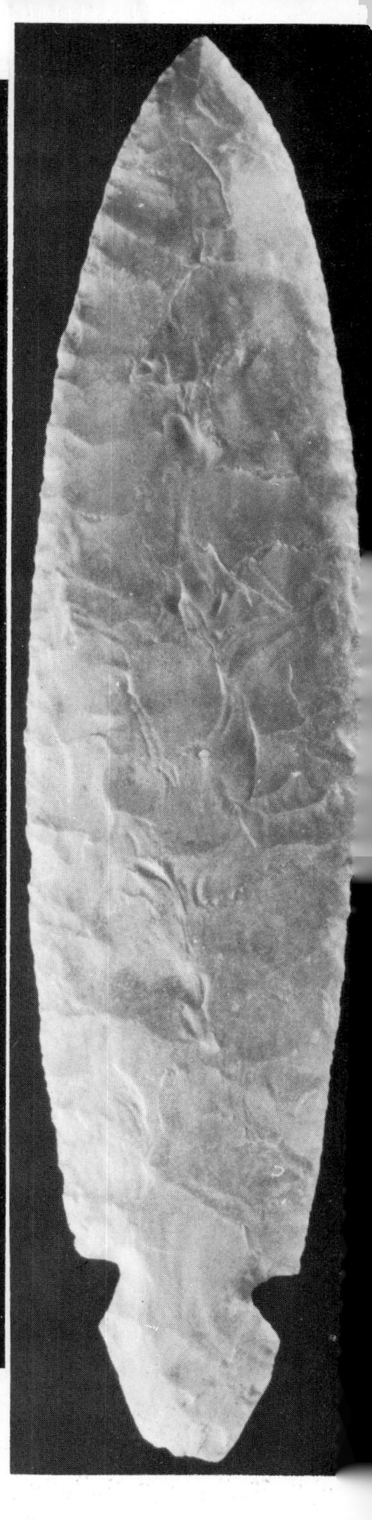

G10, $2500-$4500
Lee Co., MS. Found with Benton points in same cache.

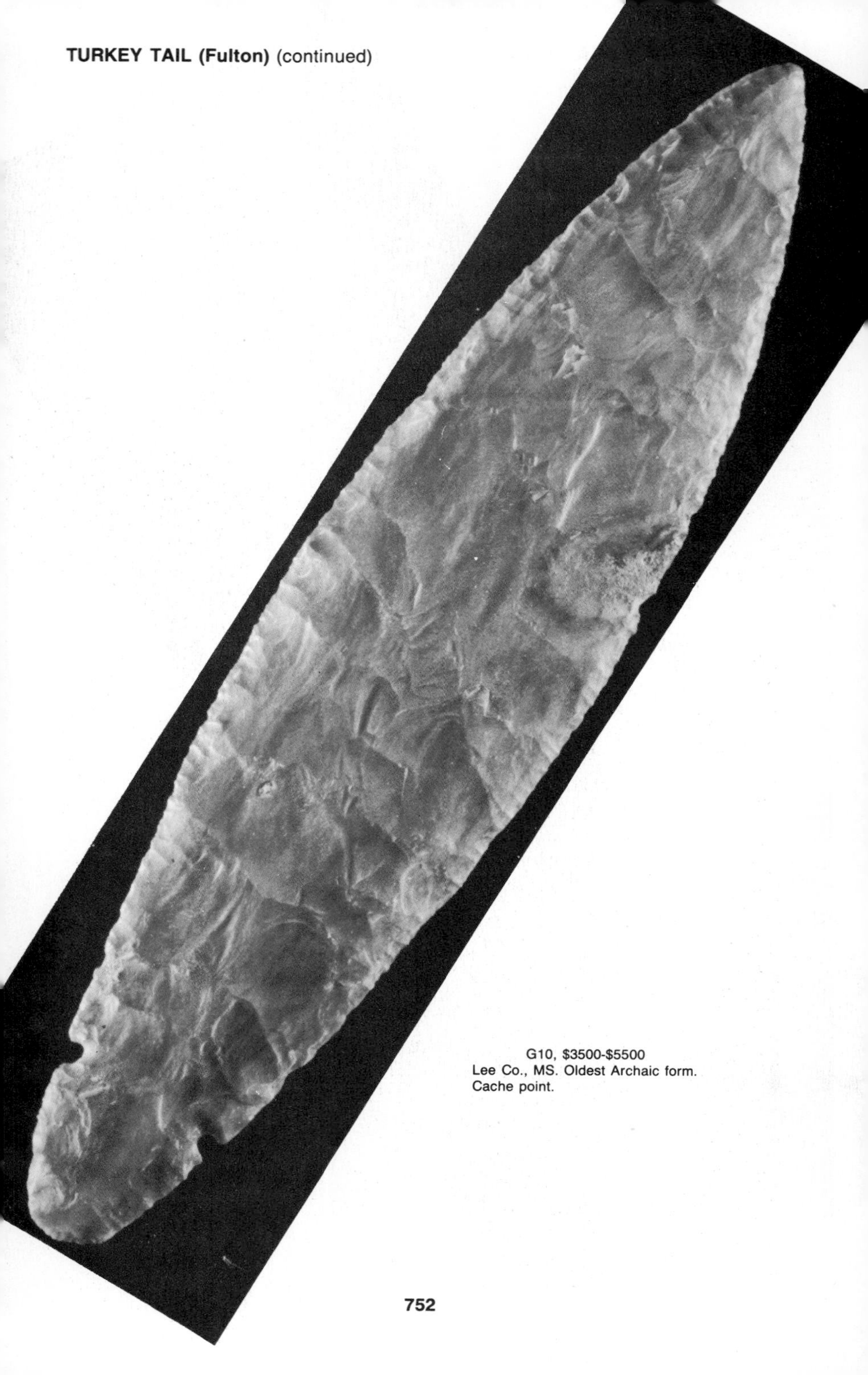

G10, $3500-$5500
Lee Co., MS. Oldest Archaic form.
Cache point.

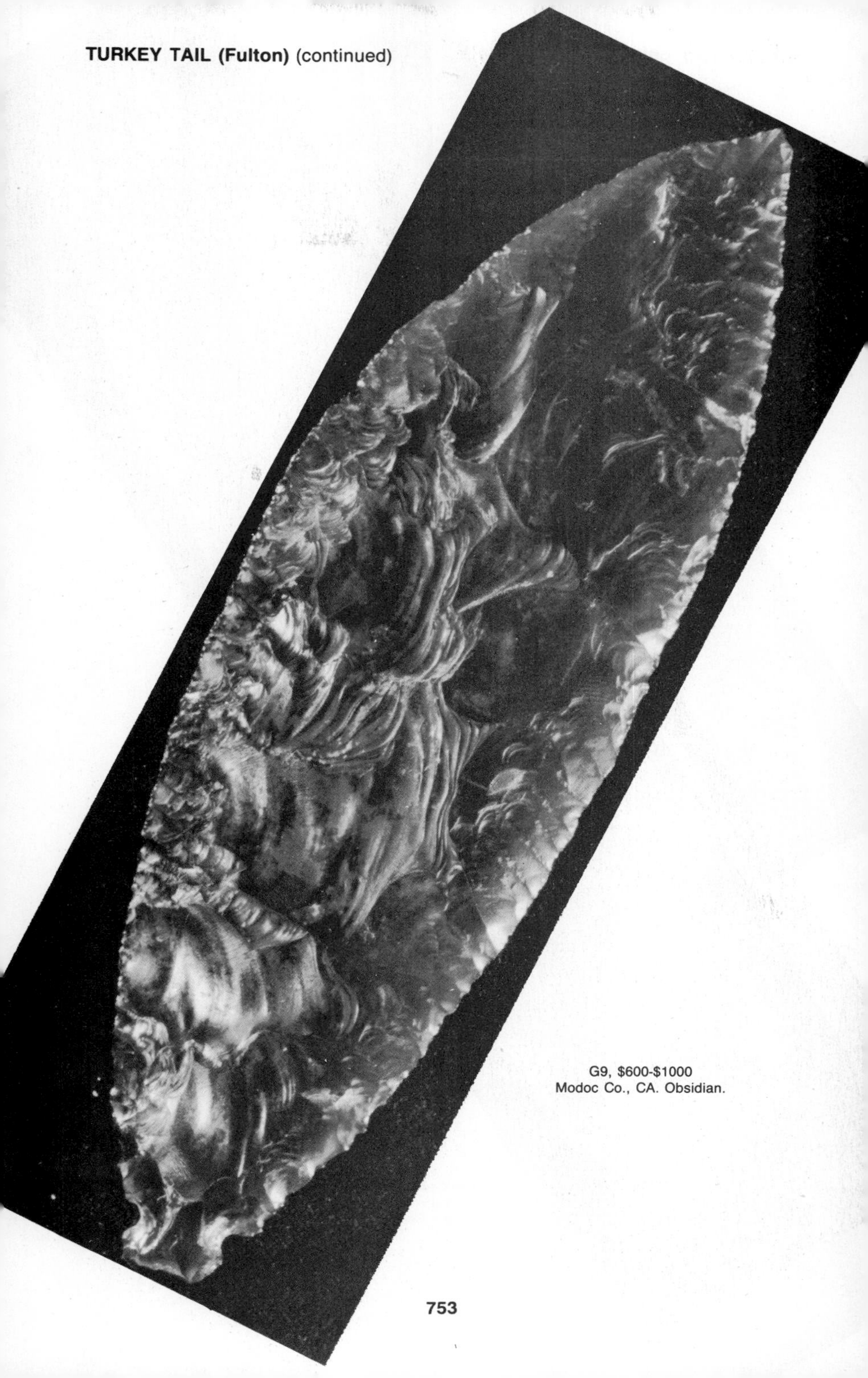

G9, $600-$1000
Modoc Co., CA. Obsidian.

G9, $700-$1200
Hardin Co., TN. Note very fine secondary flaking.

G10, $2500-$4500
Lee County, MS. Classic double notch form. Only a few are known. Cache point.

TURKEYTAIL (Harrison), Late Archaic to Woodland, 4000 - 2500 B.P.

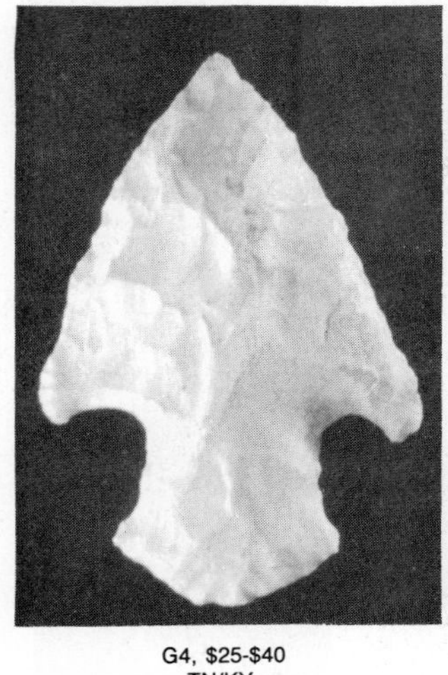
G4, $25-$40
TN/KY.

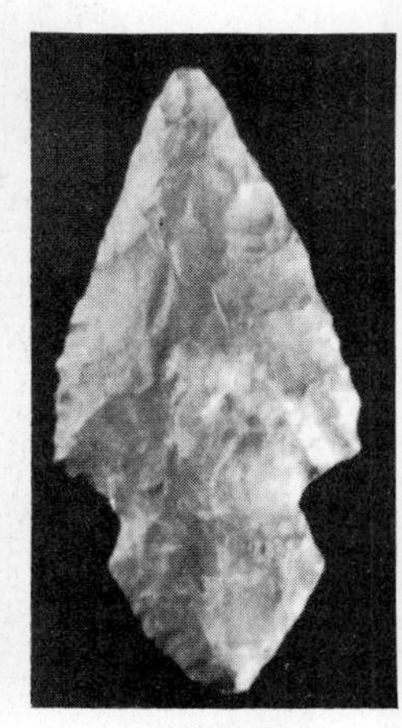
G2, $3-$5
Humphreys Co., TN.

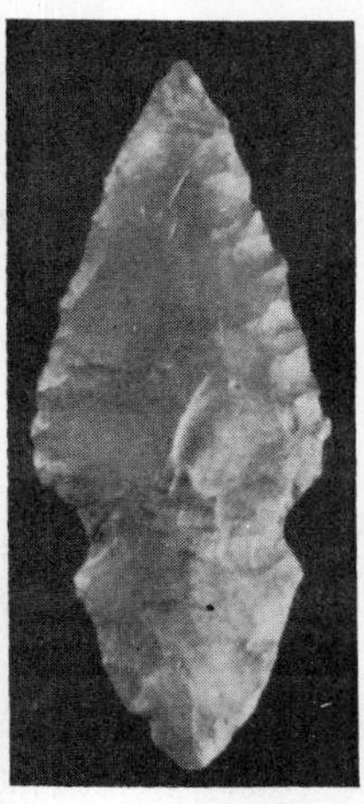
G3, $5-$8
Humphreys Co., TN.

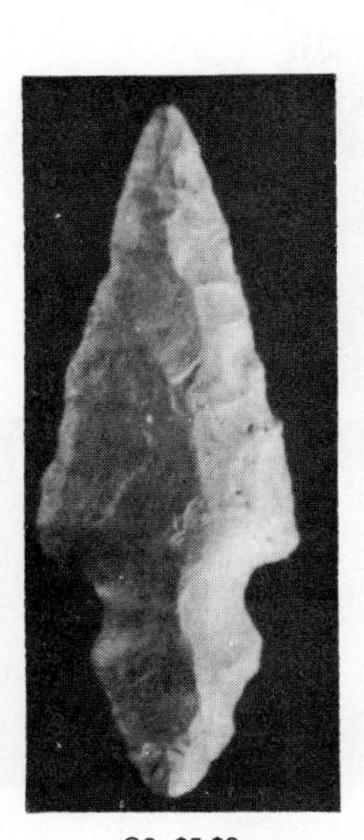
G3, $5-$8
Humphreys Co., TN.

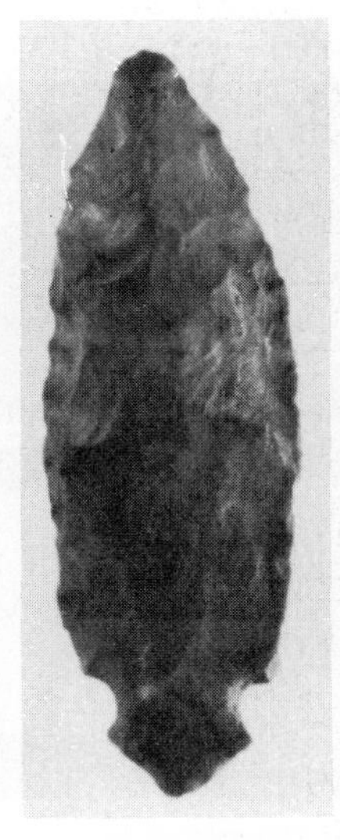
G2, $2-$4
Cookeville, TN.

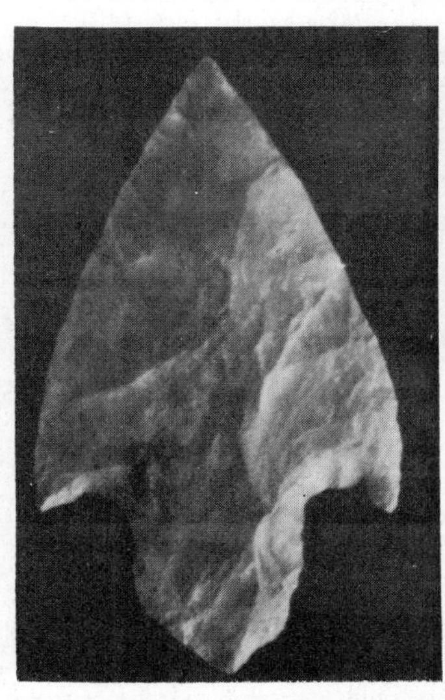
G4, $25-$40
Humphreys Co., TN. Dover chert.
Very thin and excellent.

LOCATION: Midwestern to Eastern states. **DESCRIPTION:** A medium to large size, narrow, elliptical blade with tapered, horizontal or barbed shoulders, and an elongated, diamond-shaped stem in the form of a turkey's tail. Large examples may have fine pressure flaking on one edge of each face. Made by the Adena culture.

G4, $25-$35
Henry Co., TN.

G5, $50-$80
Logan Co., KY.

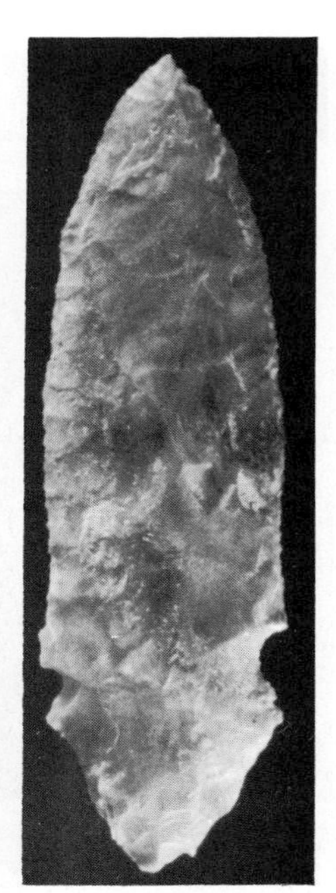

G3, $20-$35
Davidson Co., TN.

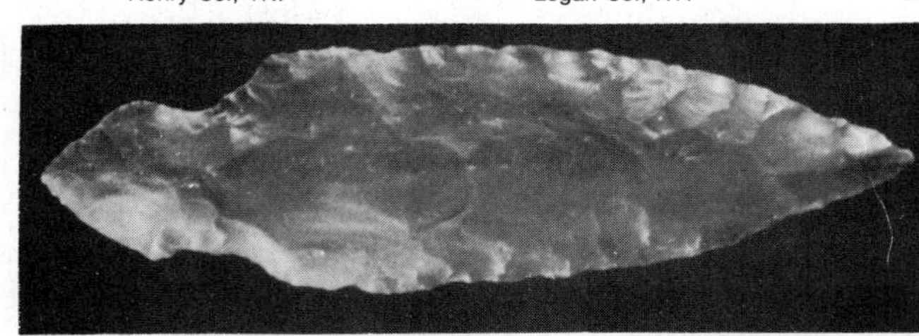

G4, $25-$35
Stewart Co., TN.

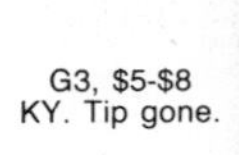

G3, $5-$8
KY. Tip gone.

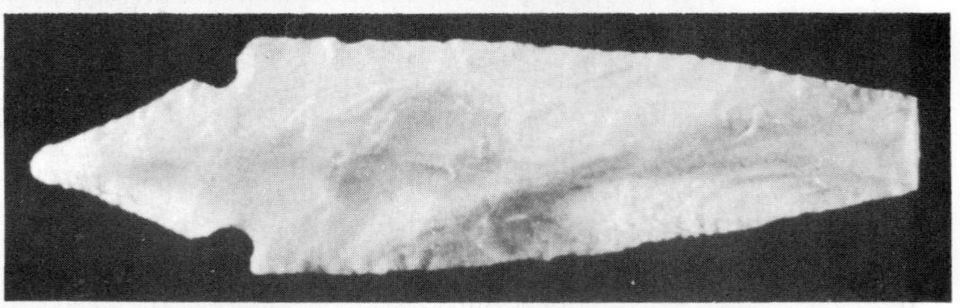

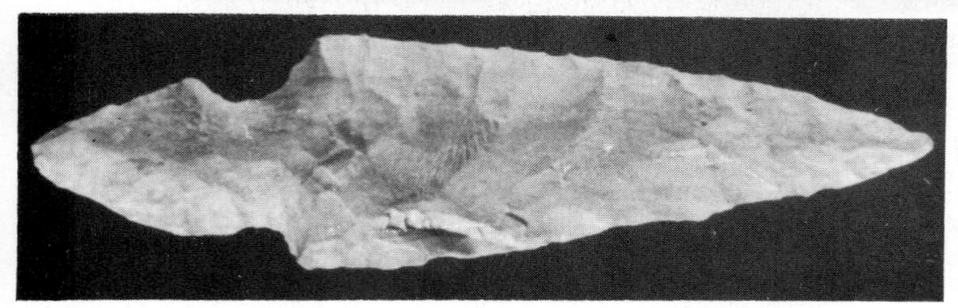

G3, $20-$35
Humphreys Co., TN.

G4, $25-$35
Humphreys Co., TN.
Unnotched form.

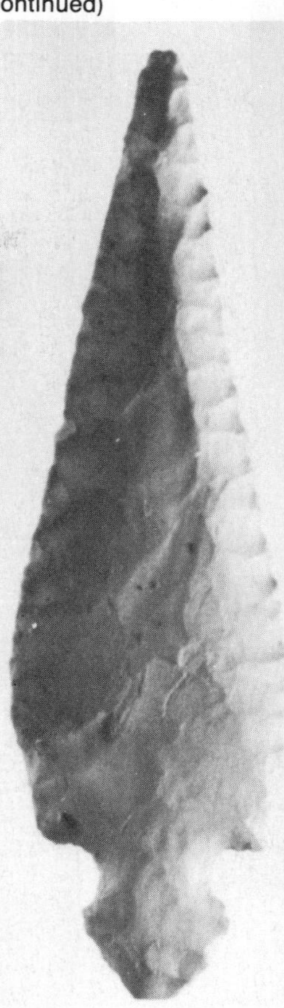

G6, $120-$180
Humphreys Co., TN.

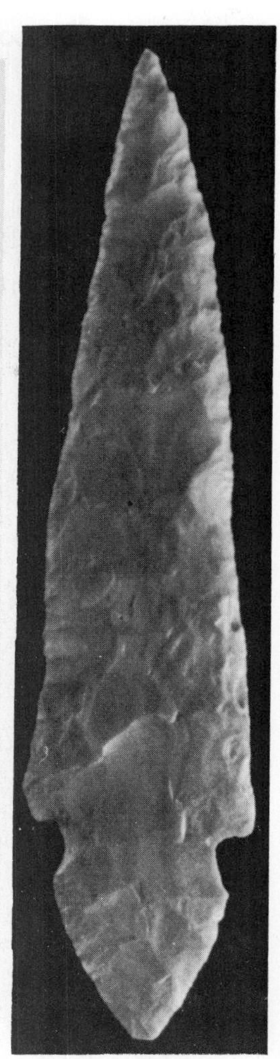

G9, $400-$600
SW KY.

G10, $600-$1000
Humphreys Co., TN.

G10, $800-$1500
Humphreys Co., TN. Very thin and High quality. Dover chert.

G10, $800-$1500
Humphreys Co., TN. Excellent quality. Dover chert.

G7, $250-$450
Wells Co., IN.

G6, $200-$300
Todd Co., KY.

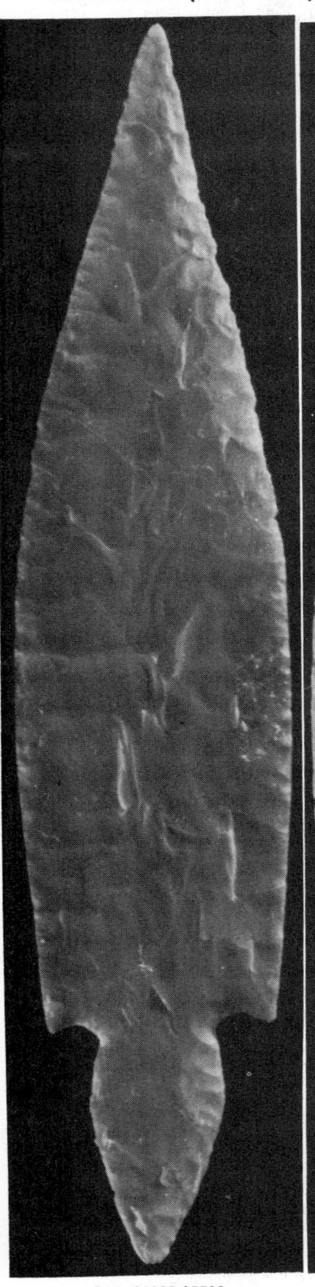

G10, $3000-$5500
Mid KY. Cache.

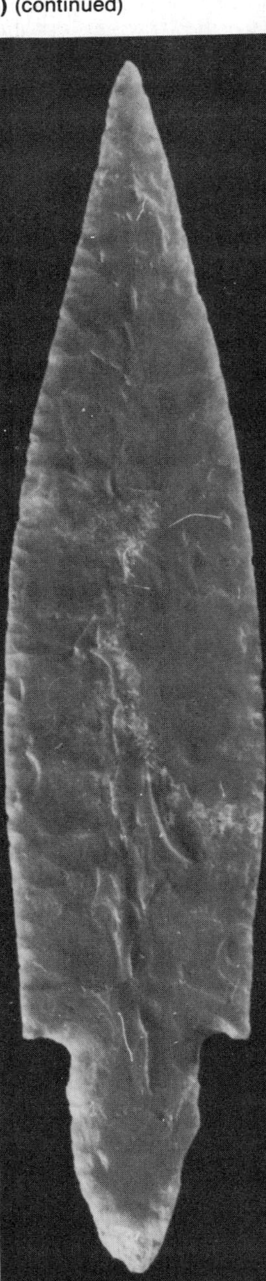

G10, $2500-$4500
Mid KY. Cache.

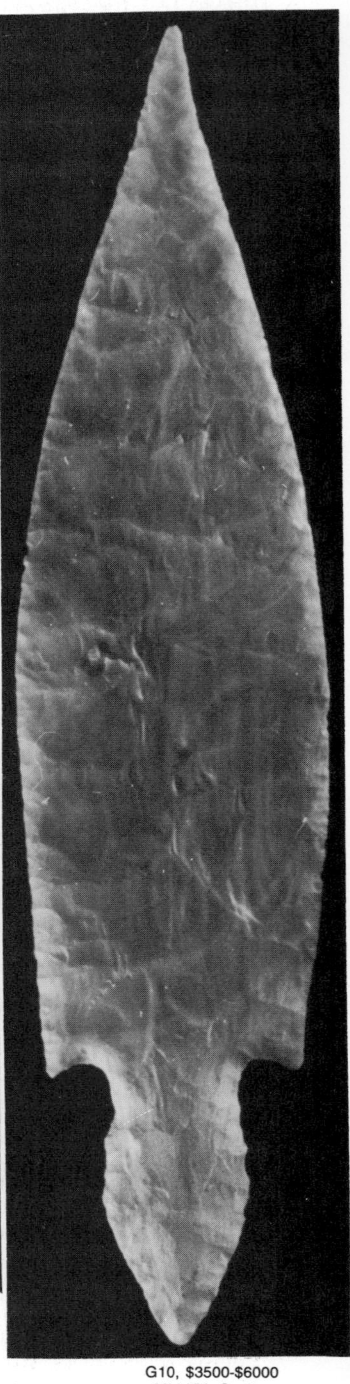

G10, $3500-$6000
Mid KY. Cache.

TURKEYTAIL (Hebron), Late Archaic to Woodland, 4000 - 2500 B.P.

G8, $30-$50
Garrard Co., KY.

LOCATION: Midwestern states. **DESCRIPTION:** A medium to large size blade with rounded, barbed shoulders, and a very narrow, rounded base. Made by the Adena culture.

UNION SIDE NOTCHED - Late Paleo, 10000 - 8000 B.P.

(Also see Decatur Blade and Hardaway Blade)

G6, $10-$20
Laurens Co., GA.

LOCATION: Southern Southeastern states. **DESCRIPTION:** A medium to large size, broad blade with weak side notches. Base can be straight to slightly concave or convex.

UMATILLA - Mississippian to Historic, 800 - 200 B.P.

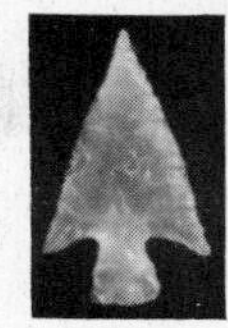

G9, $30-$50
Umatilla Co., OR.

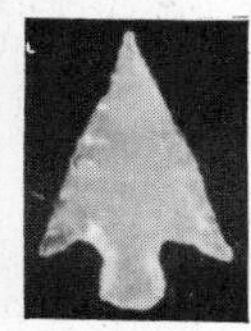

G8, $25-$40
Umatilla Co., OR.

G9, $35-$60
Wasco Co., OR.

G9, $35-$60
Umatilla Co., OR.

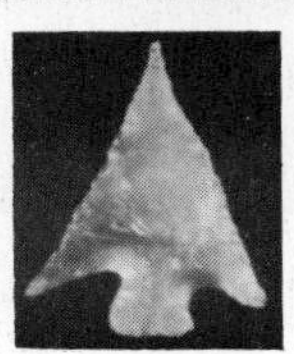

G9, $35-$70
Wasco Co., OR.

LOCATION: Northwestern states. **DESCRIPTION:** A small size barbed point with a rounded base. Tip and barbs are sharp.

UVALDE - Mid-Archaic to Woodland, 6000 - 1500 B.P.

(Also see Big Sandy, Fox Valley, Frio, Hoxie, LeCroy, Pedernales, Rice Lobbed, Stanly and Val Verde)

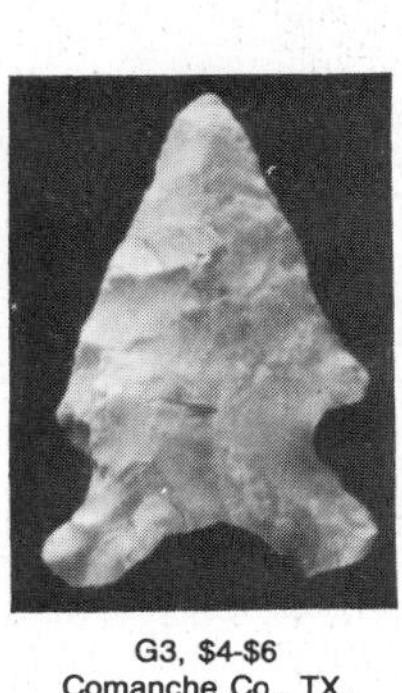

G3, $4-$6
Comanche Co., TX.

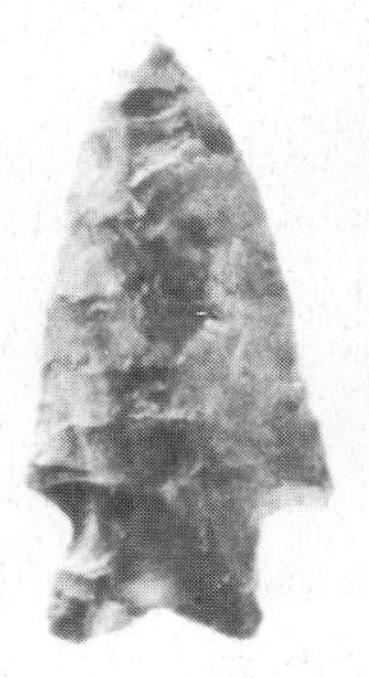

G3, $4-$6
Comanche Co., TX.

G8, $45-$70
Comanche Co., TX.

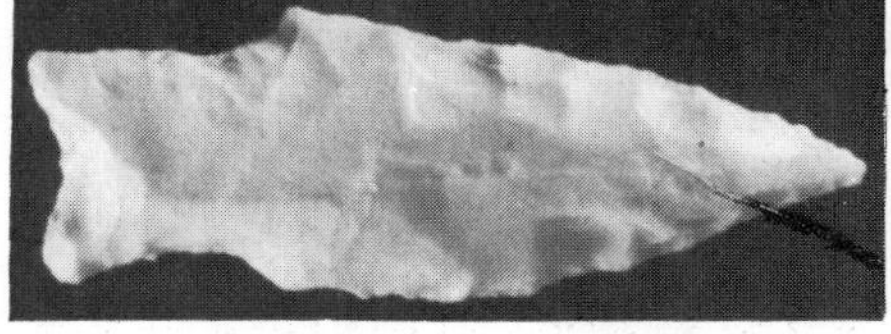

G2, $3-$5
Comanche Co., TX.

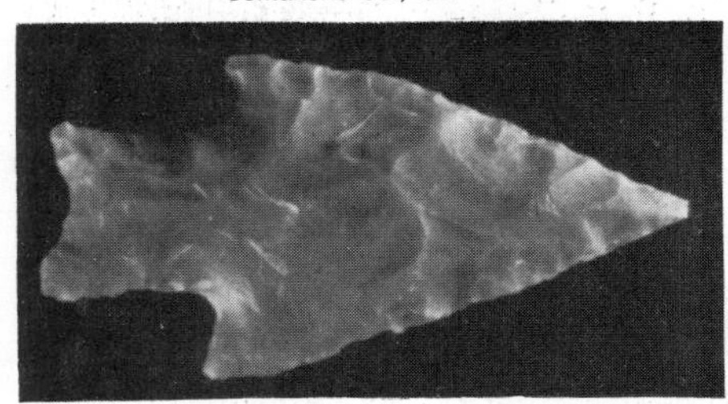

G5, $10-$20
Bell Co., TX.

G5, $10-$20
Comanche Co., TX.

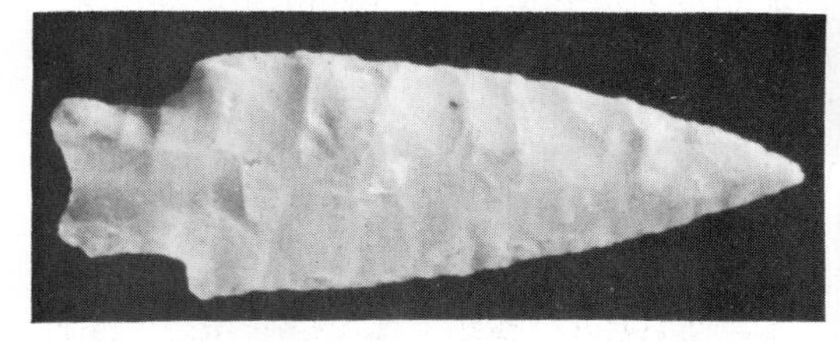

G4, $6-$10
Comanche Co., TX.

LOCATION: Midwestern to Southeastern states. **DESCRIPTION:** A medium size, bifurcated stemmed point with barbed to tapered shoulders. Some examples are serrated. The *Frio* point is similar but is usually broader and the ears flare outward more than this type.

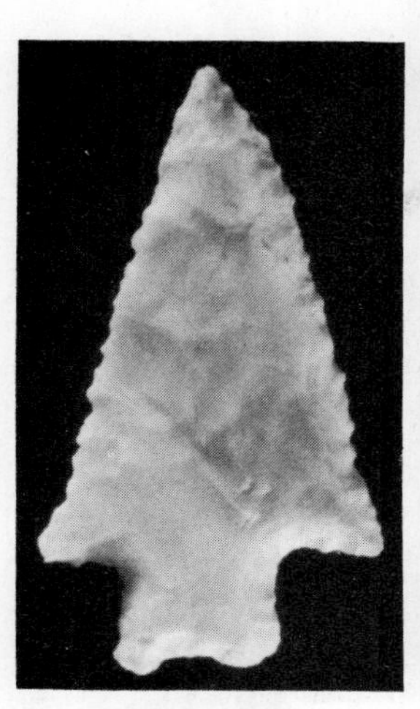

G5, $10-$20
Comanche Co., TX.

G8, $40-$60
Bell Co., TX.

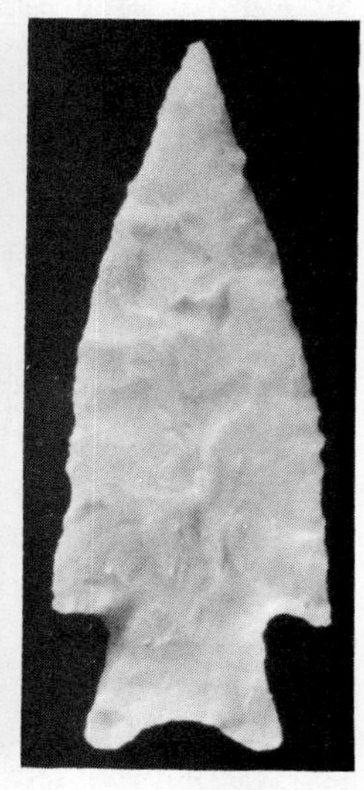

G8, $40-$60
Comanche Co., TX. Right hand bevel on opposite blade faces.

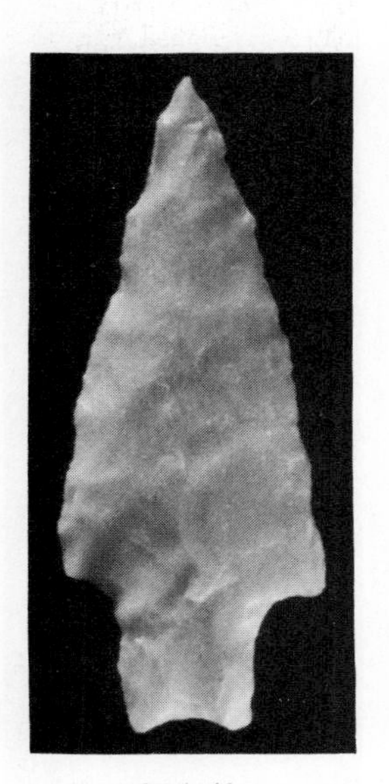

G3, $4-$6
Comanche Co., TX.

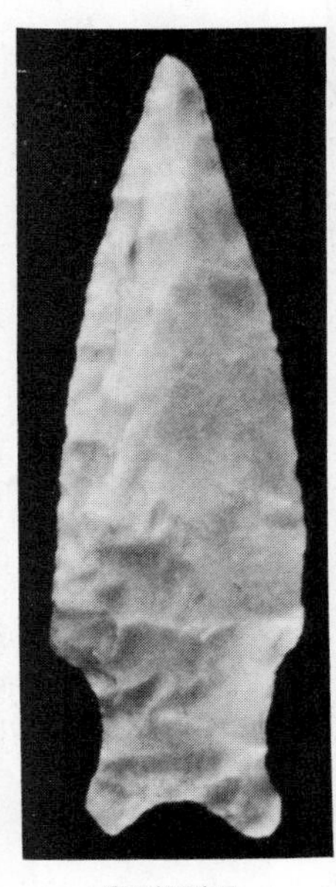

G7, $25-$40
Comanche Co., TX.

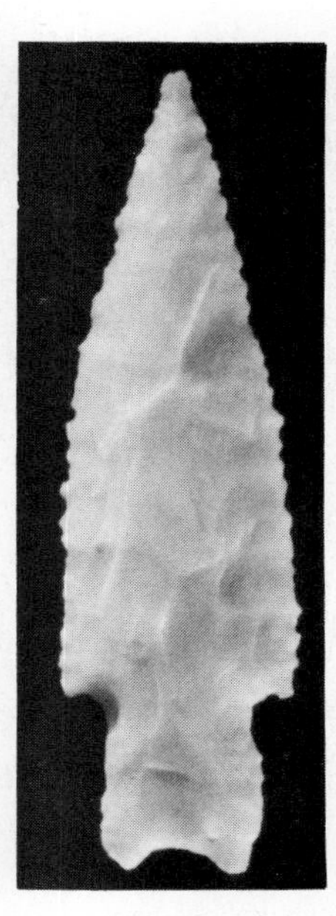

G7, $25-$40
Comanche Co., TX.

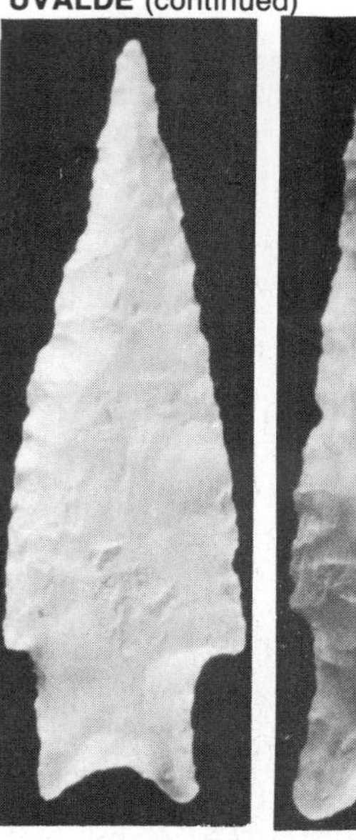

G7, $25-$40
Comanche Co., TX.

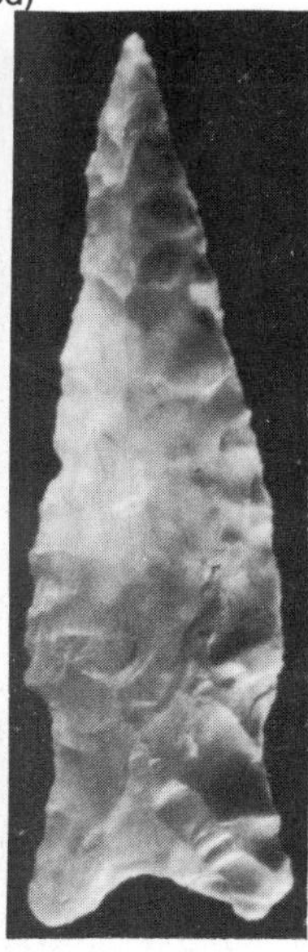

G7, $25-$40
Austin, TX.

G9, $90-$150
Comanche Co., TX. Note serrated edges.

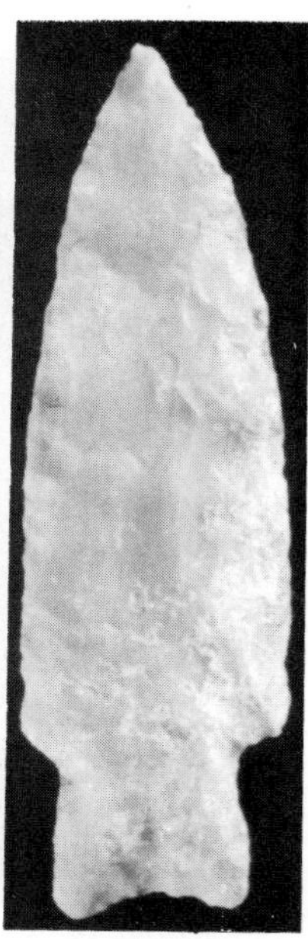

G7, $30-$50
Comanche Co., TX.

G7, $30-$50
Comanche Co., TX.

G6, $25-$45
Waco, TX.

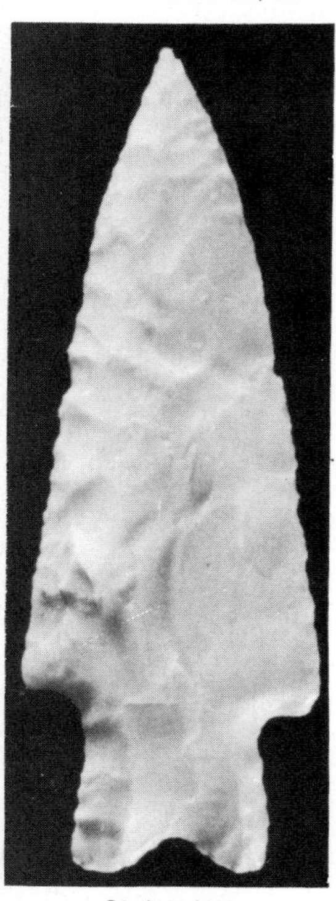

G9, $100-$200
Comanche Co., TX. Classic.

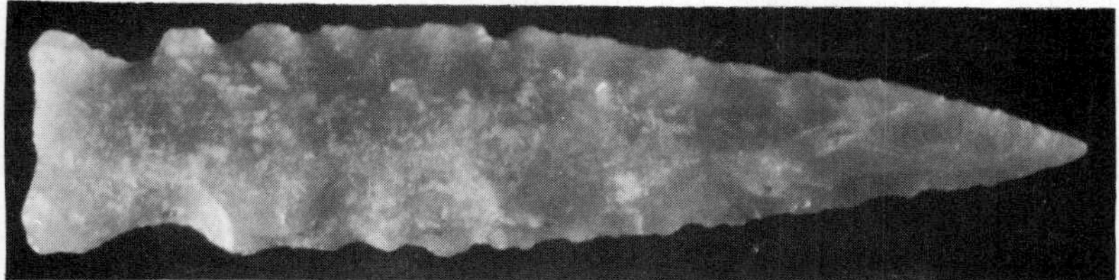

G6, $25-$45
Austin, TX.

G8, $45-$70
Austin, TX.

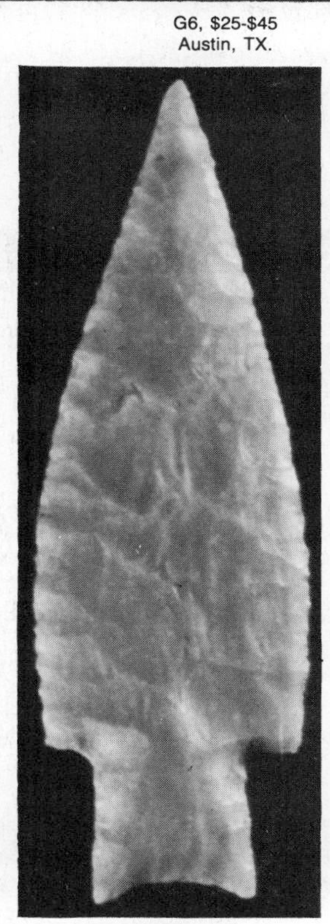

G10, $250-$450
Austin, TX.

G10, $250-$400
Austin, TX.

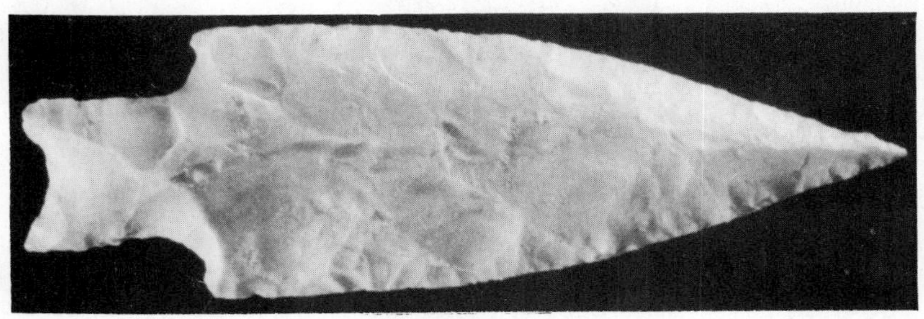

G9, $150-$250
Austin, TX.

UVALDE (continued)

G10, $250-$400
Austin, TX.

UWHARRIE (See Hamilton)

VAL VERDE - Mid to late Archaic, 5000 - 3000 B.P.

(Also see Langtry, Pedernalis and Uvalde)

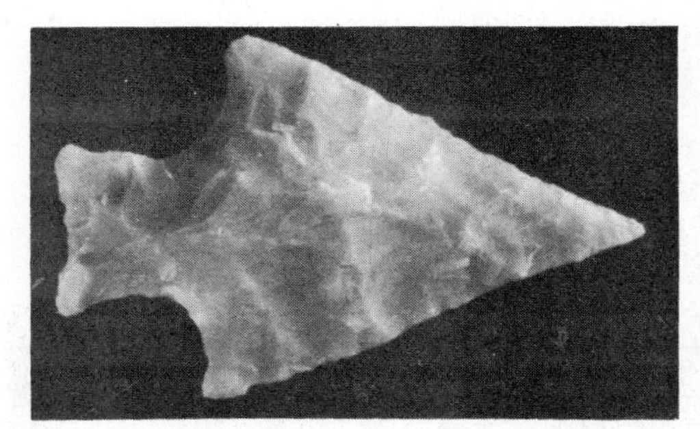

G8, $40-$70
Comanche Co., TX.

LOCATION: Midwestern states. **DESCRIPTION:** A medium size point with outward flaring tapered shoulders, an expanding stem and a concave base. On some examples the basal corners form auricles.

VALINA - Woodland, 2500 - 1000 B.P.

(Also see Madison, Matamoros, Morrow Mountain and O'Leno)

G4, .50-$1
Dunlap, TN.

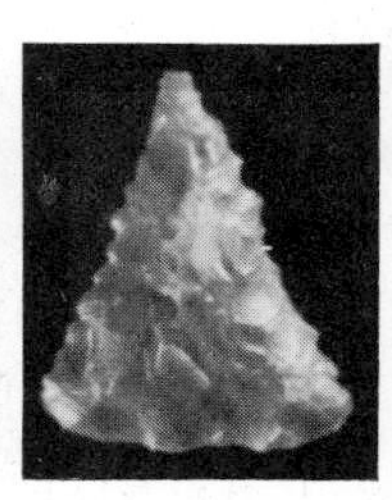

G5, $1-$2
Meigs Co., TN.

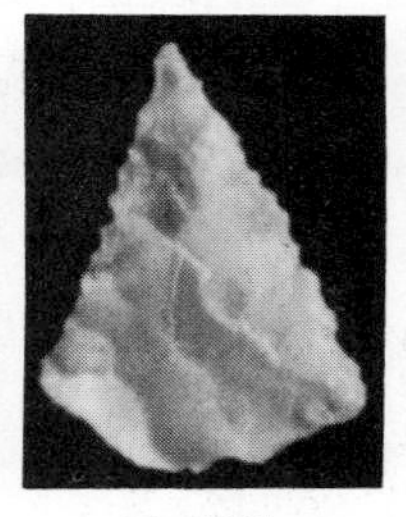

G4, .50-$1
Meigs Co., TN.

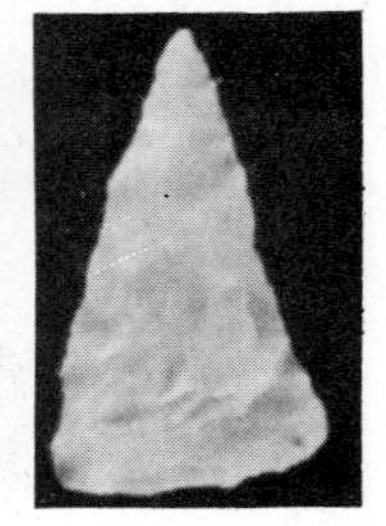

G3, .25-.50
SE TN.

LOCATION: Eastern states. **DESCRIPTION:** A small size, broad triangle with rounded basal corners and a convex base.

VENTANA-AMARGOSA - Mid-Archaic, 7000 - 5000 B.P.

(Also see Colonial, Dallas, Rose Springs and Yavapai Stemmed)

G4, $2-$4
Yavapai Co., AZ.

G5, $3-$5
Yavapai Co., AZ.

G6, $6-$8
Yavapai Co., AZ.

LOCATION: Southwestern states. **DESCRIPTION:** A small to medium size point with a roughly parallel stem and weak horizontal shoulders.

VICTORIA - Early Archaic, 8000 - 6000 B.P.

(Also see Stanfield)

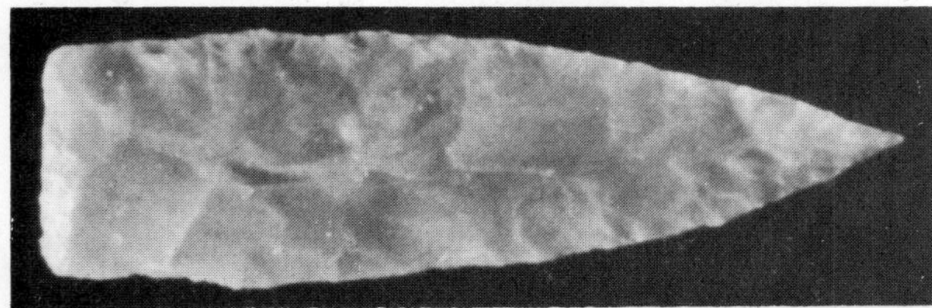

G7, $45-$70
Bell Co., TX.

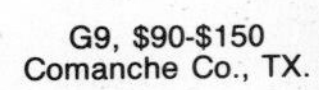

G9, $90-$150
Comanche Co., TX.

LOCATION: Midwestern states. **DESCRIPTION:** A medium to large size, narrow, lanceolate blade with a straight base. The hafting area is separated from the blade by weak shoulders.

WACISSA - Early Archaic, 9000 - 6000 B.P.

(Also see Abbey, Arredondo, Bolen, Kirk & White Springs)

G2, $2-$4, Henry Co., AL.

G3, $3-$5, Leon Co., FL.

WACISSA (continued)

G4, $8-$15
Dale Co., AL.

G8, $36-$60
Henry Co., AL. Classic.

G6, $20-$35
Lee Co., GA.

G7, $35-$50
Sou. GA.

G8, $40-$70
Aucilla Rv., FL.

G7, $30-$50
Lee Co., GA.

LOCATION: Southern Southeastern states. **DESCRIPTION:** A small to medium size, thick, short, broad stemmed point that is beveled on all four sides. Shoulders are moderate to weak and horizontal to slightly barbed. Some examples are serrated.

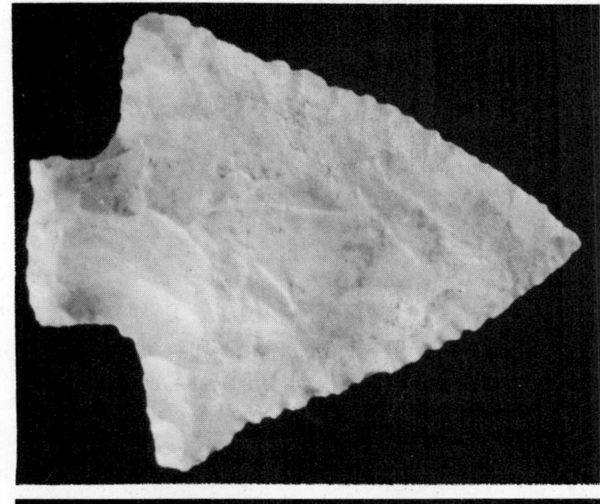

G8, $350-$550
Dodge Co., GA.

WADE - Late Archaic to Woodland, 4500 - 2500 B.P.

(Also see Buck Creek, Culbreath, Eva, Hamilton Stemmed, Motley & Smithsonia)

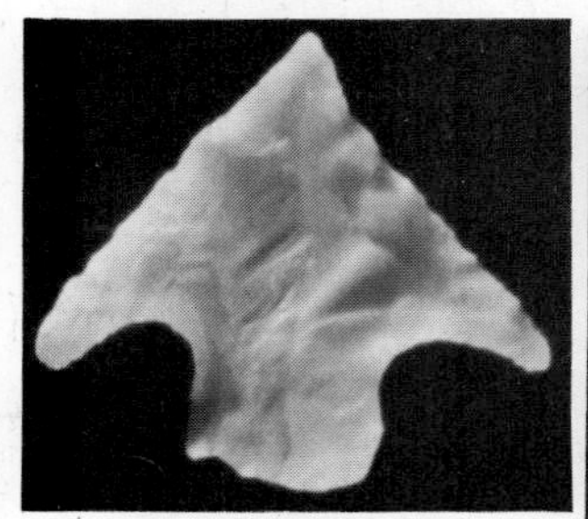

G5, $10-$20
Dayton, TN.

G2, $2-$4
Meigs Co., TN. Broken tang.

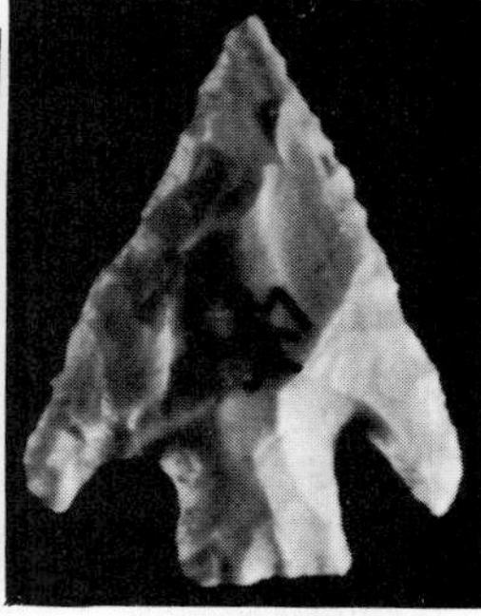

G4, $6-$10
Decatur, AL.

G5, $10-$20
Putnam Co., TN.

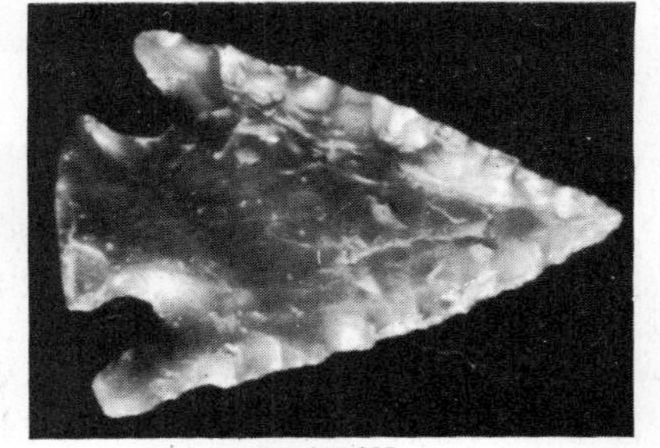

G6, $15-$25
Fentress Co., TN.

LOCATION: Southeastern states. **DESCRIPTION:** A medium to large size, broad, well barbed, stemmed point. The blade is straight to convex. The stem is straight to expanding. On some examples, the barbs almost reach the base. Has been found with *Motley* points in caches.

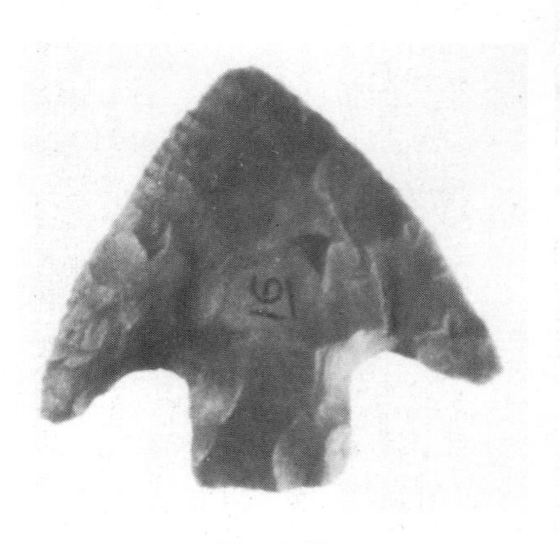

G5, $10-$20
Florence, AL.

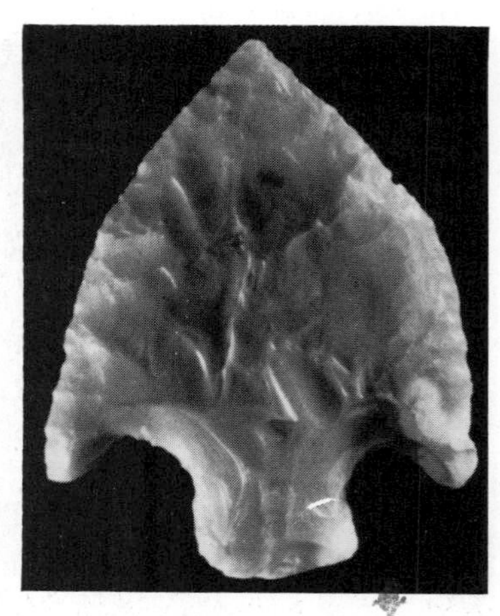

G5, $10-$20
Decatur, AL.

G4, $6-$10
KY.

G3, $4-$6
Huntsville, AL. Snapped base.

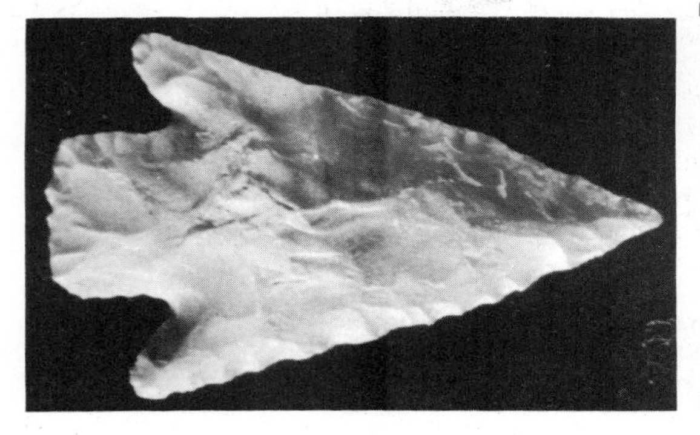

G8, $40-$60
Christian Co., KY.

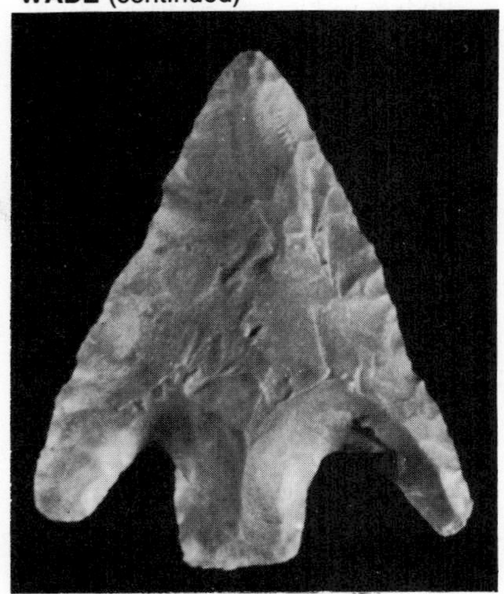

G7, $25-$40. Hardin Co., TN.

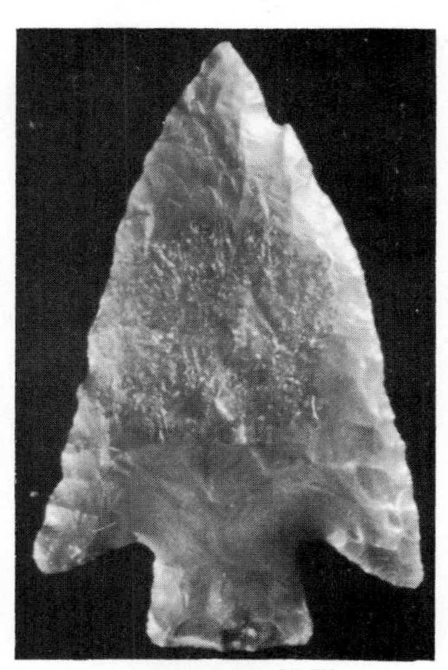

G6, $15-$25. SE TN.

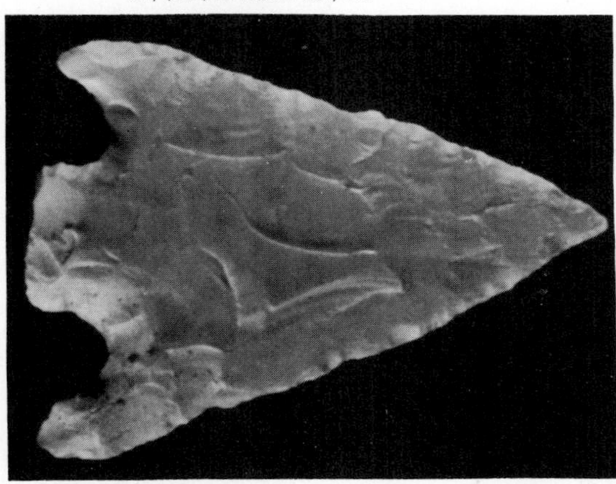

G6, $15-$25. Lyon Co., KY.

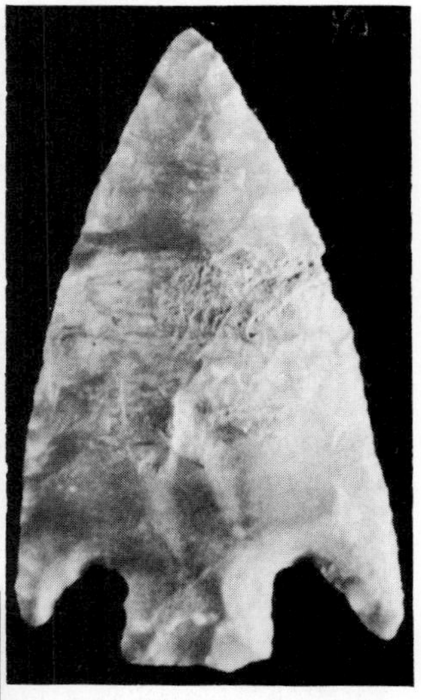

G7, $25-$40
Walker Co., AL.

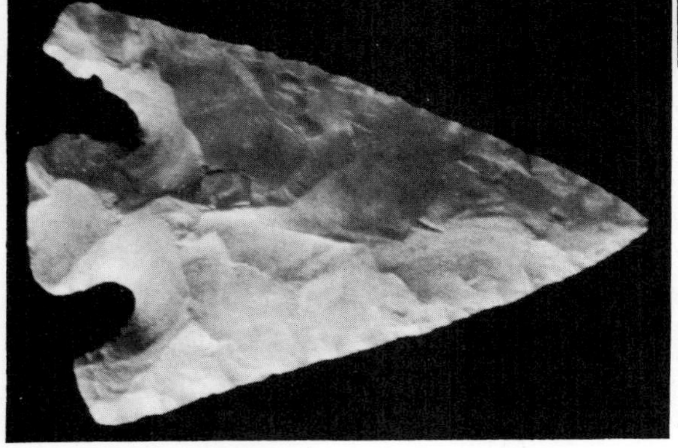

G8, $40-$60, Dayton, TN.

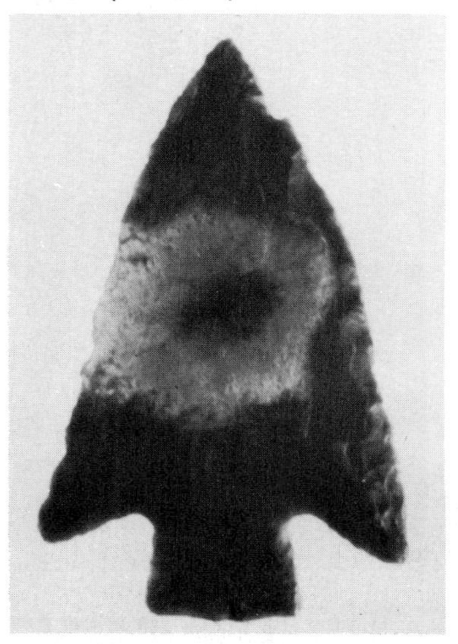

G7, $25-$40
SE TN. Note large translucent spot in center of blade.

G9, $90-$150
Wayne Co., TN. Cache blade.

G8, $40-$60
Dayton, TN.

G8, $40-$60
Clarksville, TN.

WADLOW - Woodland, 3000 - 1500 B.P.

(Also see Adena Blade, Cobbs Triangular, Red Ochre and Tennessee River)

G7, $70-$100
Florence, AL.

G6, $70-$100
Florence, AL.

LOCATION: Midwestern to Southeastern states. **DESCRIPTION:** A large to very large size, broad, parallel sided blade with a straight to convex base. Some examples are almost triangular shaped; others have fine pressure flaking on the blade edges, but most do not.

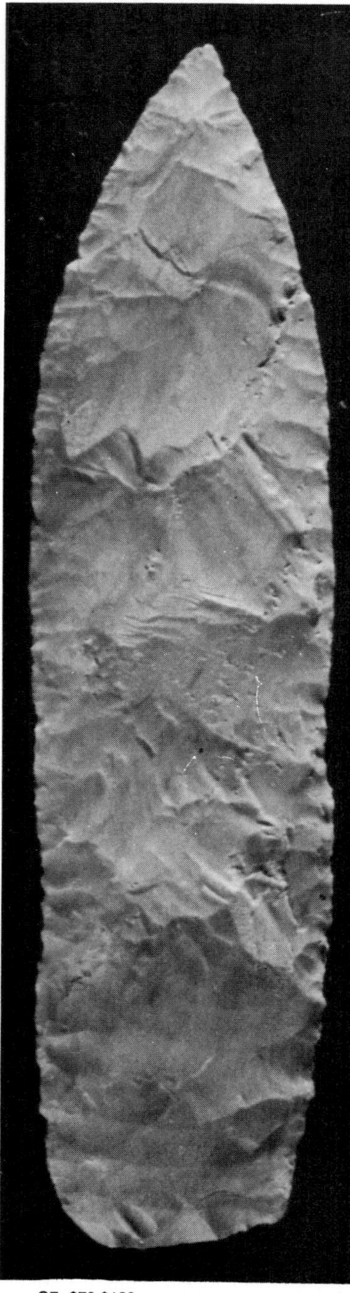

G7, $70-$120
Florence, AL.

G7, $80-$150
Morgan Co., TN. Broken & glued.

WALLER KNIFE - Early Archaic, 9000 - 5000 B.P.

(See Corner Tang Knife & Edgefield Scraper)

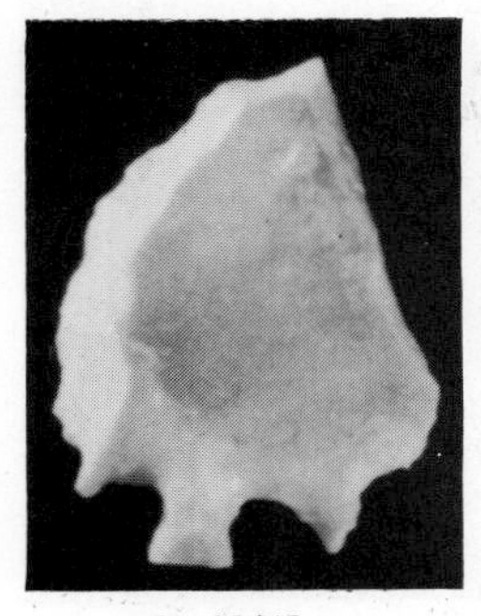

G4, $8-$15
Bird Lake, FL.

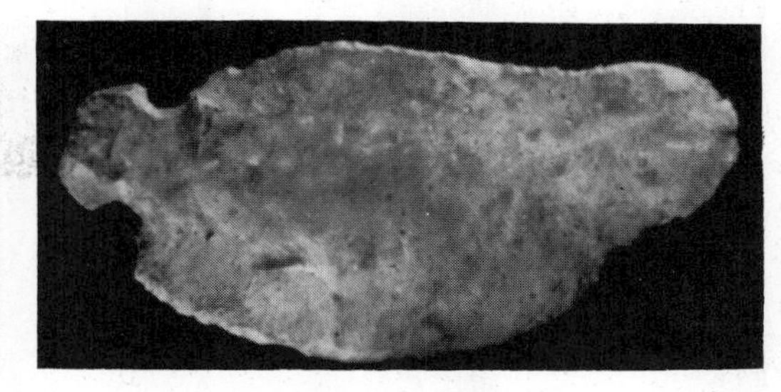

G6, $10-$20, Sante Fe Rv., FL.

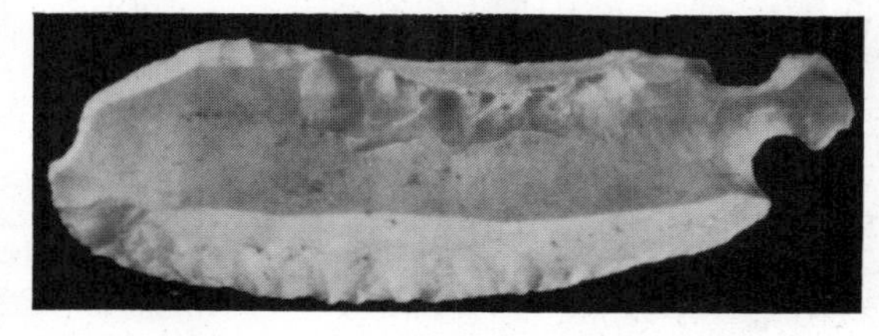

G8, $20-$30
Seminole Co., GA.

LOCATION: Southern Southeastern states. **DESCRIPTION:** A medium size double uniface knife with a short, notched base, made from a flake. Only the cutting edges have been pressure flaked.

WARATAN - Woodland, 3000 - 1000 B.P.

(Also see Potts, Wacissa and Yadkin)

G5, $5-$8
Southampton Co., VA.

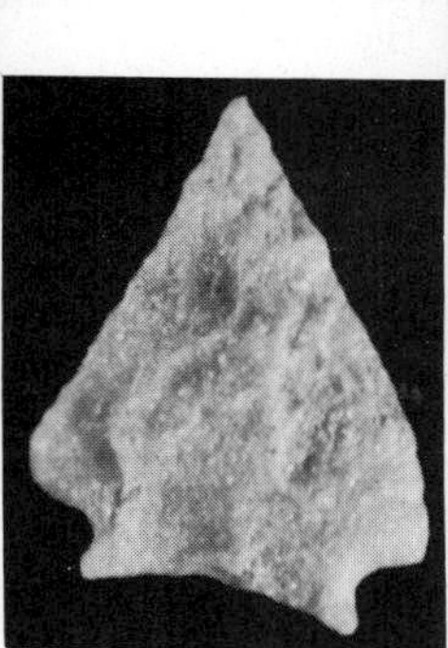

G6, $8-$15
Southampton Co., VA.
Classic Form.

G5, $5-$8
Sussex Co., VA.

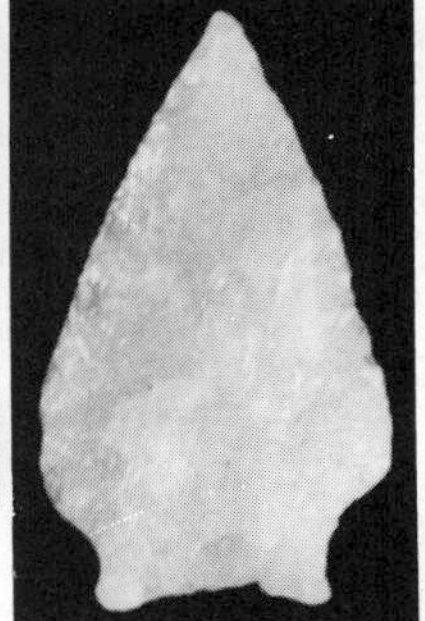

G5, $6-$10
Sussex Co., VA.

LOCATION: Far Eastern states. **DESCRIPTION:** A medium to large size point with usually broad, tapered shoulders, weak corner notches and a very short, broad, concave base. The base expands on some examples giving the appearance of ears or auricles.

G8, $15-$30
Southampton Co., VA.

G7, $12-$20
Davidson Co., NC. Classic.

G4, $4-$6
Dunlap, TN.

WASHINGTON - Woodland, 3000 - 1500 B.P.

(Also see Durant's Bend and Nova)

G8, $5-$8
Dallas Co., AL.
Classic.

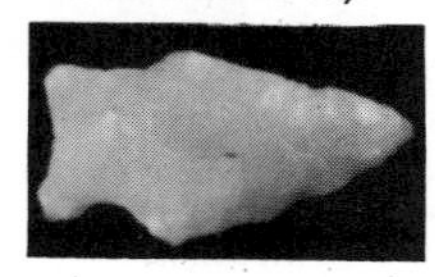

G6, $4-$6
Bethany, WV.

LOCATION: Southeastern states. **DESCRIPTION:** A small size, serrated, corner to side notched point with a concave, expanded base.

WASHITA - Mississippian, 800 - 400 B.P.

(Also see Harrell)

G2, $1-$3
Comanche Co., TX.

G2, $1-$3
Comanche Co., TX.

G2, $1-$3
Comanche Co., TX.

G2, $1-$3
Hamilton Co., TN.

G5, $4-$6
Comanche Co., TX.

G2, $1-$3
Comanche Co., TX.

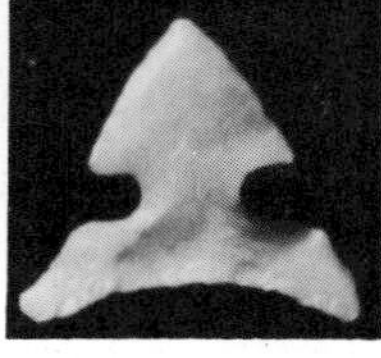

G8, $30-$65
WA/OR.

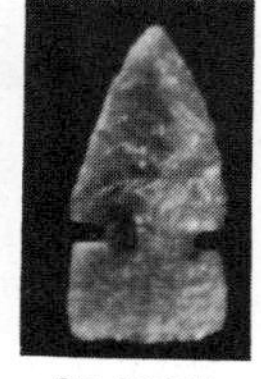

G7, $8-$15
OR.

G9, $45-$70
Florence, AL.

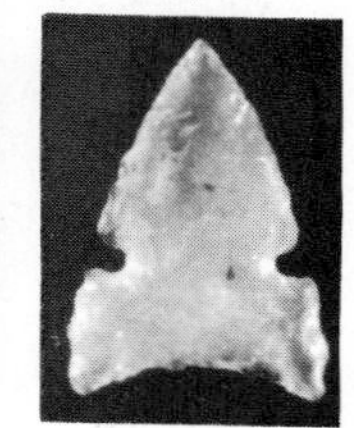

G8, $25-$40
Clearwater Co., ID.
Agate. Classic.

LOCATION: Midwestern states. **DESCRIPTION:** A small size, triangular, thin, side notched point with a concave base.

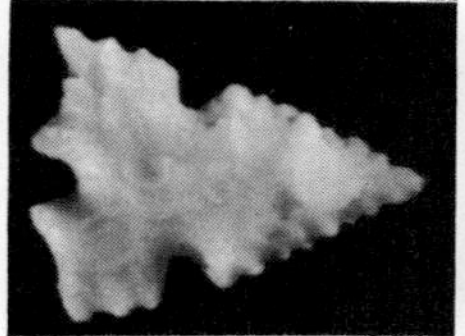
G8, $25-$40
Comanche Co., TX.

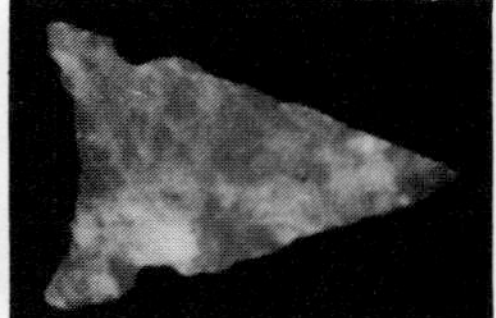
G7, $8-$15
AR.

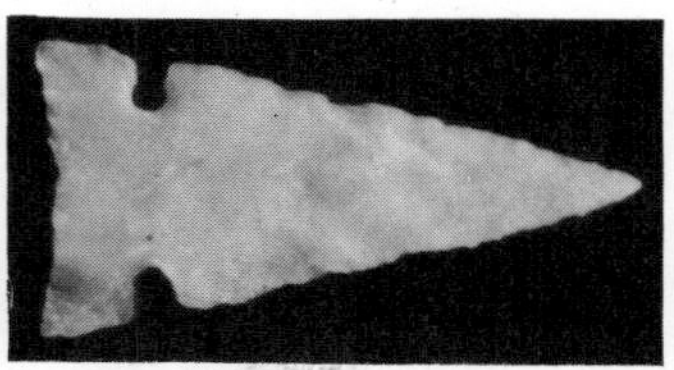
G9, $35-$60
WA/OR.

WATEREE - Woodland, 3000 - 1500 B.P.

(Also see Will's Cove)

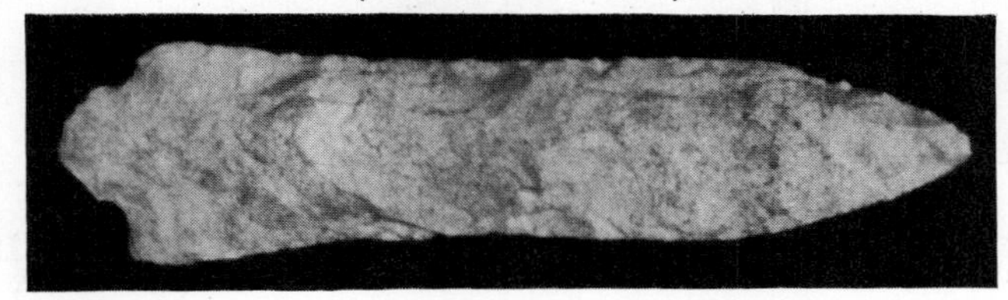
G8, $20-$35. Fairfield Co., SC. Slate. Very rare. Similar to North Carolina's Will's Cove.

LOCATION: Far Eastern states. **DESCRIPTION:** A medium size, narrow point with a recurvate blade, horizontal shoulders and a very short stem.

WAUBESA (See Adena-Waubesa)

WELLS (See Adena-Wells)

WHEELER EXCURVATE - Transitional Paleo, 10000 - 8000 B.P.

(Also see Angostura, McKean and Pinto Basin)

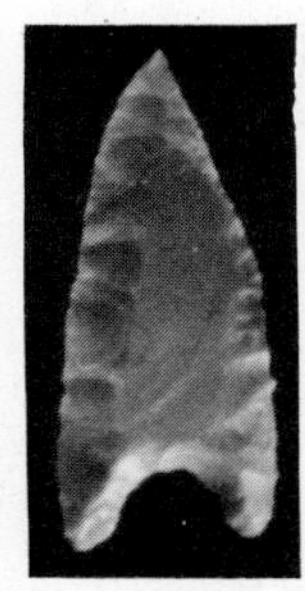
G5, $90-$150
Limestone Co., AL.
Quad site.

G5, $90-$150
Limestone Co., AL.
Quad site.

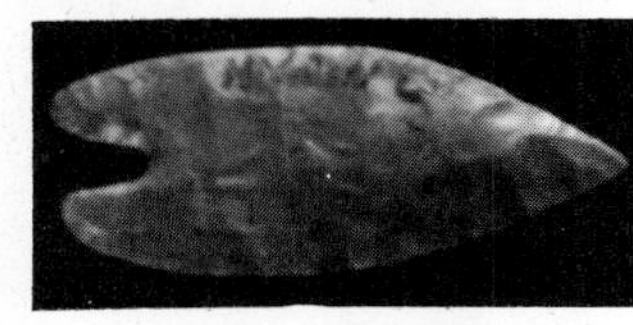
G9, $800-$1500
Hardin Co., TN. Classic.

G8, $700-$1200
Limestone Co., AL. Classic.

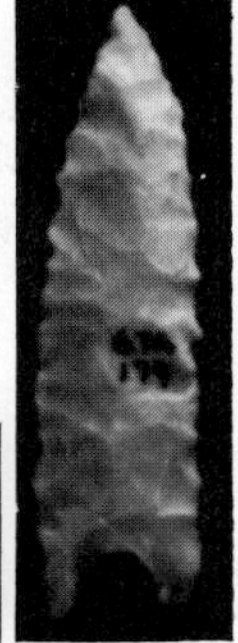
G7, $350-$650
Limestone Co., AL.
Quad site.

LOCATION: Southeastern states. **DESCRIPTION:** A small to medium size, lanceolate point with a deep concave base that is steeply beveled. Some examples are fluted, others are finely serrated and show excellent quality collateral flaking. Most bases are deeply notched but some examples have a more shallow concavity. Basal grinding is absent. The ears on some examples turn inward. Blade edges are excurvate. **I.D. KEY:** Base form and flaking style.

G3, $25-$45
Lawrence Co., AL.

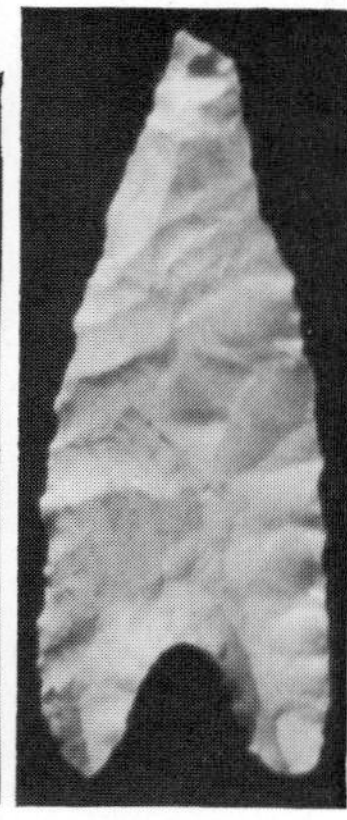

G3, $30-$50
Limestone Co., AL.

G7, $350-$650
Colbert Co., AL. Rare fluted form.

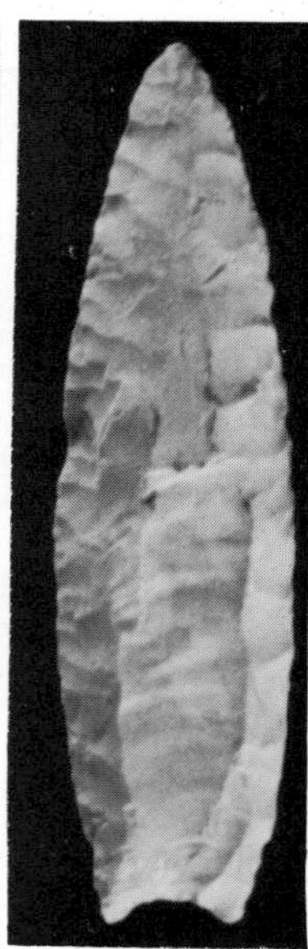

G8, $700-$1200
Hardin Co., TN. Rare fluted form. Fort Payne chert.

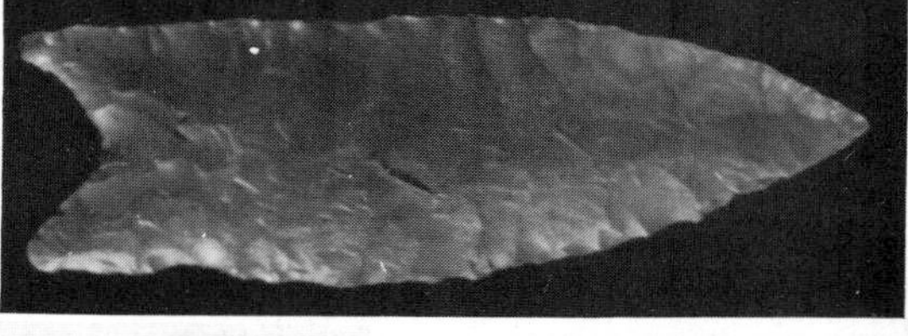

G7, $350-$650
Lauderdale Co., AL.

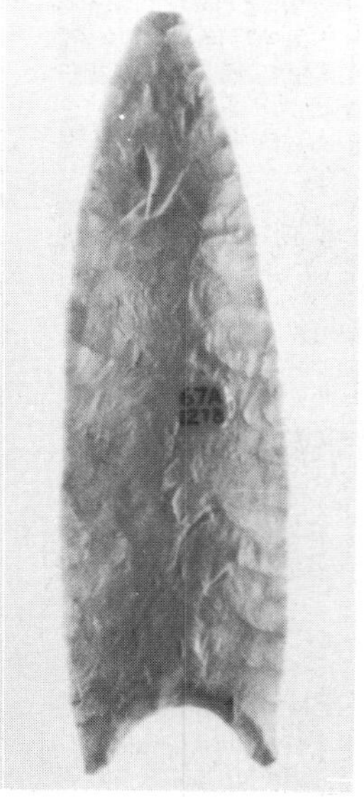

G8, $700-$1200
Limestone Co., AL. Quad site. Tip nick. Note steeply beveled base. No basal grinding.

G7, $250-$450
N. AL.

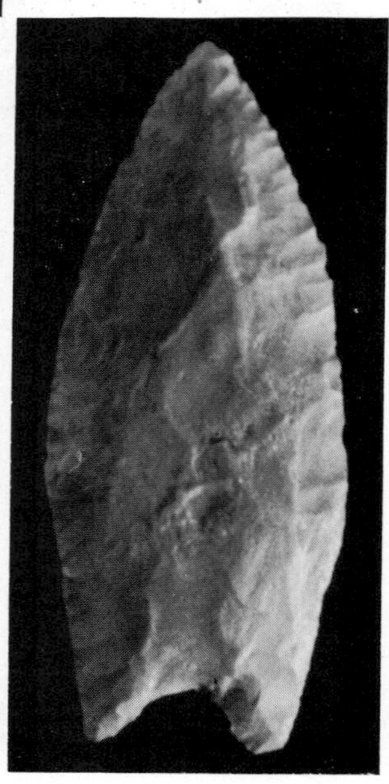

G7, $250-$500
SW KY.

WHEELER EXPANDED BASE - Transitional Paleo 10000 - 8000 B.P.

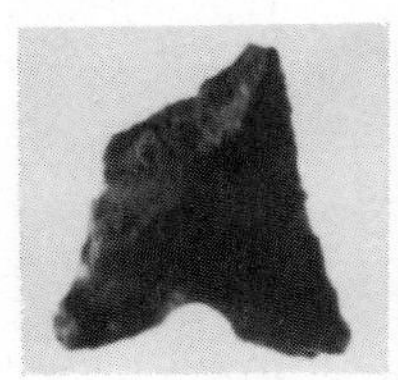
G1, $5-$10
Coffee Lake, AL.

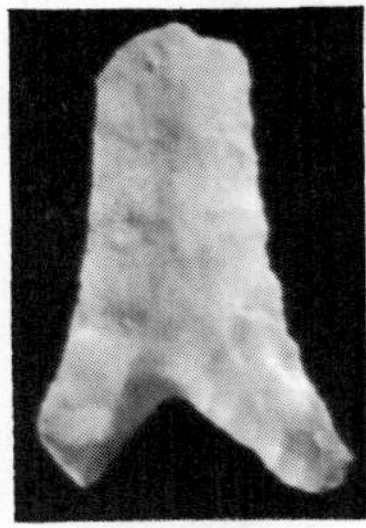
G1, $10-$20
Lincoln Co., TN.

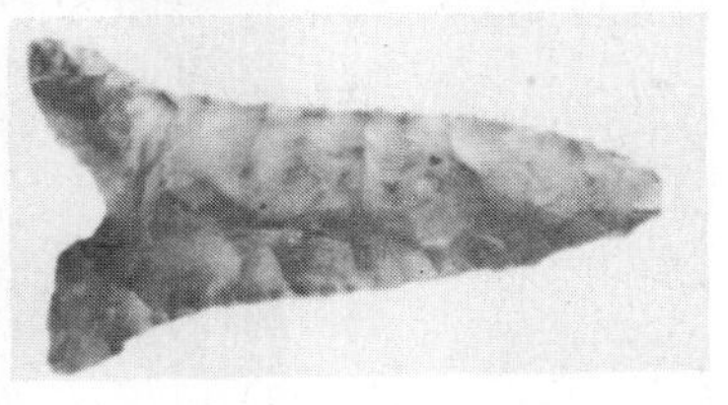
G5, $120-$250
Savannah, TN. Note collateral flaking. Minor tip nick. Rare.

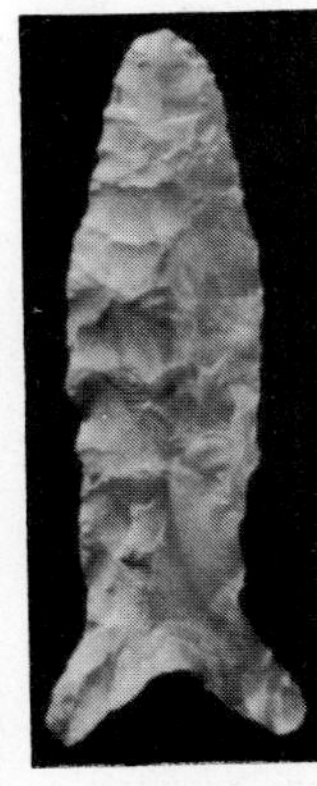
G3, $30-$70
W. TN. Buffalo Rv. chert.

G10, $4500-$8000
Hardin Co., TN. Patinated Dover chert. Very thin. Torque blade. Flaked to the center, both sides.

G2, $20-$40
Coffee Lake, AL. Broken.

LOCATION: Northwest Alabama and southern Tennessee. **DESCRIPTION:** A small to medium size, very narrow, thin, lanceolate point with expanding, squared ears forming a "Y" at the base which is "V" notched. Most examples have high quality collateral flaking. This very rare type has been found on *Wheeler* sites in the type area. Scarcity of this type suggests that it was not in use but for a short period of time. **I.D. KEY:** Notch and ears.

WHEELER RECURVATE - Transitional Paleo, 10000 - 8000 B.P.

(Also see Gower, Hanna & Patrick)

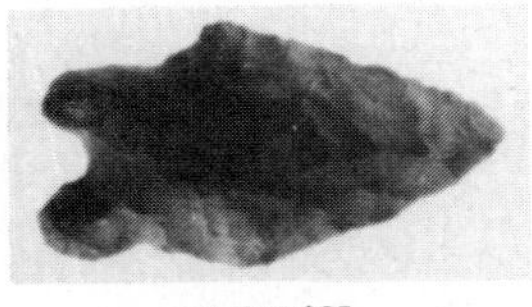
G3, $15-$25
SE TN.

G4, $20-$35
SE TN.

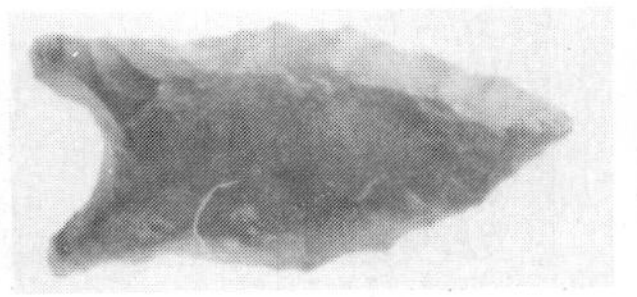
G6, $50-$80
SE TN.

LOCATION: Southeastern states. **DESCRIPTION:** A small to medium size, lanceolate point with recurved blade edges and a deep concave base that is steeply beveled. The blade edges taper towards the base, forming the hafting area. Basal grinding is absent. Rare examples are fluted.

WHEELER RECURVATE (continued)

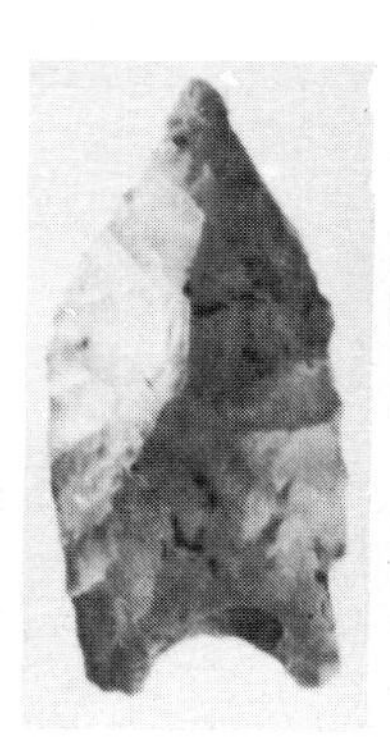

G5, $25-$40
Florence, AL.

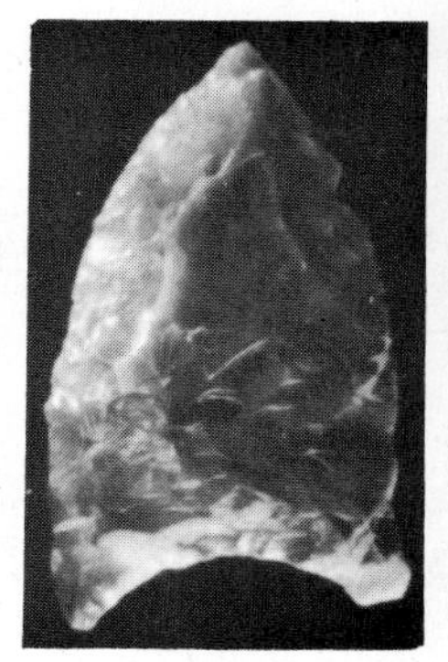

G6, $50-$80
Madison Co., AL.

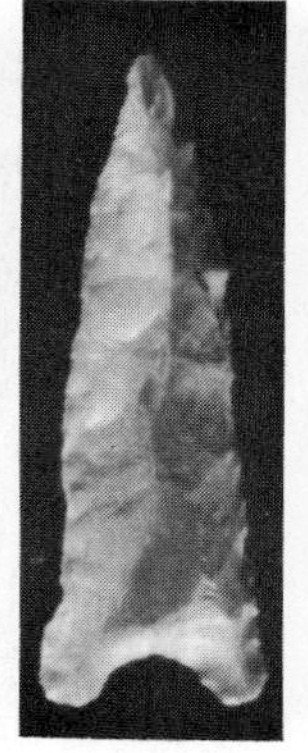

G5, $40-$60
Lawrence Co., AL.

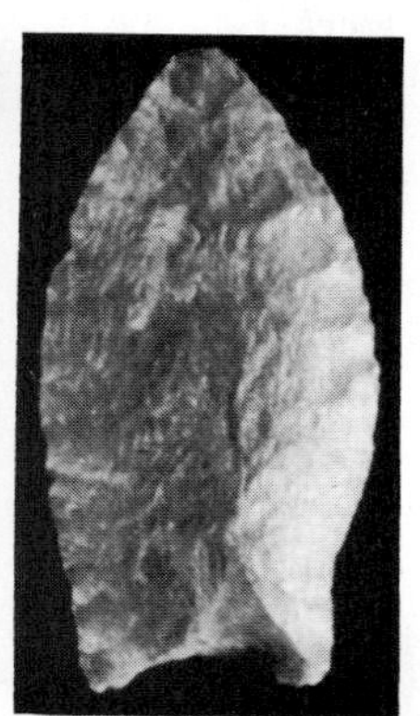

G7, $90-$150
W. TN.

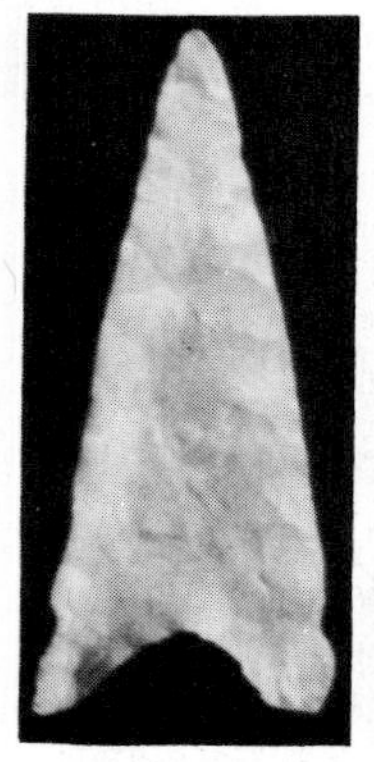

G5, $40-$60
Huntsville, AL.

G7, $90-$150
SE TN.

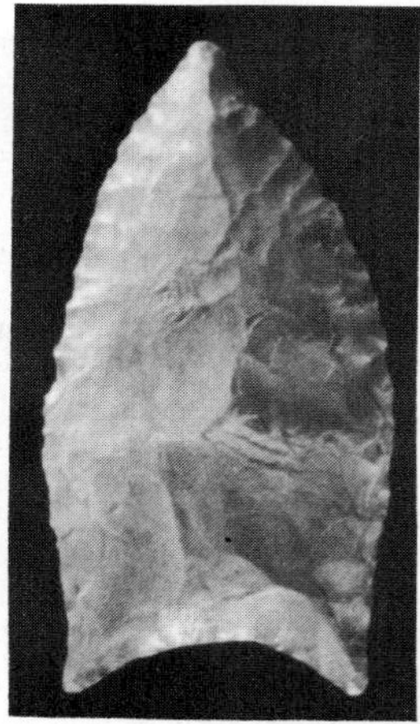

G7, $120-$200
Coffee Lake, AL.

G9, $500-$900
Trigg Co., KY. Classic.

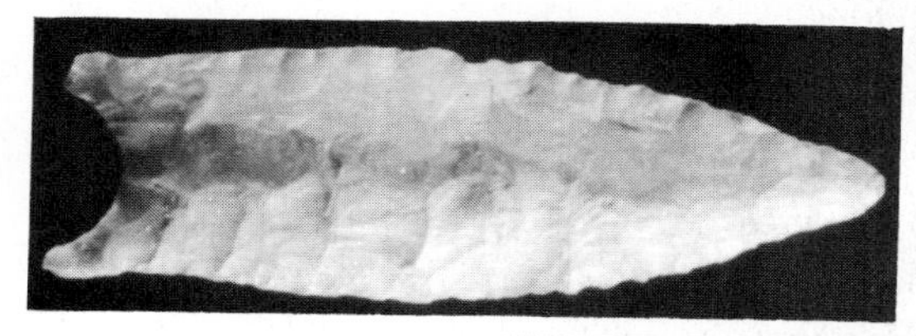

G8, $350-$700
Smith Co., TN. Classic.

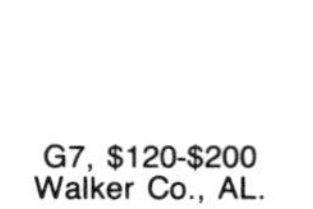

G7, $120-$200
Walker Co., AL.

WHEELER RECURVATE (continued)

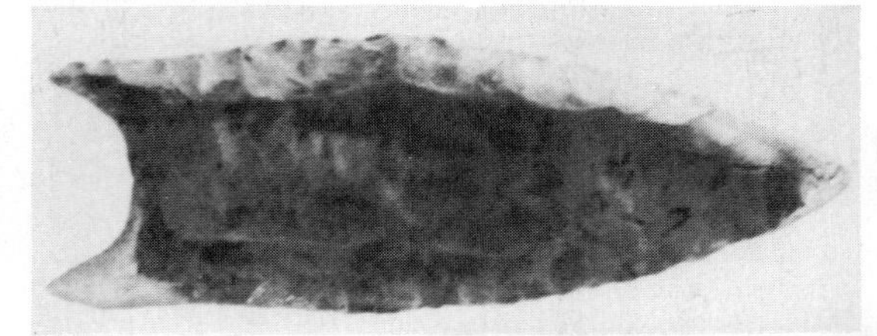

G5, $70-$120
Florence, AL. Tip & ear restored. Rare fluted form.

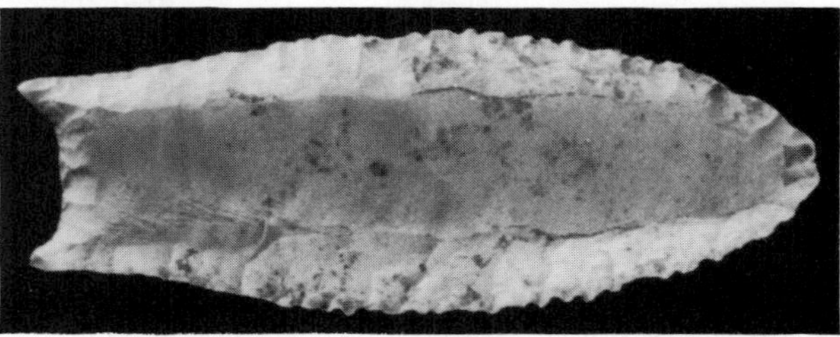

G9, $2500-$4000
Colbert Co., AL. Rare fluted and serrated form.

WHEELER TRIANGULAR - Transitional Paleo, 10000 - 8000 B.P.

G6, $90-$120
Colbert Co., AL.

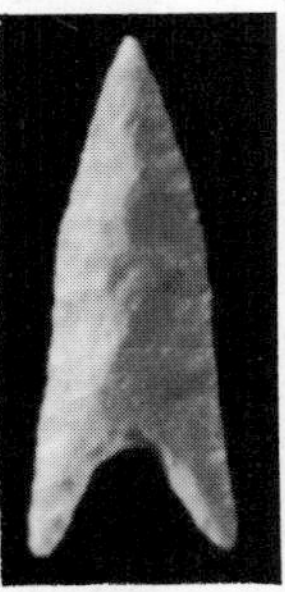

G8, $350-$600
Hardin Co., TN.

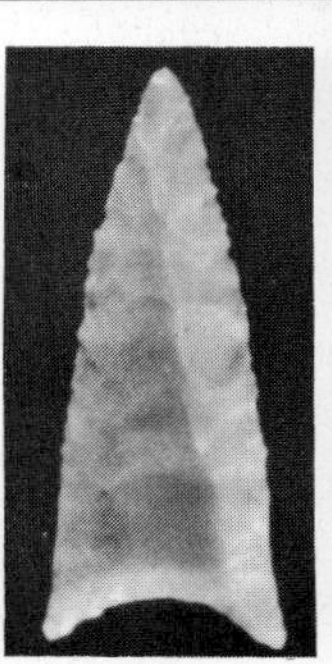

G7, $200-$300
Limestone Co., AL. Fluted.

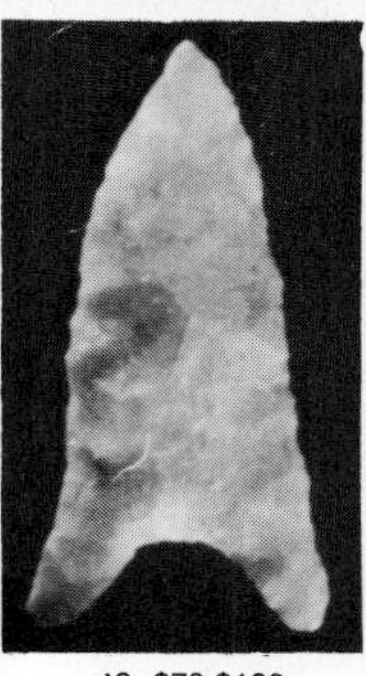

G6, $70-$100
Limestone Co., AL.

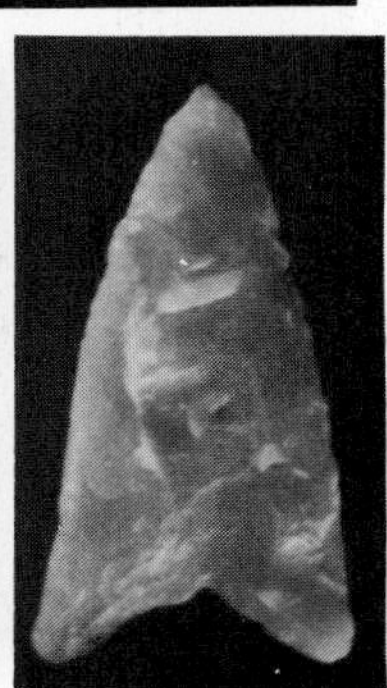

G5, $25-$40
Wilcox Co., AL.

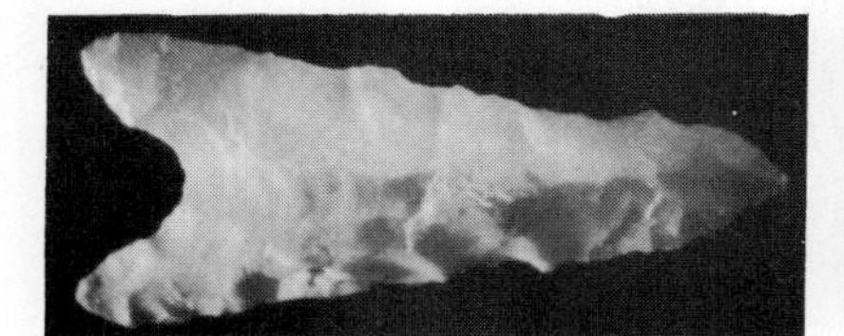

G5, $30-$50
Colbert Co., AL.

G7, $250-$400
Lawrence Co., AL.

LOCATION: Southeastern states. **DESCRIPTION:** A small to medium size, lanceolate point with straight sides and a deep concave base that is steeply beveled. On some examples, the ears point inward toward the base. This is a rare form and few examples exist. **I.D. KEY:** Beveled base and Paleo flaking.

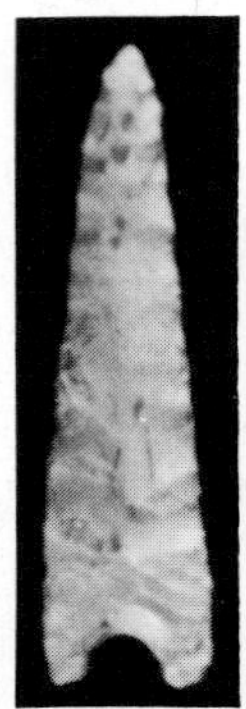

G8, $350-$600
Colbert Co., AL.

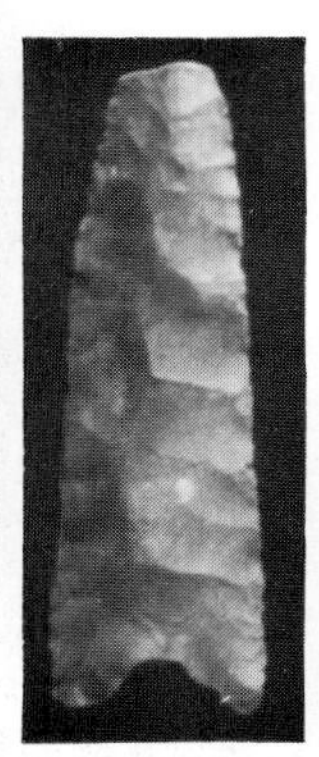

G3, $15-$25
Panola Co., MS.
Tip damage.

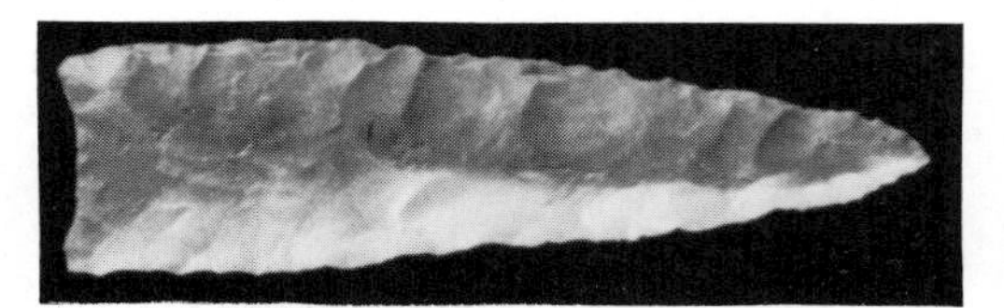

G6, $60-$90
Decatur, AL.

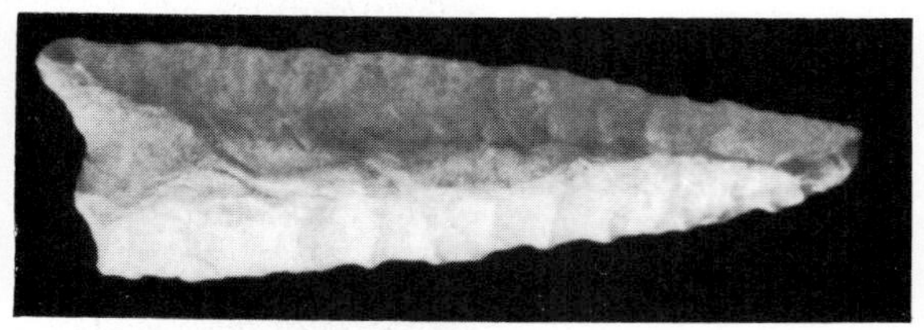

G2, $10-$20
Limestone Co., AL.
Tip & ear nick. Note collateral flaking to a median ridge.

G10, $4500-$8000
Limestone Co., AL. Quad site.
Outstanding and classic.

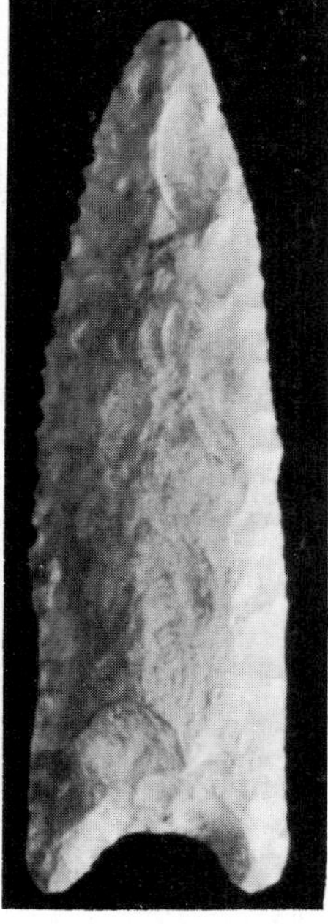

G8, $400-$600
SW KY.

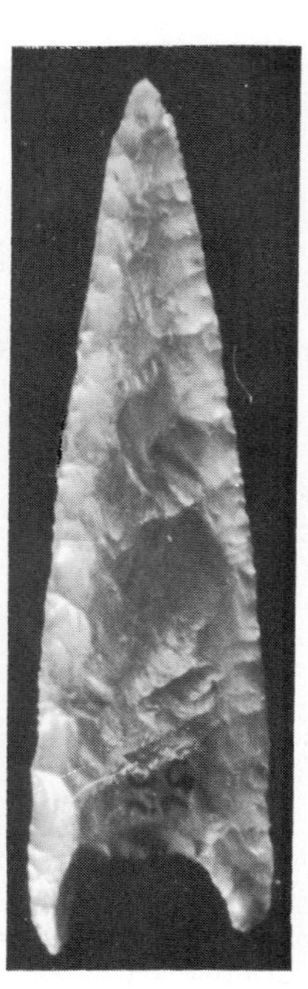

G7, $150-$250
Left: Actual point with tip missing and replaced with wax. Florence, AL. Deep red jasper. **Right:** Cast of point used in Alabama type book for this type.

WHITE SPRINGS - Early to mid-Archaic, 8000 - 6000 B.P.

(Also see Benton, Potts and Wacissa)

G3, $3-$5
N. AL. Vein quartz.

G6, $6-$10
Limestone Co., AL.

G8, $12-$20
Limestone Co., AL. Classic.

G7, $8-$12
Florence, AL.

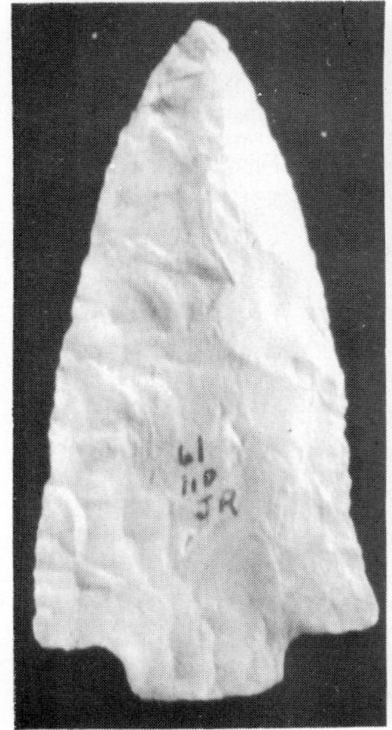

G8, $12-$20
Limestone Co., AL.

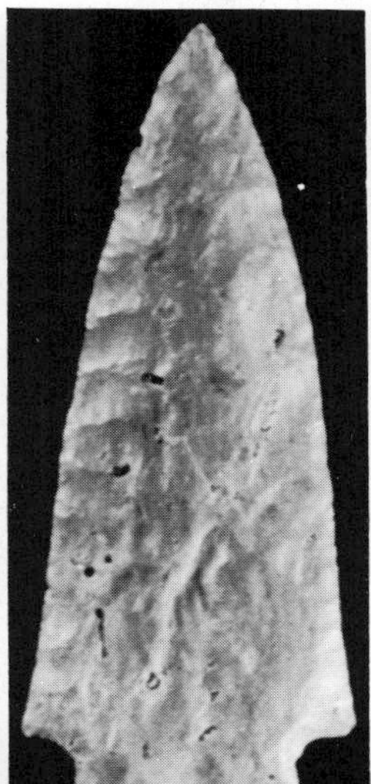

G10, $40-$70
Colbert Co., AL. Classic.

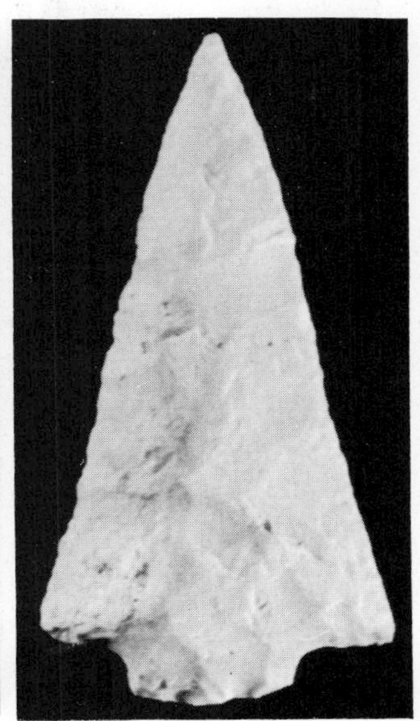

G9, $15-$25
Madison Co., AL.

LOCATION: Southeastern states. **DESCRIPTION:** A medium size, broad, triangular point with a medium to wide very short straight stem. Shoulders are usually square and the base is straight, slightly convex or concave. **I.D. KEY:** Short base and early flaking.

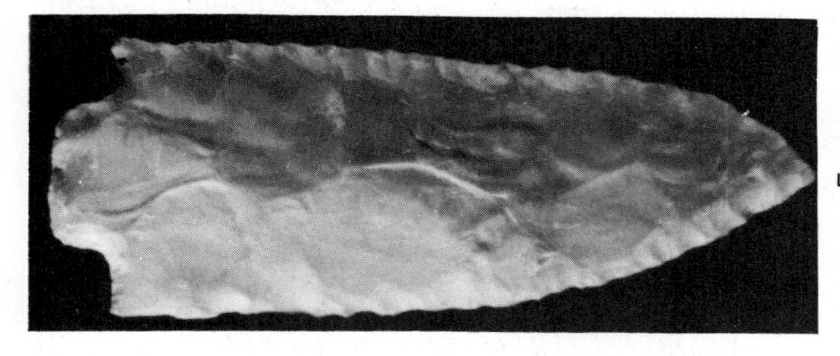

G9, $30-$50
Limestone Co., AL.

WILLIAMS - Mid-Archaic to Woodland, 6000 - 1000 B.P.

(Also see Beacon Island, Big Slough, Marcos and Palmillas)

G1, $1-$3
Comanche Co., TX.

G6, $10-$20
Comanche Co., TX.

G3, $2-$4
Comanche Co., TX.

G4, $4-$6
Austin, TX.

G8, $50-$80
Comanche Co., TX. Classic.

G5, $8-$15
Comanche Co., TX.

LOCATION: Midwestern states. **DESCRIPTION:** A medium to large size, barbed point with an expanded, rounded base. Some examples have tapered shoulders.

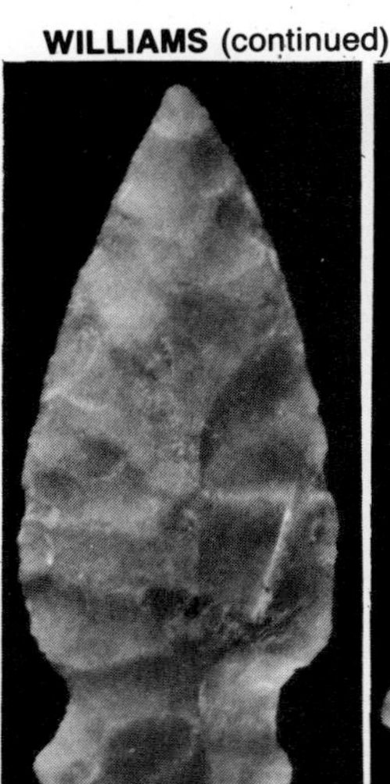

G6, $15-$25
Comanche Co., TX.

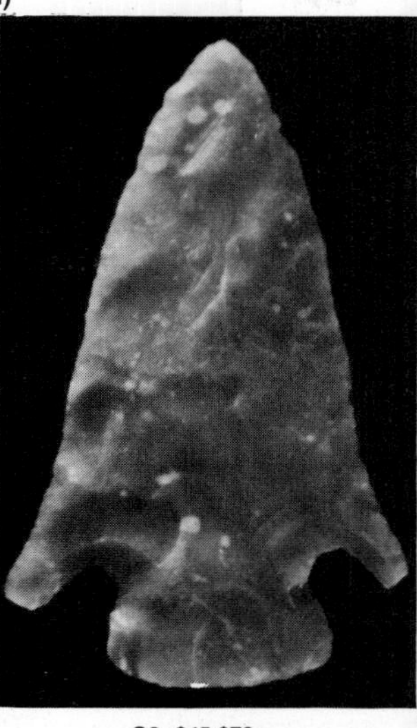

G8, $45-$70
Comanche Co., TX.

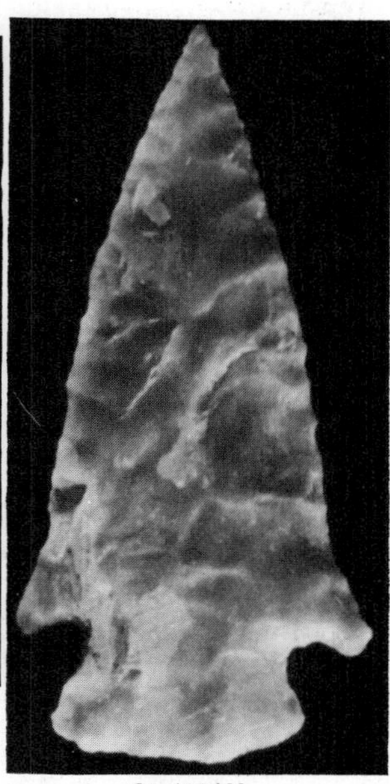

G9, $55-$80
Austin, TX.

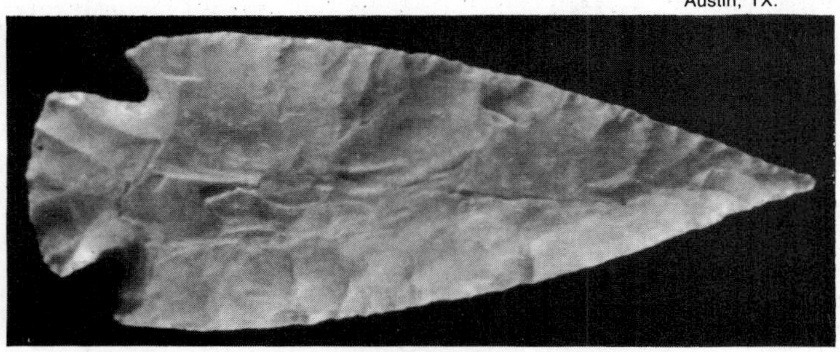

G10, $160-$300
Austin, TX. Thin and classic.

WILL'S COVE - Woodland, 3000 - 1000 B.P.

(Also see Wateree)

G3, $1-$3
York Co., SC. Slate.

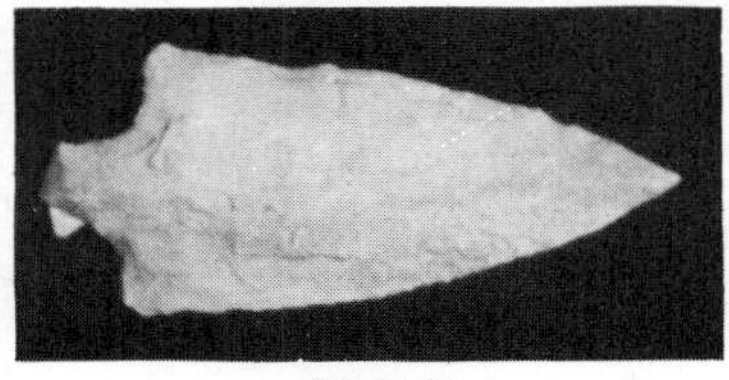

G2, $1-$2
Kershaw Co., SC. Slate.

LOCATION: Far Eastern states. **DESCRIPTION:** A medium size, very narrow point with tapered shoulders and a short, narrow stem with parallel sides, and a straight base.

WILL'S COVE (continued)

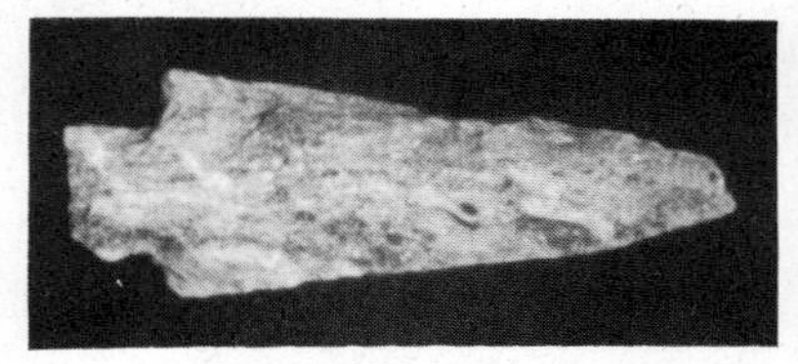

G1, .25-.50
Kershaw Co., SC. Slate.

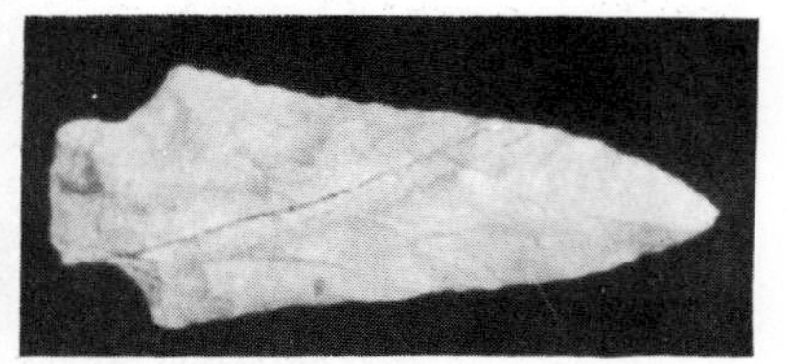

G7, $5-$8
Union Co., SC. Vein quartz.

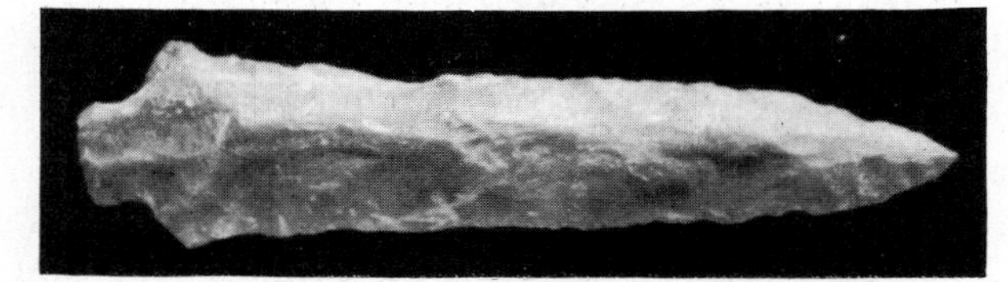

G6, $4-$6
Guilford Co., NC.

YADKIN - Woodland to Mississippian, 2500 - 500 B.P.

(Also see Camp Creek, Hamilton, Levanna, O'Leno and Nolichucky)

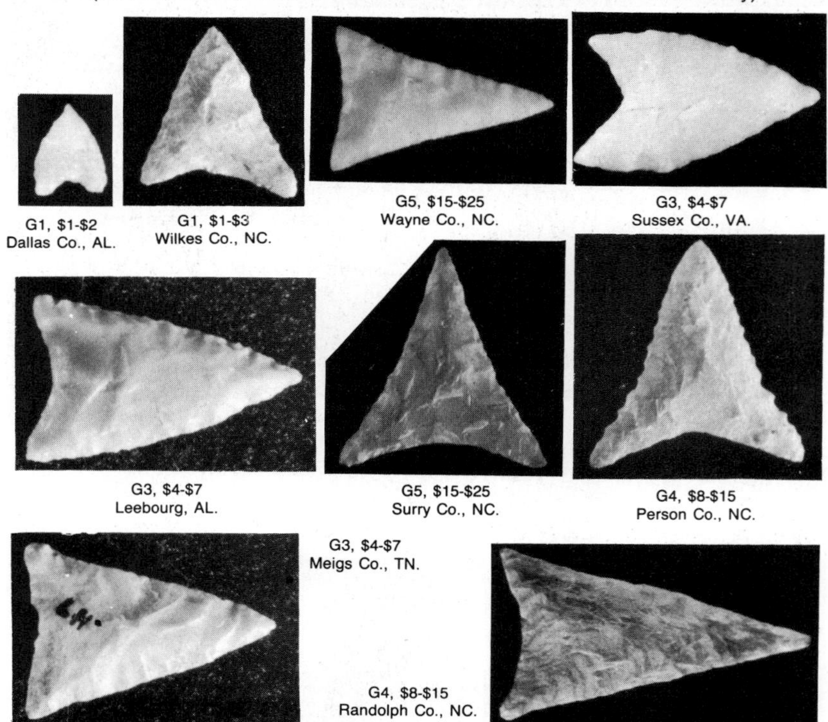

G1, $1-$2
Dallas Co., AL.

G1, $1-$3
Wilkes Co., NC.

G5, $15-$25
Wayne Co., NC.

G3, $4-$7
Sussex Co., VA.

G3, $4-$7
Leebourg, AL.

G5, $15-$25
Surry Co., NC.

G4, $8-$15
Person Co., NC.

G3, $4-$7
Meigs Co., TN.

G4, $8-$15
Randolph Co., NC.

LOCATION: Southeastern and Eastern states. Type site is Yadkin River in central North Carolina. **DESCRIPTION:** A small to medium size, broad based, fairly thick, triangular point with a broad, concave base and straight to convex to recurved side edges. Called *Levanna* in New York.

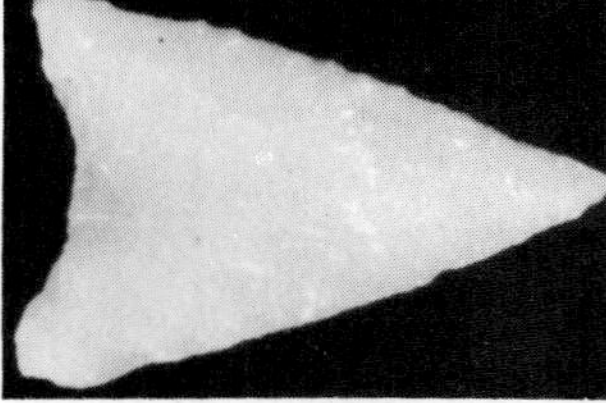

G4, $8-$15
Randolph Co., NC.

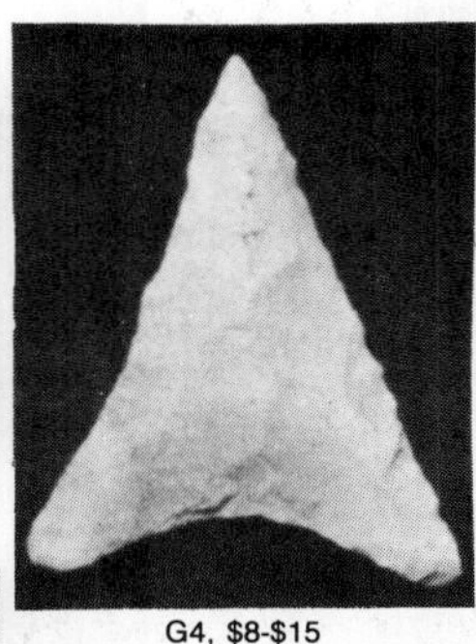

G4, $8-$15
Newberry Co., SC. Slate.

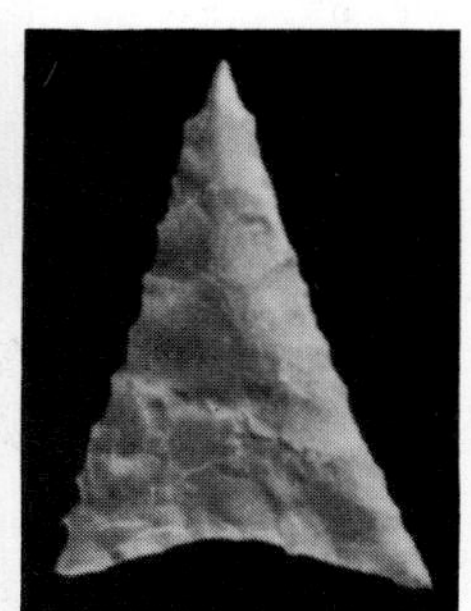

G7, $45-$90
Wayne Co., NC.
Donnaha tip.

G4, $8-$15
Moore Co., NC. Milky quartz.

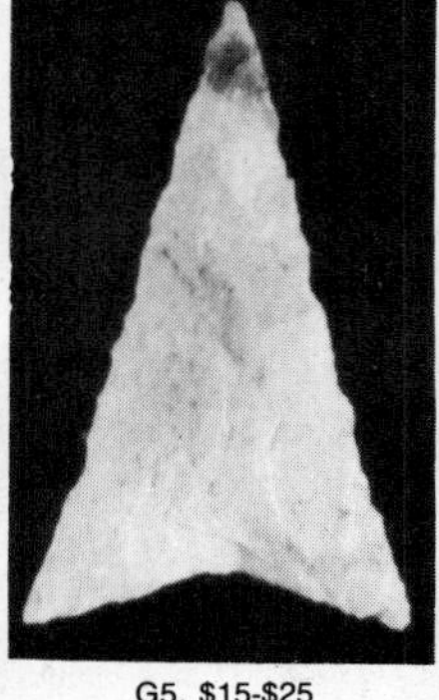

G5, $15-$25
Moore Co., NC.

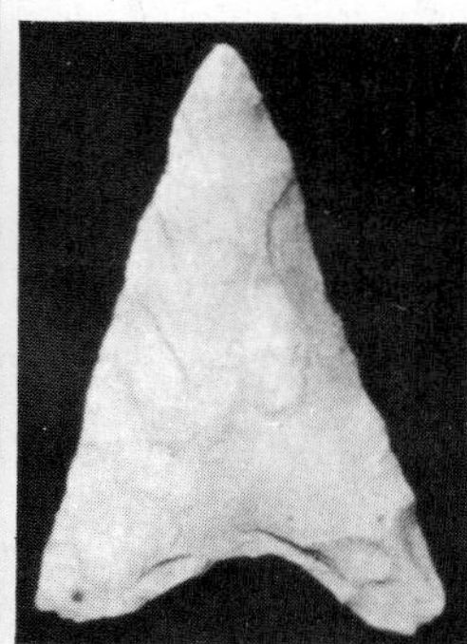

G3, $5-$8
Union Co., SC. Slate.

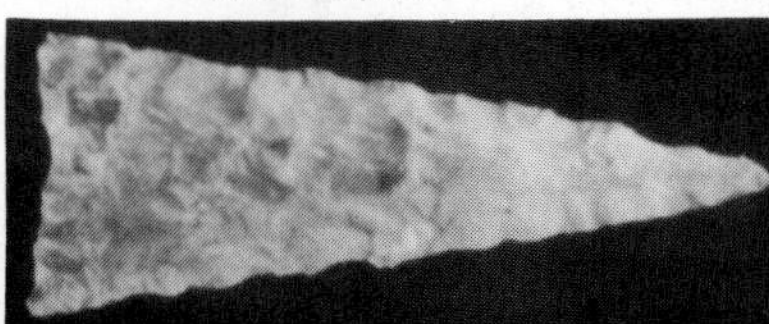

G4, $8-$15
Stokes Co., NC.

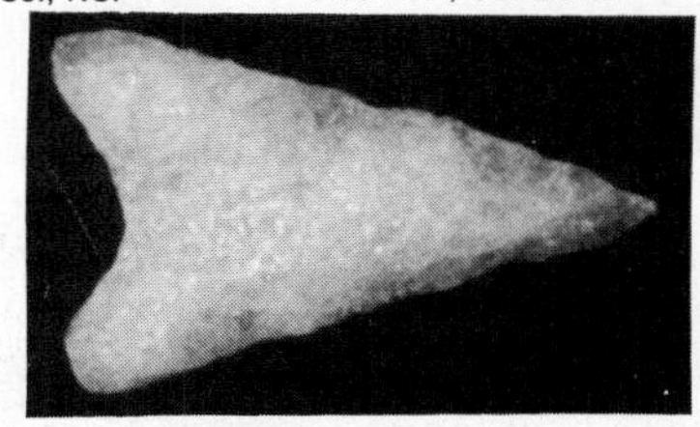

G4, $8-$15
Newberry Co., SC. Vein quartz.

G4, $8-$15
SC.

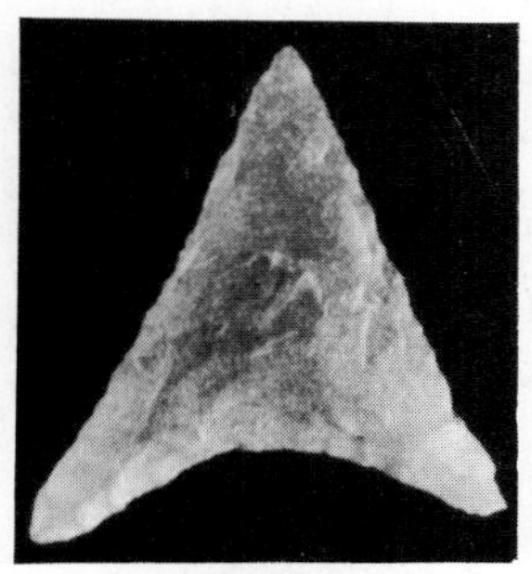

G5, $15-$25
Danville Co., VA.

G5, $20-$30
Randolph Co., NC.

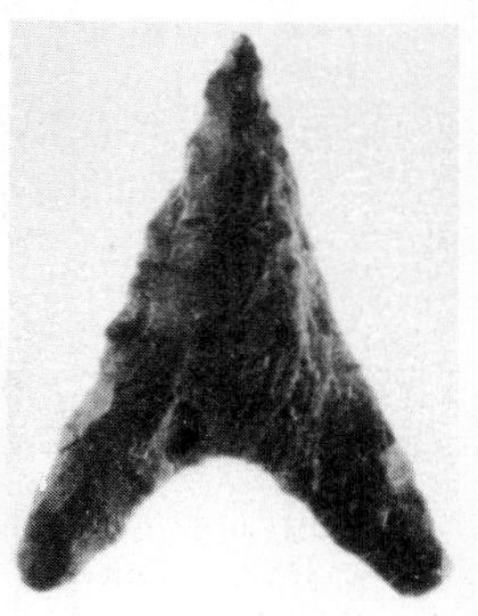

G5, $15-$25
Randolph Co., NC.

G7, $35-$60
Iredell Co., NC. Milky quartz.

G5, $15-$25
Wayne Co., NC.

G6, $25-$40
Stokes Co., NC.

G7, $35-$60
Wake Co., NC.

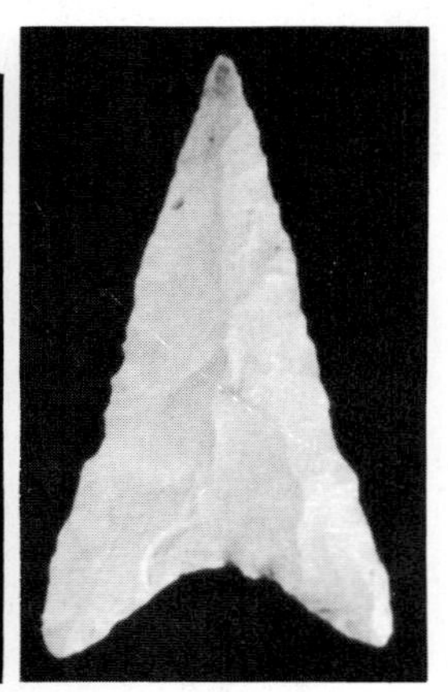

G6, $25-$40
Stokes Co., NC.

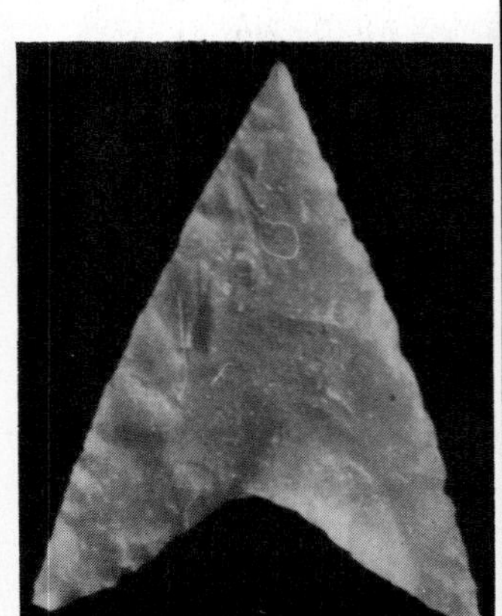

G7, $35-$60
Allendale Co., SC.

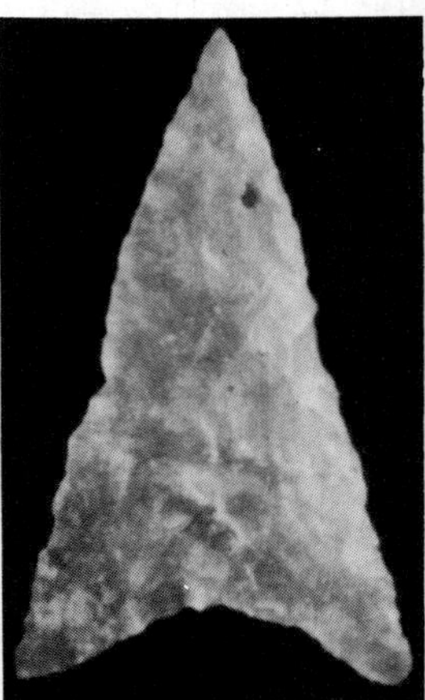

G6, $25-$40
Lee Co., GA.

G7, $35-$60
Wake Co., NC.

G8, $50-$80
Montgomery Co., NC.

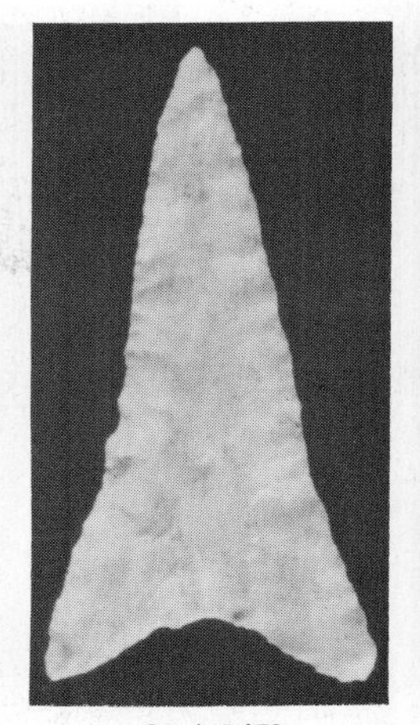

G7, $45-$70
Allendale Co., SC.

G6, $25-$40
Rockingham Co., NC.

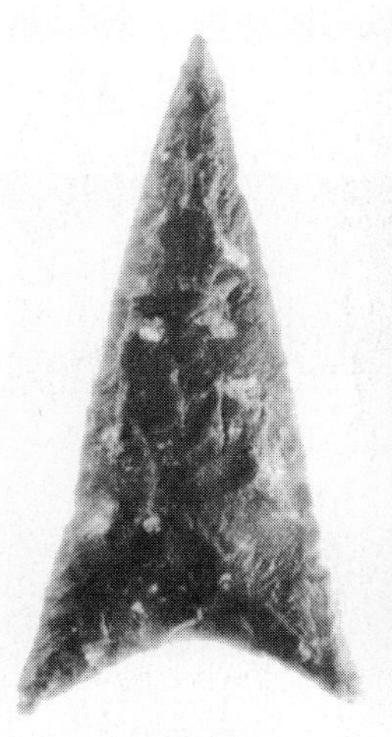

G9, $80-$120
Montgomery Co., NC.
Yadkin River. Rhyolite.

G8, $60-$100
Central NC.

G9, $120-$200
Montgomery Co., NC. Classic.

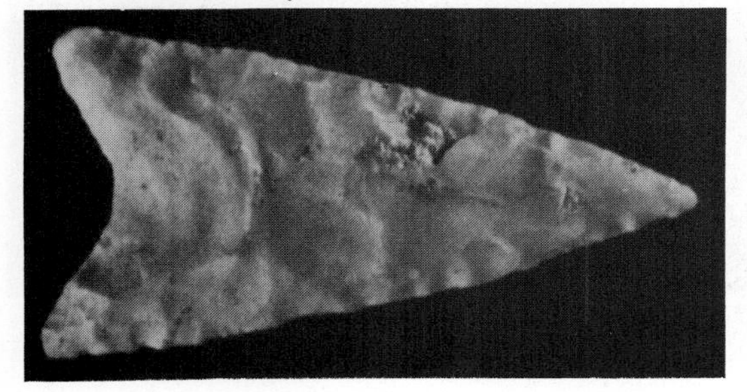

G8, $70-$120
SC.

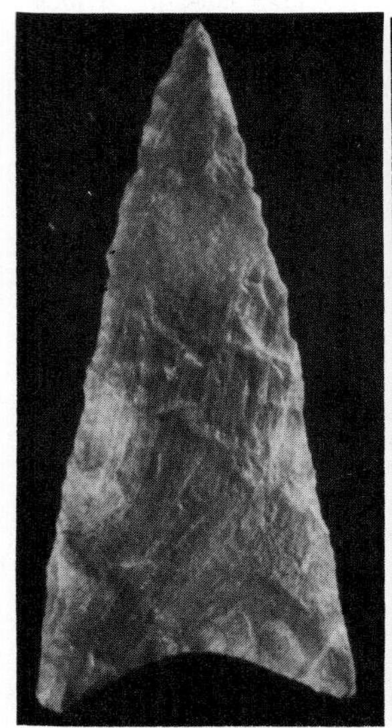

G9, $90-$160
SC.

G8, $60-$100
SC.

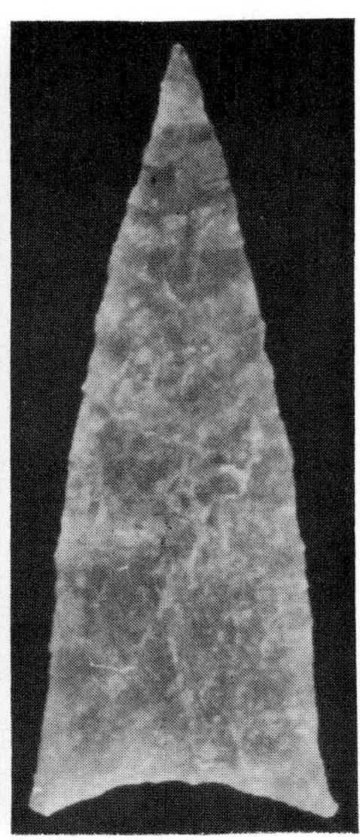

G9, $120-$200
Allendale Co., SC.

G9, $90-$150
Randolph Co., NC.

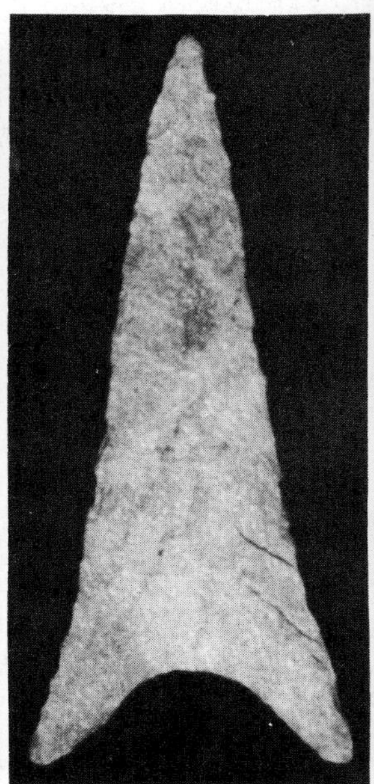

G9, $90-$150
Fairfield Co., SC. Slate.

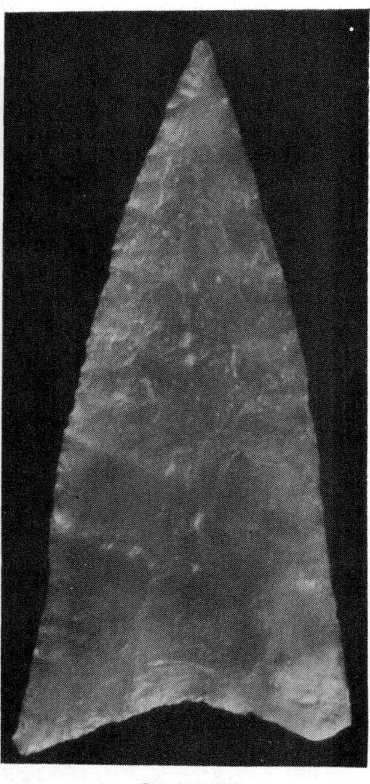

G7, $40-$75
Allendale Co., SC.

G10, $350-$700
Allendale Co., SC.

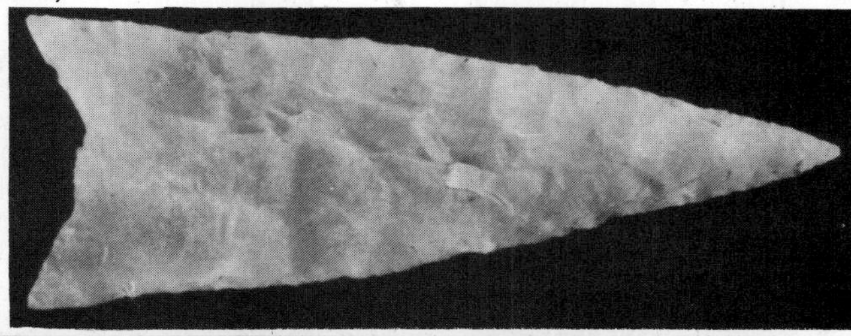

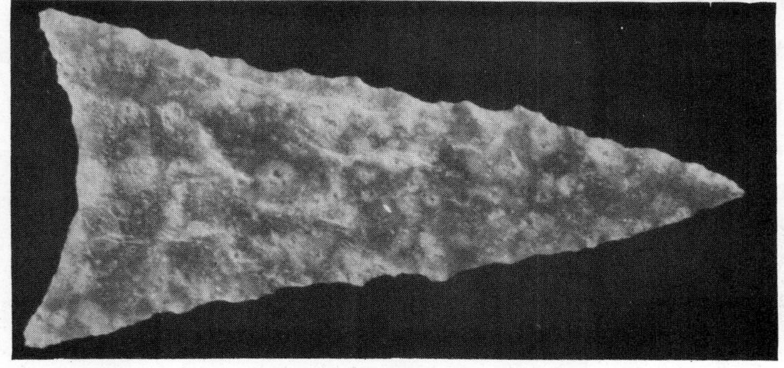

G10, $350-$600
Charleston, SC. Cooper River.

YADKIN-EARED - Woodland to Mississippian, 2500 - 500 B.P.

(Also see Candy Creek, Hardaway, Nolichucky, Potts and Waratan)

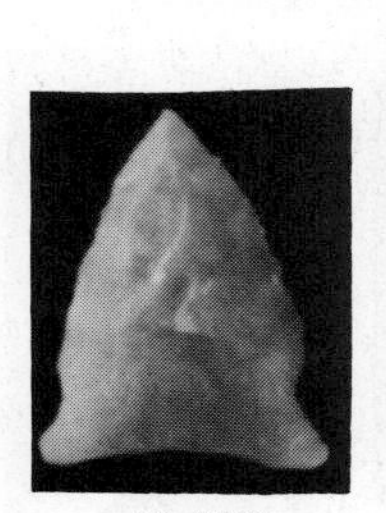

G3, $4-$6
Greene Co., NC.

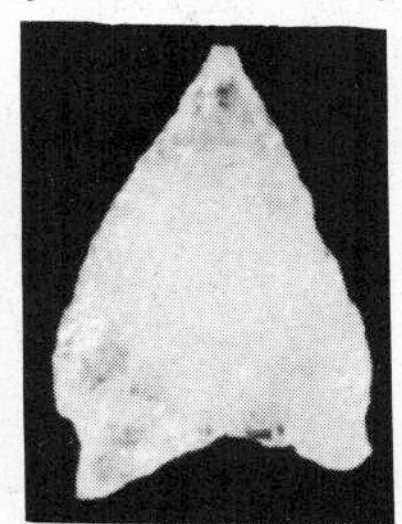

G1, $2-$3
Chatham Co., NC.
Milky quart.

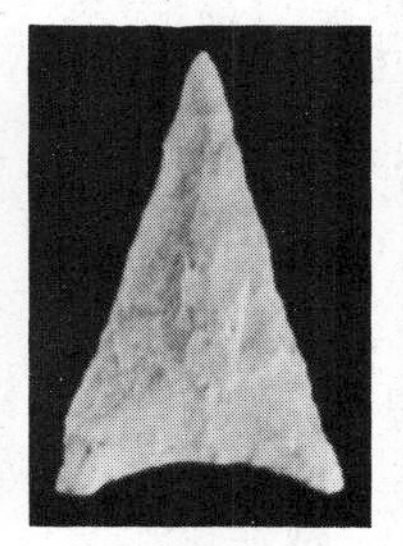

G2, $2-$4
Stokes Co., NC.

G3, $4-$6
Montgomery Co., NC.

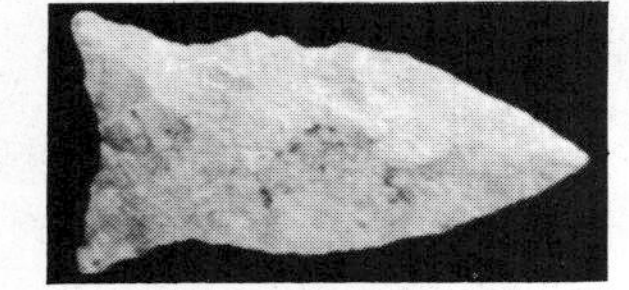

G3, $4-$6, Montgomery Co., NC.

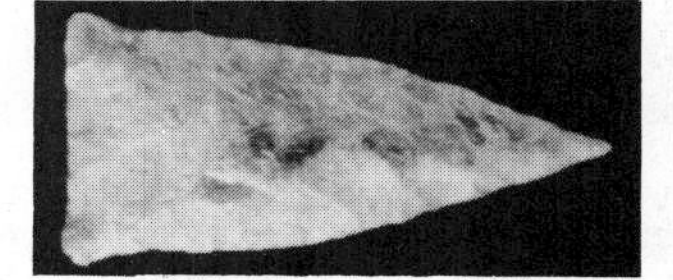

G3, $4-$6. Surry Co., NC.

LOCATION: Far Eastern states, esp. North Carolina. **DESCRIPTION:** A small to medium size triangular, auriculate point with a concave base. The ears are produced by a shallow constriction or notching near the base. The notches are steeply beveled on one edge of each face on some examples.

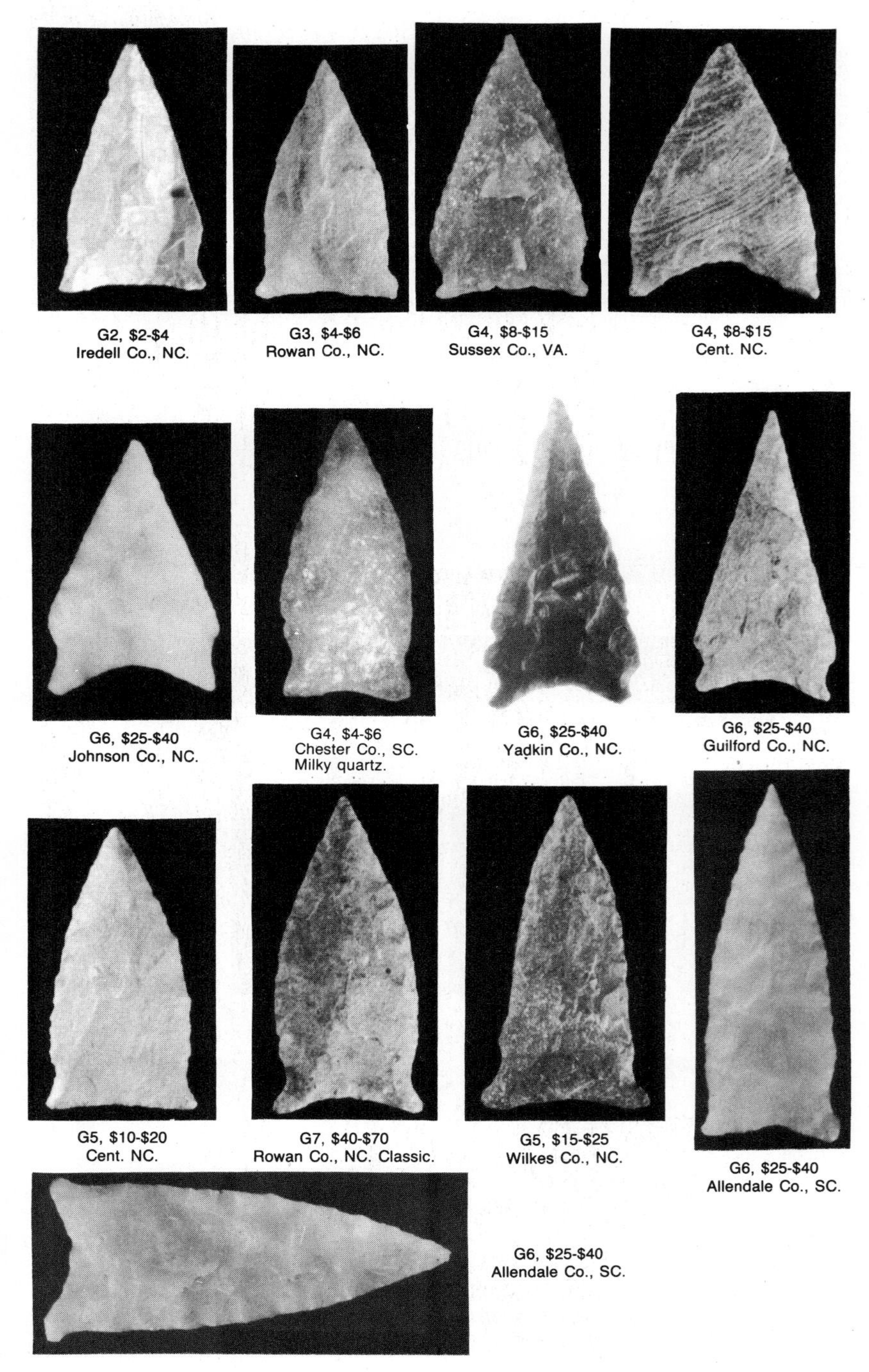

G2, $2-$4
Iredell Co., NC.

G3, $4-$6
Rowan Co., NC.

G4, $8-$15
Sussex Co., VA.

G4, $8-$15
Cent. NC.

G6, $25-$40
Johnson Co., NC.

G4, $4-$6
Chester Co., SC.
Milky quartz.

G6, $25-$40
Yadkin Co., NC.

G6, $25-$40
Guilford Co., NC.

G5, $10-$20
Cent. NC.

G7, $40-$70
Rowan Co., NC. Classic.

G5, $15-$25
Wilkes Co., NC.

G6, $25-$40
Allendale Co., SC.

G6, $25-$40
Allendale Co., SC.

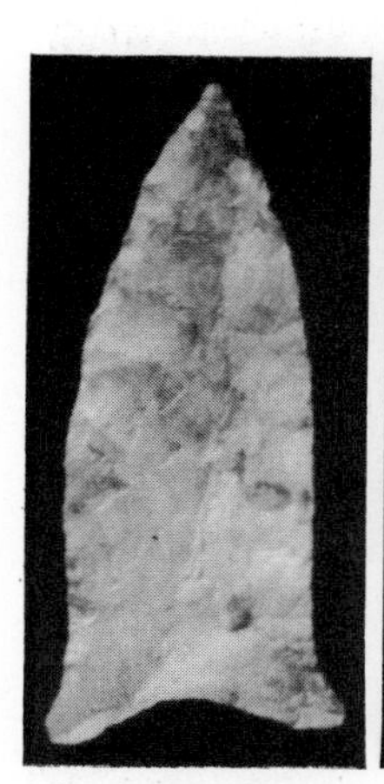

G6, $25-$45
Allendale Co., SC.

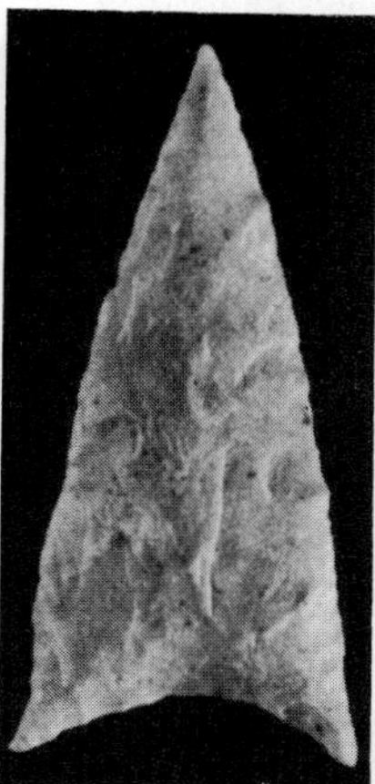

G10, $120-$250
Iredell Co., NC.

G6, $25-$45
Sussex Co., VA.

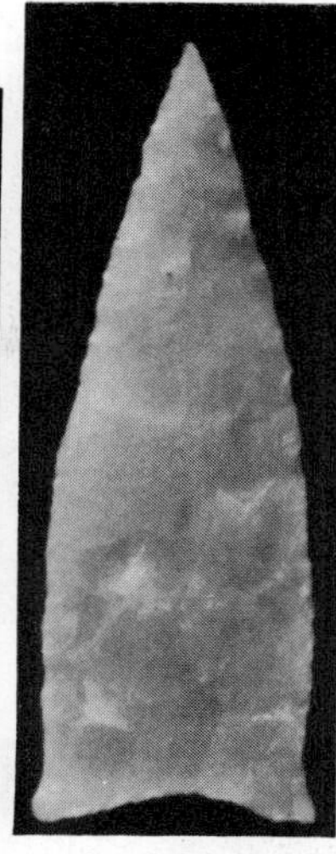

G10, $180-$300
Allendale Co., SC.

G7, $40-$70
Stokes Co., NC.

G5, $15-$25
Yadkin Co., NC.
Blade nicks.

G9, $90-$150
Montgomery Co., NC.

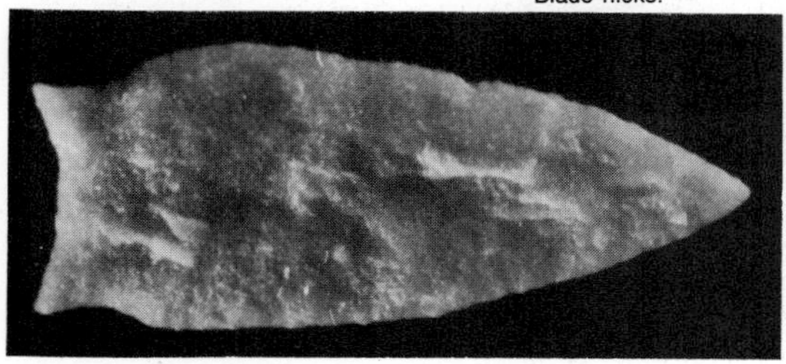

G9, $90-$150
Cent. NC.

YARBROUGH - Woodland, 2500 - 1000 B.P.

(Also see Darl, Hoxie, Kent, Lange, Travis and Zorra)

G2, $1-$2
Waco, TX.

G4, $2-$4
Comanche Co., TX.

G5, $3-$5
Comanche Co., TX.

G4, $2-$4
Comanche Co., TX.

G3, $2-$3
Waco, TX.

G3, $1-$3
Waco, TX.

G6, $6-$10
N. AL. Classic.

G9, $30-$50
Comanche Co., TX.

G8, $20-$30
Bell Co., TX.

G5, $5-$8
Comanche Co., TX.

LOCATION: Midwestern states. **DESCRIPTION:** A medium size, narrow point with a long rectangular stem that has slightly concave sides. The shoulders are very weak and tapered. The stem edges are usually ground.

YARBROUGH (continued)

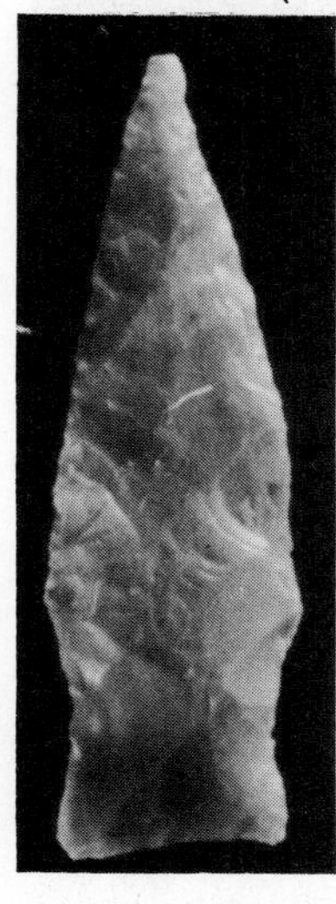

G5, $4-$6
Bell Co., TX.

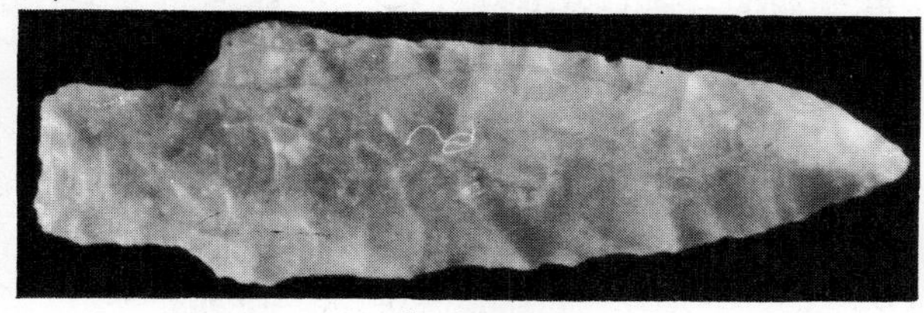

G7, $10-$20
Comanche Co., TX.

G6, $6-$10
Bell Co., TX.

YAVAPAI STEMMED - Mid to late Archaic, 5000 - 3000 B.P.

(Also see Pedro and Ventana-Amargosa)

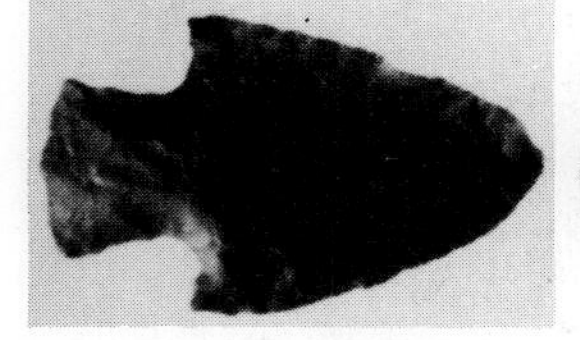

G7, $4-$7
Yavapai Co., AZ.

G5, $2-$4
Yavapai Co., AZ.

G3, $1-$2
Yavapai Co., AZ.

LOCATION: Southwestern states. **DESCRIPTION:** A small to medium size point with horizontal to tapered shoulders and a horizontal to expanding stem.

YOUNG - Mississippian, 1000 - 400 B.P.

(Also see Ebenezer, Catan, Montgomery, Morrow Mountain and Tampa)

G1, .10-.25
Waco, TX.

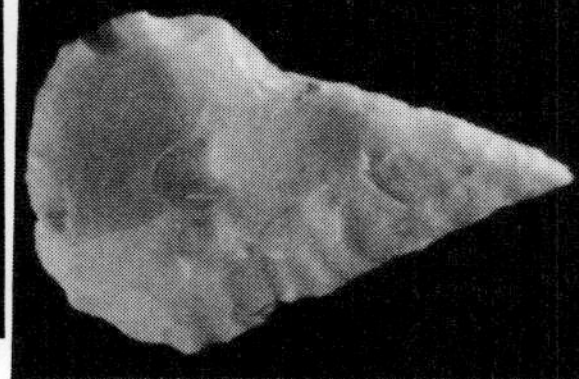

G5, $1-$2
Comanche Co., TX.

G3, .50-$1
Comanche Co., TX.

LOCATION: Midwestern states. **DESCRIPTION:** A small size, crudely chipped, elliptical shaped, usually round base point made from a flake. One side is usually uniface.

ZORRA - Mid-Archaic, 6000 - 4000 B.P.

(Also see Darl, Lange, Nolan and Travis)

G9, $90-$150
Austin, TX.

G6, $15-$25
Austin, TX. Georgetown flint.

G8, $50-$90
Austin, TX. Classic form.

G7, $35-$50
Austin, TX.

G10, $280-$500
Austin, TX. Excellent quality.

LOCATION: Midwestern states. **DESCRIPTION:** A medium to large size point with tapered shoulders and a stem that is usually flat on one face and beveled on both sides of the opposite face. Otherwise identical to *Nolan*. Most have needle tips and good quality flaking.

BIBLIOGRAPHY

Alabama Projectile Point Types, by A.B. Hooper, III. Albertville, AL, 1964.

Album of Prehistoric Man, by Tom McGowen, Illustrated by Rod Ruth, Rand McNally and Co., Chicago-New York-San Francisco, 1975.

American Indian Almanac, by John Upton Terrell, Thomas Y. Crowell Co., New York, NY, 1974.

American Indian Point Types of North Florida, South Alabama and South Georgia, by Son Anderson, 1987.

American Indian Ways of Life, by Thorne Deuel, Illinois State Museum, Springfield, IL, 1968.

Americans Before Columbus, by Elizabeth Chesley Baity, The Viking Press, New York, NY, 1951.

America's Beginnings—The Wild Shores, by Loften Snell, National Geographic Society, Washington, D.C., 1974.

America's Fascinating Indian Heritage, The Readers Digest Association, Inc., Pleasantville, NY, 1978.

Americans in Search of their Prehistoric Past, by Stuart Struever and Felicia Antonelli, Holter Anchor Press, Doubleday New York, 1979.

The Arkansas Archeologist, Bulletin, Vol. 19, Univ. of Arkansas, Fayetteville, Ark, 1978.

The Ancient Civilizations of Peru, by J. Alden Mason, Penguin Books Ltd., Middlesex, England, 1968.

The Ancient Kingdoms of the Nile, by Walter A. Fairservis, Jr., N.A.L. Mentor Books, The North American Library, Thomas Y. Crowell Co., New York, N.Y., 1962.

Ancient Native Americans, by Jesse D. Jennings, editor, W.H. Freeman & Co., San Francisco, CA, 1978.

Antiquities of Tennessee, by Gates P. Thurston, The Robert Clarke Co., Cincinnati, OH, 1964.

An Archaeological Survey and Docementary History of the Shattuck Farm, Andover, Mass, (Catherine G. Shattuck Memorial Trust), Mass. Historical Commission, March, 1981.

Archaeology, by Dr. Francis Celoria, Bantam Books, New York, N.Y. 1974.

Archaeology-Middle America (A science program) - U.S.A., Nelson Doubleday, Inc., 1971.

The Archaeology of Essex County, by Gwenn Wells, Essex Life, Summer, 1983.

Arrowheads and Projectile Points, by Lar Hothem, Collector Books, Paducah, KY, 1983.

Arrowhead Collectors Handbook, produced by John L. Sydman, Charles Dodds (author), Danville, Iowa, 1963.

Artifacts of North America (Indian and Eskimo), by Charles Miles, Bonanza Books, Crown Publ., Inc., New York, NY, 1968.

Beginners Guide to Archaeology, by Louis A. Brennan, Dell Publishing Co., Inc., New York, NY, 1973.

The Bog People (Iron-Age Man Preserved), by P.V. Glob, Faber and Faber, London, 1965.

The Book of Indians, by Holling C. Holling, Platt and Munk Co., Inc., New York, NY, 1935.

The Chattanooga News-Free Press, Thursday, Nov. 14, 1989, page B5, U.P.I. dateline, Los Angeles, CA article by James Ryan.

Cherokee Indian Removal From the Lower Hiwassee Valley, by Robert C. White, A Resource Intern Report, 1973.

The Cherokees, Past and Present, by J. Ed Sharpe, Cherokee Publications, Cherokee, NC, 1970.

The Columbia Encyclopedia Edition, Clarke F. Ansley, Columbia University Press, New York, NY, 1938.

The Corner-Tang Flint Artifacts of Texas, University of Texas, Bulletin No. 3618, Anthropological Papers, Vol. 1, No. 3618, 1936.

Cro-Magnon Man, Emergence of Man Series, by Tom Prideaux, Time-Life Books, New York, N.Y., 1973.

The Crystal Skull, by Richard Garvin, Pocket Books-Simon & Schuster, Inc., New York, N.Y., 1974.

Cypress Creek Villages, by William S. Webb and G. Haag, University of Kentucky, Lexington, KY, 1940.

Death on the Prairie, by Paul I. Wellman, Pyramid Books, Pyramid Publications, Doubleday and Co., Inc., New York, 1947.

Digging Into History, by Paul S. Martin, Chicago National History Museum, Chicago, IL, 1963.

Duck River Cache, by Charles K. Peacock, published by T.B. Graham, Chattanooga, TN, 1954.

Early Man, by F. Clark Howell, Time-Life Books, New York, N.Y., 1965.

Early Man East of the Mississippi, by Olaf H. Prufer, Cleveland Museum of Natural History, Cleveland, Ohio, 1960.

Etowah Papers, by Warren K. Moorehead, Phillips Academy, Yale University Press, New Haven, CT, 1932.

Eva-An Archaic Site, by T.M.N. Lewis and Madelin Kneberg Lewis, University of Tennessee Press, Knoxville, TN, 1961.

Field Guide to Point Types of the State of Florida, by Son Anderson and Doug Puckett, 1984.

Field Guide To Point Types (The Tennessee River Basin), by Doug Puckett, Custom Productions (printer), Savannah, TN, 1987.

A Field Guide to Southeastern Point Types, by James W. Cambron, Decatur, AL.

A Field Guide to Stone Artifacts of Texas Indians, by Sue Turner and Thomas R. Hester, 1985, Texas Monthly Press.

Field Identification of Stone Artifacts of the Carolinas, by Russell Peithman and Otto Haas, The Identifacs Co., 1978.

The First Americans (Emergence of Man), by Robert Claiborne, Time-Life Books, New York, N.Y., 1973.

Flint Blades and Projectile Points of the North American Indian, by Lawrence N. Tully, Collector Books, Paducah, KY, 1986.

Flint Type Bulletin, by Lynn Mungen, curator, Potawatomi Museum, Angola, IN, 1958.

Flint Types of the Continental United States, by D.C. Waldorf and Valerie Waldorf, 1976.

Fluted Points in Lycoming County, Penn., by Gary L. Fogelman and Richard P. Johnston, Fogelman Publ. Co., Turbotville, Pennsylvania.

The Formative Cultures of the Carolina Piedmont, by Joffre Lanning Coe, New Series—Vol. 54, part 5, The American Philosophical Society, 1964.

Fossil Man, by Michael H. Day, Bantam Books, Grosset & Dunlap, Inc., New York, NY, 1971.

Frontiers in the Soil, (Archaeology of Georgia), by Roy S. Dickens and James L. McKinley. Frontiers Publ. Co., Atlanta, Ga, 1979.

Geological Survey of Alabama, Walter B. Jones, Geologist, University of Alabama, 1948.

The Great Histories-The Conquest of Mexico, The Conquest of Peru, Prescott, edited by Roger Howell, Washington Square Press, Inc., New York, N.Y., 1966.

Guide to the Identification of Certain American Indian Projectile Points, by Robert E. Bell, Oklahoma Anthropological Society, Norman, OK, 1958, 1960, 1968.

A Guide To The Identification Of Florida Projectile Points, by Ripley P. Bullen, Kendall Books, 1975.

A Guide to the Identification of Virginia Projectile Points, by Wm Jack Hranicky and Floyd Painter, Special Publ. No. 17, Archaeological Society of Virginia, 1989.

Handbook of Alabama Archaeology, by Cambron and Hulse, edited by David L. DeJarnette, University of Alabama, 1986.

A Handbook of Indian Artifacts from Southern New England, drawings by William S. Fowler, Mass. Archaeological Society.

A History of American Archaeology, by Gorgen R. Willey and J.A. Sabloff, Thomas and Hudson, Great Britain, 1974.

Hiwassee Island, by T.M.N. Lewis and Madeline Kneberg, University of Tenn. Press, Knoxville, TN, 1946.

In Search of the Maya, by Robert L. Brunhouse, Ballentine Books-Random House, Inc., New York, NY, 1974.

The Incredible Incas, by Loren McIntyre, National Geographic Society, Washington, D.C., 1980.

Indian Aratifacts, by Virgil Y. Russell & Mrs. Russell, Johnson Publ. Co., Boulder, CO, 1962.

Indian Relics and Their Story, by Hugh C. Rogers, Yoes Printing and Lithographing Co., Fort Smith, AR, 1966.

Indian Relics and Their Values, by Allen Brown, Lightner Publishing Co., Chicago, IL, 1942.

Indian Relics Price Guide, by Lynn Munger, published by Potawatomi Museum, Angola, IN, 1961.

Indiana Archaeological Society Yearbook, The Indiana Archaeological Society, 1975-1986.

Indianology, by John Baldwin, Messenger Printing Co., St. Louis, Mo, 1974.

Indians and Artifacts in the Southeast, by Bert W. Bierer, published by the author, State Printing Co., Columbia, SC, 1979.

Indians of the Plains, by Harry L. Shapino, McGraw-Hill Book Co., Inc., New York, NY, 1963.

An Introduction to American Archaeology (Middle & North America), by Gordon R. Willey, Printice-Hall, Inc., Englewood Cliffs, NJ, 1966.

Ishi-In Two Worlds (The Last Wild Indian in North America), by Theodora Kroeber, Univ. of Calif. Press, Berkeley & Los Angeles, 1965.

Journal of Alabama Archaeology, David L. DeJarnette, editor, University of Alabama, 1967.

Man's Rise to Civilization, by Peter Faro, Avon Books, The Hearst Corp., New York, NY, 1968.

Massachusetts Archaeological Society, Bulletin of the, by William S. Fowler, Vol. 25, No. 1, Bronson Museum, Attleboro, Mass, Oct., 1963.

The Mighty Aztecs, by Gene S. Stuart, National Geographic Society, Washington, D.C., 1981.

The Mississippian Culture, by Robert Overstreet & Ross Bentley, Preston Printing, Cleveland, TN, 1967.

The Missouri Archaeologist (The First Ten Years, 1935-1944), The Missouri Archaeological Society, Inc., Columbia, MO, 1975.

The Missouri Archaeologist Edition, Carl H. Chapman, University of Missouri, Columbia, MO.

The Mound Builders, by Henry Clyde Shetrone, D. Appleton-Century Co., New York, NY, 1941.

Mysteries of the Past, by Lionel Casson, Robert Claiborne, Brian Fagan and Walter Karp, American Heritage Publ., Co., Inc., New York, N.Y., 1977.

The Mysterious Maya, by George E. and Gene S. Stuart, National Geographic Society, Washington, D.C., 1983.

National Geographic, National Geographic Society, Numerous issues, Washington, D.C.

The Neanderthals, The Emergence of Man Series, by George Constable, Time-Life Books, New York, N.Y., 1973.

New World Beginnings (Indian Cultures in the Americas), by Olivia Vlahos, Fawcett Publ., Inc., Greenwich, CT, 1970.

North Amerian Indian Artifacts, by Lar Hothem, Books Americana, Florence, AL, 1980.

North American Indian Arts, by Andrew Hunter Whiteford, Golden Press-Western Publ. Co. Inc., New York, N.Y., 1970.

North American Indians-Before the coming of the Europeans, by Phillip Kopper (The Smithsonian Book), Smithsonian Books, Washington, D.C.

Notes in Anthropology, by David L. DeJarnette & Asael T. Hansen, The Florida State University, Tallahassee, FL, 1960.

Paleo Points, Illustrated Chronology of Projectile Points, by G. Bradford, published by The author, Ontario, Canada, 1975.

The Papago Indians of Arizona, by Ruth Underhill, Ph. D., U.S. Dept. of The Interior, Bureau of Indian Affairs, Washington, D.C.

The Plants, (Life Nature Library), by Frits W. Went, Time-Life Books, New York, N.Y., 1971.

Pocket Guide to Indian Points, Books Americana, Inc., Florence, AL, 1978.

Prehistoric Art, R.E. Grimm, editor, Greater St. Louis Archaeological Society, Wellington Print., St. Louis, MO, 1953.

Prehistoric Artifacts of North America, John F. Berner, editor, The Genuine Indian Relic Society, Inc., Rochester, IN, 1964.

Prehistoric Implements, by Warren K. Moorehead, Publisher, Charley G. Drake, Union City, GA, 1968.

Prehistoric Implements, by Warren K. Moorehead, Publisher, Charley G. Drake, American Indian Books, Union City, GA, Arno Press, Inc., New York, NY, 1978.

Projectile Point Types in Virginia and Neighboring Areas, by Wm. Jack Hranicky and Floyd Painter, Special Publ. No. 16, Archaeological Society of Virginia, 1988.

Projectile Point Types of the American Indian, by Robert K. Moore, published by Robert K. Moore, Athens, AL.

A Projectile Point Typology for Pennsylvania and the Northeast, by Gary L. Fogelman, Fogelman Publ. Co., Turbotville, Pennsylvania.

Projectile Points of the Tri-Rivers Basin, (Apolachicola, Flint and Chattahoochee), by John D. Sowell & Udo Volker Nowak, Generic Press, Dothan, Alabama, 1990.

The Redskin, Genuine Indian Relic Society, Inc., published by the Society, East St. Louis, IL, 1964.

Relics of Early Man Price Guide, by Philip D. Brewer, Athens, AL, 1988.

Secrist's Simplified Identification Guide (Stone Relics of the American Indian), by Clarence W. Secrist, published by the author, Muscatine, Iowa.

Selected Preforms, Points, and Knives of the North American Indian, by Gregory Perino, Vo. No. 1, Idabel, Ok., 1985.

Shoop Pennsylvania's Famous Paleo Site, Fogelman Publ., Co., Turbotville, Pennsylvania.

Solving The Riddles of Wetherill Mesa, by Douglas Osborne, Ph. D., National Geographic, Feb., 1964, Washington, D.C.

Southern Indian Studies, By The Archaeological Society of N.C., University of North Carolina, Chapel Hill, NC, 1949.

Stone Artifacts of the Northwestern Plains, by Louis C. Steege, Northwestern Plains Publ., Co., Colorado Springs, CO.

Stone Implements of the Potomac Chesapeake Province, by J.W. Powell, 15th Annual Report, Bureau of Ethnology, Washington, DC, 1893-1894.

Story in Stone (Flint types of Central & Southern U.S.), by Valerie and D.C. Waldorf, Mound Builder Books, Branson, MO, 1987.

Sun Circles and Human Hands, Emma Lila Fundaburk & Mary Douglas Foreman, editors. Published by the editors, Paragon Press, Montgomery, AL, 1957.

Ten Years of the Tennessee Archaeologist, Selected Subjects, J.B. Graham, Publisher, Chattanooga, TN.

Tennessee Anthropologist, Vol. XIV, No. 2, Fall, 1989, U.T. Knoxville, 1989.

Tennessee Archaeologist, T.M.N. Lewis and Madeline Kneburg, University of Tennessee, Knoxville, TN.

Tennessee Anthropologist, Vol. 14, No. 2, 1989. The Quad Site Revisted, by Charles Faulkner.

A Typology and Nomenclature of New York Projectile Points, by William A. Ritchie, Bulletin No. 384, New York State Museum, NY, 1971.

U.S. News and World Report (Weekly News Magazine) article by William F. Allman and Joannie M. Schrof—"Last Empires of the Americas," April 2, 1990 issue, Washington, DC.

The Vail Site (A Paleo Indian Encampment in Maine), by Richard Michael Gromeley, Bulletin of the Buffalo Society of Natural Science, Vol. No. 30, Buffalo, NY, 1982.

Walk with History, Joan L. Franks, editor, Chattanooga Area Historical Assn., Chattanooga, TN, 1976.

Who's Who in Indian Relics, by H.C. Wachtel, publisher, Charley G. Drake, American Indian Books, Union City, GA, 1980.

The World Atlas of Archaeology (The English Edition of "Le Grand Atlas de Parcheologie"), executive editor—James Hughes, U.S. & Canada, G.K. Hall & Co., Boston, Mass., 1985.

World Book Encyclopedia, Field Enterprises, Inc., W.F. Quarrie and Company, Chicago, Ill., 1953.

The World of the American Indian (A volume in the Story of Man Library), National Geographic Society, Jules B. Billard—Editor, Washington, DC, 1989.